◎Harden's

BEST UK
RESTAURANTS
2020

INDEPENDENT AND UNBIASED REVIEWS OF OVER 2,800 RESTAURANTS

'IT WILL TELL YOU WHAT DINERS ACTUALLY LIKE, AS OPPOSED TO MERE RESTAURANT CRITICS'
— RICHARD VINES, CHIEF FOOD CRITIC, BLOOMBERG

Put us in your client's pocket!

Branded gift books and editions for iPhone

call to discuss the options on 020 7839 4763.

Follow Harden's on Instagram and Twitter @hardensbites

© **Harden's Limited 2019**

ISBN 978-1-916076-11-2

British Library Cataloguing-in-Publication data: a catalogue record for this book is available from the British Library.

Printed in Britain by SRP, Exeter

Front cover images: (top) Coal Office, London, (middle) The Five Fields, London, (bottom) Bancone, London

Assistant editors: Bruce Millar, Clodagh Kinsella, Antonia Russell
Designers: (text) paulsmithdesign.com, (cover) Egelnick and paulsmithdesign.com

Harden's Limited
Beta Space, 25 Holywell Row, London EC2A 4XE

Would restaurateurs (and PRs) please address communications to 'Editorial' at the above address, or ideally by email to: editorial@hardens.com The contents of this book are believed correct at the time of printing. Nevertheless, the publisher can accept no responsibility for errors or changes in or omissions from the details given.

◎Harden's 100

The UK's 100 Best Restaurants for 2020, as dictated by Harden's annual survey of diners

1 Fraiche, Oxton (7)

2 The Five Fields, London (13)

3 Mana, Manchester (-)

4 Restaurant Sat Bains, Nottingham (23)

5 Moor Hall, Aughton (30)

6 Hambleton Hall, Hambleton (10)

7 The Ledbury, London (5)

8 Kitchen Table at Bubbledogs, London (14)

9 Core by Clare Smyth, London (11)

10 Casamia, The General, Bristol (1)

11 Restaurant Nathan Outlaw, Port Isaac (4)

12 L'Enclume, Cartmel (31)

13 Umu, London (-)

14 Waterside Inn, Bray (9)

15 Belmond Le Manoir aux Quat' Saisons, Belmond, Great Milton (16)

16 Etch, Hove (-)

17 Mãos, London (43)

18 Endo at Rotunda, London (-)

19 Adam Reid at The French, Midland Hotel, Manchester (-)

20 Lumière, Cheltenham (61)

21 The Araki, London (3)

22 Texture, London (2)

23 Hakkasan, London (48)

24 Winteringham Fields, Winteringham (8)

25 Orwells, Shiplake (-)

26 Sushi Tetsu, London (15)

27 Amaya, London (68)

28 Andrew Fairlie, Gleneagles Hotel, Auchterarder (55)

29 Adam's, Birmingham (22)

30 Little Fish Market, Brighton (99)

31 Restaurant Martin Wishart, Edinburgh (18)

32 Roganic, London (76)

33 Le Cochon Aveugle, York (91)

34 Gymkhana, London (-)

35 Hipping Hall, Kirkby Lonsdale (-)

36 Dastaan, Ewell (-)

37 House of Tides, Newcastle upon Tyne (-)

38 Sorrel, Dorking (21)

39 Indian Accent, London (24)

40 Morston Hall, Morston (26)

41 The Peat Inn, Cupar (58)

42 The Neptune, Old Hunstanton (50)

43 Opheem, Birmingham (-)

44 Artichoke, Amersham (28)

45 Sosban And The Old Butcher's, Menai Bridge (-)

46 Le Gavroche, London (25)

47 La Dame de Pic London, Four Seasons Hotel, London (6)

48 Zuma, London (66)

49 The Fordwich Arms, Fordwich (-)

50 Lympstone Manor, Exmouth (20)

"AT GUSBOURNE WE EMBRACE TRADITION
BUT READILY CHALLENGE CONVENTION,
EVEN TO MAKE WHAT MIGHT SEEM LIKE
VERY SMALL DIFFERENCES TO THE
FINISHED WINE. ATTENTION TO DETAIL
IS OFTEN THE DIFFERENCE BETWEEN
GREAT AND EXCEPTIONAL."

CHARLIE HOLLAND
WINEMAKER

GUSBOURNE.COM

◎Harden's 100

The UK's 100 Best Restaurants for 2020, as dictated by Harden's annual survey of diners

51 Lake Road Kitchen, Ambleside (-)	76 Babur, London (-)
52 Purnells, Birmingham (59)	77 The Blackbird, Bagnor (-)
53 Roski, Liverpool (-)	78 The Sportsman, Seasalter (49)
54 Paul Ainsworth at No. 6, Padstow (-)	79 Club Gascon, London (-)
55 Raby Hunt, Summerhouse (51)	80 The Moorcock Inn, Sowerby Bridge (-)
56 The Whitebrook, Whitebrook (-)	81 Northcote, Langho (-)
57 Bohemia, Jersey (-)	82 Frog by Adam Handling, London (98)
58 Stark, Broadstairs (-)	83 Midsummer House, Cambridge (38)
59 La Petite Maison, London (-)	84 Trinity, London (88)
60 21212, Edinburgh (-)	85 The Ninth London, London (-)
61 Alyn Williams, Westbury Hotel, London (-)	86 Caractère, London (-)
62 Ikoyi, London (-)	87 Skosh, York (-)
63 Ynyshir, Eglwys Fach (44)	88 Seven Park Place, St James's Hotel, London (-)
64 Hunan, London (41)	89 Indian Essence, Petts Wood (-)
65 A Wong, London (-)	90 La Trompette, London (74)
66 Roka, London (-)	91 Crab House Cafe, Weymouth (-)
67 Chez Bruce, London (77)	92 Joro, Sheffield (-)
68 1921 Angel Hill, Bury St Edmunds (-)	93 Kahani, London (-)
69 Elystan Street, London (84)	94 Ormer Mayfair, Flemings Mayfair Hotel, London (-)
70 StreetXO, London (-)	95 The Box Tree, Ilkley (19)
71 OOTY, London (-)	96 The Barbary, London (-)
72 Black Swan, Oldstead (29)	97 John's House, Mountsorrel (-)
73 Restaurant MCR, Manchester (-)	98 Pollen Street Social, London (83)
74 Gravetye Manor, East Grinstead (-)	99 The Small Holding, Goudhurst (-)
75 Number One, Balmoral Hotel, Edinburgh (71)	100 Trishna, London (92)

Exmoor Caviar
MADE IN ENGLAND

www.exmoorcaviar.com   info@exmoorcaviar.co.uk   tel.: 08454 349 587
563-565 Battersea Park Road London SW11 3 BL, U.K.

 @londonfinefoods   @londonfinefoods   @londonfinefoods

CONTENTS

Marcus, The Berkeley, London

The Barn at Moor Hall, Aughton

Opheem, Birmingham

RATINGS & PRICES

Ratings

The ratings in this guide are derived statistically and with the judgement of the editors from ratings provided by ordinary diners in the Harden's diner survey. For more details see opposite. Our rating system does not tell you as most guides do that expensive restaurants are often better than cheap ones! What we do is compare each restaurant's performance as judged by the average ratings awarded by reporters in the survey with other similarly-priced restaurants. This approach has the advantage that it helps you find whatever your budget for any particular meal where you will get the best 'bang for your buck'.

The following qualities are assessed:

F	—	Food
S	—	Service
A	—	Ambience

The rating indicates that, **in comparison with other restaurants in the same price-bracket**, performance is…

5	—	Exceptional
4	—	Very good
3	—	Good
2	—	Average
1	—	Poor

Prices

The price shown for each restaurant is the cost for one (1) person of an average threecourse dinner with half a bottle of house wine and coffee, any cover charge, service and VAT. Lunch is often cheaper. With BYO restaurants, we have assumed that two people share a £7 bottle of off-licence wine.

Small print

Telephone number – including area code.

Map reference – shown immediately after the telephone number.

Full postcodes – for non-group restaurants, the first entry in the 'small print' at the end of each listing, so you can set your sat-nav.

Website and Twitter – shown in the small print, where applicable.

Last orders time – listed after the website (if applicable); Sunday may be up to 90 minutes earlier.

Opening hours – unless otherwise stated, restaurants are open for lunch and dinner seven days a week.

Credit and debit cards – unless otherwise stated, Mastercard, Visa, Amex and Maestro are accepted.

Dress – where appropriate, the management's preferences concerning patrons' dress are given.

SRA Star Rating – the sustainability index, as calculated by the Sustainable Restaurant Association see page 12 for more information.

YOUR CONTRIBUTION

Every year this guide is based on the Harden's annual survey of ordinary diners.

For our 29th survey, the total number of diners who took part numbered 7,500, and, between them, they contributed 50,000 individual reports.

The survey takes place online each year (and in print for a small number of long-term participants), and anyone is free to sign up. Some of our diners (or 'reporters' as we sometimes call them in the text) have been taking part for over 20 years. The survey invites diners to nominate their favourite restaurant, where they had the best meal of the last 12 months and so on. Diners also award marks for Food, Service and Ambience together with leaving a short comment.

We then take the raw feedback and subject it to a rigorous statistical number-crunching exercise. Ratings for highly commented-on restaurants are derived almost entirely by statistical analysis. Where the level of feedback is lower, editorial judgement plays more of a part.

At a time when a recent study suggested that as many as 1/3 of the reviews on TripAdvisor are paid for by the restaurants they cover, we believe there is an ever-greater need for trusted sources such as the Harden's annual diner survey. For while obviously folks can attempt to stuff the Harden's ballot too, the high degree of editorial oversight plus the historical data we have both about the restaurants and also about those commenting makes it much harder to succeed. In this way Harden's can socially source restaurant feedback, but – vitally – curate it fully as we do so. It is this careful curation which provides extra 'value-added' for diners.

How we determine the ratings

In the great majority of cases, ratings are arrived at statistically. This essentially involves 'ranking' the average survey rating each restaurant achieves in the survey – for food, service and ambience – against the average ratings of the other establishments in the same price-bracket.

(This is essentially like football leagues, with the most expensive restaurants going in the top league and the cheaper ones in lower leagues. The restaurant's ranking within its own particular league determines its ratings.)

How we write the reviews

The tone of each review and the ratings are largely determined by the ranking of the establishment concerned, which we derive as described above.

At the margin, we may also pay some regard to the proportion of positive nominations (such as for 'favourite restaurant') compared to negative nominations (such as for 'most overpriced').

To explain why a restaurant has been rated as it has, we extract snippets from survey comments ("enclosed in double quotes"). On well-known restaurants, we receive several hundred reports, and a short summary cannot possibly do individual justice to all of them.

What we seek to do – without regard to our own personal opinions – is to illustrate the key themes which have emerged in feedback from diners on any particular restaurant.

Coal Office, London

SURVEY MOST MENTIONED

These are the restaurants which were most frequently mentioned by reporters. (Last year's position is given in brackets.)

1	J Sheekey (1)	21	Noble Rot (29)
2	Le Gavroche (4)	22	Galvin La Chapelle (-)
3	Chez Bruce (3)	23	Brat (-)
4	Clos Maggiore (2)	24	Trinity (18)
5	Scott's (5)	25	The Cinnamon Club (21)
6	The Ledbury (6)	26=	Pollen Street Social (23)
7	Core by Clare Smyth (13)	26=	La Poule au Pot (22)
8	The Wolseley (10)	28=	The Ritz (40)
9	Brasserie Zédel (11)	28=	Gordon Ramsay (37)
10	La Trompette (9)	30	Bentley's (31)
11	Gauthier Soho (8)	31	The Five Fields (25)
12	The River Café (12)	32	Bleeding Heart Restaurant (28)
13	Gymkhana (7)	33	Murano (-)
14	Hide (-)	34=	Pied À Terre (33)
15	The Ivy (14)	34=	Trishna (-)
16	AWong (15)	36	Medlar (-)
17	Bocca Di Lupo (24)	37=	Kerridge's Bar & Grill (-)
18=	Indian Accent (-)	37=	Trullo (-)
18=	Andrew Edmunds (17)	37=	Le Caprice (19)
20	The Delaunay (16)	40	Elystan Street (30)

J Sheeke

SURVEY NOMINATIONS

Top gastronomic experience	Best breakfast/ brunch	Most disappointing cooking	Most overpriced restaurant
1 Core by Clare Smyth (6)	1 The Wolseley (1)	1 Oxo Tower (2)	1 The River Café (1)
2 Le Gavroche (2)	2 Dishoom (5)	2 The Ivy (3)	2 Gordon Ramsay (4)
3 The Ledbury (1)	3 Caravan (6)	3 The Ivy Grills &	3 Oxo Tower (3)
4 Chez Bruce (3)	4 The Delaunay (2)	Brasseries (1)	4 Sexy Fish (2)
5 La Trompette (4)	5 The Ivy Grills &	4 Le Gavroche (-)	5 Le Gavroche (8)
6 Pied À Terre (-)	Brasseries (3)	5 Hide (-)	6 Hide (-)
7 Gauthier Soho (5)	6 Côte (8)	6 Gordon Ramsay (7)	7 The Ivy Café (-)
8 Frog by Adam Handling (-)	7 Cecconi's (10)	7 Chiltern Firehouse (9)	8 J Sheekey (-)
9 Hide (-)	8 Granger & Co (4)	8 Kerridge's Bar & Grill (-)	9 Sushisamba (9)
10 10 The Five Fields (10)	9 Breakfast Club (7)	9 Scott's (-)	10 Hutong (-)
	10 10 Hawksmoor (-)	10 Union Street Café (-)	

Favourite	Best for romance	Best bar/pub food	Best for business
1 Chez Bruce (1)	1 Clos Maggiore (1)	1 Harwood Arms (1)	1 The Wolseley (1)
2 Le Gavroche (7)	2 La Poule au Pot (2)	2 The Anchor & Hope (2)	2 Hawksmoor (3)
3 The Ledbury (3)	3 Andrew Edmunds (3)	3 The Anglesea Arms (4)	3 The Delaunay (2)
4 The River Café (-)	4 Chez Bruce (7)	4 The Wells Tavern (5=)	4 Bleeding Heart Restaurant (5)
5 La Trompette (8)	5 Bleeding Heart	5 Canton Arms (7)	5 The Dining Room, The Goring
6 Gauthier Soho (4)	Restaurant (4)	6 The Ladbroke Arms (5=)	Hotel (-)
7 Trinity (-)	6 Le Gavroche (5)	7 The Drapers Arms (-)	6 Scott's (4)
8 J Sheekey (9)	7 The Ledbury (-)	8 The Guinea Grill (-)	7 The Ivy (10)
9 The Wolseley (5)	8 Café du Marché (8)	9 The Wigmore, The	8 Galvin La Chapelle (-)
10 Clos Maggiore (-)	9 Gauthier Soho (6)	Langham (-)	9 Goodman (-)
	10 The Ritz (-)	10 The Coach (-)	10 Coq d'Argent (-)

SURVEY HIGHEST RATINGS

FOOD	SERVICE	AMBIENCE	OVERALL

£100+

FOOD	SERVICE	AMBIENCE	OVERALL
1 The Five Fields	1 The Five Fields	1 The Ritz	1 Pied à Terre
2 Bubbledogs, Kitchen Table	2 Pied à Terre	2 Pied à Terre	2 Bubbledogs, Kitchen Table
3 Texture	3 The Ledbury	3 Bubbledogs, Kitchen Table	3 The Five Fields
4 The Ledbury	4 Le Gavroche	4 Oblix	4 The Ledbury
5 Pied à Terre	5 Bubbledogs, Kitchen Table	5 The Ledbury	5 Core by Clare Smyth

£75–£99

FOOD	SERVICE	AMBIENCE	OVERALL
1 Zuma	1 Caractère	1 Clos Maggiore	1 Launceston Place
2 Launceston Place	2 Chez Bruce	2 Spring Restaurant	2 Roux at Parliament Sq
3 Roganic	3 Noizé	3 Launceston Place	3 Caractère
4 Roux at Parliament Sq	4 Launceston Place	4 Rules	4 Chez Bruce
5 Roka	5 Roux at the Landau	5 Roux at Parliament Sq	5 Roka

£60–£74

FOOD	SERVICE	AMBIENCE	OVERALL
1 Frog by Adam Handling	1 Il Portico	1 La Poule au Pot	1 Cornerstone
2 Cornerstone	2 Caraffini	2 Andrew Edmunds	2 Brat
3 Brat	3 Oslo Court	3 Rex Whistler	3 Smith's Wapping
4 Twist	4 Quilon	4 The Wolseley	4 Clarke's
5 Anglo	5 Smith's Wapping	5 Oslo Court	5 Cabotte

£45–£59

FOOD	SERVICE	AMBIENCE	OVERALL
1 The Barbary	1 The Barbary	1 Brasserie Zédel	1 The Barbary
2 Babur	2 Babur	2 San Carlo Cicchetti	2 Barrafina
3 Barrafina	3 Barrafina	3 Barrafina	3 Babur
4 A Wong	4 A Wong	4 40 Maltby Street	4 40 Maltby Street
5 Bombay Palace	5 40 Maltby Street	5 Ognisko	5 Bombay Palace

£44 or less

FOOD	SERVICE	AMBIENCE	OVERALL
1 Dastaan	1 Monmouth Coffee Co	1 Dishoom	1 Padella
2 Padella	2 Kaffeine	2 Churchill Arms	2 Monmouth Coffee Co
3 Pizza Pilgrims	3 Paradise Hampstead	3 Kiln	3 Dishoom
4 Homeslice	4 Dastaan	4 Mercato Metropolitano	4 Dastaan
5 Lahore Kebab House	5 Kiln	5 Padella	5 Kiln

SURVEY BEST BY CUISINE

These are the restaurants which received the best average food ratings (excluding establishments with a small or notably local following).

Where the most common types of cuisine are concerned, we present the results in two price-brackets. For less common cuisines, we list the top three, regardless of price.

British, Modern

£60 and over		Under £60	
1	The Five Fields	1	The Dairy
2	Bubbledogs, Kitchen Table	2	40 Maltby Street
3	The Ledbury	3	Lamberts
4	Launceston Place	4	The Anchor & Hope
5	5 Roganic	5	Noble Rot

French

£60 and over		Under £60	
1	Le Gavroche	1	Casse-Croute
2	La Dame de Pic London	2	Café du Marché
3	The Ninth London	3	The Wells Tavern
4	La Petite Maison	4	Le Relais de Venise
5	La Trompette	5	Comptoir Gascon

Italian/Mediterranean

£60 and over		Under £60	
1	Theo Randall	1	Padella
2	Bocca Di Lupo	2	Bancone
3	Murano	3	Sorella
4	River Café	4	L'Amorosa
5	Locanda Locatelli	5	San Carlo Cicchetti

Indian & Pakistani

£60 and over		Under £60	
1	Amaya	1	Dastaan
2	Gymkhana	2	Babur
3	Indian Accent	3	Bombay Palace
4	Kutir	4	Lahore Kebab House
5	Café Spice Namaste	5	Dishoom

Chinese

£60 and over		Under £60	
1	Hakkasan	1	A Wong
2	Hunan	2	Singapore Garden
3	Yauatcha	3	Yming
4	China Tang	4	Kym's by Andrew Wong
5	Min Jiang	5	Royal China

Japanese

£60 and over		Under £60	
1	Umu	1	Sushi Tetsu
2	Endo at Rotunda	2	Takahashi
3	Zuma	3	Chotto Matte
4	Roka	4	Chisou
5	The Araki	5	Jin Kichi

British, Traditional

1	St John Smithfield
2	The Ritz
3	Scott's

Vegetarian

1	Gauthier Soho
2	The Frog
3	Vanilla Black

Burgers, etc

1	Hawksmoor
2	Goodman City
3	Burger & Beyond

Pizza

1	Pizza Pilgrims
2	Homeslice
3	Oliveto

Fish & Chips

1	Toff's
2	fish!
3	North Sea Fish

Thai

1	Smoking Goat
2	Kiln
3	Farang

Steaks & Grills

1	Hawksmoor
2	Goodman City
3	Flat Iron

Fish & Seafood

1	Cornerstone
2	Angler
3	J Sheekey

Fusion

1	Brat
2	Twist
3	108 Garage

Spanish

1	Barrafina
2	Sabor
3	José

Turkish

1	Kyseri
2	Oklava
3	Mangal 1

Lebanese

1	Crocker's Folly
2	Maroush
3	Yalla Yalla

Flor, London

Hide, London

Gloria, London

THE RESTAURANT SCENE

The squeeze on the market loosens... just

There are 174 newcomers in this year's guide. Although this is the fourth-best year we have recorded, this figure is well off the peaks seen in 2017 and 2018 which scored 200 and 193 respectively.

Closures, however, remain at a near-record level. At 110, they are the third highest-ever recorded since we started keeping count in 1992. They are narrowly exceeded only by last year's chart-topping 117 and the 113 recorded in the 2004 guide, which resulted from the savage hit the trade took as a result of the second gulf war and SARS epidemic.

Net openings (openings minus closures) grew weakly to 64: a rather mediocre performance. In the last ten years only two years have seen a worse result (last year and 2012).

The feeling that the market is still in the doldrums is reinforced by the ratio of openings to closures. At 1.6:1, it represents only a slight gain from last year's 1.4:1, and is well below the 29-year average of 2.1:1. Previous slumps in activity have generally been followed by a sharp rebound either back to, or above, the long-term average. You have to go back to the deep recession of the early 1990s to find as limp a recovery as the one currently underway.

Only the strong survive

One of the eye-catching features of the last year has been the number of high profile casualties. The failure of Jamie's Italian was major news, although it came as a surprise only to those who had not bothered to read this guide, which had awarded it dire marks for six years previously. Eventually gravity intervened.

Jamie's problems have become emblematic of the crisis in casual dining, which has also taken its toll on a slew of other chains, with seemingly daily announcements of CVAs (Creditor Voluntary Agreements) or closures. Abokado, Byron, Polpo, Ed's Easy Diner, Giraffe...

Looking at the more upscale chains and indies that Harden's reporters tend to focus on, what have been notable are the number of casualties amongst long-running well-known names, who chose this year to give up the ghost. Fifteen shuttered itself of course, but also Hedone, The Providores, Shepherd's, Kensington Place, maze, The Red Fort, Sonny's, Asia de Cuba, and Great Queen Street. Also small multiples of quality such as Rök, Picture and Foxlow. Doubtless the glory days of many of the above had passed, but at another time, many of them would have soldiered on.

It is a truism of entrepreneurial texts that just to stand still it is necessary for any business constantly to reinvent itself. That is ever-more the case in the London restaurant scene where any site that is not performing at its peak, will quickly be reformatted under the same brand or a new one.

The tough get going... less so to the burbs

The good news is that London's restaurateurs are a much more formidable bunch than when this guide was first published. The last three decades have seen an incredible rise in the professionalism of the trade. Opportunities continue to present themselves to those with witty new formats or sufficient passion to excel at the old ones.

But whereas in recent years much of the excitement has been focused on hipster enclaves in the East End, this year saw openings much more targeted on Central London (with 82 newcomers).

Away from the centre, activity was very much more evenly spread than it has typically been in recent times. East London led the way, but only by a whisker (with 27 openings) closely followed by both South London (with 26) and West London (25). The only laggard was North London which – after a promising year last year – reverted to being the tail end charlie (with just 14 newcomers).

Modern British cuisine (53) is by far and away the most popular for newcomers, with Italian (17), Indian (10) and Japanese (9) the next most numerous.

A good year for the girls...

Core by Clare Smyth enters the top-10 Most Mentioned restaurants this year. Taylor Bonnyman's Five Fields – head chef Marguerite Keogh – scored the survey's highest food mark. Newcomer of the year at Harden's Restaurant Awards 2019 was Caractère: Emily Roux's venture in partnership with husband Diego Ferrari.

The hottest of the hot

Every year, we do an editors' pick of the ten most significant openings of the year. This year our selection is as follows:

Bancone	Darby's
Bright	Endo at Rotunda
Bob Bob Cité	Emilia
Caractère	Gloria
The Coal Office	Kutir

Prices

The average price of dinner for one at establishments listed in this guide is £59.28 (compared to £55.76 last year). Prices have risen by 6.3% in the past 12 months (up on 4.8% in the preceding 12 months). This rate compares with a general annual inflation rate of 2.1% for the 12 months to July 2019, yet further accelerating the trend seen in the last three years by which London restaurant bills have seen price rises running significantly higher than UK inflation generally. Restaurants are a people-heavy business, though, and with UK wage growth having picked up to 4%, an above-inflation rise in restaurant bills is to be expected.

OPENINGS AND CLOSURES

Openings (174)

Adam Handling Chelsea
Allegra
Angelina
AOK Kitchen
Arcade Food Theatre
Arros QD
Baba G's *(NW1)*
BabaBoom *(N1)*
Bancone
Bao & Bing
Baozi Inn *(SE1)*
Berto
The Betterment
Black Dog Beer House
Black Radish
Bloomsbury Street
 Kitchen
Brasserie of Light
Bright
Brixton Laundry
Brook House
Bubala
Bun House *(WC2H)*
Burger & Beyond
by Chloe *(SE1,W1)*
Casa Fofó
Caviar Kaspia
Le Cellar
Cent Anni
Ceru *(W1)*
Charlie's
Church House
Circolo Popolare
Coqfighter
Le Comptoir Robuchon

Curry House Coco
 Ichibanya
Da Terra, Town Hall
 Hotel
Daffodil Mulligan
Dandy
Darby's
Davies and Brook,
 Claridge's Hotel
Decimo
Din Tai Fung *(WC1)*
Double Standard
E&O Chelsea *(SW3)*
Eggslut
Emilia's Crafted Pasta *(E1)*
Emilia
Endo at Rotunda
Fare
Farzi Cafe
Fatt Pundit
Fishworks *(WC2)*
Flat Iron *(E1)*
Flesh and Buns *(W1)*
Flor
Folie
Fortnum's Bar &
 Restaurant, Royal
 Exchange
400 Rabbits *(SE27)*
Four Legs at The
 Compton Arms
Franzina Trattoria
Fucina
Fugitive Motel
Garden Room
Gezellig
Gloria

Gold
Grays & Feather
Gridiron, COMO
 Metropolitan London
The Halal Guys
Hankies Marble Arch *(W1)*
Hard Rock Café *(W1 x2)*
Harlequin
Harrods Dining Hall
Haya
Hello Darling
Heritage
Imperial Treasure
Ippudo London *(WC2)*
Isla
Kaki
Kanishka
Kin and Deum
Kol
KoolCha
KPH
Kricket *(W12, SW9)*
Kuku Riku
Lagom at Hackney
 Church Brew Co.
Laksamania
Legare
Lina Stores *(N1)*
Lino
Locket's
The Lore of the Land
Loyal Tavern
Lucknow 49
Lucky Cat
Madame Pigg
Manzi's
Mao Chow

Maremma
Market Hall Victoria
Master Wei
Mathura
Melabes
Mimo
Moio
Moncks of Dover Street
Monsieur Le Duck
Myrtle
Nandine
No. 5 Social
No. Fifty Cheyne
Norma
Nutshell
O'ver *(SW1)*
The Oak *(SW11)*
104 Restaurant
Onima
OOTY
Orasay
Pachamama East *(EC2)*
Paradise
Parrillan
Passyunk Avenue
Pasta Remoli *(W3, E20)*
Pasticceria Marchesi 1824
Patri *(W13,W6)*
Peg
Le Petit Citron
Pick & Cheese
Les Platanes
Poppy's 3 *(W6)*
Le Pot de Terre
Pucci Mayfair
Roast *(W1)*
Robata

Roe
Sambal Shiok
The Sea, The Sea
Seabird
Señor Ceviche *(W1)*
Sette
Shanghai Modern
Silo
Siren
Sloane Street Deli
Snackbar
Soane's Kitchen
Spiritland *(SE1, N1)*
St Martin's Lane Kitchen
Stem & Glory *(EC1)*
Suzi Tros
10 Heddon Street
The Buxton
The Restaurant at The
 Capital
The Yard, Great Scotland
 Yard Hotel
Top Cuvee
Trivet
Vardo
Vinegar Yard
Wild Food Cafe *(WC2)*
Wild Rice & Mamasan
Xier
XR
Yeni
Yopo
Zia Lucia *(W14)*

Closures (110)

L'Absinthe
L'Ami Malo
Andi's
Annies *(SW13)*
Asia de Cuba, St Martins
 Lane Hotel
L'Atelier de Joel
 Robuchon
Babel House
The Balcon, Sofitel St
 James
Barbecoa *(EC4)*
Beck at Browns, Browns
 Hotel
Bellanger
Bonhams Restaurant
The Brackenbury
Bradys
La Buvette
Ceremony
Chilly Katz

Claw Carnaby
Dip in Brilliant
Drakes Tabanco
Edwins
Eight Over Eight
Essence Cuisine
Fayre Share
Fera at Claridge's,
 Claridge's Hotel
Fifteen
Foxlow *(W1, EC1, SW12)*
Gabys
Gastronhome
Gaylord
Gazelle
Gazette *(SW1)*
Ginger & White *(NW3)*
Great Queen Street
Hedone
Heirloom
Jackson & Rye Chiswick
 (W4)
Jackson & Rye *(W1)*

James Cochran EC3
 (EC3A)
Jamie's Italian *(all branches)*
Kensington Place
Kensington Square
 Kitchen
Kerbisher & Malt *(SW4)*
Kiru
Kulu Kulu *(WC2, SW7)*
Lantana Cafe *(NW1)*
Lardo Bebè *(E8)*
Little Social
Lokhandwala
Londrino
Lupita *(WC2)*
Magpie
Marianne
MASH Steakhouse
maze
Mint Leaf *(SW1)*
Morada Brindisa Asador
 (W1)
Mustard
Neo Bistro

Nuala
On The Bab Express *(W1)*
On the Dak
Outlaw's at The Capital
The Palmerston
Parabola, Design
 Museum
Pescatori
Peyotito
Picture *(W1 x2)*
Pitt Cue Co
Polpetto
Popeseye *(N19)*
La Porchetta Pizzeria
 (EC1, N4, NW1)
The Providores and Tapa
 Room
Quantus
Red Fort
Rivea, Bulgari Hotel
Rök *(N1, EC2)*
Rotorino
Rox Burger

Sapling
Schmaltz Truck
Serge et Le Phoque
Shepherds
Social Wine & Tapas
Sonnys Kitchen
Southam Street
Stem
Taylor Street Baristas
 (all branches)
Toms Kitchen *(E1, E14)*
Tommi's Burger Joint
 (SW3)
The Trafalgar Dining
 Rooms
Tratra
28-50 *(W1, EC4)*
VIVI
Waterloo Bar & Kitchen
Wellbourne
Workshop Coffee
 Holborn *(EC1)*

Flor, London

Core by Clare Smyth, London

Coal Office, London

Decimo, London

LONDON DIRECTORY

A CENA TW1 £50 343

418 RICHMOND ROAD 020 8288 0108 1–4A

Upmarket local in St Margaret's – close enough to Twickers for a meal before or after the rugby – that earns solid ratings for its "great Italian cooking" and "very friendly service". New owner chef Tom Rowlandson has introduced weekend brunches. / TW1 2EB; @acenarestaurant; 10 pm; closed Mon L & Sun D; booking max 6 may apply.

A WONG SW1 £59 553

70 WILTON RD 020 7828 8931 2–4B

"He's won my heart, and my taste buds…" – Andrew Wong's Pimlico venture "a short walk from Victoria Station" is the survey's No. 1 Chinese nowadays due to its "absolutely amazing", "elevated cuisine, beautifully plated and full of flavour". At lunch time, the attraction is "dim sum as you've never tasted it before" – "mouthwatering and so delicate", with special mention to the "incredible soup dumplings" – while at night there's "a brilliant tasting menu, taking you on a whistle-stop tour of Chinese culinary delights". "Happy" and "super-efficient" staff also rate special mention. "Plush the decor is not" – in fact the ground floor can seem "an oddly canteen-ish environment" – but, by contrast, the basement bar "has a beautiful 'secret club' feel to it". See also Kym's. / SW1V 1DE; www.awong.co.uk; @awongSW1; 10.15 pm; closed Mon L & Sun; credit card required to book.

THE ABBEVILLE SW4 £46 333

67-69 ABBEVILLE RD 020 8675 2201 11–2D

"Reliable local with better-than-pub fare"; an attractive, and well-established gastropub (which looks more like a wine bar – complete with opening frontage in summer – than a trad boozer), which sits at the heart of 'Abbeville Village' life. / SW4 9JW; www.theabbeville.co.uk; @threecheerspubs; 10.30 pm, Sun 9 pm.

ABD EL WAHAB SW1 £62 332

1-3 PONT STREET 020 7235 0005 6–1D

Surprisingly little feedback on this posh Lebanese, swankily located near Belgrave Square – the London outpost of a well-known, Beirut-based chain with 18 branches in the Arab world. Such as we have suggests it's good all-round, but doesn't set the world on fire. / SW1X 9EJ; www.abdelwahab.co.uk.

THE ABINGDON W8 £59 334

54 ABINGDON RD 020 7937 3339 6–2A

With its "cosy red-leather booths" to the rear and attractive dining room and bar, this posh gastropub has been a "locals' favourite" of chichi backstreet Kensington for 21 years. The food is "above average (fantastic steaks!)" and there's a "decent wine list" – "what's not to like?". / W8 6AP; www.theabingdon.co.uk; @theabingdonw8; Tues-Sat 10.30 pm, Sun-Mon 10 pm.

ABOUT THYME SW1 £56 343

82 WILTON RD 020 7821 7504 2–4B

"Like a home away from home", this Pimlico stalwart keeps regulars happy with a "lovely range of tapas" and Spanish classics, "supervised brilliantly by the amazing host, Issy". "In an age of ever-changing restaurants, it's a great pleasure to enjoy such consistency over many years." / SW1V 1DL; www.aboutthyme.co.uk; 10 pm; closed Sun.

ABU ZAAD W12 £30 332

29 UXBRIDGE RD 020 8749 5107 8–1C

"Plentiful and delicious Syrian specialities make it worth trying out this Shepherd's Bush café". It has a "slightly unpromising exterior", but a "superb atmosphere" inside, and it's "good value too". "Just go!" – "you won't be leaving hungry". / W12 8LH; www.abuzaad.co.uk; @abuzaaduk; 11 pm, Sat & Sun midnight; No Amex.

ADAM HANDLING CHELSEA SW1 334

THE BELMOND CADOGAN, 75 SLOANE STREET 020 7199 8370 6–2D

Sloane Street's old Cadogan Hotel – formerly a creaky, old Chelsea anachronism – has been transformed to join the über-luxurious Belmond portfolio: it now provides a "gorgeous" and luxurious backdrop to a meal ("perfect to impress a client in Chelsea"). Wunderkind chef, Adam Handling, is in charge of the dining room, and fans say that his individualistic cuisine is "knock-out": "from the bread with chicken-butter onwards, everything about this menu is now the best of modern British". However, there's also a slightly worrying proportion of disgruntled reports too: "as a massive fan of Adam Handling's Frog restaurants and even his cooking at Caxton Grill back in the day, I was anticipating greatness from AH Chelsea. But the food was sorely disappointing, confused, and as such, very overpriced. Hoping the food matches its surroundings soon!" / SW1X 9SG; www.adamhandlingchelsea.co.uk; @AHChelseaLDN.

ADAMS CAFÉ W12 £34 353

77 ASKEW RD 020 8743 0572 8–1B

"Greasy spoon by day, North African bistro by night" – this "so friendly" Shepherd's Bush institution run by Anglo-Tunisian couple Frances and Abdel Boukraa has been "treasured by locals for 25 years". "The grills (fish, lamb, chicken) are the high points, all delicious!", but "don't miss the home-made pickles and harissa – they're highly addictive". They are licensed these days, but you can still BYO (wines only, £6 corkage). / W12 9AH; www.adamscafe.co.uk; @adamscafe; 10 pm; closed Sun.

ADDIE'S THAI CAFÉ SW5 £38 432

121 EARL'S COURT RD 020 7259 2620 6–2A

"Fantastic Thai food at very reasonable prices" is the reason this basic Earl's Court canteen "has been around for over 20 years". "You can't fault it" for "real street food" that "far outperforms rivals and chains". / SW5 9RL; www.addiesthai.co.uk; 11 pm, Sun 10.30 pm; No Amex.

ADDOMME SW2 £54 433

17-21 STERNHOLD AVENUE 020 8678 8496 11–2C

"They use the best ingredients, the pizzas are extremely good, and Nadia and her husband are always lovely hosts" at their family-run joint, next to Streatham Hill station. "Sometimes it can get a bit crammed and noisy, but hey, it's a pizza place". / SW2 4PA; www.addomme.co.uk; @PizzAddomme; 11 pm.

THE ADMIRAL CODRINGTON SW3 £55 333

17 MOSSOP ST 020 7581 0005 6–2C

In a chichi backstreet, a posh boozer that's well-known to the denizens of Chelsea: it serves "a revisited version of typical pub food" in its rear dining room, which boasts a big, retractable glass skylight for warm days. / SW3 2LY; www.theadmiralcodrington.co.uk; @TheAdCod; 10 pm, Thu-Sat 11 pm, Sun 9 pm; No trainers.

Baltic SE1

AFGHAN KITCHEN N1　£29　3 3 2

35 ISLINGTON GRN　020 7359 8019　9–3D

"Decent food but seriously cramped!" – that's long been the trade-off at this tiny, barely decorated caff, by Islington Green, whose small selection of interesting curries makes it a "great local". / N1 8DU; 11 pm; closed Mon & Sun; Cash only; no booking.

AGLIO E OLIO SW10　£47　3 3 2

194 FULHAM RD　020 7351 0070　6–3B

"Honest", "fresh-tasting pasta and Italian staples" have won a major fanclub for this "unobtrusive" but "buzzy and very good-value institution" near Chelsea & Westminster Hospital. "Service is high-speed" and there's a "fun atmosphere" – but be warned, it's "not for the hard of hearing". / SW10 9PN; www.aglioeolio.co.uk; 11.00 pm.

AKIRA AT JAPAN HOUSE W8　£88　2 3 3

101-111 KENSINGTON HIGH STREET 020 3971 4646　6–1A

"Would have expected a lot more from a Japanese restaurant within Japan House" is too often the verdict on this venue within the Japanese Government's year-old showcase for all things Nipponese, which occupies Kensington's former Derry & Toms department store. The place is not without advocates of its "attractive" design and "beautiful presentation" but even fans acknowledge it's "on the expensive side" and some critics report really bad trips with "overly complex and heavy", or even "shockingly bad" dishes. / W8 5SA; www.japanhouselondon.uk; @japanhouseldn.

AL DUCA SW1　£59　2 2 2

4-5 DUKE OF YORK ST　020 7839 3090 3–3D

To avoid breaking the bank in swanky St James's, this long-established Italian is worth remembering thanks to its "reasonable food at sensible prices". On the downside, "there's no real ambience", but it can be fun to take a coffee at a pavement table and watch the world walk by". / SW1Y 6LA; www.alduca-restaurant.co.uk; 11 pm; closed Sun.

AL FORNO　£43　3 4 4

349 UPPER RICHMOND RD, SW15 020 8878 7522　11–2A 2A KING'S RD, SW19　020 8540 5710　11–2B

These "buzzing family-run Italians" in southwest London create "an exceptional atmosphere" for large parties of all ages – and "they won't break the bank". "Despite the celebratory brouhaha, they produce a very respectable menu of traditional dishes – fish stew, duck, pizza on demand" – "even the veggies are catered for". "Expect noise and old people dancing." / 10 pm-11 pm.

ALAIN DUCASSE AT THE DORCHESTER W1　£133　2 3 3

53 PARK LN　020 7629 8866　3–3A

Now a dozen years old: Alain Ducasse's UK flagship is a "subtly decorated and beautiful" – some would say "spectacular" – looking chamber on Park Lane, which perennially divides opinion between those who say it "never lets you down" and opponents who say it "never fails to disappoint". The latter camp have had the upper hand pretty much since the day it opened: they acknowledge a meal here is "a treat", but focus their fire on the "ludicrous prices", and the fact that its level of achievement is so "overhyped" by Michelin, who – seemingly on the grounds of Gallic cultural imperialism – insist on awarding this superstar Frenchman three stars, when one or two would be more than adequate! / W1K 1QA; www.alainducasse-dorchester.com; 9.30 pm; closed Mon, Sat L & Sun; Jacket required.

ALBERTINE W12　£50　3 3 5

1 WOOD LANE　020 8743 9593　8–1C

The attractively "louche and convivial atmosphere" of this Shepherd's Bush veteran, opposite and long pre-dating Westfield shopping centre, is redolent of the 1970s, when the "great little wine bar" was opened by chef Allegra McEvedy's mother. Now co-owned by McEvedy, whose "interesting short seasonal menu" is available in the bar and upstairs restaurant. / W12 7DP; albertine.london; @albertineLDN; closed Sat & Sun; No Amex.

ALEION N10　£48　3 3 3

346 MUSWELL HILL BROADWAY 020 8883 9207　1–1B

"A very small, friendly local" in the centre of Muswell Hill for over two years now; mostly it serves "delicious", light brunch-friendly fare from breakfast onwards ("lovely healthy salad options"), but there's a more substantial menu of simple, modern bistro dishes by night. / N10 1DJ; www.aleion.co.uk; @Aleion346.

THE ALFRED TENNYSON SW1　£64　3 3 3

10 MOTCOMB STREET　020 7730 6074 6–1D

Smartly kitted-out and scenically located Belgravia pub, originally launched (under the same owners) as the Pantechnicon Dining Rooms, with a happening ground-floor bar and less frenetic first-floor dining room. Upstairs in particular, the quality of the fit-out is much plusher than your typical corner-boozer. / SW1X 8LA; thealfredtennyson.co.uk; @TheTennysonSW1; 10 pm, Sun 9.30 pm.

ALI BABA NW1　£29　3 2 2

32 IVOR PL　020 7723 5805　2–1A

"An enduring curio that never disappoints and is so engagingly different" – this family run dining room, off the top end of Baker Street, is entered through a take-away, and offers genuine Egyptian cooking at prices that are a snip, in a genuinely Egyptian (if not always particularly polished) manner. / NW1 6DA; alibabarestaurant. co.uk; @alibabalondon; midnight; Cash only.

ALLEGRA E20

MANHATTAN LOFT GARDENS, 20-22 INTERNATIONAL WAY　14–1D

Ex-Chiltern Firehouse head chef Patrick Powell's first solo venture, on the seventh floor of Stratford's new Manhattan Loft Gardens building, opened too late for any reports in our survey. Powell's dedication to sustainability has extended to buying Kent farmland to provide Allegra with local ingredients. / E20 1GQ; www.allegra-restaurant.com; @allegraLDN.

ALOUNAK W14　£27　3 3 3

10 RUSSELL GDNS　020 7603 1130　8–1D

"I started eating at Alounak when it was in a container in a car park round the corner" twenty-five years ago, and this Iranian café over the tracks from Olympia remains a "favourite BYO" to this day, with its "consistently good Persian comfort food": in particular "superb kebabs". (A Bayswater 'Alounak' is still in operation, but seems now to operate independently of W14.) / W14 8EZ; alounakrestaurant.com; 11.30 pm; No Amex.

ALYN WILLIAMS, WESTBURY HOTEL W1　£107　4 5 3

37 CONDUIT ST　020 7183 6426　3–2C

"Outstanding cooking, with first-class service" consistently hits the bullseye at this relatively unsung venue, tucked away at the back of a luxury Mayfair hotel. There's a "thoughtful" approach to the meal, with "chefs coming out to tell you about dishes" – while some diners are "invited into the kitchen to meet Alyn". It's a "very comfortable" set-up and "the space between tables is incredible by modern restaurant standards, which creates the intimacy that a romantic meal requires". And, especially at lunch, the elegant room's lack of windows and natural light adds to the cocooning nature of the experience. / W1S 2YF; www.alynwilliams.com; @Alyn_Williams; 10.30 pm; closed Mon & Sun; Jacket required.

AMAYA SW1 £87 5|3|3

HALKIN ARCADE, 19 MOTCOMB ST
020 7823 1166 6–1D

"Cracking Indian fine dining-with-a-twist" is to be had at this "congenial" and moodily "cavernous" Belgravia fusion-venture (under the same ownership as Chutney Mary and Veeraswamy). The tapas-style dishes, prepared in an open kitchen over the grill, deliver "vibrant" and "fabulous flavours", and rank amongst London's very best. Overall, it's "a bit expensive", but a "super, super, super-lovely experience". / SW1X 8JT; www.amaya.biz; @theamaya_; 11.30 pm, Sun 10.30 pm.

THE AMERICAN BAR SW1 £80 2|4|3

16 - 18 SAINT JAMES'S PLACE
020 7493 0111 3–4C

"The beautiful cocktails are the best" at this plush and cosy hideaway, at the end of a St James's mews. Foodwise, there's a Mediterranean-inspired brasserie menu, or hold out for the summer BBQs in the courtyard. / SW1A 1NJ; thestaffordlondon.com/the-american-bar; @StaffordLondon; 10 pm.

AMETSA AT COMO THE HALKIN SW1 £83 3|3|2

5 HALKIN ST 020 7333 1234 2–3A

Notable for its associations with San Sebastian superstar chef Arzak, this hotel dining room, a chic-but-austere space near Belgrave Square, suffers from a "disappointing lack of atmosphere" (just like its predecessor, Nahm, long RIP). Opened with great fanfare five years ago, its highly ambitious Basque-inspired cuisine has never really won it the reputation anticipated for it on opening, but gradually improving ratings year-by-year suggest that it shouldn't be written off, and that the tyre men were wrong to deprive Ruben Briones of his star last October. "Having been with different friends, we realise it isn't to everyone's taste, but we love offbeat elements throughout the menu, and everything looks so beautiful. They lost their Michelin star but we think the food is better than ever" / SW1X 7DJ; www.comohotels.com/thehalkin/dining/ametsa; 10 pm; closed Mon L & Sun.

L'AMOROSA W6 £54 4|4|3

278 KING ST 020 8563 0300 8–2B

"It's a privilege to have such a high-class local Italian on our doorstep – I love it!", say Hammersmith foodies, thrilled by the "authentic food at affordable prices" ("fab pasta" in particular) which draws fans from across West London; it's prepared by ex-Zafferano chef/patron, Andy Needham, in slightly quirky, split-level premises, in a row of shops near Ravenscourt Park. The "warm welcome" from staff helps the occasion feel "special." / W6 0SP; www.lamorosa.co.uk; @LamorosaLondon; Tues - Sat 10pm; closed Mon & Sun D.

AMRUTHA SW18 £31 4|4|2

326 GARRATT LANE 020 8001 4628 11–2B

"Deservedly loved" – this "friendly, little 'vegan soul food'" yearling in Earlsfield serves "delicious", meat-free dishes, created by Arvin Suntaramoophy and Shyam Kotecha. It's a total budget option – not only can you BYO (no corkage) but you pay as much as, or little as you feel the meal is worth. You may have to queue: not only do the locals love it, but it regularly features as #1 in TripAdvisor's London rankings. / SW18 4EJ; www.amrutha.co.uk.

ANARKALI W6 £33 3|2|2

303-305 KING ST 020 8748 1760 8–2B

After a "welcome return" and revamp following an extended period of closure, this stalwart of Hammersmith's restaurant row (est 1972) continues to provide a "very relaxing" setting for chef Rafiq's consistently "enjoyable" curries. / W6 9NH; www.anarkali-finedining.com; @anarkalidining; midnight; closed Mon L & Sun L; No Amex.

THE ANCHOR & HOPE SE1 £54 4|3|2

36 THE CUT 020 7928 9898 10–4A

"Still nailing it after all these years" – this "unpretentious but brilliant" Southwark boozer near the Young Vic was again very narrowly beaten into No. 2 place amongst London's best gastropubs (by the Harwood Arms), but maintains a massive fanclub, and "you still have to queue to get a table". The draw is its "hearty" British cooking – "always-fascinating-and-unusual" dishes (often using game or offal) "delivering great flavours and textures". Top Tip – you can book for Sunday lunch. / SE1 8LP; www.anchorandhopepub.co.uk; @AnchorHopeCut; 10.30 pm, Sun 3.15 pm; closed Mon L & Sun D; No Amex; no booking.

ANDINA £52 4|3|3

31 GREAT WINDMILL STREET, W1
020 3327 9464 4–3D
157 WESTBOURNE GROVE, W11
020 3327 9465 7–1B
1 REDCHURCH ST, E2 020 7920 6499 13–1B

"Quite stunning food at a consistently high level", led by "fresher-than-fresh ceviche" and other "flavoursome dishes", earns improving ratings for Martin Morales's small Peruvian group, inspired by the cooking of the Andes. "Fabulous to visit" – "the room is permanently sunny – or is that just the pisco sours?". The Notting Hill venue includes a bakery. / www.cevichefamily.com/andina; @AndinaLondon.

THE ANDOVER ARMS W6 £49 3|4|4

57 ALDENSEY RD 020 8748 2155 8–1B

A "great", "traditional pub" in a cute warren of Hammersmith backstreets, which has been somewhat gentrified by successive managements, but which has 'kept it real' as a community boozer better than most. Steak is the top tip on the "good value" menu. / W6 0DL; www.theandoverarms.com; @theandoverarms; 10 pm, Sun 9 pm; No Amex.

ANDREW EDMUNDS W1 £61 3|3|5

46 LEXINGTON STREET 020 7437 5708 4–2C

"Perfect for dîner à deux" – the "quaint", "rustic and candle-lit" interior of this "Dickensian" Soho "staple" remains one of the capital's most romantic destinations, and its long-term ownership by antique print dealer Andrew Edmunds gives it a "charming and unpretentious" style of a rare kind, and fostered by his "genial" staff. "Yes, it's cramped" ("you squeeze in at a tiny table with lots of noise") and the "honest" and "straightforward food" – though "perfectly decent" – avoids fireworks. As an overall experience, though, it offers "excellent value" particularly due to the owner's collection of wine: 'Andrew still makes other lists look a rip-off' with "prices not much more than retail" for some fine vintages and "ever changing additions to the blackboard that are a pleasure to explore". The ground floor is the safest bet – by comparison the basement can appear "dull". / W1F 0LP; www.andrewedmunds.com; 10.45 pm, Sun 10.30 pm; No Amex; booking max 6 may apply.

ANGELINA E8 £54 5|4|3

56 DALSTON LANE 020 7241 1851 14–1A

"A clever, Italian-Japanese fusion that actually works well, who knew!?" – this tiny and original six-seater in Dalston inspires nothing but love amongst early reporters. "If you're bored of the endless tasting-menus trend in the food scene, the one here is top notch" – with five courses for £39 (or you can order individually at £9 per plate). "Bargain!" – "I went back the next day..." / E8 3AH; angelina.london.

ANGELUS W2 £75 3|4|2

4 BATHURST STREET 020 7402 0083 7–2D

"A serious wine list complements the good-quality Gallic cuisine" at former Gavroche sommelier Thierry Tomasin's clever conversion of a Lancaster Gate mews pub into an art nouveau bistro. The "old-fashioned service" is excellent, but prices are high, given the slightly off-the-beaten-track location. / W2 2SD; www.angelusrestaurant.co.uk; @AngelusLondon; 11 pm, Sun 10 pm.

ANGIE'S LITTLE FOOD SHOP W4 £44 3|2|2

114 CHISWICK HIGH ROAD 020 8994 3931 8–2A

"Sublime blueberry pancakes... flavour-packed avocado toast... luscious cakes" – typical of the light-ish bites that make Angie Steele's artfully distressed café a Chiswick brunch, light lunch and coffee favourite. / W4 1PU; www.angieslittlefoodshop.com; 7 pm, Sun 6 pm; L only.

ANGLER, SOUTH PLACE HOTEL EC2 £92 433

3 SOUTH PL 020 3215 1260 13–2A

Gary Foulkes's "classy" cuisine – "always perfect" fish and seafood, from a menu showcasing sustainable British Isles produce – maintains this "City gem" as the culinary star of D&D London at present. Occupying the "cool and refined" top floor of a hotel near Broadgate, it's "a great place for a business lunch, with excellent light": "one wall is virtually all window, overlooking the neighbouring blocks" (and there's a terrace for sunny days). "It's pricey, but you are slap bang in the heart of the Square Mile." / EC2M 2AF; www.anglerrestaurant.com; @Angler_London; 10 pm; closed Sat L; May need 8+ to book.

THE ANGLESEA ARMS W6 £62 444

35 WINGATE RD 020 8749 1291 8–1B

"The perfect pub" – this "brilliant all-round" hostelry, in a leafy sidestreet near Ravenscourt Park, is one of London's top gastropubs: a status it's maintained for two decades now. Its "seasonal" cooking is "unfussy but universally well-prepared and tasty", "the wine list is very reasonable, there's great cask beer and it's "always full and humming". Service has had its ups and downs over the years: "it's better than ever" at present: "friendly but not overwhelming". Top Tip – "T-bone night is fantastic and exceptional value". / W6 0UR; www.angleseaarmspub.co.uk; @_AngleseaArmsW6; 10 pm, Fri 11 pm, Sat & Sun 10 pm; closed weekday L; no booking.

ANGLO EC1 £71 532

30 ST CROSS STREET 020 7430 1503 10–1A

"It's all about the food" – "thought-provoking flavour combinations that hit all the right notes" – at Mark Jarvis's "incredible" venture, where the main options (other than a three-course menu at lunch) are six- or seven-course tasting menus (alongside "drink pairings which segue into cider and sour beers for dessert – another sign of a willingness to break the mould"). "Service is less polished" though: ditto the surroundings – a "soulless", "minimal room stuck in lawyer-land" near Hatton Garden. Still, "it's hard to find the words to describe just what good value it is". Come on Michelin, wake up and give the lad a star. / EC1N 8UH; www.anglorestaurant.com; @AngloFarringdon; 9.30 pm; closed Sun; booking max 4 may apply.

ANIMA E CUORE NW1 £49 552

129 KENTISH TOWN RD 07590 427171 9–2B

"Fab creative Italian food" – "an ever-changing menu with great homemade pasta" is "served with charm in the most unpretentious environment", at this "tiny BYO café" in Kentish Town. With ratings improving every year, locals are smitten by this "lovely hidden gem", so the only problem is the increasing

difficulty of grabbing a seat – but then again "they're expanding, so perhaps it'll become a little easier to get a table". / NW1 8PB; @animaecuoreuk; 9 pm, Sun 2.30 pm.

ANJANAAS NW6 £38 422

57-59 WILLESDEN LANE 020 7624 1713 1–1B

"Humble, family-run" venture that's become a "go-to Indian in Kilburn" on the strength of the "beautiful flavours" on its "superb Keralan menu": "great value for such high quality", which some even compare favourably with nearby legend Vijay. A word of warning: "they need to make sure the Deliveroos don't take precedence over customers present". / NW6 7RL; www.anjanaas.com.

ANNIE'S W4 £52 344

162 THAMES RD 020 8994 9080 1–3A

This "enviable local star" from former Sticky Fingers director Lorraine Angliss knows exactly its doing after more than 15 years in Strand-on-the-Green – and its ratings are always very dependable. The menu may not be the most exciting in town, but it's "varied" and contributes to a "totally relaxing" meal. In September 2019, its Barnes sibling gave up the ghost – perhaps the closure of Hammersmith Bridge was knocking trade? / W4 3QS; www.anniesrestaurant.co.uk; @annieschiswick; 10 pm, Fri & Sat 10.30 pm.

THE ANTHOLOGIST EC2 £56 222

58 GRESHAM ST 0845 468 0101 10–2C

This very "convenient" and sizeable bar-restaurant from Drake & Morgan, near the Guildhall, is valued for its efficiency and reliable (if pretty standard) menu. Nothing about it will set the world on fire, but it's a pleasant and versatile standby that can be pressed into action for any number of occasions. / EC2V 7BB; www.theanthologistbar.co.uk; @theanthologist; 11 pm, Thu & Fri 1 am; closed Sat & Sun.

L' ANTICA PIZZERIA NW3 £49 443

66 HEATH ST 020 7431 8516 9–1A

"A Hampstead institution", this "small" Neapolitan with a "classic, buzzy-pizzeria ambience" is "the real deal and excellent value" – so it's "always packed, especially at weekends (when you can't reserve)". There's also a range of appetizers and pasta dishes, and a spin-off branch in New Barnet. / NW3 1DN; www.anticapizzeria.co.uk; @AnticaHamp; 10.30 pm; Mon-Thu D only, Fri-Sun open L & D.

L'ANTICA PIZZERIA DA MICHELE NW1 £47 323

199 BAKER STREET 020 7935 6458 2–1A

The London franchise of the 19th-century Neapolitan pizzeria that featured in the film 'Eat, Pray, Love' is a "buzzy, noisy" crowd-pleaser in touristy Baker Street that serves

"delicious and massive pizzas". / NW1 6UY; anticapizzeriadamichele.co.uk.

ANTIPODEA RICHMOND TW9

30 HILL STREET 020 8940 4727 1–4A

"An excellently seasoned burger" is typical of the "big portions of rather tasty" food at this popular, "friendly and pleasantly appointed", all-day modern bistro in Richmond. There are also (less commented-on) branches in Kew, Putney and Notting Hill. / TW9 1TW; antipodea.co.uk; @AntipodeaLondon.

AOK KITCHEN W1 £86 224

52-55 DORSET STREET 020 3889 9400 2–1A

A "beautiful room", with Instagram-friendly blossom trailing from the ceiling, helps win positive early reports on this ambitious (rather clunkily-named) new Marylebone restaurant (upstairs) and bakery (downstairs), where the focus is on "healthy cooking that's 100% free from gluten, dairy and refined sugar". Some negative feedback, however, although not massively so, contributes to a slightly mixed rep overall: "no pun intended, it was only OK". / W1U 7NQ; www.aokkitchen.co.uk.

APPLEBEE'S FISH SE1 £64 422

5 STONEY ST 020 7407 5777 10–4C

"Superb fish – not overcooked – in generous portions" is the USP at this Borough Market café, where you can "sit outside for a lovely lunch". Service came under fire from several reporters this year: "are they becoming a little slapdash?" / SE1 9AA; www.applebeesfish.com; @Applebeesfish; Thu-Sat 11 pm; closed Sun; No Amex.

APULIA EC1 £56 332

50 LONG LN 020 7600 8107 10–2B

This "friendly little place" on the edge of Smithfield Market "serves delicious, hearty Puglian-style food", including "proper southern Italian pizza with fresh and authentic ingredients". This year's worst report? – "A likeable place: the sort you would want round the corner." / EC1A 9EJ; www.apuliarestaurant.co.uk; 10 pm; closed Sun D.

AQUA KYOTO W1 £85 224

240 REGENT ST (ENTRANCE 30 ARGYLL ST) 020 7478 0540 4–1A

"This huge restaurant above Regent Street" with a sizeable rooftop setting (from the Hong Kong-based group also at The Shard) serves "surprisingly good Japanese food" and "feels like a nightclub, with bouncers, red carpets, loud music, moody lighting and a sexily groomed, exuberant clientele". It's "very buzzy, very loud and great for people-watching". A neighbouring rooftop sibling, aqua nueva, does similar things with a Hispanic menu but doesn't inspire the same level of feedback. / W1B 3BR;

Ametsa at COMO The Halkin SW1

www.aqua-london.com; @aqualondon; 10.30 pm, Thu-Sat 11 pm; closed Sun D.

AQUA SHARD
SE1 £112 1️⃣1️⃣4️⃣

LEVEL 31, 31 ST THOMAS ST 020 3011 1256 10–4C

"The views are fantastic from the top of the Shard", but prices for the "very ordinary food" are "totally outrageous" – "hardly value for money unless you're a hedge-fund manager". Some reporters "would never return", but others are "glad they went". Just remember – "this is a place to be seen and to see from, rather than a magnet for food-lovers". Top Tip – "don't miss the urinals – they're the best in London". / SE1 9RY; www.aquashard.co.uk; @aquashard; 10.45 pm.

AQUAVIT SW1 £83 3️⃣2️⃣3️⃣

ST JAMES'S MARKET, 1 CARLTON ST 020 7024 9848 4–4D

This two-year-old, near Piccadilly Circus – in the glossy St James's Market development – is an offshoot of one of Manhattan's most celebrated restaurant stalwarts, and here, as in NYC, "everything is made following Nordic traditions creating really delicious dishes" with "great Scandinavian fish and meat" ("even the bread is something you won't forget". But while to some reporters its big windows and expensive decor are "truly glamorous", to others the ambience is "cold" – "a bit see-and-be-seen, and somehow a bit soulless". / SW1Y 4QQ; www.aquavitrestaurants.com; @aquavitlondon.

ARABICA BAR AND KITCHEN
SE1 £52 3️⃣4️⃣3️⃣

3 ROCHESTER WALK 020 3011 5151 10–4C

"Outstandingly flavoursome Middle Eastern fare" is delivered "fast" – and with "warm and helpful service" – at this "lively and noisy" venue on the edge of foodie Borough Market. "Just the place after visiting the market stalls, or the Shard". A second 100-seater site is planned to open in autumn 2019 in King's Cross, but the menu will be quite a departure. / SE1 9AF; www.arabicabarandkitchen; @ArabicaLondon; 10.30 pm, Sat 11 pm, Sun 8.30 pm; closed Sun D.

THE ARAKI W1 £369 5️⃣3️⃣2️⃣

UNIT 4 12 NEW BURLINGTON ST 020 7287 2481 4–3A

"Sushi as an art form, with every piece designed to the last detail" is at the heart of an unforgettable trip to this illustrious Mayfair nine-seater, where Marty Lau is the new master after maestro Matsuhiro Araki returned to Japan in spring 2019. The place is "sooooooooooo expensive", but what's been striking ever since its debut in 2014 is how few diners begrudge the mesmerising bill, instead appreciating the intense, personal theatricality of the endeavour; and the "exceptional quality and sourcing of the ingredients". Early feedback on the new regime says it's "not affected by the loss of Mr Araki, and still a very special experience" – whether Michelin maintain its three-star rating in autumn 2019 remains to be seen… / W1S 3BH; www.the-araki.com; seatings only at 6 pm and 8.30 pm; D only, closed Mon.

ARCADE FOOD THEATRE
WC2

CENTRE POINT, 103-105 NEW OXFORD STREET 5–1A

A new style of food hall for central London; this industrial-chic space on the ground floor of Centre Point has seven kitchens, three bars, a coffee shop and bakery and an 'incubation-focused space'. Stalls at the summer 2019 opening were Lina Stores, Pophams, TOU by TA TA, Pastorcito, Oklava, Flat Iron, Casita do Frango and Chotto Matte. / WC2H 8LH; www.arcade-london.com.

ARIANA II NW6 £25 3️⃣3️⃣2️⃣

241 KILBURN HIGH RD 020 3490 6709 1–2B

"Seriously tasty Afghan food" has made this "niche venue" a long-time north London favourite (the original Ariana was founded by another branch of the family in New York in the 1980s). It's "handy for the Kiln Theatre" (formerly the Tricycle) and "BYO so very cheap 'n' cheerful indeed". Top Tip – "the mantu (minced lamb in steamed pastry) are worth the trip alone". / NW6 7JN; www.ariana2restaurant.co.uk; @Ariana2kilburn; midnight.

ARK FISH E18 £40 3️⃣4️⃣2️⃣

142 HERMON HILL 020 8989 5345 1–1D

Solidly high ratings again this year for this South Woodford chippy, whose owning family are fish 'n' chips royalty (having previously run Lisson Grove's famous Seashell); fish comes daily from Billingsgate. / E18 1QH; www.arkfishrestaurant.co.uk; @ArkfishLondon; 9.45 pm, Fri & Sat 10.15 pm, Sun 8.45 pm; closed Mon; No Amex; no booking.

ARLO'S £51 3️⃣2️⃣2️⃣

47 NORTHCOTE ROAD, SW11 11–2C 1 RAMSDEN ROAD, SW12 020 3019 6590 11–2C

"Top-quality steaks" – "cooked to perfection" – and at "reasonable prices" make this three-year-old Balham steakhouse and its Battersea satellite "great for carnivores". Non-meat-eaters are catered for on a daily brunch menu.

ARROS QD W1 £86 4️⃣4️⃣4️⃣

64 EASTCASTLE STREET 020 3883 3525 3–1D

"A fantastic paella" is the signature dish at Quique Dacosta's very well-publicised (well, he does have three Michelin stars back in Alicante) two-floor, Spanish newcomer, which opened in June 2019: too late to receive a huge volume of survey feedback (so the ratings should be seen as indicative). Such as we have is brimming with enthusiasm all-round, both for results from the extensive menu (not just paella, but skewers, grilled and roasted fish and meats) and for the "really good atmosphere for a restaurant just north of Oxford Street". The newspaper critics have painted a mostly upbeat, but more mixed, picture. / W1W 8NQ; www.arrosqd.com; @QiqeDacosta.

ARTHUR HOOPER'S
SE1 £50 3️⃣3️⃣3️⃣

8 STONEY ST AWAITING TEL 10–4C

"Brilliant value… market bustle… great modern menu – we love it", declare fans of this "upmarket" wine bar with (mainly Italian) small plates – "another good option for a great tapas meal in Borough Market". It took the name of the greengrocer who previously occupied the site. / SE1 9AA; www.arthurhoopers.co.uk; @arthurhoopers; 10.30 pm, Fri & Sat 11.30 pm; booking max 6 may apply.

L'ARTISTA NW11 £43 3️⃣3️⃣3️⃣

917 FINCHLEY RD 020 8731 7501 1–1B

"Tucked under the railway arches", by the tube at Golders Green, this very family-friendly local landmark and celebration spot has been serving "great pasta and pizza" along with a good dose of old-school jollity for 35 years. "You won't be disappointed" – "cheap 'n' cheerful it really is". / NW11 7PE; www.lartistapizzeria.com; 11.30 pm.

ARTUSI SE15 £48 432

161 BELLENDEN RD 020 3302 8200 1–4D

A "limited seasonal menu knocks it out of the park" at this "star neighbourhood restaurant" in Peckham (named after Pellegrino Artusi, the 19th-century 'godfather of Italian cuisine'). There's a "laid-back, hipster" vibe, while the "simple and cheap ingredients are well chosen and delivered at a compelling price". / SE15 4DH; www.artusi.co.uk; @artusipeckham; 10.30 pm, Sun 8 pm; closed Mon L.

ASAKUSA NW1 £33 522

265 EVERSHOLT ST 020 7388 8533 9–3C

Vaguely Tyrolean, beamed decor is nobody's idea of a Japanese restaurant at this slightly odd venture, near Mornington Crescent tube. No complaints about the outstanding value sushi and other fare though: "good and varied as ever, with many choices for Japanese drinks too, including sake". / NW1 1BA; asakusa.has. restaurant; 11.30 pm, Sat 11 pm; D only, closed Sun.

ASSAGGI W2 £68 331

39 CHEPSTOW PL 020 7792 5501 7–1B

"Having been the biggest fan since the first day Assaggi opened, I'm now struggling with the prices!" – a constant refrain in feedback on this offbeat, first-floor Bayswater pub dining room, which for many years was a contender as London's top Italian. No-one's suggesting the cooking's gone down the tubes – in fact some regulars believe that "standards are as good as they were fifteen years ago" – but "the room and ambience need updating", and even many reporting an "excellent" meal nevertheless leave feeling "fleeced". / W2 4TS; www.assaggi.co.uk; @assaggi3; 11 pm; closed Sun; No Amex.

ASSAGGI BAR & PIZZERIA W2 £62 333

39 CHEPSTOW PLACE 020 7792 5501 7–1B

"Extraordinarily good pizzas", "very good negronis" and "no burgers" are served at this bar, which boasts "the style of Mayfair transplanted to Notting Hill". It's upstairs from Assaggi, and from the same team, in the former pub they share, and these days seems the less risky bet. Top Tip – "try the truffle pizza in winter and English asparagus with San Daniele ham in summer". / W2 4TS; www.assaggi.co.uk; @Assaggi3; No bookings.

ASTER RESTAURANT SW1 £68 222

150 VICTORIA ST 020 3875 5555 2–4B

"For a pre-Hamilton meal", this D&D London operation has proved "a welcome addition to Victoria eating choices": "perfect for a better-than-quick, better-than-casual, meal". It's not an area over-blessed with options, though, and there is an element of 'in the land of the blind, the one-eyed man is king'. The cuisine – no longer with Nordic influences since Helena Puolakka left in early-2019, but now, under Bjoern Wassmuth, in the 'Grand European Café' mould – is "variable, if nothing to complain about". And the modern setting – to fans "the most characterful option in the new Nova development canyons" – can feel "like eating in an airport". / SW1E 5LB; www.aster-restaurant.com; @AsterVictoria; 9.30 pm.

ATARI-YA £43 421

20 JAMES ST, W1 020 7491 1178 3–1A
1 STATION PDE, W5 020 8896 3175 1–3A
75 FAIRFAX ROAD, NW6 020 7328 5338 9–2A

Some of "the best (reasonably affordable) sushi in London" can be found at these supermarket/ cafés operated by a Japanese food importer. But it's all about the "fresh and addictive" plates – "service is a bit rough and ready when they're busy" and the ambience "lacks soul". / www.sushibaratariya.co.uk; W1F Mon-Wed 10 pm, Thu-Sat 10.30 pm, W1T Mon-Sat 10 pm, E8 Sat 4 pm; NW6 closed Mon, W5 closed Mon .

THE ATLAS SW6 £49 444

16 SEAGRAVE RD 020 7385 9129 6–3A

This "cracking, traditional English pub", "tucked away in the backstreets" a short walk from West Brompton tube, has earned an enviable reputation for "interesting" Mediterranean cooking, backed up by "premium wines" and "some of London's best real ale", over more than two decades. "The Victorian-style cosy interior and spacious, sunny terrace makes it perfect for all occasions" – the outside is now even more of an attraction given the smart and expanded garden enabled by the new development next door. / SW6 1RX; www.theatlaspub.co.uk; @theatlasfulham; 10 pm.

AUGUSTINE KITCHEN SW11 £54 443

63 BATTERSEA BRIDGE RD 020 7978 7085 6–4C

This "great local French bistro" offers "well priced and very well executed" dishes, based on the cuisine of Evian on the shore of Lake Geneva. It's "easily missed in its location" just south of Battersea Bridge. / SW11 3AU; www.augustine-kitchen.co.uk; @augustinekitchen; closed Mon & Sun D.

AULIS LONDON W1 £195 554

SOHO - ADDRESS ON BOOKING 020 3948 9665 –

Lakeland-based uber-chef Simon Rogan's eight-seater development kitchen offers "a fascinating and unique experience", featuring "some of the most creative dishes in London". Diners pre-book (at £195 a head) and go to a secret Soho address, where a dozen surprise courses and paired wines are prepared in front of them by two chefs. "We went for our anniversary but the other six diners pulled out; what could have been awkward became a once-in-a-lifetime exclusive pampering!". / W1; aulis. london; @AulisSimonRogan.

AUTHENTIQUE EPICERIE & BAR NW5 £46 343

114-116 FORTESS ROAD 020 3609 6602 9–2C

"A must for wine-lovers" – this year-old combination of wine bar, restaurant and shop in Tufnell Park is a "real treasure-trove", showcasing the produce of the French-speaking world, including 650 wines. "Given the retail side of the operation, you could just buy the stuff and eat it all at home, but it would be a shame to miss out on the buzz" – and the "fresh and well-presented small menu". Top Tip – "book a table if you don't want to sit on a stool". / NW5 5HL; authentique-epicerie.com.

THE AVALON SW12 £53 344

16 BALHAM HILL 020 8675 8613 11–2C

"A great pub!" (part of the Three Cheers Pub Co) down Balham way, with smart interior and gorgeous, big outside garden, and where steaks and 'artisan pizzas' are mainstays of a comprehensive menu: "even if the pub was boring, I'd come back time and again for the fantastic food!" / SW12 9EB; www.theavalonlondon.com; @threecheerspubs; 10.30 pm, Sun 9 pm.

L'AVENTURE NW8 £72 345

3 BLENHEIM TERRACE 020 7624 6232 9–3A

"A romantic hideaway obscured, by climbing plants, from passers-by" – Catherine Parisot's St John's Wood institution has just celebrated its 40th anniversary, serving "classic French cuisine" that is "unchanged in years". "It is old-fashioned but never boring, conventional but not too formal, simple but not too basic, traditional but still progressive". To the relief of her many fans, Madame C is targeting her half-century here: "she is always there to come and talk to you, the waiters are very friendly and they want you to have a good time". / NW8 0EH; www.laventure.co.uk; 11 pm; closed Sat L & Sun.

THE AVENUE SW1 £53 333

7-9 ST JAMES'S STREET 020 7321 2111 3–4D

This "slick and professional" modern brasserie in the heart of St James's from D&D London is "very popular at lunchtime with business people" – in particular for the "glass-fronted private room which allows for confidential conversation without being stuffy". "The location is easy to get to", and the food "caters for all tastes". / SW1A 1EE; www.avenue-restaurant.co.uk; @avenuestjames; 10.30 pm; closed Sat L & Sun.

AVIARY EC2 £64 223

10TH FLOOR, 22-25 FINSBURY SQUARE 020 3873 4060 13–2A

"A pleasant location overlooking the City" is the headline attraction at this 10th-floor eyrie on Finsbury Square, which has a big outside terrace. "The food is fine but not very inspiring, and service can be a bit away with the fairies" – maybe try it out for brunch. / EC2A 1DX; aviarylondon.com; @AviaryLDN.

AWESOME THAI SW13   £32   342

68 CHURCH RD   020 8563 7027   11–1A

"Family-run, friendly and popular" – an easy-going but efficient Thai local, which does a roaring trade at least in part due to its location, bang opposite the busy Olympic Studios indie cinema in Barnes. That said, the food is "delicious and inexpensive" and "feels like authentic home cooking". / SW13 0DQ; www.awesomethai.co.uk; 10.30 pm, Sun 10 pm; Mon-Thu D only, Fri-Sun open L & D.

LE BAB W1   £47   423

**TOP FLOOR, KINGLY COURT
020 7439 9222   4–2B**

"Posh kebabs bring the late-night, post-pub favourite to a new level" at this "fun little place at the top of Kingly Court", thanks to "quality ingredients and a standard of cooking (and imagination) not available elsewhere". / W1B 5PW; www.eatlebab.com; @EatLeBab; 10 pm, Sun 7 pm; booking max 6 may apply.

BABA G'S   43–

**724 STABLES MARKET, NW1 07725 230995
9–2B
POP BRIXTON, 49 BRIXTON STATION ROAD,
SW9 07725 230995   11–1D**

"Everything here is great, but I totally loved the paneer burger" – an alternative to the best-selling bhangra burger on the menu of these popular pop-ups, in POP Brixton and now also Vinegar Yard, SE1. After over ten years in the game, the business shifted up a gear in May 2019 (too late for survey feedback) with the opening (flush with £300k of investment having won BBC2's 'My Million Pound Menu') of the new forever-home listed here: a 50-seater in Camden Town's Stables Market. / www.bhangraburger.com; @BabaGsfood.

BABABOOM   £34   322

**189 UPPER STREET, N1 07715 525203
9–2D
30 BATTERSEA RISE, SW11 07809 903181
11–2C**

"A great local for a quick dinner" – these cheery pitstops in Battersea and Islington offer superior kebabs and mezze, alongside craft beer and other drinks. Top Tip – bottomless frozen margaritas with their weekend brunch deal. / www.bababoom.london; @bababoomlondon.

BABETTE SE15   £45   333

57 NUNHEAD LANE   020 3172 2450   1–4D

Nunhead ain't overburdened with super eating options, and this French-owned, converted old Truman pub is one of the best: "its sharing boards are tops for a cheap 'n' cheerful meal"; and "it never fails to give great customer service". / SE15 3TR; www.babettenunhead.com; @babettenunhead; 11 pm, Fri & Sat midnight, Sun

5 pm; closed Mon & Tue, Wed & Thu D only, Fri & Sat L & D, Sun L only.

BABUR SE23   £57   554

119 BROCKLEY RISE   020 8291 2400   1–4D

"In Forest Hill… who knew?"; this "off-the-beaten-track" culinary mecca has, in fact, been "brilliant for years" (it opened in 1985) and "these guys just keep on delivering the goods". It's not just the "magnificent cooking", often featuring game, or "seriously divine cocktails" (some of them "super spicy") – the ambience too "is strikingly elegant given the mundane locale" of the distant south London 'burbs. Top Tip – "best experienced when they do their special seasonal menus and events". / SE23 1JP; www.babur.info; @BaburRestaurant; 11.30 pm; No shorts.

BACCO TW9   £59   332

39-41 KEW RD   020 8332 0348   1–4A

The well-priced pre-show menu is popular with Richmond's theatre-goers at this "excellent local Italian" – handy for both the Orange Tree and Richmond Theatres – it's a "calm and pleasant" standby for "well-cooked cuisine". / TW9 2NQ; www.bacco-restaurant.co.uk; @BaccoRichmond; 11 pm; closed Sun D.

BAGERIET WC2   £12   433

24 ROSE ST   020 7240 0000   5–3C

"The best cinnamon buns", "freshly cooked cakes" and "good coffee" make this "tiny Swedish café a good pitstop for cultural activities in Covent Garden". "Just a pity it's so small you can't always get in". / WC2E 9EA; www.bageriet.co.uk; @BagerietLondon; 7 pm; L & early evening only, closed Sun; No bookings.

BALA BAYA SE1   £64   322

**ARCH 25, OLD UNION YARD ARCHES, 229
UNION STREET   020 8001 7015   10–4B**

"Unusual, imaginative and tasty Israeli cuisine" takes centre stage at this "lively modern Tel Aviv-style café" with cocktail bar, in a Southwark railway arch, from former Ottolenghi chef Eran Tibi. / SE1 0LR; balabaya.co.uk; @bala_baya; 11.30 pm, Sun 5 pm; closed Sun D.

BALADY NW11   £23   342

750 FINCHLEY ROAD   020 8458 2064   1–1B

"Israeli street food with attitude" – in particular the "lovely falafels" – win nothing but praise for this top "cheap 'n' cheerful" kosher bar in Temple Fortune (where most surfaces are wipe clean). It's no criticism of the place to say that Giles Coren awarding it 9/10 this year may have been over-egging the shakshuka a little. / NW11 7TH.

BALTHAZAR WC2   £73   224

4 - 6 RUSSELL ST   020 3301 1155   5–3D

"This American-style French brasserie" in Covent Garden – an offshoot of Keith McNally's downtown NYC institution – has a

"great atmosphere any time of day": "love the decor as you enter". It's "a large space but a very cosy one", and, say fans, "not outrageously priced considering its position and what it must have cost to create". But at times it's "a victim of its own success – packed, loud and slow, with staff trying heroically to cope", and "the food is not exactly world-shattering", just "fine in a 'here's one I prepared earlier and heated up' sort of way". Top Tip – "it's very good for breakfast, which is less costly than other meals here". / WC2B 5HZ; www.balthazarlondon.com; @balthazarlondon; midnight, Sun 11 pm.

BALTIC SE1   £66   334

74 BLACKFRIARS RD   020 7928 1111   10–4A

"A real surprise" near The Cut – this well-established fixture (which opened in 2001) has a relatively "humble entrance", which opens onto a "great space": an intriguingly converted Georgian factory, with a fun bar, and an unexpectedly large, "light-filled" dining room. The cuisine is enjoyably unusual too: "modern Polish – not the usual heavy, East European dishes", but "gutsy" and "always imaginative, with new and traditional choices". Go easy on the vodka though: over 60 varieties, all served straight from the deep freeze in frozen glasses. / SE1 8HA; www.balticrestaurant.co.uk; @balticlondon; 11.15 pm, Sun 10.30 pm; closed Mon L.

BANCONE WC2   £47   543

**39 WILLIAM IV STREET   020 7240 8786
5–4C**

"Superbly-flavourful" pasta dishes at "extremely good-value" prices – especially for the West End – make Louis Korovilas's "handy" yearling "one of the better options in the tourist centre" of town, just off Trafalgar Square. Some reporters feel it's "let down by the long, narrow shape of the restaurant", but more commonly it's judged an "elegant, buzzing, if packed space". / WC2N 4DD; www.bancone.co.uk; @bancone.pasta.

BANG BANG ORIENTAL NW9   £43   223

399 EDGWARE ROAD   NO TEL   1–1A

"A recreation of a Singapore food court", this vast space in Colindale has a "huge choice of different Oriental foods" – "everything from dim sum to Korean". The main challenge is that "quality varies hugely" – "not everything is a hit but it's never dull, kids love it, and it's full of Asian families". Top Tip – "the bao from mainland China are excellent" / NW9 0AS; www.bangbangoriental.com; @Bangbangofh.

BÁNH BÁNH   £42   332

**46 PECKHAM RYE, SE15 020 7207 2935
1–4D
326 COLDHARBOUR LANE, SW9
020 7737 5888 11–2D**

"A small but well-executed menu" and "great cocktails" win general applause for this "tasty, cheap 'n' cheerful local Vietnamese" in Peckham Rye, now with a Brixton spin-off. The Nguyen family use their chef-grandmother's recipes from 1940s Saigon. / www.banhbanh.com; @BanhBanhHQ

BANNERS N8　£52　2 3 4

21 PARK RD　020 8348 2930　9–1C

"Perfect for breakfast" – Juliette Banner's "very family-friendly", neighbourhood diner has been a treasured staple of Crouch End life since it opened in 1992 (and chef Tim Peterman has been in charge of the stoves all this time too). By contrast, its wacky mix of world food cuisine makes it "a bit of an unreliable option for dinner" though. / N8 8TE; www.bannersrestaurant.com; 11 pm, Fri 11.30 pm, Sat midnight, Sun 10.30 pm; No Amex.

BAO　£38　4 3 3

31 WINDMILL ST, W1 020 3011 1632　5–1A
53 LEXINGTON ST, W1 07769 627811　4–2C
13 STONEY STREET, SE1 020 3967 5407　10–4C
NETIL MARKET, 13-23 WESTGATE STREET, E8　NO TEL　14–2B

"A hole-in-the-wall type place, but some of the best buns in London!" – these "hipsterish", if "haphazard" Taiwanese cafés in Soho, Fitzrovia, and now also Borough, have made a big name for their "sensationally tasty" steamed buns and other "inventive, delicious plates": superb "homely food at very reasonable prices". The new SE1 branch, opened in Spring 2019, has a grab-and-go delivery hatch and a karaoke room upstairs; and both here and in Fitzrovia you can book – at Soho you run the gauntlet of a big queue and it's more "rushed". / baolondon.com; @bao_london; W1F Mon-Wed 10 pm, Thu-Sat 10.30 pm, W1T Mon-Sat 10 pm, E8 Sat 4 pm; W1F & W1T closed Sun, E8 open Sat L only; W1 no bookings, E8 takeout only.

BAO & BING W1　£40　3 3 4

22 PADDINGTON STREET　020 3873 7271　2–1A

For a fun night out with the girls, promising early-days reports on this slick new cocktail and dining concept, in Marylebone, from the former CEO of the Ping Pong dim sum chain (similar DNA here), which mixes tasty bao buns and other Taiwanese, street-food fare ('inspired by night street markets of Taipei and Jiufen', apparently) with yummy cocktails, and sleek design (to 'take you all the way back to the 1950s and 1960s teahouses of Xinyi district'). / W1U 5QY; www.baoandbing.com; @baoandbing.

BAOZI INN　3 3 3

24 ROMILLY STREET, W1 020 7287 6877　5–3A
8 SOUTHWARK STREET, SE1 10–4C

"Spicy noodles and tasty bao make for a dependable staple for quick eats in Chinatown" at the original Newport Court branch of this growing chain: the brainchild of Wei Shao, who helped popularise Sichuan cuisine with Bar Shu back in the day. A Soho offshoot followed in 2018, and mid-August 2019 saw the launch of a new three-storey, 120-cover, flagship near Borough Market (and there's also a stall in Market Halls Victoria). The exact offering

varies from branch to branch but, in general, meals are "extremely satisfying and reasonably priced". / baoziinn.com.

THE BAPTIST GRILL, L'OSCAR HOTEL WC1　£91　3 4 4

2-6 SOUTHAMPTON ROW　020 7405 5555　2–1D

A former HQ of the Baptist Church provides the gracious quarters for this swish, new Holborn hotel, whose luxurious dining room's cuisine is produced by Tony Fleming (who held a Michelin star at his former gaff, The Angler). Thin feedback supports the view that this late-2018 opening remains somewhat off-the-radar for many Londoners, but such as we have suggests it's worth discovering: "I used to go to Baptist Council meetings in the building so was intrigued to see how it had worked out: the answer is well! I also worried from some of the hotel's descriptions that it would all be a bit up-itself, but it was better than I expected: the cooking was very good indeed – not too fussy and full of flavour – and there's a very good wine list too. Service was OK: I could have just done without the waiters' psychedelic jackets…" / WC1B 4AA; baptistgrill.com.

BAR BOULUD, MANDARIN ORIENTAL SW1　£72　3 3 3

66 KNIGHTSBRIDGE　020 7201 3899　6–1D

"Consistency has always been key" at this NYC-import in the basement of a landmark Knightsbridge hotel, "so it's not surprising it reopened after the fire here and did not skip a beat". Oft touted by some for "the best hamburger in town" ("beating the specialist chains"), it actually "offers a surprisingly wide range of dishes, although the French bistro options tend to be best", and fans say they are delivered "with just the right amount of friendliness". It's very much casual luxury, however, and there's also quite a widely held view that "for such a glamorous hotel, everything here is distinctly average", especially at very Knightsbridge prices. Top Tip – in summer, you can now dine outside on the 'Bar Boulud Terrace' overlooking Hyde Park (first-come first-served, weather permitting). / SW1X 7LA; www.barboulud.com; @barbouludlondon; 11.45 pm, Sun 10.45 pm; No trainers.

BAR DOURO SE1　£56　4 4 4

ARCH 25B FLAT IRON SQUARE, UNION ST 020 7378 0524 10–4B

A "unique menu" of "delicious Portuguese tapas" that "really pack flavour" makes this authentically tiled bar near Borough Market "just a delight"; especially in summer when its "lovely outdoor seating area" makes it "an ideal place to spend an afternoon." "The knowledgeable staff have great wine recommendations" from the "interesting" all-Portuguese list. / SE1 1TD; www.bardouro.co.uk; @BarDouro; 11.30 pm; booking max 4 may apply.

BAR ESTEBAN N8　£53　3 4 3

29 PARK RD　020 8340 3090　1–1C

"Brilliant upmarket tapas" have Crouch Enders purring that "we're lucky to have this as our local Spanish restaurant". It's run by "lovely people" and has some "really interesting Spanish wines from smaller vineyards". Top Tip – "paella lunches at the weekend are great fun with the kids". / N8 8TE; www.baresteban.com; @barestebanN8; 9.30 pm, Fri & Sat 10.30 pm, Sun 9 pm; closed weekday L; booking max 8 may apply.

BAR ITALIA W1　£34　2 3 5

22 FRITH ST　020 7437 4520　5–2A

"A special place" – "frozen in time and all the better for it" – this atmospheric Soho institution defies caffeine fashion and is as perfect a location for a cup of coffee today as it was when it opened in 1949. It operates 24/7 – and don't even think of bringing your laptop... / W1D 4RF; www.baritaliasoho.co.uk; @TheBaristas; open 24 hours, Sun 4 am; No Amex; no booking.

THE BARBARY WC2　£52　5 5 4

16 NEAL'S YARD　AWAITING TEL　5–2C

"If fantastic food is your priority rather than comfort", make a bee-line for The Palomar's "fun" and "intimate" younger sibling in Neal's Yard, which majors in "the most tasty and exciting" North African-inspired tapas, all served at the bar. "In theory this is everything I dislike in a restaurant: countertop seating only, loud music, and sharing-plates. But it blew every prejudice out of the water. The food was exquisite – lots of flavours I hadn't had before – and the ones I had, perfectly produced. Fantastic wine, wonderful atmosphere; and despite being alongside fellow diners at the counter, it felt private and relaxed. A really special evening". "I'd go all the time if only you could book!" / WC2H 9DP; www.thebarbary.co.uk; @barbarylondon; 10 pm, Sun 9 pm; no booking.

LA BARCA SE1　£68　3 3 3

80-81 LOWER MARSH　020 7928 2226　10–4A

"A lovely and cosy, family-run Italian", "handily placed near Waterloo", which "has been a feature of the area for years" (well over 30). It's always been "quite expensive", but for traditional trattoria fare it's a "go-to" for some diners, including as a business lunch spot. / SE1 7AB; www.labarca-ristorante.com; @labarca1976; closed Sat L & Sun; Booking max 12 may apply.

BARRAFINA　£59　5 5 5

26-27 DEAN STREET, W1 020 7813 8016　4–1D
10 ADELAIDE ST, WC2 020 7440 1456　5–4C
43 DRURY LN, WC2 020 7440 1456　5–2D
COAL DROPS YARD, N1　9–3C

"The tapas is perfection and the equal of Cal Pep in Barcelona" at the Hart Bros' "vibrant" chain of small (typically 30 covers) no-bookings bars, which its vast fanclub acclaim as the "the best tapas in London or in the UK or perhaps even in Europe north of the Pyrenees!", with "delicious, ultra-fresh seafood" a particular highlight. The preparation at the counter is "still a great piece of theatre" and – buoyed by its "exceptional, friendly, enthusiastic and knowledgeable staff" – helps create a feelgood experience. "Don't be put off by the queuing – it's part of the fun: sipping on Cava and nibbling on Jamon as you snake your way to the front of the line!". This year, the group added a "slick outfit in the new Coal Drops Yard development" – "it lacks a bit of the charm and vibe of those in Soho and Covent Garden, but the edibles are still very edible!" / www.barrafina.co.uk; 11 pm, Sun 10 pm; no booking, max group 4.

BARRICA W1 £55 3 3 3

62 GOODGE ST 020 7436 9448 2–1B

"Popular for a good reason", this Goodge Street spot is valued for "authentic tapas, served fast and fresh, with knowledgeable and friendly Spanish staff to guide you through the choices". It's "great value" for central London, but can get "hot and cramped", with the "buzzy and loud" atmosphere rising to "raucous" on busy evenings. / W1T 4NE; www.barrica.co.uk; @barricatapas; 10.30 pm; closed Sun.

BARSHU W1 £47 4 2 2

28 FRITH ST 020 7287 6688 5–3A

"Spice heaven!" – this "old favourite" is "worth a detour north of Shaftesbury Avenue" to "experience genuinely interesting and mouth-popping Sichuan specials" – so "be brave when you order". The food-writer, China expert and consultant "Fuchsia Dunlop's touch makes it a regional Chinese diamond in the Chinatown rough". / W1D 5LF; www.barshurestaurant.co.uk; @BarshuLondon; 10.30 pm, Fri & Sat 11 pm.

BEARS ICE CREAM W12 £7

244 GOLDHAWK ROAD 020 3441 4982 8–1B

An ice cream parlour with a difference – a mouthwatering selection of toppings, all mixed with just one flavour of ice – from an Icelandic recipe – at this simple little shop (with small garden), on the busy gyratory north of Ravenscourt Park. More reports please! / W12 9PE; www.bearsicecream.co.uk; @bears_icecream; 8.30 pm; L & early evening only; No bookings.

BEAST W1 £107 2 2 2

3 CHAPEL PL 020 7495 1816 3–1B

"An amazing place for steaks and spider crab... but, my god, is it expensive!" Nothing changes at Goodman group's candle-lit, surf 'n' turf extravaganza, just off Oxford Street, which bills itself as 'a unique gastronomic experience featuring Norwegian King Crab and hand-selected, dry-aged Nebraskan Angus beef. But, after five years in operation, what's actually most striking is how little feedback we receive nowadays... / W1G 0BG;

www.beastrestaurant.co.uk; @beastrestaurant; 10.30 pm; closed Mon & Sun; May need 7+ to book.

THE BEGGING BOWL SE15 £49 4 3 2

168 BELLENDEN RD 020 7635 2627 1–4D

Spicy scoff "continues to impress at this authentic and very busy Peckham fixture" – a corner site with terrace, which has been a well-known feature of the local food scene since 2012 (and was refurbed in December 2018). It's not Thai-run: chef and co-owner Jane Alty worked at David Thompson's much-vaunted Nahm (long RIP) back in the dim and distant past. / SE15 4BW; www.thebeggingbowl.co.uk; @thebeggingbowl; 9.45 pm, Sun 9.15 pm; no booking.

BELLAMY'S W1 £62 3 4 4

18-18A BRUTON PL 020 7491 2727 3–2B

"Everybody is smartly attired which makes a nice change" at Gavin Rankin's (ex-MD of Annabel's) "old-fashioned-in-a-good-way" bastion: "a picture-lined dining room", tucked away in a quiet mews, which – to those of a blueblooded disposition – makes "a much more attractive choice than some of its flashier Mayfair rivals". "Well-drilled", traditionally-attired staff deliver "classic" – if "fairly simple" – Anglo/French cuisine and, in particular, the package makes "an excellent choice for a business lunch" (of the kind where "a couple of dry Martinis before you get started will not raise an eyebrow"). / W1J 6LY; www.bellamysrestaurant.co.uk; 10.30 pm; closed Sat L & Sun.

BELVEDERE RESTAURANT W8 £72 2 4 5

OFF ABBOTSBURY RD IN HOLLAND PARK 020 7602 1238 8–1D

"There's not a better setting in London for romance" than this 17th-century former ballroom inside Holland Park: "a walk to the restaurant through the greenery is a joy, the space itself is elegant and light; and in the summer, the terrace offers al fresco dining overlooking the formal gardens". Some reports still talk of the "pretty ordinary" modern British food and "adequate" service that's often dogged the place, but overall feedback was more positive this year: "its lean years of so-so food and service are behind it" – "it's a shame more people don't go". / W8 6LU; www.belvedererestaurant.co.uk; @BelvedereW8; 11 pm, Sun 3.30 pm; closed Sun D.

BENARES W1 £104 2 2 2

12A BERKELEY SQUARE HOUSE, 020 7629 8886 3–3B

Mixed reports this year on this swish first-floor Indian, in the heart of Mayfair, which severed ties in August 2018 with its original founder. Fans say it's "still excellent, despite Atul Kochhar's departure", serving "very nicely balanced, spiced and well-prepared" Indian cuisine that offers "a real twist compared to what's usually found in the UK". Its ratings

have waned, though, with gripes re-emerging about its "windowless", slightly "dull" interior, but more concerningly about cooking that "may not justify the price tag": "just go to Dishoom, get better food, have more fun and save your cash!" / W1J 6BS; www.benaresrestaurant.co.uk; @benaresofficial; 10.45 pm, Sun 9.45 pm; closed Sun L; No trainers; booking max 10 may apply.

BENTLEY'S W1 £90 3 3 3

11-15 SWALLOW ST 020 7734 4756 4–4B

"We always sit at the bar and enjoy superb oysters!" – so say fans of the "more casual downstairs" at Richard Corrigan's "elegant" stalwart, near Piccadilly Circus, which some diners prefer over the "quieter" (prettier) upstairs dining rooms. Now over a century old, this remains one of the capital's favourite destinations for fish that's "invariably good" and "classic seafood" (with lobster, oysters, "epic fish pie", "top fish 'n' chips with mushy peas" and "the best dressed crab in town" all rating mention). Most diners love its "very relaxed" style (although one or two feel staff can be a bit "over-familiar"), and there are pitfalls to its super-handy West End location: it can seem "rather touristy"; "tables are closely packed"; and prices are a bit "elevated". Top Tip – "fabulous outside terrace: summer lunch in the alleyway is bliss". / W1B 4DG; www.bentleys.org; @bentleys_london; 10.30 pm, Sun 10 pm; No shorts; booking max 8 may apply.

BERBER & Q £52 4 4 4

ARCH 338 ACTON MEWS, E8 020 7923 0829 14–2A
EXMOUTH MARKET, EC1 020 7837 1726 10–1A

The tang of Tel Aviv-meets-North African tastes infuse the lipsmacking charcoal-grilled meats (and also the veg) at Josh Kat's Haggerston railway arch, which is mostly a walk-in style place (though there are a few tables for bookings). But, in fact, it's the more recent Exmouth Market spin-off that inspires more feedback nowadays: "Having Shawarma Bar in the title might make it sound like a kebab-shop but, it's actually an unassumingly intimate restaurant, with great sharing plates and grill dishes that don't break the bank". And "it really punches above its weight in terms of the seriously delicious Israeli/Eastern Mediterranean dishes it turns out (the rotisserie chicken is amazing) complemented by an exciting, low-intervention wine list".

BERENJAK W1 £57 4 4 4

27 ROMILLY STREET 5–2A

"Fun and trendy" Persian newcomer in Soho – a busy, small (35-seater), no-bookings dive that's part of JKS Restaurants's portfolio, where the seats at the counter look onto a grill, rotisserie and clay oven. On the menu from Iranian chef Kian Samyani, "gentrified" kebabs (arguably "it's really all about the meat", this place), flatbreads and mezze that are "interesting and full of flavour". / W1D 5AL; berenjaklondon. com.

Bancone WC2

Bleeding Heart Restaurant EC1

BERNARDI'S W1 £66 343

62 SEYMOUR STREET 020 3826 7940
2–2A

A stylish modern Italian where Marylebone meets Bayswater. It's "particularly good for a late, louche lunch", although it can be "difficult to carry on a conversation" with the associated "buzz". The food? – "inconsistent but really enjoyable nevertheless". / W1H 5BN; www.bernardis.co.uk; @BernardisLondon; Mon - Sat 10.30pm, Sun 9.30pm.

THE BERNERS TAVERN W1 £93 214

10 BERNERS ST 020 7908 7979 **3–1D**

To be "blown away by the decor" – with its "beautiful high ceiling and sense of spaciousness" – is still the dominant reaction to Jason Atherton's glam dining room inside Ian Shrager's Edition hotel, north of Oxford Street. "Wish the food could be at the same level as the interior" is another common theme, however, as is ever-more "arrogant" or "haphazard" service, and there's a general feeling that, on current form, the place is "serving a transient market with its glorious setting rather than focussing on the product and delivery". / W1T 3NP; www.bernerstavern.com; @bernersTavern; 11.45 pm, Sun 10.15 pm.

BERTO N7

155 HOLLOWAY ROAD **9–2D**

From the owners of Zia Lucia, this smallish (40-cover), summer 2019 newcomer aims to bring a similar experimental approach to pasta to that which has won Zia Luca a following for pizza, using different flours for its homemade creations. 'Pasta – Roll with it' is the catchy motto. / N7 8LX; berto.uk.

BEST MANGAL £40 432

619 FULHAM RD, SW6 020 7610 0009 **6–4A**
104 NORTH END RD, W14 020 7610 1050
8–2D
66 NORTH END RD, W14 020 7602 0212
8–2D

Every postcode boasts its own "best kebab in London", but this trio in Fulham haa a better claim than most after 23 years' service: "all freshly made and truly delicious", fans say they're "one in a million!" / www.bestmangal.com; midnight, Sat 1 am; no Amex; book online.

THE BETTERMENT W1

THE BILTMORE, 39-44 GROSVENOR SQUARE 020 7629 9400 **3–2A**

Due to open in September 2019, Hilton's new luxury Mayfair hotel has signed Jason Atherton's Social Company to oversee all the food; former City Social head chef Paul Walsh will be heading up the stoves at this all-day, brasserie-style operation. The debut is bang opposite the recent opening from Atherton's former employer, Gordon Ramsay's Lucky Cat, and much has been made in the press of the two 'going head-to-head'. / W1K 2HP; lxrhotels3.hilton.com/lxr/biltmore-mayfair/dine.

BIBENDUM SW3 £134 334

81 FULHAM RD 020 7589 1480 **6–2C**

"The iconic architecture of the Michelin building", in South Kensington, helps make its first-floor dining room (converted by Sir Terence Conran, and opened in 1987) a modern classic, and provides a "stunning" location for a meal (in particular at lunch). Claude Bosi is entering his third year at the stoves now, and wins strong praise from most diners for his "first-class-but-rich" French cuisine, which creates some "wow" moments. A minority, though, feel the cooking here "is not up to the very high standard Bosi set when in Ludlow and Mayfair", and consider prices "exorbitant": "I thought tiny, overpriced portions of nouvelle cuisine were a thing of the past… until I ate here". / SW3 6RD; www.bibendum.co.uk; @bibendumltdSW3; 11 pm, Sun 10.30 pm; booking max 12 may apply.

BIBENDUM OYSTER BAR SW3 £55 334

MICHELIN HOUSE, 81 FULHAM ROAD 020 7581 5817 **6–2C**

"Expensive for what it is but very enjoyable" – the unchanging equation over the years at this luxurious seafood café, off the beautiful and atmospheric foyer of the Michelin building. Nowadays part of Claude Bosi's regime, he has added hot items (fish pie, moules, fish 'n' chips etc) to an offer that has traditionally focussed on raw seafood and cold platters. / SW3 6RD; www.bibendum.co.uk; @bibendumrestaurant; 10 pm; closed Sun D; no booking.

BIBIMBAP SOHO £34 332

10 CHARLOTTE ST, W1 020 7287 3434
2–1C
11 GREEK ST, W1 020 7287 3434 **5–2A**
39 LEADENHALL MKT, EC3 020 72839165
10–2D

For a Korean bite on the go, try these Soho and Fitzrovia canteens (and there's also a take-away in the City's Leadenhall Market), whose trade bibimbaps (rice with a topping) make for "delicious food, served quickly and at great prices". Top Tip – "Korean Fried Chicken is a naughty-but-nice treat packed full of flavour". / 11pm, EC3 3 pm; W1 Sun, EC3 Sat & Sun; no bookings.

BIG EASY £61 323

12 MAIDEN LN, WC2 020 3728 4888 **5–3D**
332-334 KING'S RD, SW3 020 7352 4071
6–3C
CROSSRAIL PL, E14 020 3841 8844 **12–1C**

"Good basic BBQ and fried foods" plus "similar lobster and seafood options" (and "live music is another plus") have kept this gen-u-ine American crabshack an always-packed-and-noisy feature of the King's Road for nearly 30 years. "Good-sized portions" and good times are also reported at its newer, if less-established ,spin-offs in Covent Garden and Canary Wharf. / www.bigeasy.co.uk; @bigeasytweet; Mon-Thu 11 pm, Fri & Sat 11.30 pm, Sun 10.30 pm.

THE BINGHAM TW10 £66 345

61-63 PETERSHAM ROAD 020 8940 0902
1–4A

"A super-pretty location" helps make the dining room of this Richmond boutique hotel – rebranded this year as the Bingham Riverhouse – "unbeatable for a special meal". To accompany the "lovely ambience", and "great views over the Thames", the food is an attraction in itself: "the menu reflects the seasons well and is always delivered to a high standard". / TW10 6UT; www.thebingham.co.uk; @thebingham; 10 pm; closed Sun D; No trainers.

THE BIRD IN HAND W14 £53 434

88 MASBRO ROAD 020 7371 2721 **8–1C**

"Not your average pub selling pizzas… these are the real deal… some of the best ever!" This stylish pub-conversion in the backstreets of Olympia is cousin to the Oak chain, and has a similarly high quality offering. "The locals obviously know they're onto a good thing as it's busy on a Tuesday night…" / W14 0LR; www.thebirdinhandlondon.com; @TBIHLondon; 10 pm, Sun 9.15 pm; booking weekdays only.

BISTRO AIX N8 £62 223

54 TOPSFIELD PDE, TOTTENHAM LN
020 8340 6346 **9–1C**

A "long-time, local favourite" – this "relaxed", retro bistro brings the classic flavours of France to Crouch End. Chef-proprietor Lynne Sanders and her team send "reliably good food" out from the kitchen. / N8 8PT; www.bistroaix.co.uk; @bistroaixlondon; 10 pm, Fri & Sat 11 pm; Mon-Thu D only, Fri-Sun open L & D; No Amex.

BISTRO MIREY
SW6   £55   433

98 LILLIE ROAD   020 3092 6969   8–2D

"Striving hard" in a tough location – near the gyratory at the top of North End Road Market – your heart goes out to this "useful and pleasant small Italo-Japanese bistro' owned by 'chef' Mirey and Ko Ito. "Simple classics like steak and chips are well executed", but there are also Japanese notes that add an interesting slant to familiar dishes. / SW6 7SR; www.bistromirey.com; @bistromirey.

[CLOSED watermark overprinted]

BISTRO UNION
SW4   £57   322

40 ABBEVILLE RD   020 7042 6400   11–2D

Clapham-star Trinity's younger sibling gains solid ratings for bringing affordable British bistro fare to the smart 'Abbeville Village' enclave. One or two diners "expect slightly better" from a patron of Adam Byatt's calibre though – "adequate but didn't quite hit the spot". / SW4 9NG; www.bistrounion.co.uk; @BistroUnion; 10 pm, Sun 8 pm; booking max 8 may apply.

BISTRO VADOUVAN
SW15   £63   443

30 BREWHOUSE LANE   020 3475 3776   11–2B

"Really interesting, Asian-fusion notes" to the essentially modern European dishes – "serious cooking, bursting with flavour" – aren't the only good feature of this Indian-run two-year-old: it has a "great location near Putney Bridge", and service is "super-friendly". "It's good to have somewhere reasonable in Putney, which is not well served by restaurants". / SW15 2JX; bistrovadouvan.co.uk; @BistroVadouvan; 10 pm.

BISTROTHEQUE
E2   £68   324

23-27 WADESON ST   020 8983 7900   14–2B

"This crisp, clean, chic warehouse" with "big industrial windows" in Cambridge Heath is, say fans, the "perfect, perfect, perfect spot for a lovely weekend brunch" or a "lush lunch with oysters and Champagne". A hipster haven for 15 years, it still rates well for its "delicious food" and an atmosphere boosted by live music. / E2 9DR; www.bistrotheque.com; @Bistrotheque; 10.30 pm, Fri & Sat 11 pm; closed weekday L.

BLACK AXE MANGAL
N1   £53   433

156 CANONBURY ROAD   NO TEL   9–2D

"Unique! Hard rock, offal, penises on the walls, skateboards… all plus rocking cooking from an ex-St John chef" – KISS fan, Lee Tiernan's tiny kebab dive near Highbury Corner is "not a place for everyone", but his massively spicy flatbreads "take this kind of dish to the next level", and, for its adoring fanclub, "a brilliant

vibe and superb food make it a must-go". / N1; www.blackaxemangal.com; @blackaxemangal; 10.30 pm, Sun 3 pm; D only Mon-Fri, Sat L & D, Sun L only; no booking.

BLACK BEAR BURGER
E1   £10   53–

BOXPARK SHOREDITCH, 2-10 BETHNAL GREEN ROAD   NO TEL   13–2B

"Amazing and well-considered burgers, plus delicious, crunchy chips" help win very high ratings for this pop-up brand, which has now graduated to Boxpark Shoreditch. The backstory works well: one of the founders grew up on a Devon beef farm: all meat is sourced from the south west from native breeds that are grass-fed and dry-aged on the bone; bacon is from outdoor-bred pigs in the east of England… / E1 6GY; www.blackbearburger.com; @BlackBearBurger.

BLACK DOG BEER HOUSE
TW8   £52   433

17 ALBANY ROAD   020 8568 5688   1–3A

"An amazing newcomer, head and shoulders above the competition locally" – this autumn 2018 opening in Brentford is the brainchild of an Aussie and Canadian couple, Pete and Ash, who have gone for it with their 14 kegs, five real ales, five real ciders and in-house brewery (Fearless Nomad). All this plus a consistently highly-rated menu serving an eclectic mix of funked-up gastro-fare. "You need to book but it's totes fab". / TW8 0NF; www.blackdogbeerhouse.co.uk; @blackdogbeerhse.

BLACK PRINCE
SE11   £46   332

6 BLACK PRINCE RD   020 7582 2818   2–4D

"Good-quality bar food and an exceptional Sunday lunch" continue to win tips for this Kennington hostelry (which film buffs will recognise from the 2014 movie Kingsman). / SE11 6HS; www.theblackprincepub.co.uk; 11 pm.

BLACK RADISH
SW19   £68   443

28 RIDGWAY   020 8617 3960   10–2B

"No choice, but it doesn't matter as everything is delicious" – on weekend evenings there's only a five-course tasting option available at this Wimbledon Village newcomer, and at other services choice is very limited: but judging by the high marks awarded by its local fanclub, no-one minds (in contrast to The Evening Standard's Fay Maschler, who panned the place). / SW19 4QW; www.blackradishsw19.com; @BlackRadishSW19.

BLACK ROE W1   £76   333

4 MILL STREET   020 3794 8448   3–2C

"A club vibe" and "amazing cocktails" help fuel the fun scene at this Hawaiian-inspired Mayfair fixture. The speciality is poké and other "expensive Pacific Rim foods" – sceptics feel dishes are "well done but on the whole lack that special something" but on most accounts

results are "very flavoursome". / W1S 2AX; www.blackroe.com; @blackroe; 10.45 pm; closed Sun.

BLACKLOCK   £45   344

24 GREAT WINDMILL ST, W1   020 3441 6996   4–3D
28 RIVINGTON STREET, EC2   AWAITING TEL   13–1B
13 PHILPOT LANE, EC3   020 7998 7676   10–3D

"Oh my! A meat-lovers' feast awaits!" at these "carnivorous havens", where "evidently very well-sourced produce is expertly cooked and served in great platters of meaty delight!" ("go when you are hungry!"). There are "superb-value steaks", but it's the "mouthwateringly scrumptious" chops that inspire more feedback. Soho and the City occupy "urban-chic" basements, whereas Shoreditch is above-ground and more "warehouse-y". Top Menu Tip – "bargain basement prices on Butchers Block Monday, with £10 corkage if you bring your own wine!" / theblacklock.com; @BlacklockChops.

BLANCHETTE   £56   423

9 D'ARBLAY ST, W1   020 7439 8100   4–1C
204 BRICK LANE, E1   020 7729 7939   13–1C

"Just fab!", say fans of this pair of "rather crammed" French bistros in Soho and Brick Lane offering "delightful and different dishes in a good atmosphere". Served as small or sharing plates, the food is generally "interesting and imaginative", and the "service friendly, if a tiny bit flaky at times". / 11 pm, Sun 9 pm.

BLANDFORD COMPTOIR
W1   £66   333

1 BLANDFORD STREET   020 7935 4626   2–1A

"Wonderful bistro food" – "surprisingly fancy, but very well executed" – matches up to a notably "interesting and well-priced wine list" at this "delightful little wine bar" in Marylebone from Xavier Rousset, the youngest-ever Sommelier of the Year. / W1U 3DA; blandford-comptoir.co.uk; @BlandfordCompt; 10 pm; No Amex.

BLEECKER BURGER   £22   521

205 VICTORIA ST, SW1   NO TEL   2–4B
UNIT B PAVILION BUILDING, SPITALFIELDS MKT, E1   07712 540501   13–2B
BLOOMBERG ARCADE, QUEEN VICTORIA STREET, EC4   AWAITING TEL   10–3C

"There is no finer burger in town: end of!" – Zan Kaufman's tiny group "keeps things simple… and they smash it!". "If you want mega-stacked, crazy combos, with layers and layers of toppings falling out of the side, there are numerous other (excellent) options in London. But if you want the best patties, made with the best aged beef, un-mucked-about-with and served by a bunch of nice people, then Bleecker is just the best there is".

BLEEDING HEART RESTAURANT EC1 £76 334

**BLEEDING HEART YD, GREVILLE ST
020 7242 8238 10–2A**

"A bit of a one-off" – this sprawling, Dickensian, subterranean warren is "hidden away in a cobbled yard that itself is tucked away behind Hatton Garden". "Though very handy for the City, it has a very romantic feel to it", with "quiet out-of-the-way arches and alcoves", but is as well-suited to conspiratorial business lunches as it is to "evening romance". A "superb wine list" adds lustre to fairly traditional Gallic cuisine that's a little "pricey" but "dependable". Top Tip – "excellent-value set menu". / EC1N 8SJ; bleedingheart.co.uk; @bleedingheartyd; 10.30 pm; closed Sat & Sun.

BLIXEN E1 £59 223

**65A BRUSHFIELD STREET   020 7101 0093
13–2C**

Elegant styling – the venue is a former bank made over in the style of a European brasserie – and a handy position by Spitalfields Market help win brunch and business recommendations for this all-day venture. Its ratings are indifferent though, and it takes some flak for "poorly executed food that doesn't merit the price charged". / E1 6AA; www.blixen.co.uk; @BlixenLondon; 11 pm, Sun 8 pm.

BLOOMSBURY STREET KITCHEN WC1

**9-14 BLOOMSBURY STREET   020 7666 2044
2–1C**

The promising, but hitherto under-exploited mix of Mediterranean and Japanese small plates is the crux of the menu offering at this August 2019 opening, which promises 'a modern, day-to-night, neighbourhood restaurant and bar… complemented by a diverse variety of wines, sake and signature cocktails'. / WC1B 3QD; bloomsburystreetkitchen.co.uk; @BloomsStKitchen.

BLUEBIRD SW3 £83 234

350 KING'S ROAD   020 7559 1000   6–3C

This smart D&D London conversion of a Modernist 1920s car showroom on a prominent King's Road site leaves reporters impressed by the venue if rather underwhelmed by the cuisine – "beautiful restaurant and nice service, they just need to up their game food-wise". Situation normal, then, at this large space, which has never really capitalised fully on its potential. / SW3 5UU; www.bluebird-restaurant.co.uk; @bluebirdchelsea; 10.30 pm, Sun 9.30 pm.

BLUEPRINT CAFÉ SE1 £62 334

**28 SHAD THAMES, BUTLER'S WHARF
020 7378 7031 10–4D**

"One of the best views in the capital", over Tower Bridge and the Thames, is the highlight of any meal at this venue from D&D London, on the first floor of the former Design

Museum. Beyond that, there's "no problem with the food or cooking", which can be "surprisingly delicious" nowadays. / SE1 2YD; www.blueprintcafe.co.uk; @BlueprintCafe; 10.30 pm; closed Mon & Sun; no booking.

BOB BOB CITÉ EC3 £88

**LEVEL 8, 122 LEADENHALL STREET
020 3928 6600 10–2D**

Three years and £25m later, Leonid Shutov's City sibling to Soho fave-rave, Bob Bob Ricard, finally burst forth onto the London restaurant scene just as our survey was closing in June 2019. Occupying the third floor of the City's 'Cheesegrater' (aka the Leadenhall Building), it looks a little like a Sci-Fi re-imagining of the decadent Soho original, complete with booths, and new-look 'Presser pour Champagne' buttons. Early feedback (too thin for a full rating) is ecstatic in terms of its potential for business entertaining – bolstered by a comprehensive wine list (with options up to £10k), and Eric Chavot's luxury-brasserie menu – but that fit-out's not going to pay for itself, and the bill is confirmation of the fact. / EC3V 4PE; www.bobbobcite.com; @bobbobcite.

BOB BOB RICARD W1 £98 235

**1 UPPER JAMES STREET   020 3145 1000
4–2C**

"OTT-opulent decor, with a 'push for champagne' button in each booth" have carved a big name for Leonid Shutov's fantastical Soho haunt, whose "high novelty factor" is extremely romantic ("you just have to take a date"). When it comes to Eric Chavot's menu of luxurious classics ("amazing beef Wellington" for example) results undisputedly taste "very nice", but the food is "expensive for what it is, and you get more adventurous cooking at the same price-bracket elsewhere". / W1F 9DF; www.bobbobricard.com; @BobBobRicard; 11.15 pm, Sat midnight, Sun 11.15 pm; closed Sat L; Jacket required.

BOB'S LOBSTER SE1 £37 343

UNIT 71, ST THOMAS STREET 10–4C

"Very fresh lobster, oysters, crab, etc, plus a good choice of wines by the glass" (as you'd expect from the team behind Bedales of Borough) win praise from a small fanclub for this railway arch below London Bridge station – the permanent site for a pop-up whose hallmark is a roving fleet of VW camper vans. / SE1 3QX; www.bobslobster.com; @BOBs_Lobster.

BOCCA DI LUPO W1 £61 543

12 ARCHER ST   020 7734 2223   4–3D

"Italian peasant-food fit for a king" – Jacob Kenedy's "exceptional and distinctive" fixture, a short stroll from Piccadilly Circus, has carved a massive foodie following with its "wonderfully eclectic and ever-changing range of traditional dishes from across the country" (categorised by region, and available in 'small' or 'large

sizes'), with the "exciting" results "so simple and delicious you cannot believe it". "And they're complemented by a staggering wine list" which "is itself a trip through Italy" ("it's worth having a detailed conversation with the wine waiter to discover outstanding vintages at sensible prices" with "lots of interesting options by the glass"). "Unsurprisingly, the place is always jammed", and the "busy, café-style" interior with "closely packed tables" is such that "while mostly delightful, it's bloody noisy" ("if not slightly manic"). But the "efficient and friendly staff" help keep the mood upbeat. Some guests "prefer the counter" – "there's great kitchen theatre perched on the bar stools". / W1D 7BB; www.boccadilupo.com; @boccadilupo; 11 pm, Sun 9.30 pm; booking max 10 may apply.

BOCCONCINO RESTAURANT W1 £108 222

19 BERKELEY ST   020 7499 4510   3–3C

In a prime Mayfair location, this "noisy", Russian-owned Italian wins acceptable ratings, but divides reporters on the subject of value: fans hail it as "wonderful all-round, with a variety of choice and well-presented dishes" (including "top pizza"), but sceptics "although the food is decent, it's majorly overpriced, in particular the wine list". / W1J 8ED; www.bocconcinorestaurant.co.uk; @BocconcinoUK; 10.45 pm.

AL BOCCON DI'VINO TW9 £66 445

**14 RED LION STREET   020 8940 9060
1–4A**

"Always a surprise" – you get what you're given (there's no menu choice) at chef Riccardo Grigolo's set-price Venetian feast in Richmond: an unqualified delight, with multiple courses of "amazing, delicious food" and "excellent service", creating "an atmosphere rarely found elsewhere". / TW9 1RW; www.nonsolovinoltd.co.uk; @alboccondivino; 11 pm; closed Mon, Tue L & Wed L; No Amex.

BODEAN'S £45 222

**10 POLAND ST, W1 020 7287 7575   4–1C
25 CATHERINE ST, WC2 020 7257 2790
5–3D
4 BROADWAY CHAMBERS, SW6
020 7610 0440   6–4A
225 BALHAM HIGH ST, SW17 020 8682 4650
11–2C
169 CLAPHAM HIGH ST, SW4 020 7622 4248
11–2D
201 CITY RD, EC1 020 7608 7230 13–1A
16 BYWARD ST, EC3 020 7488 3883 10–3C**

"A nice, laid-back American buzz" has helped win a loyal following over the years for this small chain of Kansas City-style diners: one of the first in London to bring BBQ indoors. "It's a fun place" (in the right mood) and the food is "decent" and in man-sized portions, but "not particularly special". / www.bodeansbbq.com; 11 pm, Sun 10.30 pm, NW10 10 pm, Fri & Sat 11 pm; booking: min 8.

BOISDALE OF BELGRAVIA SW1 £77 3|2|3

15 ECCLESTON STREET   020 7730 6922   2–4B

"High-quality manfood" (steaks, burgers and other 'proper' main dishes) and a "clubby atmosphere" of whisky, cigars (on a dedicated terrace) and live jazz are the key ingredients at Ranald MacDonald's Scottish-themed Belgravia haunt, which has offshoots in Mayfair, the City and Canary Wharf. It's "not for everyone" – one nay-sayer complained of "worse than pub food" – but for a certain sort of bloke it's "the perfect place – he'll leave happy, content and very satisfied". / SW1W 9LX; www.boisdale.co.uk/belgravia; @boisdale; midnight; closed Sat L & Sun.

BOISDALE OF BISHOPSGATE EC2 £75 3|2|2

SWEDELAND COURT, 202 BISHOPSGATE 020 7283 1763 10–2D

"A complete contrast from the exterior bustle of Bishopsgate" – this Caledonian-themed wine bar (ground floor) and restaurant (basement) provides the same gutsy (some feel "heavy"), meaty Scottish fare of the Belgravian original, and is consistently decently rated food-wise. / EC2M 4NR; www.boisdale.co.uk; @Boisdale; 11 pm; closed Sat & Sun.

BOISDALE OF CANARY WHARF E14 £69 2|3|4

CABOT PLACE   020 7715 5818 12–1C

"For a total dining experience, night out, or even Saturday BBQ", fans of the "spacious-yet-intimate" E14 spin-off from Ranald Macdonald's well-known Belgravian applaud its "eclectic brilliance", and cigar-lovers particularly enjoy the "wonderful humidor and private smoking balcony". The cuisine can seem "expensive for what it is", but even some critics acknowledge: "you don't really go for the food – the entertainment is top-notch, and the great selection of spirits helps dampen any pain from the bill". / E14 4QT; www.boisdale.co.uk/canary-wharf; @boisdaleCW; 11 pm, Wed-Sat midnight, Sun 4 pm; closed Sun D.

BOMBAY BRASSERIE SW7 £72 3|3|2

COURTFIELD ROAD   020 7370 4040   6–2B

This upmarket fixture in South Kensington – on the Indian dining scene in London since 1982 – doesn't make waves nowadays, but still earns solid praise for producing consistently "very good food". Current owner Taj Hotels have spruced up the interior, although the odd reporter is "not keen on the current look". / SW7 4QH; www.bombayb.co.uk; @Bbsw7; 11 pm, Sun 10.30 pm; closed Mon L.

BOMBAY BUSTLE W1 £73 4|3|3

29 MADDOX STREET   020 7290 4470   4–2A

The "fantastic", "properly spicy and tasty" Indian cooking at this Mayfair two-year-old is "definitely of the quality and invention of Jamavar" – its celebrated stablemate nearby. Taking inspiration from Mumbai street and comfort food invites the comparison to an "upmarket Dishoom", while the departure of founding chef Rohit Ghai has thus far only had limited impact on the excellent ratings. / W1S 2PA; www.bombaybustle.com; @BombayBustle.

BOMBAY PALACE W2 £47 5|4|3

50 CONNAUGHT ST   020 7723 8855   7–1D

"A wonderful taste of India!" – the cooking at this plush venue tucked away behind Marble Arch has returned to the heights following an extended period of closure after a fire a few years ago. "The makeover looks great" and "the food is still consistent and authentic", according to relieved regulars. / W2 2AA; www.bombay-palace.co.uk; @bombaypalaceW2; 10.45 pm.

BON VIVANT WC1 £57 3|2|3

75-77 MARCHMONT ST   020 7713 6111   9–4C

"Like an everyday restaurant in a minor French town", this "very busy" Bloomsbury bar/bistro is a "noisy but great fun" neighbourhood amenity: "some dishes are more successful than others" but most are délicieux. / WC1N 1AP; www.bonvivantrestaurant.co.uk.

BONE DADDIES £40 3|3|3

NOVA, VICTORIA ST, SW1   NO TEL   2–4B
30-31 PETER ST, W1 020 7287 8581   4–2D
46-48 JAMES ST, W1 020 3019 7140   3–1A
WHOLE FOODS, KENSINGTON HIGH ST, W8 020 7287 8581   6–1A
24 OLD JAMAICA ROAD, SE16 10–4D
THE BOWER, 211 OLD STREET, EC1 020 3019 6300 13–1A

"Incredibly filling bowls of ramen" – backed up by "interesting menus of delicious food, served quickly with a smile" – attract an enthusiastic crowd to this small chain of hip Japanese-style fast-food bars, although feedback supports the view that "the original in Soho is by far the best". The founder, Aussie-born, Nobu-trained chef Ross Shonhan, has spun off a series of "Asian-fusion" concepts – Flesh & Buns, Shack-Fuyu and his latest, Poke-Don. / www.bonedaddies.com/restaurant/bermondsey; 10 pm, Thu-Sat 11 pm, Sun 9.30 pm; W1, W8, SE16 no bookings.

BONNIE GULL £59 5|3|3

21A FOLEY ST, W1 020 7436 0921   2–1B
22 BATEMAN STREET, W1 020 7436 0921 5–2A

"Like being by the sea in the centre of London!" – this "tiny-but-perfectly-formed" Fitzrovian offers a "wide range of carefully sourced, skilfully prepared, seasonal fish"; and

"if the dining room's a bit noisy and crowded, that's part of the experience" ("you get to know the adjoining table pretty well"), although in the summer months there's also "outside seating in the quiet street". Its even smaller Soho 'shack' spin-off – with a counter at the front and a few tables to the rear – opened a couple of years ago, and scores similarly highly. / www.bonniegull.com; @BonnieGull.

BONOO NW2 £51 4|4|3

675 FINCHLEY ROAD   020 7794 8899   1–1B

"The consistently excellent Indian street food" at this family-run local in Child's Hill – "mostly sharing-plates served tapas-style" – "is tastier and more varied than what's on offer at fancier places in central London". / NW2 2JP; www.bonoo.co.uk; @bonoohampstead; 10.30 pm.

THE BOOKING OFFICE, ST PANCRAS RENAISSANCE HOTEL NW1 £78 2|1|4

EUSTON ROAD   020 7841 3566   9–3C

A "beautiful location" is the particular reason to seek out this this all-day operation, which oldies still recall as the grand ticket office of St Pancras station: nowadays converted in all its Victorian splendour, with an attractive atrium attached. It's "a bit pricey" and "service is all over the place", but – particularly for breakfast, or Sunday lunch – it can be an atmospheric choice on account of food that's "reliable if not spectacular". / NW1 2AR; www.bookingofficerestaurant.com; @StPancrasRen; 11 pm.

BOQUERIA £50 4|3|3

192 ACRE LN, SW2 020 7733 4408 11–2D
278 QUEENSTOWN ROAD, SW8 020 7498 8427 11–1C

"A really interesting menu" of "wonderful modern-style tapas and sharing plates" contributes to "a Spanish gastronomic experience" at this "vibrant" duo in Battersea and Clapham. "The young staff are always so friendly and welcoming". / www.boqueriatapas.com; @BoqueriaTapas.

IL BORDELLO E1 £52 3|3|3

METROPOLITAN WHARF, 70 WAPPING WALL   020 7481 9950 12–1A

"Wapping's favourite" for more than 20 years – this "classic local Italian trat" scores well for its "friendly service", "and the food remains terrific". There's a recurrent complaint – rare elsewhere – that "portions are too large", but to both management and happy regulars this is without doubt a badge of honour. / E1W 3SS; www.ilbordello.com; 11 pm, Sun 10.30 pm; closed Sat L.

BORO BISTRO SE1 £44 2|3|3

6-10 BOROUGH HIGH ST   020 7378 0788 10–3C

"Interesting and very edible food in 'tapas mode'", at "very reasonable prices", is on offer at this contemporary Franco-Hispanic bistro in Borough Market. "Charming service" from "efficient and friendly staff" adds to its attractions – along with "plenty of outdoor tables" for summer scoffing. / SE1 9QQ; www.borobistro.co.uk; @borobistro; 10.30 pm, Mon & Sun 9 pm; closed Mon & Sun; booking max 6 may apply.

THE BOTANIST   £55   2️⃣2️⃣2️⃣
**7 SLOANE SQ, SW1 020 7730 0077   6–2D
BROADGATE CIRCLE, EC2 020 3058 9888
13–2B**

This pair of "casual", well-located all-day brasseries serve an "eclectic menu" from breakfast on, but it's the "friendly ambience that's a real winner". The Sloane Square branch is "very Chelsea" – "great for lunch" and "wonderfully convenient pre- and post-show for Cadogan Hall or Royal Court". / thebotanist.uk.com; @botanistchester; SW1 breakfast 8, Sat & Sun 9, SW1 & EC2 11 pm.

BOUDIN BLANC
W1   £71   3️⃣3️⃣4️⃣

5 TREBECK ST   020 7499 3292   3–4B

"It feels like a proper Gallic bistro"; and this 'petit coin' of Mayfair's cute and atmospheric Shepherd Market is reasonably "authentic" all-round – "the classic French cooking takes you away on holiday" all without leaving W1, and it's most popular as a place for wooing a date. / W1J 7LT; www.boudinblanc.co.uk; 11 pm.

The Five Fields, SW3

BOULESTIN SW1   £76   2️⃣2️⃣2️⃣
5 ST JAMES'S ST   020 7930 2030   3–4D

A "perfect courtyard – practically unique for the West End" is a good feature of this "expensive French bistro", which serves "classic but well-executed food". Named after an iconic Covent Garden dining room of the 1920s, it was revived on this site in St James's (once L'Oranger, RIP) a few years ago, but never really made waves and went into administration last year. "Under new management (and it shows)", it still seems "slightly overpriced" but elicited supportive, if mixed feedback this year: "They didn't know what a Kir is. Not great for a restaurant named after a famous chef. Will try again but for now, a work in progress…" / SW1A 1EF; www.boulestin.com; @BoulestinLondon; 10.30 pm; closed Sun; No trainers.

BOULEVARD WC2   £53   2️⃣3️⃣3️⃣
40 WELLINGTON ST   020 7240 2992   5–3D

In the tourist hell of Covent Garden, this traditional brasserie is easily missed but worth remembering for a "cheap 'n' cheerful" bite. Even those who say "it's not too inspiring" feel it's "hard to fault for a speedy pre-theatre meal": "just like half the brasseries in France – classic dishes, realisation can be mediocre, but very reasonably priced". / WC2E 7BD; www.boulevardbrasserie.co.uk; @BoulevardWC2; 11 pm, Fri & Sat 11.30 pm, Sun 10.30 pm.

BOURNE AND
HOLLINGSWORTH BUILDINGS
EC1   £54   3️⃣2️⃣4️⃣
42 NORTHAMPTON RD 10–1A

"Lush surroundings" set a stylish tone at this "trendy", five-year-old venue on a "hard-to-find" Farringdon corner, not far from Exmouth Market. It's a 'multi-faceted' venue – a jumble of bar, café, restaurant, club, and private dining space – from a design team whose portfolio includes Pizza East and Riding House Café. "Fab cocktails" are maybe its most reliable attraction, although the food is consistently well-rated too. / EC1R 0HU; www.bandhbuildings.com.

BOWLING BIRD
EC1   £51   4️⃣4️⃣3️⃣
44 CLOTH FAIR   020 7324 7742 10–2B

"Ranks with the best beef I've ever had in London" is typical of the high praise earned by this smart two-year-old. "Mind you, it is right next to Smithfield" – a fact reflected in its straight-to-the-point menu – "and the maître d' knows just the right wine to wash it down with". It occupies an architectural gem of a townhouse once home to Sir John Betjeman. / EC1A 7JQ; bowlingbird.com.

BOXCAR BUTCHER & GRILL
W1   £56   4️⃣4️⃣3️⃣
23 NEW QUEBEC ST   020 3006 7000   2–2A

"Top burgers…", "good-value and tasty steaks…", "good Sunday roast…" – such are the attractions of this all-day Marylebone butcher, deli and steakhouse (part of the Cubitt House group). / W1H 7SD; boxcar.co.uk; @BoxcarLondon.

BRACKENBURY WINE ROOMS
W6   £58   2️⃣3️⃣3️⃣
**111-115 HAMMERSMITH GROVE
020 3696 8240   8–1C**

An "interesting wine list" is backed up by "reliable and quite imaginative food" at this modern and "very friendly" wine bar (with a sunny terrace) on a leafy Hammersmith corner. Wines are available pre-paid and by the glass to encourage experimentation, and can be bought by the bottle from the attached shop. There's another branch in Kensington. / W6 0NQ; winerooms.london/brackenbury; @Wine_Rooms; 11.30 pm, Sun 10.30 pm.

BRADLEY'S NW3   £64   2️⃣2️⃣2️⃣
25 WINCHESTER RD   020 7722 3457   9–2A

This "friendly" neighbourhood spot with a "tasty" modern European menu has done stalwart service in a Swiss Cottage sidestreet for the best part of three decades. "They have a monopoly for convenience to the nearby Hampstead Theatre", and serve an "efficient and stress-free" pre-theatre spread. The harsh would say the quality of the cooking can be "so so" – if it was a notch higher, this could be quite a destination. / NW3 3NR; www.bradleysnw3.co.uk; @bradleysnw3; 10 pm; closed Sun D.

BRASSERIE
BLANC   £56   2️⃣2️⃣2️⃣

"Fair all-round, if by no means special" is a justifiable, if slightly harsh verdict on Raymond Blanc's contemporary brasserie chain, whose branches are generally handy and well-appointed, and whose EC2 and SE1 outlets are often voted as "a decent place for a business meet up/dinner". If it were not "trading on the name" of one of the country's most famous chefs, its "reasonable" level of cooking might seem more laudable and less "formulaic". / www.brasserieblanc.com; most branches close between 10 pm & 11 pm; Threadneedle and Chancery lane closed Sun.

BRASSERIE OF LIGHT
W1   £64   2️⃣2️⃣4️⃣
**400 OXFORD STREET   020 3940 9600
3–1A**

"For sheer glamour and Damien Hirst's Pegasus, this gets my vote" – Richard Caring's "lavish" and "wonderfully buzzy" (at times "ear-splittingly loud") newcomer on the first floor of Selfridges (but with its own entrance) is "visually stunning, with a fit-out that creates talking points and enjoys marvellous views of Oxford Street". Its brasserie fare ranks somewhere between "better-than-you-might-expect" and "mediocre", and service can be "amateur", but serious criticisms are absent. "Populated mostly by ladies who shop and lunch", it was also nominated by numerous reporters for "a great and glitzy date": "something about department store dining can actually be quite sexy, and this extravagant presentation kind-of works…" Top Tip: "Would recommend for a drink at the bar as the space is gorgeous, and with pink loos being so OTT it made us smile". / W1A 1AB; www.brasserie-of-light.co.uk.

BRASSERIE TOULOUSE-
LAUTREC SE11   £61
**140 NEWINGTON BUTTS   020 7582 6800
1–3C**

Nightly live entertainment jazzes up this bravely-located fixture, near Kennington's cinema museum, which serves a variety of brasserie fare, majoring in steaks and other meaty, traditional Gallic dishes. Limited feedback this year, but all positive, including as a breakfast option. / SE11 4RN;

www.btlrestaurant.co.uk; @btlrestaurant; 10.30 pm, Sat & Sun 11 pm.

BRASSERIE ZÉDEL
W1   £45   2 3 5

20 SHERWOOD ST   020 7734 4888   4–3C

"You'll be so dazzled by the place that you may be inclined to overlook the food" – Corbin & King's "improbably glamorous" recreation of an "archetypal buzzing Parisian brasserie" is "so handy, being just by Piccadilly Circus tube" and provides "unmistakable value for such opulent and elegant surroundings in the very centre of London". The "huge", Grade I listed chamber is an "amazing Art Deco underground ballroom"; "a wonderfully blingy, brightly-lit space with gold everywhere". The "straightforward" French brasserie fare (soupe à l'oignon, boeuf bourguignon, steak haché…) from a huge menu is mundane by comparison… in fact it's pretty mundane full stop. But whereas the odd critic brands results as "terrible", most reporters feel that "you'd have to be a miserable sod to complain about anything at these prices" – "inevitably there are slips along the way and food can be inconsistent, but you get more bang for your buck here than at virtually any other London restaurant" (in particular "prix-fixe menus are astonishing value"). Top Tip – "there is also a beautiful Bar Americain". / W1F 7ED; www.brasseriezedel.com; @brasseriezedel; 11.45 pm, Sun 10.45 pm.

BRAT E1   £61   5 5 4

**FIRST FLOOR, 4 REDCHURCH STREET
NO TEL   13–1B**

"Totally living up to the hype!" – Tomos Parry's "cool ex-pub, first-floor dining room" (above Smoking Goat) was Harden's top newcomer last year, and "pulls off what so many Shoreditch restaurants aspire to" with "its phenomenal food from the open kitchen; its relaxed-but-highly-competent style; and its lack of expense". "And the wood-panelled dining room is a welcome change from the usual warehouse-style in the area". The Basque-influenced cuisine, much of it cooked over an open wood fire, majors in fish – "never overcooked, with a hint of smokiness after a roasting over hot embers" – in particular the "to-die-for", signature turbot (for which the restaurant is named) which is "positively Mediterranean in its fresh deliciousness". "The room is small and tables are close together" but no-one seems to care: "the buzz of the place simply tells you that here are a lot of folks really enjoying their dinner". It helps that "the staff are almost as good as the food: enthusiastic, knowledgeable, and clear in their explanations of the menu". All this, plus a "brilliant, wide-ranging and value-for-money wine list". / E1 6JJ; www.bratrestaurant.com; @bratrestaurant.

BRAWN E2   £61   5 3 4

49 COLUMBIA ROAD   020 7729 5692   14–2A

"By rights this place ought to have gone off by now, it's been going too long still to be fashionable!". But this East End sibling to the West End's Terroirs – "a gorgeous modern space" on Columbia Road – shows no sign of going downhill like its stablemate. "Ed Wilson is back at the helm full time and the kitchen purrs like a Rolls". "Every week brings different choices, but always with amazing products and a quality of small plates that's without a doubt at the top level". And there's a "great selection of natural wines" from all over Europe. "Why doesn't it have a Michelin star yet? They have delivered on an exceptional level of cooking for almost a decade now, and managed to remain creative, inventive and original in the meantime". / E2 7RG; www.brawn.co; @brawn49; 11 pm; closed Mon L & Sun D; No Amex.

BREAD STREET KITCHEN
EC4   £74   2 2 3

10 BREAD STREET   020 3030 4050   10–2B

This "warehouse-style" outfit from Gordon Ramsay near St Paul's provides a handy amenity for business-lunchers and, out of business hours, has a "great atmosphere for families and groups". But while it's generally decent, especially for brunch, it's rather "overpriced for what it offers" and apt to be "let down by average cooking and service". / EC4M 9AJ; www.breadstreetkitchen.com; @breadstreet; 11 pm, Sun 8 pm.

BREAKFAST CLUB   £42   3 3 3

**33 D'ARBLAY ST, W1 020 7434 2571   4–1C
2-4 RUFUS ST, N1 020 7729 5252 13–1B
31 CAMDEN PAS, N1 020 7226 5454   9–3D
12-16 ARTILLERY LN, E1 020 7078 9633
13–2B**

An "outstanding array of breakfasts" – "from egg and chips to huevos rancheros" – "in a buzzing atmosphere" that lasts well into the evening has driven the enormous popularity of this café chain. "Book ahead though, or be ready for a long queue at the door". The convivial party feel is fuelled by cocktails as the day wears on. / www.thebreakfastclubcafes.com; @thebrekkyclub; SRA-Food Made Good – 3 stars.

BREDDOS TACOS   £49   4 2 3

**82 GOSWELL ROAD, EC1 020 3535 8301
10–1B**

"We were taken there by a Mexican who reckons it's the most authentic in London!" – these "friendly-if-chaotic, little taco stops" hit the spot with "interesting flavour combinations" on "a tiny menu that manages to have something for everyone". / breddostacos.com; @breddostacos.

BRICIOLE W1   £52   3 3 2

20 HOMER ST   020 7723 0040   7–1D

"Fresh, interesting and authentic Italian dishes" make this Marylebone deli/trattoria "an easy choice for family gatherings". It started out as a spin-off from Latium in Fitzrovia, which closed last year (RIP). / W1H 4NA; www.briciole.co.uk; @briciolelondon; 10.15 pm.

BRICK LANE BEIGEL BAKE
E1   £5   4 1 1

159 BRICK LN   020 7729 0616 13–1C

This epic, "super-cheap" Jewish deli (nowadays "obviously in overseas guide books given the numbers of tourists in the line") has been famous forever, thanks to its "delicious home-made beigels" and "incredible salt beef", plus its 24/7 opening (and queue). Staff "can be very rude", but "the brutal service is part of the charm". Top Tip – "forget the beigel and have salt beef in a superb onion platzel – at £4.50 it's one of London's culinary bargains". / E1 6SB; www.beigelbake.com; @BeigelBake; open 24 hours; Cash only; No bookings.

BRIGADIERS EC2   £55   5 4 4

**BLOOMBERG ARCADE, QUEEN VICTORIA
STREET   020 3319 8140 10–3C**

"Mindblowing!" – this "colonially-themed" yearling in the City's Bloomberg Arcade is "another smash hit from JKS" and "probably the best place to eat in the Square Mile" right now. Occupying a "comfortable (slightly macho) sequence of little rooms", staff are notably "patient and helpful", while foodwise "the focus is on Indian sharing plates" with "insanely good" grilled meats (lamb chops in particular), plus "all your local curry favourites, dressed up with wonderful, perfumed aromatics and dazzling dips". "They don't pull any punches when it comes to heat in dishes either", and "there's a strong drinks menu too" – you can see "thought has gone into the beer selection". With numerous TV screens, "it's a great place to watch sports" ("they even have a pool table!") / EC2R; brigadierslondon.com; @brigadiersldn.

BRIGHT E8   £74   5 4 3

**NETIL HOUSE, 1 WESTGATE STREET
020 3095 9407 14–2B**

"Beautiful food, with elegance and full, intense flavours" from a menu of "simple, high-quality dishes", backed up by a list of "natural wines from top importers" – all served in a "laid back", semi-industrial space (formerly Ellory, RIP) – wins adulation for this yearling in London Fields, from the team behind fooderati fave-rave P Franco. / E8 3RL; www.brightrestaurant.co.uk.

THE BRIGHT COURTYARD
W1   £70   3 2 2

43-45 BAKER ST   020 7486 6998   2–1A

North of Portman Square, in a somewhat nondescript office block setting (complete with atrium seating for some diners), this Marylebone Chinese has won a big reputation for its innovative cuisine. Its ratings are more middling this year, however, with one or two reporters feeling that "even if the food is exceptional, it does not warrant such high prices". / W1U 8EW; www.lifefashiongroup.com; @BrightCourtyard; 10.45 pm, Thu-Sat 11.15 pm.

BRINKLEY'S SW10 £64 2 2 3

47 HOLLYWOOD RD 020 7351 1683 6–3B

John Brinkley's "stalwart of Chelsea nightlife" provides "a good service to the Eurotrash and ageing lotharios brigade". "The food won't set the world alight", but it's a "buzzy" venue, with a "great garden conservatory". / SW10 9HX; www.brinkleys.com/brinkleys-restaurant.html; @BrinkleysR; 11.30 pm; closed weekday L.

BRIXTON LAUNDRY SW9

374 COLDHARBOUR LANE 11–2D

Opening in November 2019, at Walton Lodge in Brixton: an all-day neighbourhood café, restaurant and wine shop from Melanie Brown, who used to work with Peter Gordon and launched The New Zealand Cellar and Australian Cellar. In the morning it will offer pastries and other light bites, and in the evening cocktails and a menu of more substantial dishes. / SW9 8PL.

BROOK HOUSE SW6 £59 3 2 4

65 NEW KING'S ROAD 11–1B

Mark Dyer and Eamonn Manson (formerly of The Sands End and The Brown Cow) have taken over this traditional pub overlooking Eel Brook Common, which wins praise for its "top-class" cooking (too posh to be called pub grub) and "super ambience". "They need to improve the inconsistent service", however. / SW6 4SG; brookhousefulham.com.

BROOKMILL SE8 £43 2 3 3

65 CRANBROOK ROAD 020 8333 0899 1–4D

It's worth knowing about this "light, airy and comfortable renovation" of a Victorian boozer complete with cute beer garden, according to Deptford-based regulars: "nothing will unduly quicken the pulse but everything's reassuringly pleasant: solidly-executed pub-grub, a decent selection of beers on tap, and BT Sport & Sky for the footie (though it never gets too rowdy)". / SE8 4EJ; www.thebrookmill.co.uk; @thebrookmillpub; 10 pm, Sun & Mon 9 pm.

THE BROWN DOG SW13 £52 3 3 3

28 CROSS STREET 020 8392 2200 11–1A

This "hidden gem" in the cute 'Little Chelsea' enclave of Barnes is "awkward to find if you're not a local, but that's probably why it's retained its character". It changed hands last year, but seems to have held onto its rep as a "reliable gastropub" – you need to book for the "great Sunday lunch". There's outdoor seating in the backyard, and dogs and children are welcome. / SW13 0AP; www.thebrowndog.co.uk; @browndogbarnes; 10 pm, Sun 9 pm.

BROWN'S HOTEL, THE ENGLISH TEA ROOM W1 £79 3 4 4

ALBEMARLE ST 020 7493 6020 3–3C

"So comfortable and homely, yet chic and stylish too" – this "classic" British hotel lounge is not quite as famous or grand as the nearby Ritz Palm Court, but nevertheless has a massive following for its "scrumptious afternoon tea" ("if at a price", of course). Top Tips – it's "'Teatox' is decadently delicious whilst not being too heavy"; and this is also "a central location for a business breakfast, with very good food". / W1S 4BP; www.roccofortehotels.com; No trainers.

BRUNSWICK HOUSE CAFÉ SW8 £60 3 2 5

30 WANDSWORTH RD 020 7720 2926 11–1D

This Georgian mansion-turned-architectural salvage shop is a "wonderful old building in a location you'd least expect it, overlooking Vauxhall Cross's huge gyratory system – and worth the trip!" for the "fun" and unexpected discovery of the "vibrant, buzzy bohemian bistro" it contains. Eating "amidst antiques a-plenty", you can enjoy "unusual breakfasts", "decent cocktails" and "excellent southwest French cuisine", the work of well-known chef, Jackson Boxer. Service, though, can be "a bit off the ball". / SW8 2LG; www.brunswickhouse.london; 10 pm; closed Sun D.

BRYN WILLIAMS AT SOMERSET HOUSE WC2 £66 3 3 3

SOMERSET HOUSE 020 7845 464 2–2D

This avowedly 'veggie-centric' concept from Welsh chef Bryn Williams (of highly rated Odette's in Primrose Hill) gives top billing to vegetables and fruit, although the menu still offers plenty for carnivores to chew on. It occupies the quirky chamber, right at the back of Somerset House with Thames views, that once housed The Admiralty (RIP) – an intriguing location, but also one smart enough for doing business. From a fair number of reports, there is mostly praise for dishes that are "beautifully prepared and served" – a "detox set lunch with no meat or fish in sight was really inspiring and exciting". / WC2R 1LA; www.bryn-somersethouse.co.uk; @bwsomersethouse.

BUBALA E1

65 COMMERCIAL STREET 13–2C

Following a number of sell-out events across London, this Middle Eastern venture's first permanent site opened near Spitalfields as we went to press. The team's CVs incorporate Berber & Q and also The Palomar family; a boldy-flavoured, fully vegetarian menu of sharing plates is promised, inspired by Tel Aviv's modern cafés. / E1 6BD; www.bubala.co.uk.

BUBBLEDOGS W1 £52 3 4 4

70 CHARLOTTE ST 020 7637 7770 2–1C

"Hot dogs and Champagne – how could that be wrong?", asks a fan of Sandia Chang's unlikely-sounding Fitzrovia concept bar, which shares premises with her husband James Knappett's tasting-menu-only Kitchen Table (see also). What's more, "excellent burgers" paired with "London's most accessible list of Champagnes (including some crackers by the glass) qualifies as cheap and ridiculously cheerful". / W1T 4QG; www.bubbledogs.co.uk; @bubbledogsUK; 9 pm; closed Sun.

BUBBLEDOGS, KITCHEN TABLE W1 £179 4 4 4

70 CHARLOTTE ST 020 7637 7770 2–1C

"One of a kind!": James Knappett's "phenomenal" Fitzrovia 20-seater – entered via the hotdog-and-Champagne bar that shares its name (see Bubbledogs) – "takes creative gastronomy to a new level" and is "well deserving of its second Michelin star". Cooking behind a horseshoe-shaped counter with the kitchen at its centre, "the chefs are good company", and their conversation helps "nail the balance between a very interesting gastronomic journey and a lovely 'feel-at-home' atmosphere". Dishes "celebrating high quality produce are effortlessly executed and perfectly sized"; and "with enough innovation to keep you interested, while not alienating anyone". "One of the best meals of my life" – "I barely noticed that it lasted three hours!" / W1T 4QG; www.kitchentablelondon.co.uk; @bubbledogsKT; seatings only at 6 pm & 7.30 pm; D only, closed Mon & Sun.

BUCKET W2 £50 3 4 3

107 WESTBOURNE GROVE 020 3146 1156 7–1B

Mussels, prawns, calamari and other seafood by the, er, bucket-load is the promise at this "lovely local" yearling on the Bayswater/Notting Hill border – a "comfortable" modern bistro with simple-but-effective decor, serving "a wide selection of very fresh fish and seafood" (in small metal pails) that's "very good value". Top Tip – oyster happy hour 4pm-7pm weekdays and 4pm-6pm on weekends, when oysters are £1 each with any bottle, jug, cocktail or bucket of beers. / W2 4UW; www.bucketrestaurant.com.

BUEN AYRE E8 £61 4 3 2

50 BROADWAY MARKET 020 7275 9900 14–2B

"As close as you can get to Buenos Aires without leaving London" – this Argentinian parrilla is one of hip Broadway Market's longest-serving foodie hotspots, and serves "amazing steaks, and a great wine list for reds". / E8 4QJ; www.buenayre.co.uk; 10 pm, Fri & Sat 10.30 pm, Sun 10 pm; No Amex.

THE BUILDERS ARMS
SW3 £58

13 BRITTEN ST   020 7349 9040   6–2C

This attractive Chelsea backstreet pub – "good food"; "a good place to watch the rugby" – closed for a refurb this summer, following our survey. Its sale to Hippo Inns returns it to the ownership of Rupert Clevely, who sold former owner Geronimo to Young's in 2010. / SW3 3TY; www.thebuildersarmschelsea.co.uk; @BuildersChelsea; 10 pm, Thu-Sat 11 pm, Sun 9.30 pm; no booking.

THE BULL N6 £51 343

13 NORTH HILL   020 8341 0510   9–1B

This grand old Highgate pub with an in-house microbrewery has a "great range of their own beers, and some good nibbles to go along with them". More substantial fare includes "very good roasts", and staff are "particularly helpful". / N6 4AB; thebullhighgate.co.uk; @Bull_Highgate.

BULL & LAST NW5 £66 333

168 HIGHGATE RD   020 7267 3641   9–1B

"Cannot wait for this gem of a place to reopen!" – Kentish Town's brilliant Heath-side destination has been closed for most of the last year, as it turns itself into a six-bedroom pub-with-rooms. Set to re-open in late-2019, here's hoping they haven't mucked up what's ranked as north London's top gastropub in recent years. / NW5 1QS; www.thebullandlast.co.uk; @thebullandlast; 10 pm, Sun 9 pm.

BUMPKIN £58 223

**102 OLD BROMPTON RD, SW7
020 7341 0802   6–2B
WESTFIELD STRATFORD CITY, THE
STREET, E20 020 8221 9900 14–1D**

"A sort of neighbourhood bistro, just beyond the touristy influence of the South Kensington museums" – the main survivor of an erstwhile chain (there's also a Stratford sibling no-one talks about) "offering British upmarket pub food", which is variable to good. It's "a nice and warming place", but it can become "rather busy and noisy"; and "service, while cheerful and pleasant, is extremely variable". / www.bumpkinuk.com; 10 pm, Sun 9 pm; closed Mon.

BUN HOUSE WC2 £14 433

26-27 LISLE STREET   5–3A

"Recently moved from Soho to Chinatown into a new, bigger and better space" – Z He and Alex Peffly's venture is a "#1 spot for a quick, cheap meal": "buns are filled with authentic Chinese flavours and the dough is so soft it feels like you're eating clouds!". Meanwhile, back at the original Greek Street site, this husband-and-wife team have transformed their old premises into Wun's, which opened in July 2019: see also. / WC2H 7BD; bun.house; @8unhouse.

BURGER & BEYOND
E1 £53 533

147 SHOREDITCH HIGH STREET 13–1B

"Some of the best burgers in London" – including a "sublime, fried, hot fish burger" and "a real vegetarian burger (that isn't pretending to be anything other than a real, delicious vegetarian burger)" – make it well worth discovering this hip new Shoreditch diner. When it comes to going 'beyond', "some of the tapas style starters are worth trying too" (cauliflower cheese balls, fried chicken bites…) / E1 6JE; burgerandbeyond.co.uk; @burgerandbeyond.

BURGER &
LOBSTER £60 323

**HARVEY NICHOLS, 109-125
KNIGHTSBRIDGE, SW1 020 7235 5000
6–1D
26 BINNEY ST, W1 020 3637 5972   3–2A
29 CLARGES ST, W1 020 7409 1699   3–4B
36 DEAN ST, W1 020 7432 4800   5–2A
6 LITTLE PORTLAND ST, W1 020 7907 7760
3–1C
18 HERTSMERE ROAD, E14 020 3637 6709
12–1C
40 ST JOHN ST, EC1 020 7490 9230 10–1B
BOW BELLS HS, 1 BREAD ST, EC4
020 7248 1789 10–2B**

The cut-price surf 'n' turf at this "fun, relaxed and reliable" operation "never fails" – "have a lobster roll as a starter, then a burger as a main". Under the same ownership as the Goodman steakhouses, the London-based chain has consolidated to nine domestic branches plus the Smack lobster roll delivery-only spinoff, while expanding internationally in the US, Middle East and southeast Asia. / www.burgerandlobster.com; @Londonlobster; 10.30 pm-11 pm, Sun 8 pm-10 pm; WC1 & EC2 closed Sun; booking: min 6.

BUSABA EATHAI £51 322

"Decent Thai food from a regularly changing menu" has earned solid ratings this year for this chain of communal Asian diners, which has seen improved feedback since the closure of its branches outside London last year. The group was founded 20 years ago by Alan Yau as the follow-up to his hit creation Wagamama, and has its strongest presence in the West End, where the branches are "a useful pre-theatre pitstop". / www.busaba.co.uk; @busabaeathai; 11 pm, Fri & Sat 11.30 pm, Sun 10 pm; W1 no booking; WC1 booking: min 10.

BUTLERS WHARF CHOP
HOUSE SE1 £70 334

36E SHAD THAMES   020 7403 3403 10–4D

This business-friendly D&D London venue plays to its strengths: the spectacular Tower Bridge setting, plus a well-constructed menu of meaty, classic British dishes. Originally part of Sir Terence Conran's 'Gastrodome' project in the 1990s, fans "have been coming here for years" and for a simple grill in prime Thames-side territory, it's worth remembering.

/ SE1 2YE; www.chophouse-restaurant.co.uk; @BWChophouse; 11 pm.

BY CHLOE 322

**4-5 LANGHAM PLACE, W1   3–1C
DRURY HOUSE, 34-43 RUSSELL STREET,
WC2 020 3883 3273   5–2D
GROUND FLOOR, ICON AT THE O2,
PENINSULA SQUARE, SE10 12–1D
6 DUCHESS WALK, ONE TOWER BRIDGE,
SE1 10–4D**

A single Covent Garden branch has quickly become a chain of four for Chloe Coscarelli and Samantha Wasser's NYC-based, fast-food, vegan chain, with openings this year near Tower Bridge, by Oxford Circus and in the O2. It's mass catering for sure (with salads, fish 'n' chips, sarnies), junk-ish even (burgers, mac 'n' cheese, fries, cupcakes) but, for an everyday vegan fix from brunch onwards, no chain is covering the ground quicker. / www.eatbychloe.com; @eatbychloe.

BYRON £37 122

Will the July 2019 adoption of a vegan burger option help turn around the fortunes of this once-market-leading burger chain, which lost nearly 1/3 of its branches in 2018 during a much-publicised CVA (Company Voluntary Agreement)? Still-plummeting ratings suggest it still has a mountain to climb with reports of food that's "not up to scratch" and "branches that seem unloved". But even so, it maintains a big following who want to see management succeed: the "formula may need a bit of refreshment", they say, but "it's a brand that does not deserve to be sneered at!" HOLD THE FRONT PAGE: In August 2019, the chain took a dramatic further step towards a complete turnaround… a new logo! / www.byronhamburgers.com; most branches 11 pm.

C&R CAFÉ W1 £31 422

3-4 RUPERT CT   020 7434 1128   4–3D

"Cheap but very tasty Malaysian food" provides a "compelling reason" to choose this well-established fixture in a Chinatown alleyway. (Its former Bayswater sibling still has 'C&R' in the title, but is now separately run as a Japanese izakaya.) / W1D 6DY; 11 pm.

CABOTTE EC2 £71 454

48 GRESHAM ST   020 7600 1616 10–2C

"A stunning treasure trove of Burgundy wine" is just one of the attractions of this "buzzy and down-to-earth" two-year-old, near the Guildhall. The serving crew are "super friendly" and "knowledgeable", while the regional French cuisine from head chef Edward Boarland is "luscious, beautiful, and nourishing (almost comfort food, but the quality is super-high". Often tipped as a top choice for business entertaining, it's nevertheless "one of the very few such City restaurants in which you would want to actually spend your own money!" / EC2V 7AY; www.cabotte.co.uk; @Cabotte_; 9.30 pm.

CAFÉ BELOW EC2 £35 333

ST MARY-LE-BOW, CHEAPSIDE
020 7329 0789 10–2B

"Escape the feel of the City for very reasonable home cooked-food" in the ancient crypt of Bow Bells church. "There are no better dining establishments in the Square Mile: affordable, great service, good food with delicious daily changing salads" including "excellent veggie and vegan options". Depending on when you go, it's either a "quiet" space or quite a "noisy" one. / EC2 6AU; www.cafebelow.co.uk; @cafebelow; 2.30 pm; L only.

CAFÉ DEL PARC N19 £47 553

167 JUNCTION ROAD   020 7281 5684   9–1C

"What an amazing find" in Tufnell Park – "a tiny kitchen behind a small counter in a converted Victorian shop that turns out delicious, flavour-packed, tapas-style, Moorish-influenced dishes to a handful of tables". There's "no menu, they just bring what they think you'll like" – and reporters are unanimous that it is "beautifully inspired and enjoyable": "the best Mediterranean cooking I've had outside the Med". / N19 5PZ; www.delparc.com; @delParc; 10.30 pm; open D only, Wed-Sun; No Amex; booking D only.

CAFÉ DU MARCHÉ EC1 £52 335

22 CHARTERHOUSE SQ   020 7608 1609   10–1B

"Just the kind of spot you expect on the market square of a small French town" – this "delightful stalwart, hidden at the back of a cobbled mews off Charterhouse Square, is an "unchanging old friend" to its big fanclub. "Convivial, candlelit and very romantic", its menu is "not gourmet, but it delivers classic Gallic cuisine served with a lot of charm"; and regular jazz helps "adds to the great ambience" in the evening. / EC1M 6DX; www.cafedumarche.co.uk; @cafedumarche; 10 pm; closed Sat L & Sun.

CAFÉ EAST SE16 £28 522

100 REDRIFF RD   020 7252 1212 12–2B

"The pho served here is the real thing – authentic, tasty and never fails", is a commonly held view of this long-running and good-value Vietnamese canteen in Surrey Quays. "They also serve the best summer rolls I've ever encountered". / SE16 7LH; www.cafeeastpho.co.uk; @cafeeastpho; 10.30 pm, Sun 10 pm; closed Tue; No Amex; No bookings.

CAFÉ IN THE CRYPT, ST MARTIN IN THE FIELDS WC2 £32 214

DUNCANNON ST   020 7766 1158   2–2C

"Lovely, airy underground café in the large, rambling and atmospheric crypt of St Martin-in-the-Fields that's "very useful for a quick lunch" by Trafalgar Square. There's always "something for everyone", including "good and varied soups" – and "it's for a good cause". / WC2N 4JJ; stmartin-in-the-fields.org/cafe-in-the-crypt; @smitf_london; 8 pm, Wed 10.30 pm, Thu-Sat 9 pm, Sun 6 pm; L & early evening only; No Amex; May need 5+ to book.

CAFÉ MONICO W1 £49 224

39-45 SHAFTESBURY AVENUE   020 3727 6161   5–3A

This would-be-instant-classic Theatreland brasserie – artfully designed by the Soho House group using the name of an 1877 original – "could be great for its location", right amongst the bright lights of Shaftesbury Avenue, and has a fine interior. But the food falls very short – which is "a real shame": the menu of French and Italian classics "promises so much" but too often "delivers nothing!"; and, for somewhere so central, the venue inspires remarkably little feedback. / W1D 6LA; www.cafemonico.com; @cafemonico; midnight, Fri & Sat 1 am.

CAFE MURANO £63 222

33 ST JAMES'S ST, SW1 020 3371 5559 3–3C
34 TAVISTOCK STREET, WC2 020 3535 7884 5–3D
36 TAVISTOCK ST, WC2 020 3371 5559 5–3D

"Perhaps hopes were too high?" – Angela Hartnett's spin-off Italians in Covent Garden and St James's inspire a lot of feedback, but much of it is mixed. Fans do applaud her for "succeeding where most others fail in establishing a couple of cheaper ventures that follow her style, but do not feel part of a factory-made chain; and which provide some excellent, simple Italian cooking and carefully chosen wines". But for many sceptics, the gloss is taken off the experience either by "food that's fine but not exceptional; not-wholly-interested service; or a lack of ambience" (WC2 can be "very noisy". She must be doing something right however, as in June 2019 she submitted plans to take over the Bermondsey site some will recall as Zucca (RIP) to become her next outlet. Top Tip – "a useful stop pre-theatre but the set menu never seems to meet expectations, so it's better to stick with the à la carte". / www.cafemurano.co.uk; 11 pm, Sun 4 pm, Pastificio 9 pm, ; Pastificio closed Sun.

CAFÉ SPICE NAMASTE E1 £62 543

16 PRESCOT ST   020 7488 9242 12–1A

"Some of the best Indian food in town" – "Cyrus and Pervin Todiwala are delightful hosts" and the "dated outside" of their City-fringe HQ "gives no clue that a meal here will be so delicious". The cuisine offers "a different take on traditional Indian" (mixing Parsi and Goan dishes with more pan-Indian inspirations) and its longstanding "authenticity" and "creativity" is a continued joy, as is the "genuinely friendly way that TV-chef Cyrus T, OBE comes out to chat with guests". "As good as you'll get in Mumbai… and the traffic isn't as bad!" / E1 8AZ; www.cafespice.co.uk; @cafespicenamast; 10.30 pm; closed Sat L & Sun.

CAFFÈ CALDESI W1 £75 323

118 MARYLEBONE LN   020 7487 0754 2–1A

"Authentic and exceptional" Italian cuisine, with "classics done well" alongside "seasonal and Tuscan specials", hits the spot at this family-run Marylebone venue. The upstairs dining room "can be a bit austere if less than half full", and there's also an informal bar and café downstairs. / W1U 2QF; www.caldesi.com; 10.30 pm, Sun 9.30 pm.

CAKES AND BUBBLES W1 £86 344

HOTEL CAFE ROYAL, 10 AIR ST   020 7406 3310   4–4C

Albert Adrià (pastry chef back in the day at his brother Ferran's world famous El Bulli) operates this marbled café, overlooking Regent Street, near Piccadilly Circus. When it comes to the menu, the clue is in the name, and on most accounts his "original", delectable sweet creations – including the signature cheesecake – may be "a little pricey", but are "simply legendary". / W1B 4DY; www.cakesandbubbles.co.uk.

THE CAMBERWELL ARMS SE5 £50 533

65 CAMBERWELL CHURCH ST   020 7358 4364   1–3C

"The menu is SO enticing and the food SO delicious that it is difficult to imagine better pub food than at The Camberwell Arms" – "buzzy" sibling to the famous Anchor & Hope. "When on song (and not full of refugees from nearby Peckham) this is one of the best gastropubs in London". "The wine list is very interesting, with some out-of-the-norm bottles that are modestly priced; and the cocktails are gluggable too". / SE5 8TR; www.thecamberwellarms.co.uk; @camberwellarms; 10 pm; closed Mon L & Sun D.

CAMBIO DE TERCIO SW5 £68 433

161-163 OLD BROMPTON RD   020 7244 8970   6–2B

Abel Lusa's "little corner of Spain on the Old Brompton Road" has pioneered upscale Hispanic cuisine in London for 25 years with "tasty creations that wow the diner" alongside "a joy of a wine list – not cheap but with an exceptional selection". It's a "destination of choice for every mood and occasion, be it just for tapas or a full meal" – or, if you're Rafa Nadal, if you're in town for a game of tennis… / SW5 0LJ; www.cambiodetercio.co.uk; @CambiodTercio; 11.15 pm, Sun & Mon 10.45 pm.

CAMBRIDGE STREET SW1 £66 334

52 CAMBRIDGE ST   020 3019 8622   2–4B

This "fun" all-day haunt in an otherwise dull corner of Pimlico has "all the on-trend

Circolo Popolare W1

gastropub menu options you could hope for, but everything is done really well for once". It makes "the perfect breakfast/ brunch spot" – when "trade can be manic". / SW1V 4QQ; www.cambridgestreetcafe.co.uk; @TheCambridgeSt; 9.30 pm, Sat 10 pm, Sun 8.30 pm.

CAMILLO BENSO W1   223

8-10 BLENHEIM STREET   020 7629 8889   3–2B

This formal Mayfair yearling – offshoot of a top Milanese establishment – achieved very limited and mixed survey feedback, in keeping with the drubbing it received from The Sunday Times's Marina O'Loughlin: "portions seem small… the food's good but not exceptional, and expect to pay dearly for it". / W1S 1LJ; www.camillobenso.co.uk; @camillobensoLDN.

CAMINO   £53   222

3 VARNISHERS YD, REGENT QUARTER, N1 020 7841 7330   9–3C
THE BLUE FIN BUILDING, 5 CANVEY ST, SE1 020 3617 3169 10–4B
2 CURTAIN ROAD, EC2 13–2B
15 MINCING LN, EC3 020 7841 7335 10–3D

A "good choice of drinks" helps fuel the "buzzy" style of this "good value" Hispanic group. Some reporters feel its tapas offering is rather "standard", but most reports are of "good tapas at good prices". / www.camino.uk.com; 11pm, EC3 Sat 10 pm, Sun 10pm; EC2 closed Sun, EC3 closed Sat & Sun.

CAMPANIA & JONES E2   £43   443

23 EZRA ST   020 7613 0015 14–2A

Rustic former cowshed that's one of the quainter diversions when visiting Columbia Road Flower Market. On limited feedback, we received nothing but good ratings this year for its Italian cooking, but the weight of custom at busy times means service can suffer. / E2 7RH; www.campaniaandjones.com; 10.30 pm.

CANNIZARO HOUSE, HOTEL DU VIN SW19   £60   113

WEST SIDE, WIMBLEDON COMMON   020 7943 0345 11–2A

The "very pleasant surroundings" of an "excellent dining room overlooking Cannizaro Park" are let down by the consistently disappointing meals and "don't care" attitude of staff at this Hotel du Vin outfit. "Someone rescue it – it's a waste of a fantastic space". / SW19 4UE; www.hotelduvin.com/locations/wimbledon; @HotelduVinBrand; 10 pm.

CANTINA LAREDO WC2   £62   222

10 UPPER ST MARTIN'S LANE, ST MARTIN'S COURTYARD   020 7420 0630 5–3C

"Sitting by the windows on a summer's evening makes for a great pre-theatre outing" at this American-owned Mexican in Covent Garden. "Top frozen margaritas" and "guacamole made at your table" add to the experience. / WC2H 9FB; www.cantinalaredo.co.uk; @CantinaLaredoUK; 10 pm, Fri & Sat 10.30 pm, Sun 9 pm.

CANTO CORVINO E1   £63   323

21 ARTILLERY LANE   020 7655 0390 13–2B

"Outstanding seasonal food with very helpful and friendly service" gets a thumbs-up for this modern Italian by Spitalfields Market. There's a "great wine list – including by-the-glass from the Coravin system", and it's also highly recommended for a business breakfast – "much better than the Breakfast Club opposite, and no queue". / E1 7HA; www.cantocorvino.co.uk; @cantocorvinoE1; 10 pm.

CANTON ARMS SW8   £51   434

177 SOUTH LAMBETH RD   020 7582 8710 11–1D

"The best gastropub I've found in London" – this Stockwell operation is "a winner for an uncomplicated but thoroughly satisfying meal", especially "for those who enjoy expertly prepared cuts of high-quality meat". "It's similar in standard to the Anchor & Hope (its famous Southwark sibling) but better because it's quieter, with a more relaxed atmosphere". To cap it all, it's "still a proper pub, where you're welcome for a quiet pint". / SW8 1XP; www.cantonarms.com; @cantonarms; 10.30 pm; closed Mon L & Sun D; No Amex; no booking.

CAPEESH E14   £56   333

4 PAN PENINSULA SQUARE   020 7538 1111 12–2C

On the 48th-floor of a Canary Wharf skyscraper, right by South Quay DLR – this glossy two-year-old, Italian restaurant and 'Sky Bar' certainly enjoys amazing panoramas. As yet, it still generates only relatively limited feedback, but such as there is says it avoids the usual curse of rooms with a view, serving decent pizza, steaks and other Italian fare. There's ent's at the weekend, with live DJs on Friday, and Saturday is club night. / E14 9HN; www.capeesh.co.uk; @capeeshlondon.

LE CAPRICE SW1   £75   244

20 ARLINGTON ST   020 7629 2239   3–4C

"Even at the bar, one feels like a star… and there are often real stars eating as well!" – this "timeless and elegant" brasserie, tucked away near The Ritz has endured well within Richard Caring's empire and, although the cooking "has fallen away a bit", the overall package remains many a savvy Londoner's favourite. "Staff are upbeat" and "make you feel well looked after", and its buzzy atmosphere "makes other posh rivals feel flat and stuffy": "some nights it zings, sometimes it just feels like an efficient machine, but either way, it's a top night out", particularly on a date. (A spin-off brand, Caprice Café, is due to open its first branch in late 2019 in North Audley Street in Mayfair). / SW1A 1RJ; www.le-caprice.co.uk; @CapriceHoldings; 11.30 pm, Sun 10.30 pm; May need 6+ to book.

CARACTÈRE W11   £83   554

209 WESTBOURNE PARK ROAD 020 8181 3850   7–1B

"Absolutely the best new restaurant in the past year or so" – the Roux dynasty have come up trumps with this "great newbie in the Notting Hill 'hood", on the site of Bumpkin (RIP). It's the brainchild of Michel Roux's daughter Emily Roux and her husband Diego Ferrari (former head chef at Le Gavroche). "Just around the corner from The Ledbury, but half the price and less formal" – it provides a "fabulous all-round experience", founded on "outstanding" and "creative" cooking "born out of two great cuisines: French and Italian". (However, "the unusual menu layout does take a moment to puzzle out", with headings like Curious, Subtle and Greedy). "Impeccable service" and the "very comfortable" space, decorated with "quirky touches" complete the experience. Top Tip – "don't miss the celeriac 'cacio e pepe'". / W11 1EA; www.caractererestaurant.com.

CARAFFINI SW1   £62   354

61-63 LOWER SLOANE ST   020 7259 0235 6–2D

"The maitre d' remembered me from over 10 years ago and treated me like I'd given them my patronage every day of those 10 years!" – this "neighbourhood" stalwart trattoria is "a staple of the area" south of Sloane Square: "unchanging from year to year" and "like a home from home" for its many (generally silver-haired) regulars. "The menu may not have changed in years, but who cares?" – it's "always reliable, and well-priced for the locale" – and its USP is "wonderful staff", who "treat you like royalty" and are so "friendly" ("they knew exactly how to banter with my grumpy daughter and exactly when to point out a good wine on the list"). "Heaven help us when it finally changes hands…" / SW1W 8DH; www.caraffini.co.uk; 11 pm; closed Sun.

CARAVAGGIO EC3   £60   322

107-112 LEADENHALL ST   020 7626 6206 10–2D

"Smart and rather business-like" stalwart, near Leadenhall Market, that's one of the City's longer-established expense-account venues. Even those who feel that the experience is "all a bit 'staged'" say it "nevertheless serves great Italian cuisine"; and reporters who feel that "after 20 years it's a tad tired" still say that "it's always a pleasant visit". / EC3A 4DP;

www.etruscarestaurants.com; 10 pm; closed Sat & Sun.

CARAVAN £54 2 2 3

YALDING HOUSE, 152 GREAT PORTLAND STREET, W1 020 3963 8500 2–1B
1 GRANARY SQ, N1 020 7101 7661 9–3C
METAL BOX FACTORY, 30 GREAT GUILDFORD ST, SE1 020 7101 1190 10–4B
11-13 EXMOUTH MKT, EC1 020 7833 8115 10–1A
22 BLOOMBERG ARCADE, QUEEN VICTORIA STREET, EC4 020 3957 5555 10–3C

"So many amazing, creative options for brunch" together with "renowned coffee" ("meticulously sourced and roasted in-house") have made these "loud", "brash", "buzzy" and "quite hip" haunts – particularly the well-known Granary Square branch – key destinations, particularly at the weekend. When busy, however, service can be "hit and miss"; and the food has sometimes been a let-down of late: "it feels like random, trendy ingredients are thrown into dishes so they can charge more for them, rather than for culinary interest or flavour". / www.caravanonexmouth.co.uk; @CaravanResto; 10.30 pm, Sun 4 pm; closed Sun; no bookings for weekend brunch.

CAROUSEL W1 £52 4 4 3

71 BLANDFORD ST   020 7487 5564   3–1A

"A brilliant idea that never disappoints" – this Marylebone venue hosts "a different guest chef every week", flying in "some of the most exciting cooks in the world, who deliver an astonishing range of food". Lunch from the crack in-house team is also "terrific and great value", comprising "small plates full of original flavours". / W1U 8AB; www.carousel-london.com; @Carousel_LDN; one seating only, at 7 pm; closed Mon L & Sun L.

THE CARPENTER'S ARMS W6 £57 3 3 3

91 BLACK LION LN   020 8741 8386   8–2B

"If Carlsberg made gastropubs...", fans of this backstreet Hammersmith hostelry near leafy St Peter's Square say it would be just like this, with a "roaring fire, beautifully-lit room, well-assembled wine list, and a menu which is driven by quality ingredients (and also with a garden that's perfect for a romantic summer evening: twinkling lights and lots of greenery"). Not all feedback is so upbeat though: critics say it's "rather expensive for what it is, with hit and miss service". / W6 9BG; www.carpentersarmsw6.co.uk; 10 pm, Sun 9 pm.

CASA BRINDISA SW7 £56 3 3 4

7-9 EXHIBITION RD   020 7590 0008   6–2C

Acres of pavement seating are the most eye-catching feature of this "buzzing" operation (run by the well-known Spanish food importers), which sits on the ant-trail between South Kensington tube station and the museums (go on a sunny day). It's "reliably enjoyable" for a "cheap 'n' cheerful" meal as the dishes are reliably good, but it's mostly chosen for its convenience rather than its foodie potential. / SW7 2HE; www.brindisatapaskitchens.com/restaurant/casa-brindisa-south-kensington; @TapasKitchens; 11 pm, Sun 10 pm; booking max 8 may apply.

CASA DO FRANGO SE1 £44 3 4 4

32 SOUTHWARK STREET   020 3972 2323 10–4C

"Grilled chicken is the centrepiece" (frango means chicken in Portuguese) and is done in three different ways: peri peri, lemon, and garlic-and-oregano – at this "buzzing", airy and artfully converted yearling, not far from Borough Market. "Sides, salads and especially the custard tarts are of a very high standard too, and service, like the room, is bright and cheery". A sibling stall is now open in Centre Point's Arcade Food Theatre, see also. / SE1 1TU; www.casadofrango.co.uk; No bookings.

CASA FOFÓ E8 £57 5 3 3

158 SANDRINGHAM ROAD   020 8062 2489 14–1B

"Paradise for serious foodies" – "a street notorious for once being crime-ridden is now home to Hackney's best-value dining experience: £39 for a seven-course tasting menu", according to practically all reports on ex-Pidgin chef, Adolfo de Cecco's "intimate-feeling" foodie venture. "Thoughtful food is excellently executed by a team with evident passion" and if "a few technical slip-ups can creep in, the charming, passionate service (often by the chefs themselves) more than makes up for this". / E8 2HS; www.casafofolondon.co.uk.

CASA PASTÓR & PLAZA PASTÓR N1 £64 3 2 3

COAL DROPS YARD   9–3C

"Decent Mexican food finally arrives in the 'hood" – the Hart Bros' Latino newcomer in the new Coal Drops Yard development mixes "a bit of party atmosphere" with the "authentic" flavours of Central America ("the frijoles charros give me that beany homey hit that has finally filled the void left when I moved from San Francisco!"). Top Tip "great kids menu with DIY tacos". / N1C 4AB; www.tacoselpastor.co.uk; @Tacos_El_Pastor.

CASA TUA WC1 £41 4 3 3

106 CROMER STREET   020 7833 1483 9–4C

"Delicious, fresh pasta" is a particular highlight of the "reasonably-priced homemade food" at this "cosy corner-Italian in the atmospheric backstreets of Bloomsbury" (within walking distance of King's Cross). / WC1H 8BZ; www.casatuacamden.com/kings-cross; @casatuagastro.

CASSE-CROUTE SE1 £56 4 4 4

109 BERMONDSEY ST   020 7407 2140 10–4D

"The Gallic bistro you kept looking for on holiday in France, but never found…" – this "tiny" and "cramped" Bermondsey venue provides a "small but ever-changing menu" of "the kind of memorable, old-school, traditional regional dishes it can be hard to find in Paris these days" ("boeuf en croute with gorgeous jus, tarte tatin etc"). "Booking is a must". / SE1 3XB; www.cassecroute.co.uk; @CasseCroute109; 10 pm, Sun 4 pm; closed Sun D.

CATFORD CONSTITUTIONAL CLUB SE6 £40 3 3 4

CATFORD BROADWAY   020 8613 7188 1–4D

"An oasis in the middle of the culinary desert" that is downtown Catford: the atmosphere – like the name – at this big ("cavernous") and retro-looking gastropub channels the 1950s by the simple expedient of retaining the decor of the former Conservative club on the site. A smart modern menu is backed up by craft ales and ciders. (Lewisham Council owns the freehold and plans to redevelop it to provide affordable housing, while leaving CCC intact.) Top Tip – cute suntrap garden. / SE6 4SP; catfordconstitutionalclub.com; @CatfordCCClub; 10 pm.

CAVIAR KASPIA W1

1A CHESTERFIELD STREET AWAITING TEL   3–4B

Since it closed in 2000 (on the site which became Bellamy's), this luxury Parisian-based brand (fondée 1927) has lacked a London outlet. Following a successful pop-up last

Casa do Frango SE1

year, this opening on the site of Mayair's former Chess Club aims to bring it back more permanently. Originally scheduled for April, the actual launch date had yet to be announced in September 2019. / W1J 5JF; www.caviarkaspia.com.

CAY TRE £43 3|3|2

42-43 DEAN ST, W1 020 7317 9118 5–2A
301 OLD ST, EC1 020 7729 8662 13–1B

The "fantastic" Vietnamese food at these canteens "is by far the best I've found, and I've tried a number of places in London" – although "it isn't the best for ambience". There are two to choose between, although the Soho site attracts more feedback than the Hoxton original these days. Top Tip – "the banh cuon (steamed rice roll) has me travelling across town with a craving!". / www.caytrerestaurant.co.uk; @CayTreLondon; 11 pm, Fri & Sat 11.30 pm, Sun 10.30 pm; booking: min 8.

CECCONI'S £85 2|2|4

19-21 OLD COMPTON STREET, W1
020 7734 5656 5–2A
5A BURLINGTON GDNS, W1 020 7434 1500
4–4A
58-60 REDCHURCH STREET, E2
020 3841 7755 13–1C
THE NED, 27 POULTRY, EC2 020 3828 2000
10–2C

"There's always such a buzz at any time" at the original Cecconi's, "tucked away behind the Royal Academy" – a "bustling" and "sophisticated" all-day Italian brasserie, whose "open, bright, pavement terrace" helps make it a big favourite amongst the St James's set, be it "for an upmarket business breakfast", or as "a treat during a day's shopping in the West End". When it comes to the cooking, it "can be a bit hit or miss, but is generally good". Nowadays owned by Soho House, the brand is being rolled out, but its diverse family of spin-offs echo rather than replicate the original. There's a City outlet in The Ned's capacious food hall, which like Mayfair is "fun" and "an excellent place to do business" of a less formal kind. Beyond that, the food is "reliable" but pretty "basic at the price", and the setting can be "the noisiest ever". A Soho pizza spot carries the name, on which there's little feedback. New in September 2018, the Shoreditch branch is "a very good addition as a real neighbourhood restaurant", with a "nice bar", and a generally "winning formula", including for brunch. / cecconis.co.uk.

THE CEDAR RESTAURANT £41 3|3|2

65 FERNHEAD ROAD, W9 020 8964 2011
1–2B
202 WEST END LANE, NW6 020 3602 0862
1–1B
81 BOUNDARY ROAD, NW8 020 3204 0030
9–3A

Understated trio of "good neighbourhood Lebanese" in Hampstead, Maida Vale and St John's Wood; "consistently tasty food" is served "in huge portions for the hungry at reasonable prices". / www.thecedarrestaurant.co.uk; @Cedarlebanese.

CELESTE AT THE LANESBOROUGH SW1 £131 2|2|4

HYDE PARK CORNER 020 7259 5599 6–1D

Dining in this grand hotel by Hyde Park Corner is a "truly amazing experience" and the food – overseen by Paris-based uber-chef Eric Fréchon – is by most accounts "lovely". But this "most exceptional night out" requires you "to forget what it will inevitably cost!" – "it would be hard to be good enough to justify these prices" – which might explain why there can be "quite a few empty chairs". / SW1X 7TA; @TheLanesborough; 10.30 pm.

LE CELLAR EC1 £37 3|4|3

130 ST JOHN STREET 020 7689 9115
10–1A

Promising initial feedback on this tiny, wine, cheese, charcuterie and tapas newcomer in Clerkenwell, whose backers include wine buyer Anthonin Charlier (formerly at Cellar and Club Gascon). French and Spanish flavours are to the fore – "a really happy discovery: both food and wine are great, but the service makes the place". / EC1V 4JS; lecellar.co.uk.

CENT ANNI SW19 £53 3|3|3

33 HIGH STREET 020 3971 9781 11–2B

A new 100-seater Italian in Wimbledon village (in the site that was formerly Cau, RIP), which avoids pizza, and serves 'proper' dishes at relatively affordable prices. Some results are "so so", but its initial ratings are promising. / SW19 5BY; centanni.co.uk.

CEPAGES W2 £64 4|3|4

69 WESTBOURNE PARK ROAD
020 3602 8890 7–1B

"Sexy sharing dishes and a dark romantic setting" earn a big thumbs-up for this "fabulous French tapas bistro in deepest Westbourne Park", with an "open brickwork vibe and a couple of coveted tables outside for the hot weather". Wine is taken seriously, prices are "gentle", and it's "one of the few places one can enjoy fresh foie gras cooked rare or à point". / W2 5QH; www.cepages.co.uk; @cepagesWPR; 11 pm, Sun 10 pm.

CERU £35 4|3|4

11 D'ARBLAY STREET, W1 020 3195 3002
4–1C
7-9 BUTE ST, SW7 020 3195 3001 6–2C

"Brilliant", "fresh" and "unusual" Levantine flavours; "cheerful and helpful staff"; and "sunnily charming decoration" ensure these "above-average", modern Middle Eastern bistros are "invariably lively and bustling". The SW7 branch is a well-known fixture of the 'Petit France' enclave of South Kensington, while its year-old spin-off has made a good start establishing itself at the top end of Soho – "you can understand the popularity when food of such a high standard is produced at such very reasonable prices". / www.cerurestaurants.com; @CeruLondon.

CEVICHE £60 3|3|4

17 FRITH ST, W1 020 7292 2040 5–2A
ALEXANDRA TRUST, BALDWIN ST, EC1
020 3327 9463 13–1A

"Still the best Peruvian cuisine in London and still a go-to for a reliable, enjoyable meal out" with "tons of atmosphere" – so say fans of Martin Morales's "vibrant and fun" Latino cantinas in Soho and Shoreditch, known for their "street-ish dishes with interesting combos" and "lovely pisco sours". Ratings came off the boil a little this year, though, with the view aired by one or two reporters that "you can get much better ceviche at much better prices elsewhere". / www.cevicheuk.com; @cevicheuk; W1D 11pm, Fri & Sat 11.30 pm, Sun 10 pm, EC1V 10.30 pm, Fri & Sat 11.30 pm; EC1V closed Sun.

CHAMPOR-CHAMPOR SE1 £58 3|3|2

62 WESTON ST 020 7403 4600 10–4C

"Unusual Thai cooking with interesting Malay influences" has for many years drawn a steady flow of diners to a sidestreet near Guy's Hospital, now in the shadow of the Shard. "Service is quick and helpful", and the "small, slightly cramped" restaurant "has a lovely hideaway table for a romantic dinner". / SE1 3QJ; www.champor-champor.com; @ChamporChampor; 10 pm; D only.

CHARLIE'S W1

BROWN'S HOTEL, ALBEMARLE STREET
020 7493 6020 3–3C

Trinity's celebrated chef, Adam Byatt, is set to relaunch this stately panelled dining room of the foyer of one of Mayfair's most historic hotels, nowadays owned by Rocco Forte (whose late father, Lord Charles Forte inspired the name of this new venture). Adam is the latest in a succession of chefs (most recently Heinz Beck, of Beck at Browns, RIP) who have somehow failed to hit a home-run in this potentially splendid, traditional chamber. According to the PR we should expect an 'evolution of great British cuisine… while embracing a bygone era of service with a sense of theatre'. / W1S.

CHARLOTTE'S £54 3|2|3

6 TURNHAM GREEN TER, W4 020 8742 3590
8–2A

This "reliable" bistro and gin bar near Turnham Green tube has always been "a pleasure to eat in" for 10 years, with "very good cooking, decent wines, and friendly, helpful staff". It is part of the long-established Ealing-based group whose original venue, Charlotte's Place, has closed down following a disastrous fire last year (RIP). / www.charlottes.co.uk; W4 midnight, Sun 11 pm, W5 9.30pm, Sun 4pm, W5 midnight.

CHELSEA CELLAR SW10 £46 4|4|4

9 PARK WALK 020 7351 4933 6–3B

"Romantic, quaint and cosy basement" near Chelsea & Westminster Hospital that earns high marks across the board for its "classy and delicious" Italian cicchetti, plus a seasonal menu of larger plates and 250 wines (also available as off sales). "The owners really take care to look after you" and "clearly put everything into this place". / SW10 0AJ; www.thechelseacellar.co.uk; @chelseacellar; midnight.

CHETTINAD W1　£43　4|3|2

16 PERCY ST　020 3556 1229　2–1C

"Simply delicious south Indian cuisine" from the state of Tamil Nadu – including "the best dosas ever" – means this "justly popular independent" in Fitzrovia "is very different from your usual curry house". "I'm slowly working my way through the menu and have yet to find something I don't like". / W1T 1DT; www.chettinadrestaurant.com; @chettinadlondon; 11 pm, Sun 10 pm; No Amex.

CHEZ BRUCE SW17　£84　5|5|4

2 BELLEVUE RD　020 8672 0114 11–2C

"Still peerless as a neighbourhood restaurant delivering exquisite, modern French cuisine" – Bruce Poole's immaculate "mainstay of South West London", by distant Wandsworth Common, is – for the 15th year in succession – the survey's No. 1 favourite restaurant, and "well worth the trip south of the river". "Whether you are going for a celebratory meal, or just a casual lunch or supper", "its consistency is astonishing, and comes at fabulously reasonable prices" (especially given the "little extra touches like Parmesan biscuits at the beginning of a meal, and chocolate truffles and palmiers at the end"). "What's brilliant about the seasonal cooking is its perfect, pure – not gastronomic – tastes and palate: classics are flawlessly cooked, and there is innovation without it being bound in any way to the latest fads and fashions". And "although there must be heaps going on behind the scenes, the set-up manages to be effortlessly elegant in an unpretentious style that feels like it comes easy to them", with "engaging" staff who are "professional without being obsequious". IF there's a gripe, it's that the "bright and compact" room that most reporters feel is "delightful" and "fitting for pretty much any occasion" (especially a romantic one) is, for a small minority, too "cramped" and un-fancy. / SW17 7EG; www.chezbruce.co.uk; @ChezBruce; 10 pm, Fri & Sat 10.30 pm, Sun 9 pm.

CHEZ ELLES E1　£58　4|4|4

45 BRICK LN　020 7247 9699 13–2C

"Top-quality French food in a totally unpretentious environment is served up with knowledge" at this really charming Brick Lane bistro, with an inviting selection of croques monsieurs at lunch. / E1 6PU; www.chezellesbistroquet.co.uk; @chezellesbistro; 10.30 pm; closed Mon, Tue L & Sun D.

CHICAMA SW10　£60　4|2|4

383 KING'S ROAD　020 3874 2000　6–3C

"Terrific ceviche" – and other "interesting and generally excellent Peruvian-style fish dishes" – dominate the menu at this "really busy and buzzy place" on the King's Road; a two-year-old offshoot of Marylebone's Pachamama. / SW10 0LP; www.chicamalondon.com; @chicamalondon.

CHICK 'N' SOURS　£43　4|3|3

1 EARLHAM STREET, WC2 020 3198 4814 5–2B

62 UPPER STREET, N1 020 7704 9013　9–3D

390 KINGSLAND RD, E8 020 3620 8728 14–2A

"Massive flavours, great vibe" and the "best chicken wings tasted in a long time" (#nextlevel) add up to "heaven in a chintzy, porcelain bowl", say fans of this "great value" concept based in Haggerston, now with branches in Covent Garden and Islington. "It's not just about the chicken – yes, it's mega-crispy and yes, it's super-juicy, but what sets Chick 'n' Sours apart are the garnishes, sides and sauces" – many of them Asian-inspired, such as "the yummy, smashed, spicy, peanuty, cucumber side". / www.chicknsours.co.uk; @chicknsours.

CHILLI COOL WC1　£35　4|2|1

15 LEIGH ST　020 7383 3135　2–1D

"A favourite for authentic spicy Chinese food", this "grungy and basic" student-friendly canteen in Bloomsbury does a wonderful line in lip-tingling Sichuan noodle dishes. The "largely Asian clientele is an effective endorsement of its quality". / WC1H 9EW; www.chillicool.co.uk; 10.15 pm; No Amex.

THE CHILTERN FIREHOUSE W1　£104　1|1|3

1 CHILTERN ST　020 7073 7676　2–1A

Five years on from its heyday as London's hottest celeb hangout, this "gorgeous" Marylebone destination is a "contender for the most overpriced in town", and attracts increasingly caustic comments: "how this poseur-filled dump hasn't been found out yet is a complete mystery: with food that's 'all fur coat and no knickers', and service which – if you're not a member of the smart set or the Z-list – is appalling". Some folks still respond to its shiny glamour, though: "the food is tasty and aesthetically pleasing… as are most of your fellow diners. Finish things off in the very sexy bar – if the romance doesn't spark, ditch each other for the beautiful staff...". / W1U 7PA; www.chilternfirehouse.com; 10.30 pm.

CHINA TANG, DORCHESTER HOTEL W1　£103　3|3|4

53 PARK LN　020 7629 9988　3–3A

"Excellent, but expensive" – the late Sir David Tang's stunning take on Art Deco-era Shanghai has always had vertiginous pricing, but its dependable cooking and "buzzy vibe" have silenced its sterner critics over the years,

and the worst anyone has to say about it this year is that it's "good but not spectacular". Set in the basement of the Dorchester Hotel and newly refurbished in early 2019, arguably its best feature is its "wonderful cocktail list" and beguiling small bar. / W1K 1QA; www.chinatanglondon.co.uk; @ChinaTangLondon; 11.45 pm.

CHISOU　£65　4|4|2

22-23 WOODSTOCK STREET, W1 020 7629 3931　4–1A

31 BEAUCHAMP PL, SW3 020 3155 0005 6–1D

"Marvellous, exquisite Japanese food", including "super-fresh fish" and "the best sushi in town that won't break your wallet", is served at this "very professional" Mayfair outfit. Popular with Vogue staffers, who call it the 'Condé Nast canteen', it has a "cosy" offshoot buried in a luxurious corner of Knightsbridge. / www.chisourestaurant.com; 10.30 pm, Sun 9.30 pm.

CHIT CHAAT CHAI SW18　£35　4|4|3

356 OLD YORK ROAD　020 8480 2364 11–2B

"What a find!" – "superb and authentic Indian street food" developed at a market stall is now found in a permanent home by Wandsworth Town station. "Passionate owner Tania is always there to talk about the menu". / SW18 1SS; chitchaatchai.com; @ChitChaatChai; 10 pm, Sun 9 pm.

CHOKHI DHANI LONDON SW11　£58　3|4|3

UNIT 2, 2 RIVERLIGHT QUAY, NINE ELMS LANE　020 3795 9000 11–1D

In the "desert" of Vauxhall's riverside developments, this year-old offshoot of one of India's best-known luxury restaurant groups occupies the smartly furnished ground floor of one of the new blocks, and specialises in Rajasthani cuisine. Feedback is still relatively limited, but such as there is says it's been an "excellent arrival". / SW11 8AW; www.chokhidhani.co.uk; @cdgchokhidhani; 22.45pm, Sun 21;45pm.

CHOTTO MATTE W1　£59　4|3|4

11-13 FRITH ST　020 7042 7171　5–2A

"Exquisite food and cocktails" – "an amazing blend of flavours danced across my tongue!" – and "a great vibe (particularly for late-night dining)" help make this Japanese-Peruvian fusion haunt in Soho a "fun and buzzy" (if "loud", especially when the music's cranked up) destination for a night on the tiles. / W1D 4RB; www.chotto-matte.com; @ChottoMatteLDN; 1 am, Sun 11 pm.

CHRISKITCH N10　£42　4|3|3

7A TETHERDOWN　020 8411 0051　1–1C

"Fabulous, healthy food" ("excellent salads"), delicious brunches, and "a bread board to die for" are all attractions at this inexpensive, "rather tiny" neighbourhood fixture in Muswell Hill. "Take-away is a good option if it's too cold/wet to sit outside". / N10 1ND; www.chriskitch.com; @chriskitchfood; 6 pm, Sat & Sun 5 pm; L & early evening only; May need 3+ to book.

CHRISTOPHER'S
WC2   £86   2️⃣2️⃣3️⃣

18 WELLINGTON ST   020 7240 4222   5–3D

This classic American surf 'n' turf restaurant and cocktail bar has a "lovely atmosphere" thanks to its setting in a very grand townhouse, and has been a Covent Garden stalwart for almost 30 years. "Perhaps it's showing its age, but it's still reliable and in a useful location". The food could be better, although reporters single out the "generally excellent steaks" for praise. / WC2E 7DD; www.christophersgrill.com; @christopherswc2; May need 6+ to book.

CHUCS
£85   2️⃣3️⃣3️⃣

31 DOVER ST, W1 020 3763 2013   3–3C
97 OLD BROMPTON ROAD, SW7
020 8037 4525   6–2B
226 WESTBOURNE GROVE, W11
020 7243 9136   7–1B
SERPENTINE SACKLER GALLERY, WEST CARRIAGE DRIVE, W2 0207 298 7552   7–2D

Part of the eponymous luxury clotheswear brand – these retro-glam cafés are mostly located in-store, but the portfolio now also boasts the "beautiful building by the Serpentine Sackler Gallery" designed by Zaha Hadid. Perhaps because their price-tag is not exactly 'bargain basement', feedback is somewhat limited, but there's a fairly clear picture of chic Italian dishes that, while "good and tasty", can seem "nothing special" given the Monte Carlo-esque bill. Any such caveats do not seem to be getting in the way of the chain's ongoing expansion however, most recently into Kensington. / www.chucsrestaurants.com; W1 & SW1 11.30 pm, Sun 6 pm; W11 10.30 pm, W2 8 pm; W2 closed Monday.

CHURCHILL ARMS
W8   £39   3️⃣2️⃣5️⃣

119 KENSINGTON CHURCH ST
020 7792 1246   7–2B

"Top-value Thai food with personality – love it!". This slightly "bonkers" pub near Notting Hill Gate looks normal enough, until you discover its "quirky butterfly conservatory at the rear": "a hustling and bustling" venue serving "tasty", spicy scoff at prices that are "amazingly low for the area". "Still a winner" after over thirty years' service: in particular it's "a great choice for eating with friends". / W8 7LN; www.churchillarmskensington.co.uk; @ChurchilArmsW8; 10 pm, Sun 9.30 pm.

CHUTNEY MARY
SW1   £89   4️⃣4️⃣3️⃣

73 ST JAMES'S STREET   020 7629 6688   3–4D

"Still very much an institution, even though it moved from its original SW10 location": this "buzzy, glitzy high-end Indian" – nowadays in St James's – delivers a formidable, all-round formula of "delightful" nouvelle Indian cuisine: "the variety and quality of the menu is truly impressive", backed up by "a well-matched list of wines and whiskies". Top Top – "sitting in the bar area is more fun than the main restaurant". / SW1A 1PH; www.chutneymary.com; @TheChutneyMary.

CHUTNEYS NW1
£21   3️⃣2️⃣2️⃣

124 DRUMMOND ST   020 7388 0604   9–4C

"Fresh and tasty" veggie fare and an "amazing lunch buffet" make this "ridiculously cheap" curry house a perennial favourite in Euston Station's 'Little India'. "I've been going here for literally decades and have introduced many happy fans to the delights of Chutneys" – "the service could be a bit friendlier but when you're getting all you can eat for well under a tenner, who cares?". "The decor of the ground floor has improved over the years, although the basement is less attractive". / NW1 2PA; www.chutneyseuston.uk; 11 pm; No Amex; May need 5+ to book.

CIAO BELLA WC1
£48   3️⃣4️⃣4️⃣

86-90 LAMB'S CONDUIT ST   020 7242 4119   2–1D

This "time-warp classic Italian trattoria" – a Bloomsbury fixture for more than 35 years – is "fun, bubbly, and has food as Mama would have made it" (somewhere between "delicious" and "not bad"). "The buzzy atmosphere makes you feel like you've stepped in off the streets of Rome", and with its "1970s food at 1990s prices, the place deserves a medal" for value. Top Tip – "charming with young children". / WC1N 3LZ; www.ciaobellarestaurant.co.uk; @CiaobellaLondon; 11.30 pm, Sun 10.30 pm.

CIBO W14
£60   4️⃣5️⃣3️⃣

3 RUSSELL GDNS   020 7371 6271   8–1D

"Just like being in Italy, with none of the pretensions of so many chef-centric London restaurants" – this "family-run" veteran between Olympia and Holland Park is "amazingly underexposed; you'd probably walk straight by it". Regulars swear by its "excellent staff, comfortable tables and amazing food", and it's long been touted by some cognoscenti as "the best Italian in west London". / W14 8EZ; www.ciborestaurant.net; 10.30 pm; closed Sat L & Sun D.

CIGALA WC1
£68   2️⃣2️⃣1️⃣

54 LAMB'S CONDUIT STREET
020 7405 1717   2–1D

Fans warm to the "reliably, bare-boards, no-fancy-business" style of this well-regarded Hispanic on an attractive Bloomsbury street,

which does a good line in "authentic tapas". But, especially as it's short on creature comforts, the bill does feel "rather expensive for what it is": "why oh why don't they spend some money on the decor?". / WC1N 3LW; www.cigala.co.uk; @cigalalondon; 10.45 pm, Sun 9.45 pm.

CIGALON WC2
£61   4️⃣4️⃣4️⃣

115 CHANCERY LANE   020 7242 8373   2–2D

"Exceptional Provençal cuisine" – "light and full of fresh flavours" – ensures that dining is "always a real pleasure" here, in what is itself a "lovely, light and airy" glass-roofed venue (once an auction room for books) on Chancery Lane, whose "well-spaced tables" make it a good choice for a business lunch in legal-land. Part of Pascal Aussignac's Club Gascon group, it has its own cocktail bar, Baranis, downstairs. / WC2A 1PP; www.cigalon.co.uk; @cigalon_london; 10 pm; closed Sat & Sun.

CINNAMON BAZAAR
WC2   £49   3️⃣3️⃣3️⃣

28 MAIDEN LANE   020 7395 1400   5–4D

This Covent Garden outpost of a grandee of modern Indian cuisine "means you get the quality of The Cinnamon Club at a more affordable price" – "really interesting food", "spiced with expertise". There's a particularly useful pre-theatre menu. / WC2E 7NA; www.cinnamon-bazaar.com; @Cinnamon_Bazaar.

THE CINNAMON CLUB
SW1   £92   3️⃣2️⃣3️⃣

OLD WESTMINSTER LIBRARY, GREAT SMITH ST   020 7222 2555   2–4C

"Still a classic" – this "elegant" destination in "Westminster's lovely former library" has long been one of London's most pre-eminent posh Indians; and its "interesting and idiosyncratic" cuisine has made it "something of an institution" (including amongst the politico classes – "being within division bell distance of Parliament, there's a fair chance of spotting a well-known face or two"). Its enjoyment was "tempered by episodes of wobbly service over the last year", however, and those who found the staff "over-stretched" were more likely to judge it "too expensive". / SW1P 3BU; www.cinnamonclub.com; @cinnamonclub; 10.30 pm; closed Sun; No trainers; booking max 14 may apply; SRA-Food Made Good – 2 stars.

CINNAMON KITCHEN
£56   4️⃣3️⃣3️⃣

4 ARCHES LANE, SW11 02039555480 11–1C
9 DEVONSHIRE SQ, EC2 020 7626 5000 10–2D

"Bright, interesting flavours" from an evolved menu that's "delicately prepared" win a thumbs up for Vivek Singh's "well-appointed" duo of modern Indians. The original, inside a large atrium within a City development, benefits from a big 'outside' terrace; its year-old sibling occupies a railway arch within the new Battersea Power Station development. / www.cinnamon-kitchen.com; @CinnamonKitchen.

Casa Pastor & Plaza Pastor N1

CIRCOLO POPOLARE W1 £46

40 RATHBONE SQUARE *5–1A*

Hot on the heels of launching smash-hit Gloria, the Big Mamma Group opened this even-more-ambitious follow-up – a larger (280-seat), Sicilian in Fitzrovia – in June 2019. Early press reports say they've absolutely nailed it for a second time, with their trademark maximalist pizzazz, which here incorporates an interior complete with spirit bottles lining the walls, festoons of foliage and twinkly fairy lights; and a pun-tastic menu of pizza by the metre. / W1T 1HX; www.bigmammagroup.com/en/trattorias/circolo-popolare; @bigmammagroup.

CITY BARGE W4 £51 333

27 STRAND-ON-THE-GREEN   020 8994 2148 *1–3A*

"A beautiful situation on the river" in picturesque Strand-on-the-Green is the prime reason to seek out this "friendly local", but its pub grub is consistently well-rated too. In summer there are small terraces with table service to the front and rear of the pub too. / W4 3PH; www.citybargechiswick.com; @citybargew4; 11 pm, Fri & Sat midnight, Sun 10.30 pm.

CITY SOCIAL EC2 £99 333

TOWER 42, 25 OLD BROAD ST **020 7877 7703** *10–2C*

"Spectacular views" reward a trip to the 24th floor of the City's Tower 42, run since 2014 by Jason Atherton's empire – "an elegant dining room, whose bar is quite sexy at night time with the lights of London on display". Unsurprisingly, it's most recommended as a "reliable option" for business entertaining, a service it carries out with aplomb. A foodie paying their own way, however, might judge the cuisine "OK, but nothing overly exciting". / EC2N 1HQ; www.citysociallondon.com; @CitySocial_T42; 10.30 pm; closed Sat & Sun; booking max 4 may apply.

CLARETTE W1 £83 333

44 BLANDFORD ST   020 3019 7750 *3–1A*

These "refitted pub premises" are in their second year as a Marylebone wine bar, brought to us by a part of the family which owns world-famous claret, Château Margaux. Winning solid ratings for its "smart small-plates of French bistro cooking" and "great service" – it's "all very nice, but too expensive" to attract much feedback… unless you're tempted by a glass of 1999 vintage Margaux for £160. / W1U 7HS; www.clarettelondon.com; @ClaretteLondon.

CLARIDGES FOYER & READING ROOM W1 344

49 BROOK STREET *3–2B*

"We've tried other places (including The Ritz) for afternoon tea, but come back here". This "iconic hotel" in the heart of Mayfair combines "art deco elegance with warm scones and piano music", and "because its tea is served in the hotel foyer, there's just the right amount of background activity for a near-perfect, tea-time experience". Also there's a "fabulous breakfast here: ideal for a visiting Aussie or American uncle, with everything from the kippers to the perfect salmon and scrambled egg". / W1K 4HW.

CLARKE'S W8 £71 454

124 KENSINGTON CHURCH STREET **020 7221 9225** *7–2B*

"Never failing to excel, even after years and years…" – Sally Clarke's Kensington HQ (opened in 1984) is nowadays a "classic"; and even those who say "it's a bit of a time warp nowadays", concede that her California-inspired cuisine is nigh-on as "modern and fresh" as ever. "The moment you step in, often to be welcomed by Sally herself, you know you are in for a wonderful evening, with imaginative but unpretentious dishes that are impeccably prepared – with great ingredients that are allowed to stand out – while service is always professional and present-without-hovering". The atmosphere here has always been slightly divisive: for a few "dull" or "formal", but to most diners – "with its artwork, soothing colors, and low noise level to allow plenty of engaging conversation" – romantic and "always a delight". / W8 4BH; www.sallyclarke.com; @SallyClarkeLtd; 10 pm; closed Sun; booking max 14 may apply.

THE CLIFTON NW8 £56 344

96 CLIFTON HILL   020 7625 5010 *9–3A*

"It's not only the fact that Edward VII was a regular", which makes this hostelry hidden away in St John's Wood "a great local". It started out as a Victorian hunting lodge where the future king conducted his affair with the actress Lillie Langtry, was a pub, and then – after a period of being vacant – was rescued from the developers to pave the way for its relaunch a couple of years ago. Modern day attractions include a "Sunday roast that's particularly good", while "the new conservatory comes recommended". / NW8 0JT; www.thecliftonnw8.com; @thecliftonnw8.

CLIPSTONE W1 £74 443

5 CLIPSTONE STREET   020 7637 0871 *2–1B*

"Not at all what you would expect from the outside!" – "fabulous flavours and clever cooking abound" at Will Lander and Daniel Morgenthau's "highly sophisticated" neighbourhood venture, whose understatedly hip premises occupy a deceptively humble-looking corner-site in Fitzrovia. It also features an "exceptional and interesting wine list by glass: I go online after to see what wines I should be buying at home!" / W1W 6BB; www.clipstonerestaurant.co.uk; @clipstonerestaurant; 11 pm.

CLOS MAGGIORE WC2 £83 345

33 KING ST   020 7379 9696 *5–3C*

"I saw a guy go down on bended knee to his girlfriend… she said yes!" This "luxurious and magical" haven – somewhat unexpectedly located "in the heart of Covent Garden" – continues to "live up to its reputation as the most romantic restaurant in London", and "for a meal with that special someone, you won't find much better", especially if you can bag a table (book months in advance) for the "blossom-festooned conservatory" (which some reporters feel is essential to a successful visit; to others it's merely "the icing on the cake"). Unusually for somewhere "oozing romance", standards elsewhere "are not compromised to deliver a memorable experience": "the food might not be the absolute pinnacle of modern British cuisine", but "it's more-than-competent" and "the star gourmet attraction is a wine list of almost biblical proportions". Top Tip – "lunch/pre theatre set menus offer superb value for the excellent quality". / WC2E 8JD; www.closmaggiore.com; @Clos_Maggiore; 11 pm, Sun 10 pm.

THE CLOVE CLUB EC1 £183 332

SHOREDITCH TOWN HALL, 380 OLD ST **020 7729 6496** *13–1B*

In terms of media profile, Daniel Willis, Johnny Smith and chef Isaac McHale's groundbreaking, east London six-year-old is one of the capital's culinary titans: the highest UK restaurant in the famous World's 50-best ranking of global gastronomic champions (one of only two UK names to be thus-recognised). Occupying a neutrally-decorated chamber within Shoreditch's gracious old town hall – with blue-tiled open kitchen on view – the experience features prodigiously-edgy combinations using seasonal British ingredients, and is centred on an extended tasting menu (although there is also a cut-down version available Monday to Thursday, which has a mere six courses; as well another cut-down option at lunch of just four courses). The restaurant also makes a particular feature of thoughtful non-alcoholic and 'ambient tea' drinks pairings to complement its more traditional wine options – an innovation other big names would do well to follow. Does it live up? For many reporters the answer is still yes, with lavish praise for its "lush", "exceptionally creative cuisine", "unusually knowledgeable service" and "remarkable wine". However the "pretentiously unpretentious" interior (no tablecloths of course) lacks charge for somewhere now so famous; and overall the average ratings here are starting to look thoroughly middling in terms of London's other 'heavy hitting' names, by which yardstick its Top 50 placement just doesn't stack up. Flabbergasting pricing is another issue: even fans acknowledge "you need to remortgage your home to go", and 1 in 3 reporters now vote it their most overpriced meal of the year. Oh, and you have to pay in advance… / EC1V 9LT; www.theclove.club; @theclove.club; 9.30 pm; closed Mon L & Sun; SRA-Food Made Good – 1 stars.

CLUB GASCON
EC1   £107   443

**57 WEST SMITHFIELD   020 7600 6144
10–2B**

"The cuisine of southwest France is constantly re-invented to a superb level" at Pascal Aussignac and Vincent Labyrie's influential establishment by Smithfield Market, which marked its 20th anniversary last year with a major overhaul. "The sumptuous atmosphere" has been retained, and Aussignac "continues to surprise and excite" with a "creative and imaginative menu that changes monthly". / EC1A 9DS; www.clubgascon.com; @club_gascon; 9 pm, Fri & Sat 9.30 pm; closed Sat L & Sun.

THE COACH EC1   £60   423

26-28 RAY STREET   020 3954 1595 10–1A

Under chef-director, ex-Racine chef Henry Harris, Harcourt Inns have created a real "neighbourhood asset" with this year-old venture in Clerkenwell, winning a steady stream of satisfied reports of its "very competent", "high-class pub-food": "an interesting menu with unusual items" of a gutsy Gallic nature. "Downstairs is more noisy", with a "buzzy" bar at the front, "lovely, glazed-sided restaurant" and a "small terrace garden that's lovely on a sunny day"; upstairs is more elegant and leisurely. / EC1R 3DJ; www.thecoachclerkenwell.co.uk; @thecoachldn.

COAL OFFICE N1   £51   344

2 BAGLEY WALK   020 3848 6085   9–3C

"Shame it's impossible to get a table", at Assaf Granit's "happening" ("loud and busy") Israeli newcomer – "possibly now the best restaurant in the new King's Cross quarter", and one of the smash hits of the year. With its "amazing location" – a "very cool", Victorian ex-industrial building, with "funky Tom Dixon decor" ("his designer stuff strewn everywhere") and an "enticing terrace" – it has "an easy casual vibe", boosted by "such happy service". For newbies, "the menu takes a little explanation" and delivers "zingy, appetising, rich" small plates which amaze many diners, although they can also seem "to be trying too hard" and "portions aren't massive". Top

Tip – "the bread is outstanding". / N1C 4PQ; coaloffice.com; @coaloffice.

COAL ROOMS
SE15   £54   443

11A STATION WAY   020 7635 6699   1–4D

"A must-visit, right by Peckham station" – whose converted Grade II ticket office houses this "excellent" two-year-old: a stand-out even by the area's lofty standards. "Robust, even macho" dishes, from the smoker and robata grills, are central both to the open kitchen and the menu. Top Tip – "worth a visit for the WC alone" – beautifully restored, old, Victorian bogs. / SE15 4RX; www.coalrooms.com; @coalrooms; 10 pm, Sun 6 pm.

THE COAL SHED
SE1   £59   333

ONE TOWER BRIDGE   020 3384 7272 10–4D

In the shiny new developments south of Tower Bridge, this stylish, but "down-to-earth" two-year-old (sibling to an original in Brighton) has a "wide menu" – from "delicious seafood" to mouthwatering steak – but it's perhaps the "very meaty" dishes that score the highest approval ratings (charcoal grilled British beef cuts are a mainstay of the menu, and the Moroccan goat dish, when it's on, is terrific). Top Tip – "perfect before a show at the new Bridge Theatre" ("I'd go to a performance just as an excuse to dine at The Coal Shed!") / SE1 2AA; www.coalshed-restaurant.co.uk; @TheCoalShed1.

CÔBA N7   £39   432

244 YORK WAY   07495 963336   9–2C

"Hard to find but worth the trip": this hard-surfaced pub-conversion – with plain walls and hanging filament lights – sits in the nondescript wastes north of King's Cross, not far from Caledonian Road Tube. Why visit? "A really good variety of Vietnamese dishes" (majoring in BBQ), prepared by Aussie chef, Damon Bui. / N7 9AG; www.cobarestaurant.co.uk; @cobafood; 10 pm; booking D only.

COCOCHAN W1   £52   322

38-40 JAMES ST   020 7486 1000   3–1A

Between Selfridges and St Christopher's Place – a "busy and quite noisy" haunt, where some reporters are very impressed by its Pan-Asian small plates (including sushi and dim sum dishes), but others feel that they're "not exciting, but OK". / W1U 1EU; www.cocochan.co.uk; @cocochanlondon; 11pm; Booking max 6 may apply.

COLBERT SW1   £74   224

51 SLOANE SQ   020 7730 2804   6–2D

"A slice of Paris in Sloane Square", this hugely popular brasserie rendezvous is "great for people-watching" and its "atmospheric" faux-period decor evokes "a gallery of film noir scenes". But while it's incredibly convenient for those out-and-about in Chelsea, or visiting a production at The Royal Court,

there's something slightly transitory about the experience that makes it the least engaging of Corbin & King's ventures. Even fans concede its Gallic brasserie fare is "not exceptional" or that it feels like "a treadmill that verges on a money-making machine rather than a relaxed venue". Top Tip – "they do breakfast just right". / SW1W 8AX; www.colbertchelsea.com; @ColbertChelsea; 11 pm, Fri & Sat 11.30 pm, Sun 10.30 pm.

LA COLLINA NW1   £57   232

17 PRINCESS RD   020 7483 0192   9–3B

In a quiet location below Primrose Hill, this little Italian – specialising in Piedmontese cuisine – has long been a feature of the area, and has built a very loyal, local following. Reports were a little more hit-and-miss this year on the food front, but fans say that "the garden on a summer's day more than makes up for any average dishes". / NW1 8JR; www.lacollinarestaurant.co.uk; @LacollinaR; 10.15 pm, Sat-Sun 9.15 pm; closed Mon L; booking max 8 may apply.

THE COLLINS ROOM
SW1   £92   234

**THE BERKELEY HOTEL, WILTON PLACE
020 7107 8866   6–1D**

"'Pret-a-Portea' remains the most creative afternoon tea, bar none!" and is "always an amazing delight, both for the eyes and the lips" (this year, its beautifully crafted cakes inspired by fashion catwalks came with a Dior tie-in to match the exhibition at the V&A). "Sitting in the light and airy Collins Room is a treat" in itself too, but while for other occasions the food is "always of a high standard" then for a full meal "do not go hungry as portions can be small". / SW1X 7RL; www.the-berkeley.co.uk/ restaurants-bars/collins-room; @TheBerkeley; 10.45 pm, Sun 10.15 pm.

LE COLOMBIER
SW3   £82   343

**145 DOVEHOUSE STREET   020 7351 1155
6–2C**

"A little corner of France in the SWs" – Didier Garnier's "comfortable and old-fashioned" French brasserie "on a tucked-away site (with a large outside terrace for the summer) has, for just over two decades, maintained a massively loyal following, particularly amongst "older Chelsea residents", on the strength of its "classic" (if rather "no frills") cuisine; "an excellent wine list with prices that are hard to beat"; and notably "courteous" service. "Tables are packed closed" though, and "it's noisy when busy". / SW3 6LB; www.le-colombier-restaurant.co.uk; 10.30 pm, Sun 10 pm.

COLONY GRILL ROOM, BEAUMONT HOTEL
W1 £85 223

THE BEAUMONT, 8 BALDERTON STREET, BROWN HART GARDENS 020 7499 9499 3–2A

In late 2018, Corbin & King lost the management contract for this luxurious Art Deco hotel near Selfridges (to the Barclay family), including its "exceptional-looking", 1920s NYC-style grill room. However for a certain kind of swish American experience, it still nails it: for example, even a reporter who thinks "it's tailed off a bit since leaving the care of C&K" feels "it's still a must-visit to experience the classic, US-country-club style"; and the "transatlantic, slightly retro cuisine" that goes with that ("very rich – but great if that's to your taste"). On the flip side, a cynical view is that it's at risk of becoming "a theme park for nostalgic Americans longing for the food of their childhood". Top Tip – "a wonderful breakfast" for business or pleasure. / W1K 6TF; www.colonygrillroom.com; @ColonyGrillRoom; midnight, Sun 11 pm.

THE COLTON ARMS
W14 £56 234

187 GREYHOUND ROAD 020 3757 8050 8–2C

Backing onto the rear of Queen's Club in Baron's Court (and with a cute small garden for sunny days) – "a good, standby local pub" given a very stylish revamp a couple of years ago, and serving "a decent array of dishes". "The ambience varies a bit depending on where you are sat in the dining room". / W14 9SD; www.thecoltonarms.co.uk; @thecoltonarms; 10 pm, Sun 8 pm.

COMPTOIR GASCON
EC1 £59 323

63 CHARTERHOUSE ST 020 7608 0851 10–1A

"Excellent duck dishes and super duck-fat chips" capture the flavour of southwest France at this offshoot of nearby Club Gascon in Smithfield. It's a "niche restaurant that sticks to its knitting and does it well", with a "very competitive lunch-time offering providing a good-quality meal at a very nice price". / EC1M 6HJ; www.comptoirgascon.com; @ComptoirGascon; 10 pm, Thu & Fri 10.30 pm; closed Mon & Sun.

COMPTOIR LIBANAIS
£46 212

The "consistently tasty food" at these bright and quirky Levantine cafés makes them ideal for a "quick lunch", or "breakfast when you want something more than the usual full English". There are "plenty of options for veggies", although service can be "a little sloppy and chaotic". / www.lecomptoir.co.uk; 10 pm (SW 8 pm), W1C & E20 Sun 8 pm; W12 closed Sun D; no bookings.

CON GUSTO SE18
£56 344

NO 1 STREET 020 8465 7452 12–2D

"In a developing part of Woolwich (an area with lots of blocks of expensive flats going up all along the Thames waterfront, in the grounds of the old Woolwich Arsenal)", this tiny, former guardroom provides a "quirky", pre-Victorian setting ("exposed brick and candle-light") for a meal. "The menu is small (like the place) but tempting – unlike many Italian restaurants where dishes often seem to be an Anglicised fudge, here the food tastes authentic". / SE18 6GH; www.congusto.co.uk.

IL CONVIVIO SW1
£68 343

143 EBURY ST 020 7730 4099 2–4A

This longstanding "local gem" in Belgravia is a "properly Italian restaurant". Currently on great form under chef Cedric Leri, "the food is better than ever, the service ever delightful, the room continues to please" – but "it's rarely full, which is an eternal mystery". / SW1W 9QN; www.etruscarestaurants.com/il-convivio; 10.45 pm; closed Sun.

COOPERS RESTAURANT & BAR WC2
£50 343

49 LINCOLN'S INN FIELDS 020 7831 6211 2–2D

Stuck looking for a comfortable bite near the LSE? – try this staple of legal-land, typically packed with barristers from Lincoln's Inn. It's unlikely to knock your socks off with culinary fireworks, but regulars say a meal here is "always a pleasure, with a great choice of dishes at good-value prices", and applaud the "professional" staff who "go the extra mile". / WC2A 3PF; www.coopersrestaurant.co.uk; @coopers_bistro; 10.30 pm; closed Sat & Sun; no booking.

COPPA CLUB TOWER BRIDGE
EC3 £45 235

THREE QUAYS WALK, LOWER THAMES STREET 020 7993 3827 10–3D

"The Christmas igloo during December was one of the nicest experiences ever…" – "the absolutely stunning location on the Thames is perfect for a summers day…" – "you can snuggle up on a sofa in front of the fire during the winter months…"; "the food is a bit so-so, but who cares?": all are comments from fans of this all-day 'club without membership' near Tower Bridge. It's part of a growing chain, with most branches in the Thames Valley, and a (much less interesting) sibling in a bank-conversion looking across the road to St Paul's Cathedral. / EC3R 6AH; www.coppaclub.co.uk; @coppaclub; 11 pm, Sun 10 pm; Booking max 6 may apply.

COQ D'ARGENT
EC2 £80 234

1 POULTRY 020 7395 5000 10–2C

"On a warm summer's day, the roof garden is a secluded and delightful place to escape the pressure of the Square Mile", say fans of D&D London's long-established, 7th-floor perch, just a stone's throw from Bank. Squarely aimed at a "very City clientele", it's a "swanky expense-accounter venue", whose starched napery will not disappoint your visiting client from NYC"; and where a meal can be started with preprandial drinks on the terrace. Fans feel it offers "high quality, well-prepared" French cuisine – the more downbeat version is that it's "pricey for what it provides": either way, you get "a great view!" / EC2R 8EJ; www.coqdargent.co.uk; @coqdargent1; 9.45 pm; closed Sun D; booking max 10 may apply.

COQFIGHTER W1
£26 532

75 BEAK STREET 020 7734 4001 4–2C

"Scrumptious, Korean-style, fried-chicken burgers – so crunchy, and topped with the most excellent flavour combinations", plus K-wings, bao, and other finger-lickin' goodies have won a big fanclub for these Aussie-owned pitstops, which graduated in June 2019 from two Boxpark locations (in Shoreditch and Croydon) to this new Soho permanent-home, with its mix of communal and small tables, on, wait for it, Beak Street… / W1F 9SS; www.coqfighter.com.

CORA PEARL WC2
£66 323

30 HENRIETTA STREET 020 7324 7722 5–3D

"One of the more individual, thoughtful places opening up in Covent Garden – this "lively", "very enjoyable little sister of Kitty Fisher" opened in mid-2018, and inspires many reports of "simple, luxurious food" from "an incredibly attractive menu" of "delicious, little, sharing bites". "Decent-without-being-exceptional" is another school of opinion on the cooking, though, and middling ratings overall take into account seating that's "so cramped" and service that's "at times, pushy, brisk and hurried". Top Tip – "I'm not sure what they did to the chips but they transcended any normal form of potato – order a bowl each as you won't want to share!" / WC2E 8NA; www.corapearl.co.uk; @CoraPearlCG.

CORAZÓN W1
£45 343

29 POLAND STREET 020 3813 1430 4–1C

Laura Sheffield's "fun, friendly and very good value" Mexican, just off Oxford Street, is a useful centrally located addition to London's taco scene. "Interesting veggie options" plus "delicious pulled pork tacos" means everybody's "pretty happy". / W1F 8QR; www.corazonlondon.co.uk; @corazon_uk.

CORE BY CLARE SMYTH
W11 £122 544

92 KENSINGTON PARK RD 020 3937 5086 7–2B

"The third Michelin star must be on its way" say fans of Clare Smyth's "world class" one-year-old, which – after its "brilliant start" – is much "better than Restaurant Gordon Ramsay Royal Hospital Road" (her former gig); and was the most-nominated restaurant in the survey this year for providing London's top gastronomic experience. Occupying the Notting Hill venue that some still recall as Leith's (long RIP), she has created a "smart-but-unintimidating" space, where "superb, friendly, and unpompous staff" steer a course between "slight informality" (no tablecloths) and being "highly professional". And "Clare and head chef Johnnie always make time to say hello". "So much original thought has gone in" to the "masterfully-blended dishes, showing occasional idiosyncratic touches" to create "precise, exquisite morsels that look like art on a plate and taste fabulous (if at a high price tag)". "Words aren't enough to describe the journey your taste buds go on!". "Unfortunately, however, it has become almost impossible to book". Top Menu Tip – "I never thought a potato could taste that good!" / W11 2PN; www.corebyclaresmyth.com.

CORK & BOTTLE
WC2   £56   2 2 4
**44-46 CRANBOURN ST   020 7734 7807
5–3B**

"The wine bar all others aspire to be" (of an old school nature) – this characterful cellar just off Leicester Square is closing in on its 50th year, and has seen little change in that time. "The food, while a bit of an eighties throwback, is perfectly good for soaking up a few glasses" – and "you can't beat the ham & cheese pie", biggest seller on the menu since 1978. Owner Will Clayton, who took over from the legendary Don Hewitson, has opened branches in Bayswater and Hampstead – but it will take them years to match up to the original. / WC2H 7AN; www.thecorkandbottle.co.uk; @corkbottle1971; 11.30 pm, Sun 10.30 pm; no booking D.

CORNER ROOM E2 £51   3 2 3
PATRIOT SQ   020 7871 0461 14–2B

Bethnal Green's old town hall – nowadays a boutique hotel – houses this 30-seater overseen by chef, Simon Shand. Although it lacks the profile it once did, the limited feedback we received this year was all positive: in particular "the fixed price, five-course menu is excellent value for good, modern British cuisine". / E2 9NF; www.townhallhotel.com/cornerroom; @townhallhotel; 9.30 pm, Thu-Sat 10 pm.

CORNERSTONE E9 £63   5 4 4
3 PRINCE EDWARD ROAD, 14–1C

"In a rather unlikely location, tucked away around the corner from Hackney Wick station" – Tom Brown's stellar yearling is one of the "most impressive" arrivals of the last year or so. His "super-fresh" fish dishes "are inventively conceived and perfectly executed" from an "original menu"; and served in an artfully "plain" and "relaxed" environment, which "brings the area's industrial heritage to the fore, while injecting a hint of Scandi chic". Staff are "very accommodating" too, and – with the open kitchen centre stage – "it's lovely watching the chefs at work". A few reporters consider it "a victim of hype", but, for the overwhelming majority, it's well "worth the

expedition". / E9 5LX; cornerstonehackney.com; @Cornerstone_h_w.

CORRIGAN'S MAYFAIR
W1   £108   3 3 3
**28 UPPER GROSVENOR ST   020 7499 9943
3–3A**

"Classic and club-like (without being oppressive)" – Richard Corrigan's spacious Mayfair HQ, just off Park Lane, offers a traditionally luxurious experience, focused on "unfussy", top-quality British cuisine (from head chef, Aidan McGee). Its ratings looked less secure this year, though, with mounting concerns about its vertiginous pricing – to fans "even if it's expensive, the quality is there", but to foes it now seems "extremely overpriced" to an extent some feel is "ludicrous". Top Tip – "superb value set lunch". / W1K 7EH; www.corrigansmayfair.com; @CorriganMayfair; 10 pm; closed Sat L; Booking max 12 may apply.

CÔTE   £57   2 2 2

"Top choice when meeting up is more important than the food!" – Richard Caring's "brisk" modern brasseries are "a cut-above most other chains" and were once again the survey's most-mentioned national multiple, on the strength of their "very convenient" and often picturesque locations; and an experience generally that's "safe" and affordable (set menus in particular are very "competitively priced"). That said, even many of its legions of fans don't suggest that their performance will set the world on fire: "menus offer a range of formulaic dishes, some more wowing than others", with "basic options such as steak-frites" or burger often touted as the best of the "rather unadventurous" selection. "Service can vary" but usually "problems are swiftly resolved" and staff keep things "speedy" enough. / www.cote.co.uk; 11 pm; closed Sun.

COUNTER CULTURE
SW4   £47   4 4 2
16 THE PAVEMENT   020 8191 7960 11–2D

"Fun, buzzy, hipster, and tiny" – Robin Gill's 16-seater in Clapham (an offshoot of his Dairy, next door) is known for its "novel and ever-changing", small-plates cuisine based around 'pickling, fermenting, curing and bottling the best of the season's produce'. "You don't go for comfort though!", given its bum-numbing stools. It won high ratings this year, but may be about to get even better: star ex-Stem chef Sam Ashton Booth joined in July 2019 and is set to introduce a new menu 'The Allotment', with produce supplied by Bedfordshire-based co-collaborator, Jake 'Wiggo' Ball (who does the growing). / SW4 0HY; www.countercultureclapham.co.uk; @culturesnax; no booking.

THE COW W2   £62   3 3 4
**89 WESTBOURNE PARK RD   020 7221 0021
7–1B**

"A long-time local favourite" celebrating its 25th anniversary this year: Tom Conran's Irish-themed gastroboozer on the Notting

Hill-Bayswater border is "always relaxed", with "reliably good food" (both in the bustling downstairs bar, and the cute, cramped first floor). Despite its name, the focus is on seafood (oysters washed down with a pint o' Guinness being the classic choice here). / W2 5QH; www.thecowlondon.co.uk; @TheCowLondon; 11 pm, Sun 10 pm; No Amex.

COYA   £81   4 3 4
**118 PICCADILLY, W1 020 7042 7118   3–4B
UNIT 1C ANGEL COURT, 31-33
THROGMORTON ST, EC2 020 7042 7118
10–2C**

"A real culinary tour of the best of Peru, with mouthwatering ceviche, smoky grilled meats and show-stopping desserts" ("we were blown away by the freshness and amazing flavour combinations"), "… all washed down with a pisco sour or two", helps inspire rave reviews this year for this Latino duo – an "impressive-looking subterranean bar/restaurant in Mayfair", and a similarly "buzzy and relaxed" set-up in the City, tucked away behind the Bank of England. "It's best if someone else is paying" of course, but past flak about whopping prices was absent this year. / www.coyarestaurant.com.

CRAFT LONDON
SE10   £65   4 4 3
PENINSULA SQUARE   020 8465 5910 12–1D

"You dine very well" from a "really interesting and different menu", hosted by "informative staff", in the restaurant at Stevie Parle's multi-level operation by the O2 Centre. "The bars are pretty good as well" – "brilliant for cocktails, fantastic for people-watching" – and there's a café on the ground floor. / SE10 0SQ; www.craft-london.co.uk; @CraftLDN; 10.30 pm (cafe 6pm); cafe L only; restaurant D only, Sat L & D, closed Mon & Sun.

CRATE BREWERY AND
PIZZERIA E9   £31   4 3 4
**7, THE WHITE BUILDING, QUEENS YARD
020 8533 3331 14–1C**

In a "lovely spot" across the canal from the Olympic Park (near Hackney Wick station), and with a big waterside terrace, this "very buzzy" and achingly East End microbrewery serves brilliant pizza ("especially if you like them thin-based") and "great own-brewed beers". After a successful CrowdCube fundraiser, the first floor is about to become a venue in itself – and further boost its cutting edge cred – importing zero-waste eco-project Silo (see also) from Brighton. / E9 5EN; www.cratebrewery.com; @cratebrewery; 10 pm, Fri & Sat 11 pm.

CROCKER'S FOLLY
NW8   £54   3 3 4
23-24 ABERDEEN PL   020 7289 9898   9–4A

"Very ornate interiors" at this "fascinating pub" were created thanks to a misguided late-Victorian entrepreneur who thought a major railway terminus would be built in St John's Wood. For the last few years, it's been a new departure for the Maroush group, and – after

Core by Clare Smyth W11

Coal Office N1

a poor start dabbling with traditional British cuisine – it's "getting better now that they've returned to their Lebanese roots". Mezze and kebabs in a pub may seem an odd mix and it is "a difficult place to get to", but by all accounts it's worth the effort. / NW8 8JR; www.crockersfolly.com; @crockersfolly.

THE CROOKED WELL
SE5   £53   3|3|3

16 GROVE LN   020 7252 7798   1–3C

"A great Camberwell local" fitted out with wittier design than you find in your typical greige gastropub; and which "fits the bill for posh pub food... not to mention its cool bar for some pre-dinner gin cocktails". / SE5 8SY; www.thecrookedwell.com; @crookedwell; 10.30 pm; closed Mon L; No Amex; booking max 6 may apply.

THE CROSS KEYS
SW3   £59   3|4|4

**1 LAWRENCE STREET   020 7351 0686
6–3C**

"Eager staff", a proper "local pub atmosphere" and a "great menu" of modern British dishes make this a "real discovery" just a stone's throw from the Thames. The oldest boozer in Chelsea (est. 1708), it has served pints to luminaries including JMW Turner, Dylan Thomas and Bob Marley. / SW3 5NB; www.thecrosskeyschelsea.co.uk; @CrossKeys_PH; 10 pm, Sun 9 pm.

THE CRYSTAL MOON
LOUNGE, CORINTHIA HOTEL
LONDON SW1   £87   2|4|4

WHITEHALL PLACE   020 7321 3150   2–3C

"Sitting under the giant chandelier [careful, it weighs two tons!] eating far too much food is a real treat", when you have afternoon tea in the swish lounge of this luxurious five-star, off Embankment: an occasion for which it's becoming increasingly well-known. It's "a really outstanding offering, served by staff who are clearly versed in the different teas on offer, as well as the delicious sandwiches and cakes". / SW1A 2BD; www.corinthia.com/en/hotels/london/dining/afternoon-tea.

CUB N1   £92   4|4|3

153-155 HOXTON ST   020 3693 3202   14–2A

"Just as much a political statement as a meal", this "low-waste, little venue" in Shoreditch is co-owned by Doug McMaster of Brighton's acclaimed zero-waste restaurant Silo, and a similar eco-friendly approach is showcased here. "It serves up a series of challenging plates of principally foraged food from a fixed multi-course menu, alongside cocktails that fall a little outside the usual comfort zone", and wins consistently high ratings (albeit from a relatively small fanclub). See also Silo. / N1 6PJ; www.lyancub.com; @mrlyan; Online only.

THE CULPEPER E1   £61   3|2|4

40 COMMERCIAL ST   020 7247 5371   13–2C

"The lovely first-floor dining room is a particular favourite" at this thoughtfully converted Spitalfields gastropub with its own rooftop garden (complete with summer BBQ). "Friendly" and "unpretentious", its cooking pleases all reporters (but misses the raves it once attracted). / E1 6LP; www.theculpeper.com; @TheCulpeper; midnight, Fri & Sat 2 am, Sun 11 pm; SRA-Food Made Good – 3 stars.

CUMBERLAND ARMS
W14   £56   3|3|3

29 NORTH END RD   020 7371 6806   8–2D

"Just around the corner from Olympia", it's worth knowing about this well-rated pub, in the not-particularly-auspicious northerly reaches of the North End Road. In the same stable as Earl's Court's excellent Atlas, it delivers "a very enjoyable meal, with a good quality menu and a lovely atmosphere". / W14 8SZ; www.thecumberlandarmspub.co.uk; @CumberlandArms; 10 pm, Sun 9.30 pm.

CURRY HOUSE COCO
ICHIBANYA WC2   £18

**17 GREAT NEWPORT STREET
020 3904 5633   5–3B**

Near Leicester Square tube and need a quick bite? – maybe grab a meal at this simple December 2018 newcomer: the first London outpost of Japan's largest (1,000-strong) chain specialising in kare raisu dishes – curry and rice: over 40 different rice toppings are available, including hamburgers, scrambled eggs and fried oysters. / WC2H 7JE; ichibanya.uk.

CUT, 45 PARK LANE
W1   £122   3|2|2

45 PARK LN   020 7493 4545   3–4A

"I've had better, but if cost is irrelevant…" – this "good but exceedingly pricey" US-style steakhouse in a Park Lane hotel is part of a global brand from celeb chef Wolfgang Puck, the second most famous Austrian-born American in LA. The menu lists 16 steaks, up to a Japanese pure wagyu rib eye from Kyushu at heart-stopping £160. "And did I mention it was expensive? Somehow we racked up a bill of almost £100 for two full English breakfasts with coffee". / W1K 1PN; www.45parklane.com; @45ParkLaneUK; 10.30 pm.

CUT + GRIND N1   £35   3|3|3

THE URBANEST BUILDING, 25-27 CANAL REACH   9–3C

"Some of the juiciest burgers out there" are prepared at this two-year-old King's Cross indie (with outlets at Boxpark Wembley and the Lexington Angel in Islington), which minces its beef onsite every day and offers two veggie versions. / N1C 4DD; www.cutandgrindburgers.com; @cngburgers.

CYPRUS MANGAL
SW1   £40   4|3|2

45 WARWICK WAY   020 7828 5940   2–4B

"Succulent kebabs, hummus and tabouleh" make this highly rated Turkish-Cypriot grill one of the "best options" in Pimlico – "rapid service without many smiles, and good value". / SW1V 1QS; www.cyprusmangal.co.uk; 10.45 pm, Fri & Sat 11.45 pm.

DA GIUA EC1   £56   3|4|2

105 WHITECROSS STREET   020 7374 6713   13–2A

Now over a year old, this newish establishment, between Old Street and Barbican, operates on a site that's seen other ventures come and go, and those who know the area say it's "good to have someone operate something that's working": a "cut-above-the-average, local Italian" at "sensible prices", including "excellent pizza". Top Tip – "a truffle-based menu looked excellent as did the truffle that was brought out for my appreciation when I expressed an interest". / EC1Y 8JH; dagiua.com.

DA MARIO SW7   £43   3|3|3

15 GLOUCESTER RD   020 7584 9078   6–1B

Near the Royal Albert Hall and needing a "reasonably priced" bite? This fun Italian is surprisingly smart given its affordable prices, and its food – majoring in pizza – is consistently well rated. It claims to have been 'Princess Diana's local pizzeria' (and is not shy about promoting the connection via pics on the walls). Top Tip – budget party cave in the cellar. / SW7 4PP; www.damario.co.uk; 11.30 pm.

DA MARIO WC2 £53 2|3|3

63 ENDELL ST   020 7240 3632   5–1C

An "old-fashioned, warm and lovely Italian", whose "comforting" 'throwback' style is at odds with its very central Covent Garden location. The family who ran ran it for so many years retired in August 2018, however, and – though the staff remain – some old-timers are concerned: "since the change of ownership the standard of cooking in this much-loved restaurant seems to have slipped, while the prices have increased. However its proximity to theatres means it is still busy". / WC2H 9AJ; www.da-mario.co.uk; 11.15 pm; closed Sun.

DA TERRA, TOWN HALL HOTEL E2 £32 5|4|4

8 PATRIOT SQUARE   020 7062 2052 14–2B

"A very fine effort by Brazilian chefs with a good team. I hope they succeed!" Paulo Airaudo and Rafael Cagali's ambitious East End newcomer is the latest inhabitant of this space in Bethnal Green's former town hall (which has, over the years, housed Lee Westcott's The Typing Room and Nuno Mendes's Viajante) where a series of wizard small plates (from either an eight-course or eleven-course menu) are delivered, often by the chefs themselves, from the open kitchen. It's yet to generate a huge depth of feedback, but in terms of dazzling ratings it's scored as one of the more interesting arrivals this year; and a very worthy successor to its brilliant predecessors on this site. / E2 9NF; www.daterra.co.uk.

DADDY BAO SW17 £33 4|3|3

113 MITCHAM ROAD   020 3601 3232 11–2C

Sibling to Peckham's Mr Bao, this casual, small Tooting yearling similarly specialises in steamed buns and other tasty Taiwanese treats, and wins nothing but very good ratings for its cooking. / SW17 9PE; www.daddybao.com.

DAFFODIL MULLIGAN EC1

70-74 CITY ROAD 13–1A

The foodie 'Murphia' is out in force with this late-2019 newcomer, backed by famous chef Richard Corrigan (who first made his name over 20 years ago at a different Mulligan's, then 'of Mayfair'), fellow Irishman John Nugent, and King's Place owner Peter Millican (see Rotunda at King's Place). On the site south of Old Street vacated by Nuala (RIP), we are promised a bar serving proper Irish food, plus regular live music and spoken word gigs. Sláinte. / EC1Y 2BJ; @CorrigansFood.

THE DAIRY SW4 £53 5|4|5

15 THE PAVEMENT   020 7622 4165 11–2D

"One of south west London's best restaurants with a great team and food ethos" – Robin Gill's "very casual and hipster" haunt provides "imaginative, skilful small-plate cooking in the heart of Clapham, with good use of seasonal ingredients and information on their sourcing". A "trendy and stripped" space, "it's a bit long and thin, so some tables feel cramped"; and

"the menu could be slightly more varied for the regular customer"; but "it's still a lovely meal on any occasion". / SW4 0HY; www.the-dairy.co.uk; @thedairyclapham; 9.45 pm; closed Mon, Tue L & Sun D.

DALLOWAY TERRACE, BLOOMSBURY HOTEL WC1 £72 3|2|4

16-22 GREAT RUSSELL ST   020 7347 1221 2–1C

With its foliage and fairy lights, it's hard to believe that this hotel terrace (with fully retractable roof) is just two minutes' walk from grungy Centre Point. Feedback is limited, mostly focusing on its afternoon tea possibilities: "great cocktails too in the adjoining Coral room". / WC1B 3NN; www.dallowayterrace.com; @DallowayTerrace; 10.30 pm.

LA DAME DE PIC LONDON EC3 £120 4|4|3

10 TRINITY SQUARE   020 7297 3799 10–3D

"A truly world-class representative of London dining" – the Pic family's "plush" two-year-old, within a monumental five-star hotel (the Port of London Authority's former HQ), provides a "stunning-if-pricey" destination that nowadays ranks in London's culinary top tier; and its heart-of-the-city location by Tower Hill makes it a natural for wining and dining particularly important prospects. The "calm, white-walled dining room" provides a "chic" and "beautiful" setting for a meal, service is "attentive but un-pushy", but its highest rated feature is its "sensational", "superbly refined" modern French cuisine. / EC3N 4AJ; ladamedepiclondon.co.uk; @FSTenTrinity; No shorts.

DANDY SE1

35 MALTBY STREET   AWAITING TEL 10–4D

From a shipping container in London Fields to a short-lived restaurant on Newington Green, and now – in the former home of Monmouth Coffee on Maltby Street – this latest, crowdfunded incarnation also has Matt Wells (co-founder of The Dairy) as partner and is slated to open in the second half of 2019. Plans include a bar and ultimately an in-house brewery; on the menu – inventive, seasonal dishes. / SE1 3PA; dandy.restaurant.

DAPHNE'S SW3 £77 2|3|4

112 DRAYCOTT AVE   020 7589 4257   6–2C

"So civilised" – this Chelsea stalwart was founded in 1967 by Daphne Rye, the theatrical agent who discovered Richard Burton; and a couple of decades later found fame as Princess Di's favourite haunt. But beyond a local well-heeled crowd its social caché is more limited nowadays, and, despite being part of Richard Caring's Caprice group, it generates only a middling amount of feedback. The Italian cooking is somewhere between dependable and unexciting… especially at the price: "we go for old time's sake, but really the food is average".

/ SW3 3AE; www.daphnes-restaurant.co.uk; @DaphnesLondon; 11 pm, Sun 10 pm.

DAQUISE SW7 £56 2|2|2

20 THURLOE ST   020 7589 6117   6–2C

"Faded old-world charm and traditional hearty food" ("stuffed cabbage most enjoyable with potato vodka") are the hallmarks of this "historic Polish gem" (est 1947) near South Ken tube, where legendary restaurant critics Jonathan Meades and the late AA Gill used to meet regularly for lunch. Even if dishes can be "stodgy" they are "wonderfully authentic" and in "robust portions", and act as a portal to "the distant past". / SW7 2LT; www.daquise.co.uk; @GesslerDaquise; 11 pm; No Amex.

DARBY'S SW11 £74 4|4|4

3 VIADUCT GARDENS ROAD, EMBASSY GARDENS 11–1D

Amidst the mushrooming luxury developments of Vauxhall's once-neglected south bank, Robin and Sarah Gill's (The Dairy, Counter Culture, Sorella) biggest venture to-date occupies the ground floor of one such new building, near the new American Embassy. Set around a large central bar with counter – and following an Irish-American theme (incorporating Robin's Irish heritage) – the culinary emphasis is ingredient-led as the website makes clear: '… our single philosophy is: We have a wonderful product, let's try not to feck it up'. It's a comprehensive offering, complete with in-house bakery, large open kitchen with grill, cold storage (showing off steaks and fresh fish), an oyster bar, and a big outside terrace. It opened just as the survey was closing, but early feedback is of food that's "fresh, interesting and delicious" – "the ragu was the best I have eaten anywhere ever!" / SW11 7AY; www.darbys-london.com; @robingillchef.

DARJEELING EXPRESS W1 £47 4|3|3

6-8 KINGLY STREET   020 7287 2828   4–2B

"The small menu really delivers on taste and price" with "some absolutely amazing dishes", at Calcutta-born Asma Khan's former supper club, now in hugely popular, permanent quarters off Carnaby Street. The "friendly" staff, including an all-women kitchen team of self-described 'housewives', ensure there's a real "home-cooked" flavour to the enterprise. / W1B 5PW; www.darjeeling-express.com; @Darjeelingldn; 10 pm, Sun 4 pm.

THE DARTMOUTH CASTLE W6 £57 3|4|4

26 GLENTHORNE RD   020 8748 3614   8–2C

A short stroll from un-lovely Hammersmith Broadway, this atmospheric pub (with outside terrace) surprises with its characterful style and quality cooking. "It's getting busier and busier during the week, but weekends can be surprisingly quiet". / W6 0LS; www.thedartmouthcastle.co.uk; @DartmouthCastle; 9.30 pm, Sun 9 pm; closed Sat L.

DARWIN BRASSERIE

EC3 £74 2 2 5

**1 SKY GARDEN WALK 033 3772 0020
10–3D**

"Go for the spectacular views alone",
"especially at night with the city lights twinkling
below", from the "unique perspective" of this
all-day brasserie at the top of the Walkie-
Talkie tower. "The menu is limited and fairly
expensive", but – on most accounts – "the food
is surprisingly good" for the location. / EC3M
8AF; skygarden.london/darwin; @SG_Darwin.

DASTAAN KT19 £39 5 4 3

447 KINGSTON RD 020 8786 8999 1–4A

"Perfectly executed north Indian food" from
a pair of former Gymkhana chefs has made
this apparently-modest, outer-suburban curry
house a site of pilgrimage, despite its "bizarre
setting just off the Ewell bypass". "The food
is in pretty much perfect inverse correlation
to the location", and "sets a new benchmark
for Indian food and service" – no wonder it's
"booked solid". Top Tip – "the lamb chops
alone are worth the Uber". / KT19 0DB;
dastaan.co.uk; @Dastaan447; Booking weekdays
only.

DAVIES AND BROOK,
CLARIDGE'S HOTEL W1

49 BROOK STREET 3–2B

Gordon Ramsay… Simon Rogan… next in
the series of celeb-chefs to occupy Claridge's
gorgeous Art Deco restaurant is NYC-chef
Daniel Humm, of Manhattan's acclaimed
Eleven Madison Park. The replacement for
Rogan's Fera at Claridges was set to open
in summer 2019, but will now do so in the
autumn, following Humm's split from his
long-term business partner Will Guidara, and
the need to buy out his share of the restaurant
group behind the opening, 'Make it Nice'. /
W1K 4HW; www.claridges.co.uk/restaurants-bars/
davies-and-brook.

DAYLESFORD
ORGANIC £60 3 1 2

**44B PIMLICO RD, SW1 020 7881 8060 6–2D
6-8 BLANDFORD ST, W1 020 3696 6500
2–1A
76-82 SLOANE AVENUE, SW3 AWAITING
TEL 6–2C
208-212 WESTBOURNE GROVE, W11
020 7313 8050 7–1B**

Lady Bamford's four organic farm-shop cafés in
London make "perfect brunch venues" before
stocking up on non-packaged 'zero-waste'
goodies from her Cotswolds farm. They're also
"nice for people-watching" – although, while
the "previously terrible service has improved a
lot", "staff are often overwhelmed when things
get busy". / www.daylesfordorganic.com; 7 pm
- 10 pm, Sun 3 pm - 4 pmGL56 8pm, Sun 4pm,
SW3 Mon 7pm, 10pm, Sun 4pm, W11 Mon 7pm,
9.30pm, sun 4pm, SW11 8pm Sun 3pm, W1U Mon
7pm, 9.30 and sun 4pm; W11 no booking L.

DEAN STREET TOWNHOUSE

W1 £67 2 3 5

69-71 DEAN ST 020 7434 1775 4–1D

"Wonderful when it's cold outside – with warm
fires burning to make it very welcoming" – and
blessed with a nice terrace for summer: this
all-day Soho House brasserie (part of their
hotel, in the heart of Soho) exudes just the right
design pheromones to keep it permanently
packed. "Just the job for a power breakfast – it
serves decent kippers, cracking kedgeree and a
full English that deserves the name". At other
times its English comfort food (when did you
last see mince and potatoes on a menu?) neither
greatly adds nor detracts from the experience.
/ W1D 3SE; www.deanstreettownhouse.com;
@deanstreettownhse; 11.30 pm, Fri & Sat
midnight, Sun 10.30 pm.

DECIMO WC1

**THE STANDARD, 10 ARGYLE ST
020 3981 8888 9–3C**

Peter Sanchez-Inglesias's famous Bristol
restaurant, Casamia, was voted by Harden's
reporters the UK's best in last year's survey,
so this October 2019 opening on a hip, new
hotel rooftop opposite King's Cross will be one
of the most closely-watched of late 2019. The
venture will offer Spanish and Mexican cuisines
in an 114-cover space, whose view takes in the
magnificent Gothic rooftops of St Pancras. /
WC1H 9JE; www.decimo.london.

DEFUNE W1 £89 4 3 2

34 GEORGE ST 020 7935 8311 3–1A

"Perfect sushi" and other "top-notch modern
Japanese" food has drawn a steady crowd to
this "sedate" Marylebone veteran for the last
35 years (it claims to be the 'longest running
Japanese restaurant in London'). No-one's
ever been that wild about the interior – the
focus is very much on the (expensive) food:
"you'll leave happy but broke…" / W1U 7DP;
www.defune.com; 10.45 pm, Sun 10.15 pm.

DEHESA W1 £58 2 2 3

25 GANTON STREET 020 7494 4170 4–2B

Especially "on a rainy night, snuggled up
in the window by candlelight", this small
modern tapas restaurant off Carnaby Street
can still be a valued haunt. But its ratings
have dropped sharply in the past two years
as the Salt Yard Group changed hands. "The
food used to be really delicious: the ideas are
still good" – the "brilliant inclusion of Italian
elements in the tapas" – but the realisation
nowadays can be "mediocre". / W1F 9BP;
www.saltyardgroup.co.uk/dehesa; @DehesaSoho;
10.45 pm, Sun 9.45 pm.

DELAMINA £42 4 4 2

**56-58 MARYLEBONE LANE, W1
020 3026 6810 3–1A
151 COMMERCIAL STREET, E1
020 7078 0770 13–2B**

"Part of the new craze for 'modern-Israeli-
style' cuisine" – self-taught chef, Limor Chen

(with the help of partner Amir) provides "a
different take on the ubiquitous Ottolenghi or
Palomar approach" at this low-key restaurant
near the Wigmore Hall – a kind of "British
Middle Eastern food", which "features lots of
vegetables, like the spicy okra tempura and
charred cauliflower, which are delicious (and I
don't normally go for veg'!)". "Nice people run
the place" too, which is decked out with the
"on-trend, stripped-back, filament-lightbulb
look". Its "buzzing and fun" E1 spin-off inspires
less feedback, but gets an equally good rep.

THE DELAUNAY

WC2 £67 2 4 4

55 ALDWYCH 020 7499 8558 2–2D

Corbin & King's "grand café", just off Aldwych,
is less showy than its Piccadilly stablemate The
Wolseley, but nevertheless "a class act", whose
"luxurious" decor, "restrained acoustics",
well-spaced interior ("the large room never
feels packed even when it's full") and "brisk",
"very professional" service make it "especially
good for business lunches" in 'Midtown'.
But it's also "fabulous for breakfast", not to
mention "a great option for pre-theatre" and
a top choice for afternoon tea ("lovely cakes,
scones… good choice of proper loose teas").
"The Mitteleuropean food isn't the most
gastronomically exciting, but there's always
something on the menu for everyone" (and with
"lots of dishes rarely found in London: wild
boar sausage, bratwurst, tarte flambé, etc)".
Top Tip – "the Delaunay Counter is excellent
for coffee". / WC2B 4BB; www.thedelaunay.com;
@TheDelaunayRest; midnight, Sun 11 pm.

DELFINO W1 £58 3 3 2

121A MOUNT ST 020 7499 1256 3–3B

"Brilliant pizzas" (alongside "typical trattoria
dishes") are served at this Mount Street
Italian: "good for quick business lunches" and
offering notably "great value in the heart of
Mayfair". It "could do with some investment
in decor and ambience" though. / W1K 3NW;
www.finos.co.uk; 10 pm; closed Sun.

DELHI GRILL N1 £29 3 3 2

21 CHAPEL MKT 020 7278 8100 9–3D

"One of the best simple curry shops in town"
– this "friendly" Punjabi 'dhaba' (roadside
food stall) in Islington's Chapel Market "has
improved if anything over the years and is
usually busy these days". Top Tip – "try the
railway lamb". / N1 9EZ; www.delhigrill.com;
@delhigrill; 10.30 pm; Cash only.

DELICATESSEN

NW3 £66 3 2 2

46 ROSSLYN HILL 020 7700 5511 9–2A

"Possibly the best of the new kosher restaurants
beyond Golders Green" – this Hampstead two-
year-old excels (in a barely competitive field,
admittedly) with its "interesting", "modern
Middle Eastern dishes" in "huge portions"
from ex-Ottolenghi chef Or Golan. Service,
by contrast, can seem "a bit amateur". / NW3
1NH; delicatessen.company.

DEPARTMENT OF COFFEE AND SOCIAL AFFAIRS
EC1 £14 **3** **4** **3**

14-16 LEATHER LN 020 7419 6906 10–2A

"Could this be the best coffee in London?" – this speciality chain has grown from this Leather Lane site to 15 around the capital in 10 years, and is, by all accounts, "exceptional" – "definitely worth going out of the way for a brew". "Staff are friendly", and sandwiches, salads and cakes are prepared fresh every day at a central in-house kitchen and bakery. / EC1N 7SU; departmentofcoffee.com; @DeptOfCoffee; 5.30 pm, Sat 4 pm; L only; No bookings.

DIN TAI FUNG
3 **3** **3**

CENTRE POINT, TOTTENHAM COURT ROAD, WC1 AWAITING TEL   5–1A
5-6 HENRIETTA STREET, WC2   5–3D

"Crazily long queues marked the inaugural week" of the UK's first 250-seat branch in Covent Garden of this legendary Asian soup, dumpling and noodle chain: established in 1972 in Taipei, and now also set to open a second branch near Centrepoint. "For anyone who's been to DTF in the Far East, the first London one may come across as a slightly unnecessarily puffed-up version of what is at heart a fantastically efficient and good-value, shopping-mall brand". "Dumplings, of many and various forms, are uniformly good (quality-control at this cult brand is notoriously anal)" and aficionados of the chain mostly feel "it lives up to the standards of branches in well-established locations in Asia". But, they also warn that: "as per my experience in Singapore etc, they're not about to change your concept of what a good xiao long bao, etc, can be". / www.dintaifung-uk.com.

THE DINING ROOM, THE GORING HOTEL
SW1 £99 **3** **5** **4**

15 BEESTON PL 020 7396 9000 2–4B

"Still glowing from its Royal Wedding connection" (and nowadays with a Royal Warrant to show for it) – this once-sleepy, nowadays increasingly fashionable, traditional British five-star hotel is situated conveniently behind Buck House. Established in 1910, it is still run by the Goring family, who have been investing heavily of late, with the creation of Siren (see also) and the recent relaunch of the hotel's bar. Its "delightfully old-school" dining room is a "perennial stalwart", whose "quintessentially-British menu" was slightly bizarrely starred by Michelin a few years ago. That's not to say that the cooking is not "traditional and of high quality", but the real reason why this is the perfect venue for lunching your maiden aunt or "wowing visiting prospective clients" isn't the food, but its "impeccable", "old-fashioned" service and the "impressive surroundings" of this "light, elegant and high-ceilinged" chamber (whose "roomy tables allow for serious business discussions"). No surprise that prices are a tad "steep". Top Tip – afternoon tea in the adjoining lounge can be "crowded" but otherwise is as it would be done by Disney – "like a fantasy step back in time" – "we went wild for the sandwiches and scones which were offered in abundance!" / SW1W 0JW; www.thegoring.com; @TheGoring; 9.30 pm; closed Sat L; No jeans; booking max 8 may apply.

DININGS
£79 **5** **4** **2**

22 HARCOURT ST, W1 020 7723 0666 9–4A
WALTON HOUSE, WALTON ST, SW3 020 7723 0666 6–2C

"Crazy combinations, truly awesome at times" continue to wow all who taste the "meticulous" sushi and other modernised Japanese dishes at this duo of venues – an "awkward and tired-looking basement" in Marylebone (under chef Tomonari Chiba) and a "much-cooler-than-the original" setting in Knightsbridge (under chef Masaki Sugisaki). "I've wandered all round the menu with friends, and each bite was terrific". / dinings.co.uk.

DINNER BY HESTON BLUMENTHAL
SW1 £128 **2** **2** **2**

MANDARIN ORIENTAL, 66 KNIGHTSBRIDGE 020 7201 3833 6–1D

"If you can overlook the stratospheric prices, and don't go often enough to tire of the historical menu" ("we've all heard about the Meat Fruit now, thanks!"), then Heston Blumenthal's Knightsbridge dining room can, say fans, "still deliver stand-out dishes with precise execution, Heston-eque flourishes" and "bold and exciting flavours". Even supporters, though, caution that "you must get someone else to pay" ("even with great cooking, the bill's terrible value") and to its worst critics it's becoming "a horrible and stale experience", especially given an environment that feels ever-more "soulless and hotel-like". / SW1X 7LA; www.dinnerbyheston.com; @dinnerbyheston; 10.30 pm.

DIP & FLIP
£34 **3** **2** **2**

87 BATTERSEA RISE, SW11   NO TEL 11–2C
115 TOOTING HIGH ST, SW17   NO TEL 11–2C
62 THE BROADWAY, SW19   NO TEL   11–2B

"It's all about the gravy – a game changer!", say fans of this south London burger chain, where beef or lamb, thin-sliced in baps comes with succulent juices for dipping. In August 2019 they announced the closure of the Brixton branch, leaving Battersea, Tooting and Wimbledon. / www.dipandflip.co.uk; @DipFlippo; 10 pm, Thu-Sat 11 pm; SW9 & SW17 booking: 8 min.

DIRTY BURGER
£34 **3** **3** **2**

86 THE BROADWAY, SW19 0203 859 1122 11–2B
ARCH 54, 6 SOUTH LAMBETH RD, SW8 020 7074 1444   2–4D
13 BETHNAL GREEN RD, E1 020 7749 4525 13–1B

"High-quality burgers" hit the spot at this funky small chain which "does the simple things well". The outlets are "fab for families and kids – there's something for everyone and puddings are a great crowd-pleaser". / www.eatdirtyburger.com; 10 pm-midnight, Fri & Sat 11pm-2 am, Sun 8 pm-11 pm; no bookings.

DISHOOM
£44 **3** **4** **5**

22 KINGLY ST, W1 020 7420 9322   4–2B
12 UPPER ST MARTINS LN, WC2 020 7420 9320   5–3B
THE BARKERS BUILDING, DERRY STREET, W8 AWAITING TEL   6–1A
STABLE ST, GRANARY SQ, N1 020 7420 9321 9–3C
7 BOUNDARY ST, E2 020 7420 9324 13–1B

"There aren't many restaurants where I will queue for nearly two hours to get a table but it's worth the wait!" – This "madly popular" Mumbai-inspired chain "has taken London by storm" and is now the capital's most mentioned chain. Even if the heady days of its Covent Garden debut are long gone, criticisms that it's "too popular for its own good" are most notable by their absence; and instead its "a firm favourite" for its massive army of fans who feel "it never fails to impress". The "buzzy, Indian, faux-retro vibe" ("I felt transported to the Parsi eating houses of Bombay in the 1960s") helps set up a "crazy, frenetic atmosphere"; and even if the "noise levels are pretty bad", "somehow it all comes together". It helps that service is "always punctual and friendly" (respect: it's such a busy chain), and the tapas-y food – though no longer as bleeding edge as it once seemed – still feels "vibrant", with a selection of dishes that's "far from run-of-the-mill" ("recommended by all our Indian friends!"), plus "an exceptional list of drinks". Breakfast here is unexpectedly "a true thing of beauty" too: "so different" in a brilliant way. "You can book during the day, but not at night" – "the wait is tedious, but the buzzer system works well" and cocktails at the bar help blur time. In mid 2019, the chain acquired the former Jamie's Italian site next to its original WC2 branch in order to expand its footprint. Top Tips – "black dahl is still the best" and "the bacon naan is the greatest restaurant breakfast dish of all time!". / www.dishoom.com; @Dishoom; 11pm, Thu-Sat midnight; breakfast 8, Sat & Sun 9; booking: min 6 after 5.45 pm.

DIWANA BHEL-POORI HOUSE
NW1 £25 **3** **2** **1**

121-123 DRUMMOND ST 020 7387 5556 9–4C

Perhaps "the best of the bunch among the Indian restaurants along Drummond Street near Euston" – this "no-frills institution" has served a "varied South Indian vegetarian menu" to a mixed crowd of students and office workers for the best part of 50 years. Its "terrific value" (and BYO policy) means it can be "too crowded for comfort", but while the interior is "sketchy" it's a joy to any style anoraks who want to know what a late 1960s canteen actually looked like. / NW1 2HL; www.diwanabph.com; @DiwanaBhelPoori; 11 pm, Sun 10 pm; No Amex; May need 10+ to book.

DOKKE E1 £54 3 4 3

IVORY HOUSE, 50 ST KATHARINE'S WAY
020 7481 3954 10–3D

"Sensational Asian-fusion cooking, with the freshest of ingredients" creates an "exciting" culinary experience at this small waterside café, in St Katharine Docks. "The team is friendly and you can chat to the chef – who is a real artist – as he works in the open plan kitchen area, adjacent to your table". / E1W 1LA; www.dokke.co.uk; @dokkelondon; 10 pm; booking max 10 may apply.

THE DON EC4 £67 3 3 3

THE COURTYARD, 20 ST SWITHIN'S LANE
020 7626 2606 10–3C

A "perfect City lunch-spot", handily located just a short cheque-bounce away from the Bank of England, with "plenty of space between tables" and "a cracking wine list". A French menu is "well executed and served" to a very "consistent standard". For the cellar bistro, see Don Bistro & Bar. / EC4N 8AD; www.thedonrestaurant.com; @thedonlondon; 10 pm; closed Sat & Sun; No shorts.

THE DON BISTRO AND BAR EC4 3 3 3

21 ST SWITHIN'S LN 020 7626 2606 10–3C

Down below The Don, this less-formal bistro section occupies a tightly-packed and atmospheric historic cellar, which originally housed Sandeman's port and sherry business. A little cheaper, it's just as business-friendly in its way as up-above, although here the ambience is less formal, and, oh what a shame, no mobile signal… / EC4N 8AD; www.thedonrestaurant.com/bistro; @TheDonLondon; 10 pm; closed Sat & Sun.

DONOSTIA W1 £57 4 4 3

10 SEYMOUR PL 020 3620 1845 2–2A

This Basque tapas bar near Marble Arch serves "imaginative dishes" including "very tasty pintxos, with some especially good vegetarian options", backed up by a notably "excellent selection of wines". Any negatives are marginal: "tables are a bit small for many tapas", and "it's hard to pace a meal as food can all arrive at once". Named after the Basque for San Sebastian, its sibling Lurra is nearby. / W1H 7ND; www.donostia.co.uk; @DonostiaW1; 11 pm; closed Mon L; booking max 8 may apply.

DORCHESTER GRILL, DORCHESTER HOTEL W1 £105 3 4 4

53 PARK LANE 020 7629 8888 3–3A

This "sophisticated and impressive" Mayfair chamber has had its ups and downs in recent times, and despite scoring a respectable level of customer satisfaction in the last couple of years, still comes nowhere near realising its potential as one of the capital's best traditional dining rooms. It's all change at the hotel, though, with the June 2019 appointment of Stefan Trepp as Executive Chef (replacing Henry Brosi who'd

been in-post for 20 years); and with the July 2019 hiring of 26-year-old Tom Booton, who shifts over from heading the kitchen at the highly rated Alyn Williams at the Westbury. Can this potentially magnificent dining room now finally regain its place as one of London's foremost dining venues? / W1K 1QA; www.thedorchester.com; @TheDorchester; 10.15 pm, Sat 10.45 pm, Sun 10.15 pm; No trainers.

DOTORI N4 £37 4 3 2

3A STROUD GREEN RD 020 7263 3562 9–1D

"Brill sushi and mouth-numbingly spicy Korean hotpots" draw a bustling crowd of overseas students to this "unprepossessing" operation near Finsbury Park tube – once "the best-kept secret in town". But word has spread about the "sensational Korean and Japanese food for £10-£20 a head" – "authentic and in huge portions". Cash only and no booking. / N4 2DQ; www.dotorirestaurant.wix.com/dotorirestaurant; 10.30 pm, Sun 10pm; closed Mon; No credit cards; no booking.

DOUBLE STANDARD WC1

THE STANDARD, 10 ARGYLE ST
020 3981 8888 9–3C

Part of a trendy, US hotel-chain's summer 2019 opening, opposite King's Cross station – this ground-floor, street-facing 'neighbourhood' bar has Adam Rawson in charge (he will also look after Isla, a garden restaurant). Double Standard promises casual drinking and dining, with draft beers and classic cocktails in a Shawn-Hausman-designed space. See also Decimo and Isla. / WC1H 8EG; www.standardhotels.com/london/features/standard_london_isla.

DRAGON CASTLE SE17 £41 4 3 3

100 WALWORTH RD 020 7277 3388 1–3C

"If you want an Asian fix", this huge, "very Cantonese" operation near Elephant & Castle is a "south London legend", with "around 1,000 dishes on the menu" – including "consistently excellent dim sum that's fresh and varied". Low prices make it "most affordable" and help make it "suitable for all kinds of groups: families, friends and greedy gourmets alike". / SE17 1JL; www.dragoncastlelondon.com; @Dragoncastle100; 11 pm, Sun 10 pm.

THE DRAPERS ARMS N1 £58 3 3 4

44 BARNSBURY STREET 020 7619 0348 9–3D

"Fantabulous Sunday roast" heads the "good mix of pub fare and some more lively dishes" at this well-run and "very busy" Islington gastroboozer: one of the best known in that 'hood. It has an "interesting wine list at reasonable prices, too". / N1 1ER; www.thedrapersarms.com; @DrapersArms; 10.30 pm; No Amex.

THE DRAWING ROOM AT THE DUKES HOTEL SW1 £73

35 SAINT JAMES'S PLACE 020 7318 6574 3–4C

Limited feedback on the eateries of this posh St James's hotel, but its afternoon tea did catch reporters' attention this year. Served in the "beautifully-decorated" drawing room or conservatory, it wins praise for its "very generous portions" and "exceptional service" ("staff treated my young nieces with such kindness, and really catered to their needs in a thoughtful manner"). Out with the girls? – go for the MarTEAni… / SW1A 1NY; www.dukeshotel.com.

DROPSHOT COFFEE SW19 4 3 4

281 WIMBLEDON PARK ROAD 11–2B

"A fantastic, cool, addition to Southfields!" – this neighbourhood corner-café (named for its close proximity to Wimbledon tennis) is serious about its coffee, featuring single-origin house espresso from Brixton roasters Assembly, plus ever-changing guest espresso and filter-coffee options. They do a "great brunch" too. / SW19 6NW; dropshotcoffee.co.uk.

THE DRUNKEN BUTLER EC1 £72 4 4 4

20 ROSEBERY AVENUE 020 7101 4020 10–1A

Chef Yuma Hashemi presides over an open kitchen – combining contemporary European small plates with influences from his boyhood in Iran – at this unusual Clerkenwell yearling. In the evenings, you choose from either a short (five-course) tasting menu or a long seven-course one. Sundays are given over to traditional Persian feasting, which fans suggest is the biggest draw here: "a meal to remember, with beautiful flavours and textures": "tahdig (the caramelised crust at the bottom of a pot of rice) was a thing of utter beauty". / EC1R 4SX; www.thedrunkenbutler.com; @SYumaHashemi; Mon & Tue 2 pm, Wed-Sat 10 pm; Online only.

THE DUCK & RICE W1 £62 3 2 3

90 BERWICK ST 020 3327 7888 4–2C

This "nice take on typical Chinese dishes", served "tapas-style in a gastropub" on Soho's Berwick Street, is the creation of Asian restaurant maestro Alan Yau. Four years on, however – while it's perfectly decently rated – there is little evidence that he has conjured another winner on the scale of his earlier hits, Wagamama and Hakkasan. / W1F 0QB; www.theduckandrice.com; @theduckandrice; 11 pm, Fri & Sat 11.30 pm, Sun 10 pm.

DUCK & WAFFLE
EC2 £86 224

110 BISHOPSGATE, HERON TOWER
020 3640 7310 10–2D

"At midnight, perched high above London in this flashy 40th-floor restaurant, it's thrilling watching the lights of the traffic; and the signature duck & waffle dish with maple syrup was like none we have tasted before" – that's the fanboy view on this luxury diner at the top of the City's Heron Tower, and the fact that it's open 24/7 makes it a big brunch destination. Sceptical diners were more in evidence this year, though, criticising the "stodgy and unbalanced" menu, or "food that's average, but a bill that's WAY above average": "once you take away the hype, that you can eat in the middle of the night and it's up a skyscraper, it's actually nothing special". "Getting a reservation can be difficult, though: book way ahead and eat at a strange hour!" / EC2N 4AY; www.duckandwaffle.com; @DuckandWaffle; open 24 hours.

THE DUCK TRUCK
E1 £15 533

LAMB STREET 07919 160271 13–2B

"Mouthwateringly delicious duck" – "not just wraps", but other dishes such as confit duck, pulled duck or duck steaks in a brioche bun – win a massive thumbs-up for this "unusual, quirky and quite unique" street-food star, permanently parked up by Spitalfields Market. "Best chips I've eaten in a very long time… and the duck is pretty good too!" / E1 6EA; www.theducktruck.com; @TheDuckTruck1.

DUCKSOUP W1
£61 434

41 DEAN ST 020 7287 4599 5–2A

"So hip, so uncomfortable, so cool it aches" – this funky Soho bar combines natural/biodynamic wines, Italian-North African small plates and sounds on vinyl. For fans, it's a combination that "just makes me happy" – with its "delicious ingredient-led seasonal food, this place just gets better and better". As for the "odd and cloudy" vino – "we were complete natural wine cretins and left knowing ever so slightly more, with a new favourite drink". / W1D 4PY; www.ducksoupsoho.co.uk; @ducksoup; 10.30 pm; closed Sun D; May need 3+ to book.

THE DUKE OF RICHMOND PUBLIC HOUSE & DINING ROOM E8
£50 323

316 QUEENSBRIDGE ROAD 020 7923 3990 14–1A

"A beautiful old boozer on the Dalston/Haggerston border", restored and revamped in mid-2018 as a "cracking local gastropub", with chef Tom Oldroyd (formerly of the Polpo group; see also Oldroyd N1). He has put a traditional French twist on its gastropub fare, helping to win an enthusiastic fanclub, with cod's roe starter, "fab burger" and "top Sunday lunch" singled out for particular praise. "If the place looks familiar, it was previously a seafood restaurant (The Richmond) and

before that a cheap 'n' cheerful bistro with weird classical artefacts (LMNT)… and long before that a dodgy boozer." / E8 3NH; www.thedukeofrichmond.com; @dukeofrichmond_.

DUKE OF SUSSEX
W4 £60 223

75 SOUTH PDE 020 8742 8801 8–1A

"A very traditional pub", prominently situated on a corner by Acton Green Common, with a fine old bar, attractive, airy rear dining room and "lovely patio garden, ideal for the summer". Its gastropub cooking includes a number of less usual "Spanish tapas-style plates". While the food can be "tasty and well-presented", ratings suggest it somewhat undershoots its potential. / W4 5LF; www.thedukeofsussex.co.uk; @thedukew4; 10.30 pm, Sun 9.30 pm.

DUM BIRYANI W1 £55 322

187 WARDOUR STREET 020 3638 0974 3–1D

"Magnificent biryanis" are served in a 'dum' – a heavy pot – at this two-year-old Indian café just south of Oxford Street, the first venture from Dhruv Mittal, who quit his job in the City and retrained as a chef in Mumbai. "All the individual spices, often quite unusual ones, could be identified and appreciated", and there's a "good choice for vegetarians". But the basement setting isn't its strongest point. / W1F 8ZB; dumlondon.com; @dumlondon; 10.30 pm, Sun 10 pm; May need 5+ to book.

THE DUSTY KNUCKLE BAKERY E8 433

CAR PARK, ABBOT STREET 020 3903 7598 14–1A

"A bakery in an old car park in Dalston which gives apprenticeships to troubled 16-25 year olds: delicious seeded sourdoughs and focaccia are both made into the most outrageous and amazing sandwiches". / E8 3DP; www.thedustyknuckle.com; @thedustyknuckle.

Decimo WC1

DYNAMO £45 433

200-204 PUTNEY BRIDGE RD, SW15
020 3761 2952 11–2B

16-18 RITHERDON ROAD, SW17
020 8767 3197 11–2C

"Lovely wood-fired pizzas and imaginative salads" make this "friendly cycle-themed coffee shop" in Putney (and its Balham sibling) a "great place for brunch on the way back from a cycle round Richmond Park". Early rouleurs will find breakfast from 7.30am, and there's "ample bike parking". / www.the-dynamo.co.uk; @WeAreTheDynamo.

THE DYSART PETERSHAM
TW10 £77 344

135 PETERSHAM ROAD 020 8940 8005 1–4A

"An excellent setting" is the particular plus of this smart Arts & Crafts pub, near Richmond Park, but its appeal goes well beyond its leaded windows, log fires and flagstone floors. Kenneth Culhane's "innovative" cuisine is "very accomplished" and "often excels", to the point that some cognoscenti consider it deserves much wider culinary recognition. / TW10 7AA; www.thedysartarms.co.uk; @dysartpetersham; Mon - Tue closed, Wed - Sat 9.30 pm, Sun 3.30 pm; closed Sun D.

E MONO NW5 £17 421

285-287 KENTISH TOWN ROAD
020 7485 9779 9–2B

"Succulent-tasting kebabs" at this "great value", family-run Turkish joint (which adopted its name from the original Victorian signage) were "recommended by Giles Coren" some years ago – and our reporters have consistently backed his judgement: "their success is deserved". / NW5 2JS; emono.co.uk.

E&O £56 333

392 KING'S RD, SW3 020 7349 9934 6–3B
14 BLENHEIM CR, W11 020 7229 5454 7–1A

"Still vibrant and alive after all these years" – Will Ricker's Notting Hill haunt survived its heady A-list celebrity of the early noughties, and even though critics say "you go here to show off your body, or your new friends, to whoever's around", its ethos has actually remained surprisingly un-snooty over the years. Foodwise, it's "no longer breaking new ground with its pan-Asian tastes and mixtures", but remains a "very fun" option for a superior cocktail with some "eclectic", SE Asian fusion bites. In mid-2019, its King's Road sibling, Eight Over Eight – already something of a chip off the old block – was refurbed and relaunched as E&O Chelsea.

THE EAGLE EC1   £45   4|3|3

159 FARRINGDON RD   020 7837 1353 10–*1A*

"This original gastropub still has amazing, genuine food with real flavours". Almost 30 years since its launch near Exmouth Market, it's still a "boisterous and scruffy pub" where "friendly chefs in the open kitchen talk about their food with love – they're keeping it real despite the gentrification and hipsterfication of the entire area". / EC1R 3AL; www.theeaglefarringdon.co.uk; @eaglefarringdon; 10.30 pm; closed Sun D; No Amex; no booking.

EARL SPENCER SW18   £51   3|2|3

260-262 MERTON RD   020 8870 9244 11–*2B*

Despite its trafficky Southfields location, this well-known Edwardian roadhouse has an unexpectedly "attractive" interior and is "consistently bang on form", with food that's "a cut-above your usual gastropub"; plus "an excellent range of beers and spirits". / SW18 5JL; www.theearlspencer.com; @TheEarlSpencer; 11 pm; Mon-Thu D only, Fri-Sun open L & D.

EARTH KITCHEN N16   £26   3|2|2

11-17 STOKE NEWINGTON ROAD
020 3873 2345 14–*1A*

"Try and snag a corner banquette for great E8 people-watching" if you visit this quirky venue – the dining room of a Dalston (technically speaking Shacklewell) events venue where ex-St John chef Chris Gillard delivers some excellent, gutsy dishes. On nights when the venue has a noisy gig though, it can fall down as a foodie experience: "they need to decide if they're a bar and disco, or a restaurant, because diners don't want both at once: the waiters were sidetracked mixing cocktails and the DJ an irritant". / N16 8BH; www.earth-kitchen.co.uk; @EarthKitchenN16.

EAT 17   £50   3|3|3

UNIT A 77 FULHAM PALACE ROAD, W6
020 8521 5279   8–*2C*
28-30 ORFORD RD, E17 020 8521 5279   1–*1D*
64-66 BROOKSBYS WALK, E9 020 8986 6242
14–*1C*

"In the heart of Walthamstow Village", this "great neighbourhood spot" – a Spar supermarket with kitchen attached – wins praise for its "quality" cooking ("the 2019 Harden's description of pub-type grub underplays its standard and originality"). "Very relaxed and welcoming for young children", the venture's best-known innovation is bacon jam, which you can buy by the jar in various flavours. Other branches have opened in Hackney and, most recently, Hammersmith (somewhat better-served areas, so these respective branches

are somewhat less of a local lifeline). / www.eat17.co.uk; @eat_17; 9.30 pm, Fri & Sat 10 pm, Sun 8 pm.

EAT TOKYO   £32   3|2|2

16 OLD COMPTON ST, W1 020 7439 9887
5–*2A*
50 RED LION ST, WC1 020 7242 3490   2–*1D*
27 CATHERINE ST, WC2 020 3489 1700
5–*3D*
169 KING ST, W6 020 8741 7916   8–*2B*
18 HILLGATE ST, W8 020 7792 9313   7–*2B*
14 NORTH END RD, NW11 020 8209 0079
1–*1B*
628 FINCHLEY RD, NW11 020 3609 8886
1–*1B*

"Genuine", "pleasingly quirky" and "unflashy" – these "humble", extremely popular cafés offer "excellent-value Japanese food" from decent ingredients in "large portions" and are "always full" of "Japanese students and other Asian locals". The "brusque" service is "a little haphazard, as is the seating". / www.eattokyo.co.uk; Mon-Sat 11.30 pm, Sun 10.30 pm; phone bookings only.

ECO SW4   £39   3|3|3

162 CLAPHAM HIGH ST   020 7978 1108
11–*2D*

"Classic pizzas, cooked simply and well in a nice, buzzy room" has kept Franco Manca creator, Sami Wasif's Clapham hang-out, in biz for over 25 years: "it's always reliable, and you can nearly always get a table". / SW4 7UG; www.ecorestaurants.com; @ecopizzaLDN; 11 pm, Fri & Sat 11.30 pm.

EDERA W11   £64   3|3|3

148 HOLLAND PARK AVE   020 7221 6090
7–*2A*

"Lovely… if a little pricey" – this "smart casual" (and business-friendly) Holland Park Italian has survived over a good number of years thanks to its "interesting" Sardinian dishes and an overall feeling of quality: "it doesn't outscore others on specifics, but the whole package works well – professional but not sleek, good but not gastronomic – a favourite". / W11 4UE; www.edera.co.uk; 11 pm, Sun 10 pm.

EGGSLUT W11

185 PORTOBELLO ROAD   7–*1B*

Egg-citing Notting Hill arrival of a California-based chain majoring in… you guessed it… which beamed down from La-La Land into Portobello in late-summer 2019, too late for survey feedback. Signature dish is 'The Slut': a coddled egg on potato puree in a jar, plus sliced baguette. / W11 2ED; www.eggslut.com; @EggSlutLA.

EKTE NORDIC KITCHEN EC4   £53   3|2|2

2-8 BLOOMBERG ARCADE   020 3814 8330
10–*3C*

"Odd location in the midst of the City for a modern Scandinavian restaurant" – Soren Jessen's (of No.1 Lombard Street) "spacious"

yearling in the new Bloomberg HQ has "quality Scandi decor with an open kitchen", but its clean-living associations are perhaps slightly at odds with its site, amongst all the money factories. "The smørrebrød (open sandwiches), particularly the pickled herring, are fantastic and the small but thoughtful wine list and menu are well thought out", but it can "seem quite pricey for what you get". / EC4N 8AR; www.ektelondon.co.uk; @ektelondon.

ELECTRIC DINER W11   £51   2|2|3

191 PORTOBELLO RD   020 7908 9696
7–*1B*

For "a perfect end to a Saturday morning on Portobello Road", some still recommend this US-diner-style haunt. But while it's fine if you're a trustafarian working off a hangover, or just posing around Portobello, you wouldn't cross town. / W11 2ED; www.electricdiner.com; @ElectricDiner; 11 pm, Fri & Sat midnight, Sun 10 pm.

ELLA CANTA W1   £85   3|3|3

INTERCONTINENTAL LONDON PARK LANE, PARK LANE   020 7318 8715   3–*4A*

"Authentic Mexican street food" stars in the "not-at-all-street-food setting" of the Park Lane Intercontinental hotel in this two-year-old from celebrated Mexico City chef Martha Ortiz. The food both "looks and tastes amazing", although – not surprisingly, given the location – it is "expensive for what it is". / W1J 7QY; www.ellacanta.com; @ellacantalondon.

ELLIOT'S CAFÉ SE1   £59   4|4|4

12 STONEY ST   020 7403 7436 10–*4C*

"The kind of place you could eat at any day of the week" – this open-fronted wine bar and café stalwart looking onto Borough Market wins consistent praise for its "punchy plates", many of them from a wood-fired oven; and "well-priced wine" (with "a good selection by the glass")… so "invent any reason, just go". / SE1 9AD; www.elliotscafe.com; @elliotscafe; 10 pm; closed Sun.

ELYSTAN STREET SW3   £88   5|5|3

43 ELYSTAN STREET   020 7628 5005   6–*2C*

Phil Howard "is going from strength to strength" at his "vibrant and lively" three-year-old, tucked away in a chichi Chelsea backstreet, where survey ratings scaled new heights this year. Deceptively, the slightly "austere" room "has the feel of a high-quality, neighbourhood local, but standards of food and service are, by contrast, top class". "Phil has gone back to basics" with his culinary approach and his "beautiful, clever dishes are a delight": "really inspired cooking using seasonal ingredients and recipes" with a "light touch" and "superb precision". Famously, he's more 'flexitarian' in approach than when he was at The Square and "while it's not a vegetarian restaurant, it delivers some of the most interesting gastronomic vegetarian dishes ever!" Service is "outstanding" too – "interested, engaged and good communicators". / SW3 3NT; www.elystanstreet.com; @elystanstreet.

EMBER YARD W1 £58 `3` `3` `4`

60 BERWICK STREET   020 7439 8057   3–1D

Up-and-down reports on this "lovely" Soho haunt, specialising in wood-fired, Mediterranean, grilled dishes – part of Salt Yard Group (all of which was absorbed into the Urban Pubs portfolio in November 2018). Fans applaud the "delicious tapas from this ever-reliable family" but quite a few reports express disappointment: "maybe there's a sense it isn't quite what it was". / W1F 8SU; www.emberyard.co.uk; @emberyard; 11 pm, Sat midnight, Sun 10 pm; booking max 13 may apply.

EMILIA'S CRAFTED PASTA £47 `4` `4` `3`

77 ALIE STREET, E1 020 3358 0317 13–2C UNIT C3 IVORY HOUSE, ST KATHARINE DOCKS, E1 020 7481 2004 10–3D

This two-year old in the picturesque surroundings of St Katharine Docks is "still serving great, home-made pasta". It's had a spin-off nearby in Aldgate since February 2019: "a welcome addition to the original (where you can't always get a table), with the same fab food". / www.emiliaspasta.com; @emiliaspasta.

EMILIA W1 £74 `4` `4` `3`

7 HAUNCH OF VENISON YARD 0207 468 5868   3–2B

"Perfect Emilia-Romagna food… and I know because I'm from there!" This "deeply impressive" Mayfair newcomer occupies the small-but-stylish space, off the rear of Bonhams auction house (with its own street entrance) that was formerly Bonhams (RIP). Run by the same (non-Italian) team as Clipstone, Portland and the Quality Chop House (Will Lander and Dan Morgenthau), the "delicate" cuisine is "enchanting", service is "classy" and, at lunch, the upstairs space is "lovely and light". Unsurprisingly though, prices give nothing away. / W1K 5ES; emiliarestaurant.co.uk.

THE EMPRESS E9 £50 `3` `4` `3`

130 LAURISTON RD   020 8533 5123 14–2B

Well-known pub close to Victoria Park, whose gentrification predates much of up-and-coming East London. "It's what a neighbourhood joint should be about", with changing menus providing sufficient interest and variety to keep regulars returning time and again. / E9 7LH; www.empresse9.co.uk; @elliottlidstone; 10 pm, Sun 9 pm; closed Mon L; No Amex.

ENDO AT ROTUNDA W12 £184 `5` `5` `4`

WHITE CITY, 101 WOOD LANE 020 3972 9000   1–2B

A "sensational Japanese sushi experience", "prepared and served by a true entertainer and showman", wins near-perfect marks

for Endo Kazutoshi's (former sushi chef at Zuma) 16-seat newcomer, in the rotunda atop the former BBC Television Centre in White City – nowadays transformed as a huge, glam apartment complex by Nick Jones of Soho House. The venture invites some comparisons with the early days of Mitsuhiro Araki at The Araki, although here the much glossier setting arguably lives up more to the inevitably stratospheric price tag: "a highly informative experience of great intimacy: not cheap, but a lot less than a plane ticket to Japan…". (On the basis that the comparison with The Araki is warranted, Michelin will likely hand this place two stars in autumn 2019). / W12 7FR; www.endoatrotunda.com.

ENEKO BASQUE KITCHEN & BAR WC2 £78 `4` `4` `3`

1 ALDWYCH   020 7300 0300   2–2D

"Top-notch Basque food in a great location" in Aldwych has earned much-improved ratings this year for chef Eneko Atxa, whose home restaurant Azurmendi is a regular on 'world's best' lists. It's "so wonderful to be able to taste some of his adventurous flavours in London" – "wasn't sure of the basement setting" (a recurrent gripe), "but loved the open kitchen and the food was extraordinary". / WC2B 4BZ; www.eneko.london; @OneAldwych; 11 pm, Sun 10 pm.

ENOTECA ROSSO W8 £60 `2` `2` `3`

276-280 KENSINGTON HIGH STREET   07384 595191   8–1D

"Go for the wine: there's a great selection" focused solely on Italy at this Kensington yearling, with bottles lining many of the walls. Even fans can note that the food (pasta, cheese and meat boards, salads) "is not as good", but it avoids any harsh critiques. Brunch here is also a possibility. / W8 6ND; www.enotecarosso.com.

ENOTECA TURI SW1 £83 `3` `4` `2`

87 PIMLICO ROAD   020 7730 3663   6–2D

"Astonishing Italian wine list: bravo signor Turi!" – Giuseppi and Pamela Turi are "now firmly ensconced in Pimlico having successfully weathered the transfer" three years ago from a more neighbourhood-y site near Putney Bridge (which they inhabited for over 20 years) to this much posher postcode; and they have brought with them their "amazing" cellar, which is perhaps London's most notable selection of Italian vintages. They have also replicated their "delightful" personal touch at this "comfortable" new venue, and fans say "the food has really raised its game since the SW15 days": "simple dishes, beautifully prepared". Its ratings slipped a fraction this year though, with quite a few gripes that it seems increasingly "pricey". / SW1W 8PH; www.enotecaturi.com; @EnotecaTuri; 10.30 pm, Fri & Sat 11 pm; closed Sun; booking max 8 may apply.

THE ENTERPRISE SW3 £65 `2` `3` `4`

35 WALTON ST   020 7584 3148   6–2C

Providing "faithful" service to an expensively dressed clientele in one of Chelsea's prettiest streets – this "lovely local" (too posh really to qualify as a 'gastropub') has an excellent buzz and consistently well-rated food. As always, though, there's the odd grumble here about its price level. / SW3 2HU; www.theenterprise.co.uk; 10.30 pm, Sun 10 pm.

L'ESCARGOT W1 £64 `3` `2` `4`

48 GREEK STREET   020 7439 7474   5–2A

"Beautiful, old-fashioned surroundings" imbue this "classy" Gallic favourite (est 1927) with a "lovely old-school atmosphere", and – if you're looking for a "classic" French meal (Chateaubriand, coq au vin, tournedos Rossini, boeuf bourguignon, profiteroles) in the heart of Soho, it has few rivals nowadays. Its rating slipped a fraction this year, though, on the back of a couple of less wholehearted endorsements: "mainly good, but not as exceptional as your last review implied". / W1D 4EF; www.lescargot.co.uk; @LEscargotSoho; 11.30 pm; closed Sun D.

EST INDIA SE1 £43 `3` `3` `3`

73-75 UNION STREET, FLAT IRON SQUARE 020 7407 2004 10–4B

If the food market in Flat Iron Square doesn't take your fancy, remember this consistently good modern basement Indian, serving a wide mix of options, including a number of south Indian dishes like dosas; good with families too. / SE1 1SG; www.estindia.co.uk; @EstIndiaLondon; 11 pm, Sun 10.30 pm.

ESTIATORIO MILOS SW1 £98 `3` `2` `4`

1 REGENT ST   020 7839 2080   4–4D

"The most beautiful fish counter ever" is the dramatic centrepiece of Costas Spiladis's "classy" four-year-old (part of an LA, Miami, etc international group), and – with its "roomy" quarters clad in white marble sourced from mountains outside Athens – it brings a "glammed up Greek atmosphere" to the fringe of St James's. Its fans extol "the best fish in London" and gorgeous seafood that's "second to none", but sceptics caution that "it's priced so that only oligarchs can afford to eat it", and to an extent that can seem "extortionate". Top Tip – by contrast, lunch and pre-theatre deals represent "incredible value". / SW1Y 4NR; www.milos.ca/restaurants/london; @Milos_London; 12.15 am.

ETHOS W1 £33 `4` `2` `3`

48 EASTCASTLE ST   020 3581 1538   3–1C

"Just wonderful for tasty and healthy food" – a five-year-old vegetarian, "self-service restaurant where you weigh the food you take from the buffet" and pay accordingly, occupying a "clean and modern" unit a short walk from Oxford Circus: "a great concept", where "the food's all delicious". Top Tip – vegan and gluten-free afternoon teas can be hard to find, but are options here. / W1W 8DX; www.ethosfoods.com; @ethosfoods; 10 pm, Sat 9.30 pm, Sun 4 pm; May need 6+ to book.

EVELYN'S TABLE AT THE BLUE POSTS W1   £86   4 5 3

28 RUPERT STREET   07921 336010   4–3D

"So much fun and such a pleasure" – "it's a bit hard to find" (below a cocktail bar, in the cellar of the 275-year-old Blue Posts pub, in Chinatown), but this tiny, year-old sibling to The Palomar and The Barbary is well worth discovering. A "cosy and super-relaxed" 11-seater, with a couple of tiny tables; the food is Italian in inspiration but focused on prime UK ingredients, especially fish brought from Cornwall daily. "The cramped counter gives you a ringside view on some exceptional cooking with a priority on freshness and flavour". / W1D 6DJ; theblueposts.co.uk.

EVEREST INN SE3   £36   3 3 3

41 MONTPELIER VALE   020 8852 7872   1–4D

"Lovely" Nepalese specialities are the menu highlights at this "reliably good local Indian" in Blackheath. Some reporters had the odd issue with the service – "if they could sort that out, this place would be amazing". / SE3 0TJ; www.everestinnblackheath.co.uk; 11.30 pm, Fri & Sat midnight.

LA FAMIGLIA SW10   £65   2 3 4

7 LANGTON STREET   020 7351 0761   6–3B

Thanks in part to its "beautiful garden", this "very friendly", old-favourite trattoria (est 1966) in a posh and pretty Chelsea sidestreet has attracted more than its fair share of Hollywood A-listers and royalty over the decades, and is particularly popular with the well-heeled locals as a place to bring the little darlings ("as the name says, it is good for families, but it's very busy at weekends"). Opinions split somewhat on how its long service has affected the realisation of its "real Italian cooking": "unchanged for 40 years – just lovely" vies with "hasn't changed in 50 years, very uninspiring". / SW10 0JL; www.lafamiglia.co.uk; @lafamiglia_sw10; 11 pm, Sun 9 pm.

FANCY CRAB W1   £64   3 3 2

92 WIGMORE STREET   020 3096 9484   3–1A

"Unbelievably delicious crab" – of the Arctic red king variety, served cold with dipping sauces or baked over charcoal – is presented fast-food-style alongside other seafood and fish at this two-year-old concept in Marylebone. To fans, it's a "great idea" to offer luxury ingredients at such "good value", although limited feedback suggests it's yet fully to win hearts and minds amongst reporters. / W1U 3RD; www.fancycrab.co.uk; @fancycrabuk.

FARANG N5   £44   4 4 2

72 HIGHBURY PARK   0207 226 1609   9–1D

"Miles more interesting than most Thais" – with food "so hot it makes your eyes water… but in a very good way" – Sebby Holmes's now-permanent Highbury venture (on the old site of San Daniele, RIP) is earning prominence amongst London's new-wave Thais. "Favourable comparisons are made with Som Saa, Kiln and Smoking Goat", approving "zero compromise in the spicing on a short, season-dependent menu". / N5 2XE; www.faranglondon.co.uk; @farangLDN; 10.30 pm, Sun 5 pm; closed Mon & Sun D; No Amex.

FARE EC1   £57   3 3 4

11 OLD STREET   0203 034 0736   13–1A

"Chic-looking, but down-to-earth, east London joint" from the folks behind Sager + Wilde, which has opened near Silicon Roundabout on the Clerkenwell/Shoreditch borders. A comprehensive wine list, and "some good coffee" create much of its appeal, and there's also an "unpretentious and not ridiculously overpriced" array of pizzas and "interesting" small plates. / EC1V 9HL; farelondon.com; @Farebarcanteen.

FARMACY W2   £63   4 4 3

74 WESTBOURNE GROVE   020 7221 0705   7–1B

"Vegan at its best", agree fans of this contemporary Californian-style operation from Camilla Fayed (daughter of the former Harrods owner, Mohamed Al-Fayed). The cooking is "interesting and highly competent", and while "vegan food can often be bland, that's not the case here" – so "if you want your first vegan experience, it's the place to come". / W2 5SH; www.farmacylondon.com; @farmacyuk; 11 pm, Sun 7 pm; SRA-Food Made Good – 2 stars.

FARZI CAFE SW1   £53   4 4 4

8 HAYMARKET   0203 981 0090   4–4D

In the heart of the West End, this decidedly glam newcomer scored better in our survey than the mixed rep it received in press reviews. The first UK outpost of a 30-strong international chain hailing from India and the Gulf, its repertoire of tapas-y offerings are very much of the funky, evolved school of Indian cuisine, and reporters salivate over "an amazing choice of inventive dishes" that are "far better than you would expect" in this touristy locale. / SW1Y 4BP; www.farzilondon.com.

FATT PUNDIT W1   £55   3 3 2

77 BERWICK STREET   020 7287 7900   4–1C

Hakka (Indo-Chinese cuisine) is centre-stage at this new Soho 60-seater, where its few early-days reviews are brimming with enthusiasm, particularly regarding the "excellent" food. You kick off with spicy 'momo' (Tibetan dumplings) and move onto the interesting selection of mains (dishes including crab, rabbit, venison…). There's even a "sizzling brownie dessert to

die for". / W1F 8TH; www.fattpundit.co.uk; @FattPundit.

FENCHURCH RESTAURANT, SKY GARDEN EC3   £91   4 3 4

20 FENCHURCH ST   033 3772 0020 10–3D

"It is rare to encounter a five-star ambience, as well as welcoming service, and a high standard of food, all at once in the City" and, on pretty much all accounts, there's "no better place if you're looking for an exceptional evening location" than the 37th floor of the 'Walkie Talkie' ("go for a walk in the garden... with a drink... take in the amazing view…"). As the survey was concluding in June 2019, chef Dan Fletcher left for Somerset, and a new chef, George Farrugia (ex-Bob Bob Ricard) joined this operation run by caterers 'rhubarb' – hopefully the good all-round performance will survive the upheaval. / EC3M 3BY; skygarden.london/fenchurch-restaurant; @SG_Fenchurch; 10.15 pm; booking max 7 may apply.

LA FERME   £47   3 3 3

154 REGENT'S PARK ROAD, NW1   9–3B
102-104 FARRINGDON RD, EC1
020 7837 5293 10–1A

This "excellent local" bistro in Primrose Hill – "there should be one on every high street" – has a "good buzz" and does "a nice line in deconstructed versions of French classics". The original La Petite Ferme near Exmouth Market is a "lovely little" venue "offering brilliant value".

FEZ MANGAL W11   £28   5 4 3

104 LADBROKE GROVE   020 7229 3010   7–1A

"Exceptional kebabs; firm, fresh salads; and lovely service in a larger but still chaotic setting" earn consistent rave reports for this Ladbroke Grove Turk. "The new Fez Mangal is glitzier without losing its soul" – and it's still "amazing value", with "wonderful food at typically £15 per head" – helped by the BYO policy. / W11 1PY; www.fezmangal.com; @FezMangal; 11.30 pm; No Amex.

FIDDIE'S ITALIAN KITCHEN NW3   £36   3 3 2

13 NEW COLLEGE PARADE   020 7586 5050   9–2A

"Fun and lively, with a management who make you feel extremely welcome" – this simple, 'Italian kitchen' in Swiss Cottage serves pizza and pasta plus somewhat more ambitious dishes: it's all "delicious and good value for money". / NW3 5EP; fiddiesitaliankitchen.com; @FiddiesItalian.

50 KALÒ DI CIRO SALVO WC2   £33   4 3 2

7 NORTHUMBERLAND AVENUE
020 7930 9955   2–3C

The best pizza in Europe outside of Italy is, according to a recent Top-50, to be found at this summer 2018 import direct from Napoli

Fumo WC2

– a "huge" space that's part of a hotel just off Trafalgar Square (but with its own dedicated entrance). 50 Kalò means 'good dough' in the local Naples dialect and most reports say it has indeed "captured the essence of good pizza making": "super light crusts, with amazing charring on the dough, delivering fantastic textures and taste"; and "varied, high quality toppings" too. Some reporters feel that to call it the best in London is hype, but all reports agree this is "simple-but-yummy food that definitely hits the spot". / WC2N 5BY; www.50kalò.it; no booking.

FINK'S SALT AND SWEET
N5   £37   3 4 3

**70 MOUNTGROVE ROAD   020 7684 7189
9–1D**

On a Highbury street corner, this coffee shop/deli is the kind of place locals "love to just drop into, providing there's a free table". "The menu's varied, whether you're veering towards breakfast or the lunch end of brunch, the coffee's excellent… and I recently discovered how great their evening food is, too". / N5 2LT; finks.co.uk; @FinksLondon.

FISCHER'S W1   £69   2 2 4

**50 MARYLEBONE HIGH STREET
020 7466 5501   2–1A**

"Reminiscent of a grand café in turn-of-the-century Vienna" – Corbin & King's "warm, cosy, and gemutlich" operation has "a Mittel-european vibe of posh coats, lipstick and gossip", and is just the place to hole up on a winter's day in particular. Its "broad and comforting menu" of Austro-Germanic fare does have many fans (who say "the schnitzel is a must-have"), but can also seem "stodgy and also rather overpriced". Top Tip – "if you've never had Gröstl for breakfast, go now! Birchermüsli… Kassler Ham and boiled eggs on proper rye sourdough… herrings and kippers. And yes, strudel IS an acceptable breakfast food! With Einspanner coffee (topped with whipped cream), a lovely start to the day. Embrace the atmosphere… and don't make any plans for lunch!" / W1U 5HN; www.fischers.co.uk; @FischersLondon; 11 pm, Sun 10 pm.

FISH CENTRAL
EC1   £37   3 4 3

149-155 CENTRAL ST   020 7253 4970 13–1A

"Dependably good fish" at "outstandingly good value-for-money" prices is the hallmark of this veteran, family-run, central chippy (est. 1968). "Been coming here for years and never had a bad dish" – no wonder it's a "cabbies' haunt". Top Tip – "one of the few post-Barbican options on Saturday nights". / EC1V 8AP; www.fishcentral.co.uk; @fishcentral1968; 10.30 pm, Fri 11 pm; closed Sun.

FISH IN A TIE
SW11   £36   3 3 3

105 FALCON RD   020 7924 1913 11–1C

"A hidden gem of a bistro near Clapham Junction", the focus here is on Mediterranean food at "exceptional prices", especially if you order from the set menu options. The name is misleading: it's not a fish restaurant, although it does serve some seafood dishes. / SW11 2PF; www.fishinatie.com; midnight, Sun 11 pm.

FISH MARKET EC2 £70   2 2 2

16A NEW STREET   020 3503 0790 10–2D

This seafood specialist in a converted warehouse near Liverpool Street – part of the D&D London operation – "looks good" and does have fans who feel it delivers outstanding fish. Ratings are undercut this year, though, by several moans that it "over-promises and under-delivers". / EC2M 4TR; www.fishmarket-restaurant.co.uk; @FishMarketNS; 10.30 pm; closed Sun.

FISH! SE1   £63   4 2 2

CATHEDRAL ST   020 7407 3803 10–4C

"A wonderful range of fresh fish is cooked to order" at this "buzzing", glass-fronted venue just by Borough Market. "It gets it right much more often than it gets it wrong" nowadays and is "well worth a visit". / SE1 9AL; www.fishkitchen.co.uk; @fishborough; 11 pm, Sun 10.30 pm.

FISHWORKS   £65   3 2 2

**7-9 SWALLOW ST, W1 020 7734 5813   4–4C
89 MARYLEBONE HIGH ST, W1
020 7935 9796   2–1A
2-4 CATHERINE STREET, WC2
020 7240 4999   5–3D**

"Good fresh fish, simply cooked" is the offer at this trio of seafood bistros (entered via a fishmongers at the front), which are "solid and reliable without being spectacular" – with the bonus, in the case of the Mayfair branch, of finding "really good value so close to Piccadilly". The May 2019 opening of the new Covent Garden venue signals an upswing of a brand that has been in the doldrums since its peak in the late 1990s. / www.fishworks.co.uk; W1B 10.30 pm, Fri & Sat 11 pm; W1U 10.30 pm.

FIUME SW8   £64   2 2 4

**CIRCUS WEST VILLAGE, SOPWITH WAY
020 3904 9010 11–1C**

"The location, near Battersea Power Station, absolutely makes this venue" – a 120-seater run by D&D London, which boasts fine views of the Thames and a big outside terrace. By comparison, "food and service are, well… fine". / SW8 5BN; www.danddlondon.com/restaurant/fiume; @FiumeLondon.

THE FIVE FIELDS
SW3   £112   5 5 4

**8-9 BLACKLANDS TER   020 7838 1082
6–2D**

"More like the Elysian fields!": Taylor Bonnyman's "congenial" but "unpretentious" Chelsea HQ (founded in 2013) doesn't court publicity, but emerged with the survey's highest food rating this year. With its "sophisticated" interior, "spectacular wine list" and "wonderful" service – "impeccably timed, professional, yet warm" – it's long been hailed as an "outstanding all-rounder". But it has hit a particularly impressive and consistent culinary stride in recent times, with not a single negative report received this year (and we received many reports). Head chef, Marguerite Keogh "strives for perfection, and the care and attention to detail of ingredients processed and plated is second to none", delivering "divinely flavoured dishes" in a mould that's "classic in style, but very modern in execution" – "witty and inventive, without being up itself or over-fussy". Much of the produce is sourced from the restaurant's own garden in East Sussex. Choose at lunch or dinner from a prix fixe three-course menu or alternative tasting option. / SW3 2SP; www.fivefieldsrestaurant.com; @The5Fields; 10 pm; D only, closed Mon & Sun.

FIVE GUYS   £21   3 2 1

"When all you want is an old-school burger", these US-based arrivals of recent years really "hit the spot" – you can "build your own", with "tons of accessories"; plus "seriously addictive fries", "thick milkshakes", and "more soda flavours than is reasonable". "The eat-in experience is as depressing as McDonald's, though, in fact perhaps more so – "some branches have a strangely gloomy ambience" – but fans feel that "if you don't mind 1980s-rock, a trip can still be surprisingly fun". / @FiveGuysUK; 10.30 pm, Fri & Sat 11 pm, Sun 10 pm; no bookings.

500 N19   £49   3 3 3

782 HOLLOWAY RD   020 7272 3406   9–1C

"Lovely, authentic and interesting Italian food" is on the menu at this "great neighbourhood restaurant" near Archway, named after the equally "small and fabulous" Fiat Cinquecento.

Founder Mario Magli learned his chops under the late Antonio Carluccio and Gennaro Contaldo, Jamie Oliver's mentor, before setting up in his own right 12 years ago. / N19 3JH; www.500restaurant.co.uk; @500restaurant; 10.30 pm, Sun 9.30 pm; Mon-Thu D only, Fri-Sun open L & D.

500 DEGREES SE24 £34 322

153A DULWICH ROAD 020 7274 8200 11–2D

Named for the temperature of its wood-fired oven, this Herne Hill three-year-old delivers "authentic Neapolitan pizza" and not much else, although the "tiramisu is not bad". (Also with branches in Brixton and Crystal Palace.) / SE24; www.500degrees.co; @500degreesuk; 11 pm, Sun 10 pm.

FLANK E1 443

THE KITCHENS, OLD SPITALFIELDS MARKET NO TEL 13–2C

Thomas Griffiths's stall in Spitalfields Market receives very consistently high ratings from reporters (and he now also has a unit in Market Halls Victoria too). The street-food style fare – brisket sandwich, dumplings, fried-chicken sandwich – belie a sophisticated and sustainable 'modern British, nose-to-tail cooking' approach. / E1 6EW; www.flanklondon.com; @tomgriffchef.

FLAT IRON £33 444

17 BEAK ST, W1 020 3019 2353 4–2B
17 HENRIETTA ST, WC2 020 3019 4212 5–3C
9 DENMARK ST, WC2 NO TEL 5–1A
47-51 CALEDONIAN RD, N1 9–3D
112-116 TOOLEY STREET, SE1 10–4D
88-90 COMMERCIAL STREET, E1 13–2C
77 CURTAIN ROAD, EC2 NO TEL 13–1B

"They put the price up from £10 to £11, but it still can't be faulted!" – for a "a great steak, without any frills" this "always busy, lively and buzzy" chain remains "a winning formula": "it's so nice to have a simple menu choice, and what they do, they do very well"; this includes the very impressively "friendly and professional service-with-a-smile". One catch: "you have to put up with no bookings", so "be prepared to queue". But "if you want a great meal on a budget: go visit!" / www.flatironsteak.co.uk; @flatironsteak; Golbourne 10 pm, Covent Garden 11 pm, other branches 11.30 pm; bookings only in W10.

FLAT THREE W11 £61 333

120-122 HOLLAND PARK AVE 020 7792 8987 7–2A

"The kitchen really is doing something different, sending out delicious and original dishes with a mixed Scandinavian and Japanese/Korean heritage" at this "under-the-radar restaurant, hidden away beneath a shop" in Holland Park. All reports suggest it's "definitely worth a visit", but there are caveats: service can be "indifferent" and even fans can find the prices over-egged. / W11 4UA; www.flatthree.london; @infoflat3; 9.30 pm.

FLAT WHITE W1 £14 443

17 BERWICK ST 020 7734 0370 4–2D

London's original Flat White was served at this early-wave, Kiwi coffee stop, which first hit Soho's Berwick Street Market in 2005; and its legendary brews and "great staff" have maintained a fair following over the last 15 years. Its brunch-friendly options include pastries, smashed avos on toast and homemade banana bread. / W1F 0PT; www.flatwhitesoho.co.uk; @flatwhitesoho; L only; Cash only; No bookings.

FLESH AND BUNS £54 233

32 BERNERS STREET, W1 020 3019 3492 3–1D
BONE DADDIES, 41 EARLHAM STREET, WC2 020 7632 9500 5–2C

"A great night out, with fab food and drinks" is the accepted wisdom on Ross Shonhan's rocking izakayas, whose original, Soho-basement location looks set to be eclipsed by its new Fitzrovia sibling – an impressively large (170 covers) space, which adds Peruvian-Nikkei fusion-dishes and an expanded range of smoked meats to its more-established repertoire of Japanese faves (sushi, sashimi, filled steamed buns). It's "amazing food that will leave you feeling VERY FULL". Ratings are dragged down, though, by reporters who find the flavour combinations "odd", or the overall package too expensive. Top Tip – "given that the main menu can be pricey: the set menu before 6pm or tasting menu is by far the best way to go". / www.fleshandbuns.co.

FLOR SE1

1 BEDALE STREET 020 3319 8144 10–4C

James Lowe and John Ogier – of epic Shoreditch legend Lyle's – plus backers JKS Restaurants launched this all-day bakery and wine bar venture in Borough Market in mid-July, too late for survey feedback. The offering stretches from coffee and croissants in the morning, through small plates at lunch, to a more wine-bar vibe in the evening. Early press reports are predictably adulatory… but they are probably correct. / SE1 9AL; florlondon.com.

FLORA INDICA SW5 £46 444

242 OLD BROMPTON RD 020 7370 4450 6–2A

"Really delicious modern Indian cooking" is making its mark at this two-year-old in Earl's Court, which is further differentiated by its "surprising steampunk decor" – a tribute to the intrepid Scottish botanists who catalogued the flora of the subcontinent in the Victorian era. There's a "good selection of wines by the glass as well as bottle". / SW5 0DE; www.flora-indica.com; @flora_indica; 1 am.

FLOTSAM AND JETSAM SW17 £35 333

4 BELLEVUE PARADE 020 8672 7639 11–2C

"Go at the right time to avoid all the yummy mummies", to get the best from this "great but often excessively busy neighbourhood brunch spot". "Aussie influence shines through the menu, and is reflected in the quality of coffee served. It has a good little sun-trap for outside seating, and is perfectly located for a post-brunch walk on Wandsworth Common". / SW17 7EQ; www.flotsamandjetsamcafe.co.uk; @_flotsam_jetsam; 5 pm; L only; No bookings.

FLOUR & GRAPE SE1 £43 433

214 BERMONDSEY ST 020 7407 4682 10–4D

"A fantastic, local pasta-and-wine restaurant" (the clue is in the name) on Bermondsey high street, which makes an excellent cheap 'n' cheerful choice. The pasta dishes themselves are "simple", but their realisation is "a cut-above most other pasta restaurants" and when it comes to the vino, there are 25 options by the glass (all Italian). / SE1 3TQ; www.flourandgrape.com; @flourandgrape; 10 pm, Sun 9 pm; closed Mon; booking max 6 may apply.

FM MANGAL SE5 £39 342

54 CAMBERWELL CHURCH ST 020 7701 6677 1–3C

Ten-year-old Turkish grill in Camberwell, where the "gracious service" starts with a "free bread and onion appetiser (a real treat)", and carries on with "finely cooked" lamb, meat and vegetables accompanied by "huge fresh salads". It's "a simple proposition, but done well". / SE5 8QZ; midnight; No Amex; no booking.

FOLEY'S W1 £52 442

23 FOLEY STREET 020 3137 1302 2–1B

"Imaginative and tasty cooking" of a "very high quality", taking its cue from modern pan-Asian cuisines, wins steadily high ratings for chef Mitz Vora (ex-Palomar) at his Fitzrovia three-year-old, and service is generally "fast and friendly" too. Only one negative: the "very tight seating arrangements". / W1W 6DU; www.foleysrestaurant.co.uk; @foleyslondon.

FOLIE W1

37 GOLDEN SQUARE AWAITING TEL 4–2C

Frenchman Guillaume Depoix has taken over a corner site in Golden Square (previously a PizzaExpress), with a view to opening 'the perfect Soho brasserie' in November 2019 (a brave post-Brexit move, we think). He has extensive front-of-house experience, with four years in London under his belt, plus Alain Ducasse's Plaza Athénée. / W1F 9LB.

FORMAN'S E3 £59 433

STOUR RD, FISH ISLAND 020 8525 2365
14–2C

This in-house restaurant of the famous smoked salmon smokery (est. 1905) on the River Lea is a "lovely place to eat the best smoked fish, with a great view" – in fact, two views: from a viewing gallery over the smokery, and across to the Olympic stadium next door. For West Ham fans, it's ideal for a pre-match lunch; for everybody else, "a bit out of the way, but worth the schlep". / E3 2NT; www.formans.co.uk/restaurant; @formanslondon; 9 pm; Closed Mon-Wed, Thu & Fri D only, Sat open L & D, closed Sun D.

FORTNUM & MASON, THE DIAMOND JUBILEE TEA SALON W1 £78 344

181 PICCADILLY 020 7734 8040 3–3D

"Amazing, incredible, unlimited everything and WOW!" – for a "quintessential afternoon tea experience", the "elegant, calm and bright" third-floor dining room of The Queen's favourite grocer offers a "fine" (and "extremely filling") experience, encompassing "a tea selection to die for", "wonderfully inventive cakes", and "delicious and plentiful sandwiches and scones". "Yes, it is a bit pricey, but it's an experience to be savoured, and the posh doggie bag they give you means dinner is sorted too…" / W1A 1ER; www.fortnumandmason.com; @Fortnums; 7 pm, Sun 6 pm; L & afternoon tea only; No trainers.

THE FORTNUM'S BAR & RESTAURANT EC3 £69 233

THE ROYAL EXCHANGE 020 7734 8040
10–2C

"Making the best of an amazing space at the Royal Exchange" – Fortnum's have taken over the operation formerly run by D&D London with this luxurious pitstop in the Exchange's magnificent courtyard: not a great place to save money, but "perfect for small plates, plus a glass or two of champers". / EC3V 3LR; www.fortnumandmason.com/restaurants/the-bar-and-restaurant-at-the-royal-exchange; @Fortnums.

45 JERMYN STREET SW1 £73 334

45 JERMYN STREET, ST. JAMES'S
020 7205 4545 3–3D

"Elegant yet relaxed" – Fortnum & Mason created "a real winner" a couple of years ago with this "beautiful bar/dining room", whose "fabulous cocktails" and "stylish" cuisine make a "smart-but-not-overpowering" replacement for the crusty Edwardian buttery, The Fountain (RIP), which it replaced. Handy for business, it's also a popular early morning choice for a "cosseting and superb breakfast" ("exactly what I need to recover after the overnight from New York!"). Top Menu Tip – Beef Wellington, with the sauce flambéed at the table. / SW1Y 6DN; www.45jermynst.com; @45JermynSt; 11 pm, Sun 10.30 pm; closed Sun D.

40 MALTBY STREET SE1 £52 444

40 MALTBY ST 020 7237 9247 10–4D

This "natural wine bar with excellent food" has become a "must-eat fixture" for London foodies, where chef Steve WIlliams produces a daily chalked-up menu of "incredible" small plates, to be consumed in the no-frills surroundings of a Victorian railway arch on the lines into London Bridge station, which houses the Gergovie biodynamic wine import business. There are "interesting gems" on the wine list, "but don't try to navigate on your own – explain to the sommelier what style you're looking for and take the advice". As for the food: "genuinely the most impressive 'sausage roll' I've had in my life – I was truly in heaven, and had to have two". / SE1 3PA; www.40maltbystreet.com; @40maltbystreet; 9.30 pm; closed Mon, Tue, Wed L, Thu L, Sat D & Sun; No Amex; no booking.

FORZA WIN SE15 £53 443

UNIT 4.1, 133 COPELAND RD
020 7732 9012 1–4D

"An unexpected treat despite the location" – a former warehouse at the back of an industrial building in Peckham – this ex-pop-up Italian serves "really original food at very good prices", including "easily some of the best pasta in London". "You feel the people working here really love what they do, and it shows in the food – it's seriously happy food". / SE15 3SN; www.forzawin.com; @forzawin.

400 RABBITS £27 432

143 EVELINA ROAD, SE15 020 7732 4115
1–4D
30-32 WESTOW ST, SE19 020 8771 6249
1–4D

"Creative pizzas" on a 'London sourdough' base meet a changing list of craft beers at this "vibrant" southeast London group which has spread from Crystal Palace to Nunhead and, this year, West Norwood. It's apparently named after the progeny of a conjugal union between the Aztec gods of fermenting and brewing. Top Tip – "if it's on, the octopus special pizza is incredible". / www.400rabbits.co.uk; @4hundredrabbits.

FOUR LEGS AT THE COMPTON ARMS N1

4 COMPTON AVENUE 020 7354 8473 9–2D

A new kitchen team have livened up the menu at this Arsenal supporters' pub, which is said to have inspired George Orwell's fictional, idealised pub The Moon Under Water. Early press reports are excited about its mix of pub grub and somewhat fancier fare. / N1 2XD; www.comptonarms.co.uk.

FOUR SEASONS £49 411

11 GERRARD STREET, W1 020 7287 0900
5–3A
12 GERRARD ST, W1 020 7494 0870 5–3A
23 WARDOUR ST, W1 020 7287 9995 5–3A
84 QUEENSWAY, W2 020 7229 4320 7–2C

"The service is passable and the ambience is poor" at this group in Chinatown and Bayswater – "but you only go for one thing: the barbecued/roast meat", especially the "famous" and "perfect Cantonese roast duck and the char siu pork". They might be "a bit too authentic these days", but they're still "hard to beat for Chinese food". / www.fs-restaurants.co.uk; 11pm, Fri & Sat midnight, W2 11.30 pm, Sun 11 pm; all branches ex W2 closed Sun.

FOX & GRAPES SW19 £61 324

9 CAMP RD 020 8619 1300 11–2A

"The best pub on Wimbledon Common", this renovated late-Georgian boozer serves "good-quality" English roasts on Sunday) and is ideal as a reward for a good walk. / SW19 4UN; www.foxandgrapeswimbledon.co.uk; @thefoxandgrapes; 10 pm, Sun 9.30 pm.

FRANCO MANCA £35 332

One of the victors in the casual dining downturn: this mushrooming multiple has become the survey's most-mentioned pizza chain – "it beats PizzaExpress hands down" nowadays (of which owner David Page was once CEO) thanks to pizza that's "so much more tasty" than PE's, with "gorgeous sourdough bases" and "excellent toppings" and "all for a very reasonable price", so no-one minds the "cheap 'n' cheerful" style of its "loud, very busy and noisy" branches. / www.francomanca.co.uk; Mon-Sat 11 pm, Sun 10.30 pm; no bookings.

FRANCO'S SW1 £63 344

61 JERMYN ST 020 7499 2211 3–3C

Classic St James's Italian, whose convivial and civilised quarters amd "totally reliable food" make it "one of the best all-rounders in the area" and, in particular, "a good choice for a business lunch" (or breakfast, which is very good here). It was opened in 1946 by the Wiltons group, and emerged from a major refurb in autumn 2019 with a new bar, refreshed decor and a menu shake-up. "Despite its popularity (and vintage), it retains a freshness both in the food and the service", and while by no means cheap, regulars say "it always delivers". / SW1Y 6LX; www.francoslondon.com; @francoslondon; 10.30 pm; closed Sun.

FRANTOIO SW10 £70 344

397 KING'S RD 020 7352 4146 6–3B

The flamboyant owner, Bucci, creates "a great atmosphere" and helps present a "really good menu for both meat and fish lovers" at this "fun" World's End trattoria. It's a real "favourite" among locals: "I love, love, love this place! Been going for 20 years and it's like walking into a family gathering". / SW10 0LR; www.frantoio.co.uk; 11 pm.

FRANZINA TRATTORIA SW9

395 COLDHARBOUR LANE   07802 473444   11–2D

Chef Pietro Franz has now left Pop Brixton for this simple, stripped-down, forever home where he serves Sicilian small plates and pasta. Little survey feedback so far – more reports please. / SW9 8LQ; franzinatrattoria.com; @franzinabrixton.

FREAK SCENE W1   £46   544

54 FRITH STREET   07561 394 497   5–2A

"I approached with trepidation… but everything was delicious!" – this "fun and laid-back", open-kitchen dining experience in Soho delivers a "casual but impressive" meal centred on "surprising-in-a-totally-good-way", Pan-Asian small plates, delivered by "dynamic" staff. A former pop-up – it's the creation of an ex-Nobu team, with Aussie chef Scott Hallsworth and partner Phar Shaweewan. / W1D 4SL; www.freakscene.london; @freakscene.

FREDERICK'S N1   £62   345

106 CAMDEN PASSAGE   020 7359 2888   9–3D

"Tucked away in Camden Passage", this Islington institution is "still going strong after all these years" and remains a real "go-to place for family celebrations" for many north Londoners; as well as "a great place for a romantic dinner". "The ordinary fascia hides a true gem inside", leading onto "a modern, spacious and stylish interior" where the top seats are in the "lovely, light and airy back area". It's not a foodie kind of place, but the cooking is "contemporary and varied (the set menu never disappoints)", and "staff are par excellence, always professional, but fun and cheery". / N1 8EG; www.fredericks.co.uk; @fredericks_n1; 11 pm; closed Sun.

THE FRENCH HOUSE W1   £65   345

49 DEAN STREET   020 7437 2477   5–3A

"Oozing rustic, Gallic charm of yesteryear" – the "lovely, intimate room" above Soho's famous Francophile watering hole (where de Gaulle is said to have composed his 'À tous les Français' speech during WWII, rallying the French people) oscillates over the years between being a forgotten-about curio, and sporadic partnerships with brilliant chefs (e.g. St John's Fergus Henderson, who started out here) that lead to its re-discovery. The arrival of Neil Borthwick (Mr Angela Hartnett) at the end of last year sees it riding another high – "it's smashing to have this old-favourite reborn under such good hands" – and his "great, old-fashioned, gutsy French menu" ("short, but with dishes which seem dragged from a distant memory") are "top class", while service is "fabulously friendly" too. A few reporters, though, feels "it doesn't live up to

the hype" or that "while great to have it back, it's still a work in progress…" / W1D 5BG; www.frenchhousesoho.com; @FrenchHouseSoho.

FRENCHIE WC2   £83   322

18 HENRIETTA STREET   020 7836 4422   5–3C

Gregory (nicknamed 'Frenchie' by Jamie Oliver at Fifteen) & Marie Marchand's stylish three-year-old is "a treat, with all its signature dishes imported from their charming Parisian venue of the same name", delivering "beautiful French food", served in a lovely, stylishly-neutral, modern space. Despite the arrival last year of Dale Sutton (the executive head chef of their French operations) however, ratings continue to head south here, and critics feel it's "lost its edge" since its stellar early days. No question, though, it's a "fun" and "useful spot in Covent Garden" that many still extol as the site of their best meal of the year. / WC2E 8QH; www.frenchiecoventgarden.com; @frenchiecoventgarden; 10.30 pm.

THE FROG   £73   553

35 SOUTHAMPTON STREET, WC2   020 7199 8370   5–3D
45-47 HOXTON SQUARE, N1   020 3813 9832   13–1B

"Eating at The Frog is like allowing your palate to go to a firework display" – Adam Handling and his teams create a series of dishes of "always-surprising ingenuity, with quirky presentation and mixture of ingredients" both at his Hoxton Square original and his even-more-successful Covent Garden flagship. Both locations offer a mixture of à la carte and tasting menus – the latter incorporating vegan and vegetarian alternatives as well as beer-matching and wine-matching options. The results inspire massive support,not just for being "a well-devised journey expertly executed", but for food that's "wow, wow, wow beyond delicious!". In keeping with the main man's free-thinking philosophy (and, at E1, a big emphasis on sustainability), his locations have a youthful energy at odds with the fayne dining ethos: an approach that also seems to inspire "impeccable service" from his staff (with a special shout-out to his sommelier – "I've never been disappointed when asking Kelvin for a recommendation!"). Where his taste is a tad more divisive is the ambience – to fans admirably un-stuffy and energetic, but to critics slightly "odd" or "nondescript", and with "loud and dreadful music" in N1. Top Menu Tip – "those cheese doughnuts are the stuff of legend". See also Adam Handling Chelsea. / www.thefrogrestaurant.com; @TheFrogE1.

LA FROMAGERIE   £49   343

2-6 MOXON ST, W1   020 7935 0341   3–1A
52 LAMB'S CONDUIT ST, WC1   0207 242 1044   2–1D
30 HIGHBURY PARK, N5   020 7359 7440   9–2D

A "mouthwatering array of wonderful cheeses" – they stock from the UK, Ireland, France and Italy – is the most obvious reason to pay a visit to these cafés-cum-cheese shops. But

they also serve excellent snacks and meals throughout the day, making the most of "fresh seasonal ingredients". / www.lafromagerie.co.uk; @LaFromagerieUK.

THE FRONTLINE CLUB W2   £64   224

13 NORFOLK PL   020 7479 8960   7–1D

The ground floor of an international journalists' club, with photo-reportage as wall decoration: this charming dining room near Paddington Station is particularly worth knowing about as a smartish option in what's still a very thinly provided area. Its modern British cooking is "a little hit and miss", but while it only "sometimes lives up to the space" it seldom goes badly awry. One problem: "with all those photos of heroic war reporting on the wall, one feels a bit of a wimp". / W2 1QJ; www.frontlineclub.com; @frontlineclub; 11 pm; closed Sat L & Sun; booking max 6 may apply.

FUCINA W1   £66

26 PADDINGTON STREET   020 7058 4444   2–1A

Kurt Zdesar – who has been involved with such illustrious names as Nobu, Hakkasan, Chotto Matte and Ping Pong – and Stefano Stecca (most recently executive chef at Toto's) opened this "spacious" and glamorous-looking Italian newcomer in late-2018 in Marylebone, with a focus on organic ingredients. Early-days feedback was limited, but some "delicious" if pricey food is reported, and the main quibble about the interior is that its moody lighting can leave it "rather dark". / W1U 5QY; fucina.co.uk; @FucinaLondon.

FUGITIVE MOTEL E2

199 CAMBRIDGE HEATH ROAD   020 3974 4455   13–1D

A 140-seater 'craft bar and kitchen' near some soon-to-be developed railway arches in hip Bethnal Green that opened in June 2019, too late for any survey feedback. It's open from breakfast on – at lunch and thereafter the main menu offering is pizza. / E2 0EU; fugitivemotel.bar; @fugitive_motel.

FUMO WC2   £52   333

37 ST MARTIN'S LANE   020 3778 0430   5–4C

This "fabulous, fun and buzzy" three-year-old next door to the Coliseum, from the national San Carlo group, has won a good following. It specialises in "tasty" cicchetti or Venetian small plates, and provides an "unexpectedly friendly and attractive welcome in the West End": "ideal for a light lunch" and "good for pre-theatre". / WC2N 4JS; www.sancarlofumo.co.uk/fumo-london; @sancarlo_fumo.

GALLERY MESS, SAATCHI GALLERY SW3 £62 233

**DUKE OF YORKS HQ, KINGS ROAD
020 7730 8135 6–2D**

A big outside terrace is a key feature of Charles Saatchi's attractive gallery café, which overlooks the green next to Duke of York's Square on the King's Road. Foodwise, it is most recommended for its afternoon tea possibilities, but it's tolerably rated for a light bite at other times too. / SW3 4RY; www.saatchigallery.com/gallerymess; @gallerymess; 11 pm, Sun 7 pm; closed Sun D.

GALLIPOLI £41 233

**102 UPPER ST, N1 020 7359 0630 9–3D
120 UPPER ST, N1 020 7226 8099 9–3D**

"Tasty, good-value Turkish food" and "a warm welcome" make these "jolly" (lots of "dangly decorations") Ottoman-themed stalwarts just "the sort of bistro you'd be pleased to have near you". / www.cafegallipoli.com; @CafeGallipoli; 11pm - midnight.

GALVIN AT THE ATHENAEUM W1 £72 122

**ATHENAEUM HOTEL, 116 PICCADILLY
020 7640 3333 3–4B**

Fans of the Galvin Bros' regime at this luxurious five-star hotel near Hyde Park Corner still applaud it as a "solid, nice and efficient" option, whose "good-value set deals" add to its possibilities as a "glam lunch venue". Its ratings took a major hit this year, however, with too many reports of "complete disappointment" and "no generosity over the pricing" – at present it's "really not up to the standards of their other ventures". / W1J 7BJ; www.athenaeumhotel.com; @galvinathenaeum; 10.30 pm.

GALVIN AT WINDOWS, PARK LANE LONDON HILTON HOTEL W1 £122 335

22 PARK LN 020 7208 4021 3–4A

"Breathtaking panoramic views over central London" make this "refined", 28th-floor eyrie a natural place for a date or celebration – or "to impress out-of-towners" – and "sipping a cocktail whilst looking at our great city is a special experience" (try to secure a window table when you book). Standards by-and-large avoid the complacency typical of rooms with a view: service is "professional" and most diners feel the cooking is "wonderful and beautifully presented". Naturally the experience is fully priced but… Top Tip – "set lunch is excellent value". / W1K 1BE; www.galvinatwindows.com; @GalvinatWindows; 10 pm, Thu-Sat 10.30 pm, Sun 3 pm; closed Sat L & Sun D; No trainers; booking max 5 may apply.

GALVIN HOP E1 £70 333

35 SPITAL SQ 020 7299 0404 13–2B

This haute-gastropub near Spitalfields Market is next to brothers Chris and Jeff's deluxe Galvin La Chapelle, and serves "high-quality bistro-style food". Ratings have improved in the past 12 months as the transition from its former guise, Café à Vin, has bedded in. / E1 6DY; www.galvinrestaurants.com/section/62/1/galvinhop; @Galvin_brothers; 10.30 pm, Sun 9.30 pm; booking max 5 may apply.

GALVIN LA CHAPELLE E1 £96 445

35 SPITAL SQ 020 7299 0400 13–2B

The "most enchanting setting" – "an out-of-this-world conversion of an old church" (to be precise, the chapel of a Victorian school) – makes the Galvin Bros' Spitalfields HQ one of London's most "beautiful" restaurants. It provides a "special" backdrop "for keen business deals, or to impress your new love-interest" (and is "a particular attraction for guests from overseas"). There are "high standards across the board", including "fantastic" modern French cuisine; a "classy wine list"; and "smart, swift, discreet service". / E1 6DY; www.galvinlachapelle.com; @galvin_brothers; 10.30 pm, Sun 9.30 pm; No trainers; booking max 8 may apply.

THE GAME BIRD AT THE STAFFORD LONDON SW1 £99 353

16-18 ST JAMES'S PLACE 020 7518 1234 3–4C

The "old-world comfort and glamour" of a quiet St James's hotel dining room provides the setting for "studiedly English food" – "a seasonal mix of classic and modern dishes" including "excellent roast beef from the trolley on Sundays." "Exceptionally good service" at "discrete tables which feel very private" and "a superb wine list" add to its attractions, particularly for entertaining clients. No surprises, though, that "it's pricey for what you get". Top Tip – "a prandprandial cocktail in the famous American Bar is highly recommended". / SW1A 1NJ; thestaffordlondon.com/the-game-bird; @TheGameBirdLON; 10 pm.

GANAPATI SE15 £42 443

38 HOLLY GROVE 020 7277 2928 1–4D

For "ace food" and "an upbeat local boho vibe" – "Ganapati does it every time". Chef Claire Fisher opened this small Peckham venue 15 years ago after travelling around South India. "Everything is home-made from the pickles to the parathas and you can even buy jars of pickle to take home" – and there's a "fantastic choice for veggies and vegans too". Top Tip – "great lunchtime thali for £8.50". / SE15 5DF; www.ganapatirestaurant.com; 10.30 pm, Sun 10 pm; closed Mon; No Amex.

THE GARDEN CAFE AT THE GARDEN MUSEUM SE1 £46 323

5 LAMBETH PALACE RD 020 7401 8865 2–4D

"A light and airy space" overlooking a "simply lovely garden" – the pavilion at Lambeth's Garden Museum is an oasis of tranquillity in a grungy part of town. The two-year-old venture operates as a full-on restaurant for lunch and dinner; and its "ambitious, unpredictable, mainly seasonal menu" is "well executed" by chefs Harry Kaufman and George Ryle, who know their chops after stints in St John and Padella respectively. "Service can sometimes make you feel a bit of a nuisance for asking for attention…" / SE1 7LB; www.gardenmuseum.org.uk; @GardenMuseumLDN; 5 pm, Sat 3.30 pm; L only; No Amex; Booking max 12 may apply.

GARDEN ROOM WC2 £71 223

**27-31 CHARING CROSS ROAD
020 3962 7275 5–4B**

"Really lovely views of London" are the reason to discover this new cocktail bar – a roof garden in the West End, on the tenth floor of the Assembly hotel, run by the hip folks from Bourne & Hollingsworth. Feedback, to-date, is limited and cautious though: hit a bum time and there's "zero atmosphere", and the food, though serviceable, "could be so much more than it is". / WC2H 0LS; www.bandhgardenroom.com.

LE GARRICK WC2 £55 334

10-12 GARRICK STREET 020 7240 7649 5–3C

"A delightful throwback to the French bistros of the 1980s, set over a couple of floors, with tables crammed into nooks and crannies" – this Covent Garden stalwart is "very romantic, with its candles and cosy booths". The "traditional, unpretentious food" is "good value" while the "staff are so friendly": if you're in a hurry pre-theatre, "they put you through fast without seeming to hassle you", but "if you have more time they let you linger". / WC2E 9BH; www.legarrick.co.uk; @le_garrick; 10.30 pm, Sun 5pm; closed Sun.

THE GARRISON SE1 £57 333

99 BERMONDSEY STREET 020 7089 9355 10–4D

"Pub food at its finest, with some real stand-out dishes" has kept this operation near the antiques market at the forefront since the early days of Bermondsey's booming food scene. "The menu's good, but the specials are worth eating every time". / SE1 3XB; www.thegarrison.co.uk; @TheGarrisonSE1; 10 pm, Fri & Sat 10.30 pm, Sun 9 pm.

THE GATE £53 422

**22-24 SEYMOUR PLACE, W1 020 7724 6656 2–2A
51 QUEEN CAROLINE ST, W6 020 8748 6932 8–2C
87 ALLITSEN ROAD, NW8 020 7833 0401. 9–3A
370 ST JOHN ST, EC1 020 7278 5483 9–3D**

"Standards remain high" at Michael and Adrian Daniel's "veggie stalwart" chain – in particular at the W6 original in a "convivial", offbeat building south of Hammersmith

Helix EC3

Broadway, which some consider "the best vegetarian in town" thanks to "inventive" food that's "wow-amazing... even for a committed carnivore". Its spring 2019 opening in St John's Wood is also going down well – launching as the second highest scoring member of the group with "a fabulous and very varied selection of vegan and vegetarian food". The W1 operation in Seymour Village and EC1 branch near Sadler's Wells are slightly less highly rated, but the tenor of practically all reports hails "thoughtful and tasty fare, catering to a range of dietary requirements". / thegaterestaurants.com; @GateRestaurant; 10 pm, Sun 9.30 pm NW8 10.15pm, Sun 9.15 pm, W6 Sun 9:15 pm.

GAUCHO   £80   2 2 2

Emerging from a financial rescue package (that has seen the owner of M Restaurants, and former Gaucho CEO, Martin Williams, return to the helm), this moodily decorated Argentinian steakhouse chain still somewhat divides reporters. Prime Latino cuts feature alongside a "well-curated" South American wine list, and even despite its difficulties, detractors don't say the food is dire, merely that the experience can appear "dull" given the "eye-watering bills". Better reports overall, though, do suggest some return to form, with a greater proportion of diners once again inclined to find it "good fun" and "expensive for a reason". Top Tip – look out for their bottomless 'beef & bottle' deals. / www.gauchorestaurants.co.uk; @gauchogroup; 11 pm, Thu-Sat midnight; WC2, EC3V , EC1M closed Sun.

GAUTHIER SOHO
W1   £77   4 4 3

21 ROMILLY ST   020 7494 3111   5–3A

"Why he has not regained his Michelin star is quite beyond me", say fans of Alexis Gauthier's immensely popular and accomplished venture, which lost its gong in 2012, and which the Tyre Man has pointedly (pointlessly?) ignored ever since. "You have to ring the doorbell to gain entrance" to this quirky old Georgian townhouse in Soho, whose "charming, old-world" dining rooms are on different floors separated by a somewhat "rickety staircase". But whereas its culinary style could once be easily pigeon-holed as "classic" Gallic gluttony – with "exquisite, inventive dishes, beautifully presented" – the main man's banishment of foie gras in 2015, his ongoing conversion to veganism, and his well-known 'Les Plantes'

vegan tasting menu (a feature since 2016) is taking the place further and further out of the mainstream. On most accounts results remain utterly "outstanding" whether or not you are a meat eater, but ratings dipped a tad this year on the back of some regulars noting a slight "slip in standards". Sometimes the concern is general ("needs a bit of a revamp"). More often, though, it's linked to the shift away from meat ("getting tired of the vegan 'foie gras' canapés and yearning for the old-style ones"). But, quibbles aside, his achievement in maintaining high standards during such a big shift is impressive, and it will be more so if he fulfills his promise next year and goes entirely vegan. Hats off to AG for "embracing the concept and importance of a plant-based diet and doing wonderful things to vegetables!" / W1D 5AF; www.gauthiersoho.co.uk; @GauthierSoho; 9.30 pm, Fri & Sat 10.30 pm; closed Mon & Sun; booking max 7 may apply.

LE GAVROCHE
W1   £140   4 5 4

43 UPPER BROOK ST   020 7408 0881   3–2A

"Elegance... discreet service... classic French cuisine – they never go out of fashion", and nowhere else in London can match Michel Roux Jr's "grande dame of the London restaurant scene" for "perfect, old-school Gallic gastronomy". Founded (on Sloane Street) in 1967 by his father Albert, this famous culinary temple has operated in Mayfair just around the corner from the former US embassy since 1982 and with MasterChef-maestro Michel at the stoves since 1991. Menus (with no prices in the lady's version) are perused in the smallish ground floor lounge, before descending to the "dark and moody basement with its elaborate table ornaments". To a few doubters the style is too "stuffy and formal" (or, alternatively, too dated and 1980s-tastic) – but to most visitors (some of whom are regulars of many decades' standing) the milieu makes it "one of the capital's best dining rooms, setting the perfect scene for any posh liaison"; with "soft furnishings and a layout that means one may hear and converse in quiet and relative privacy; and where it's refreshing to find the standard of dress amongst the patrons still includes a suit and tie". "Attention to detail and personal enjoyment shows in every aspect of the experience": cooking is "superbly judged both in its selection and preparation", and the "wine list is the work of an afternoon – hugely pleasurable to read and to attempt to absorb its width and variety!". "Smooth, unobtrusive

service" under maître d' Emmanuel Landré, is "impeccable" – "ideally pitched from when you step through the door to the final farewell"; and Michel (usually in attendance) "is a charmer as well as a brilliant chef", with "the personal visit from Le Patron making a special meal very special". The bill? "It's barely affordable, but worth saving for": "a classic example of the rule, 'you get what you pay for' and, while expensive, good value for money". Top Tip – "the renowned set lunch deserves every bit of its reputation": "perhaps the best value prix fixe deal in town" and "always a top experience". / W1K 7QR; www.le-gavroche.co.uk; @michelrouxjr; 10 pm; closed Sat L & Sun; Jacket required.

GAZETTE   £53   3 3 3

79 SHERWOOD CT, CHATFIELD RD, SW11
020 7223 0999 11–1C
147 UPPER RICHMOND RD, SW15
020 8789 6996 11–2B

This Gallic duo in Clapham and Putney (Balham is now closed, RIP) score well for "lovely classic French bistro food", "good vibes from friendly staff" and a "really good value prix fixe lunch". They also run sightseeing meals on luxury double-decker buses in London and Paris. Top Tip – "seasonal offerings (e.g. fondue, morilles etc) keep the menu interesting". / www.gazettebrasserie.co.uk; 11 pm.

GEALES W8   £60   2 2 2

2 FARMER ST   020 7727 7528   7–2B

In 1999 the Geale family sold out of this genteel, pre-war (est 1939) fish 'n' chip restaurant, off Notting Hill Gate, and since 2006 it's been operated by Concept Venues (with a second branch in Dubai!). Nowadays it lacks the faithful following of yesteryear, but reports suggest it's still "fine if close by, if not for a detour". / W8 7SN; www.geales.com; @Geales_London; 10.30 pm, Sun 10 pm; closed Mon L.

GEM N1   £39   3 3 2

265 UPPER ST   020 7359 0405   9–2D

"Friendly, with decent nosh" – this Turkish-Kurdish café near Angel "really is a little gem, with prices that are more than fair for the quality of the food". The exceptional value for the locations means it "can get very crowded". / N1 2UQ; www.gemrestaurant.org.uk; @Gem_restaurant; 11 pm, Sun 10 pm; No Amex.

GEORGE IN THE STRAND
WC2   £62   3 3 3

213 STRAND   020 7353 9638   2–2D

"Surprisingly good food and charming service" make it worth remembering this historic hostelry (refurbed in recent times), near the Royal Courts of Justice. You can eat in the ground floor bar, or in the upstairs 'Pig and Goose' restaurant. / WC2R 1AP; www.georgeinthestrand.com; @thegeorgestrand; 10pm, Fri & Sat 10.30pm, Sun 9pm.

GERMAN GYMNASIUM
N1 **£72** 2 2 4

1 KING'S BOULEVARD   020 7287 8000
9–3C

"What a fantastic building!". This D&D
London bar/restaurant occupies a "huge"
and "interesting" former Victorian gym –
"handily located, slap bang next to King's
Cross" – and despite a tendency to feel
"cavernous" and to become very "loud" ("you
can feel a bit like you're eating in an aircraft
hanger") provides a "stunning" location. Its
intriguing focus on German cuisine, and
wines in particular, does win it gastronomic
recommendations, but all too often the "stodgy"
food "is really nothing special". Even so, as
a watering hole, a business rendezvous, or
brunch spot, it has a big following. / N1C 4BU;
www.germangymnasium.com; @TheGermanGym;
11 pm, Sun 9 pm.

GEZELLIG WC1   **£73** 4 3 2

HOLBORN HALL, 193-197 HIGH HOLBORN
020 3004 0004   5–1D

"You can tell head chef Graham Long trained
with Phil Howard", given the "precise" modern
European dishes at this June 2019 newcomer,
in Holborn's old Town Hall (on the fringe of
Covent Garden). It opened just as the survey
concluded, but the few initial reports were
already wowed by its 350-bin wine selection. /
WC1V 7BD; www.gezellig.co.uk; @gezelligLND.

GIACOMO'S NW2   **£45** 3 3 2

428 FINCHLEY RD   020 7794 3603   1–1B

"Consistently good, basic Italian cooking" has
kept this family-run Childs Hill venue busy
through two decades. There's "nothing fancy"
to it beyond a "warm welcome from happy
people". / NW2 2HY; www.giacomos.co.uk; 10
pm.

THE GILBERT SCOTT
NW1 **£73** 3 2 4

EUSTON RD   020 7278 3888   9–3C

"It's such a wonderful building" – the
spectacular neo-Gothic riot of St Pancras
Station – and Marcus Wareing's "fabulously
grand" and "buzzing" dining room near the
Eurostar platforms "seduces with its ambience"
("it's all rather 'Orient Express'"). Judged as
a foodie destination alone, appreciation of
its distinctively traditional, British cuisine is
sometimes dogged by gripes about dishes
that are "not up-to-scratch" (or incidents
of "clunky" service), but most reports
applaud its "very pleasant" approach and
"excellent menu that's always evolving, so
the food stays interesting". / NW1 2AR;
www.thegilbertscott.co.uk; @Thegilbertscott; 11
pm, Sun 9 pm; booking max 7 may apply.

GINGER & WHITE
HAMPSTEAD NW3 **£13** 3 3 3

4A-5A, PERRINS CT   020 7431 9098   9–2A

Cutely-sited Hampstead café – a chic and
highly rated coffee stop (beans care of Square

Mile Coffee Roasters) whose all-day breakfasts,
toasties and buns are ideal for brunching
with beauteous Hampstead types. It no
longer has a Belsize Park sibling. / NW3 1QS;
www.gingerandwhite.com; L only; No Amex; no
booking.

GINZA ONODERA
SW1 **£96** 3 3 2

15 BURY ST   020 7839 1101   3–3D

Stately Japanese venue – from an international
chain based in Tokyo's upmarket Ginza –
that's "de luxe, although not OTT"; with
"very good food and top-notch service".
It's not so dissimilar to Matsuri (RIP), the
previous occupant of this refurbished ("not
for the better") St James's basement, below a
department store. / SW1Y 6AL; onodera-group.
com/uk; @Onodera_London; 10 pm.

THE GLASSHOUSE
TW9 **£81** 4 3 3

14 STATION PDE   020 8940 6777   1–3A

"A five-star experience" – this posher-than-usual
neighbourhood haunt, by Kew Gardens tube
station is "the lowest profile in the Chez Bruce
stable". Arguably "the dining room itself is a
little uninspiring, but it has a good atmosphere
when it's full", and the operation generally
shows "similar care and professionalism"
to its siblings, down to the "expert cuisine";
"well chosen, affordable wine list"; and "top
cheeseboard". After a rocky patch, long term
fans feel it's "sprung back to form", but scores
have yet to hit their old highs here, and a more
representative view is that "it's not as superlative
as it was, but of very high quality nevertheless".
/ TW9 3PZ; www.glasshouserestaurant.co.uk;
@The__Glasshouse; 10.30 pm, Sun 10 pm;
booking max 8 may apply.

GLORIA EC2   **£58** 3 3 4

54-56 GREAT EASTERN STREET 13–1B

"If Wes Anderson did Italian restaurants, they
might be something like this"; and this "very
2019" Shoreditch newcomer – whose glam,
pastiche decor apes a thriving 1960s ristorante –
feels "like popping to the Amalfi Coast for lunch
without the air travel!". Definitely, it's not one
for food purists, who can condemn what they
see as "overhyped, Instagram-led, bog-standard,
fake cooking". Don't take it too seriously,
though, and it's superb "fun", service is
"prompt and smooth-running", and the calorie-
laden scoff – with echoes of 1970s Britalian
– is "generously portioned" and "surprisingly
good". / EC2A 3QR; www.bigmammagroup.com;
@bigmammagroup.

GO-VIET SW7   **£57** 4 3 2

53 OLD BROMPTON RD   020 7589 6432
6–2C

"Refined Vietnamese food" – "with clean,
fresh flavours" – is showcased at this two-year-
old South Ken flagship of former Hakkasan
chef Jeff Tan, who also owns Viet Food in
Chinatown. Top Tip – "the weekend lunch
menu is a steal for the quality". / SW7 3JS;

vietnamfood.co.uk/go-viet; @govietnamese; 10 pm,
Fri & Sat 10.30 pm.

LA GOCCIA WC2   **£58** 2 2 4

FLORAL COURT, OFF FLORAL STREET
020 7305 7676   5–3C

"Outside in the courtyard on a summer's
day is a very pleasant experience" at this
good-looking, all-day Italian (complete with
wood-fired oven) in Covent Garden's recently
constructed Floral Court development. No
gripes about the food, but it's not especially
cheap, and service is "charming" but can be
"wayward". / WC2E 9DJ; petershamnurseries.
com/dine/la-goccia; @PetershamN .

GODDARDS AT GREENWICH
SE10 **£27** 3 4 3

22 KING WILLIAM WALK   020 8305 9612
1–3D

"Crammed with tourists and locals every
lunchtime, getting a taste of history", this
"genuine and friendly" Greenwich fixture is
one of the last purveyors of traditional pie
'n' mash left in London. The "pies haven't
changed since 1890" – although they do
now offer a veggie version with soya. /
SE10 9HU; www.goddardsatgreenwich.co.uk;
@GoddardsPieMash; 7.30 pm, Fri & Sat 8 pm; L &
early evening only.

GÖKYÜZÜ   **£33** 2 2 2

26-27 GRAND PDE, GREEN LANES, N4
020 8211 8406   1–1C
THE MALL, SELBORNE ROAD, E17   1–1D
SOUTHEND ROAD, E4 020 8527 4927 14–1C

"Very lively and noisy with families and
children" – the "large" Harringay original of
this small Turkish group is twenty years old,
and remains "understandably popular, given
its reasonable prices": "the food is good and
plentiful and just keeps coming", and "the
grilled meats are just yummy". There are
now spin-offs in Chingford, Walthamstow and
Finchley. Top Tip – "doggy bags are readily
provided". / gokyuzurestaurant.co.uk.

GOLD W11   **£66**

95 PORTOBELLO ROAD   020 3146 0747
7–2B

On the former site of Portobello Gold (RIP),
this long-standing Portobello haunt has been
utterly revamped by Mahiki-founder Nick
House, who has taken its look from grunge to
glam. In its new incarnation, there's a garden
room (with retractable roof) and a party room
on the second floor. Chef Theo Hill used to
work at The River Café, while the front of
house has worked at various Soho House
venues. / W11 2QB; goldnottinghill.com.

GOLD MINE W2   **£34** 4 2 2

102 QUEENSWAY   020 7792 8331   7–2C

"The special roasted duck is rightly acclaimed
as the best in London" according to fans of this
"crowded" Bayswater Cantonese – although
its near neighbour the Four Seasons is also a

rival for that crown. "Expect long queues", "friendlier service than some of its competitors" and a "slightly chaotic atmosphere". / W2 3RR; 11 pm.

GOLDEN DRAGON W1 £44 | 3 2 2

28-29 GERRARD ST 020 7734 1073 5–3A

A "straightforward Chinatown classic": this long-standing, "very authentic" destination provides a "good central location for inexpensive – and always reliable – dim sum" as well as roast meat. / W1 6JW; www.gdlondon.co.uk; 11.30 pm, Fri-Sun midnight.

GOLDEN HIND W1 £36 | 3 2 2

73 MARYLEBONE LN 020 7486 3644 2–1A

"Still my favourite fish 'n' chips in Marylebone" – this centenarian (est. 1914) "ticks all the boxes" and is "fantastic value". The reporter who complained that "you can no longer bring your own wine" will be pleased to learn that BYO was restored this summer, with £5 corkage (wine and cocktails are also on the menu). / W1U 2PN; www.goldenhindrestaurant.com; 10 pm; closed Sat L & Sun.

GOOD EARTH £61 | 3 3 2

233 BROMPTON RD, SW3 020 7584 3658 6–2C
143-145 THE BROADWAY, NW7 020 8959 7011 1–1B
11 BELLEVUE RD, SW17 020 8682 9230 11–2C

"A huge cut-above a 'regular' Chinese!" – this "well-run", well-established family-run chain in Knightsbridge, Balham and Mill Hill (and Esher) offers an "upmarket" experience that's "always reliable": "not cheap but worth it". "If feels like a bit of a 1990s throwback and I like it for that!" / www.goodearthgroup.co.uk; Mon-Sat 10.45 pm, Sun 10 pm; NW7 11.15 pm, Sun 10.45 pm, KT10 10.30 pm, Sun 10.15pm.

GOODMAN £92 | 4 3 3

24-26 MADDOX ST, W1 020 7499 3776 3–2C
3 SOUTH QUAY, E14 020 7531 0300 12–1C
11 OLD JEWRY, EC2 020 7600 8220 10–2C

"Sustaining their excellent reputation": these NYC-style steakhouses offer a solid and comfortable, rather than a particularly vibey environment, but when it comes to the quality of their meat – sourced in the UK, US and Spain; and dry-aged on-site – they are "second to none"; and the City branch, in particular, slugs it out with its nearby rival Hawksmoor as a favourite haunt of carnivorous expense-accounters. "Expensive but always a treat". / www.goodmanrestaurants.com; 10.30 pm; closed Sun.

GOPAL'S OF SOHO W1 £45 | 3 3 2

12 BATEMAN ST 020 7434 1621 5–2A

"For a cuzza in Soho", this "good Indian in the centre of all the action" is just the job thanks to its "flavoursome and so tasty" cooking and "top

price/quality ratio". Family run since 1988, its unfashionably traditional basement setting is also a great antidote when you're sick of being dazzled by trendy new restaurant design-concepts. / W1D 4AH; www.gopalsofsoho.co.uk; 11.30 pm, Sun 11 pm.

GORDON RAMSAY SW3 £160 | 3 3 2

68-69 ROYAL HOSPITAL RD 020 7352 4441 6–3D

"Are people just deducting points because it has Gordon's name?" – that's the suspicion raised by fans of the world-famous TV-chef, who – like Michelin – consider his modern French cuisine "simply unbeatable", and extol his "early-noughties-time-warp-style" Chelsea HQ (currently presided over by head chef Matt Abé) as "the best in London". The answer is no! – the problem is the equally sizeable number of diners who feel "safety first is the word here", and that by the standards of top, world-class culinary genius it "doesn't really hit the mark": "OK-ish, but too often run-of-the-mill" or "merely average (except for the price… which is outrageous!)". / SW3 4HP; www.gordonramsay.com; @GordonRamsay; 10.15 pm; closed Sat & Sun; No jeans; booking max 9 may apply.

GORDON'S WINE BAR WC2 £39 | 2 2 5

47 VILLIERS ST 020 7930 1408 5–4D

"An old favourite – but still the best place to meet friends in London" – this lovingly preserved, 1890s wine bar by Embankment station has a huge outside terrace and "atmospheric cellars" lit by candles. "This is not about the food (which is perfectly OK, just very limited) or the grumpy staff – it's about the wine and the ambience, delivered here in spades". "How wonderful to take someone who's never been before, to experience the atmosphere", either as a boozy hideaway in winter, or for a BBQ by the park in summer. / WC2N 6NE; gordonswinebar.com; @GordonsWineBar; 11 pm, Sun 10 pm.

GOURMET BURGER KITCHEN £33 | 2 2 2

"Hitting the spot when nothing but a burger will do", say devotees of the original upmarket burger chain that started with a single outlet in 2001. Losses of £4.6million last year led to the closure of 24 sites around the country, but the number of reporters complaining of "generally indifferent" meals is still relatively minor compared to those who still see it as "a safe bet for the kids" or "sensibly priced and reliable, suggesting it's a franchise worth saving. / www.gbkinfo.com; most branches close 11 pm, Sun 10.30 pm; book online.

GOYA SW1 £41 | 3 2 3

34 LUPUS ST 020 7976 5309 2–4C

"Basic tapas at its best", "decent paella" and a "good selection of wines" have been the order of the day at this "reasonably priced" Spanish

local in Pimlico for 25 years. "The menu never changes, but the food's always good". / SW1V 3EB; www.goyarestaurant.co.uk; midnight, Sun 11.30 pm.

GRANARY SQUARE BRASSERIE N1 £53 | 2 1 3

1 GRANARY SQUARE 020 3940 1000 9–3C

"Very flashy decor" – and (it is claimed) 'the largest al fresco dining terrace in north London' – help entice diners to this "busy and buzzy" King's Cross yearling from Richard Caring's Ivy Collection, and sharing all the 'affordable glam' design ethos of the group. Everyone finds it an agreeably "lively place" but beyond that views are sharply divided: and whereas fans report "good quality brasserie food at all times of day", critics dismiss "ordinary" food and "uninterested service" that's "not up to their pretentions" or the "ambitious prices". / N1C 4AB; www.granarysquarebrasserie.com; Booking max 12 may apply.

GRAND TRUNK ROAD E18 £55 | 4 3 2

219 HIGH STREET 020 8505 1965 1–1D

"An exceptional local" – this Woodford three-year-old (from the ex-manager and ex-head chef of Mayfair's Tamarind) delivers "a real treat of modern, well-spiced food", and draws fans from north London to Essex. On the downside, the "noisy" room "could be more cosy". / E18 2PB; www.gtrrestaurant.co.uk; @GT_Road; 10.30pm; closed Mon & Sun D.

GRANGER & CO £51 | 3 2 3

237-239 PAVILION RD, SW1 020 3848 1060 6–2D
175 WESTBOURNE GROVE, W11 020 7229 9111 7–1B
STANLEY BUILDING, ST PANCRAS SQ, N1 020 3058 2567 9–3C
THE BUCKLEY BUILDING, 50 SEKFORDE ST, EC1 020 7251 9032 10–1A

"Despite the eternal, off-putting queues, brunching is always such a treat" at Aussie celeb-chef, Bill Granger's "very buzzy" ("crowded and noisy") hang-outs. "Old favourite options given a creative spin" feature amidst the "excellent choice of delicious options" and there's an appealing "freshness" to the dishes. The Notting Hill original still inspires most feedback, but all outlets – King's Cross, Clerkenwell and Chelsea – have their followings. For any occasion other than brunch they provoke less interest. Top Tip – "OMG, those ricotta pancakes are amazing!" / Mon-Sat 11 pm, Sun 10 pm.

GRAYS & FEATHER WC2 | 3 4 4

26 WELLINGTON STREET 0203 948 4900 5–3D

Promising, if limited, early feedback on this modern 'wine parlour' – recently opened by wine expert Andrew Gray (a merchant with a business at the Southbank Food Market) on a corner-site near Covent Garden (the erstwhile office-space of a Mr Charles Dickens); and with an excellent list of 70 wines: "limited food, but what they do is lovely; tiny space, but it's gorgeous, and well worth a visit, especially as staff are so lovely". / WC2E 7DD; www.graysandfeather.com; @GraysandFeather.

GREAT NEPALESE
NW1 £42 3 3 2

48 EVERSHOLT ST 020 7388 6737 9–3C

"Delicious and different food and caring hosts who explain its origins" have kept fans loyal to this otherwise nondescript fixture, down the side of Euston Station, for over 50 years. Some of the food is fairly standard north Indian fare – the Nepalese specialities are the way to go. / NW1 1DA; www.great-nepalese.co.uk; 11.30 pm, Sun 10 pm.

THE GREEN ROOM, THE NATIONAL THEATRE
SE1 £48 2 2 2

101 UPPER GROUND 020 7452 3630 2–3D

For some reporters, the National Theatre's "brisk" in-house diner delivers on the "plain good food near the theatre" you'd hope for, so "it's a shame" that the "food is complacently ordinary" for too many others to make it a reliable recommendation. Top Tip – "best when you can sit in the garden". / SE1 9PP; www.greenroom.london; @greenroomSE1; 10.30 pm, Sun 7 pm.

GREENBERRY CAFÉ
NW1 £46 3 3 4

101 REGENTS PARK ROAD 020 7483 3765 9–2B

"A perfect favourite for brunch" – this "welcoming" café, "quite idyllically located" on Primrose Hill's cute main drag, is not a foodie destination, but a popular all-day hub for breakfast, a bite, or a bun with a brew. "The line outside was a hint that it would deliver… and so it did!" / NW1 8UR; greenberrycafe.co.uk; @Greenberry_Cafe; 10 pm; closed Mon D & Sun D; No Amex.

THE GREENHOUSE
W1 £140 3 3 3

27A HAYS MEWS 020 7499 3331 3–3B

"Down a quiet street in Mayfair", this calm and luxurious temple of gastronomy is a well-known stalwart (est 1977), that's a particular "old-favourite" for those who recall its days under Gary Rhodes. Nowadays part of Marlon Abela's restaurant empire, it has held two Michelin stars since 2014, which were successfully retained by new chef Alex Dilling, who joined in mid 2018. Harden's regulars likewise report a "seamless transition" that's "given a new lease of life" to the kitchen: acclaiming his "thoughtfully sequenced" and "exciting" tasting menus, which manage not to be eclipsed by one of London's most comprehensive wine lists. The experience comes at "hedge fund prices" though, and the continuing ethos of classic gastronomy for its own sake continues to leave some

folks with a "stuffy, stilted, and pretentious" impression. "It was bordering on the comical at times – I recall no less than four servers engaged in simultaneously spooning a rather flat Parmesan foam on to our plates with such pomp and ceremony that my guest and I could barely hold back the tears of laughter. I felt like I was misbehaving in church, but this is far from being a sacred place…" / W1J 5NY; www.greenhouserestaurant.co.uk; @greenhouse27a; 10.30 pm; closed Sat L & Sun.

THE GREYHOUND CAFE
W1 £61 3 2 3

37 BERNERS STREET 020 3026 3798 3–1D

First European outpost of a Thailand-based chain – a sizeable operation in Fitzrovia that's now in its second year. Some "lovely spicy combinations" help create a "really interesting menu" but views divide a little on the trendily-designed space: "lacking atmosphere" to some but "lovely" and "den-like" to others. / W1T 3LZ; www.greyhoundcafe.uk.

GRIDIRON, COMO METROPOLITAN LONDON
W1 £80

19 OLD PARK LANE 020 7447 1080 3–4A

Little survey feedback as yet on this late-autumn 2018 opening right on Park Lane – a contemporary 'live fire' steakhouse occupying the space which older hipsters may recall as the Met Bar. The Observer's Jay Rayner felt it was a 'so-nearly-but-not quite' experience, but the team behind it is impressive with Richard H Turner (ex-Hawksmoor) and Colin McSherry (Nuala, Clove Club). / W1K 1LB; www.gridironlondon.com.

GRUMBLES SW1 £47 3 3 4

35 CHURTON ST 020 7834 0149 2–4B

"Very characterful", ancient bistro, which has been a feature of Pimlico for over 50 years (est 1964). It's treasured by its regulars, who come from near and far, for its rustic style and "top-value" dishes: essentially Anglo/French (moules marinière, escargots in garlic butter, fillet steak, fish 'n' chips, burgers), freshened up with some eclectic international additions over the years (Thai-style duck breast, quinoa and feta salad…). / SW1V 2LT; www.grumblesrestaurant.co.uk; @grumblesbistro; 10.45 pm, Sun 10.30 pm.

GUGLEE £38 3 3 2

7 NEW COLLEGE PDE, NW3 020 7722 8478 9–2A
279 WEST END LN, NW6 020 7317 8555 1–1B

This pair of "quirky", modern curryhouses bowl up "terrific food" including some "great Goan dishes" to happy customers in West Hampstead and Swiss Cottage. They win solid praise even from reporters who generally "don't like the new wave of fancy Indians". / www.guglee.co.uk; 11 pm.

THE GUILDFORD ARMS
SE10 £46 3 4 3

55 GUILDFORD GROVE 020 8691 6293 1–3D

"One of the best in the Greenwich area" – this three-storey Georgian tavern has a "beautiful garden" and "sits away from the main drag, so it's not overly packed and touristy". Chef Guy Awford is a well-known name in these parts having cooked at Inside (RIP) for many years, and is credited with some "brilliant cooking" here too. In mid 2019 it closed, to be totally transformed, with re-opening set for September 2019: if they get it half right, this will become Greenwich's No. 1 destination. (Ratings are based on past performance: not yet post-revamp). / SE10 8JY; www.theguildfordarms.co.uk; @GuildfordArms_; 10 pm, Sun 9 pm; closed Mon.

THE GUINEA GRILL
W1 £75 3 3 3

30 BRUTON PL 020 7409 1728 3–3B

"Splendid old pub" in a cute Mayfair mews whose adjoining "old school" grill-house – "various small rooms packed with tables" – may be "noisy and less-than-comfortable", but is "an institution" for those fond of a "fabulous steak" or meat pie. "Superb beef and lamb are cooked on the open charcoal grill (you can choose your cut on the way in)" and the meat is of "consummate quality". With its "excellent real ale" it's a "good place for the boys" but its "sky-high prices" can deepen the impression of catering for a "principally male, expense-account clientele". Top Tip – in early 2019, landlord Oison Rogers started opening for breakfast: "full English in meaty portions". / W1J 6NL; www.theguinea.co.uk; @guineagrill; closed Sat L & Sun.

THE GUN E14 £67 2 2 4

27 COLDHARBOUR 020 7515 5222 12–1C

"The views alone make it worth a visit" to this Grade II listed Docklands pub operated by Fuller's. Directly opposite The O2, with extensive conservatory and terrace seating, it's a "great little spot on the river", with "upscale food and service". / E14 9NS; www.thegundocklands.com; @thegundocklands; 10 pm, Sun 7 pm.

GUNPOWDER £48 4 3 3

ONE TOWER BRIDGE, 4 CROWN SQUARE, SE1 AWAITING TEL 10–4D
11 WHITES ROW, E1 020 7426 0542 13–2C

"BOOM! Excellent, sometimes-fiery fare" ("they don't hold back on the spicing") "hits the spot" with "great creative flavours" at this duo of Indian tapas-style haunts. The "tiny", "so-noisy, full-on and not-so-relaxing" original sits near Spitalfields, while the "bigger" (but also "buzzing and noisy") second branch near Tower Bridge is the better-known nowadays, similarly well-rated and "handy for the Bridge Theatre". Top Menu Tips – "superb lamb chops and sublime venison doughnuts". / www.gunpowderlondon.com; @gunpowder_ldn.

Gloria EC2

Flor SE1

GUSTOSO RISTORANTE & ENOTECA SW1 £48 3 3 3

33 WILLOW PL   020 7834 5778   2–4B

"This very decent Italian" is a "hidden gem just a stone's throw from Victoria Station" – "improbably located in the culinary desert behind Westminster Cathedral" – with "ever-improving traditional dishes" made from "fresh ingredients" delivered by "friendly staff" in a "pleasing", relatively modern setting. / SW1P 1JH; www.ristorantegustoso.co.uk; @GustosoRist; 10.30 pm, Fri & Sat 11 pm, Sun 9.30 pm.

GYMKHANA W1 £77 5 4 4

42 ALBEMARLE ST   020 3011 5900   3–3C

"Still at the top of its game" – the Sethi's "posh Indian" in Mayfair is "worth the hype" and remains the most-mentioned Indian in the survey on account of "memorable and beautifully flavourful" cuisine delivered by "warm and friendly staff" in an enveloping, old-colonial-style setting: "get a booth on the ground floor and prepare to be transported!" Top Menu Tip – "How I love the tandoori lamb chops. After a marinade in spices, these thick pieces of meat become so succulent, tender and taste-laden, are magnificently presented and really delicious on the eager palate!". NB: Just as the survey closed, in June 2019, a fire gutted the restaurant and according to its website it remains "closed until further notice". / W1S 4JH; www.gymkhanalondon.com; @GymkhanaLondon; 10.30 pm; closed Sun.

HACHÉ £42 3 4 2

95-97 HIGH HOLBORN, WC1 020 7242 4580 2–1D
329-331 FULHAM RD, SW10 020 7823 3515 6–3B
24 INVERNESS ST, NW1 020 7485 9100 9–3B
37 BEDFORD HILL, SW12 020 8772 9772 11–2C
153 CLAPHAM HIGH ST, SW4 020 7738 8760 11–2D
147-149 CURTAIN RD, EC2 020 7739 8396 13–1B

"Still some of the best burgers around", say fans of this French group, whose Gallic je ne sais quoi lends a certain superiority to the offering, while service is "friendly and speedy". Its seventh outlet opened in Kingston early in 2019, at a time when rival mid-market operators were struggling. / www.hacheburgers.com; 10.30 pm, Fri-Sat 11 pm, Sun 10 pm; WC1 Sat & Sun.

HAI CENATO SW1 £61 3 2 2

2 SIR SIMON MILTON SQUARE, 150 VICTORIA ST   020 3816 9320   2–4B

"Some of the best pizza in town" – "with really delicious, springy crusts and interesting flavour combinations" – is the big tick at Jason Atherton's take on New York Italian dining in Victoria's Nova development. But even some who say "the food is great" say "it's let down by below-par ambience and service: one for the lunchtime crowd". / SW1H 0HW; haicenato.

co.uk; @haicenato; 10 pm, Sun 9.30 pm; booking max 6 may apply.

HAKKASAN £101 4 2 3

17 BRUTON ST, W1 020 7907 1888   3–2C
8 HANWAY PL, W1 020 7927 7000   5–1A

"Hakkasan has been setting the standard for modern Chinese food in London for ages now", with the nightclubby, "dimly lit" original ("I had difficulty reading the menu and even seeing the food!"), opening "in a tiny, narrow lane with an anonymous entrance" near Tottenham Court Road in 2001; and although both it and its easier-to-find Mayfair spin-off's styling "is a little bling bling" they continue to serve "seriously lovely" food and "refreshing" cocktails. There are drawbacks, which have also changed little over the years: it's "very noisy", staff can seem "bored" or "totally dismissive", and "your wallet will have a hangover in the morning". / www.hakkasan.com; 12.30 am, Sun 11.15 pm; W1 12.30 am, Thu-Sat 12.45 am, Sun midnight; no trainers, no sportswear.

THE HALAL GUYS WC2 £17 3 3 2

14-15 IRVING STREET   020 8706 0307   5–4B

"Finally a US brand that delivers the goods!" This "cheap 'n' cheerful newcomer" – a fast food caff with outside seating just off Leicester Square – is the first UK outpost of a 27-year-old, NYC-brand that started as a hot dog stand, but where now the focus is on halal street food (hot sandwiches, or bowls with meat or falafel), which early reports say is "superb value". The roll-out is already ongoing: a second branch opened in Earl's Court in Summer 2019. / WC2H 7AU; thehalalguys.com; @HalalGuys.

HAM NW6 £57 3 2 3

238 WEST END LANE   020 7813 0168   1–1B

"A brilliant neighbourhood restaurant: actually far better than a typical neighbourhood restaurant!" – so say fans of Matt Osborne's West Hampstead yearling, serving a "changing (if limited) menu of small-plates. Ratings overall are undercut, though, by those who find its performance "overhyped" or "disappointing after a great start". / NW6 1LG; www.hamwesthampstead.com/ham; @hamwhampstead/.

HAM YARD RESTAURANT, HAM YARD HOTEL W1 £60 2 3 4

1 HAM YD   020 3642 1007   4–3D

Sitting in the cute courtyard of this "immaculately kept" newish hotel, you would never dream you were a two-minute stroll from Piccadilly Circus, and – in colder weather – its "quirky modern/traditional conservatory" is also a lovely destination. In keeping with other Firmdale hotels, the food avoids fireworks, but they have an "excellent-value set lunch and pre-theatre menu", and some would argue it's "the best place in town for afternoon tea – served on quirky china with hand-stitched white

table linen and not at all rushed". / W1D 7DT; www.firmdalehotels.com/hotels/london/ham-yard-hotel/ham-yard-bar-restaurant; @Firmdale_Hotels; 11.30 pm, Sun 10.30 pm.

THE HAMPSHIRE HOG W6 £54 2 3 3

227 KING STREET   020 8748 3391   8–2B

Near Hammersmith's un-lovely town hall, this sizeable 'pub & pantry' has a particularly attractive dining area, looking onto its large garden, and you can also eat in the large bar. Even those who feel "there's not a great menu choice" say a meal here is "an OK experience". / W6 9JT; www.thehampshirehog.com; @TheHampshireHog; 10 pm, Sun 4 pm; closed Sun D.

HANKIES 4 2 2

61 UPPER BERKELEY STREET, W1 020 7958 3222   2–2A
67 SHAFTESBURY AVENUE, W1 020 7871 6021   5–3A

Anirudh Arora's year-old, north Indian, street-food café on the West End's ever-bustling Shaftesbury Avenue also has a new outpost in a smart hotel dining room, near Marble Arch. The duo's title refers to classic Roomali Roti: bread, hand spun into thin sheets, cooked and folded into a 'hankie', and both branches win praise for "great food at a relatively small price".

HANS' BAR & GRILL SW1 £71 2 3 3

164 PAVILION ROAD   020 7730 7000   6–2D

"A good addition to the area, but standards can be a bit rough and ready" is a balanced view on this "nice, bright venue" in a super-cute enclave off Sloane Street that's part of nearby luxury boutique hotel, 11 Cadogan Gardens. On most accounts, its "all-day menu is not too expensive for the area" making it a versatile choice for a meet-up in Chelsea; but there's the odd 'off' report of meals "offering a masterclass of how not to do it". / SW1X 0AW; www.hansbarandgrill.com; @HansBarGrill; 10.30pm.

THE HARCOURT W1 £60 3 4 4

32 HARCOURT STREET   020 3771 8660   7–1D

"Restaurant-quality", "Scandi-influenced", "delicious" food has helped carve a major reputation for this five-storey gastropub, in "a quiet Marylebone backwater that's handy for Paddington". Beautifully decorated: "it's still just discernibly a pub, but an extremely well presented one". / W1H 4HX; www.theharcourt.com; @theharcourtldn; 11 pm, Fri & Sat 11.30 pm, Sun 10 pm.

HARD ROCK CAFÉ 234

**150 OLD PARK LANE, W1 020 7287 4600
3–4B
CRITERION BUILDING, 225-229 PICCADILLY,
W1 020 7287 4600 4–4D
HARD ROCK HOTEL, GREAT CUMBERLAND
PLACE, W1 020 7479 5078 2–2A**

Since 1971, this age-old rocker has grown from its first site, near Hyde Park Corner, to 186 globally, and this year saw the group reinvest massively in the capital, with not just a new hotel (on the site that was once The Cumberland) by Marble Arch, but also with the July 2019 opening of a 19,000 sq ft, multi-level, new London flagship at Piccadilly Circus. The latter opening includes a menu shake-up, which introduces an unsuspecting world to new culinary delights, including the '24-Karat Gold Leaf Steak BurgerTM'; (as well as the retail opportunities of 'the world's largest Rock Shop'"). For silver-haired reporters (who were alive for the chain's founding) – a generation by-and-large untroubled by the hipster burger revolution – the "generously meaty" patties of the original are "still the best", and one early report on the hotel says its restaurant "really rocks" too…. Even allowing for cynicism about the effects of nostalgia on the tastebuds, the brand fares better in the survey than most mass-market offerings. / www.hardrockcafe.com/location/london; @HardRockLondon.

HARE & TORTOISE £39 332

**11-13 THE BRUNSWICK, WC1 020 7278 9799
2–1D
373 KENSINGTON HIGH ST, W14
020 7603 8887 8–1D
156 CHISWICK HIGH RD, W4 020 8747 5966
8–2A
38 HAVEN GRN, W5 020 8810 7066 1–2A
296-298 UPPER RICHMOND RD, SW15
020 8394 7666 11–2B
90 NEW BRIDGE ST, EC4 020 7651 0266
10–2A**

"Brilliant for a quick pitstop", these Japanese-inspired pan-Asian canteens consistently churn out "a great selection of fresh and tasty dishes" (sushi, noodles, laksa,…) at an "impressive speed" – you can watch a "gaggle of chefs in action with an array of woks". Established in 1996, the group has lived up to its name, expanding slowly to six sites while its rivals have proliferated – and, in some cases, crashed and burned. / www.hareandtortoise-restaurants.co.uk; 11 pm; EC4 10.30, Fri 11 pm; EC4 closed Sun; W14 no bookings.

HARLEQUIN SW6 £68 444

**194 WANDSWORTH BRIDGE ROAD
020 7736 7169 11–1B**

"An amazing, new, local addition" – James Erasmus (a South African chef who has graduated from The Ledbury and Harwood Arms stable) is cooking up a storm at his casual, neighbourhood newcomer, in the depths of deepest Fulham, presenting a monthly changing seasonal menu, with a parallel vegetarian option. Someone forgot to tell him that nobody ever opens a really good restaurant on the Wandsworth Bridge Road! / SW6 2UF; www.harlequinrestaurant.co.uk.

HARRODS DINING HALL SW1

HARRODS, 87-135 BROMPTON ROAD 6–1D

The Grade II, 1920s tiled splendour of Harrods Meat & Fish Hall has been revamped and re-imagined as London's poshest food court, with bars dedicated to sushi, pasta, grills (wagyu, rotisserie chicken) and 'Harrods signature fish 'n' chips'. There's also the 26-seat Kama run by Vineet Bhatia, selling 'modernised, regional Indian classics'. The centrepiece is a wine bar, with more than 100 vintages sold by the glass and snacks from Caviar House & Prunier. / SW1X 7XL; www.harrods.com/en-gb/restaurants.

HARRY MORGAN'S NW8 £46 333

**29-31 ST JOHN'S WOOD HIGH ST
020 7722 1869 9–3A**

"Nobody does better salt beef" than this veteran NYC-style kosher deli: a St John's Wood institution since 1948 that's "packed to heaving on a Saturday". Don't expect innovation – it's a place to "stick to the favourites". / NW8 7NH; www.harryms.co.uk; @morgan_hm; 10 pm.

HARRY'S BAR W1 £64 223

**30-34 JAMES STREET 020 3971 9444
3–1A**

Richard Carling's cutely-situated yearling north of Oxford Street – his second 'accessible' version of Mayfair's famous Harry's Bar (which is still very much members only) – hasn't yet hit the same level of satisfaction as its Knightsbridge sibling, Harry's Dolce Vita. But most diners like its "spacious" interior and "good atmosphere", and even those who say the food's "distinctly average" can still feel "it's a useful casual-dining addition". / W1U 1EU; www.harrys-bar.co.uk.

HARRY'S DOLCE VITA SW3 £67 335

27-31 BASIL STREET 020 3940 1020 6–1D

Emptied your wallet at Harrods and need to recover over a bowl of pasta and glass of fizz? – Richard Caring's "fun" and "nicely buzzing" Italian brasserie, near the store's rear entrance, can be just the job. Now two years old, its fanbase primarily seems to extend to shoppers and other miscellaneous Knightsbridge types, as it elicits limited survey feedback; but all reports praise its "great consistency in a fun setting with attentive and engaging staff". / SW3 1BB; www.harrysdolcevita.com.

HARWOOD ARMS SW6 £74 433

WALHAM GROVE 020 7386 1847 6–3A

"Fabulous game" is a highpoint of the "simple food, cooked to perfection" ("mouthwatering meat so tender the knife just fell through it") at this "super-fine" hostelry in the distant backstreets of Fulham – for the second year, the survey's No. 1 gastropub. Full credit goes to head chef Sally Abé for her "top flight" evolution of traditional dishes, but it can't harm to have input from backers who include Brett Graham of The Ledbury, and also the UK's most prominent game chef, Mike Robinson. Aside from the small amount of space dedicated purely to drinking, it feels like an honest-to-goodness, fairly unreformed boozer. Top Menu Tips – "venison scotch egg is to die for, as is the Sunday roast". / SW6 1QP; www.harwoodarms.com; @HarwoodArms; 9.30 pm, Sun 9 pm; closed Mon L; credit card required to book.

HASHI SW20 £44 342

54 DURHAM RD 020 8944 1888 11–2A

A "very good local Japanese": consistently one of the best in the enclave around Raynes Park. Top Menu Tip – notably good sushi. / SW20 0TW; 10.30 pm; closed Mon; No Amex.

HATCHED SW11 £71 542

**189 SAINT JOHN'S HILL 020 7738 0735
11–2C**

Shane Marshall's highly accomplished, if spartan Battersea venture (formerly called Darwin) serves "a very small menu of exquisite modern British food" that's well above-par for its anonymous location. "You wouldn't know it was there unless someone told you." / SW11 1TH; www.hatchedsw11.com; @HatchedSW11.

THE HAVELOCK TAVERN W14 £52 323

57 MASBRO RD 020 7603 5374 8–1C

"Top local gastropub" in an Olympia backstreet that's "better run" nowadays than during its original heyday, and after more than 20 years still "always delivers" a "well thought-out menu"; and can be surprisingly "buzzing and hectic" for such a tranquil location. / W14 0LS; www.havelocktavern.com; @havelocktavern; 10 pm, Sun 9.30 pm.

HAWKSMOOR £85 433

**5A AIR ST, W1 020 7406 3980 4–4C
11 LANGLEY ST, WC2 020 7420 9390 5–2C
3 YEOMAN'S ROW, SW3 020 7590 9290
6–2C
16 WINCHESTER WALK, SE1 020 7234 9940
10–4C
157 COMMERCIAL ST, E1 020 7426 4850
13–2B
10-12 BASINGHALL ST, EC2 020 7397 8120
10–2C**

Huw Gott and Will Beckett "do the 'casual excellence' thing very well indeed" and their still über-fashionable steakhouse chain (founded in 2006) occupies a niche in the hearts of London's fooderati like no other, with its "distinctly clubby" ("big, loud and busy") style, its "to-die-for cocktails" and its "top steaks": British-bred and "char-grilled to perfection over wood fires, with deliciously indulgent sides". Ratings for such a phenomenon have sometimes seemed middling in comparison to its renown – a reflection of the very full pricing that's always been their policy. That said, despite some accusations that "it's all gone downhill in recent times", its grades actually bounced back significantly this year, and remain in line with its past best. The City branch in particular shines. "Dark dens and out-of-this-world quality beef are the cornerstones of dealmaking. What deal would not reach a happy ending fuelled by a perfectly cooked rib-eye, grilled bone marrow, and beef dripping fries? Throw in a bottle or two of bordeaux and that IPO is around the corner!" Top Tips – "£5 corkage on Monday BYO is an incredible deal" and starting the day at the Guildhall branch: "if anyone can do a better breakfast I'd love to try it!" / www.thehawksmoor.com; 10.30 pm; W1 & WC2 Fri & Sat 11 pm, Sun 9pm-10 pm; EC2 closed Sat & Sun.

HAYA W11

184A KENSINGTON PARK ROAD   7–1B

This September 2019 newcomer on Notting Hill's Kensington Park Road is to be an all-day restaurant riding the current wave of Tel Aviv-inspired diners, featuring healthy sharing-plates. / W11 2ES; haya.london.

HAZ   £53   2 2 2

9 CUTLER ST, E1 020 7929 7923 10–2D
14 FINSBURY SQUARE, EC2 020 7920 9944 13–2A
34 FOSTER LN, EC2 020 7600 4172 10–2B
64 BISHOPSGATE, EC2 020 7628 4522 10–2D
112 HOUNDSDITCH, EC3 020 7623 8180 10–2D
6 MINCING LN, EC3 020 7929 3173 10–3D

"Straightforward Turkish food at a relatively sensible price (for the Square Mile)" is the simple proposition at this "useful" and well-established small chain. They get pretty "packed and noisy at lunchtime with a boisterous City clientele". / www.hazrestaurant.co.uk; 11.30 pm; EC3 closed Sun.

HÉLÈNE DARROZE, THE CONNAUGHT HOTEL W1   £155   3 4 4

CARLOS PL   020 3147 7200   3–3B

Hélène Darroze's luxurious Mayfair temple of gastronomy, within Mayfair's most blueblooded hotel, is celebrating its tenth year with a two-month closure, to re-open in September 2019. A revamp is promised, care of French design house, 'Pierre Yovanovitch Architecture d'Intérieur' (whose aesthetic, we are told in the PR, 'focuses on bold re-imaginings of historic spaces, combining the contemporary with luxury materials'). There will also be the addition of a new chef's table and dedicated Armagnac room; plus a new menu 'rooted in Hélène's culinary style, with a larger focus on British producers and suppliers'. The survey consensus on its former incarnation could be summarised as "exceptional cuisine albeit at extortionate prices" to appeal to "a crowd of plutocrats and their lawyers, and very old-money types": we've maintained last year's rating on the conservative assumption that its new incarnation will be a case of 'plus ça change'… / W1K 2AL; www.the-connaught.co.uk;

@TheConnaught; 10 pm, Sun 9 pm; closed Mon & Sun; No trainers.

HELIOT STEAK HOUSE WC2   £63   3 3 3

CRANBOURN STREET   020 7769 8844   5–3B

"Exceptional value set deals" (particularly at lunch and pre-theatre) provide reason to discover this unusually situated grill, in the former dress circle of the converted theatre that nowadays houses the UK's largest casino (right by Leicester Square tube) and looks down on the gambling tables below. Casino owner Simon Thomas prides himself on the quality of the steaks and wines on offer, and it shows. / WC2H 7AJ; www.hippodromecasino.com; @HippodromeLDN; midnight, Sat 1 am, Sun 11 pm.

HELIX EC3   £82   2 3 5

30 ST MARY AXE   0330 1070816 10–2D

"The wow factor" of its "remarkable views by day or night" helps make this "fun and busy" space – the top three stories of this landmark City tower (originally restricted to those working in the Gherkin, now open to the public) – a "good choice for a special occasion". The catering has its fans too, although critiques include that it can be "ordinary" or "very expensive". Top Tip – "good set menu". / EC3A 8EP; searcysatthegherkin.co.uk/helix-restaurant; @SearcysGherkin.

HELLO DARLING SE1   £43   2 3 3

131 WATERLOO ROAD   020 7401 9603   10–4A

Limited feedback to-date on this new, 'playful restaurant and botanical bar' next to The Old Vic serving 'killer botanical cocktails' alongside 'eclectic sharing-plates' from Natalie Coleman, winner of MasterChef 2013. One early reporter voiced sentiments similar to the Evening Standard's Fay Maschler: "it's a fun, new opening but with fairly average food". / SE1 8UL; www.hellodarling.london; @HelloDarlingLDN.

HENRIETTA BISTRO WC2   £56   3 3 3

HENRIETTA STREET   020 3794 5313   5–3C

Southwestern France and northern Spain are inspiration for the "interesting menu" at this "lovely" yearling bistro in a boutique Covent Garden hotel (which has a "very good bar" too). / WC2E 8NA; www.henriettahotel.com.

HEREFORD ROAD W2   £50   4 4 3

3 HEREFORD RD   020 7727 1144   7–1B

Chef Tom Pemberton's "consistently excellent neighbourhood resto" in Bayswater has a sharp focus on "very good seasonal British produce, very well cooked", and is "a bargain for the quality". "I've been eating here since I gate-crashed the opening in 2007, and

I've never been disappointed". / W2 4AB; www.herefordroad.org; @3HerefordRoad; 10.30 pm, Sun 10 pm.

HERITAGE W1   £75

18 RUPERT STREET   020 3995 7500   4–3D

This new, Swiss venture landed in Soho in June 2019, too late for any survey feedback. Its aesthetic is a world away from the cod-chalet style of its most obvious, age-old competitor, St Moritz. From fondue, raclette and rösti to barbecuing prime cuts of meat and fresh seafood on table-top charbonnade grills – the (highly priced) Alpine menu designed for sharing is served in a swish, modern setting. / W1D 6DF; www.heritagerestaurant.co.uk.

THE HERO OF MAIDA W9   £60   2 2 3

55 SHIRLAND RD   020 7266 9198   7–1C

Is it the strain of fast expansion at Harcourt Inns? This gentrified Maida Vale boozer, which was one of the group's original properties, opened to great acclaim last year thanks to its "great Henry Harris menu". But reports after a year of operation are mixed. For its supporters, "churning out dishes like sweetbreads, rabbit and brain shows it isn't your average pub", and its "famous Sunday lunch is hard to beat". But a number of former fans scent "a steady descent to mediocrity": they feel staff can appear "unconcerned" or "ditsy", and think the food is "priced as something very special but sub-par". / W9 2JD; theheromaidavale.co.uk; @TheHeroofMaida; 10 pm, Sat & Sun 11 pm.

THE HERON W2   £48   4 3 1

1 NORFOLK CR   020 7706 9567   9–4A

The "scruffy basement of a pub" in Bayswater is the setting for what some in the fooderati believe to be "hands-down the best authentic Thai cooking in London" – "food like you'd have in Thailand". Top Tip – "the bbq pork neck is melt-in-your-mouth". / W2 2DN; www.theheronpaddington.com; @theheronpaddington; 11 pm, Sun 10.30 pm; May need + to book.

HICCE N1   £48   2 3 4

COAL DROPS YARD   020 3869 8200   9–3C

"In revitalised Coal Drops Yard" – Angela Hartnett protégée Pip Lacey's late-2018 opening is generally credited as "an excellent addition to the new development". But while just about everyone loves its "beautifully designed and buzzy" interior, when it comes to her "interesting dishes, cooked over wood, mainly for sharing", then opinions are more divided. "Some truly unusual combinations" make it a brand-new-favourite for some diners, but even fans sometimes note that "the ratio of tiny portion size to high cost is a problem", and for others the cooking is "just not memorable enough": "confused and far too expensive for what was delivered". Top Tip – it's pronounced 'ee-chay'. / N1C 4AB; www.hicce.co.uk; @hiccelondon.

HIDE W1 £143 3 5 4

85 PICCADILLY 020 3146 8666 3–4C

"An extraordinary restaurant for an extraordinary occasion!" – Up the "beautiful staircase" accessed through Hide Ground (see also), "no expense has been spared in the creation of this exquisite restaurant", and the "cool" and incredibly spacious first-floor dining room of this Russian-owned yearling provides an impressively luxurious backdrop, "especially if you bag one of the tables facing Green Park". You can choose from either the six-course or nine-course tasting menu, which comes with a vegetarian alternative (and a shorter, "more affordable" option at lunch) and there's the "astonishing complement" of "nearby Hedonism Wines' incomparable 6,000-strong list, as they will run your preferred bottle over if it's not in the restaurant's own cellar". When it comes to Ollie Dabbous's Scandi-inspired cooking, most reporters feel that "thankfully the food lives up to the posh surroundings", delivering "precise, light and intriguing" cuisine that's a "worthy successor to Dabbous". "Impeccable", "helpful" and "charming" service adds further to the mood. "OMG it's oligarch prices" though, leaving doubters – who also feel some plates are a tad "over-engineered" – to conclude that "the biggest impression it leaves is the dent in your wallet!" / W1J 8JB; www.hide.co.uk.

HIDE GROUND W1 £81 3 4 4

85 PICCADILLY 020 3146 8666 3–4C

As a way of dipping your toe into the Hide 'waters', the ground floor of this huge, Russian-backed project near Green Park tube is the safest place to start, offering a selection of menus from early morning onwards, and with a grazing menu, in addition to the ("punishingly expensive") à la carte. As with Above, this likewise is a "beautifully designed and spacious set-up that's good for more than just business but certainly good for a working lunch". Top Tips – "wonderful breakfasts, with a coffee list too" and "lovely afternoon tea watching the world go whilst trying a variety of teas". / W1J.

HIGH ROAD BRASSERIE W4 £49 2 3 3

162-166 CHISWICK HIGH RD 020 8742 7474 8–2A

"A suntrap outside and buzzy atmosphere" help make this fashionable Soho House haunt – prominently situated near Turnham Green Terrace – Chiswick's premier brunch spot. Fans say the "food's always good" too, but critics are less convinced ("imagine your worst greasy spoon breakfast, then multiply the bill by five…") / W4 1PR; highroadbrasserie.co.uk; @HRBrasserie; 11 pm, Fri & Sat midnight, Sun 10 pm; booking max 8 may apply.

HIGH TIMBER EC4 £67 3 3 3

8 HIGH TIMBER STREET 020 7248 1777 10–3B

"Simple, well-prepared steaks" and "an excellent wine list (before you even get to

visiting the cellar itself)" are the main treats in store at this South African-owned wine bar. Its "out-of-the-way but still central setting" by the Wobbly Bridge and directly opposite Tate Modern really comes into its own "when you can sit outside in the summer" (otherwise the nearby Thames merely sets the scene as you arrive and depart). / EC4V 3PA; www.hightimber.com; @HTimber; 10 pm; closed Sat & Sun.

HISPANIA EC3 £68 3 3 3

72-74 LOMBARD STREET 020 7621 0338 10–2C

"In the City but without off-the-chart prices" – this spacious fixture occupies a comfortable, somewhat rustically themed two-floor site, by the Bank of England, and serves "good quality Spanish food". "Good for a business meal", but also relatively "fun". / EC3V 9AY; www.hispanialondon.com; @hispanialondon; 10pm, Mon 9.30 pm; closed Sat & Sun.

HIX W1 £77 1 2 2

66-70 BREWER STREET 020 7292 3518 4–3C

"Needing to recover its imagination": Mark Hix needs somehow to reboot his Soho HQ. On the plus side, it's potentially a "lovely" venue – a vaguely Manhattan-esque room, with an attractive cellar cocktail bar – and service is typically "welcoming" (if not always on-the-ball). On the downside, its fish-heavy menu remains far too expensive, and "there seems to be little thought about how to produce something interesting with the ingredients at hand". / W1F 9UP; www.hixrestaurants.co.uk/restaurant/hix-soho; @HixRestaurants; 11.30 pm, Sun 10.30 pm.

HIX OYSTER & CHOP HOUSE EC1 £66 2 2 2

36-37 GREENHILL RENTS, COWCROSS ST 020 7017 1930 10–1A

The first of Mark Hix's London ventures – this white-tiles-and-marble chophouse near Smithfield has often somewhat divided reporters. Fans see it as "the go-to place for modern British seasonal classics, from steaks to the fish of the day"; sceptics judge it "very noisy and busy, with average food, and trading on its reputation". / EC1M 6BN; www.hixrestaurants.co.uk/restaurant/hix-oyster-chop-house; @hixchophouse; 11 pm, Sun 9 pm; closed Sat L; No trainers.

HOLBORN DINING ROOM WC1 £78 3 2 3

252 HIGH HOLBORN 020 3747 8633 2–1D

"Savoury pastry heaven" – "outstanding pies, steak puddings and beef Wellington" are the orders of the day at this "fabulous" dining room on the edge of the City, where Chef Calum Franklin oversees a "great menu" also featuring British charcuterie and grills. The setting is "a little hotel-like" but "tables are nicely spaced" helping to make it a big hit with business types. Top Tip – "pick up a takeaway

pie from the Pie Room"; and there's "an excellent breakfast, to boot". / WC1V 7EN; www.holborndiningroom.com; @HolbornDining.

HOLLY BUSH NW3 £50 2 2 3

22 HOLLY MOUNT 020 7435 2892 9–1A

This "quaint relic from the 18th century" is a Grade II listed tavern on an attractive Georgian side-street in Hampstead. It serves "a fairly restricted menu" of "unmodernised pub food", which can fit the bill for a Sunday roast or simple meal, but critics feel the cooking "really ought to be better". / NW3 6SG; www.hollybushhampstead.co.uk; @thehollybushpub; 10 pm, Sun 9 pm.

HOME SW15 SW15 £61 3 3 2

146 UPPER RICHMOND ROAD 020 8780 0592 11–2B

This yearling all-day brasserie near East Putney tube "has succeeded where several other restaurants have failed", by following a formula of "good food and value for money". "It knocks the socks off the Bill's or Brew and their wannabes". / SW15 2SW; www.homesw15.com; @homesw15.

HOMESLICE £38 4 3 3

50 JAMES STREET, W1 020 3034 0621 3–1A
52 WELLS ST, W1 020 3151 7488 2–1B
13 NEAL'S YD, WC2 020 7836 4604 5–2C
2 TELEVISION CENTRE, 101 WOOD LANE WHITE CITY, W12 020 3034 0381 1–2B
374-378 OLD ST, EC1 020 3151 1121 13–1B
69-71 QUEEN STREET, EC4 020 3034 0381 10–3C

"Messy… but so tasty!" – the "best pizzas ever" win nothing but rave reviews for these "easygoing and fun" outlets (backed by the late Terry Wogan's sons, Mark and Alan), which were out-scored only by the very narrowest margins by Pizza Pilgrims this year as London's best. "If you like funky topping combos, this is the place for you". NB: Ry Jessup, the Kiwi who originally founded the chain, moved on from the business after the survey closed in summer 2019, but we have maintained the rating. / www.homeslicepizza.co.uk; @homesliceLDN; 11 pm, Sun 10 pm (ex WC2H 10.30 pm); no booking.

The Harcourt W1

HONEST BURGERS £29 3|3|3

"A chain that defies the image of chains!" – "by far the tastiest of the 'gourmet' burger groups has yet to succumb to the typical slip-in-quality as it grows", and is nowadays the most-mentioned burger multiple in the survey. It has "taken the mantle from Byron" in recent years, with both a "better, less formulaic approach" and also a "slower and steadier opening programme": a combination that's "maintained the basic fundamentals of a decent, un-mucked-up formula". "Half restaurant/ half fast food in style, there are no starters and only ices for dessert, so you are in and out inside an hour. But, if you are looking for a good quality quick bite, this is the place for you". "It knocks out great-value, no-nonsense burgers, still serves them medium rare in flagrant defiance of food hygiene fascism, does the best veggie burger around (more of a fritter), and now does the famous 'bleeding' vegan burger, oozing beetroot juice for those requiring the illusion of meat with their veg". Other winning features include "addictive rosemary chips", "interesting specials (which vary by branch)" and "great beers on draught" from local breweries. / www.honestburgers.co.uk; @honestburgers; 10 pm-11 pm; SW9 closed Mon D; EC3 closed Sat & Sun; no bookings.

HONEY & CO W1 £60 5|3|3

25A WARREN ST 020 7388 6175 2–1B

"No duds on the fabulous menu" at Sarit Packer and Itamar Sruolovich's "small-but-perfectly-formed" café, near Warren Street tube, where plate-lickingly-yummy Middle Eastern dishes (and you MUST leave space for a cake afterwards) are "made with love and served with a smile". It's "always very busy", though, and you need to shoehorn yourself into some of the seats. / W1T 5JZ; www.honeyandco.co.uk; @Honeyandco; 10.30 pm; closed Sun; No Amex.

HONEY & SMOKE W1 £59 4|3|2

216 GREAT PORTLAND STREET 020 7388 6175 2–1B

"Plentiful and nourishing Israeli dishes" (with "a delicious mix of spices and textures") win waves of praise for Honey & Co's younger, larger grill-house spin-off, south of Great Portland Street tube. It's a "busy and lively" ("frantic" and "very noisy") venue, popular with large parties, but whose "1970s-style plastic moulded chairs" can seem "strangely utilitarian" (unless you are someone who appreciates "the authenticity of Middle Eastern café culture"). / W1W 5QW; www.honeyandco.co.uk/smoke; @Honeyandco; 11.30 pm; closed Mon & Sun.

HOOD SW2 £53 4|3|3

67 STREATHAM HILL 020 3601 3320 11–2D

"If Streatham Hill can still be called up-and-coming, this local is leading the pack"; a "great casual place with very good food, and a nice range of craft beers, all at a reasonable price". / SW2 4TX; www.hoodrestaurants.com; @HoodStreatham; 11 pm.

HOPPERS £48 4|3|3

49 FRITH ST, W1 NO TEL 5–2A
77 WIGMORE STREET, W1 020 3319 8110 3–1A

"Authentic Sri Lankan food (just like my friend's mum used to make)" has won fame for JKS Restaurants's "buzzy" ("not much elbow room at busy times") and "fun", street-food cafés, which – although not quite as "novel" as when they first opened – are still "simply sensational" for most reporters. "Obviously you must have a hopper" (a rice pancake), and also "the curries are delicious, especially the seafood one", as are the "really tasty dosas". And "it's unbelievable that you can have a table filled up with exciting food at less than £30 a head, including drinks!". "While the original location (Soho) is better, it's nice that you can book at St Christopher's Place". / www.hopperslondon.com; @HoppersLondon.

HOT STUFF SW8 £28 3|4|2

19-23 WILCOX RD 020 7720 1480 11–1D

In the heart of Vauxhall, Raj Dawood's little Indian canteen pre-dates the street food revolution (est 1988), and has a loyal following who award high ratings to its down-to-earth style and zesty scoff. / SW8 2XA; www.welovehotstuff.com; 10 pm; closed Mon; No Amex; No bookings.

HOUSE RESTAURANT, NATIONAL THEATRE SE1 £56 2|3|2

NATIONAL THEATRE, SOUTH BANK 020 7452 3600 2–3D

The smartest of the National Theatre's in-house dining rooms has had its high in past years, but is currently "only worth it if you're going to the theatre". The standard of cooking can vary sharply between visits: at best "really excellent and imaginative" but sometimes merely "fine" or "a bit of a production line process". / SE1 9PX; house.nationaltheatre.org.uk; @NT_House; 11 pm; D only (L served on matinee days), closed Sun.

HUBBARD & BELL, HOXTON HOTEL WC1 £63 3|3|3

199-206 HIGH HOLBORN 020 7661 3030 2–1D

Actually in Holborn not Hoxton – "an all-pleasing place, with a cool bar area" that's part of the Soho House group, tipped for its "excellent breakfasts" and "simple, classic burgers". / WC1V 7BD; www.hubbardandbell.com; @HubbardandBell; midnight, Sun 11 pm.

HUMBLE GRAPE £54 3|4|3

11-13 THEBERTON STREET, N1
020 3887 9287 9–3D
2 BATTERSEA RISE, SW11 020 3620 2202 11–2C
18-20 MACKENZIE WALK, E14 12–1C
8 DEVONSHIRE ROW, EC2 10–2D
1 SAINT BRIDE'S PASSAGE, EC4
020 7583 0688 10–2A

"An amazing choice of wines" is served by "lovely staff, who are passionate and knowledgeable about the list" at these "proper wine bars", whose liquid offering is "complemented by a very good food menu" of "well-made" dishes (small plates, plus cheese and charcuterie). The Battersea original is still the branch attracting most feedback, although the chain is spreading eastwards, and its operation in the crypt of St Bride's Church and newer Liverpool Street branch are "very competent": next stop is an opening in Canary Wharf. / www.humblegrape.co.uk; @humblegrape.

HUNAN SW1 £95 4|2|1

51 PIMLICO RD 020 7730 5712 6–2D

"Be adventurous! There's no menu but Mr Peng selects a fantastic array of dishes for you" at this Pimlico veteran (founded in 1982), which is still often acclaimed as "the best Chinese in London, bar none". "It looks ordinary from the outside (and is nothing special on the crowded inside either!)", but still diners "love the place" and the "entertaining" manner in which Mr P "treats you to a slew of scrumptious Chinese flavours… until you say you have had enough". "The wine choices are excellent too". All that said though, ratings here took a dip this year, dragged down by a small-but-vocal minority who feel the cooking risks losing some of its edge: "still love it, but the selection can be a little samey, albeit very nicely done". / SW1W 8NE; www.hunanlondon.com; 11 pm; closed Sun.

HUSH W1 £91 2|2|3

8 LANCASHIRE CT 020 7659 1500 3–2B

"Elegant without stuffiness", this smooth, "buzzy" bar/brasserie "in a courtyard down a discrete lane" off Bond Street makes "a very nice venue for a business lunch in busy Mayfair". Established 20 years ago (by founders including Geoffrey Moore, Roger's son, and Evgeny Lebedev, owner of the Evening Standard), it clearly knows its market and "offers something for most occasions". / W1S 1EY; www.hush.co.uk; 11 pm; closed Sun; booking max 12 may apply.

HUTONG, THE SHARD SE1 £106 2|2|5

31 ST THOMAS ST 020 3011 1257 10–4C

"Fabulous view" – "fittingly sky-high prices": that's the familiar trade off on the 33rd floor of the Shard, which nobody would deny is "a truly exceptional location", but where other aspects of the experience are sharply divisive. There are those who feel "this is a real luxury treat" and who praise its "high-end Chinese dishes", but a worrying proportion of reports feel the trip is "not really worth the money spent", and dismiss "pretentious" cooking, "but with an extra-big price tag". / SE1 9RY; www.hutong.co.uk; @HutongShard; 10 pm; No shorts.

IBÉRICA £59 323

ZIG ZAG BUILDING, 70 VICTORIA ST, SW1
020 7636 8650   2–4B
195 GREAT PORTLAND ST, W1
020 7636 8650   2–1B
12 CABOT SQ, E14 020 7636 8650 12–1C
89 TURNMILL ST, EC1 020 7636 8650 10–1A

From its first branch, on Great Portland Street, which opened in 2007, these "buzzy", "authentic" and relatively stylish Spanish tapas-haunts have grown into a national chain, boosted by their "consistent standards, fair quality and sensible prices" (although "service is a bit uneven"). / 11 pm, SW1 Sun 10.30 pm, E14 Sun 4pm; W1 closed Sun D.

ICCO PIZZA £18 421

46 GOODGE ST, W1 020 7580 9688   2–1C
21A CAMDEN HIGH STREET, NW1
020 7380 0020   9–3B

There are "no frills at all" at this 20-year veteran pizza-joint in Goodge Street, with a branch in Camden Town – "but the fact that you can sit down with a tasty thin-crust pizza in central London for these prices (£3.95 for a Marinara) is well worth the lack of ambience". / www.icco.co.uk; @ICCO_pizza.

ICHI BUNS W1 £48 223

24 WARDOUR STREET   5–3A

Clubby, three-floor 'Japanese Super Diner' in Chinatown that opened in 2018, with regular DJs on the dim-lit, basement level, and boatloads of retro-Japanese pop-memorabilia throughout. Alongside cocktails it provides burgers, udon and sushi – recommended strongly by some reporters, but "neither here nor there" to others. / W1D 6QJ; www.ichibuns.com; @ichibuns.

IDA W10 £50 343

222A KILBURN LANE   020 8969 9853   1–2B

"What a find!" – In a fairly obscure part of town, near the Queen's Park Estate, "a really cosy, neighbourhood Italian, serving a top selection of cheap 'n' cheerful dishes, but also more pricey ones, all freshly made and of great quality" (in particular the hand-rolled pasta). Service from husband-and-wife team Simonetta and Avi "is very professional but lively, and there's a real sense of community at play (e.g. the staff were handing out little pieces of paper with a guest's name on it, asking us to sing along for his birthday!)" / W10 4AT; www.idarestaurant.co.uk; @IdaRestaurant; 11 pm; closed Sat L & Sun; No Amex.

IKOYI SW1 £106 422

1 ST JAMES'S MARKET   020 3583 4660
4–4D

"Dazzling reinvention of African classic dishes", featuring "really unique combinations and flavours", has made this much-discussed two-year-old – from Chinese-Canadian chef Jeremy Chan and Nigerian co-founder Iré Hassan-Odukele – one of the most original of recent London openings. It's in the St James's Market development near Piccadilly Circus: an area, in contrast, with conformity to the norm", where "the vibes are a bit sterile". In the evening, the main option is a seven-course tasting menu for £75, but an extended version for £100 is also available. / SW1Y 4AH; www.ikoyilondon.com.

IL GUSCIO N5 £52 343

231 BLACKSTOCK ROAD   020 7354 1400
9–1D

This "great little Sardinian restaurant" in Highbury serves up "excellent food (large amounts of it), in a very convivial atmosphere". It's "the perfect local for when we can't face cooking, or want a midweek treat, or are meeting friends, or want a quick pre-dinner drink... in fact, it's good on pretty much any occasion". Kids are welcome, and will love the "amazing pizzas". / N5 2LL; www.ilgusciohighbury.co.uk; 10.30 pm, Fri & Sat 11 pm.

IMPERIAL TREASURE SW1 £104 222

9-10 WATERLOO PLACE   020 3011 1328
4–4D

"Everything about this place is wow!… including the breathtaking bill!" – This extremely swanky, late-2018 newcomer occupies a "beautiful old banking hall, with butter-soft leather banquettes, and tasteful furniture" just off Pall Mall. It's the first London branch of a Singaporean chain with branches throughout mainland China and Hong Kong as well as elsewhere in Asia. "Don't forget to pre-order your £100 Peking duck with pancakes!", which has become something of a cause célèbre in (generally unfavourable) newspaper reviews of its opening, although whether the result is "magnificent", or "a tasteless rip off" at "obscene prices" is likewise debated by Harden's reporters. Ultimately ratings here are dragged down by the vocal minority of critics, but supporters say "you wouldn't complain about the prices if it were French". / SW1Y 4BE; www.imperialtreasure.com.

INDIA CLUB, STRAND CONTINENTAL HOTEL WC2 £29 222

143 STRAND   020 7836 4880   2–2D

"Step back in time with shades of the 1950s" – "you could imagine Nehru walking through the door" – at this "atmospheric all-Indian" curry house on the Strand, close to the Indian High Commission, that was recently saved from redevelopment. "The food is decent value at a remarkably low price" – although it's "not really the point". "After lunch in the rather bleak dining room, coffee in the cocktail bar seems positively luxurious". Top Tip – BYO from the hotel bar. / WC2R 1JA; www.theindiaclub.co.uk; @hostelstrandcon; 10.50 pm; booking max 6 may apply.

INDIAN ACCENT W1 £82 542

16 ALBEMARLE STREET   020 7629 9802
3–3C

"From the amuse bouche and blue cheese naan onwards, we were blown away!" – this "impeccable" Mayfair spin-off from a famous New Delhi venture is in contention as "the best-of-the-best of London's new wave of fine dining Indians": "maintaining classic, traditional flavours" but with "an impressive balance of refinement and power" to create "deliciously tantalising" dishes. Service is "patient" and "warmly welcoming", while the interior – though certainly "smart" and "tastefully understated" – can also seem "very stereotypically Mayfair", or "too businessy". / W1S 4HW; indianaccent.com/london; @Indian_Accent.

INDIAN MOMENT SW11 £41 322

44 BATTERSEA RISE   020 7223 6575 /
020 7223 1818 11–2C

In Clapham's busy 'Nappy Valley', this "great local Indian" earns consistent ratings for its "well-cooked food" with subtle spicing. Its modern dining room is far from spacious and can descend into "bedlam in the evenings, when it's full of screamers… not all of them young!". / SW11 1EE; www.indianmoment.co.uk; @indianmoment; 11.30 pm, Fri & Sat midnight.

INDIAN OCEAN SW17 £31 343

214 TRINITY RD   020 8672 7740 11–2C

This "old-school Indian" keeps its long-term Wandsworth Common regulars "very happy" with a "good range of dishes" – not all of them the usual suspects. Everything is "done perfectly, and it's not too expensive". / SW17 7HP; www.indianoceanrestaurant.com; 11.30 pm, Sat 11.45 pm, Sun 11 pm.

INDIAN RASOI N2 £37 322

7 DENMARK TERRACE   020 8883 9093
1–1B

"High-quality, very tasty and authentic dishes" inspired by the Mughal-era cuisine of northern India make this "cramped" Muswell Hill curry house "way better than most". / N2 9HG; www.indian-rasoi.co.uk; 10.30 pm; No Amex.

INDIAN ZING W6 £57 432

236 KING ST   020 8748 5959   8–2B

The "amazing", "top-quality cuisine" at Manoj Vasaikar's consistently high-rated Ravenscourt Park venue "proves that you don't need to go into central London to get really excellent, authentic Indian food". A long-time favourite – the late Michael Winner was a fan – it serves "Michelin star quality cuisine without the wannabe nonsense" in a tightly packed space. / W6 0RS; www.indian-zing.co.uk; @IndianZing; 11 pm, Sun 10 pm.

INKO NITO W1 £51 3|3|4

55 BROADWICK STREET 4–2B

LA's Art District housed the first branch of this Roka-lite concept (same founder), and this Soho yearling, with its "manifestly cool decor" (from a California design agency) delivers well all-round (even if it's maybe "a little expensive"), especially if you are in the mood for a meal combining "a fun bar ambience" with "simple yet exciting" Korean/Japanese dishes. / W1F 9QS; www.inkonitorestaurant.com/london-soho.

IPPUDO £47 3|3|3

3 CENTRAL SAINT GILES PIAZZA, WC2 020 7240 4469 5–1B
31A VILLIERS STREET, WC2 5–4D
1 CROSSRAIL PL, E14 020 3326 9485 12–1C

"Top ramen with great broth and good combinations", win fans for this genuinely Japanese chain (originating in Fukuoka), which has branches in Holborn, Embankment and Canary Wharf. Ratings, though, fall short of the top heights at the hands of those who feel its food is "not bad, but not memorable". A fourth branch is to open in Fitzrovia in autumn 2019. / www.ippudo.co.uk; @IppudoLondon.

ISHTAR W1 £54 3|3|2

10-12 CRAWFORD ST 020 7224 2446 2–1A

"A finesse not often found in Turkish restaurants" helps set this "comfortable" Marylebone establishment apart: the food is "tasty", with particularly good value set menus, and service "pleasant and friendly". / W1U 6AZ; www.ishtarrestaurant.com; 11.30 pm, Sun 10.30 pm.

ISLA WC1

THE STANDARD HOTEL, 10 ARGYLE STREET 9–3C

This hip American hotel opened in summer 2019 with several restaurants, including this garden restaurant overseen by Adam Rawson which offers a 'seasonal menu, featuring light proteins and a predominantly natural wine list'. He will also be looking after ground-floor, street-facing 'neighbourhood' bar, Double Standard (see also, and rooftop restaurant Decimo too). / WC1H 8EG; www.standardhotels.com/london/features/standard_london_isla.

ITALO SW8 £46 4|3|4

13 BONNINGTON SQUARE 020 7450 3773 11–1D

"Grab a seat outside either at the counter shelf or at one of the tables" of this ten-year-old deli "in an off-the-beaten track, verdant garden square in Vauxhall" for an authentic lunchtime treat from a short Italian menu. In colder weather you eat inside at a few closely-packed tables surrounded by shelves of produce. / SW8 1TE; italodeli.co.uk.

THE IVY WC2 £83 2|2|3

1-5 WEST ST 020 7836 4751 5–3B

"An old favourite, but the diffusion-brand has tarnished its name" – it feels like this Theatreland legend is steadily being sacrificed for the greater good of its growing stable of spin-offs. Many supporters do still feel its "comforting" menu delivers "reliable, traditional British food" in a "classy and buzzy" setting and that the trip is "still worth it (especially if you can get into the adjoining Ivy Club)". But scores here are heading inexorably south across the board, supporting the many former regulars who feel the place "misplaced its soul, serving food that's decidedly average at best" and "lost its caché" to the extent it's "a shadow of its former self". / WC2H 9NQ; www.the-ivy.co.uk; @TheIvyWestSt; 11.30pm, Thu-Sat midnight, Sun 10.30 pm; No shorts; booking max 6 may apply.

THE IVY CAFÉ £56 1|1|3

96 MARYLEBONE LN, W1 020 3301 0400 2–1A
120 ST JOHN'S WOOD HIGH ST, NW8 020 3096 9444 9–3A
75 HIGH ST, SW19 020 3096 9333 11–2B
9 HILL STREET, TW9 020 3146 7733 1–4A

"Trading on The Ivy's name, but nothing like the real thing": outlets of Richard Caring's sub-sub-brand are "squarely bistro in nature" and proving less successful than their brasserie namesakes in capturing diners' affections. True, some do tout them as a "dependable if unexciting" choice, but – lacking the pizzazz which carries the experience at their grander cousins – the focus falls more on the "bland, by-numbers" food and service that's "neither here nor there". Top Tip – "Prefer breakfast to the expensive lunch and dinner options". / 11 pm, Fri & Sat 11.30 pm, Sun 10.30 pm; SW19 11 pm, Sun 10.30 pm; midnight.

THE IVY GRILLS & BRASSERIES £60 2|2|4

26-28 BROADWICK ST, W1 020 3301 1166 4–1C
1 HENRIETTA ST, WC2 020 3301 0200 5–3D
197 KING'S RD, SW3 020 3301 0300 6–3C
96 KENSINGTON HIGH ST, W8 020 3301 0500 6–1A
ONE TOWER BRIDGE, 1 TOWER BRIDGE, SE1 020 3146 7722 10–4D
DASHWOOD HOUSE, 69 OLD BROAD ST,, EC2 020 3146 7744 10–2D

"Maybe the brand is a bit stretched", but Richard Caring's bold expansion is paying off by-and-large, certainly in commercial terms, and – though most branches' average food-rating is run-of-the-mill – by the standards of large chains, the group delivers a consistent-enough formula, whereby folks accept predictable nursery fodder in return for a dependable dose of 'affordable glamour'. The "beautiful and festive" Ivy Chelsea Garden (SW3) is the best known in the stable and it's particularly "wonderful if you manage to get a table in their fabulous garden". The "big and buzzy" Ivy Kensington Brasserie (W8) is less highly rated, but nevertheless fills a vital niche in the local market for a comfortable, atmospheric and versatile rendezvous ("its bar is also a fun place for a drink"). The City branches (The Ivy Tower Bridge, The Ivy City Garden EC2) and Canary Wharf outlet (The Ivy in the Park, E14) are the highest rated all-round (perhaps reflecting the ongoing lack of convivial spaces out east). "Awesome views" at Tower Bridge are distinct client-pleasers. Other branches taking above-average flak include The Ivy Soho Brasserie, W1 ("busy mayhem" with "slow and disorganised service") and The Ivy Market Grill, WC2 ("nothing special, rather overpriced, and very busy"). See also Granary Square Brasserie. / ivycollection.com.

Hide W1

JACOB THE ANGEL
WC2 £25 **3 3 3**

16A NEAL'S YARD   NO TEL   5–2C

"Yummy bakes and great caffeine" help make this tiny coffee house (just 10 covers) in Seven Dials – from the owners of The Palomar – particularly "good for a solo breakfast". / WC2H 9DP; www.jacobtheangel.co.uk; No bookings.

JAFFNA HOUSE
SW17 £26 **3 2 2**

90 TOOTING HIGH ST   020 8672 7786 11–2C

"Incredible thalis at awesome prices", inspire a dedicated band of devotees to the authentic Sri Lankan and South Indian specialities served up in this "homely dining room": "maybe not the best, but certainly the best-value lunch in Tooting". / SW17 0RN; Www.jaffnahouse.uk; 11.30 pm.

JAMAVAR W1 £84 **3 3 3**

8 MOUNT STREET   020 7499 1800   3–3B

"Boldly flavoured" nouvelle Indian cuisine served in a "dark and clubby", colonial-theme setting puts Leela Palace's Mayfair two-year-old in London's premier league, if not perhaps quite at the top of the table: "not as memorable as some top names, but definitely a favourite". But while it's "a good attempt at taking Indian cuisine to the next level", it lacks the stunning verve fans recall from when it first opened: "a fun evening out, but it will need to do better again to match the best of the best". / W1K 3NF; www.jamavarrestaurants.com; @JamavarLondon.

JASHAN N8 £37 **4 4 2**

19 TURNPIKE LN   020 8340 9880   1–1C

This "old-school curry house in far Turnpike Lane" serves up "wonderful dishes" from a "menu very different from the norm in suburban Indian restaurants" (although the atmosphere is "dreary"). Fans say it's "really fabulous – we go almost every week!". / N8 0EP; www.jashan.co.uk; @indian_jashan; 10.15 pm, Fri & Sat 10.30 pm; D only; No Amex; May need 6+ to book.

JEAN-GEORGES AT THE
CONNAUGHT W1 £114 **2 3 3**

THE CONNAUGHT, CARLOS PLACE
020 7107 8861   3–3B

It's as a site for an exceptional afternoon tea – with fusion-flavoured finger sarnies adding some brio to the traditional experience – or a "chic brunch" that this posh brasserie, in a conservatory addition to Mayfair's most upper-crust of hotels, excites enthusiasm. When it comes to star NYC-chef, Jean Georges Vongerichten's "unusual" main menu – from pizza to caviar via truffle cheeseburger (and minus the SE Asian notes for which the chef is most famous) – it can seem like a "stunning and relaxing" experience… or merely "overpriced", "tired and lacking flavour". / W1K 2AL; www.the-connaught.co.uk/mayfair-restaurants/jean-georges; @TheConnaught; 11 pm.

JIDORI £23 **4 3 2**

15 CATHERINE STREET, WC2   5–3D
89 KINGSLAND HIGH ST, E8   020 7686 5634
14–1A

"Yakitori heaven" ("everything is so yummy") is to be found at this minimalist duo, specialising in Japanese skewers, which opened in Covent Garden in 2018 after a successful first venture in Dalston. The trade-off is "very simple Muji/utilitarian" decor "but who cares when the food's this nice". (Versatile Aussie chef Brett Redman is behind it, in partnership with Natalie Lee-Joe). It also has a karaoke room. / www.jidori.co.uk; @JidoriUK.

JIKONI W1 £75 **3 3 4**

21 BLANDFORD STREET   020 70341988
2–1A

A "delicious and interesting fusion of the familiar and unfamiliar" – and of chef Ravinder Bhogal's mixed Indian, East African, Middle Eastern and British heritage – this Marylebone two-year-old is "always delightful". "A quaint layout with comfy print cushions makes it feel smaller than it is", while "staff are friendly if perhaps not always expert". / W1U 3DJ; www.jikonilondon.com; @JikoniLondon.

JIN KICHI NW3 £48 **5 4 3**

73 HEATH ST   020 7794 6158   9–1A

"Outstanding" Japanese cooking ("we dream about it!") has made this stalwart "izakaya-style" venue one of Hampstead's best foodie destinations for decades; and it attracts fans from across north London and beyond. "And it's not all about sushi" – yakitori ("grilled delicacies) are also a speciality here, and "the hotpots are brilliant too". "Service is lovely", and the only drawback is its diminutive size – "so get a reservation if you can". Top Tip – "sit by the grill upstairs for the treat of watching the chef at work". / NW3 6UG; www.jinkichi.com; 11 pm, Sun 10 pm; closed Mon L.

JINJUU W1 £62 **4 4 3**

16 KINGLY ST   020 8181 8887   4–2B

This "modern Korean" basement off Carnaby Street does a great line in "delicious but different food" served in "cool surroundings": it "delivers on the staples – fried chicken, dumplings, etc – while more unusual modern interpretations also hit the target", such as "terrific tofu sliders". In June 2019, Korean-American TV chef Judy Joo severed her ties with the venture, but we've maintained the rating for the time being. / W1B 5PS; www.jinjuu.com; @JinjuuSoho; 11.30 pm, Thu-Sat 1 am, Sun 9.30 pm.

JOE ALLEN WC2 £51 **2 2 3**

2 BURLEIGH ST   020 7836 0651   5–3D

"Seemingly relocated brick-by-brick, table-by-table" – this "casual and fun" haunt in Covent Garden's (a 1970s spin-off from NYC's famous Theatre District staple) moved a couple of years ago, leaving its original basement home for this new two-level location just a minute's walk away. It's a surprisingly faithful reproduction, and regulars of decades standing feel "it still works and seems unchanged"; and, as a place to refuel before or after a show, it still has a large fanclub, despite a "perennially ordinary" level of cooking…sadly also preserved in the move. Top Menu Tip – "the secret's been out about the off-menu burger for many, many years now", and it's the best bet. / WC2E 7PX; www.joeallen.co.uk; @JoeAllenWC2; 11.30 pm, Fri & Sat 12.30 am, Sun 10 pm.

JOE PUBLIC SW4 £18 **4 3 2**

4 THE PAVEMENT   020 7622 4676 11–2D

"Fab pizzas" – "brilliant option of just buying a slice: America meets Clapham!" – have made this tiny outfit in a former public convenience beside Clapham Common a big favourite among locals wanting an ultra-quick bite. "Just love this place – you can eat alone and not feel lonely". / SW4 7AA; www.joepublicpizza.com; @JoepublicSW4; midnight, Sun 11pm; No bookings.

JOLENE N16 £61 **3 2 3**

20 NEWINGTON GREEN   0203 887 2309
1–1C

"This too-kool-for-school hangout in Newington Green" – a yearling bakery/café/restaurant from Primeur and Westerns Laundry founders Jeremie Cometto-Lingenheim and David Gingell – is "full to the rafters with Stokie's coolest hipsters with good reason – the food is spot-on". The vibe, all 'unaltered grains milled onsite', gets up one or two reporters' noses though, who feel "its mincing pomposity makes it the Jacob Rees-Mogg of the Hackney restaurant scene!" / N16 9PU; www.jolenen16.com.

JOLLIBEE SW5 £13 **1 2 1**

180-182 EARLS COURT ROAD
020 7244 7444   6–2A

Over 1,000 people queued for its opening, but if you're not Filipino, chances are you won't 'get' this Earl's Court fast-food diner, which has introduced the capital to the delights of authentic 'chickenjoy', yumburger and Jolly Spaghetti (with sweet tomato and hot dog sauce) – "really not special!" / SW5 9QG; www.jollibee.com.ph/international; @Jollibee.

JONES & SONS
N16 £52 **3 4 3**

STAMFORD WORKS, 3 GILLETT STREET
020 7241 1211 14–1A

"You can't go far wrong", according to the more-than-local fanclub of this open-plan venture, hiply located near Dalston Station; and serving "excellent, modern British food from a frequently changing menu" that's "good value". Top Tip – bottomless brunch. / N16 8JH; www.jonesandsonsdalston.com; @JonesSons; 10 pm, Fri & Sat 11 pm, Sun 7 pm; booking max 7 may apply.

THE JONES FAMILY KITCHEN SW1 £47 4️⃣3️⃣3️⃣

7-8 ECCLESTON YARD   020 7739 1740   2–4B

"The best beef in the area (Belgravia/ Pimlico)... nuff said" – this "shiny", year-old sibling to Shoreditch's Jones Family Project is part of the "beautiful" Eccleston Yards courtyard development: "a fantastic addition to SW1" that doesn't feel at all like somewhere around the corner from Victoria Coach Station. As well as steak, it features a fairly broad selection of modern British brasserie fare (including plenty of fish), much of it from the Josper charcoal oven; plus a decent list of cocktails and wine. Top Tip – for coeliacs there's a dedicated gluten-free menu. / SW1W 9AZ; www.jonesfamilyproject.co.uk; @JonesShoreditch .

THE JONES FAMILY PROJECT EC2 £58 3️⃣3️⃣4️⃣

78 GREAT EASTERN STREET   020 7739 1740 13–1B

"Upstairs is 1970s, retro-cocktail fun! – the basement is an atmospheric restaurant", at this Shoreditch venue. "Outstanding, juicy steak perfectly cooked (with very good side dishes – the best being the truffled mac 'n' cheese)" is the headline feature in culinary terms, but there's a dish to suit most tastes on the wide-ranging brasserie-style menu. / EC2A 3JL; www.jonesfamilyproject.co.uk; @JonesShoreditch; 10.30 pm, Sun 6 pm.

JOSÉ SE1 £53 5️⃣4️⃣5️⃣

104 BERMONDSEY ST   020 7403 4902   10–4D

"There's no finer tapas outside Spain" than at José Pizarro's "outstanding, if authentically tiny" Bermondsey bar: "very buzzy and busy, as a tapas bar should be" providing "absolute classic dishes, prepared with attention to detail and with perfect produce". "It looks chaotic when you turn up and you have to queue outside with your wine. However the system they have works because you're soon seated and ready to enjoy some of London's best tapas"; "highly recommended". / SE1 3UB; www.josepizarro.com; @Jose_Pizarro; 10.15 pm, Sun 5.15 pm; closed Sun D; no booking.

JOSÉ PIZARRO EC2 £62 4️⃣3️⃣2️⃣

BROADGATE CIRCLE   020 7256 5333 13–2B

The vibrancy of the star Spanish chef's tapas has always seemed slightly at odds with the glossy-but-corporate location of this outlet, in the midst of the City's Broadgate Circle. Even those who don't vibe with the place, though, acclaim its "friendly" style, and the cooking is rated from very good to exceptional. / EC2M 2QS; www.josepizarro.com/jose-pizarro-broadgate; @JP_Broadgate; 10.45 pm, Sat 9.45 pm; closed Sun.

JOY KING LAU WC2 £43 3️⃣3️⃣2️⃣

3 LEICESTER ST   020 7437 1132   5–3A

"In a crowded Chinatown field", this three-story Cantonese institution just off Leicester Square "is a dependable crowd-pleaser" with a "good price-to-quality ratio": "the queues outside speak for its popularity". Highlights from the "reliable menu" include "fab dim sum every time", "yummy char sui" and "legendary soft shell crab", all delivered by staff who "although rushed off their feet are generally smiley and friendly". Top Tip – "the ground floor is a better experience than the higher floors". / WC2H 7BL; www.joykinglau; 11.30 pm, Sun 10.30 pm.

JUGEMU W1 £43 5️⃣2️⃣3️⃣

3 WINNETT ST   020 7734 0518   4–2D

"Under the direction of a single, passionate and precise chef" (Yuya Kikuchi), this brilliantly "authentic" little (about 20 seats) izakaya in Soho produces some marvels, with dazzling sushi being the top pick on the menu. Don't go if you're in a hurry. / W1D 6JY; jugemu-uk. crayonsite.com; @jugemu_uk.

THE JUGGED HARE EC1 £60 3️⃣2️⃣2️⃣

49 CHISWELL STREET   020 7614 0134   13–2A

This game-themed gastropub next to the Barbican has a solid following for its "excellent game and seriously good local produce" from an "interesting and well-executed menu". Clearly, it's best to come in game season (August-February), but at other times the kitchen gets by on rare-breed beef, goat and seafood options, and an "amazing Sunday roast – pricey but worth it". Arguably, the interior "doesn't lift the spirits, but there's a sheer lack of decent alternatives around the Barbican". / EC1Y 4SA; www.thejuggedhare.com; @thejuggedhare; 11 pm, Thu-Sat midnight, Sun 10.30 pm.

JULIE'S W11 £56

135 PORTLAND RD   020 7229 8331   7–2A

At last! Since 2015 this Holland Park icon of louche 1970s living – an intriguing subterranean labyrinth of differently-styled chambers – has promised that it will reopen, and it finally looks set to happen in September 2019, in time for its 50th year in business. Its updated looks are unknown as yet, but they have recruited a good chef in the form of Shay Cooper, who held a Michelin star at his previous gig, The Goring. / W11 4LW; www.juliesrestaurant.com; @JuliesW11; 11 pm.

K10 £33 3️⃣2️⃣2️⃣

3 APPOLD ST, EC2 020 7539 9209 13–2B
MINSTER CT, MINCING LN, EC3
020 3019 2510 10–3D
(TAKEAWAY ONLY) 15 QUEEN STREET, EC4 10–2C
(TAKEAWAY ONLY) 78 FETTER LANE, EC4 10–2A

"Good value" sushi, sashimi and other Japanese dishes trundle past your seat at these two 'kaiten' (conveyor-belt) operations in the City, tempting you to help yourself. It makes a fun, fast and efficient way to grab lunch. The chain also has takeaway and delivery options for evenings. / www.k10.com; Mon-Fri 3 pm; Closed D, closed Sat & Sun; no booking .

KAFFEINE £15 3️⃣5️⃣4️⃣

15 EASTCASTLE ST, W1 020 7580 6755 3–1D
66 GREAT TITCHFIELD ST, W1
020 7580 6755   3–1C

This "stylish and serious", coffee-shop operation with two sites in Fitzrovia is "still one of the best independents in London", 10 years after pioneering modern Antipodean-style coffee culture in the UK. They serve "brilliant coffee" (naturally), "a nice range of pastries" and "excellent sandwiches", and have a "good vibe at both locations". "Only the slightly monastic seating lets things down" – and there's "not enough" of it! / kaffeine.co.uk/Eastcastle; @kaffeinelondon; 6 pm, Sun 5 pm; no bookings.

KAHANI SW1 £70 5️⃣4️⃣3️⃣

1 WILBRAHAM PLACE   020 7730 7634   6–2D

Ex-Tamarind executive chef, Peter Joseph (raised in Tamil Nadu) is cooking up a storm at his "smart" September-2018 newcomer, "tucked away behind Cadogan Hall" near Sloane Square. Even a reporter who considers it "expensive" feels "it's certainly amongst London's Top-5 Indians", and there's little but high esteem for its "refined", "thoughtfully prepared" cooking: "distinct and light" dishes featuring "favourite flavours but raised to a fine dining experience, including a tasting menu option". / SW1X 9AE; www.kahanirestaurants.com.

KAI MAYFAIR W1 £127 3️⃣2️⃣2️⃣

65 SOUTH AUDLEY ST   020 7493 8988   3–3A

"If you want Chinese food at its best", numerous reporters award top marks to Bernard Yeoh's luxurious Mayfair fixture, which has held a Michelin star for the last 10 years now, and which is unusual in boasting a heavyweight wine list featuring many of the world's most famous vintages. Even those who say it's "brilliant" acknowledge it's decidedly "not cheap" however. / W1K 2QU; www.kaimayfair.co.uk; @kaimayfair; 10.45 pm, Sun 10.15 pm.

Harwood Arms SW6

KAIFENG NW4 £71 3|2|2

51 CHURCH ROAD 020 8203 7888 1–1B

The divide in opinions on this smart, kosher-Chinese stalwart in Hendon has been unvarying since the year dot – to fans it's "the best Chinese food ever eaten" but to critics the most "overpriced". / NW4 4DU; www.kaifeng.co.uk; @KaifengKosher; 10 pm; closed Fri & Sat.

KAKI N1 £48 3|2|1

125 CALEDONIAN ROAD 020 7278 0004 9–3D

"Superb-if-rustic" Sichuan cuisine – "off-the-wall, especially if you aren't accustomed to it – has won instant acclaim, including amongst newspaper critics, for this newcomer by Regent's Canal: "a weird space that feels like a hastily converted pub" (which it is). Its overall ratings however, due to those who feel "the food didn't live up to the positive reviews (Coren, Maschler…)", or who "find the flavours a bit one-dimensional". / N1 9RG; www.kakilondon.com.

KANADA-YA £39 5|3|2

3 PANTON ST, SW1 020 7930 3511 5–4A
64 ST GILES HIGH ST, WC2 020 7240 0232 5–1B
35 UPPER STREET, N1 020 7288 2787 9–3D

"The best ramen in London – such a rich, meaty broth with just the right amount of fatty unctuousness" – is served at this franchise of a Japanese-owned brand, with branches in the West End and now Angel. The "nice, slurpy noodles" are "a firm favourite, great for cold days, hangovers, comfort food", and come with a small selection of side dishes and rice. / www.kanada-ya.com; @KanadaYa_LDN; 10.30 pm, Sun 8.30 pm; WC2 no bookings.

KANISHKA W1 3|3|2

17-19 MADDOX STREET 020 3978 0978 4–2A

"Off to a great start", with "superb" cuisine, say fans of Atul Kochhar's "upmarket" (and sizeable: 130 covers) new venture on a site that was previously the Mayfair branch of 28:50 (RIP), and which specialises in the "strongly flavoured", relatively undiscovered cuisine of India's north-eastern states (bordering Tibet and China). It's "not cheap" however, and while "some star dishes" are reported "some of the rest are a little more forgettable", while the interior design is "relaxing and warm" to some tastes, but – to others – can appear "cold" or "incoherent". / W1S 2QH; kanishkarestaurant. co.uk; @kanishka_maddox.

KAOSARN £26 4|2|3

110 ST JOHNS HILL, SW11 020 7223 7888 11–2C
181 TOOTING HIGH STREET, SW17 11–2C
BRIXTON VILLAGE, COLDHARBOUR LN, SW9 020 7095 8922 11–2D

"Delicious food and incredibly reasonable prices" ensure that this family-run Thai trio in South London (Brixton, Battersea and Tooting) are "hard to beat – especially with BYO". You eat "authentically, but very quickly!" / SW9 10 pm, Sun 9 pm; SW11 closed Mon L; no credit cards; no bookings.

KAPPACASEIN SE16 £9 4|3|2

1 VOYAGER INDUSTRIAL ESTATE 07837 756852 12–2A

Cheese, cheese and more cheese – in toasties, or as raclette – have made Bill Oglethorpe's market stall one of the linchpins of Borough Market. Since 2017, you can also visit their dairy in nearby Bermondsey, although you can only actually eat-in there on Saturday morning and lunchtime. / SE16 4RP; www.kappacasein.com; @kappacasein; 2pm; Sat L only; Cash only; No bookings.

KASHMIR SW15 £46 3|3|2

18-20 LACY ROAD 07477 533 888 11–2B

Billed as England's only Kashmiri specialist, this Putney three-year-old offers something "genuinely different from the standard Indian fare" – and it's "always delicious". Chef Rohit Razdan and his wife Shweta have previously had restaurants in New Delhi and Singapore. / SW15 1NL; www.kashmirrestaurants.co.uk; @KashmirRestUK; 10.30 pm, Fri & Sat 11 pm.

KASPAR'S SEAFOOD AND GRILL, THE SAVOY HOTEL WC2 £92 3|4|4

THE STRAND 020 7420 2111 5–3D

"The river views are super if you're lucky enough to get a table by the windows", in The Savoy's "plush, calm dining room, at the back of the hotel", which many still recall as The Savoy River Restaurant. Most reports are of fish and seafood "to savour", plus "expert service in beautiful surroundings", although even fans can feel that "it's quite a pricey treat", and some sceptics say that, "while pleasant, standards are not as outstanding as you'd expect from The Savoy". Perhaps its good ratings will improve even further with the July 2019 recruitment of Joost Bijster as head chef. Top Tip – head here for a "perfect breakfast". / WC2R 0ER; www.thesavoylondon.com/ restaurant/kaspars-at-the-savoy-restaurant; @TheSavoyLondon; 11 pm.

KATEH W9 £53 4|3|2

5 WARWICK PL 020 7289 3393 9–4A

Cute Little Venice bistro, where "consistently excellent Persian food" is matched with a "fine southern European wine list". "When it's packed with elegant Iranians, you know you're in the right place". / W9 2PX; www.katehrestaurant.co.uk; @RestaurantKateh; 11 pm; closed weekday L.

THE KATI ROLL COMPANY W1 £22 4|2|2

24 POLAND STREET 020 7287 4787 4–1C

"You'll be lucky to get a seat at this bustling, Indian street-food outlet" in Soho – London outpost of an NYC-chain with six Manhattan locations. It serves "excellent, wholesome south-Asian-style filled rolls" – "there's a huge variety of rolls to choose from" – and "Bollywood posters and songs make up for what's a very compact space". / W1F 8QL; www.thekatirollcompany.com; @KatiRollCompany.

KAZAN £52 3|3|2

77 WILTON RD, SW1 020 7233 8298 2–4B
93-94 WILTON RD, SW1 020 7233 7100 2–4B

"Reliably gratifying Turkish food" – "the best in this part of London" – is the calling card for this Pimlico duo, opposite each other close by Victoria Station. Service is "fast", with a "lively cosmopolitan atmosphere". / www.kazan-restaurant.com; 10.15 pm, Sun 9.15 pm.

THE KEEPER'S HOUSE, ROYAL ACADEMY W1 £60 2|2|3

ROYAL ACADEMY OF ARTS, BURLINGTON HOUSE, 020 7300 5881 3–3D

In the bowels of the RA, this subterranean venue (with bar, garden and dining room) is praised by fans for providing "reliable food in a civilised space". Typically for Peyton & Byrne though, it doesn't impress everyone, with the odd report of some "terrible" dishes. / W1J 0BD; www.royalacademy.org.uk/keepers-house; @TheKeepersHouse; 11.30; closed Sun.

KEN LO'S MEMORIES SW1 £68 3|2|2

65-69 EBURY ST 020 7730 7734 2–4B

"Expensive though reliable, like an old friend" – the late Ken Lo's Belgravia operation has won improved marks for its high-quality Oriental cuisine in the past year. Fans say it's "as good as always and good value for the area", taking it as a sign of quality that the clientele is made up of "regulars, not tourists: people are here because of the food". / SW1W 0NZ; www.memoriesofchina.co.uk; 11 pm, Sun 10.30 pm.

KENNINGTON TANDOORI SE11 £54 3|4|3

313 KENNINGTON RD 020 7735 9247 1–3C

Kowsar Hoque's Kennington fixture is "definitely not your regular curry house" – whatever your game. If it's cricket, it's "the only place to enjoy a meal post-Test at The Oval". If it's politics, it's "famous for its popularity with politicians from all sides: you're quite likely to find Ken Clarke eating alone reading The Economist", while David Cameron had his 'last supper' as PM delivered to Number 10 Downing Street. / SE11 4QE;

www.kenningtontandoori.com; @TheKTLondon;
No Amex.

THE KENSINGTON WINE ROOMS W8 £65 233

127-129 KENSINGTON CHURCH ST
020 7727 8142 7–2B

Forty wines by the glass, and 150 by the bottle are the main 'gourmet' attraction at this modern wine bar, near Notting Hill Gate (which, over the years, has added siblings in Fulham and Brackenbury Village). To accompany the liquid refreshment, there's substantial fare like steaks and seared fish, or you can stick to the "great bar platters". / W8 7LP; winerooms.london/kensington; @wine_rooms; 11.30 pm.

KERBISHER & MALT W6 £27 322

164 SHEPHERD'S BUSH RD 020 3556 0228
8–1C

"I know of no better chippie... apart from the interior", say fans of this ten-year-old venture by Brook Green, whose white-tiled walls and bum-numbing chairs can make it feel "rather Spartan"; and where attractions include ethically sourced fish and home-made curry sauce. As the chain it spawned has shrunk away, though, feedback on this, the original branch, has become much less adulatory, and sceptics feel "it used to be a lot better" and can sometimes be "disappointing" now. / W6 7PB; www.kerbisher.co.uk; @Kerbisher; 10 pm; closed Mon.

KERRIDGE'S BAR & GRILL SW1 £92 334

WHITEHALL PLACE 020 7321 3244 2–3C

TV-star Tom Kerridge "has clearly tried to bring a touch of his Marlow pub, The Hand & Flowers to the formal and plush surroundings of the Corinthia" with this much-awaited, late-2018 opening. This massive and potentially "cavernous" chamber has now been successfully cosied-up from its former incarnation as Massimo (RIP), with a big bar area; "clubby" dark decor; and with "rotisseries and meat-maturing cabinets lining one side of the room". "The food, likewise, is a little more hearty and traditional – with a Kerridge twist – than the expected, hotel-fine-dining experience". "Prices, however, remain very much high end", and diners are slightly divided on the overall outcome. A few critics feel the experience "doesn't match the hype", and is "a mismatch of average pub grub with one of London's most exclusive hotels". For a big majority of diners, though, it "fires on all cylinders", combining an "impressive-but-relaxed room" with "suitably professional but informal service" and "interesting and delicious" cooking of a type in line with TK's celebrity persona: "it was probably the most expensive fish 'n' chips I have ever had, but I can't wait to go back!" Top Tip – well spaced tables help make it good for less formal business occasions. / SW1A 2BD; www.kerridgesbarandgrill.co.uk; @kerridgesbandg.

KILN W1 £35 544

58 BREWER STREET NO TEL 4–3C

"Stonkingly good SE Asian small-plates" – "spiced to perfection and tasty beyond words" – are delivered from the "more-than-interesting menu" of Ben Chapman's "brilliant value" Thai BBQ (sibling to Shoreditch's Smoking Goat): "it's the kind of punchy and earthy food that you'd normally only encounter in Thailand in non-touristy places". "Thoughtful" staff help manage the "tiny" space – a "fun", "very, very busy" and "crowded" Soho environment, "blending in a bit of hipster attitude". It's "hard to get a seat", though, and "there can be some very long waiting times". Top Tip – eating perched at the ground floor counter is a good option: it's "fascinating watching the chefs doing their stuff". / W1F 9TL; www.kilnsoho.com.

KIN AND DEUM SE1 £44 523

2 CRUCIFIX LANE 020 7357 7995 10–4D

"Epic Thai cuisine" from "an interesting and varied" menu, "including the old favourites along with some more-innovative choices" distinguishes this contemporary, white-walled, new pub-conversion near London Bridge, on the site that was formerly Suchard's Freehouse (RIP) but has been transformed into this newcomer by the owner's children. / SE1 3JW; www.kindeum.com; @kin_deum.

KIPFERL N1 £46 323

20 CAMDEN PASSAGE 020 77041 555
9–3D

A slice of Vienna in Camden Passage that's "more than a coffee shop" (with "terrific brews and cakes") but also "a lovely casual lunch or dinner spot" with "great" Austrian specialities including "perfect schnitzel". A Ladbroke Grove offshoot closed down in early 2019. / N1 8ED; www.kipferl.co.uk; @KipferlCafe; 9.25 pm; closed Mon.

KIRAKU W5 £48 432

8 STATION PDE 020 8992 2848 1–3A

"Basic café serving Ealing's Japanese enclave" (situated near Ealing Common tube): "sushi is of high quality, service is warm – even if the surroundings are a little plain – and it's very reasonably priced: a winner!" / W5 3LD; www.kiraku.co.uk; @kirakulondon; 10 pm; closed Mon; No Amex.

KITCHEN W8 W8 £72 443

11-13 ABINGDON ROAD 020 7937 0120
6–1A

This under-the-radar venture, in a smart row of businesses off Kensington High Street, has supplied "unexpectedly delicious" meals to a well-heeled local crowd for 10 years – although the consistently high marks should be no surprise given that it's part-owned by star chef Phil Howard (of Elystan Street and formerly The Square). Atmosphere-wise, it's somewhere between "quietly sophisticated" and "Spartan".

/ W8 6AH; www.kitchenw8.com; @KitchenW8;
Mon-Thu 9.30 pm, Fri-Sat 10pm, Sun 9.30 pm.

KITTY FISHER'S W1 £79 333

10 SHEPHERD'S MARKET 020 3302 1661
3–4B

Named after an 18th-century courtesan, this "cosy" haunt "has real character", while "the seediness of Mayfair's Shepherd Market at night makes it romantic". "Food and service are delightful and consistent", but even so, these days it struggles to live up to the wave of hype generated at its launch, and – judged comparatively – "it's not as good as when Tomos Parry (now at Brat in Shoreditch) was head chef". / W1J 7QF; www.kittyfishers.com; @kittyfishers; 9.30 pm; closed Sun.

KNIFE SW4 £58 443

160 CLAPHAM PARK ROAD 020 7627 6505
11–2D

"Stonking steaks are the draw" at this small three-year-old, "on a rather bleak stretch of 'Claxton' (CLApham/BriXTON) highway". "The room is pretty basic" (and "intimate to the point of cramped") but fans like its "warm and slightly rustic" charm as enlivened by the "friendliest staff". "Sunday roasts are top notch" too – "you get complimentary mini Yorkshires and gravy to start; and the veg is superb". / SW4 7DE; kniferestaurant.co.uk; @KnifeLondon; 10 pm, Sun 4 pm; closed Mon, Tue & Sun D.

KOJI SW6 £89 334

58 NEW KING'S RD 020 7731 2520 11–1B

"The Japanese food prepared in front of you is amazing, the cocktail bar is amazing..." – Pat & Mark Barnett's "lovely Asian-fusion" haunt has unusually glam looks for somewhere near Parsons Green, and is a big local hit for a date or Big Night Out. (Older fans will remember their previous venture, Mao Tai, which they ran on the same site for over two decades). / SW6 4LS; www.koji.restaurant; @koji_restaurant; D only, Sun open L & D.

KOL WC2

108-110 SEYMOUR PLACE 2–1A

Due to open in 2020, a Mexican restaurant from Santiago Lastra, who ran Noma's Mexico pop-up back in 2017, and which looks destined to be one of the more talked-about openings of the new year. / WC2B 5DA; kolrestaurant.com.

KOOLCHA HA9 £44

BOXPARK WEMBLEY, OLYMPIC WAY
020 3744 4436 1–1A

Rohit Ghai not only opened Chelsea's Kutir this year, but this February 2019 newcomer occupying three units of the Wembley Boxpark (not the loveliest of locations, in the shadow of Wembley Stadium). As yet it's inspired little survey feedback, but if you're a fan of Indian cooking, its wide selection of dishes are said by some social media aficionados to be worth a try. / HA9 0NU; www.koolcha.co.uk.

KOYA £36 `4` `4` `3`

50 FRITH ST, W1 020 7434 4463 5–2A
BLOOMBERG ARCADE, QUEEN VICTORIA STREET, EC2 NO TEL 10–3C

"The #1 Japanese noodles in London" – especially for those who prefer udon, the fat wheat noodles eaten hot or cold that are a healthier alternative to ubiquitous ramen. The 10-year-old Soho original has been joined by a City bar in the Bloomberg Arcade, although an offshoot at Victoria Market Halls closed after only six months this year. Choose the "very interesting specials and consistently good udon – the rice dishes are nice, but not as memorable". Top Tip – "one of the few Japanese restaurants open for breakfast in the West End". / www.koyabar.co.uk; W1 10.30 pm, Sun 10pm; no bookings.

KPH W10

139 LADBROKE GROVE 7–1A

On Ladbroke Grove, this big landmark pub was taken over by Henry Harris and Harcourt Inns, with chef Ruairidh Summers at the stoves, and re-launched in mid-2019, too late for this year's survey feedback. / W10 6HJ; thekph.co.uk.

KRICKET W1 £53 `4` `4` `4`

12 DENMAN ST 020 7734 5612 4–3C

"So many layers of taste… a throwback to living in India" – their "fantastic take on subcontinental flavours and textures" has helped blaze a trail for Rik Campbell and Will Bowby's street-food brand. Since mid-2015, their "always interesting and very tasty" bites have taken them from a Pop Brixton shipping container to three permanent outlets in Soho, Brixton and White City's TV Centre. "Busy" Soho in particular is "great for counter dining". Top Menu Tips – "spot-on bhel puri", "fab chai, dazzling deep-fried chicken and delicious halwa". / W1D 7HH; www.kricket.co.uk; @kricketlondon; 10 pm.

KUDU SE15 £54 `4` `4` `4`

119 QUEEN'S RD 020 3950 0226 1–4D

"Just wow: bags and bags of flavour in every dish" – this "consistently interesting" Peckham two-year-old from chef Patrick Williams and front of house Amy Corbin (daughter of Chris) is hitting an ever-more impressive stride with its "modern and intelligent" South African-influenced cooking, service that's "gracefully informal and knowledgeable" and an interior that's "charming and relaxed, with subdued lighting". It's "generous, too – bread served with whole frying pans full of flavoured butter, for goodness sake!". "A real treat and worth the (in my case) 350-mile round trip", enthused one satisfied reporter. / SE15 2EZ; www.kudu-restaurant.com; @KuduRestaurant.

KUKU RIKU NW1 £39

UNIT 91 - 92 NORTH YARD, CAMDEN MARKET 020 3818 7499 9–2B

Rotisserie chicken from the Josper grill is the selling proposition at this new outlet in atmospheric Camden Market, which has room for 70 covers and does takeaway too. / NW1 8AH.

KULU KULU W1 £35 `3` `2` `1`

76 BREWER ST 020 7734 7316 4–3C

"Always there to satisfy a Japanese food craving": this conveyor-belt sushi-stalwart in Soho rates well for "fast, good-quality plates" – less so for the "uncomfortable stools and loud music". But nobody is complaining with "fresh hand-made tempura and salmon rolls for £4 – a steal!". It lost its spin-offs this year, though, in Covent Garden and South Kensington. / W1F 9TX; 10 pm; closed Sun; No Amex; no booking.

KUTIR SW3 £62 `5` `4` `4`

10 LINCOLN STREET 0207 581 1144 6–2D

Rohit Ghai has done it again at his late-2018 newcomer: the latest occupant of the "cosy" and "romantic" (if "on-the-quiet-side") Chelsea townhouse, which for many years was another premier Indian (Rasoi Vineet Bhatia, RIP). Practically all reports are a hymn of praise to his "faultless cooking", which has immediately propelled it into London's very top tier for nouvelle Indian cuisine. / SW3 2TS; kutir.co.uk; @kutirchelsea; No Amex; No shorts; Credit card deposit required to book.

KYM'S BY ANDREW WONG EC4 £52 `4` `3` `3`

BLOOMBERG ARCADE QUEEN VICTORIA STREET 020 7220 7088 10–3C

"Very good… but not as good as A Wong" is a common view on Andrew Wong's late-2018 opening in Bloomberg's HQ, which provides "a very different experience and menu from the Pimlico original". Foodwise the emphasis is not on dim sum, but on plates of Cantonese roast meats, and, though "refined" with "lovely clean tastes", results seem "quite pricey". And the interior, though slick, is a trifle "dull" to some tastes. Still, it's "another 'tick' for the City's rise as a dining destination", and the overall verdict is that it's "still well worth a visit". Top Tip – good value 'Sunday roast'. / EC4N 8AR; www.kymsrestaurant.com; @kymsrestaurant.

LA LLUNA N10 £56 `3` `3` `2`

462 MUSWELL HILL BROADWAY 020 8442 2662 1–1B

Modern Spanish tapas bar that's one of Muswell Hill's brighter culinary sparks, delivering "enjoyable food, served quickly and efficiently". "Tables are really packed in, intensifying the noise", but it's calmer when they open the frontage and terrace in summer. / N10 1BS; ww.lalluna.co.uk; @lallunalondon; 9 pm.

THE LADBROKE ARMS W11 £61 `3` `3` `3`

54 LADBROKE ROAD 020 7727 6648 7–2B

At the posher end of Ladbroke Grove, this smarter-than-usual local is a "comfortable" and "friendly" spot drawing a crowd of regulars – Jeremy Clarkson among them – as well as tourists. It's "always a great place to go for Sunday lunch, or indeed any other time", to sample the "small menu of modern British dishes" – even if some find it hard to accept the "high prices for what is gastropub food". / W11 3NW; www.ladbrokearms.com; @ladbrokearms; 10 pm, Sat 10.30 pm, Sun 9 pm; no booking after 8 pm.

LADY MILDMAY N1 £45 `3` `3` `3`

92 MILDMAY PARK 020 7241 6238 1–1C

This Victorian-era local on Newington Green relaunched three years ago as a gastropub and has "maintained its standards" despite rising popularity – "long may it stay that way". The blackboard menu "tries hard to cater for all tastes"… and by all accounts largely succeeds. Craft beers and "reasonably priced" wines also go down well. / N1 4PR; www.ladymildmay.com; @theladymildmaypub; 10 pm, Sun 9 pm; May need 6+ to book.

LAGOM AT HACKNEY CHURCH BREW CO. E8 £54 `4` `3` `3`

16 & 17 BOHEMIA PLACE 020 8985 3496 14–1B

"Fantastic-quality smoked meat" from Elliot Cunningham's small, permanent menu (promising 'a British-Swedish live-fire fusion') is served "in a beer-hall-style location" at this heart-of-Hackney brew pub (fka St John at Hackney), which is rated on limited early feedback (all of it very upbeat). It's set in a railway arch (of course it is!), and with a garden for sunny days. / E8; hackneychurchbrew.co.

LAHORE KEBAB HOUSE E1 £34 `5` `2` `2`

2-10 UMBERSTON ST 020 7481 9737 12–1A

"OMG!! Do not judge a book by its cover!" "The grand-daddy of cheap 'n' cheerful Pakistani kebab joints" in Whitechapel has been "an East End staple" since it opened in 1972. A "huge, echoey, tiled room, with big screens showing cricket", it's "such amazing value" and "so damn consistent, it just keeps getting bigger, busier and better". Top Tip – "step in at the off-licence next door for your booze". Top Menu Tips – "the chops are special", and it serves "the best chicken tikka ever". / E1 1PY; www.lahore-kebabhouse.com; @lahorekebabhous; midnight.

LAHPET E1 £51 `3` `2` `3`

58 BETHNAL GREEN ROAD 020 3883 5629 13–1C

"Top Burmese cuisine, with nice modernising touches" has won a fanclub for this small but growing brand, which as well as operating a 'street food kitchen' at nearby Spitalfields Market has this year-old, permanent, white-walled, communal-table canteen. Top Menu Tip – salads, in particular the tea leaf one. / E1 6JW; www.lahpet.co.uk; @Lahpet.

Indian Accent W1

LAKSAMANIA W1 £51 322

92 NEWMAN STREET   020 7637 9888   3–1D

"The best Straits cooking I've found, outside of SE Asia… indeed, having recently returned from two weeks in Singapore/Malaysia, it actually beats a lot of the hawker food I had over there!". This new operation just off Oxford Street "mostly serves laksa" (spicy noodle soup) with "up to ten different regional variations of the recipe, each one delicious". "Some dishes are merely good, but the highs really hit the top notes!". "Downstairs is larger", but more "loud, noisy, and canteeny" than the space above. / W1T 3EZ; www.laksamania.co.uk.

LAMBERTS SW12 £50 454

2 STATION PARADE   020 8675 2233 11–2C

"So lucky to have this on my doorstep!" – Joe Lambert's "firm favourite" near Balham tube has long been the area's top neighbourhood choice thanks to its "first-rate", "seasonal" cooking; "friendly and informed service"; and an agreeable ambience that's smart enough for a date or special occasion, but relaxed enough for an evening when you can't be bothered to cook. Its ratings slipped a tad this year though: not due to any grievous complaints, but a few more meals were judged "fine-but-nothing-exceptional". Top Tip – excellent-value early-week menu. / SW12 9AZ; www.lambertsrestaurant.com; @lamberts_balham; 10 pm, Sun 5 pm; closed Mon & Sun D; No Amex.

THE LANDMARK, WINTER GARDEN NW1 £84 235

222 MARYLEBONE RD   020 7631 8000 9–4A

"Among palm trees and exotic flowers", the main event in this spectacular atrium featuring an eight-storey-high glass roof is the "wonderful afternoon tea, with homemade cakes and scones"; also popular, though, is the "excellent Sunday buffet brunch, beautifully cooked and presented, with unlimited champagne". / NW1 6JQ; www.landmarklondon.co.uk; @landmarklondon; 10.15 pm; No trainers; booking max 12 may apply.

LANGAN'S BRASSERIE W1 £72 224

STRATTON STREET   020 7491 8822   3–3C

"Determinedly old-school" – this "lively", former A-list brasserie near The Ritz was opened by the legendary Peter Langan in partnership with Michael Caine in 1976. To true believers – the firm majority of its clientele – it's "an institution that always performs" and "great fun for a business meal in a boisterous setting (even if the bill ends up at more than expected… but that's life when the wine flows)". Others, though, complain of "classics done with not quite enough panache or vibrancy", and see it as "an out-of-towners kind of place harking back to the good old days when Mr L was about. He isn't and it's a shadow of its former self". / W1J 8LB; www.langansrestaurants.co.uk; @langanslondon; 11 pm, Fri & Sat 11.30 pm; closed Sun.

PALM COURT, THE LANGHAM W1 £79 334

1C PORTLAND PLACE   020 7636 1000 2–1B

They claim they invented afternoon tea, in this "elegant and refined" chamber, at the heart of the luxurious five-star hotel, opposite Broadcasting House (so "ideal for BBC expense-accounters"), and which for the big occasion provides a "beautifully presented, deliciously tasty tea, served by staff who are efficient, attentive and friendly". Top Tip – also a handy spot for a stylish pre-theatre bite. / W1B 1JA; www.palm-court.co.uk; @Langham_London; No trainers.

LANTANA CAFE £45 333

13-14 CHARLOTTE PL, W1 020 7323 6601 2–1C
GROUND FLOOR WEST, 44-46 SOUTHWARK ST, SE1 020 7403 2633 10–4B
UNIT 2, 1 OLIVER'S YD, 55 CITY RD, EC1 020 7253 5273 13–1A

With their "chilled ambience and laid-back vibe" this trio of cafés have championed Aussie-style day-time eating for more than a decade in London. "Good for breakfast, brunch and lunch", they are "not too overpriced compared with competitors", and the Shoreditch and London Bridge venues are open in the evening for drinks and dinner. / lantanacafe.co.uk; @lantanacafe; EC1 9.30 pm, Sat & Sun 3 pm; W1 3.30 pm, Sat & Sun 5 pm; NW1 closed Sun; W1 no booking Sat & Sun; NW1 no booking Sat & Sun.

LAO CAFE WC2 £39 322

60 CHANDOS PLACE   020 3740 4748   5–4C

"A funky little joint", off Trafalgar Square and "very convenient for the Coliseum", which was opened a couple of years ago by one of the founders of Rosa's Thai; and which specialises in the cuisine of neighbouring Laos. "Lots of dishes seem novel, it's certainly not like your average Thai, and the menu includes a selection of bugs! (actually quite tasty!!)". The odd Asian food connoisseur feels it falls short ("having travelled in Laos, I found it expensive and rather disappointing") but on most accounts it's "excellent" for a "cheap 'n' cheerful" bite. / WC2N 4HG; laocafe.co.uk; May need 8+ to book.

LARDO E8 £55 322

197-201 RICHMOND RD   020 8533 8229 14–1B

This "buzzy", well-known Italian (in the Arthaus building near London Fields) continues to inspire relatively limited feedback. Pizza is the most popular option foodwise, and reports say it "ticks all the boxes" for a good time. Its sibling Lardo Bebe is no more. / E8 3NJ; www.lardo.co.uk; @lardolondon; 10.30 pm, Sun 9.30 pm.

THE LAUGHING HEART E2 £56 233

277 HACKNEY ROAD   020 7686 9535 14–2A

"Quirky but delightful" Hackney wine bar and merchant, whose funky small-plates menu is, to its fans, "perfect in every way". "The owner (Charlie Mellor, ex-Brawn and Elliot's) is a king of the London wine scene, and his list drifts into natural territory without ever going down the stinky route". / E2 8NA; thelaughingheartlondon.com.

LAUNCESTON PLACE W8 £84 444

1A LAUNCESTON PL   020 7937 6912   6–1B

"In a quiet residential corner of Kensington", on a picture-book street – this "lovely and calm" pre-Victorian townhouse (established as a restaurant in 1985, and owned by D&D Restaurants since 2007) creates a sense of "privacy" that's particularly "great for a romantic evening". "Over the years there have been many changes of chef", but since Ben Murphy joined in early 2017, the food rating here has been "on an upward trajectory" and his "exciting" cuisine – "fun, whimsical, delicious" – won impressively consistent praise this year. "Surely a Michelin star is now beckoning for this young chef"? / W8 5RL; www.launcestonplace-restaurant.co.uk; @LauncestonPlace; 10 pm, Sun 9.30 pm; closed Mon & Tue L.

LAURENT AT CAFE ROYAL W1 £75

HOTEL CAFÉ ROYAL, 68 REGENT STREET 020 7406 3310   4–4C

"Set upstairs in the Café Royal" on its mezzanine level, this glitzy dining space is branded for French chef Laurent Tourondel. After its opening in mid-2018, both Giles Coren of The Times and Jay Rayner of The Guardian lined up to tear the place to shreds ("howling", "shameful pricing",…). Survey feedback regarding its steak and sushi formula is a little thin on which to rate a place of this calibre, but such reports as we have are, by contrast, upbeat: despite the odd warning of "not-so-experienced service" or a "pricey wine list", they suggest it's "very enjoyable". / W1B 4DY; www.hotelcaferoyal.com/laurent-at-cafe-royal; @HotelCafeRoyal.

THE LEDBURY
W11 £150 5|5|4
127 LEDBURY RD   020 7792 9090   7–1B

"Brett Graham never ceases to amaze" at his "simply sensational" Notting Hill fixture, celebrating its 15th year in 2020, and still idolised by its massive fanclub, who feel it stands "head and shoulders above just about any other restaurant in the capital". "Superbly crafted, beautifully balanced modern British dishes are full of wonderful contrasts of tastes and textures, using the freshest seasonal ingredients" (notably, "world-beating game"). But there's a "much more relaxed atmosphere than at most top-end 'Michelin' establishments", with many-a-compliment paid to its "easygoing, accommodating and un-fussy" staff; with kudos to sommelier Seamus Williams-Sharkey for his "light touch" and "clever advice introducing you to interesting corners of the world". Decor is sophisticated if low-key, and "while always busy, it's easy to have a conversation". / W11 2AQ; www.theledbury.com; @theledbury; 9.45 pm; closed Mon L & Tue L.

LEGARE SE1
CARDAMOM BUILDING, 31G SHAD THAMES 12–2A

Jay Patel, previously Barrafina's general manager, and Matt Beardmore, formerly senior sous chef at Trullo, are joining forces to open this 35-cover Italian in Tower Bridge in autumn 2019. / SE1 2YB; legarelondon.com.

LEMONIA NW1
£52 1|4|4
89 REGENT'S PARK RD   020 7586 7454 9–3B

"The miracle is that it doesn't change", say fans of this veteran Primrose Hill taverna: a "big, bustling, cheerful, noisy, Greek family-style restaurant that's been around forever", with particularly "warm" staff of decades' standing, who "don't just tolerate children, they positively welcome them." Never exactly a foodie hotspot, "it's time to revamp the menu…", according to one fan, who then goes on to admit "…but I've been saying that since 1978!" In truth, though, the experience here is finally starting to show its age: there have always been one or two sceptics who "wonder why everyone makes such a fuss about the place", but their number grows more numerous with each passing year. / NW1 8UY; www.lemonia.co.uk; @Lemonia_Greek; 11 pm; closed Sun D; No Amex.

LEROY EC2
£53 3|4|3
18 PHIPP STREET   0207 739 4443 13–1B

"Perfectly executed classics with a gentle twist" and other small plates with "delicious and inventive combinations" have won foodie renown for this approachable (if "rather cramped") two-year-old of the same team's original Hackney outfit, Ellory (RIP), occupying a quirky triangular site. Our reporters are a little more circumspect, and unimpressed that the venue sometimes seems to attract "the Michelin-star-chasing crowd… not what you'd want in a neighbourhood Shoreditch restaurant". / EC2A 4NP; www.leroyshoreditch.com; @leroyshoreditch; Credit card deposit required to book.

LEVAN SE15
£56 5|5|4
3-4 BLENHEIM GROVE   020 7732 2256 1–4D

"Fantastic food + great wine list + super-friendly people + brilliant music = cool vibes!" – this new restaurant and wine bar near Peckham Rye station (baby bro' to Salon in Brixton) has cracked the formula for winning fans from SE15 and beyond: a "casual-yet-special" operation, it can become "extremely busy" and "crowded". Its "incredible" small plates are a foil to the "very good wine list" and arguably a form of "wildly indulgent nursery food", but are so "creative and fun" and with "flavours that sing!" / SE15 4QL; levanlondon. co.uk.

THE LIDO CAFÉ, BROCKWELL LIDO SE24
£29 3|3|4
DULWICH RD   020 7737 8183 11–2D

"It's nice to drink coffee in winter watching hardier souls swimming by", as you enjoy an appetising bite at Brixton's marvellously preserved old lido, most often recommended for its blinding brunch. / SE24 0PA; www.thelidocafe.co.uk; @thelidocafe; 4 pm; closed Sun D; No Amex; booking max 8 may apply.

THE LIGHT HOUSE SW19
£49 3|3|3
75-77 RIDGWAY   020 8944 6338 11–2B

"One of the few, very good restaurants in Wimbledon" – although this "buzzy", 20-year veteran indie has always suffered from being "very patchy", with a "kitchen that repeatedly underperforms". When it's on song though – which is to say pretty often – it serves a quality of dishes you would expect in a much more expensive restaurant", all "efficiently and charmingly served". / SW19 4ST; www.lighthousewimbledon.com; 10.30 pm; closed Sun D.

THE LIGHTERMAN N1
£61 3|2|4
3 GRANARY SQUARE   020 3846 3400 9–3C

An "ideal location overlooking the canal and the King's Square fountains" means this King's Cross gastroboozer "books up fast – I'd go again if I could get a table". Despite the old-time name, it's a starkly contemporary grey-brick-and-glass building over several floors with a big terrace, which can get "noisy when it's rammed". But reporters say it's "fun" and the mod Brit gastro fare earns very solid ratings. / N1C 4BH; www.thelighterman.co.uk; @TheLightermanKX; Mon to Thu: 10.30pm, Fri & Sat: 11pm; Sun: 9.30pm.

LIMA FITZROVIA
£78 3|3|2
31 RATHBONE PL, W1 020 3002 2640   2–1C
14 GARRICK ST, WC2 020 7240 5778   5–3C

"Fresh, vibrant food" – full of "interesting, sharp flavours" – makes this "relaxed" Fitzrovia joint and its Covent Garden offspring ("Floral by Lima") "great places to try out Peruvian cuisine". There's a "diverse range of dishes", from "excellent ceviches to hot main courses", although "portion sizes don't really match the cost". / www.limalondongroup.com/fitzrovia; @lima_london; 10.30 pm, Sun 9.30 pm; Mon L closed.

LINA STORES
£39 4|4|4
51 GREEK STREET, W1 020 3929 0068 5–2A
20 STABLE STREET, N1   AWAITING TEL 9–3C

"A tiny restaurant with a big heart… and wonderful pasta" – the "transition from great Italian deli to restaurant is a big success" at this landmark, 75-year-old Soho store, which morphed last year from pure retail to providing an "excellent, counter-dining experience at moderate prices" nearby. "If you love pasta, this is the place to go" – "delicately silky, with the most fantastic sauces" – and it's "a brilliant stop-off before film, theatre etc". It's not going to take 75 years to turn this rip-roaring success into a chain, though: branch no. 2 opens in the second half of 2019 in one of King's Cross's 'heritage buildings' and will be 'an 100-cover outfit decorated in the same pale green-and white-stripes that diners in Soho have come to know'.

LINDEN STORES N1
£42 3|3|2
220 SAINT PAUL'S ROAD   9–2D

Worth remembering near Highbury & Islington tube – a small, white-tiled and brick-lined wine shop and neighbourhood bistro with an "interesting wine selection and nibbles", written up on the blackboard. It's run by Laura Christie (one half of Oklava) and Chris Boustead (erstwhile chef at the Opera Tavern). / N1 2LL; Www.lindenstores.co.uk; @lindenstores; Online only.

LINO EC1
£57 3|4|2
90 BARTHOLOMEW CLOSE   020 8016 5199 10–2B

This spring-2019 arrival occupies a "post-industrial space" – part of a converted linoleum factory near Barts – where the focus is on the trendy, modern British food emanating from the open kitchen, prepared by ex-Dairy head chef, Richard Falk. It is "a great newcomer in a barren area", but some mixed reports suggest it still has a way to go before it fully realises its potential (the "food is good without being outstanding…", and the "cavernous space can make conversation difficult…"). / EC1A 7BN; www.linolondon.co.uk.

LISBOA PÂTISSERIE
W10 £10 323

57 GOLBORNE RD 020 8968 5242 *7–1A*

"A little corner of authenticity in an ever-more-gentrified bit of London", this Portuguese café in North Kensington's Golborne Road has been famous for its pastéis de nata for more than 20 years – and, despite increased competition, fans swear they're "still the best custard tarts in town". / W10 5NR; none; 7 pm; L & early evening only; no booking.

LITTLE BIRD
£60 334

1 STATION PARADE, W4 020 3145 0894 *1–3A*
1 BATTERSEA RISE, SW11 020 7324 7714 *11–2C*

A "fab menu" of Asian-Med fusion dishes, 'botanical' cocktails and funky interior design add up to a "great little local restaurant" concept from Lorraine Angliss, building her Annie's and Rock & Rose west London group; Little Bird has perched in Chiswick and Battersea. / www.littlebirdrestaurants.com; @LittleBirdW4.

LITTLE DUCK THE PICKLERY
E8 443

68 DALSTON LANE 020 7249 9177 *14–1B*

A short stroll from Hackney Downs station, this year-old sibling to Ducksoup operates as a 'fermenting kitchen and eatery' (and you can buy the results by the gram or bottled as part of their The Picklery range). It also operates as a kitchen from breakfast on, serving a short menu, which varies throughout the day (you might have squid risotto, or steak in the evening); and it's later in the day that its "great list of natural wines" comes to the fore. "It feels very relaxed, serves lots of pickled stuff and the food's all good: it's a bit like going around to a friend's house, who's a very good cook and has a lot of very nice wine". / E8 3AH; www.littleduckpicklery.co.uk.

LITTLE KOLKATA
WC2 £51 432

51-53 SHELTON STREET 07712 124868 *5–2C*

"Easily missed" – "tucked away" in "an unfashionable part of Covent Garden" near Seven Dials – Prabir Kumar Chattopadhyay and Biswajit Deb Das's year-old "little gem" graduated "from a pop-up to provide homecoming in an unpretentious canteen-style outlet". "It showcases a range of interesting regional Indian dishes" including "specialities from Calcutta and Bengal" and fans say it's "a must-visit". Top Tip – "The lunchtime bento box is good value and offers a good choice." / WC2H 9JQ; www.littlekolkata.co.uk; @littlekolkatauk.

LITTLE TAPERIA
SW17 £44 333

143 TOOTING HIGH ST 020 8682 3303 *11–2C*

"Tasty tapas", served in a "slightly odd-shaped room" with a "cheery atmosphere", have created "a Tooting legend in just a few years" at this "excellent" venue dominated by a marble bar. / SW17; www.thelittletaperia.co.uk; @littletaperia; 10 pm, Fri & Sat 11 pm, Sun 9.30 pm; May need 6+ to book.

LLEWELYN'S SE24 £62 322

293-295 RAILTON RD 020 7733 6676 *11–2D*

This "all-day neighbourhood restaurant" opened two years ago in an old Victorian dining room opposite Herne Hill station, and quickly established itself as "a top local option" for many reporters; although, because it's "small", it becomes "crowded and noisy" as a result. The "admirably daily-changing menu" has Mediterranean influences and "usually offers interesting dishes" at "good prices" – they would be rated even higher were it not for a few reporters who see them as "decent enough, but nothing special". / SE24 0JP; www.llewelyns-restaurant.co.uk; @llewelynslondon; 9.30 pm; Booking max 8 may apply.

LOBOS MEAT & TAPAS
SE1 £69 433

14 BOROUGH HIGH ST 020 7407 5361 *10–4C*

"Just incredible! Every mouthful delights the tastebuds" – "punchy, powerful, memorable morsels of real food" – at this meat-centric Borough Market tapas joint, run by "people who seem interested in what they're offering". A "buzzing, little place under a railway arch", it's a "cosy" experience if sometimes a little "rushed and cramped". The Spanish team has a second branch in Soho, likewise praised for "superb tapas, and service with style but not pomp". / SE1 9QG; www.lobostapas.co.uk; @LobosTapas; 11 pm, Sun 10 pm; booking max 8 may apply.

LOCANDA LOCATELLI
W1 £98 443

HYATT REGENCY, 8 SEYMOUR ST 020 7935 9088 *2–2A*

"A restaurant of the highest calibre, which manages to be elegant and unpretentious at the same time" – Giorgio Locatelli's long-established Italian (which he, and wife Plaxy, opened in 2002) provides "a fantastic experience from start to finish". The hotel environment it sits within can seem "rather sterile", but the division of the moodily-lit dining room "breaks up what could be a large soulless space", and the ambience still feels "buzzing after all these years"; boosted by its "impeccable" and "good-humoured" service. A few diners discern "a lack of wow factor" in the cuisine, but more common is a hymn of praise to "simple ingredients combined and cooked to perfection every time". / W1H 7JZ;

www.locandalocatelli.com; 11 pm, Thu-Sat 11.30 pm, Sun 10.15 pm; booking max 8 may apply.

LOCKET'S SW1

23-27 ST JAMES'S ST *3–4C*

The owners of Wilton's and their freshly refurbished Franco's are staying busy by launching a third establishment (bringing their average opening rate up to almost one restaurant a century!) in the now re-named, wackily 1960s former Economist Plaza in St James's; it's to be a casual, all-day cafe and evening wine bar, opening October 2019. / SW1A 1HA; @wiltons1742.

LOCKHOUSE W2 £52 333

3 MERCHANT SQUARE 020 7706 4253 *7–1D*

Canalside in Paddington Basin, and with massive windows providing water views, this large bar/restaurant – occupying the high-ceilinged ground floor of one of the area's blocks – has an attractive, if not super-individual, semi-industrial design. Feedback is limited on its gastropub-ish dishes, but suggests it does what it does well. / W2 1AZ; www.lockhouselondon.co.uk; @Lockhouselondon; 23.30, Sat 5pm.

LONDON GRIND
SE1 £50 344

2 LONDON BRIDGE 020 7378 1928 *10–3C*

"Good coffee… and the food's OK too" – this Borough Market café remains one of the top caffeine hits in SE1. "It's great for breakfast" too. / SE1 9RA; www.londongrind.com; @LondonGrind; 11 pm, Sun 7 pm.

LONDON HOUSE
SW11 £61 222

7-9 BATTERSEA SQ 020 7592 8545 *11–1C*

If this Battersea venue were not owned by Gordon Ramsay, we would probably not trouble to write an entry. Not that this 'neighbourhood bar, garden, and restaurant' is too bad to burn: it just inspires little feedback, all of it humdrum: e.g. "good everyday food, chips are special, lounge is very relaxing for a drink". / SW11 3RA; www.gordonramsayrestaurants.com/london-house; @londonhouse; 11 pm, Sun 9 pm.

LONDON SHELL CO.
W2 £77 335

SHELDON SQUARE 07818 666005 *7–1C*

"A really lovely romantic trip down the canal" on a traditional barge is crowned by four courses of "delicious fish", plus pud – "great fun!". In July 2019 a second floating venue, the Grand Duchess, was added, although it stays permanently at the company mooring by Paddington Station. / W2 6EP; www.londonshellco.com; @LondonShellCo; dinner cruises depart at 7.30 pm; closed Mon, Sun & Sat L.

THE LONG BAR, THE SANDERSON W1 £49 2|4|4

50 BERNERS ST 020 7300 1400 3–1D

A "superb and quirky afternoon tea" is to be had in the atrium of this boutique hotel north of Oxford Street, with is themed around Alice in Wonderland's Mad Hatter (the 'drink me' potion here, is an invitation to indulge in Champagne!): "good value for a huge amount of attention to detail – love it!" / W1T 3NG; www.morganshotelgroup.com/originals/originals-sanderson-london/eat-drink/long-bar.

THE LORE OF THE LAND W1 £56 3|3|4

4 CONWAY STREET 020 3927 4480 2–1B

"Distressed in all the right places" – Guy Ritchie and David Beckham have channeled their inner Marie Antoinette at this spring 2019 newcomer – a Fitzrovia boozer transformed into their conception of a perfect country pub, and serving beers from Gritchie (Guy's brewery). "The food here is so much better than it needs to be, with a short, ideal menu" of incongruously-polished small plates; and "with the Sunday menu augmented by a roast". "Attentive staff and a room full of happy punters" complete the idyll. / W1T 6BB; gritchiepubs.com.

LORNE SW1 £62 5|5|3

76 WILTON ROAD 020 3327 0210 2–4B

"Lorne has gone from strength to strength since its recovery from its awful flash flood", which closed it for a significant portion of 2018 – "it's a measure of the warm feelings it generates that just about all staff came back when the restaurant reopened, as did all the regulars who had become loyalists in a relatively short period of time". Owned and run by Katie Exton and Peter Hall, it's a "tranquil space" with "no fuss and no pretentiousness", but "unexpectedly good, seasonal food for a street a stone's throw from Victoria, and lined with medium-priced, fast-food restaurants". A good chunk of its appeal lies in its "vast and interesting wine list" on which "Katie provides guidance". / SW1V 1DE; www.lornerestaurant.co.uk; 9.30 pm; closed Sun.

Kutir SW3

LOUIE LOUIE SE17 £51 3|2|3

347 WALWORTH RD 020 7450 3223 1–3C

Bright, white-walled café on a Walworth corner that makes a feature of playing vintage vinyl, and is hailed as a "fab neighbourhood spot", particularly for brunch. Also, "look out for top-class cooking at pop-up events in the evening". / SE17 2AL; louielouie.london; @LouieLouie_Ldn.

LOYAL TAVERN SE1

171-173 BERMONDSEY STREET 020 7260 2560 10–4D

Tom Cenci, former executive chef at Duck & Waffle, and Adam White from the Riding House Cafe, opened Loyal Tavern in Bermondsey in late summer 2019. It's on the site of former south east London institution Village East, once a textile factory, making use of British produce to create a 'relaxed neighbourhood environment'. / SE1 3UW; www.loyaltavern.co.uk.

LUCA EC1 £88 3|3|4

88 ST JOHN ST 020 3859 3000 10–1A

"Upscale" two-year-old in Clerkenwell that's an "unassuming-yet-special-feeling" cousin to the famous Clove Club, and whose quirky layout – "lots of different 'zones' in the restaurant, with a cosy bar at the front" and "funky" conservatory to the rear – creates a "delightful" setting for a meal. Its distinguishing culinary feature is the use of British ingredients to produce Italian cooking, alongside an "extremely pleasant Italian-biased wine list", and fans say results are "incredible". "The one gripe: as good as this is, it's pricier than you'd expect". Top Menu Tip – "love the Parmesan fries". / EC1M 4EH; luca.restaurant; @LucaRestaurant.

LUCE E LIMONI WC1 £63 4|4|3

91-93 GRAY'S INN RD 020 7242 3382 10–1A

"Glory be! A real neighbourhood spot in, of all places, Gray's Inn Road, with proper cooking by proud Sicilians". "It's my favourite family restaurant" – "Fabrizio (Zafarana) is a great host and the food is superb" and "cooked with love". Top Tip – "try the sea urchin ravioli when they have it". / WC1X 8TX; www.luceelimoni.com; @Luce_e_Limoni; 10 pm, Fri & Sat 11 pm.

LUCIANO'S SE12 £54 4|3|2

131 BURNT ASH RD 020 8852 3186 1–4D

This "great neighbourhood restaurant" in Lee is run by an Anglo-Neapolitan family. Pasta is made on the premises every day, and it has an all-day bar next door. Owner Enzo named it after his father, Luciano Masiello, who played football for Charlton Athletic before going into the catering trade. / SE12; ristorante. lucianoslondon.co.uk; @LucianosLondon; 10.30 pm, Sun 10 pm.

LUCIO SW3 £77 3|3|2

257 FULHAM RD 020 7823 3007 6–3B

"It's easy to go too often" to this "friendly" Fulham Road Italian, that has built a strong local following over 15 years. "The menu changes regularly with the seasons" and "portions are generous", but what is "spectacular value" at lunchtime becomes "expensive in the evening for almost the same menu". / SW3 6HY; www.luciorestaurant.com; 10.45 pm.

LUCKNOW 49 W1 £57 4|4|3

49 MADDOX STREET 020 7491 9191 3–2C

Dhruv Mittal (of Dum Biryani House) is behind this Mayfair newcomer, which specialises in Awadhi dishes: the cuisine of Mughal-infuenced Lucknow. Echoing the upbeat reviews it's enjoyed in the press, early-days feedback says it's a winner: "a lovely place, with attentive service, and delicious food". / W1S 2PQ; lucknowldn.com; @Lucknow_Social.

LUCKY CAT W1 £78

10-13 GROSVENOR SQUARE 020 7107 0000 3–2A

Gordon Ramsay replaced his ailing, former heavy-hitter 'maze' with this Pan-Asian Mayfair newcomer in the summer of 2019 – his first opening in the capital in the last five years (and most notable for provoking a Twitter-storm of abuse about cultural appropriation seeing as the chap he recruited to head the kitchen is the thoroughly un-Asian, ex-Sexy Fish executive chef, Ben Orpwood). The restaurant, which cost over £5 million to refurbish, aims to emulate 'the drinking dens of Thirties Tokyo and the Far East' (not the first time we've heard that one) but opened too late for survey feedback. / W1K 6JP; www.gordonramsayrestaurants.com/lucky-cat; @LuckyCatGR.

LUPINS SE1 £50 4|3|2

66 UNION ST 020 3908 5888 10–4B

This "wonderful" two-year-old is the brainchild of chefs Lucy Pedder and Natasha Cooke, whose "affordable" modern British small plates are "cooked to a very high standard" – so "full marks to these brave young women". "Handy for Tate Modern" in the Flat Iron complex, Lupins is "small", so remember to book. / SE1

1TD; www.lupinslondon.com; 10.30 pm; closed Mon D & Sun D.

LUPITA £44 3|2|2

7 KENSINGTON HIGH STREET, W8
020 3696 2930 6–1A
60-62 COMMERCIAL STREET,
SPITALFIELDS, E1 020 3141 6000 13–2C

This "fun Mexican" pair in Kensington and the City fringe serve "super-fresh, close to authentic" food and are "good value". The branch near Embankment station has closed down.

LURE NW5 £44 3|4|3

56 CHETWYND RD 020 7267 0163 9–1B

"The nicest posh chippy around" – this Dartmouth Park destination draws fans from across north London with its "fancy fish 'n' chips" and "small selection of well-cooked seafood". "It seems to be under new management, so we have to hope it keeps up standards". / NW5 1DJ; www.lurefishkitchen.co.uk; @Lurefishkitchen; 10 pm, Sun 9.30 pm; booking weekends only.

LURRA W1 £66 3|3|4

9 SEYMOUR PLACE 020 7724 4545 2–2A

"Excellent Basque cooking" and an "interesting wine list" attract high praise for this grill in Seymour Village, near Marble Arch, although the "limited menu" means "the experience is mainly for meat-lovers" – especially the "fantastic Galician steak", much of it using charcoal-grilled cuts from grass-fed cattle reared in Northern Spain. "The lovely almost secret outdoor terrace is a calm oasis in this part of town". Its stablemate, Donostia (see also), is nearby. / W1H 5BA; www.lurra.co.uk; @LurraW1; 10.30 pm, Sun 3.30 pm; closed Mon L & Sun D.

LUTYENS GRILL, THE NED EC2 £92 3|3|3

27 POULTRY 020 3828 2000 10–2C

"A great setting for high-powered, top-quality steak" – the "old bank manager's office" of the former Midland Bank HQ, bang in the middle of the City, has been transformed seamlessly by Soho House into a wood-panelled grill, with such old-world touches as beef Wellington from the trolley at lunch. Initially reserved for the club's members but now open to all-comers, it retains its clubby atmosphere and is (perhaps reassuringly) "very expensive, but worth going, even if just to marvel at the building". A "fun brunch" is a secondary attraction. / EC2R 8AJ; www.thened.com/restaurants/lutyens-grill#; @TheNedLondon.

LYLE'S E1 £92 4|3|2

THE TEA BUILDING, 56 SHOREDITCH HIGH STREET 020 3011 5911 13–1B

"Notwithstanding the hipster canteen vibe, this is the real thing!". James Lowe's "brilliantly executed", seasonal British small plates – "fresh and light, yet sturdy and filling when required" (and often "using a wood-fired oven to give that extra tang of flavour") – are complemented by "delicious bread" and "a proper list of natural wines", and have rightly won renown for his venerated foodie champion: a light-filled space at the foot of Shoreditch's iconic Tea Building. Its ratings are not quite as beyond-stellar as when the venue first opened, however, and it's no criticism to say that its No. 2 ranking in the UK according to the World's 50 Best has less to do with its "sublime" cooking, and more to do with the in-crowd criteria of the fooderati who vote for it. Top Tip – "the Lyle's Guest Chef Series programme is great". / E1 6JJ; www.lyleslondon.com; @lyleslondon; 10 pm; closed Sat L & Sun.

M RESTAURANTS £79 2|2|2

ZIG ZAG BUILDING, VICTORIA ST, SW1
020 3327 7776 2–4B
BREWERY WHARF, BREWERY LANE, TW1
020 3327 7776 1–4A
2-3 THREADNEEDLE WALK, 60
THREADNEEDLE STREET, EC2
020 3327 7770 10–2C

Martin Williams's glossily-glam steakhouses have a touch of Vegas-glitz to their ritzy design, and particularly win nominations as impressive venues for business, boosted by the range of top-quality meat (the highest grades of USDA, Wagyu and Kobe beef) and an extensive wine selection. Since the top man returned to rescue Gaucho as CEO, however, some reporters feel "it's lost its way since the wonderful early days". / www.mrestaurants.co.uk; @mrestaurants_; midnight; closed Sun.

MA GOA SW15 £44 3|4|3

242-244 UPPER RICHMOND RD
020 8780 1767 11–2B

This Putney institution "celebrated its 25th anniversary with a great party last summer – they must be getting something right!". Even if "the menu can sometimes be a bit samey", the "authentic Goan/Indian food" is "still exceptional" and the service "so friendly". "I suspect Ma Goa will still be going in 20 years' time". / SW15 6TG; www.magoaputney.co.uk; @magoalondon; 10.30 pm, Fri & Sat 11 pm, Sun 10pm.

MAC & WILD £55 3|3|3

65 GREAT TITCHFIELD ST, W1
020 7637 0510 3–1C
9A DEVONSHIRE SQUARE, EC2
020 7637 0510 10–2D

"Delicious" Scottish game and shorthorn beef, much of it from owner Andy Waugh's family estate, is showcased at his two venues in Fitzrovia and Liverpool Street. The kitchens "give an interesting modern twist to traditional dishes". / www.macandwild.com; @MacandWild.

MACELLAIO RC £48 4|3|3

6 STORE STREET, WC1 2–1C
84 OLD BROMPTON RD, SW7 020 7589 5834
6–2B
ARCH 24, 229 UNION ST, SE1 07467 307682
10–4B
124 NORTHCOTE RD, SW11 020 3848 4800
11–2C
38-40 EXMOUTH MARKET, EC1
020 3696 8220 10–1A

"Quality Italian beefsteaks" – most notably from the Piedmontese Fassone breed – are showcased in style at Genovese owner, Roberto Costa's, "unique" steakhouse group, where at each branch you "enter through the butcher's shop" and "you can tell the staff which cut you want". "The well-hung rump steak is absolutely delicious" and "a great selection of Italian wines" helps make it the perfect place to kill off an evening. / www.macellaiorc.com; @macellaiorc; 11 pm.

MACHIYA SW1 £45 3|2|2

5 PANTON ST 020 7925 0333 5–4A

"Good quality Japanese comfort food" including "proper tonkatsu – rich pork served with cabbage" – is on the menu at this rather "cramped" venue off Leicester Square from the duo behind Kanada-Ya, Aaron Burgess-Smith and Tony Lam. "Also of note is the speakeasy bar in the basement". / SW1Y 4DL; machi-ya.co.uk; @MachiyaLondon; 10.30 pm, Fri & Sat 11 pm, Sun 10 pm.

MADAME PIGG E8 £58 3|4|4

480 KINGSLAND ROAD 07956 925695
14–1A

In oh-so-now Haggerston, this neighbourhood newcomer – from chef Adam Hardiman (ex-St John and The Dartmouth Arms) – opened in November 2018, offering a seasonal, daily-changing menu. It is rated on the limited survey feedback received to date, but all of it is very upbeat, in keeping with newspaper reports and social media buzz about the place. / E8 4AE; www.madamepigg.com.

MADE IN ITALY £46 4|2|3

50 JAMES ST, W1 020 7224 0182 3–1A
249 KING'S RD, SW3 020 7352 1880 6–3C
141 THE BROADWAY, SW19 020 8540 4330
11–2B

"Top pizzas" that "taste as good as they look" are the hallmark of this 30-year Chelsea fixture, now with branches in Wimbledon and Battersea. "I couldn't stop myself from eating every last bit of the dough," reports one happy fan of the pizza, which is served by the metre. / www.madeinitalygroup.co.uk; @MADEINITALYgrp; SW3 11.30 pm; W1 11.30 pm, Sun 10.30 pm; SW19 11 pm; SW3 closed Mon .

MAGGIE JONES'S W8 £60 **2 3 4**

6 OLD COURT PL 020 7937 6462 6–1A

"Cosy, fun, old place that has been around for years and years" – a favourite in its time of Princess Margaret, who used to slip away to here from nearby Kensington Palace, and whose alias when booking provides the current restaurant's name. Its rustic, heavily-romantic style isn't dissimilar to its stablemate, La Poule au Pot, and it likewise serves "basic, traditional English dishes" designed to satisfy your hunger at a "decent price" rather than to dazzle your tastebuds. "There's a reasonable wine list too, unless you go for the magnum where they measure with a stick how much of it you've taken from the bottle: amusing to say the least but not their best vintage…" / W8 4PL; www.maggie-jones.co.uk; 11 pm, Sun 10.30 pm.

MAGURO W9 £60 **4 3 2**

5 LANARK PL 020 7289 4353 9–4A

This "spot on" Japanese near Little Venice wins consistent high ratings for its ultra-fresh sushi, sashimi and maki rolls as well as cooked dishes. Do book because it's "small and often overcrowded, but worth it for the food and welcome". / W9 1BT; www.maguro-restaurant.com; 10.30 pm, Sun 10 pm; No Amex.

MAISON BAB & KEBAB QUEEN WC2 £120 **5 4 3**

4 MERCER WALK 020 7439 9222 5–2C

"Taking the kebab to a whole new level": this sibling to Kingly Court's Le Bab occupies Covent Garden's Mercers Walk development and – in a style reminiscent of Bubbledogs – combines a regular ground floor "cheap 'n' cheerful" diner (serving regular mezze and kebabs – formula price £46), with a much more ambitious basement venue, Kebab Queen (price shown). In the cellar, behind a fake take-away shop-front, is a ten-seater venue where the initial kebab (or rather 'kebabito' as they call it) is merely the first stage of an ambitious £60 six-course tasting experience from chef Manu Canales, served directly onto a heated counter (there's no plates or cutlery). "I was completely cynical about Kebab Queen, but was bowled over by their wickedly tasty and absurdly good-value tasting menu. There's no way on earth they are making money on it?". / WC2; www.eatlebab.com; @eatlebab.

MAISON BERTAUX W1 £8 **4 4 5**

28 GREEK ST 020 7437 6007 5–2A

This "eccentric but marvellous treasure" is a Soho landmark and "one of the few remaining original London pâtisseries". "Gateaux to die for" and "wonderful tea and scones" provide a "trip down memory lane" in premises opened by a Parisian exile in 1871 and graced by Karl Marx and Virginia Woolf as well as generations of Soho bohos. / W1D 5DQ; www.maisonbertaux.com; @Maison_Bertaux; 10.15 pm, Sun 8.45 pm.

MALABAR W8 £48 **3 3 2**

27 UXBRIDGE ST 020 7727 8800 7–2B

This "high-quality" Indian has fed happy Notting Hill diners "with some style and on metal platters" for more than 30 years, and – having taken over the premises of an Italian trattoria back in the day – has always had a contemporary look. The odd regular says "is it me, or has this old favourite gotten a bit tired?", but perhaps that's more a comment on how outstanding it once was, as its overall feedback is pretty solid. / W8 7TQ; www.malabar-restaurant.co.uk; 11 pm.

MALABAR JUNCTION WC1 £41 **3 3 3**

107 GT RUSSELL ST 020 7580 5230 2–1C

Keralan specialist in Bloomsbury – an early champion of South Indian cuisine in London – serving "interesting and unusual dishes", and offering "a considerably better choice than the chains". "There's always a smiling welcome and excellent friendly service". / WC1B 3NA; www.malabarjunction.com; 11 pm.

MAM W11 £41 **4 4 3**

16 ALL SAINTS RD 020 7792 2665 7–1B

"A great addition to the Notting Hill scene", this two-year-old Vietnamese BBQ grill serves a "limited menu which one could eat pretty well every day: fresh, zingy and delicious – what more could you want?". Owner Colin Tu (of the Salvation in Noodles pho joints) serves his mother's recipe for fermented dipping sauce – MAM is pronounced 'mum' in Vietnamese. / W11 1HH; mamlondon.com.

MAMMA DOUGH £43 **3 3 3**

40 LADYWELL ROAD, SE13 1–4D
179 QUEEN'S RD, SE15 020 7635 3470 1–4D
76-78 HONOR OAK PK, SE23 020 8699 5196 1–4D
354 COLDHARBOUR LN, SW9 020 7095 1491 11–2D

"Delicious pizza dough" with top toppings have won a solid following for this "informal" South London group, now reaching as far as Sydenham. Home-made ginger beer and locally brewed craft beer, plus artisan coffee roasted in Shoreditch, complete the deal. / www.mammadough.co.uk; SW9 SE15 and SE26 10.30 pm, SE13, SE23 10pm; phone bookings only.

MANDARIN KITCHEN W2 £41 **4 3 1**

14-16 QUEENSWAY 020 7727 9012 7–2C

"Better than any lobster noodles in Asia – possibly the best in the world" is the oft-repeated superlative attached to this Queensway temple to "seafood, Chinese style". "Don't go for the ambience", however: "it's noisy and the opposite of stylish" – although it's "a bit smarter than it used to be". / W2 3RX; mandarinkitchen.co.uk; 11.15 pm.

MANGAL 1 E8 £29 **5 2 2**

10 ARCOLA ST 020 7275 8981 14–1A

"Still the best Turkish BBQ in town", say fans of the original Mangal grill that put Dalston on the carnivore's map. "I've been coming here for over 20 years and it's still one of my all-time favourite restaurants. Never fails with great food and excellent service". BYO helps keep the costs down. / E8 2DJ; www.mangal1.com; @Mangalone; midnight, Sat & Sun 1 am; Cash only; No bookings.

MANICOMIO £76 **3 2 3**

85 DUKE OF YORK SQ, SW3 020 7730 3366 6–2D
6 GUTTER LN, EC2 020 7726 5010 10–2B

It's "always a delight" to visit this sleekly modern Italian duo in Chelsea and the City, which provide an "airy, relaxing escape from the fumes". "Food and service are of a high quality", and "there's been a definite improvement over the last few years". They're "undoubtedly a bit pricey", but "nothing is cheap in these areas". The group has added a third venue, Canto Corvino, in Spitalfields (see also). / www.manicomio.co.uk; SW3 10 pm, Sun 4 pm; EC2 10 pm; EC2 closed Sat & Sun.

MANNA NW3 £56 **2 2 2**

4 ERSKINE ROAD 020 7722 8028 9–3B

Now fully vegan, this 1968-vintage Primrose Hill outfit can claim to be Europe's oldest veggie restaurant, and is still co-owned by musician Roger Swallow of the Albion Band, long-time resident in LA. The food has had its ups and downs over the decades and is nowadays mostly (if not uniformly) rated "enjoyable and tasty", even by reporters "neither vegetarian nor vegan". It closed for major refurbishments in summer 2019. / NW3 3AJ; www.mannav.com; @mannacuisine; 10 pm, Sun 7.30 pm; closed Mon.

MANUKA KITCHEN SW6 £53 **3 3 3**

510 FULHAM RD 020 7736 7588 6–4A

"Excellent, little rustic-chic local bistro" near Fulham Broadway which is a "lovely spot to eat in at any time but weekend brunch is legendary". The "intriguing menu" has some "delicious, ambitious dishes", and the owner is "delightful and charming". / SW6 5NJ; www.manukakitchen.com; @manukakitchen; 10 pm, Tue-Sat 11 pm, Sun 4 pm; closed Sun D; booking max 8 may apply.

MANZI'S (CORBIN & KING) W1

1 BATEMAN'S BUILDINGS 5–2A

Due to arrive in mid-2020, an homage to the late, great Manzi's – a once famous fish-icon of the West End – from über-restaurateurs Corbin & King; it's not on the same site (it will be off Soho Square, rather than off Leicester Square as the original was) – but will be a fish-centric offering all the same, and the aim is to be "fun

Kerridge's Bar & Grill SW1

and affordable" like Brasserie Zédel. / W1D 3EN; @corbinandking.

MAO CHOW E8 £40

159A MARE STREET NO TEL 14–2B

This mid-2019 newcomer near London Fields is riding just about all of the current food trends: it's a tiny (12 seats), no-booking, vegan, pop-up-turned-permanent BYO in east London – Insta-stardom is next, no doubt. The inventive Chinese-inspired food can also be taken away. / E8 3RH; www.mao-chow.com; No bookings.

MÃOS E2 £185 554

REDCHURCH STREET 02027 88909 13–1C

"Nuno Mendes strikes again, outside the box" at his "informal and wonderful" Shoreditch 16-seater, where a once-daily, three-hour sitting provides a "very intimate" happening, which fans hail as "the top dining experience in town". It is tucked away up a staircase in the 'nurturing' environment of the Blue Mountain School – self-described as 'a progressive vision and a physical place of contemplation' (where one can spend a ton of money on clothes and other artisanal creations). The meal takes place in a bare terracotta chamber at a shared table, and "the opportunity to watch and interact with the chefs makes the experience so much more interesting". "An ever-changing, multi-course tasting menu" is served: "inventive, challenging" and "exciting". It's "a brilliant concept" and one whose scary expense inspires not a single grumble from anyone commenting this year. And – breaking news… – with a recent change of policy, taking pics for your Insta feed is now not only allowed but encouraged. / E2 7DJ; www.maos.dinesuperb.com.

MAR I TERRA SE1 £42 233

14 GAMBIA ST 020 7928 7628 10–4A

This "charming, unpretentious neighbourhood tapas restaurant" in an old Southwark pub is a "good option near the South Bank and Young Vic theatre". "The food is reliable if a little old-fashioned" and comes in "proper portions". The place "can be noisy – the staff, however, are darlings!". There's "a private room for hire upstairs". / SE1 0XH; www.mariterra.net; 11 pm; closed Sat L & Sun.

MARCELLA SE8 £45 333

165A DEPTFORD HIGH STREET 020 3903 6561 1–3D

"Smashing it out of the park" – this two-year-old Italian, on Deptford's high street close to the station, is a prized local in these parts, with first-class pasta the highlight of a short menu, using British as well as Italian ingredients. It's the lesser-known sibling to Peckham star, Artusi. / SE8 3NU; www.marcella.london ; @MarcellaDeptfrd; midnight, Fri & Sat 1 am, Sun 4 pm; May need 6+ to book.

MARCUS, THE BERKELEY SW1 £128 333

WILTON PL 020 7235 1200 6–1D

"Outstanding in every way", say fans of Marcus Wareing's calm Belgravia temple of gastronomy: "a big room, where the setting of each table feels very private", and where the "expertly crafted and seasonal" cuisine (under chef patrons, Mark and Shauna Froydenlund) is, they feel, "expensive, but oh-so-worth it". For a large minority, though, its "daft" prices defy comprehension, and those who remember the era when Marcus himself was more regularly at the stoves feel that "compared with ten years ago, it's not a patch on what it was". / SW1X 7RL; www.marcusrestaurant.com; @marcusbelgravia; 10 pm; closed Sun; No trainers; booking max 6 may apply.

MARE STREET MARKET E8 £55 325

117 MARE STREET 020 3745 2470 14–2B

"A wonderful addition to the area" – a 10,000 square feet market inside the transformed base of a formerly run-down, Hackney office-block, which is the brainchild of Marc Francis-Baum (owner of a string of bars and pubs). With its flowers, vintage design-pieces, artisan coffee, bar, open kitchen and 'dining room' he's channeled hipster design pheromones to maximum zeitgeisty effect. It's not a majorly foodie hotspot, but "the atmosphere's buzzing, and the drinks are always flowing. Love it!" / E8 4RU; www.marestreetmarket.com.

MAREMMA SW2 £53

36 BRIXTON WATER LANE 020 3186 4011 11–2D

Brixton locals Alice Staple and Dickie Bielenberg have teamed up with ex-Bruno Loubet chef Dominique Goltinger to create this little Italian haven. It opened in early summer 2019, too late for survey feedback, but early reviews are very upbeat about its honest Tuscan cuisine. / SW2 1PE; www.maremmarestaurant.com.

MARGOT WC2 £60 243

45 GREAT QUEEN STREET 020 3409 4777 5–2D

"Old-school elegance is mixed with excellent, friendly service" at Paulo de Tarso & Nicolas Jaouën's "stylish" and "very comfortable" Italian near the Freemasons' Hall – "one of the better post-Covent Garden options", and also a useful business venue in WC2 ("an area that isn't too rich in restaurants of this calibre"). But, while fans still praise its "classic, simple, well-executed dishes", ratings slid this year amidst some concerns that it "has suffered from its popularity", producing food that seems "less enthralling" than it once did: "nice, but nothing special for the price". / WC2B 5AA; www.margotrestaurant.com; @MargotLDN.

MARKET HALL VICTORIA SW1 £35 422

TERMINUS PLACE 2–4B

Opened in November 2018 on the site that long ago was the nightclub Pacha, this 400-cover food hall hosts eleven vendors, plus three bars and a coffee stop. "Variety is the key to its strength" and – as at many similar venues – "much of the food is better-than-OK but some is not excellent". A West End branch is opening in late-2019; Fulham was the first, in the atmospheric former ticketing hall of the tube station. Top Tip – "very family friendly and you're spoilt for choice". / SW1V 1JR; www.markethalls.co.uk; @MarketHalls.

THE MARKSMAN E2 £62 433

254 HACKNEY ROAD 020 7739 7393 14–2A

"Still just about a pub", this chef-run operation near Columbia Road Market is "way, way ahead of other gastropubs, and just gets better". It serves "one of the best and most reliable roasts anywhere" – perfect after a trip to the flower market on Sunday morning – and "is sublime during the week, with great cocktails and beer selection". / E2 7SJ; www.marksmanpublichouse.com; @marksman_pub; 10 pm, Sun 8 pm; closed weekday L & Sun D.

MAROUSH £55 322

I) 21 EDGWARE RD, W2 020 7723 0773 7–1D
II) 38 BEAUCHAMP PL, SW3 020 7581 5434 6–1C
V) 3-4 VERE ST, W1 020 7493 5050 3–1B
VI) 68 EDGWARE RD, W2 020 7224 9339 7–1D
Â€˜GARDEN') 1 CONNAUGHT ST, W2 020 7262 0222 7–1D

London's longest-serving Lebanese group has served a "delicious and generous ensemble of mezze and mains" for almost four decades, remaining "admirably consistent over the years". There are currently 14 branches under various names (including Ranoush, Beirut Express, Randa); and at the outlets actually branded as 'Maroush' the "decor is a bit 1980s" especially in the sedate main dining rooms. The better bets are the "casual" cafés at the original branch and in Beauchamp Place – "for a quick meal, you can't go wrong", especially from the bargain menu of wraps. For late-night live music and belly-dancing head to the original Edgware Road branch. / www.maroush.com; most branches close between 12.30 am-5 am.

MASALA ZONE £44 334

"Fresh-tasting food with distinctive flavours" and "unpretentious, tasty thalis" make this small London group (now in its 20th year) a "go-to chain" for its fans: "amazing value for such high-quality cuisine". / www.masalazone.com; @masalazone; 11 pm, Sun 10.30 pm; W1U 9 pm; Sun 4 pm; booking: max 8 online.

MASTER WEI WC1 £24 4️⃣3️⃣2️⃣

13 COSMO PLACE 020 7209 6888 2–1D

Down a sidestreet near Russell Square – "a new place opened by the chef of Arsenal's Xi'an Impression, Wei Guirong, which is slightly more spacious, but where the menu is almost the same". "It's a simple setting, with the most amazing Shaanxi food": "great hand-cut noodles" are the headline option. / WC1N 3AP; masterwei.co.uk.

MASTERS SUPER FISH SE1 £28 3️⃣2️⃣1️⃣

191 WATERLOO RD 020 7928 6924 10–4A

"The batter's crispy, the chips just right" – plus portions are "generous" – at this "reliably good" Waterloo chippie, which draws a steady crowd of locals, passers-by and taxi drivers to be served at its "Formica tables". / SE1 8UX; masterssuperfish.com; 10.30 pm; closed Sun; No Amex; no booking, Fri D.

MATHURA SW1

4 GREYCOAT PLACE 2–4C

Hot on the heels of Kanishka, Atul Kochhar has announced his next venture to open in autumn 2019, also in collaboration with Tina English. Based in an old fire station building in Victoria, the big (200-cover) operation will, a press release informs us, 'use premium, locally-sourced British produce, while offering unique and unexpected elements which set it apart from his previous restaurants'. / SW1P 1SB; mathura.co.uk.

MATSUBA TW9 £45 4️⃣3️⃣2️⃣

10 RED LION ST 020 8605 3513 1–4A

"Lovely, tiny Japanese café run by a friendly family" (who are in fact Korean) on the edge of Richmond town-centre's one-way system – "never lets you down" (sushi is the highlight). / TW9 1RW; www.matsuba-restaurant.com; @matsuba; 10.30 pm; closed Sun.

MAX'S SANDWICH SHOP N4 £35 5️⃣4️⃣3️⃣

19 CROUCH HILL NO TEL 1–1C

Max Halley's cult Stroud Green café has won renown as an "outstanding, cheap 'n' cheerful" gourmet option, thanks to its wild, wacky and wickedly enjoyable selection of sarnies, each of which amounts to what's effectively a meal between slices of bread (be prepared to get your hands dirty). / N4 4AP; www.maxssandwichshop.com; @lunchluncheon; 11 pm, Fri & Sat midnight, Sun 6 pm; closed Sun D; No Amex; no booking.

MAZE GRILL £54 2️⃣2️⃣2️⃣

10-13 GROSVENOR SQ, W1 020 7495 2211 3–2A
11 PARK WK, SW10 020 7255 9299 6–3B
79 ROYAL HOSPITAL RD, SW3 020 7352 4448 6–3D

Neighbouring maze has gone, replaced by Lucky Cat, but Gordon Ramsay's hotel grill in Mayfair continues to plough on for the time being. Feedback is negligible compared with its heyday, but its posh grills inspired fewer disappointments this year. It also has a Chelsea spin-off on the site where the f-word chef first made his name, when it was called Aubergine (long RIP), and another on Chelsea's Royal Hospital Road (near the GR mothership): reports similarly are few, with a verdict of tolerable but mixed.

MAZI W8 £65 4️⃣4️⃣3️⃣

12-14 HILLGATE ST 020 7229 3794 7–2B

This "wonderful, buzzy" Greek in Hillgate Village, near Notting Hill Gate, "goes from strength to strength" in its reinterpretation of the traditional taverna as a "modern neighbourhood restaurant". The "fresh, delicious menu is perfect for sharing", but "you need to pick wisely otherwise it's expensive". / W8 7SR; www.mazi.co.uk; @mazinottinghill; 10.30 pm; closed Mon L & Tue L.

MEATLIQUOR £38 3️⃣3️⃣3️⃣

37-38 MARGARET STREET, W1 3–1C
6 ST CHAD'S PLACE, WC1 020 7837 0444 9–3C
17 QUEENSWAY, W2 020 7229 0172 7–2C
133B UPPER ST, N1 020 3711 0104 9–3D
37 LORDSHIP LANE, SE22 020 3066 0008 1–4D
74 NORTHCOTE ROAD, SW11 020 7228 4777 11–2C

"Irreverent pop-art-meets-punk surrounds" are the hallmark of this cult chain, home of the 'Dead Hippie' burger, washed down with 'Grog' ("powerful rum cocktails"), showcased by a new West End flagship just off Oxford Circus. "I thought I might be bored with yet another dirty burger-style place, but these are so good" for "when you need a 'filthy' treat" that's "tasty as hell" (and, moreover, "much better than GBK, Byron and so on"). / meatliquor.com; @MEATliquor; W1 midnight (Fri & Sat 2 am), N1 11 pm, SE22 midnight, Sun 10.30 pm-11.30 pm; booking: min 6.

MEATMISSION N1 £34 3️⃣3️⃣4️⃣

14-15 HOXTON MARKET 020 7739 8212 13–1B

"The messiest, most delicious burgers ever; and a good selection of craft beers as well" – still the deal at this "hip" spin-off from the Meatliquor group, which brings the worship of meat to an old Christian missionary building (complete with stained glass windows and illuminated ceiling). / N1 6HG; www.meatmission.com; @MEATmission; 11 pm, Sun 10 pm.

MEDITERRANEO W11 £67 3️⃣2️⃣3️⃣

37 KENSINGTON PARK RD 020 7792 3131 7–1A

"Always enjoyable" local Italian that's provided consistently well rated meals in Notting Hill for 21 years. Its two siblings, Osteria Basilico and Essenza, are near-neighbours on the same street. / W11 2EU; www.mediterraneo-restaurant.co.uk; 11.30 pm, Sun 10.30 pm; booking max 10 may apply.

MEDLAR SW10 £75 4️⃣4️⃣3️⃣

438 KING'S RD 020 7349 1900 6–3B

"Well worth a visit in this remote corner of Chelsea": this "outstanding oasis in Worlds End" has won a big culinary reputation, and chef Joe Mercer-Nairne "maintains high standards year-in-year-out", with a "classic French approach that's not so over-refined as to suck enjoyment out of it". "Very good ingredients are cooked with great care, love and attention, but not overdone, nor over-fancy". Service is of a very "high class" too, while the interior is "sophisticated" ("if a little cramped"). "It's another surprising omission from the Michelin star list: is it because it's at the wrong end of the King's Road?" / SW10 0LJ; www.medlarrestaurant.co.uk; @MedlarChelsea; 10.30 pm, sun 9.30pm.

MEGAN'S 2️⃣3️⃣4️⃣

571 KINGS RD, SW6 020 7348 7139 6–4A
UNIT B, 57-69 PARSONS GREEN LANE, SW6 020 7348 7139 11–1B
27 CIRCUS WEST VILLAGE, SW11 11–1C
43 BEDFORD HILL, SW12 11–2C
86 HIGH STREET WIMBLEDON, SW19 11–2B
55-57 THE PAVEMENT, SW4 11–2D

"Affordable and with a nice vibe" – these good-looking, all-day hang-outs major in brunch, but make reasonably-priced options for a relaxed meal at any time. This year, they added Wimbledon, Battersea Power Station and Clapham branches to the fast-growing stable. / megans.co.uk; @MegansCafes.

MEI UME EC3 £113 3️⃣3️⃣3️⃣

10 TRINITY SQUARE 020 3297 3799 10–3D

Delectable Asian-fusion delicacies – combining dishes of both Chinese and Japanese inspiration – win nothing but bouquets for this palatial dining room in a City five-star hotel, near the Tower of London. On the downside, cynics say "it feels like a business hotel restaurant", and one or two diners "expected more, considering the big-ticket prices". / EC3N 4AJ; www.meiume.com; @meiumelondon; 10 pm.

MELABES W8 £49 3️⃣2️⃣2️⃣

221 KENSINGTON HIGH STREET 020 7937 3003 6–1A

"Delicious Israeli-tapas and sharing-style plates at very reasonable prices" make it worth discovering this new arrival on Kensington High Street: a two-storey space where the existence of the (larger) upper floor isn't obvious from the street. "It's rather plain-looking from the outside (and once you're inside too!)" and "some soundproofing is called for". / W8 6SG; melabes.business.site; @melabes221.

MELE E PERE W1   £54   333

46 BREWER STREET   020 7096 2096   4–3C

"What a great find in Soho!" – "this quirky and funky place offers a nice twist on traditional Italian dishes", and is "so much better than the chains". "Looks tiny from the outside but has this ginormous expanse at basement level", which "can be noisy". "It's not cheap but nor is it outrageously expensive for the area and quality". There's also an on-site aperitivo bar featuring home-made vermouth. / W1F 9TF; www.meleepere.co.uk; @meleEpere; 11 pm, Sun 10 pm.

MENIER CHOCOLATE FACTORY SE1   £55   223

51-53 SOUTHWARK STREET   020 7234 9610   10–4B

Stick to the good-value, meal-with-ticket deals at the theatre restaurant of this converted Victorian chocolate factory, whose food is "honest" but rather "hit and miss", hence "not good enough to pay full stand-alone prices" – especially with foodie Borough Market just across the road. / SE1 1RU; www.menierchocolatefactory.com; @MenChocFactory; 11 pm; closed Mon & Sun D.

MERAKI W1   £62   444

80-82 GT TITCHFIELD ST   020 7305 7686   3–1C

"Imaginative Greek dishes with a twist" earn high ratings this year for this two-year-old in Fitzrovia from Arjun and Peter Waney, who seem to have imbued Hellenic cooking with the trademark glamour and excitement they brought to Japanese with Zuma and Roka. The place is "always buzzing and packed", and reporters reckon it's "pricey but worth it" for "the best Greek meal I've ever eaten". / W1W 7QT; www.meraki-restaurant.com; @meraki_lon.

MERCATO METROPOLITANO SE1   £25   423

42 NEWINGTON CAUSEWAY   020 7403 0930   1–3C

"Chocca with pop-ups" near Elephant & Castle, this "amazing" 45,000 square foot foodie market is "a great place to hang out and eat" – and is "far less crowded than Borough Market, its neighbour up the road". "The range and quality means you have to return several times to sample everything you want" from 50 different operators including an on-site Bavarian brewer. This 'sustainable community food market' is the brainchild of Andrea Rasca, who runs similar schemes in Milan and Turin. Upcoming developments include markets in Grade I listed St Mark's Church, Mayfair and Ilford's new cultural quarter and an MM Food Factory at the nearby £2.3billion Elephant Park development scheme. The only complaint is that this former paper factory

"feels like a barn and can get chilly in winter". / SE1 6DR; www.mercatometropolitano.co.uk; @mercatometropol; 11pm, Sun 9pm.

THE MERCER EC2   £61   322

34 THREADNEEDLE ST   020 7628 0001   10–2C

This banking hall conversion just moments from the Bank of England "feels like a gentleman's club" and "has become a City mainstay" for its "good-quality 'school' cooking". "They understand the 'time essence' of the business lunch", so "service comes at a good clip". / EC2R 8AY; www.themercer.co.uk; @TheMercerLondon; 9.30 pm; closed Sat & Sun.

MERCHANTS TAVERN EC2   £66   223

36 CHARLOTTE ROAD   020 7060 5335   13–1B

Following on from Neil Borthwick's departure a year ago, his wife Angela Hartnett has severed her ties with this large and elegant gastropub-style haunt that she helped create from a converted Shoreditch warehouse. The amount of feedback the place generates has declined dramatically, and the few reports we have are mixed: some say it's still very good all round, but more downbeat commentary says "this used to be very good, but our recent meal was very poor". / EC2A 3PG; www.merchantstavern.co.uk; @merchantstavern; 11 pm, Sun 9 pm.

LE MERCURY N1   £33   223

140A UPPER ST   020 7354 4088   9–2D

"Bustling" and "lovely" French-style bistro, which has been an Islington institution for almost 30 years, with its crowd-pleasing formula of a keen set price for each of the three courses (£4.95, £11.95 and £3.95 respectively): the food's not art, but with value like this, nobody cares. / N1 1QY; www.lemercury.co.uk; @le_mercury; midnight, Sun 10 pm; Mon-Thu D only, Fri-Sun open L & D.

MERE W1   £87   454

74 CHARLOTTE STREET   020 7268 6565   2–1B

"You can tell the moment you walk through the door that the people who own it are involved and want to make their guests' experience enjoyable" – that's the vibe at Monica and David Galetti's "peaceful and delightful" Fitzrovia two-year-old. "You have a relaxing drink at street level in the bar, and then it's down a flight of steps to a chic room flooded in natural light from the street outside". "The heart in the mind-blowing cooking shines through" – in particular the "wonderful, delicate, balanced tasting menu, packed with fresh seasonal ingredients"; and "it's paired with an exceptional wine list". "Staff are outstanding and the chef/patron visiting guests at their tables is a lovely touch". "Must surely get its Michelin star soon?" / W1T 4QH; www.mere-restaurant.com; @mererestaurant; Jacket & tie required.

Otto's WC1

MESON DON FELIPE SE1   £54   223

53 THE CUT   020 7928 3237   10–4A

This "modestly priced" veteran Hispanic opposite the Young Vic is invariably "packed out" from early evening. "It's my default for a quick pre-theatre supper". There's "such a vibe between 7-9pm – nobody's going to write sonnets about the food, but sometimes it's just about the good times". / SE1 8LF; www.mesondonfelipe.com; 10 pm; closed Sun; No Amex.

MEZA   £33   322

**34 TRINITY RD, SW17 07722 111299 11–2C
70 MITCHAM RD, SW17 020 8672 2131 11–2C**

"Great Lebanese food with lots of delicious veggie options" is what keeps this duo of Tooting/Clapham cafés buzzing. Yes, they're "a bit cramped", but they compensate by being "friendly and fun". / www.mezarestaurant.co.uk; @MezaRestaurants; 11 pm, Fri & Sat 11.30 pm.

LA MIA MAMMA SW3   £62   333

257 KING'S ROAD   020 7351 2417   6–3C

An "intriguing concept" – 'A rotation of Mammas' from 20 different Italian regions per year provide the hearty scoff at this welcoming Chelsea yearling, where handmade pasta is something of a feature. By all accounts, the formula works, delivering "interesting dishes not found in your typical Italian restaurant" to a consistently good standard, and – for the 'hood – it's not especially pricey either. / SW3 5EL; www.lamiamamma.co.uk; @LaMiaMamma_.

MICHAEL NADRA   £63   432

**6-8 ELLIOTT RD, W4 020 8742 0766   8–2A
42 GLOUCESTER AVE, NW1 020 7722 2800 9–3B**

"Vibrant", "thoughtful" cuisine is very consistently produced at both Michael Nadra's eponymous restaurants, in Chiswick and Camden Town. Both sites, though, are awkward in their way: the former "is a small space that's a bit of a squeeze" (window tables are best); while the latter, right next to the Regent's Canal, is a little stuck out-on-a-limb, and can seem "a little morgue-like" when it's not busy. Both sites, though, are pepped up by their "friendly" staff. / www.restaurant-michaelnadra.co.uk; @michaelnadra; 10 pm - 10.30 pm, Sun earlier.

MIEN TAY £39 322

180 LAVENDER HILL, SW11 020 7350 0721 **11–1C**
45 FULHAM HIGH ST, SW6 11–1B
122 KINGSLAND RD, E2 020 7729 3074 **14–2A**

This hard-hitting family-run quartet "kicks the pants off lots of other Vietnamese restaurants", with "food that's hard to beat" at "very reasonable prices" (the late Sunday Times food critic AA Gill raved about their pho and goat with galangal). / mientay.co.uk; @Mien_Tay; 11 pm, Sun 10 pm; E2 Sun 10.30 pm.

MILDREDS £47 333

45 LEXINGTON ST, W1 020 7494 1634 **4–2C**
200 PENTONVILLE RD, N1 020 7278 9422 **9–3D**
9 JAMESTOWN RD, NW1 020 7482 4200 **9–3B**
GROUND FLOOR THOMAS TOWER, UPPER DALSTON SQ, E8 020 8017 1815 **14–1A**

"My partner's a die-hard meat eater, but still thinks this place is the bee's knees!" – this extremely popular vegetarian chain has built on three decades of popularity for the "always-super-busy" (no bookings) Soho original, with branches in Camden Town, Dalston and King's Cross all opened in the last few years. All outlets get a good rep in the survey, with their "great choice" of "very tasty, veggie, comfort food". / @mildredslondon.

MILK SW12 £16 323

20 BEDFORD HILL 020 8772 9085 **11–2C**

For a top breakfast or brunch, a good number of Balham residents still tip their favourite Antipodean café as the best way to go locally; no bookings, you just rock up (and expect to queue at the weekend). / SW12 9RG; www.milk.london; @milkcoffeeldn; 10 pm; No bookings.

MIMO SE1 £53

1 CATHEDRAL STREET 020 3286 7777 **10–3C**

Jon and Nicole Warren, the husband-and-wife team behind San Sebastian's Mimo (which has branches in Seville, Mallorca and The Algarve) have opened a cookery school, 'experiential dining' and chef's table overlooking Borough Market, with Basque-born Joseba Lasa as chef. You book (for 1-12 guests) for the nightly two-and-a-half-hour 'experience', which incorporates a tasting menu with wines, plus cookery demonstration, around the 'rugged concrete chef's counter'. / SE1 9DE; london.mimofood.com/en; @mimo_food.

MIN JIANG, THE ROYAL GARDEN HOTEL W8 £87 335

2-24 KENSINGTON HIGH ST 020 7361 1988 **6–1A**

"With such delightful views of Kensington Gardens, the food could so easily become secondary", but the impressively glam 8th-floor of the "luxurious" Royal Garden Hotel has long been acknowledged as one of the capital's best destinations thanks to its "consistently excellent" Chinese cuisine ("better than I had in Hong Kong!"). Its ratings came off the boil slightly this year however, amidst some unfamiliar accusations that "it's going downhill and becoming very expensive": "if this is the best Beijing Duck in town, then I'm the Emperor of China!" / W8 4PT; www.minjiang.co.uk; @minjianglondon; 10 pm.

MINT LEAF LOUNGE EC2 £74 334

ANGEL CT, LOTHBURY 020 7600 0992 **10–2C**

"Light and delicate" Indian-fusion dishes and "nice cocktails" continue to maintain a fanclub for this snazzy-looking haunt, tucked away near the Bank of England. Its Trafalgar Square sibling bit the dust, though, this year (RIP). / EC2R 7HB; www.mintleaflounge.com; @MintLeafLondon; 10.45 pm.

MIRCH MASALA SW17 £26 422

213 UPPER TOOTING RD 020 8767 8638 **11–2D**

"A broad range of dishes with distinct sauces at amazing prices" makes this "basic Pakistani place" a standout on Tooting's "curry corridor": "the quality certainly merits the mediocre setting and variable service"; a favourite of Sadiq Khan, it's "often busy and noisy". Top Tips: "nihari – slow-cooked lamb shank – is memorable"; "BYO wine is a plus point, too". / SW17 7TG; www.mirchmasalarestaurant.co.uk; midnight; Cash only; No bookings.

THE MODERN PANTRY EC1 £61 222

47-48 ST JOHNS SQ 020 7553 9210 **10–1A**

In June 2019, after ten years, Anna Hansen quit the Clerkenwell haunt she founded with the backing of D&D London, leaving Robert McCleary, who'd cooked with her all that time, at the helm. Known for its eclectic, Kiwi-inspired culinary approach, it's always been a venue that's divided opinion ("others rave, but I'm not sure why") and we've maintained its existing middle-of-the-road rating for the time being. Most reliably, it's tipped as "a scrumptious brunch place" – "really good food and a light, fresh place to start the day". / EC1V 4JJ; www.themodernpantry.co.uk; @themodernpantry; 10.30 pm, Sun 10 pm.

MOIO N16 £53 333

188 STOKE NEWINGTON HIGH STREET 020 7923 7119 **1–1D**

Funky Portuguese- and Scandi-inspired dishes (a 'moio' is an arcane Iberian measure once used in the salt trade with Sweden!) set a culinarily ambitious tone at this early-2019 newcomer, occupying a simple, café-style space on Stokie's main drag. Limited feedback to-date, but all of it upbeat. / N16 7JD; moiorestaurant.com.

MOKSHA KT3 £35 443

216 KINGSTON ROAD 020 894 92211 **1–4A**

Out in the boonies of New Malden, first class ratings again – if on slightly limited feedback – for Arjun Singh Rawat and Rajeev Danga's North Indian two-year-old. / KT3 3RJ; www.moksharestaurant.uk; @Mokshanewmalden.

MOMO W1 £76 434

25 HEDDON STREET 020 7434 4040 **4–3B**

Old-timers remember when Tom Cruise and Nicole Kidman (still married) chilled in the groove-tastic basement bar at Mourad Mazouz's party-Moroccan after it first opened (in 1997) and – notwithstanding a recent menu revamp and general scrub-up (plus much less snotty service) – it's changed little over the years other than the evaporation of its A-list clientele. In fact, if anything, the "extremely tasty" North African cuisine is higher quality and better value. Top Tip – "love the outdoor garden on a scorching day". / W1B 4BH; www.momoresto.com; @momoresto; 11 pm; credit card required to book.

MON PLAISIR RESTAURANT WC2 £54 334

19-21 MONMOUTH STREET 020 7836 7243 **5–2B**

"For a romantic touch of Paris", this "archetypal" Gallic bistro in Covent Garden (dating from 1946) certainly looks the part – "a warren of rooms", which has seen numerous additions over the years, and where the "delightful" ambience is at its strongest in the oldest section of all. The cuisine is very "traditional" and, according to most diners, "still superb after so many years"; but others are more nuanced in their praise: "it's not the best French food by far, but a visit is like meeting an old friend who's been in your life for decades". Top Tip – "the pre-theatre deal is great value". / WC2H 9DD; www.monplaisir.co.uk; @MonPlaisir4; 10.30 pm; closed Sun.

MONA LISA SW10 £39 332

417 KING'S RD 020 7376 5447 **6–3B**

"Very popular workers café by day, rather trendy restaurant by night!" – this veteran at the 'wrong end' of the King's Road enjoys a "slick" double life as Chelsea's "fun cheap eat". / SW10 0LR; www.mona-lisa.business.site; 11 pm, Sun 5.30 pm; closed Sun D; No Amex.

MONCKS OF DOVER STREET W1

33 DOVER STREET   3–3C

An all-day brasserie-concept from luxury Mayfair restaurant Park Chinois: the 92-cover venue launched in July 2019, with chef Gennaro Vitto, who was previously a pastry chef at Park Chinois, at the stoves. / W1S 4NF; www.moncksbrasserie.com.

MONMOUTH COFFEE COMPANY   £7   3 5 4

27 MONMOUTH ST, WC2 020 7232 3010 5–2B
2 PARK ST, SE1 020 7232 3010 10–4C

"There really is only one winner here when it comes to coffee!" – these caffeine-havens remain the survey's No. 1 coffee company thanks to its "perfect" brews – from a "fabulous, rotating and extensive selection of beans" – delivered by "patient and helpful staff", who are "invariably lovely despite the crazy-massive queues". By Borough Market, the "rustic, no-frills SE1 branch with its communal heavy wood table" offers a "quintessential London breakfast experience, with a cult following" (foodwise, there's bread and jam, plus "beautifully-sourced pastries"). The original WC2 branch is also "lovely… if you can get a seat"; and a recent addition is a Saturday-only branch at Spa Terminus in Bermondsey SE16. / www.monmouthcoffee.co.uk; WC2 6:30 pm; SE1 6 pm; SE16 Sat 1.30 pm; closed Sun; no Amex; no booking.

MONSIEUR LE DUCK EC1   £47   4 3 3

25 CLERKENWELL ROAD   020 7247 2223 10–1A

"Duck in all its variants" ("cooked in the Gascon style") from a "limited but brilliant menu" (duck burger, confit leg, breast) – and "great frites too" – make this street-food brand a "duck-lover's delight". They were a pop-up until May 2019, when they moved into this permanent Spitalfields home (the troubled site that saw Workshop and Sarona come and go within a year). / EC1M 5RN; www.leduck.co.uk.

MORITO   £45   4 3 3

195 HACKNEY ROAD, E2 020 7613 0754 14–2A
32 EXMOUTH MKT, EC1 020 7278 7007 10–1A

"Great vibe, great food" – Moro's "busy", "tightly packed" spin-off, a few doors away along Exmouth Market, combines Spanish and North African tastes into "terrific" tapas dishes, served in a "laid back" fashion. A second, slightly larger Morito on Hackney Road, not far from Columbia Road flower market, wins equally enthusiastic approval. / EC1 10.45 pm, E2 10.30 pm, Sun 9 pm; EC1 closed Sun D; no bookings.

MORO EC1   £67   3 3 2

34-36 EXMOUTH MKT   020 7833 8336 10–1A

"Still going strong twenty years on…", "still stylish…", "still needing acoustic engineering…!" – Samuel & Samantha Clark's "unflashy" Exmouth Market legend has maintained an enormous loyal fanclub over the years. The draw is its "consistently excellent cooking, with distinctive Spanish and North African flavours" ("so fresh and vibrant"); plus "a great list of sherries and wines", all delivered in a "relaxed and buzzy" ("always noisy") setting. But, for a growing minority of regulars, it's "not always as good as yesteryear": service "if well-meaning is sometimes patchy"; and "though the old-favourite dishes are still cracked out with aplomb, they're not as adventurous as they once seemed". Such reservations tend to be quibbles, rather than full-on complaints, however, and the overall consensus is that it's "still a real favourite!" / EC1R 4QE; www.moro.co.uk; @RestaurantMoro; 10.30 pm; closed Sun D.

MORSO NW8   £60   3 4 3

130 BOUNDARY ROAD   0207 6247 412 9–3A

"This jewel-like place in a faintly unfashionable corner of St John's Wood exceeds expectations" with "fresh pasta", "friendly service", and "an exciting grappa list", plus "grappa-themed cocktails that really hit the spot". Downsides? "It is very noisy", and "the small-plates format means that bills can add up alarmingly". / NW8 0RH; www.morsolondon.co.uk; @morsolondon.

MORTIMER HOUSE KITCHEN W1   £64   3 3 4

37-41 MORTIMER STREET   020 7139 4401 3–1C

"Fun" and fashionable newcomer – a glamorous, grown-up, all-day restaurant complete with bar, on the ground floor of 'private workspace and wellbeing destination', Mortimer House in Fitzrovia. Its open kitchen is headed by Antonio 'Lello' Favuzzi (formerly of leading City Italian, L'Anima) who joined as head chef in February 2019. A versatile choice for many occasions, it is particularly tipped for business. Foodwise, one or two reporters consider the Mediterranean-via-the-Middle-East cuisine a little "average", but overall it's consistently decently rated. / W1T 3JH; www.mortimerhouse.com.

MOTHER SW11   £44   3 3 4

2 ARCHERS LANE, BATTERSEA POWER STATION   020 7622 4386 11–1C

Still relatively undiscovered by reporters, London's branch of this trendy Copenhagen pizza-stop occupies a moodily and slightly weirdly decorated arch at Battersea Power Station's Circus West Village, complete with tables hewn from big lumps of tree, spaceship lights and candles. On the few reports we received, it's worth a whirl, especially for one of its buffet brunch deals. / SW11 8AB; www.motherrestaurant.co.uk; @mother_ldn.

MR BAO SE15   £38   5 3 3

293 RYE LN   020 7635 0325   1–4D

For a "cheap 'n' cheerful" scran-fest, Frank Yeung's small Peckham café comes highly recommended by reporters as distant as Gloucester! It's all about the tasty Taiwanese bao – a total wow! / SE15 4UA; www.mrbao.co.uk; @MrBaoUK; 11 pm.

MR CHOW SW1   £88   2 1 2

151 KNIGHTSBRIDGE   020 7589 7347   6–1D

The very acme of dining glamour when it opened in 1968 – Sir Terence Conran once hailed it as a breakthrough in restaurant design – this expensive Chinese stalwart in Knightsbridge is now showing its age. "I used to love this place but the food is now old-fashioned and hasn't kept up with the times" is the politest of this year's feedback. Other reporters are blunter: "remarkable it continues to have any customers…" / SW1X 7PA; www.mrchow.com; @mrchow; midnight; closed Mon L.

MUNAL TANDOORI SW15   £28   4 4 2

393 UPPER RICHMOND ROAD, PUTNEY 020 8876 3083 11–2A

"Massive portions of happiness" describes the "fabulous Indian/Nepalese food in generous-sized dishes" at this stalwart local: on the South Circular at Putney now for 30 years. / SW15 5QL; Www.munaltandori.co.uk; @munalrestaurant.

MURANO W1   £99   4 5 3

20-22 QUEEN ST   020 7495 1127   3–3B

With its "understated" style, Angela Hartnett's "elegant-but-relaxed" HQ manages to be one of the most personal of the "luxury" central London restaurants run by a big name, particularly one in Mayfair. Under head chef, Oscar Holgado, the accomplished modern cuisine "with an Italian twist" is "first class", as is the wine list: incredibly consistent and, "if not cheap, not wildly expensive". But it's the "professional service with a smile" that sets the seal on the experience: "warm, welcoming, and less pushy than at some other top destinations". "I'd just returned from Rome and was worried I'd be disappointed, but in fact it topped things off with a level of refined luxury I enjoyed very much". / W1J 5PP; www.muranolondon.com; @muranolondon; 11 pm; closed Sun.

MYRTLE SW10   4 3 3

1A LANGTON STREET   020 7352 2411 6–3B

"Brilliantly executed, Irish-inspired food (we particularly enjoyed the black pudding – made from beef, not pork – in a potato roll; and the beef fillet with boxty)" wins high praise from early-days reporters on chef Anna Haugh's May 2019 opening, near World's End in Chelsea (named for her hero – Ballymaloe chef, Myrtle Allen – and aiming to offer 'modern European cooking with an Irish influence, using the finest Irish produce'). It's a "cosy and welcoming" space too: "part of a small, Chelsea townhouse, so quite tightly packed, with steep stairs to the upper level or down to the toilets". / SW10 0JL; www.myrtlerestaurant.com; @myrtlerest.

NANASHI EC2   £63   3 2 2

14 RIVINGTON ST   020 7686 0010 13–1B

"Super sushi and some decent hot plates too" win enthusiastic but limited feedback for this "pleasant if rather cramped" Japanese two-year-old in Shoreditch. / EC2A 3DU; www.nanashi.co.uk; Tue - Wed 10 pm, Thur - Sat 11 pm.

NANDINE SE5   4 5 3

45 CAMBERWELL CHURCH STREET   1–3C

"A marvellous alternative to generic Middle East cuisine" – this family business has graduated from Peckham Levels (where they still trade) to this new café in Camberwell, where they offer "a Kurdish take on classic Middle Eastern dishes: well spiced, utterly fresh and served with a warmth worth mentioning because it's so uncommon...". A rave August 2019 review by Jay Rayner has propelled it to becoming a fooderati talking point. / SE5 8TR; @NandineUK.

THE NARROW E14   £62   1 2 3

44 NARROW ST   020 7592 7950 12–1B

"Always disappointing for the food, but the view saves it" sums up the general attitude toward Gordo's Limehouse pub, which despite its celeb chef ownership has never reliably cut it gastronomically. The "standard brasserie fare" is "average" at the very best – it "could and should be so much better". / E14 8DP; www.gordonramsayrestaurants.com/the-narrow; @thenarrow; 10.30 pm, Sun 8 pm.

NATIVE SE1   £57   3 3 2

32 SOUTHWARK STREET   07943 934 375 10–4C

"Refreshingly innovative dishes" which "bring out the best in British ingredients" – including squirrel meat, left-overs and peelings under a strict 'zero waste' regime – "create a truly unique dining experience" at Ivan Tisdall-Downes and Imogen Davis's new and bigger venue near Borough Market, where they moved last year from their cramped Neal's Yard original. "Hidden away" behind a curtain, "the joint seems more East End than South Bank", but its "funky interior makes for a fun night out". Marks would have been higher without a significant minority who were "disappointed" by various aspects of the new venture. / SE1 1TU; www.eatnative.co.uk; @eatnativeuk.

NAUGHTY PIGLETS SW2   £57   5 5 3

28 BRIXTON WATER LN   020 7274 7796 11–2D

Joe and Margaux Sharratt's "distressed-chic Brixton/Brockwell Park fixture" continues to win "top marks" for its French-inspired

"small-plates at reasonable prices" ("if I lived next door I'd get rid of my kitchen!"). The "friendly, chatty and informal staff" and "South London style" also go down well, although the occasional reporter is "not so sure about the natural wines". The same team has opened a sister venue at Andrew Lloyd Webber's The Other Palace theatre in Victoria (see also). / SW2 1PE; www.naughtypiglets.co.uk; 10 pm, Sun 3 pm.

NAUTILUS NW6   £38   4 4 1

27-29 FORTUNE GREEN RD   020 7435 2532 1–1B

"Delicious fresh fish", "battered or crumbed in matzo meal", and "friendly" service make this classic West Hampstead chippy stand out from the crowd. Even regulars who've "been coming for years" point out that "the restaurant could do with a makeover"… but we've been saying that for nearly three decades now, so are not exactly holding our breath! / NW6 1DU; 10 pm; closed Sun; No Amex.

NEEDOO E1   £26   4 3 2

87 NEW RD   020 7247 0648 13–2D

Whitechapel Punjabi BYO that's a real match for its better-known Pakistani competitors in the East End due to its "grilled meats at bargain prices" and other "fantastic, freshly made dishes" from the sub-continent. / E1 1HH; www.needoogrill.co.uk; @NeedooGrill; 11.30 pm.

NEPTUNE, KIMPTON FITZROY LONDON WC1   £86   2 2 2

8 RUSSELL SQUARE   020 7520 1806 2–1D

"Stylish, grand-hotel decor" creates an "impressive" backdrop to a meal in the year-old incarnation of this dining room within a huge Victorian pile (fka Hotel Russell) on Russell Square. Its brasserie-style cooking is decently rated but can seem "very pricey". / WC1B 5BE; neptune.london; @Principal_Hotel.

NEXT DOOR SE22   £45   4 3 2

151 LORDSHIP LANE   020 3659 1413 1–4D

"A welcome addition to East Dulwich" and "really worth the trip" – "super-fresh fish (from the namesake Moxon's fishmonger next door)" helps this year-old venture "punch above its weight". "The whole roast fish to share is a real delight, but there are also lots of tasty small plates, which are equally satisfying". "You must book, and try and go there early, as it's small, and the best dishes don't last very long". "Not a cheap meal" especially as the "simple premises are somewhat cramped", but "well worth the money as it's so good". "Outside tables during good weather are at a premium". / SE22 8HX; www.moxonsnextdoor.com.

NICHE EC1   £56   3 3 2

197-199 ROSEBERY AVENUE 020 7837 5048 9–3D

'Gluten free but you wouldn't know it!' is the motto at this modern bistro "very handy for the Sadlers Wells theatre": "a charming and slightly

eclectic restaurant with enthusiastic staff" and "a varied menu to suit all tastes". "My gluten-free friend was delighted to find he could eat anything on the menu, and happily tucked into pie and mash, saying that you wouldn't know it was gluten-free (a point echoed by the non-gluten-free among us)". / EC1R 4TJ; www.nichefoodanddrink.com; @Nichefooddrink; 9.45 pm, Fri & Sat 10.15 pm, Sun 3.30 pm.

THE NINTH LONDON W1   £78   5 4 3

22 CHARLOTTE STREET   020 3019 0880 2–1C

"Mouth-watering food" – "French-style with a difference" – wows almost all visitors to Jun Tanaka's "informal fine-dining" joint in Fitzrovia. "The food is taken seriously but the atmosphere is grounded and relaxed" – "when I want a solid and thoughtful meal, I go here". Better still, it's "a bit of a bargain for the quality", and there's "huge value in the wine list for a Michelin restaurant". / W1T 2NB; www.theninthlondon.com; @theninthlondon; 10 pm, Thu-Sat 10.30 pm; closed Sun.

NO. 5 SOCIAL W1   £79

5 POLLEN STREET   020 7870 3730 3–2C

The mid-2019 relaunch of Little Social (RIP) over the road from the Pollen Street mothership sees it re-invented but still under the aegis of the Jason Atherton empire; this Mayfair 60-seater now sports a softer, more classically luxurious style than its siblings. It's to be a new showcase for chef Kostas Papathanasiou – whose CV incorporates The Fat Duck and The Ledbury – with a focus on seasonal, British cuisine. Top Tip – the prix fixe menu is a good deal for the area: £19.50 for 2 courses or £24.50 for 3 courses. / W1S 1NE; www.no5social.com; @no5social.

NO. FIFTY CHEYNE SW3   £81   3 4 4

50 CHEYNE WALK   020 7376 8787 6–3C

"Extremely well-appointed, and featuring an open grill" – this Chelsea newcomer, picturesquely located right by the river near Albert Bridge, bears many of the hallmarks of its elegant predecessor on the site, the Cheyne Walk Brasserie, which has undergone a complete rebuild under the watchful eye of Sally Greene (Director of The Old Vic and proprietor of Ronnie Scott's). Chef Iain Smith (formerly head chef at Social Eating House) provides the eats for the 70-seat restaurant. Top Tip – the cocktail bar and drawing room upstairs, is a particularly fab space with brilliant views. / SW3 5LR; www.fiftycheyne.com; @50Cheyne.

NOBLE ROT WC1   £58   3 4 4

51 LAMB'S CONDUIT ST   020 7242 8963 2–1D

"Allied to the magazine of the same name", Mark Andrew and Daniel Keeling's Bloomsbury three-year-old took over the "lovely", if "slightly cramped" premises that

Noble Rot WC1

were previously the marvellously old-school wine bar Vats (RIP). It has a "brilliantly curated" wine list "featuring something for everyone: from small, natural and biodynamic producers using grapes you've never heard of (from areas you didn't even know produced wine), to the grand marques of the first growth Bordeaux. There is something for everyone and the staff are ridiculously knowledgeable and keen to help guide you through as much or as little as you want". The "simple" fare that accompanies it is better-than-incidental too ("sometimes outstanding"), and prepared with "an assured touch". "It's not a place for loony foodies of the Instagram persuasion, thank God. Just really good fun!" And "all without it being daylight robbery" too. / WC1N 3NB; www.noblerot.co.uk; @noblerotbar; 10 pm.

NOBU, METROPOLITAN HOTEL W1 £100 322

19 OLD PARK LN 020 7447 4747 *3–4A*

"It no longer pulls the A-list celebs, it's no longer difficult to get a table – but the food is still exceptional" at the Japanese-South American fusion chain's original London flagship. It can be "hit or miss", though – "some days it's the real Nobu with the exquisitely prepared black cod signature dish, but at times it seems the chef has forgotten the recipe". More than 20 years after its arrival in the UK, the global brand is still expanding, with a second hotel scheduled to open in the West End in early 2020. / W1K 1LB; www.noburestaurants.com; @NobuOldParkLane; 10.15 pm, Fri & Sat 11 pm, Sun 10 pm.

NOBU BERKELEY W1 £104 322

15 BERKELEY ST 020 7290 9222 *3–3C*

"Fab but SO expensive"; the Mayfair branch of Matsuhisa Nobu's luxury, Japanese-Latino fusion brand still pleases with its "absolutely incredible food ("stunning black cod") – it even converted my non-sushi-eating husband to sushi". It's no longer a celeb-magnet nowadays however, and every year, a huge proportion of reporters complain how painfully "overpriced" it is, especially given its 'meh' decor and iffy service. / W1J 8DY; www.noburestaurants.com; @NobuBerkeleyST; 11 pm, Thu-Sat midnight, Sun 9.45 pm; closed Sun L.

NOBU SHOREDITCH EC2 £110 222

10-50 WILLOW ST 020 3818 3790 *13–1B*

In the basement of this very boutiquey, year-old Shoreditch hotel – London's first from the global Japanese-American chain – the big, airy dining room opens onto a small sunken garden. To fans, its sleek styling, wizard sushi and "perfect cocktails" make it "pricey but worth it for a special blow-out". To sceptics, though, it's all a bit 'vieux chapeau': "for what it is – an old formula with nothing innovative – it's overpriced; and you can have much better Japanese elsewhere at a fraction of the bill". / EC2A 4BH; www.nobuhotelshoreditch.com; @NobuShoreditch.

NOIZÉ W1 £79 454

39 WHITFIELD ST 020 7323 1310 *2–1C*

Mathieu Germond, former manager of Pied à Terre, "has worked his considerable magic here", and has created an "amazing wine list" with "very fair mark-ups" at his "very charming" Fitzrovia yearling (on the former site of Dabbous, RIP) – "go for his suggestions" from the "wide and interesting range, many by the glass". Ed Dutton's "delightful" French cuisine is "excellent too", showing "genuine, old-school skill", while the "tasteful decoration, with lots of natural light" and "spot-on" service ("personable" – "there when you need them and non-intrusive") "make it an ideal spot for an informal business lunch, as well as more serious entertaining". / W1T 2SF; www.noize-restaurant.co.uk; @NoizeRestaurant.

NOOR JAHAN W1 £47 343

2A BINA GDNS, SW5 020 7373 6522 *6–2B*
26 SUSSEX PL, W2 020 7402 2332 *7–1D*

"Reliably upmarket curry house" on the Earl's Court-South Ken border – a true veteran (est. 1964) whose loyal, well-heeled clientele rate its "consistency" and comforting atmosphere. Given its posh neighbourhood, it's attracted its share of slebs, with Brangelina, Gwyneth and Robbie spotted over the years. The Bayswater offshoot is similar, but less fashionably located. / W2 11.30 pm, Sun 11 pm; SW5 11.30 pm.

NOPI W1 £76 432

21-22 WARWICK ST 020 7494 9584 *4–3B*

"A wonderful treasure-house of Middle Eastern dishes" – "absolutely fabulous sharing-plates", of which the vegetarian ones "would sway even a committed carnivore with their culinary magic" – inspire many rave reviews of Yotam Ottolenghi's Soho flagship; and its "unusual wines" are also "very acceptable". "Downstairs, by the busy and interesting open kitchen, there are communal tables; the ground floor is more fashionable (busier and noisier) and, unlike at his main chain, you can book". It's no huge bargain nowadays: "the small plates are as tasty as the cookbooks suggest but portions seem in inverse proportion to the price!" / W1B 5NE; ottolenghi.co.uk/nopi; @ottolenghi; 10.30 pm, Sun 4 pm; closed Sun D.

NORDIC BAKERY W1 £13 322

14A GOLDEN SQ 020 3230 1077 *4–3C*

"Nordic sarnies and cinnamon buns are as good as ever, along with the coffee", at this Scandi fixture in Soho. "Pity about the other sites", which closed down a couple of years ago and are "greatly missed – but at least the Golden Square original is still here". / W1F 9JG; www.nordicbakery.com; 8 pm, Sat & Sun 7 pm; L & early evening only; No Amex; no booking.

THE NORFOLK ARMS WC1 £56 333

28 LEIGH ST 020 7388 3937 *9–4C*

"Great, good-value tapas" is a slightly surprising find at this classic London pub, "hiding" in sidestreet near King's Cross: "a real revelation in an area not noted for good places to eat". / WC1H 9EP; www.norfolkarms.co.uk; 11pm, Sun 10.30 pm; No Amex.

NORMA W1

8 CHARLOTTE STREET *2–1C*

Following the success of The Game Bird, the team from The Stafford London took the bold step of opening this independent non-hotel restaurant, in a Fitzrovia townhouse, in September 2019. The cooking, overseen by the Salt Yard's ex-culinary director, Ben Tish, is 'inspired by the culture of Sicily, with particular emphasis on the Moorish influences on the island's cuisine'; a crudo (raw) bar is also a feature. / W1T 2LS; thestaffordlondon.com/norma-london; @Norma_ldn.

NORTH CHINA W3 £47 433

305 UXBRIDGE RD 020 8992 9183 *8–1A*

Though its fans would differ, this "utterly reliable", "family-run" stalwart (est 1976) is by no means "the best Chinese restaurant in London" or England! It is, however, an unusually high quality operation to find deep in the 'burbs of Acton and has a much wider following than you would expect of somewhere in this location. "The food is fresh and full of flavour" and service under owner/manager Lawrence Lou is very professional and warm. / W3 9QU; www.northchina.co.uk; 11 pm, Fri & Sat 11.30 pm.

NORTH SEA FISH WC1 £47 342

7-8 LEIGH ST 020 7387 5892 *9–4C*

"The real deal!" This "popular" Bloomsbury chippy – "run by the same family for more than 40 years" – is one of the best in town, certainly of those within striking distance of the West End. "The choice is always good, and simply grilled is a fantastic option", or fried in matzo meal; and you can round off with "excellent English puddings and custard". It's a good idea to book. / WC1H 9EW; www.northseafishrestaurant.co.uk; @TheNorthSeaFish; 10 pm, Sun 9.30 pm; closed Sun D; No Amex.

THE NORTHALL, CORINTHIA HOTEL WC2   £101   323

10A NORTHUMBERLAND AVE
020 7321 3100   2–3C

"Fine if you're staying in the hotel, but not a destination restaurant", is a common verdict on this "elegant" chamber, which is currently most often tipped by non-residents as a "perfect business lunch venue": "comfortable, with good food, and you're always well looked-after". It's an impression the management of this beautiful five-star hotel, near the Embankment, is keen to change, however, and the arrival of André Garrett at the stoves from Cliveden in late-2018 was a statement of intent to zhoosh things up, as they have done with Kerridge's (see also). Since André's arrival its food rating is, in fact, little-changed (good but unmemorable), but perhaps that's all about to change: in a June 2019 interview with trade website 'Big Hospitality', he promises 'something big' including a name change, refurb, and a new dedicated restaurant entrance. / WC2N 5AE; www.thenorthall.co.uk; @CorinthiaLondon; 10.45 pm.

NORTHBANK EC4   £58   223

ONE PAUL'S WALK   020 7329 9299   10–3B

You can't argue with the location of this bar/café, right by the Wobbly Bridge, looking over to Tate Modern, and with an outside terrace in summer. It inspired limited and mixed feedback this year: fans applaud its seasonal modern British cooking and tip it as a business option, but one or two others feel "it's overpriced, with poor service, and only exists due to its view of the Thames". / EC4V 3QH; www.northbankrestaurant.co.uk; @NorthbankLondon; 10 pm; closed Sun.

NOVIKOV (ASIAN RESTAURANT) W1   £105   324

50A BERKELEY ST   020 7399 4330   3–3C

"A playground for oligarchs" – Arkady Novikov's infamously glam, Eurotrash-magnet remains one of Mayfair's most happening scenes, luring the fast crowd with its mix of light Asian bites, sushi, grills and noodles. It's not exactly somewhere to go if you're counting the pennies, but, actually, "dim sum at lunch is excellent and very reasonably priced". / W1J 8HA; www.novikovrestaurant.co.uk; @NovikovLondon; 11.15 pm; No trainers.

NOVIKOV (ITALIAN RESTAURANT) W1   £109   222

50A BERKELEY ST   020 7399 4330   3–3C

Wreathed in the über-Eurotrashy environs and telephone-number prices of Russian restaurateur Arkady Novikov's well-known, Mayfair glamour-magnet, it's hard to form a totally balanced judgement on its Italian dining room. It's fabulously "overpriced" of course, but most diners do actually feel the "classic Italian cuisine" is "proper" and "delicious".

/ W1J 8HA; www.novikovrestaurant.co.uk; @NovikovLondon; 11.45 pm.

NUOVI SAPORI SW6   £48   333

295 NEW KING'S RD   020 7736 3363   11–1B

"Honest food", "delightful service" and an upbeat atmosphere again win praise for this well-established, neighbourhood trattoria, near Parsons Green; it's good with kids too. / SW6 4RE; www.nuovisaporilondon.co.uk; 11 pm; closed Sun; booking max 6 may apply.

NUSR-ET STEAKHOUSE SW1

THE PARK TOWER KNIGHTSBRIDGE, 101 KNIGHTSBRIDGE   6–1D

First announced in July 2017, this December 2019 opening on Knightsbridge from social media sensation, Nusret Gökçe is The Park Tower hotel's answer to breathing life into the deathly dull-looking space that was for many years One-O-One (RIP). Now it's to be Salt Bae's latest branch in a steak chain that nowadays spans the globe. / SW1X 7RN; www.nusr-et.com.tr/en/home.aspx.

NUTBOURNE SW11   £59   223

29 RANSOMES DOCK, 35-37 PARKGATE RD 020 7350 0555   6–4C

"Quirky and relaxed" Battersea venue, on the waterside site long occupied by Ransome's Dock (RIP), which is run the Gladwin brothers using the same farm-to-fork formula as at their other ventures (see Rabbit and The Shed). "Great wines" from the eponymous family vineyard in Sussex are a plus, but the modern British cooking is "inconsistent", with "some hits and some misses"… but rather too many "misses". / SW11 4NP; www.nutbourne-restaurant.com; @NutbourneSW11.

NUTSHELL WC2

30 SAINT MARTIN'S LANE   5–4C

Modern Iranian cuisine is served at this August 2019 newcomer in Covent Garden, which opened too late for any survey feedback. Former head chef of The Palomar, Jeremy Borrow, will oversee the kitchen of this 85-seater, split over two floors and – as at his former gaff – featuring counter-style seating with an open kitchen. (The idea was trialled last year as a pop-up, by a different chef, Leonardo Pereira). / WC2N 4EJ; nutshelllondon.co.uk; @NutshellLondon.

O'VER   £52   433

1 NORRIS STREET, ST. JAMES'S MARKET, SW1 020 7930 9664   4–4D
44-46 SOUTHWARK STREET, SE1 020 7378 9933 10–4B

"Out-of-this-world pizza" – using seawater in the dough, and whose "toppings are inventive without being bizarre" – again inspires high praise for this "piece of Napoli in London", "on a busy street that's a little out of the way", but "not far from Borough Market". In the

evening it can be "crowded and very noisy", but staff are "always very welcoming". As of June 2019, it has a new heart-of-the-West End sibling, in the St James's Market development. / www.overuk.com.

OAK   £60   334

243 GOLDHAWK RD, W12 020 8741 7700 8–1B
137 WESTBOURNE PARK RD, W2 020 7221 3355   7–1B
39 PARKGATE ROAD, SW11 020 7924 3999 6–4C

"Tasty pizzas" top the bill at these "good-looking gastropub" conversions in Notting Hill and Shepherd's Bush, with the "excellent new addition" of a "stylish bistro" in a "stunning, huge space" on the river at Battersea. "Pizzas and starters outshine main courses, but overall very pleasant and relaxing". / W12 10.30pm, Fri & Sat 11 pm Sun 9.30pm; W2 10.30pm, Fri & Sat 11 pm, Sun 10 pm.

OBLIX SE1   £105   224

LEVEL 32, THE SHARD, 31 ST. THOMAS STREET   020 7268 6700 10–4C

"The view is spectacular" from the 32nd floor of the Shard, so "why not put the £35 it would cost to go to the viewing deck towards a meal here", in the brasserie from Rainer Becker of Zuma and Roka. "The meal is ridiculously overpriced", of course, but "the atmosphere feels special" and – though the food is not without its detractors – a relatively high proportion of diners here feel "it matches the panorama". You can choose between the West section for a restaurant-style meal or the East bar with food. / SE1 9RY; www.oblixrestaurant.com; @OblixRestaurant; 11 pm; booking max 6 may apply.

ODETTE'S NW1   £62   443

130 REGENTS PARK ROAD   020 7586 8569 9–3B

This "smart" Primrose Hill veteran of 40-odd years is "a most likeable place enhanced by the patina of time, and combined with inventive high-end cooking" from chef Bryn Williams, who has owned it for the past decade. It's "always a treat" to taste the "beautiful ingredients", which include produce from the Williams family farm in Wales; although the patron's tilt towards a Welsh and Irish heritage means it's "tempting here to overdo the carbs, cream and calories": Irish soda bread, cheesy choux nibbles, creamy tarts and caramel-sauced soufflés to name but a few…" / NW1 8XL; www.odettesprimrosehill.com; @Odettes_rest; 10 pm, Sat 10.30 pm, Sun 9.30 pm; closed Mon; No Amex.

OGNISKO RESTAURANT SW7   £54   345

55 PRINCE'S GATE, EXHIBITION ROAD 020 7589 0101   6–1C

"What a wonderful oasis of calm in the hustle of London's museum area" – this "elegant dining room of a Polish emigrés' club" (open to the general public) has a "wonderful

19th-century vibe" and is a "civilised and reliable" setting that's both "cosy in winter" and with a particularly "beautiful terrace for summer". Its "authentic traditional Polish fare" is "charmingly served" in "huge portions" with lashings of vodka and some interesting wines. / SW7 2PG; www.ogniskorestaurant.co.uk; @OgniskoRest; 11.15 pm, Sun 10.30 pm; closed Mon L; No trainers.

OKA £48 4|3|2

KINGLY COURT, 1 KINGLY COURT, W1 020 7734 3556 4–2B
251 KING'S ROAD, SW3 020 7349 8725 6–3C
71 REGENTS PARK RD, NW1 020 7483 2072 9–3B
88 CHURCH ROAD, SW13 020 8741 8577 11–1A

"Punching above their weight in terms of flavour and presentation" – this "buzzy" quartet of "medium-priced" Japanese/Asian fusion "pit-stops" are "fab little places" for a high-quality refuelling (the new Barnes site is "perfect before a film at the Olympic across the road"). / www.okarestaurant.co.uk; 10.30 pm.

OKLAVA EC2 £57 4|4|3

74 LUKE ST 020 7729 3032 13–1B

"Outstanding Turkish and Cypriot cuisine" – with an original, light spin that can come as a "real surprise" – wins plaudits for this Shoreditch venue. "Sitting at the counter watching the food being prepared is eye-opening; and owners (Selin Kiazim and Laura Christie) obviously love what they do". "It's not strictly vegetarian, but has many options if you are". / EC2A 4PY; www.oklava.co.uk; @Oklava_ldn; 10.30 pm, Sun 4 pm; booking max 6 may apply.

OLDROYD N1 £56 4|3|2

344 UPPER ST 020 8617 9010 9–3D

"Tiny, really tiny!" – Tom Oldroyd's converted Islington house is "either intimate or cramped… it's hard to decide", but "even though the space is confined, it has character" ("upstairs is slightly better"), plus it's staffed with "nice people". The draw is the "simple and well-prepared food", which is "really tasty and interesting": in the space, "how they do it is a mystery!" / N1 0PD; www.oldroydlondon.com; @oldroydlondon; 10.30 pm, Fri 11 pm, Sun 9.30 pm; Booking max 4 may apply.

OLIVETO SW1 £60 4|3|2

49 ELIZABETH STREET 020 7730 0074 2–4A

"Loud without being unpleasant", this "cheerful and buzzy" Sardinian has been a Belgravia stalwart for many years – "my son spent his formative years coming back to this place because of the huge and excellent pizzas" (and the repertoire also includes pasta and salads). Older regulars are more enamoured of the "interesting Italian/Sardinian wine list". / SW1W 9PP; www.olivorestaurants.com/oliveto; @OlivoGroup; 10.30 pm, Sun 10 pm.

OLIVO SW1 £74 3|3|2

21 ECCLESTON STREET 020 7730 2505 2–4B

"An old haunt of style and enjoyment" – this Sardinian was the original in Mauro Sanna's upmarket Belgravia group – "an absolute banker for consistency". "The freshness of the cooking and the delightfully different wines" make it a "great lunch venue", although – this being SW1 – it's "now outrageously priced". / SW1W 9LX; www.olivorestaurants.com; @OlivoGroup; 10.30 pm; closed Sat L & Sun L.

OLIVOCARNE SW1 £80 3|2|2

61 ELIZABETH ST 020 7730 7997 2–4A

"Excellent meat" puts the 'carne' into this accomplished Belgravian – part of Mauro Sanna's group of upmarket Sardinian locals – which shares the "original" cooking and "special and varied wines" of its siblings. Its austere but zany minimalist decor lacks charge but is certainly 'different'. / SW1W 9PP; www.olivorestaurants.com; 11 pm, Sun 10.30 pm.

OLIVOMARE SW1 £79 3|3|2

10 LOWER BELGRAVE ST 020 7730 9022 2–4B

"Always a-buzz with locals", this "buoyant" Sardinian seafood specialist in Belgravia is "a bit steep in its prices at £60-£70 a head, but the freshness and range of fish make it worthwhile". It was the third to open in the Olivo group owned by Mauro Sana, who seemingly "personally knows more than 70% of his clientele". / SW1W 0LJ; www.olivorestaurants.com; @OlivoGroup; 11 pm, Sun 10.30 pm; booking max 10 may apply.

OLLEY'S SE24 £39 3|3|2

65-69 NORWOOD RD 020 8671 8259 11–2D

"Generous portions of consistently excellent fish 'n' chips" have made Harry Niazi's "friendly" rustic chippie a fixture opposite Brockwell Park since 1987. It inspired the odd 'off' report this year, though: "supposedly the best chippy in the area, but we found it a huge let-down". / SE24 9AA; www.olleys.info; 10 pm, Sun 9.30 pm; No Amex.

OLYMPIC, OLYMPIC STUDIOS SW13 £52 2|2|3

117-123 CHURCH ROAD 020 8912 5170 11–1A

The all-day brasserie at the legendary recording studios-turned-indie-cinema and members' club is "popular with Barnes residents" after a "pre-film snack". Reporters agree that "breakfast and brunch – especially at one of the outside tables under the cherry trees – are good"; lunch and dinner less so: "the cuisine is over-ambitious and not well-realised". / SW13 9HL; www.olympiccinema.co.uk; @Olympic_Cinema; 11 pm, Fri & Sat midnight, Sun 10 pm.

OLYMPUS FISH N3 £37 3|3|2

140-144 BALLARDS LN 020 8371 8666 1–1B

"Fish 'n' chips as it's meant to be" – "non-greasy, tasty and in good portions" – makes this chippy a "great local" for Finchley. It's Turkish-run, which gives the option to "try fish from the charcoal grill". There's still the odd glitchy report, but one regular says that "after an off-patch recently, it's back on form", as it enters its 20th year in business. / N3 2PA; www.olympusrestaurant.co.uk; @Olympus_London; 11 pm.

ON THE BAB £36 3|3|2

36 WELLINGTON ST, WC2 020 7240 8825 5–3D
305 OLD ST, EC1 020 7683 0361 13–1B
9 LUDGATE BROADWAY, EC4 020 7248 8777 10–2A

"A good stab at proper Korean food" – these "nicely buzzing", K-pop styled pit-stops are "not subtle" but score points for their punchily flavoured bites (the fried chicken is the fave rave), served "cheaply and quickly". / onthebab.co.uk; @onthebab; EC1 & WC2 10.30 pm, Sun 10 pm; W1 & EC4 4 pm; EC4 closed Sat & Sun; W1 closed Sun; no bookings.

108 GARAGE W10 £79 4|3|2

108 GOLBORNE RD 020 8969 3769 7–1A

The "fantastic experience" of eating at this highly original and "exciting" venue – a former car repair shop off Portobello Market featuring "industrial stripped-down walls" – has been restored with the return to the kitchen of Chris Denncy, "a really inventive chef", following the loss of sibling-venture Southam Street. It's "uber trendy, but the food is of exceptional quality". / W10 5PS; www.108garage.com.

104 RESTAURANT W2 £87 4|3|3

104A CHEPSTOW ROAD 020 3417 4744 7–1B

"So glad to have 104 back on the map", say fans of this tiny 14-seater on the fringe of Notting Hill – formerly Marianne's (RIP) and now re-launched without fanfare by chef Richard Wilkins and front-of-house Matt Hough: the former of whom had worked here with Marianne Lumb before she moved onto pastures new. Early feedback on this "very pretty room" ("romantic", but "be prepared to overhear everyone else's conversation") does include the odd caveat ("excellent quality overall, but some dishes seemed overly simple; and some of the accompanying sauces had gone wrong – the lemon sabayon with the asparagus just tasted of synthetic gloop"). For the most part, however, the picture is of rave reviews for "stunning and very high quality dishes at a reasonable price for such great produce". / W2 5QS; www.104restaurant.com.

Mortimer House Kitchen W1

Lutyens Grill, The Ned EC2

101 THAI KITCHEN
W6 £38 522

352 KING ST 020 8746 6888 8–2B

"Phenomenally authentic", family-run Thai caff near Stamford Brook, on busy King Street, that's become a cult destination amongst Asian food cognoscenti for its Isaan dishes from the country's northeast, supplemented by southern seafood by 'Auntie Bee'; the food "feels like the real McCoy – and is quite challenging as a result". The place is "filled with Thai expats – what more do you need to say? Oh, it's cheap as chips". / W6 0RX; 10.30 pm, Fri & Sat 11 pm; No Amex.

1 LOMBARD STREET
EC3 £86 222

1 LOMBARD ST 020 7929 6611 10–3C

"Such a classic City venue" – former banker, Soren Jessen's smooth operation in a converted banking hall near Bank station has traded off Square Mile expense accounts for 20 years. If nobody thrills to the cuisine, nor do they tend to have very harsh words for it – "whenever I'm looking for dinner with a nice wine, I head to 1 Lombard Street where I won't be disappointed". There's a "great atmosphere at breakfast time", too. / EC3V 9AA; www.1lombardstreet.com; @1LombardStreet; 10 pm; closed Sat & Sun; booking max 10 may apply.

ONIMA W1 £86 334

1-3 AVERY ROW 020 7078 9747 3–2B

Swish, Greek-owned, late-2018 newcomer, which occupies two floors of a five-storey Mayfair townhouse (the remainder being dedicated to a bar, club, roof terrace, etc) which aims to 'brings the spirit of Mykonos to London' on a site that once housed the HQ of Cartier's watch-making empire. Ex-Novikov chef, Sicilian Carmelo Carnevale, oversees a Mediterranean/Asian mash-up of a menu, which earned solid ratings in early feedback, alongside perhaps predictable concerns about the slightly scary pricing. / W1K 4AJ; www.onimarestaurant.com.

LES 110 DE TAILLEVENT
W1 £83 233

16 CAVENDISH SQUARE 020 3141 6016 3–1B

"You will never get bored, although you might get drunk!" at this London scion of Paris's famous Taillevent group, where "you can try 110 different types of superb wine by the glass". Set in "an attractive former private banking hall" – on the opposite side of Cavendish Square from the back of Oxford Street's John Lewis – its "staff are extremely well-drilled and make everything effortless and smooth". However, "the total cost of a meal takes it out of brasserie territory", while the "seasonal French cuisine", though "enjoyable", doesn't always seem in keeping with the level of ambition that the final bill might imply. / W1G 9DD; www.les-110-taillevent-london.com; @110London; 10.30 pm; closed Sat L & Sun.

OOTY W1 £75 543

66 BAKER STREET 020 3727 5014 2–1A

"Gorgeous, perfect, elegant" Indian cuisine from former Rasoi chef, Manmeet Singh Bali, wins very high food-ratings for this Marylebone newcomer. It's on the site that was formerly well known as Galvin Bistrot de Luxe (RIP), which has been given a "beautiful", unusually tasteful makeover; "impeccable" service adds to the very civilised, if slightly "low key" tone. Fingers crossed word gets out fully, though: "it was a bit empty when we went which made it a bit of a barn: with a few more people it could have been fantastic". / W1U 7DJ; www.ooty.co.uk; @ootylondon.

OPERA TAVERN
WC2 £59 443

23 CATHERINE STREET 020 7836 3680 5–3D

"Not really a pub any more, though it certainly used to be" – this well-known tapas bar near Covent Garden operates on two atmospheric, if noisy, floors, and is a "go-to for pre-theatre dining, with superb small plates at a relatively reasonable cost for the location". "The little morsels of Spanish and Italian deliciousness haven't faltered since the Salt Yard chain was taken over" (in late-2018). In late summer 2019 it emerged from a major revamp. / WC2B 5JS; www.saltyardgroup.co.uk/opera-tavern; @saltyardgroup; 11.15 pm, Sun 9.45 pm.

OPSO W1 £59 333

10 PADDINGTON ST 020 7487 5088 2–1A

A modern take on Greek cuisine in Marylebone hailed for its "authentic food and lively atmosphere (crowded and noisy inside but good outside on a fine day)". Other plus points include "friendly, helpful service" and "a nice selection of Greek wines" – in fact, there's "little to complain about, except perhaps the pricing". A more casual street-food offshoot, Pittabun, opened off Carnaby Street last year. / W1U 5QL; www.opso.co.uk; @OPSO_london; 10:30pm, Sun 10 pm; closed Sun D.

THE ORANGE SW1 £65 323

37 PIMLICO RD 020 7881 9844 6–2D

This spruced-up gastro-boozer in an attractive square on the Pimlico-Chelsea border makes for a "fun dining experience with all the benefits of a pub". The cooking is "better than expected", with the "reliable pizzas a safe bet". / SW1W 8NE; www.theorange.co.uk; @theorangesw1; 10 pm, Sun 9.30 pm.

ORANGE PEKOE
SW13 £36 334

3 WHITE HART LN 020 8876 6070 11–1A

"A vast choice of great teas, coffees, cakes and sandwiches, plus daily specials" attract hordes of visitors to this "very popular" tea shop near the river in chichi Barnes. If you want to sit down for a proper afternoon tea, you'd be wise to book. / SW13 0PX; www.orangepekoeteas.com; @OrangePekoeTeas; 5 pm; L only.

ORASAY W11 £59 444

31 KENSINGTON PARK ROAD 020 7043 1400 7–1A

As "a welcome arrival in the area", Jackson Boxer's "friendly and unpretentious" new venture (which oldies will think of as opposite the long-RIP 192) commands a lot of support from Notting Hill locals, and it's drawing a "fun crowd", including a few famous faces. The cuisine focuses on the Hebridean islands where Boxer spent childhood summers: to fans, results are "superb", but one or two reporters feel "good ingredients are fussily assembled" to create dishes that are merely "good but not amazing". / W11 2EU; orasay.london; @Jackson_Boxer.

ORMER MAYFAIR,
FLEMINGS MAYFAIR HOTEL
W1 £100 442

7-12 HALF MOON STREET 020 7016 5601 3–4B

"A delight!" – Shaun Rankin's "exceptional" and "beautifully presented" cuisine at this posh, Mayfair hotel dining room wins acclaim from all reporters this year: "not sure why it doesn't have a stronger following – highly under-rated". He made his name on Jersey – an 'ormer' is a Channel Islands gastropod – before shifting to the capital in 2016. "It's a beautiful interior, but the basement setting can make it a bit gloomy for lunch". / W1J 7BH; www.ormermayfair.com; @ormermayfair; No shorts.

ORO DI NAPOLI
W5 £35 443

6 THE QUADRANT, LITTLE EALING LANE 020 3632 5580 1–3A

"There's no better pizza in London" ("twenty or so combinations of toppings or you can make your own as you wish"), say fans of this "humming" South Ealing spot, where "the kitchen is visible (almost indivisible) from the small and intimate dining area" presided over by "smiling, passionate staff". It's thriving in an area thick with the smoke of Neapolitan wood-fired ovens – nearby Santa Maria is another claimant as 'London's best'. / W5 4EE; www.lorodinapoli.co.uk; 11 pm.

ORRERY W1 £89 333

55 MARYLEBONE HIGH ST 020 7616 8000 2–1A

Opened by Sir Terence Conran in 1997 (on the first floor, above the eponymous Conran Shop) – this "calm and well-run", light-filled Marylebone fixture remains one of the most consistent performers in the D&D London stable. Igor Tymchyshyn has been at the stoves since 2008 (and became 'chef-patron' in 2016), and his "top quality" and "well-presented" modern cuisine is served by "accommodating and unfussy" staff in a stylish setting: a narrowly-proportioned room, with great views of the adjacent church. Top Tip – the "secret" rooftop terrace is a joy on a summer's evening". / W1U 5RB; www.orrery-restaurant.co.uk;

@The_Orrery; 10 pm, Fri & Sat 10.30 pm; booking max 8 may apply.

OSCAR WILDE LOUNGE AT CAFE ROYAL W1 £82 345

68 REGENT ST   020 7406 3333   4–4C

"One of the most magical afternoon tea locations" – "overseas guests are particularly impressed by the sumptuous surroundings" of this "OTT" rococo chamber (the original Café Royal Grill Room, dating back to 1865), which comes "with loads of mirrors and gold leaf" and flamboyant murals. "Don't go just for the room", though – "staff are great (making you feel special without being too pompous), while the sandwiches are varied and plentiful", pastries are "featherlight" and there are a variety of options for tea itself. / W1B; www.hotelcaferoyal.com/oscarwildebar; @HotelCafeRoyal; 6 pm; L & afternoon tea only.

OSLO COURT NW8 £66 354

CHARLBERT STREET   020 7722 8795   9–3A

"Like going on a 1970s cruise without leaving the shore" – this "crazy-but-fun throwback" at the foot of a Regent's Park apartment-block is certainly "one of a kind", and always "leaves you smiling". "Faultless and charming" staff of decades' standing bantering with silver-haired regulars of a not-dissimilar vintage create an atmosphere that's "half restaurant – half theatre": "there are always generations of families celebrating a birthday" and "the hubbub can be deafening, with cakes arriving at regular intervals". The "absurdly retro menu" (crudités, melba toast, steak Diane…) is seemingly unchanged from when the place opened, and delivers "overwhelming helpings of well-cooked classic dishes, washed down with very sensibly priced wine". "The renowned dessert waiter with his trolley is still there, but of late, no longer always does the same performance at the end of the meal, whereby he tells you what you want without you saying, and says 'mama saved the last piece for you!'" / NW8 7EN; www.oslocourtrestaurant.co.uk; 11 pm; closed Sun; No jeans.

OSTERIA, BARBICAN CENTRE EC2 £58 332

LEVEL 2 SILK STREET   020 7588 3008   10–1B

"I am truly surprised at the low ratings this has received in Harden's!" – Searcy's seem to have pulled their socks up at their Italian brasserie and cocktail bar, which sits in the beating heart of the Barbican arts centre (making it a natural pre-theatre option), and which by day enjoys "excellent views" over the centre's lake and St Giles Cripplegate church. Some diners do still say its overall performance is "no better than adequate", but more fans this year lauded its "excellent food from a regularly changing menu". / EC2Y 8DS; osterialondon. co.uk; @searcyslondon; 10.30 pm, Sat 11.30 pm; closed Sun.

OSTERIA ANTICA BOLOGNA SW11 £50 322

23 NORTHCOTE RD   020 7978 4771   11–2C

"For a 'local Italian' it's hard to beat" this "consistently good" trat that celebrates three decades on Clapham's foodie Northcote Road this year. "It looks and feels like an authentic taverna in Northern Italy" – "there's nothing flash and no emphasis on fancy tableware or presentation, but I've had better food here than at fancier places in town". It's "a bit dark inside", though, "so better for lunch than dinner". Top Menu Tip – "wild boar ragu". / SW11 1NG; www.osteria.co.uk; @OsteriaAntica; 10.30 pm, Sun 10 pm.

OSTERIA BASILICO W11 £63 432

29 KENSINGTON PARK RD   020 7727 9957   7–1A

"Simple, honest Italian fare done well" – with "fresh ingredients and great service" – is a combination that has served Notting HIll well for almost 30 years at this local trattoria: the senior in a group of three siblings in the same street (see also Mediterraneo and Essenza). / W11 2EU; www.osteriabasilico.co.uk; 11.30 pm, Sun 10.30 pm; no booking, Sat L.

OSTERIA DELL'ANGOLO SW1 £64 332

47 MARSHAM ST   020 3268 1077   2–4C

"Ignore the lobbyists feeding MPs and enjoy this for what it is" – a smart, traditionally decorated corner-spot that's one of the only restaurants in Westminster worth going to eat in! "Italian through and through", it features "many regional dishes" and "unusual takes on traditional pasta and main courses (including crab, rabbit and quail)"; plus an interesting, all-Italian wine list. / SW1P 3DR; www.osteriadellangolo.co.uk; @Osteria_Angolo; 10 pm; closed Sat L & Sun.

OSTERIA TUFO N4 £52 432

67 FONTHILL RD   020 7272 2911   9–1D

This "Italian gem" in Finsbury Park has locals purring with its "wonderful homemade pasta" and "brilliant service from Paola and her team" – "we were a fussy group aged 7 to 75 and the staff catered for our every desire". Yes, there's "a singing waiter", but "it's not cringe-worthy, he's really good!". / N4 3HZ; www.osteriatufo.co.uk; @osteriatufo; 10.30 pm, Sun 9.30 pm; closed Mon & Sun L; No Amex.

THE OTHER NAUGHTY PIGLET SW1 £50 432

12 PALACE STREET   020 7592 0322   2–4B

In a masterstroke of casting, Andrew Lloyd Webber recruited Brixton's Naughty Piglets team to run the restaurant at his new Other Palace Theatre in Victoria, bringing their "dependably delightful" cuisine to this "almost secret location tucked away by Buckingham Palace". / SW1E 5JA; www.theothernaughtypiglet.co.uk; booking max 10 may apply.

OTTO'S WC1 £73 443

182 GRAY'S INN ROAD   020 7713 0107   2–1D

"A joyous celebration of how restaurants used to be and how they should be"; "eccentric Otto" is "a breath of fresh French air", and his "gift of showmanship", "traditional service" and "classic Gallic cuisine" – all in a "pleasant and old-fashioned", if slightly "faded", dining room in out-of-the-way Bloomsbury – is part of a nowadays "unique" approach that most diners feel is "always a wow". "Otto's duck and lobster à la presse is superlative" (he's recently added pigeon too), "the steak tartare is London's best" and four culinary throwbacks form part of a "magnificent", unreformed, old-school menu. Caveats? – some of the food is "devastatingly cream-rich – not all modern eaters could manage it" – and "though it's all very likeable, watch out as the bill stacks up quickly". "But it's one-of-a-kind". / WC1X 8EW; www.ottos-restaurant.com; @ottosrestaurant; 9.30 pm; closed Mon, Sat L & Sun.

OTTOLENGHI £58 322

13 MOTCOMB ST, SW1   020 7823 2707   6–1D
63 LEDBURY RD, W11   020 7727 1121   7–1B
287 UPPER ST, N1   020 7288 1454   9–2D
50 ARTILLERY PAS, E1   020 7247 1999   10–2D

"A feast for the eyes and always fresh, delicious" and full of "interesting flavour" – the "unusual salads" and habit-forming cakes at Yotam Ottolenghi's starkly decorated café chain: an ongoing success-story particularly beloved of brunching yummy-mums and Guardian-reading types ("is this a restaurant or a cult?… some of the clientele on my trip seemed beyond parody"). "It's only the food that makes it worth it" though – branches are "super-busy and never enjoyable" – and, given the prices, a visit can "feel like daylight robbery". / www.ottolenghi.co.uk; N1 10.30 pm, Sun 7 pm; W11 & SW1 8 pm, Sat 7 pm, Sun 6 pm; E1 10.30 pm, Sun 6 pm; W11 & SW1 no booking.

OXO TOWER, RESTAURANT SE1 £100 111

BARGE HOUSE ST   020 7803 3888   10–3A

"Tried it again… still disappointing" – this notorious South Bank rooftop has been our No. 1 top dud for about as long as we can remember. "Yes, the views are fine, but – with its quite insipid cooking and no glamour whatsoever" – the experience here is "just dull and mediocre". At some level, "you've got to congratulate them for still getting patrons for such overpriced rubbish!" / SE1 9PH; www.harveynichols.com/restaurant/the-oxo-tower; @OxoTowerWharf; 11 pm, Sun 10 pm; booking max 8 may apply.

OXO TOWER, BRASSERIE SE1 £75 1|1|3

BARGE HOUSE ST 020 7803 3888 10–3A

"Why can't they get it right?" in the cheaper section of this South Bank landmark. "The view is superb, the setting is relaxing… if only the food lived up to it". / SE1 9PH; www.harveynichols.com/restaurants/oxo-tower-london; @oxo_tower; 11 pm, Sun 10 pm; May need 2+ to book.

THE OYSTERMEN SEAFOOD KITCHEN & BAR WC2 £63 4|3|3

32 HENRIETTA ST 020 7240 4417 5–3D

"You'll expect to look out the window at the beach and waves… yet it's Covent Garden out there!". This "fun and casual" two-year-old perhaps "feels different since they grew" (into the next door premises) in the autumn of 2018. "But you still eat cheek-by-jowl with neighbouring tables" in a "hustling-and-bustling" setting, and most reports still feel it's "just as good in its expanded space". Amongst the selection of "cracking" fish and seafood, "the oysters are a joy", "the crab's a wow"; and it's all "amazing value". "Likeable staff", too. / WC2E 8NA; oystermen.co.uk; @theoystermen.

OZONE COFFEE ROASTERS EC2 £44 3|3|4

11 LEONARD STREET 020 7490 1039 13–1A

"Damn fine coffee! Nuff said!" – "complex and expertly made" – is the focus at this "super-cool spot" in Shoreditch (the offshoot of an NZ original). The beans are "roasted downstairs" with wonderful aromas floating up from the big machines in the basement, while upstairs a "funky crowd enjoy food and drinks" from the "best breakfast" to late-night cocktails. A second London branch is scheduled to open in Bethnal Green in late-2019. / EC2A 4AQ; ozonecoffee.co.uk; @Ozonecoffeeuk; 9 pm, Sat & Sun 4.30 pm ; May need 8+ to book.

P FRANCO E5 £48 4|2|3

107 LOWER CLAPTON ROAD 020 8533 4660 14–1B

No Eater newsletter is complete without paradisical claims for this – still the online fooderati's favourite bottle shop – in gentrifying Clapton: a "funky" and "buzzy", if "very crowded" little space where "sensational wines" (of the 'natural' variety) are accompanied by "amazing" and "eclectic" small plates from an ever-changing roster of chefs: all eaten at a communal central table. / E5 0NP; www.pfranco.co.uk; Thu-Sat 10 pm, Sun 9 pm; closed Mon-Wed, Thu-Sat D only, Sun L & D; No Amex; No bookings.

PACHAMAMA 2|2|3

18 THAYER STREET, W1 020 7935 9393 3–1A
GREAT EASTERN STREET, EC2 13–1B

"Big, punchy flavours" come through from the "varied" menu at these "lively" ("we could barely hear one another above the din") Peruvians, in Marylebone and – since November 2018 – now also in Shoreditch (Pachamama East).

PADELLA SE1 £28 5|4|3

6 SOUTHWARK ST NO TEL 10–4C

"Bellissimo!" – Tim Siadatan and Jordan Frieda's Borough Market three-year-old remains one of the capital's best options on a budget. The formula is simple: "no reservations, no frills": just "superlative, freshly made pasta" from a "compact and great value menu". "Arrive ultra-early to dodge the worst of the perma-queues", although "the line moves relatively quickly, and their beeper system means you can go for a drink and come back to get your table". In September 2019, they announced a second branch is top open on Phipp Street in Shoreditch in early 2020. / SE1 1TQ; www.padella.co; @padella_pasta; 10 pm, Sun 5 pm; no booking.

PALADAR SE1 £59 4|3|3

4-5 LONDON ROAD 020 7186 5555 10–4A

"A great find in the wasteland around Elephant & Castle, where everything is South American, from ingredients, such as plantain and cassava, to the wine list and the lively clientele". A bar/restaurant (with walled garden for warmer days), it's "a great introduction to Latino food": "typical dishes such as ceviche and braised black beef are produced to a higher standard than just about anywhere else in London". Top Tip – all dishes are gluten-free, with a range of veggie and vegan options. / SE1 6JZ; www.paladarlondon.com; @paladarlondon.

PALATINO EC1 £60 4|3|2

71 CENTRAL STREET 020 3481 5300 10–1B

Chef Stevie Parle's two-year-old pasta specialist is a real "crowd-pleaser", with "consistently interesting, extremely tasty" Roman-inspired dishes emerging from its "impressively visible kitchen". It's part of a "warehouse-style" Clerkenwell work-space, but "when busy you forget the office atmosphere which can otherwise be a little cold". Top Tip – "cacio e pepe is to die for". / EC1V 8AB; palatino.london; @PalatinoLondon; 10 pm; closed Sun.

THE PALOMAR W1 £64 4|3|4

34 RUPERT STREET 020 7439 8777 4–3D

"Deafening and crowded, but that's all part of the fun" – Tel Aviv comes to Theatreland at this "interesting haven", on the fringe of Chinatown. "If you like atmosphere, too much noise, and somewhere right in the heart of things, it hits the bullseye"; and "sitting at the bar, bantering with the chefs and soaking up the superb playlist help make this a truly memorable occasion". The "stunning and stunningly different", "Israeli-influenced" small plates are "simply scrumptious" too, even if "prices are high for such a quick turnover of covers". / W1D 6DN; www.thepalomar.co.uk; @palomarsoho; 11 pm, Sun 9 pm; closed Sun L.

PAPPA CICCIA £37 3|3|2

105 MUNSTER RD, SW6 020 7384 1884 11–1B
41 FULHAM HIGH ST, SW6 020 7736 0900 11–1B

"The best pizza in the area" – "thin, very tasty" and in "large" portions – wins fans for this "friendly" family-owned trio that has built a solid following in Fulham and Putney over two decades. SW15 is primarily take-out and delivery (but has some outside seating). / www.pappaciccia.com; SW6 5RQ 11 pm, Sat & Sun 11.30 pm; SW6 3JJ 11 pm.

PARADISE W1

61 RUPERT STREET 4–2D

Replacing Soho's Spuntino (RIP) – a Sri Lankan 30-seater from a team who have been popping up around London recently, so it will have a ready-made fanclub when it opens in October 2019. The refurb is being done by the designer behind Kiln and Smoking Goat, who is aiming to keep the site's stripped-back aesthetic, but with a new 'warm-yet-raw' look. / W1D 7PW.

PARADISE BY WAY OF KENSAL GREEN W10 £55 2|2|5

19 KILBURN LANE 020 8969 0098 1–2B

For a chilled Sunday roast, vibey night out, date, birthday party, funeral wake – whatever – it's still worth considering this vast Kensal Green tavern, with seemingly endless bars, dance-floors, party rooms, and terraces, plus its gorgeous dining room and garden. The days when it was in the vanguard of London's gastropub scene are long gone, but it's still a magnet for chilled Notting Hillbillies who've strayed north; and still serves dependable grub. / W10 4AE; www.theparadise.co.uk; @weloveparadise; 10.30 pm, Fri & Sat 11 pm, Sun 9 pm; closed weekday L; No Amex.

PARADISE HAMPSTEAD NW3 £41 4|5|4

49 SOUTH END RD 020 7794 6314 9–2A

"Lovely neighbourhood Indian" near Hampstead Heath that's deservedly popular for its "tasty food from an interesting menu" and "reasonable prices". Now run by the second generation of the founder's family, who provide "exceptionally friendly service", its only drawback is that it "can be difficult to get a table". / NW3 2QB; www.paradisehampstead.co.uk; 10.45 pm.

Neptune, Kimpton Fitzroy London WC1

EL PARADOR NW1 £41 333

245 EVERSHOLT ST 020 7387 2789 9–3C

Veteran, family-run tapas bar, near Mornington Crescent, which garners consistent high praise for "home cooking of the kind you rarely find these days". What's more, there's a "pleasant garden for outdoor eating in fine weather". / NW1 1BA; www.elparadorlondon.com; 11 pm, Fri & Sat 11.30 pm, Sun 9.30 pm; closed Sat L & Sun L; No Amex.

PARANHODU SE14 £23 342

125 LEWISHAM WAY 020 3573 8175 1–4D

Down near Goldsmiths in need of a decent scoff? Don't forget this "good, independent Korean" – a five-year-old café offering "a solid representation of all the classics: nice banchan, satisfying dolsot bibimbap and kimchi tofu stews etc". / SE14 6QJ.

PARK CHINOIS
W1 £136 223

17 BERKELEY ST 020 3327 8888 3–3C

There's no denying the "seductive" pull of this opulent venture (founded in 2015 by Alan Yau and nowadays owned by an anonymous Turkish family) which brings a slice of 1920s Shanghai decadence to Mayfair. But while fans "love the dim sum selection and vibes on a busy night", saying it "ticks all the boxes", its "off-the-scale prices" inspire outrage amongst many reporters, and raise a suspicion that beneath the glamorous veneer, "it's just a bog standard Chinese". / W1S 4NF; www.parkchinois.com; @ParkChinois; 11 pm, Sun 10.15 pm; No jeans.

PARK TERRACE
RESTAURANT, ROYAL
GARDEN HOTEL
W8 £62 233

2-24 KENSINGTON HIGH ST 020 7361 0602 6–1A

With its "beautiful views over Kensington Gardens", this "quiet and comfortable" hotel restaurant makes a useful venue for lunch or afternoon tea. "The service is a perfect blend of efficiency and friendliness", while the Sunday roast – sirloin of Buccleuch beef, carved from the trolley – is "delicious". / W8 4PT; www.parkterracerestaurant.co.uk; 10:30.

PARLOUR KENSAL
NW10 £50 344

5 REGENT ST 020 8969 2184 1–2B

This "super gastropub" on Kensal Rise has a "creative, ever-changing and good-value menu" that starts with a "fantastic breakfast". The "always incredible welcome" ensures a "perfect chilled time". / NW10 5LG; www.parlourkensal.com; @ParlourUK; 10 pm; closed Mon.

PARRILLAN N1 £66 344

COAL DROPS YARD 020 7018 3339 9–3C

"An experience as well as amazing food!" – the Hart Bros' spring 2019 newcomer, in Coal Drops Yard, occupies a big, glam terrace, overlooking Regent's Canal: "it's outside only, partially protected from the rain, but with no protection from any wind". Each table has its own DIY tabletop mini-grill (the eponymous 'parrillan'): "you grill your own partially-prepared vegetables, meats and fish"; and there's also a selection of 'para picar' (Spanish nibbles). All early feedback says the formula stacks up well, but one or two diners feel the bill ends up a tad pricey. / N1C 4AB; barrafina.co.uk; @ParrillanLondon.

PARSONS WC2 £65 432

39 ENDELL STREET 020 3422 0221 5–2C

"It's the fresh fish that brings you" to this "tiny, tiny space" in Covent Garden (sibling to 10 Cases, just across the road) – a "crowded, congested and stripped-down room" that's almost "more of a seafood bar than a restaurant as you perch on stools". "There's a small menu, with a few specials painted on the walls showing the catch of the day", "all cooked to perfection behind the counter and served as soon as it's ready". "Ideal for pre-theatre, but it doesn't encourage lingering". / WC2H 9BA; www.parsonslondon.co.uk.

PASSIONE E TRADIZIONE
N15 £39 322

451 WEST GREEN ROAD 020 8245 9491 1–1C

"A top local" – this small, basic-looking two-year-old between Wood Green and Tottenham is worth remembering for its "great pizzas along with superb pastas". / N15 3PL; spinach.london; 11 pm.

PASSYUNK AVENUE
W1 £47 443

80 CLEVELAND STREET 020 3960 2251 2–1B

"Pure fast food evil (in the best kind of way)" – this retro newcomer in the shadow of the BT tower is named for the home of the Philly cheesesteak, which it serves with "great authenticity (as validated by my colleague from Philadelphia)", alongside "the best buffalo wings in London (and maybe outside of Pennsylvania)", plus other classics from Rocky Balboa's hometown like "wiz cheese and bacon tater tots". "Friendly staff" complete its down-to-earth vibe; there's also a branch in Westfield Stratford. / W1T 6NE; www.passyunk.co.uk; @passyunkavenue.

PASTA REMOLI £40 333

DICKENS YARD, 16A NEW BROADWAY, W5 020 8840 2687 1–3A

7 CLIFTON TERRACE, N4 020 7263 2948 9–1D

3 FRESH FOOD, GREAT EASTERN MARKET, WESTFIELD STRATFORD CITY, E20 020 8555 9149 14–1D

From its Finsbury Park base (next to the Park Theatre), this "cheerful" group of "good neighbourhood pasta-stops" has expanded to Ealing this year, with a Wembley branch coming soon (there's also an outlet in Westfield Stratford); all deliver "well-cooked", affordable pasta. / www.pastaremoli.co.uk; @PastaRemoli.

PASTAIO W1 £45 332

19 GANTON STREET 4–2B

"Amazing fresh pasta that's great value for central London" has carved a strong following for Stevie Parle's "loud" and buzzy Kingly Court operation for a "swift", "cheap 'n' cheerful" bite. / W1F 7BU; www.pastaio.london; @pastaiolondon.

PASTICCERIA MARCHESI
1824 W1

117 MOUNT STREET 020 8075 5380 3–3B

For a posh bun, it's hard to upstage this new Milanese import: a fashionista favourite for its superlative cakes and also serving some more substantial dishes (such as risotto) alongside cocktails and wine. Too limited feedback for a rating as yet, but all of it enthusiastic. / W1K 2AL; www.pasticceriamarchesi.com.

EL PASTÓR SE1 £43 434

7A STONEY STREET NO TEL 10–4C

"Some of the better tacos in London" have made the Hart Bros' "very crowded" taqueria one of the hits of Borough Market. "Really delicious, interesting flavours – you just want to try them all" – especially if "you love really hot, spicy Mexican food". The Harts have followed up with Casa Pastór at King's Cross (see also), Tortilleria at nearby Maltby Street, and most recently Pastorcito in the new Arcade Food Theatre at Centre Point. / SE1 9AA;

www.tacoselpastor.co.uk; @Tacos_El_Pastor; 11 pm; No bookings.

PATARA £62 343

15 GREEK ST, W1 020 7437 1071 5–2A
7 MADDOX ST, W1 020 7499 6008 4–2A
181 FULHAM RD, SW3 020 7351 5692 6–2C
9 BEAUCHAMP PL, SW3 020 7581 8820 6–1C
82 HAMPSTEAD HIGH ST, NW3 020 7431 5902 9–2A
18 HIGH ST, SW19 020 3931 6157 11–2B

"Andy Murray is a regular visitor (to the Wimbledon branch), and with good reason", report fans of this "upmarket" group. Like Sir Andy, "great service" is a particular strength, while "the food is pretty authentic" too. Now an international operation, the first of its six London venues opened in 1990. / www.pataralondon.com; @PataraLondon; 10.30 pm, Thu-Sat 11 pm.

PATERNOSTER CHOP HOUSE EC4 £61 222

1 WARWICK COURT 020 7029 9400 10–2B

This business-friendly venue overlooking St Paul's Cathedral is part of the D&D London operation and offers "pretty good steaks" cooked over charcoal, although the "ridiculous prices" are likely to deter all but expense account diners (and maybe also TV fans, as the show First Dates has been filmed here for the past six years). / EC4M 7DX; www.paternosterchophouse.co.uk; @paternoster1; 10.30 pm; closed Sat & Sun D; booking max 12 may apply.

PATOGH W1 £18 432

8 CRAWFORD PL 020 7262 4015 7–1D

"Don't let the shabby interior put you off" – this "wonderful, simple Iranian café" off Edgware Road serves "excellent and authentic Persian dishes" including "superb lamb". "I love this place" – "small, squashed and full of character", it all but defines "cheap 'n' cheerful" ("and BYOB"). / W1H 5NE; www.patoghlondon.com; 11 pm; Cash only.

PATRI 343

139 NORTHFIELD AVENUE, W13 020 3981 3388 1–3A
103 HAMMERSMITH GROVE, W6 020 8741 1088 8–1C

"Love this new Indian street-food joint" – a neighbourhood cantina in Hammersmith not dissimilar to its predecessor (Chai Naasto), refurbed, formatted and renamed by the same owners to become this current incarnation. It serves a "good selection of veg and non-veg options", and some dishes are "fantastic". There's also a branch in Northfields.

PATTY AND BUN £29 433

18 OLD COMPTON ST, W1 020 7287 1818 5–2A
54 JAMES ST, W1 020 7487 3188 3–1A
14 PEMBRIDGE RD, W11 020 7229 2228 7–2B
19 BOROUGH HIGH STREET, SE1 10–4C
36 REDCHURCH STREET, E2 020 7613 3335 13–1C
2 ARTHAUS BUILDING, 205 RICHMOND ROAD, E8 020 8525 8250 14–1B
22-23 LIVERPOOL ST, EC2 020 7621 1331 10–2D
SWINGERS CRAZY GOLF, 8 BROWN'S BUILDINGS, SAINT MARY AXE, EC3 020 3846 3222 10–2D

There's "clear blue water between Patty & Bun and other wannabe mass burger offerings" – the only drawback is "you have to queue all the time". Having started out as a pop-up, the small chain has grown to eight branches and two spin-offs: Smash Patty and Jefferies, a chicken specialist. The core of the offer is "burgers dripping in all the good stuff, loud tunes, friendly vibes and lots of napkins". Top Tip – the "legendary lamb burger always makes me smile". / www.pattyandbun.co.uk; @pattyandbunjoe; 10 pm-11.30 pm, Sun 9 pm-10pm.

PAVILION CAFE & BAKERY E9 £10 424

VICTORIA PARK, OLD FORD ROAD 020 8980 0030 14–2C

"Sambar curry is super, and a great way to start the day!" at this brunch favourite – a quaint-looking, domed café by the water in Victoria Park, where Sri Lankan options feature alongside full English and vegan breakfasts; there's offshoots in Colombia Road and Broadway Market. / E9 7DE; www.pavilionbakery.com; @pavilionbakery; 3 pm; L only; No Amex; No bookings.

THE PEAR TREE W6 £42 344

14 MARGRAVINE RD 020 7381 1787 8–2C

Entering this "quiet neighbourhood pub" in a backstreet behind Charing Cross Hospital is "like stepping back in time" into a "piece of living history" – dating from 1824, it has kept an unspoilt vintage interior and wood fires. The "good food at reasonable prices" manages to be both traditional (beef & kidney suet pudding) and modern (with a vegan menu). / W6 8HJ; www.thepeartreefulham.com; 9.30 pm, Fri-Sun 9 pm; Mon-Thu D only, Fri-Sun open L & D.

PEARL LIANG W2 £53 422

8 SHELDON SQUARE 020 7289 7000 7–1C

"Consistently excellent dim sum" – "very good for the price" as well – is the menu highlight at this "go-to" Cantonese destination in Paddington Basin. Despite its smart modern fit-out, however, the basement location can appear "noisy" and "soulless". / W2 6EZ; www.pearlliang.co.uk; @PearlLiangUK; 11 pm.

PECKHAM BAZAAR SE15 £56 333

119 CONSORT RD 020 7732 2525 1–4D

"All the dishes deliver bags of flavour and something different to the usual" at this "really interesting Balkan restaurant", "well off-the-beaten-path (even by Peckham standards)". Much is cooked on a charcoal grill so "there's a happy smoky vibe to the place", although it's "always busy" and "can feel cramped". / SE15 3RU; www.peckhambazaar.com; @PeckhamBazaar; 10 pm, Sun 8 pm; closed Mon, Tue-Fri D only, Sat & Sun open L & D; No Amex.

PECKHAM LEVELS SE15 £17

95A RYE LANE NONE 1–4D

"Tasty street-food vendors, a good pint and a great atmosphere" (plus, for families, "plenty of space for kids to scoot around") win a thumbs-up for this vibey project, converted from seven levels of an underutilised multi-storey car park. Levels five and six are the heart of the action foodwise: residents include Nandine (offshoot of a Kurdish café in Camberwell), Other Side Fried (chicken burgers) and Hao Hao chi (handmade regional Chinese street food). / SE15 4TG; www.peckhamlevels.org; @peckhamlevels.

PEG E9 433

120 MORNING LANE 020 3441 8765 14–1B

In early summer 2019 (just as our survey was getting underway), some of the backers behind P Franco and Bright opened this: another painfully hip, East End natural wine bar (on the former site of Hackney's now-defunct Legs – geddit?). This time Australian chef Byron Fini is at the stoves cooking up a small menu of light, "Japanese-izakaya-style" bar snacks – including ferments and pickles, and majoring in grilled skewers (lots of them chicken-related) – which are served in a bright, stylishly-neutral, small space that's very 'now' (communal seating, tabletops made from recycled yoghurt pots, vinyl soundtrack, etc). Foodwise, the odd disappointment is noted ("if you want Japanese, go to a Japanese restaurant") but most reports are in line with the rhapsodic write-ups it's received in the press, rating the dishes very good to exceptional. / E9 6LH; www.peglondon.co.uk; No bookings.

E PELLICCI E2 £25 355

332 BETHNAL GREEN RD 020 7739 4873 13–1D

"You don't come here for the food: the welcome and the banter are the main attraction!", say fans of the Nevio family's "buzzy" (but hipster-free) Bethnal Green greasy spoon, which is a top choice for a "simple breakfast". Architecture anoraks will also want to examine its (listed) Art Deco interior (often used as a location for TV). / E2 0AG; epellicci.has.restaurant; 4 pm; L only, closed Sun; Cash only; No bookings.

PENTOLINA W14   £57   4 5 3

71 BLYTHE RD   020 3010 0091   8–1C

This "hidden gem near Brook Green", with "authentic and imaginative home-made Italian food", is an "absolute favourite neighbourhood restaurant". "The lovely couple who own it" – chef Michele and front-of-house Heidi – "are so friendly and passionate about their cuisine", while "standards are constantly improving" – especially "now that they change the menu regularly". / W14 0HP; www.pentolinarestaurant.co.uk; 10 pm; closed Mon & Sun; No Amex.

PERILLA N16   £62   4 4 3

1-3 GREEN LANES   0207 359 0779   1–1C

"Intelligent, creative, modern British food from chef Ben Marks" is attracting widespread foodie attention at his "hip" two-year-old, whose huge picture windows overlook Newington Green. Still in his twenties, the Noma graduate wins praise for his "really great cooking and innovative thinking" – "you can really feel the kitchen's sense of excitement at diners enjoying their delicious food", and it's "very rare to get a chef of this quality in the kitchen every night". / N16 9BS; www.perilladining.co.uk; @perilladining; 10.30 pm, Sun 8.30 pm.

THE PETERSHAM WC2   £91   2 1 4

FLORAL COURT, OFF FLORAL ST   020 7305 7676   5–3C

"Like being in the country, but without leaving London": this year-old 'lifestyle destination' in a new Covent Garden development – spun out from the Richmond garden centre's famous shabby-chic restaurant – comprises a shop, florist, deli, cicchetti (Italian small plates) bar and a main restaurant. It's a lavish investment from the Boglione family, with a "beautiful atmosphere", but the food is "only just about good enough for the prices", while the "disorganised and chaotic service requires some serious work". Still, for a romantic lunch on a summer's day in the centre of town, its flower-filled courtyard is hard to beat. / WC2E 9DJ; petershamnurseries.com; @PetershamN; midnight.

PETERSHAM NURSERIES CAFE TW10   £80   2 2 5

CHURCH LANE (SIGNPOSTED 'ST PETER'S CHURCH'), OFF PETERSHAM ROAD   020 8940 5230   1–4A

"The setting is just 'wow' on a sunny day" – "a secret paradise among the plants and bushes in a greenhouse" – "but the food is such a disappointment" ("seemingly great ingredients but very mediocre cooking") nowadays at this venue near Richmond Park that became famous under former chef Skye Gyngell a decade ago. It now has a smart offshoot in Covent Garden, but there's "something missing" at the original – not to speak of "the inadequate facilities, which leave you queueing outdoors for the toilet... in January!". / TW10 7AB; www.petershamnurseries.com; 2 pm, Sat &

Sun 3.30 pm; L only, closed Mon; SRA-Food Made Good – 3 stars.

LE PETIT CITRON W6   £48   3 2 3

98-100 SHEPHERDS BUSH ROAD   020 3019 1175   8–1C

"To the Brook Green site of Mustard (RIP) and before that Café Rouge (longer RIP) comes this attractive and inexpensive new French bistro". "Not much has changed since its predecessor" (same owners, who also own Covent Garden's Joe Allen) – "the food's decent" and comes at "very reasonable prices". / W6 7PD; lepetitcitron.co.uk; @lepetitcitronw6.

PETIT MA CUISINE TW9   £52   3 3 3

8 STATION APPROACH   020 8332 1923   1–3A

This "simple, cosy French bistro" from Central Casting – gingham tablecloths, Impressionist posters, menu of Gallic classics – is a "reliable" hit with both Kew locals and visitors to the nearby botanical gardens. Top Tip – "great value set lunch" ("busy when we went on a Monday lunchtime!") / TW9 3QB; www.macuisinebistrot.co.uk; 10 pm, Fri & Sat 10.30 pm; No Amex.

PETIT POIS BISTRO N1   £58   4 3 3

9 HOXTON SQUARE   020 7613 3689   13–1B

"Delicious French food in a small space" is the prospect of this "so, so good" Gallic bistro on Hoxton Square (with a small outside terrace). Top Menu Tip – "the chocolate mousse really is to die for!" / N1 6NU; www.petitpoisbistro.com; @petitpoisbistro; 10.30 pm, Sun 9 pm.

THE PETITE COREE NW6   £45   4 3 2

98 WEST END LANE   020 7624 9209   1–1B

Not far from West Hampstead station, this well-established, modern bistro serves "small but delicious portions" of distinctive, "Asian-French fusion cuisine": no doubt a legacy of chef-owner Jae's stints working for Nobu and Hélène Darroze at the Connaught. The "limited ambience" may represent a "missed opportunity" for cooking of this style and quality – the vibe is "nice local" rather than "romantic" – but it's a "hidden gem" worth discovering. / NW6 2LU; www.thepetitecoree.com; @thepetitecoree; 9.30 pm; booking max 6 may apply.

LA PETITE MAISON W1   £114   4 3 4

54 BROOK'S MEWS   020 7495 4774   3–2B

"Beautiful, light, fresh sharing plates" bring a taste of Mediterranean sunshine to a glam Mayfair crowd at this spin-out of a famous Côte d'Azur haunt – "not the usual cream and butter of French cooking, but delectable!". Although, just as in the South of France, the arrival of the bill can induce a mild seizure. Chef Raphael

Duntoye has tweaked the original formula here for the London market – "it's nothing like the Nice original" – which he has since exported to the Middle East, Miami and most recently Hong Kong. / W1K 4EG; www.lpmlondon.co.uk; @lpmlondon; 10.45 pm, Sun 9.45 pm.

PÉTRUS SW1   £115   3 4 3

1 KINNERTON ST   020 7592 1609   6–1D

"An impressive wine vault in the middle of the dining room" provides a talking-point at Gordon Ramsay's "beautiful" and "romantic" (luxuriously anodyne) Belgravian, whose capacious wine list is one of its defining features. Russell Bateman joined as chef in mid-2018, and, according to most reports, his "fabulous" modern cuisine "ticks every box" to contribute to a "fabulous all-round experience". Ratings slid here a bit this year, though, due to concerns about value: "it's good, but so painful on the wallet". / SW1X 8EA; www.gordonramsayrestaurants.com; @petrus; 10 pm; closed Sun; No trainers.

PHAM SUSHI EC1   £42   4 3 3

159 WHITECROSS ST   020 7251 6336   13–2A

"Surprisingly great sushi" – among "the best in London" – is to be found at this "modest Japanese" near the Barbican. "I lived in Japan for 10 years, so I know good sushi when I have it". / EC1Y 8JL; www.phamsushi.com; @phamsushi; 10 pm; closed Sat L & Sun.

PHAT PHUC SW3   £30   3 3 2

CHELSEA COURTYARD, 151 SYDNEY STREET   020 7351 3843   6–3C

"Delicious Vietnamese street food" – almost certainly "the best" in this part of London – is found at this Chelsea noodle bar apparently meaning "happy Buddha". The "scrumptious prawn laksa" is technically a Singaporean dish, but who gives a ph**? / SW3 6NT; www.phatphucnoodlebar.co.uk; @Phat_PhucNoodle.

PHO   £37   3 3 2

"Fresh soup noodle with an authentic, tasty tang, straight from the streets of Hanoi" continues to win fans for these "pleasant" street-food pitstops, which provide "very enjoyable, cheap and healthy", "Viet-style" bites. / www.phocafe.co.uk; 10 pm-11pm, Sun 6.30 pm-10 pm; EC1 closed Sat & Sun; no booking.

PHOENIX PALACE NW1   £63   3 2 2

5-9 GLENTWORTH ST   020 7486 3515   2–1A

This "huge, traditional Chinese banqueting hall" – a rather 1970s space near Baker Street tube – can be "a revelation" to newbies. "It does all the typical Cantonese dishes" from a menu boasting more than 300 dishes, and is particularly well-known for its "wonderful dim sum". "The service runs like clockwork… as it has to". / NW1 5PG; www.phoenixpalace.co.uk; 11.30 pm, Sun 10.30 pm.

PICK & CHEESE WC2

KERB SEVEN DIAL MARKET 5–2C

One of the first concessions to be announced for the new Seven Dials Market from KERB (opened in late Summer 2019), is a cheese conveyor belt (yes, you read that right!) restaurant, from the owners of Camden's Cheese Bar. Twenty-five British cheeses will be delivered by the 40-metre conveyor belt. / WC2H 9HD; www.sevendialsmarket.com.

The Savoy Hotel, Thames Foyer WC2

PIDGIN E8 £78 5|3|2

52 WILTON WAY 020 7254 8311 14–1B

"I don't know how they do it, but every week there is a new, exciting and delicious menu that never seems to be repeated" at this genius foodie-mecca in Hackney, which has rightly won renown on account of its "uniquely delicious, complex-without-being-baroque" cuisine. "It has a Michelin star and, after a few mouthfuls, it's clear to see why: the food is always innovative, mixing bold ranges of flavour and ingredients, focused on seasonal produce, all served up with a 'too-cool-for-skool' vibe", by staff who "move around the incredibly-tightly-packed dining room with a balletic poise". "The wine list is short but excellently curated", but the major win is the value: "in Mayfair it would cost double". On the downside, one or two regulars feel that the food has been "more hit-and-miss" in recent times, and the self-consciousness of the enterprise is a big turn-off for some folks: "a mixture of over-earnest staff intoning the menu without smiles, and sombre presentation of food as something sacred left us underwhelmed, on both visits". "I think I prefer food to be more unobtrusive, so you can spend the evening enjoying it alongside friends and conversation, rather than having each dish explained and having to come up with the requisite 'ooh, that sounds lovely, thank you' with every course…" / E8 1BG; www.pidginlondon.com; @PidginLondon; 11 pm; closed Mon & Tue, Wed & Thu D only, Fri-Sun L & D.

PIEBURY CORNER £20 3|2|2

3 CALEDONIAN RD, N1 020 7700 5441 9–3C
209-211 HOLLOWAY RD, N7 020 7700 5441 9–2D

"Prime pies" named after legendary Gunners are available at the Holloway shop on Arsenal match days and full-time at the King's Cross venue. Their quality makes for "a pleasant surprise – with vegetarian options no afterthought", and there's also Scotch eggs, craft beers and cider. / N7 9.30 pm, Sun 5pm, N1 10 pm, Thu-Sat 11 pm, Sun 8 pm; N7 closed Mon-Wed ; no bookings.

PIED À TERRE
W1 £104 4|4|4

34 CHARLOTTE ST 020 7636 1178 2–1C

David Moore's illustrious Fitzrovian "continues to shine" under the tenure of head chef Asimakis Chaniotis, and this "elegant" townhouse remains one of London's foremost temples of gastronomy. "Letting Chef Chaniotis take you through an evening with a custom tasting menu is second to none" – "he really is a master of meat, but they have great vegetarian and vegan tasting menus too", and "there's always something new and exciting" to sample. "An impressive wine list and a great sommelier's intelligent recommendations" complete the formula. The proportions of the building are not expansive, but tables are "well-spaced" and the overall experience is an "intimate" one. / W1T 2NH; www.pied-a-terre.co.uk; @PiedaTerreUK; 10.45 pm; closed Sat L & Sun; May need 12+ to book.

PIG & BUTCHER
N1 £54 3|4|3

80 LIVERPOOL ROAD 020 7226 8304 9–3D

Craft ales and on-site butchered meat combine at this "great local pub" in Islington – where the "hearty fare" is (perhaps unsurprisingly) "great for meat-lovers". It's "buzzy and busy", so "expect to queue" at prime times. / N1 0QD; www.thepigandbutcher.co.uk; @pigandbutcher; 10 pm, Sun 9 pm; Mon-Thu D only, Fri-Sun open L & D.

PIQUE NIQUE SE1 £60 3|2|3

32 TANNER STREET 020 7403 9549 10–4D

"Sister restaurant of nearby Casse Croute" that occupies a funny, mock-Tudor building (built as a shelter) on the borders of Tanner Street Park, complete with bar and open kitchen. The traditional Gallic cuisine – though good – lacks the all-round excellence of its sibling: service, though "friendly", is "a bit more sloppy"; and the environment is "cosy but a little less so". / SE1 3LD; pique-nique.co.uk; @piquenique32.

EL PIRATA W1 £49 2|3|3

5-6 DOWN ST 020 7491 3810 3–4B

"Fast, furious" – and offering resoundingly "good value for Mayfair" – this "cheap 'n' cheerful" bar is "brilliant for a quick lunch at just over a tenner including beer", or for an early evening booze up. It serves "proper tapas" which are "OK", but it's not a foodie destination, it's a "fun" one. / W1J 7AQ; www.elpirata.co.uk; @elpirataw1; 11.30 pm; closed Sat L & Sun.

PISQU W1 £60 3|3|2

23 RATHBONE PLACE 020 7436 6123 5–1A

"Very refined food from the Amazon, full of flavour" has established this Fitzrovia two-year-old as "possibly one of the best Peruvian restaurants in London". "Often overlooked by people passing in favour of better-known Lima on the same street", it's "very different, and good value for money too". / W1T 1HZ; www.pisqulondon.com; @PisquLondon.

PIZARRO SE1 £61 4|3|3

194 BERMONDSEY ST 020 7256 5333 10–4D

Lacking the pizzazz of José P's nearby tapas-bar sibling, which is one block away, his somewhat bigger contemporary Spanish restaurant never inflames quite as much passion as its little sister. It still achieves very good ratings, though, for its "really interesting food" and "attractively priced wine list". / SE1 3TQ; josepizarro.com/pizarro-restaurant-bermondsey; @Jose_Pizarro; 10.45 pm, Sun 9.45 pm.

PIZZA DA VALTER
SW17 £45 3|2|2

7 BELLEVUE ROAD 020 8355 7032 11–2C

Solidly rated, wood-fired pizza is the staple at this spot, on foodie Bellevue Parade, overlooking Wandsworth Common, but "the dishes beyond the pizza are also very good". There's also a branch at Fulham Broadway (which doesn't inspire feedback in the survey). / SW17 7EG; www.pizzadavalter.co.uk; @pizzadavalteruk.

PIZZA EAST £58 3|2|4

310 PORTOBELLO RD, W10 020 8969 4500 7–1A
79 HIGHGATE RD, NW5 020 3310 2000 9–1B
56 SHOREDITCH HIGH ST, E1 020 7729 1888 13–1B

"Big and still with a great buzz" – these "vibey", industrial-style haunts, owned by the Soho House group, have won an impressive following with their "inventive pizzas" (lots of them meaty), grungy-cool styling and staff who – despite a fair dose of hipster cred – maintain a welcoming attitude. Its ratings came off the boil a little this year, though, and the odd reporter feels their performance is seeming more "tired". / www.pizzaeast.com; @PizzaEast; E1 11pm, Thu midnight, Fri & Sat 1am, NW5 9.30 pm, Fri & Sat 11.30 pm, Sun 10.30 pm, W10 10 pm, Thu-Sat 11pm, Sun 10.30 pm.

PIZZA METRO
SW11 £47 **4 3 3**

64 BATTERSEA RISE 020 7228 3812 11–2C

"A long-time favourite", "always full of chatter and laughter", this Battersea pizzeria was the first in town to serve by the metre (or round, if you prefer) in 1993. "Both pizzazz and pizza that are long and good". / SW11 1EQ; www.pizzametropizza.com; @pizzametropizza; 11 pm, Fri & Sat midnight; No Amex.

PIZZA PILGRIMS £41 **4 3 3**

102 BERWICK ST, W1 0778 066 7258 4–2D
11-12 DEAN ST, W1 020 7287 8964 4–1D
KINGLY CT, CARNABY ST, W1 020 7287 2200 4–2B
23 GARRICK STREET, WC2 020 3019 1881 5–3C
12 HERTSMERE RD, E14 020 3019 8020 12–1C
136 SHOREDITCH HIGH ST, E1 020 3019 7620 13–1B
15 EXMOUTH MKT, EC1 020 7287 8964 10–1A
SWINGERS CRAZY GOLF, 8 BROWN'S BUILDINGS, SAINT MARY AXE, EC3 NO TEL 10–2D

"So delicious and affordable every time!" – the Elliot brothers' "speedy and cheerful" small chain put in a stellar performance this year as London's top pizza multiple, pipping rival Homeslice by tiny decimals. "You can see the dough being made on entering: everything is very fresh, and you get crisp, thin pizzas with quality toppings". / pizzapilgrims.co.uk; @pizzapilgrims; 10.30pm, Sun 9.30 pm; WC2 11 pm, Sun 10 pm; Dean St: no booking.

PIZZAEXPRESS £50 **2 2 2**

Entering its 55th year, the granddaddy of all UK pizza chains has "survived the passing of time". These past five years have not been vintage ones for the brand, however – since its takeover by Hony Capital in 2014, "the whole experience seems a bit more soulless" and, after a continual slide, its ratings have bottomed out somewhere between "just so average" and "all-in-all not bad". As "a good introduction for kids to eating out" however, it still enjoys massive support thanks to its "kind and supportive service given to frazzled grandparents and over-excited grandsons". Some wider hope comes from the recently "much-improved" Oxford Circus branch which is the prototype of a promising new look ("newly revamped with a central bar feature, at which you can eat if you prefer, plus draught Peroni and a better menu has brought some desperately-needed vigour back to this tired chain"). "Only a few more hundred branches to refurb now..." / www.pizzaexpress.co.uk; 11.30 pm - midnight; most City branches closed all or part of weekend; no booking at most branches.

PIZZERIA PAPPAGONE
N4 £38 **3 3 3**

131 STROUD GREEN RD 020 7263 2114 9–1D

"Such a fun neighbourhood pizzeria" – this "friendly", if hectic, indie has been a Finsbury Park fixture for 21 years. They do "very competent pasta", too, and are kid-friendly to the extent of producing "pizza dough dinosaurs". / N4 3PX; www.pizzeriapappagone.co.uk; @pizza_pappagone; midnight.

PIZZICOTTO W8 £55 **4 5 3**

267 KENSINGTON HIGH STREET 020 7602 6777 8–1D

"Skip the ubiquitous PizzaExpress locations and head to this family-run sister to Il Portico" ("owned by the same family"), a few doors down, and opposite Kensington's new Design Museum. The pizzas (featuring "activated charcoal bases") are "miles better than the usual", and they also offer "freshly made pasta and traditional entrees". Top Tip – "go for the incredibly simple Sicilian deep-fried pizza dough with salt on – then ask why there aren't east London hipsters selling these!". / W8 6NA; www.pizzicotto.co.uk; @pizzicottow8; 10.30 pm, Sun 9.30 pm.

PLAQUEMINE LOCK
N1 £47 **2 4 3**

139 GRAHAM ST 020 7688 1488 9–3D

This tribute to the cuisine of Louisiana in a converted Islington canal-side boozer is "fun and different" – and possibly "the best way to try Creole and Cajun food without having to brave Homeland Security". Two years on from opening, though, it hasn't fully lived up to the expectations raised by founder Jacob Kenedy, known for his brilliant Bocca di Lupo. "The best dishes are fabulous, and genuine Southern food seems to mean a lot is fried". / N1 8LB; plaqlock.com.

LES PLATANES W1 £63

26-28 BRUTON PLACE 020 7629 5613 3–2B

In a Mayfair townhouse that was formerly the short-lived Babel House (RIP), this 'contemporary bistro de luxe' features a southern French menu from chef Thierry Laborde, and opened in mid-2019, too late for any survey feedback. In his early review, The Evening Standard's David Sexton focused on its handsome design, variably realised and expensive cuisine, impressive wine list and bargain set lunch (£25 with wine). / W1J 6NG; lesplatanes.co.uk.

PLATEAU E14 £64 **3 3 3**

4TH FLOOR, CANADA SQ 020 7715 7100 12–1C

Atop Canada Place, opposite One Canada Square tower, this D&D London operation is well-known to denizens of Canary Wharf as one of its top expense-account destinations, thanks not least to its stunning views across the development. Those not slaving in the local money mills are less inclined to make the trip (except perhaps for brunch), but Jeremy Trehout's modern European cuisine is consistently well-rated this year. Top Tip – the adjoining grill is cheaper than the main restaurant. / E14 5ER; www.plateau-restaurant.co.uk; @plateaulondon; 10.30 pm; closed Sat L & Sun.

PLOT SW17 £42 **4 3 3**

UNIT 70-72 BROADWAY MARKET, TOOTING HIGH STREET 020 8767 2639 11–2C

High marks again for this brave hipster outpost occupying one of the stalls in Tooting's covered market, and where funky, seasonal, British small plates are served at the counter. Some diners found themselves "questioning some of the combinations", but most judged results "very good". / SW17 0RL; plotkitchen.com; @plot_kitchen.

THE PLOUGH
SW14 £45 **2 2 4**

42 CHRIST CHURCH RD 020 8876 7833 11–2A

Close to leafy Richmond Park, this 18th-century inn is a "lovely local boozer", with a "nice, quaint inside" for the winter months, and a "restful outside terrace that makes a perfect setting for a drink outdoors". Service is "very friendly" too, so it's a shame they don't make a bit more of an effort on the mostly enjoyable pub grub: "they don't aim for fancy, difficult dishes, but basic execution can disappoint". / SW14; www.theplough.com; 9.30 pm, Fri & Sat 10 pm, Sun 9 pm; 12 â€© 3pm and 6.30pm â€© 9.30pm, Fri - Sat - 12 â€© 5pm and 6.30pm â€© 10pm, Sun - 12 â€© 9pm.

PLUM + SPILT MILK, GREAT NORTHERN HOTEL
N1 £74 **2 3 3**

KING'S CROSS ST PANCRAS STATION, PANCRAS ROAD 020 3388 0818 9–3C

This "beautiful" first-floor dining room is part of the restored Great Northern Hotel at King's Cross (the name derives from the Flying Scotsman's colours). By the standards of railway-related restaurants, it's a distinct cut above, with a "good-value set lunch" and "some nice options on the menu". Fair to say, though, that the cuisine is generally overshadowed by the "elegant decor", but that helps make it "a good spot for a business lunch". / N1C 4TB; plumandspiltmilk.com; @PlumSpiltMilk; 11 pm, Sun 10 pm.

POLLEN STREET SOCIAL
W1 £113 **3 3 3**

8-10 POLLEN ST 020 7290 7600 3–2C

"If I want a guest to feel special, this is where I always choose to go!" – Jason Atherton's "first class" Mayfair HQ is "a great all-rounder with a very nice, light touch to its approach": most particularly its "clever and immaculately presented food" served "with flair", but also its relaxed-yet-upscale ambience. "It's not cheap but – to quote another famous brand – quality is remembered long after the price is forgotten". "Amazing cocktails" too. / W1S 1NQ; www.pollenstreetsocial.com; @PollenStSocial; 10.30 pm; closed Sun; booking max 7 may apply.

POLPO W1   £51   1️⃣2️⃣2️⃣

41 BEAK ST, W1 020 7734 4479   4–2B
6 MAIDEN LN, WC2 020 7836 8448   5–3D
DUKE OF YORK SQ, SW3 020 7730 8900 6–2D
126-128 NOTTING HILL GATE, W11 020 7229 3283   7–2B
2-3 COWCROSS ST, EC1 020 7250 0034 10–1A

Now ten years old, Russell Norman and Richard Beatty's Venetian/Mediterranean chain faces the well-publicised challenge of a March CVA (Company Voluntary Agreement), amidst a drip-feed of branch closures. Fans do still applaud its "very convivial and fun" formula, but even they often feel it's "somewhat lost its way", with staff who can seem "overwhelmed" and serving Venetian small plates that are often "no better than fine", and at worst "uncared for" or "very mediocre". / www.polpo.co.uk; 10 pm-11 pm; W11 closed Sun & Mon, EC1M closed Sun; no bookings.

POMONA'S W2   £57   3️⃣4️⃣4️⃣

47 HEREFORD ROAD   020 7229 1503   7–1B

"Love the garden and the creative spin they put on classic brunch dishes" – hitherto the main reasons to seek out this bright Notting Hill pub conversion. With the arrival of Ruth Hansom in April 2019, however, the menu has taken on a more serious, and British-sourced, slant – very early reports are upbeat: "exquisite cooking from a fabulous new female chef". / W2 5AH; www.pomonas.co.uk; @PomonasLondon; 10 pm, Fri & Sat 10.30 pm, Sun 9 pm.

LE PONT DE LA TOUR SE1   £77   2️⃣2️⃣3️⃣

36D SHAD THAMES   020 7403 8403 10–4D

It can be "very special, particularly on a sunny day", at this well-known D&D London stalwart, thanks to its "lovely situation" (complete with large terrace) by the Thames near Tower Bridge; and it remains "a firm favourite" for a few folk, including for a date. Its famous heyday, when the Blairs and the Clintons supped on salmon and Bollinger at the height of Cool Britannia is well gone now, though, and – remarkably for what was once the City's top expense-accounter destination – of the relatively limited feedback this place now inspires, none of it plugs its suitability as a business rendezvous. The straightforward French-ified menu, likewise, elicits muted enthusiasm, although its heavyweight wine list still rates mention… as do the prices. / SE1 2YE; www.lepontdelatour.co.uk; @lepontdelatour; 10.30 pm, Sun 9.30 pm; No trainers.

POPESEYE W14   £64   4️⃣3️⃣2️⃣

108 BLYTHE RD   020 7610 4578   8–1C

"Grotty-looking, but serving top steak!" – that's been the trade-off for over two decades at this "intimate and special", but simultaneously "fairly basic" little quirk of a bistro, in the backstreets near Olympia. "If you like good steak then this is as good a place to start as any: its excellent meat, cooked perfectly, takes some beating", and is supplemented by an intriguing wine selection of well-chosen bin ends. The N19 branch is no more. / W14 0HD; www.popeseye.com; 10.30 pm; D only, closed Sun; Cash only.

POPOLO EC2   £52   5️⃣4️⃣3️⃣

26 RIVINGTON STREET   020 7729 4299 13–1B

"An amazing experience at a price that doesn't hurt your wallet" – Jonathan Lawson's "superb Italian food with Spanish and Moorish influences, and including brilliant pasta (just as good as at The River Café!)" is well-worth the trip to Shoreditch to discover his brilliantly casual and laid back little hole-in-the-wall, with counter seating at the open kitchen downstairs, and a small upstairs dining room. / EC2A 3DU; popoloshoreditch.com; @popolo_EC2; no booking.

POPPIES   £48   3️⃣3️⃣3️⃣

59 OLD COMPTON ST, W1 020 7482 2977 4–2D
30 HAWLEY CR, NW1 020 7267 0440   9–2B
6-8 HANBURY ST, E1 020 7247 0892 13–2C

Fish trade veteran Pat 'Pops' Newland started out cutting up newspapers to wrap portions at the age of 11, and has kitted out his three tourist-friendly chippies (in Soho, Spitalfields and Camden Town) in 1950s memorabilia to commemorate the era. The "no-frills" fish he serves is "excellent" and "consistently fresh" – but even fans can find it "overpriced by a long way". / 11 pm, Fri & Sat 11.30 pm, Sun 10.30 pm.

POPPY'S   3️⃣2️⃣4️⃣

129-131 BRACKENBURY ROAD, W6 020 8741 4928   8–1C
30 GREYHOUND ROAD, W6   8–2C
78 GLENTHORNE ROAD, W6 020 8748 2351 8–2C

"A really quirky taste in decor" is working out well for this little group of Thai cafés in W6. From its tiny first branch (Poppy's I) on a traficky bit of Hammersmith's one-way system, it's progressed via a branch off the Fulham Palace Road (Poppy's II) to occupy the well-known former site of The Brackenbury, RIP (Poppy's III). Nowadays, the latter is hidden behind a terrace of foliage and packed with stuffed animals, mirrors and chandeliers. Notwithstanding a rather functional level of service, its low prices for tasty scoff and BYO policy are packing 'em in.

IL PORTICO W8   £62   3️⃣5️⃣4️⃣

277 KENSINGTON HIGH ST   020 7602 6262 8–1D

This "proper, family-run Italian trattoria" in Kensington pre-dates the new Design Museum on the other side of the road by decades, and exudes "cosy", "olde world charm". That it's "family-owned and family-friendly" is key to its longevity, and has made it a "go-to restaurant" for its many long-term regulars. But "after decades, the business has passed down a generation, and young and old alike agree it's brought an improvement, with an approach that's more energetic". Its strengths are "a charming atmosphere", "authentic Emilia-Romana cuisine, instead of the usual floods of red sauce" and the "unfailing and unflappable care of owner James Chiavarini and his well-trained staff". / W8 6NA; www.ilportico.co.uk; 11 pm; closed Sun.

PORTLAND W1   £80   4️⃣4️⃣2️⃣

113 GREAT PORTLAND STREET 020 7436 3261   2–1B

"Always on form, always interesting" – Will Lander and Daniel Morgenthau's acclaimed Fitzrovian has won a serious culinary reputation over the years, with both an à la carte and tasting menu available lunch and dinner. Fans say its interior is "lovely and modern", but – despite its "charming" service – the set-up can also seem a little too no-nonsense; the focus is very much on the modern European cuisine – "every dish is a success". / W1W 6QQ; www.portlandrestaurant.co.uk; @portland113; 9.45 pm; closed Sun.

PORTOBELLO RISTORANTE PIZZERIA W11   £54   3️⃣3️⃣3️⃣

7 LADBROKE ROAD   020 7221 1373   7–2B

Just off Notting Hill Gate, this "splendid staple" wins solid marks for "great pizza, pasta and more" – including a decent array of fish showcased in a chiller-cabinet. "Authentically Italian in its chaos and delicious food", it's also "fun and child-friendly". The best seats are outside on the glorious terrace in summer (which is also very effectively covered in winter and bad weather). / W11 3PA; www.portobellolondon.co.uk; 10 pm, Fri & Sat 11 pm, Sun 10 pm.

THE PORTRAIT, NATIONAL PORTRAIT GALLERY WC2   £74   2️⃣3️⃣4️⃣

ST MARTIN'S PLACE   020 7306 0055   5–4B

"Cracking views over the rooftops of Trafalgar Square and beyond from a sun-drenched room" earn the NPG's top-floor dining room decent ratings as a venue for brunch, lunch or afternoon tea, or for an "early supper before the opera at the Coliseum". The food is "quite adequate" although "not spectacular". (There's also a Spartan café in the basement). / WC2H 0HE; www.npg.org.uk/visit/shop-eat-drink/restaurant.php; @NPGLondon; 8.30 pm; Sun-Wed closed D.

Padella SE1

LE POT DE TERRE
N8   3 | 2 | 3

34 HIGH STREET   020 8340 0099   1–1C

"A Caribbean edge" adds an "interesting twist" to the fundamentally European menu at this late-2019 newcomer, which opened without fanfare in the heart of Hornsey. "The chef has little support so expect a relaxed service!" / N8 7NX; lepotdeterre.co.uk.

POTLI W6   £44   4 | 4 | 3

319-321 KING ST   020 8741 4328   8–2B

"Exceptionally flavoured, and unusual, 'street-food' dishes" – "the spicing makes them stand out" – have earned consistently high marks for this "inventive" Indian for much of the decade. It compares well with the better-known Indian Zing just a few steps closer to Ravenscourt Park tube station, and is "well worth a try". / W6 9NH; www.potli.co.uk; @Potlirestaurant; 10.15 pm, Fri & Sat 10:30 pm, Sun 10 pm.

LA POULE AU POT
SW1   £61   3 | 3 | 5

231 EBURY ST   020 7730 7763   6–2D

"Get snuggly" at this "engaging if somewhat faded", "typically Gallic" 1960s-"throwback" in Pimlico, whose "dark", candle-lit interior and "cosy tables hidden away in nooks and crannies" make it "one of the most romantic restaurants of all time" (it's Londoners' No. 2 for romance in the survey this year). Foodwise, "there's no nonsense, no surprises" – just "very traditional French classics" that are "still passable" ("cuisine grand mére" – think calf's liver, coq au vin, cassoulet), served by "the most colourful French waiters". Top Tip – "idyllic terrace for long lunches and dinner al fresco": "you could imagine yourself in a little French marketplace having a simple bistro-style lunch". / SW1W 8UT; www.pouleaupot.co.uk; 10 pm; No trainers.

PRAWN ON THE LAWN
N1   £62   4 | 3 | 2

292-294 ST PAUL'S RD   020 3302 8668   9–2D

"Fish at its best: fresh, dressed and novel – seared, crispy and spiced; or as a mountain of fruits de mer au naturel" is the reason this "fabulous", "almost caff-like" local on Highbury Corner (which doubles as a fishmonger) is "always very busy". It's "a rarity in London", and "every bit as good as its Cornish cousin" in Padstow. One caveat: it's "far too tiny and cramped and always needs to be booked days ahead – wish they would expand". / N1 2LY; prawnonthelawn.com; @PrawnOnTheLawn; 11 pm; closed Mon & Sun; No Amex.

PRIMEUR N5   £51   3 | 3 | 3

116 PETHERTON RD   020 7226 5271   1–1C

A 1920s former car garage provides an "unusual" setting for this Stoke Newington fringe haunt, whose "look and feel (with most people at communal tables, or on counters with stools) works well", despite it being "crammed" and with "a high noise-level". There's quite a "traditional", 'bistronomy-style' menu, from which everything's "well-cooked", and there's an "interesting" list of wines (low intervention, naturellement). / N5 2RT; www.primeurN5.co.uk; @Primeurs1; 10.30 pm, Sun 5 pm; closed Mon, Tue L, Wed L, Thu L & Sun D; booking max 7 may apply.

THE PRINCESS VICTORIA
W12   £50   3 | 3 | 3

217 UXBRIDGE ROAD   020 8749 4466   8–1B

This "old Victorian gin palace" "must be one of the best pubs in the Bush", so for locals it has been "wonderful to see the Vic resurrect itself from the ashes of oblivion" (after a short period of closure last year). "The atmosphere is warm and friendly and the food is quite delicious" – "proper restaurant quality"; "they've recently added a pizza oven, and even the pizzas are a substantial cut above what you might expect". / W12 9DH; www.princessvictoria.co.uk; @threecheerspubs; 10pm, Sun 9pm.

PRINCI W1   £37   3 | 2 | 3

135 WARDOUR ST   020 7478 8888   4–1D

This "stylish and modern" Soho outpost of Rocco Princi's self-service Milanese bakery is "always buzzing" with a crowd chasing its "delicious breakfasts", "great sandwiches" and "incredible cakes"; there are "creative salads and pizzas", too (the latter are particularly good). / W1F 0UT; www.princi.com; @princi_london; 11 pm, Sun 10 pm; no booking.

PRIX FIXE W1   £48   3 | 2 | 2

39 DEAN ST   020 7734 5976   5–2A

"Unostentatious and slightly lacking in character", this "basic, cheap 'n' cheerful French-style bistro" (sibling to Pierre Victoire) offers "good, honest cooking and excellent value" in the heart of the West End – "more enjoyable, with better food, than many a swankier venue". / W1D 4PU; www.prixfixe.net; 11.30 pm.

THE PROMENADE AT THE
DORCHESTER W1   £133   2 | 4 | 4

THE DORCHESTER HOTEL, 53 PARK LANE   020 7629 8888   3–3A

"Impeccable in every way: from the quietly unintrusive pianist in the background, to the service…" – this plush Mayfair hotel lounge is an orgy of opulent soft furnishings with a spoiling afternoon tea to match (plus other luxury bites from breakfast on); "not cheap", say fans, "but actually worth every penny". / W1K 1QA; www.dorchestercollection.com/en/london/the-dorchester/restaurant-bars/afternoon-tea; @TheDorchester; 10.30 pm; No shorts.

PROVENDER E11   £41   3 | 3 | 3

17 HIGH ST   020 8530 3050   1–1D

A "happy choice for dinner" in Wanstead – this "busy", neighbourhood bistro from veteran restaurateur Max Renzland inspired the odd gripe this year, but most reports say it's "a safe bet" for traditional Gallic fare. / E11 2AA; www.provenderlondon.co.uk; @ProvenderBistro; 10 pm, Fri & Sat 10.30 pm, Sun 9 pm; booking max 10 may apply.

PRUFROCK COFFEE
EC1   £13   3 | 3 | 2

23-25 LEATHER LN   020 7242 0467   10–2A

Celebrating its 10th year, this City-fringe café near Hatton Garden takes its caffeine seriously, running its own barista training schemes and taking supplies from Square Mile Roasters and various guest roasters from all over Europe. Good light bites at lunch, too. / EC1N 7TE; www.prufrockcoffee.com; @PrufrockCoffee; L only; No Amex.

PUCCI MAYFAIR
W1   £64   3 | 3 | 3

39 MADDOX STREET   020 3887 4363   3–2C

Fans of the long-gone Pucci Pizza on the King's Road will be glad to know that it's back (if with a few tweaks). Pucci's son Rufus Albanese has revived the brand in Mayfair, serving thin-crust pizzas made to the family recipe as well as mezze: "great fun and great pizza". / W1S 1FX; puccimayfair.com; @PucciMayfair.

THE PUNCHBOWL
W1   £60   3 | 3 | 4

41 FARM ST   020 7493 6841   3–3A

Approaching its 300th birthday, this Mayfair pub is more stylish than most in the West End, partly due to its history of celebrity ownership (it was part of Madonna and Guy Ritchie's divorce settlement, with Ritchie getting The Queen of Pop's share when they split). Foodwise, it's also been a decent bet in recent times (although it did receive one 'off' report from a former fan this year). / W1J 5RP; www.punchbowllondon.com; @ThePunchBowlLDN; 11 pm, Sun 10.30 pm; closed Sun D.

PUNJAB WC2   £42   3 | 4 | 3

80 NEAL ST   020 7836 9787   5–2C

Many Londoners have tried this very traditional, north Indian veteran on the fringe of Covent Garden (founded in 1946, and now in the 4th generation of family ownership) at some time or another, but it lacks a regular local following due to its touristy location. It wins consistent praise, however – including for its support of the armed forces (10% discount to those who've served). / WC2H 9PA; www.punjab.co.uk; 11 pm, Sun 10 pm; booking max 8 may apply.

PURE INDIAN COOKING
SW6   £51   3 | 4 | 2

67 FULHAM HIGH STREET   020 7736 2521   11–1B

This "real local gem" north of Putney Bridge serves "delicious and unusual Indian food" – and is "refreshingly free from the usual clichés".

Owner Shilpa Dandekar is a "great and innovative chef" – she trained at the Taj Group and worked under Raymond Blanc – and her cooking is "beautifully presented". Only the "rather ordinary room" gets brickbats – "more prestigious surroundings required!". / SW6 3JJ; www.pureindiancooking.com; @PureCooking.

PUREZZA NW1 £45 433

43 PARKWAY 0203 884 0078 9–3B

"Truly amazing tastes recommended for both vegans and non-vegans!" help win high scores for this year-old, Camden Town offshoot of the UK's first vegan pizzeria (which first hit Brighton in 2015). Bases include sourdough, hemp and gluten-free options: "it's the best pizza I've had in a very long time!". Top Tip – kids under 10 get a free pizza when eating with their parents. / NW1 7PN; www.purezza.co.uk; @purezza; Booking max 6 may apply.

QUAGLINO'S SW1 £76 235

16 BURY ST 020 7930 6767 3–3D

D&D London's "fabulous, shimmering dining room from the Jazz Age" in fact, owes much of its glam looks to Sir Terence Conran's 1993 revamp of this massive, subterranean, 1920s ballroom in St James's – is unusual amongst high-end venues nowadays in making "fantastic entertainment" and live music a regular feature of its ritzy offering. After many years on the skids, its standards of service and posh-brasserie fare have been somewhat on the mend in recent times, and – all feedback this year was upbeat. Top Tip "Sunday brunch is worth the trip". / SW1Y 6AJ; www.quaglinos-restaurant.co.uk; @quaglinos; 10.30 pm, Fri & Sat 11 pm; closed Sun; No trainers.

THE QUALITY CHOP HOUSE EC1 £71 444

94 FARRINGDON RD 020 7278 1452 10–1A

"You either love or hate the iconic and original (and cramped and uncomfortable) Victorian booths, which are part of the charm of this Clerkenwell institution" (est 1869) , "which has not been a 'Progressive Working Class' establishment for a very long time, no matter what it says on the ancient, etched-glass windows!". Relaunched in the early 1990s in the first stages of Britain's latter-day food revival, it's been run since 2012 by Will Lander and Daniel Morgenthau and its ratings are going from strength to strength on the back of its "honest, modern-ish take on hearty traditional dishes" ("perfect for meat eaters – huge steaks") and "unusual and interesting wines". They run a deli and wine shop next door too, 'Quality Wines' which is currently a voguish haunt in its own right, with chef Nick Bramham producing a small menu of trendy small plates. / EC1R 3EA; thequalitychophouse.com; @QualityChop; 10.30 pm; closed Sun.

QUARTIERI NW6 £44 433

300 KILBURN HIGH ROAD 020 7625 8822 1–2B

"The tastiest Neapolitan pizza, with lots of delicious toppings", wins fans for this "great neighbourhood joint" in Kilburn – thanks to its combination of "fail-proof classic choices and exciting, delightful specials" delivered by "service with a smile", it's "always filled with Italians". Top Tip – "straccetti – deep-fried pizza dough with hazelnut chocolate for dessert – is out of this world!". / NW6 2DB; www.quartieri.co.uk; @quartierilondon; 11 pm.

LE QUERCE SE23 £47 433

66-68 BROCKLEY RISE 020 8690 3761 1–4D

"Distinctly regional" Sardinian cooking – "above average and at reasonable prices" – has earned a strong following for this "very good family-run trattoria" from chef Antonello Serra in Brockley Rise. Look out for "great home-made bread and specials", along with "their own ice creams and sorbets in dozens of intriguing mixtures like strawberry and pepper"; "interesting wine list" too. / SE23 1LN; www.lequerce.co.uk; @lequercerest; 9.30 pm, Sun 8.15 pm; closed Mon & Tue L.

QUILON SW1 £71 552

41 BUCKINGHAM GATE 020 7821 1899 2–4B

"Consistently excellent" Keralan cuisine – "beautifully presented and served" – from chef Sriram Aylur ensures this 20-year-old, from the luxury Taj Group, remains at the summit of modern Indian gastronomy in the capital. Despite the swish hotel decor, though, it's a decidedly low-key institution – if it wasn't for such "friendly and thoughtful staff" the ambience could become stifling and leaden here. A short walk from Buckingham Palace, it's close enough to Parliament to have its own division bell to summon MPs for a vote. Top Tip – "set lunch is tremendous value". / SW1E 6AF; www.quilon.co.uk; @thequilon; 11 pm, Sun 10.30 pm; SRA-Food Made Good – 2 stars.

QUIRINALE SW1 £68 343

NORTH CT, 1 GT PETER ST 020 7222 7080 2–4C

"One of the finest Italian restaurants in London" for almost two decades, this is "near the Palace of Westminster, so frequented by MPs, journalists and lobbyists – but don't let that put you off". This clientele might explain why "tables are the right distance apart" in the "low-ceilinged basement". Top Tip – "go in truffle season – divine". / SW1P 3LL; www.quirinale.co.uk; @quirinaleresto; 10.30 pm; closed Sat & Sun.

QUO VADIS W1 £61 335

26-29 DEAN ST 020 7437 9585 4–1D

"It feels small now that Barrafina has taken up half of the original space" following a re-jig a year ago, but the Hart Bros' "gorgeous" landmark (est 1926) remains a "discrete", "comfortable" and "fun" oasis from the bustle of Soho. Chef Jeremy Lee's seasonal menu "is frequently refreshed with innovative dishes" and, at its best, delivers "unusual but superb" riffs on British cuisine, alongside a list of "interesting wines" and "fine cocktails". Top Tip – "a bangin' place for a traditional breakfast in classy surroundings". / W1D 3LL; www.quovadissoho.co.uk; @QuoVadisSoho; 11 pm; closed Sun.

RABBIT SW3 £56 323

172 KING'S RD 020 3750 0172 6–3C

"Truly delicious tapas" showcasing "great farm-sourced food", with "some robust, well-judged flavours" win ongoing appreciation for the Gladwin brothers' five-year-old King's Road operation. There's also a "cool vibe" to the "quirkily decorated room – loved it!". / SW3 4UP; www.rabbit-restaurant.com; @RabbitResto; midnight, Mon 11 pm, Sun 6 pm; closed Mon L & Sun D.

RABOT 1745 SE1 £64 232

2-4 BEDALE ST 020 7378 8226 10–4C

"A chocolate-themed restaurant is a good idea in principle, but some dishes work better than others" is the general verdict on this Borough Market outlet of a St Lucia plantation owned by Hotel Chocolat, which "users cocoa in every

La Trompette W4

dish". "Chocolate mac 'n' cheese", anyone? What does work is the "fantastic hot chocolate", and the café/bar has a "fun atmosphere" in the evening, while "the breakfast menu is really tasty, too". / SE1 9AL; www.rabot1745.com; @rabot1745; 9.30 pm; closed Mon & Sun.

RADICI N1 £68 222

30 ALMEIDA ST 020 7354 4777 9–3D

It's a "spacious, modern and stylish" venue – on the site of Islington's Almeida (RIP) – but owners D&D London and respected chef Francesco Mazzei "really ought to up their game" here: it "beats a pizza chain", but should deliver much more. As it is, being "convenient for the Almeida Theatre" is one of the best things that reporters have to say about it: "without this neighbour they probably wouldn't survive". / N1 1AD; www.radici.uk; @radici_n1.

RAGAM W1 £35 442

57 CLEVELAND ST 020 7636 9098 2–1B

"Unpretentious but brilliant" Keralan veteran near the Telecom Tower, which offers some of the "best-value curry in London". It's "still rough as anything in terms of the building but the food consistently nails it" – including some "proper veggie choices". Top Tip – "the dosas at Ragam are the best I've found in London". / W1T 4JN; www.ragamindian.co.uk; 11 pm.

RAIL HOUSE CAFÉ SW1 £66 222

SIR SIMON MILTON SQ 020 3906 7950 2–4B

"Having read some mixed reviews, we were pleasantly surprised on a recent visit" – the Riding House Café group's "eclectically decorated", year-old unit in Victoria's Nova development again inspires somewhat up-and-down reports, but most are positive regarding its "friendly" staff and "well-presented and tasty" food, tipping it for a breakfast or coffee and a snack; outside seating in summer is a bonus. / SW1H 0HW; www.railhouse.cafe; @railhouse_cafe.

Parsons WC2

RANDALL & AUBIN W1 £61 435

14-16 BREWER ST 020 7287 4447 4–2D

"No-fuss", "fresh seafood done really well" combines with a "fun" and "buzzy" ("riotous even!) ambience, at this Soho landmark – formerly a butcher (est 1911) that morphed into a restaurant 25 years ago. "It's still excellent after all these years, like meeting an old friend – we love it". "Go for the specials, they're always worth trying". / W1F OSG; www.randallandaubin.com; @randallandaubin; 11 pm, Fri & Sat 11.30 pm, Sun 9.30 pm; booking L only.

RAOUL'S CAFÉ W9 £42 324

13 CLIFTON RD 020 7289 7313 9–4A

This "really good all-rounder" near Little Venice has long been a "very nice option for brunch/lunch" with "still some of the best eggs Benedict in London after so many years". "The ambience is much better since it's usually a little quieter nowadays". / W9 1SZ; www.raoulsgourmet.com; 10.15 pm; no booking L.

RASA £37 342

6 DERING ST, W1 020 7629 1346 3–2B (TRAVANCORE) 56 STOKE NEWINGTON CHURCH ST, N16 020 7249 1340 1–1C 55 STOKE NEWINGTON CHURCH ST, N16 020 7249 0344 1–1C

Fans of the "unbeatable, unpretentious, delicious Keralan cuisine" at the three Rasas say it's "not your standard Indian fare" – "the spicing is second to none, giving a unique, delicate and surprising balance of flavours". They also say that the Stokie original, "established over 20 years ago", is "still the best veggie curry in north London" (with meat an option at its younger Travancore spin-off across the road); and that its popular Oxford Circus offshoot is a handy – and good-value – option in the West End. All locations, though, suffer accusations that they are "not as good as they were", and – though solid – ratings in each case no longer 'smash the ball out of the park' as once they did. / www.rasarestaurants.com; N16 & Travancore N16 10.45 pm, Fri & Sat 11.30 pm, W1 11 pm, Sun 9 pm.

RAVI SHANKAR NW1 £32 322

132-135 DRUMMOND ST 020 7388 6458 9–4C

A "long-term favourite" in Euston station's Little India, this is "the place to come for your masala dosa fix: there's lots to choose from, they're big, really really tasty, and amazingly cheap". "The weekend buffet has to be the best deal in town – you can gorge yourself on delicious vegetarian food and still get change from a tenner". / NW1 2HL; www.ravishankarbhelpoori.com; 10.30 pm.

RED FARM WC2 £56 323

9 RUSSELL STREET 0203 883 9093 5–3D

"Killer dim sum combinations make for an experience not to forget" at this three-storey canteen-style import from NYC in Covent Garden, famous on Instagram for its prawn dish that looks like the ghosts in Pac-Man. Even some fans, though, query "why is it so expensive? The food's great and fun and adventurous, but simply too pricey!" / WC2B 5HZ; redfarmldn.com.

THE RED LION & SUN N6 £58 333

25 NORTH ROAD 020 8340 1780 9–1B

"Lovely on all levels" – this cosy gastropub in a leafy corner of Highgate is not the largest, but has earned a solid reputation for its "yummy food". Well-behaved dogs and children are welcome, too. / N6; www.theredlionandsun.com; @redlionandsun; 10 pm.

RED ROOSTER EC2 £68 223

45 CURTAIN ROAD 020 3146 4545 13–1B

The hugely hyped offshoot of a famous Harlem NYC soulfood kitchen, from Ethiopian-Swedish celebrity chef, Marcus Samuelsson has failed to catch fire in Shoreditch. Some reporters like it – "a foodie dream" – but too many find it a "deep disappointment" (although "Sunday lunch is worth a visit for the live entertainment"). / EC2A 4PJ; www.thecurtain.com; @RoosterHarlem; midnight, Wed 1 am, Thu-Sat 2 am, Sun 5 pm; closed Sun D.

REGENCY CAFE SW1 £16 335

17-19 REGENCY STREET 020 7821 6596 2–4C

"One of the few completely authentic greasy spoons in central London" now – this "unchanging" veteran in a Westminster side street won the Harden's Award for Best Breakfast last year: "for the full English, it's tops" and "well worth queuing for". Opened in 1946, the original Austerity Era interior makes it sought-out as a location for films (Brighton Rock, Layer Cake), and the "old school caff" atmosphere is rounded off by "the lady behind the counter who bellows when your order's ready" – "being there always lifts the spirits". / SW1P 4BY; regencycafe.co.uk.

LE RELAIS DE VENISE L'ENTRECÔTE £48 333

120 MARYLEBONE LN, W1 020 7486 0878 2–1A 50 DEAN ST, W1 020 3475 4202 5–3A 5 THROGMORTON ST, EC2 020 7638 6325 10–2C

"Bish, bash, bosh… great steak!" – "amazing result!", "You know what you're going to get", and "what you're given is very good" at this Gallic steakhouse chain which "does what it says on the tin" – a "no-decision" menu of steak-frites, served with the chain's trademark 'secret sauce', plus seconds if you're still hungry (followed by a variety of puddings). "They're busy, so be prepared to queue, and to vacate your table as soon as you've finished." / www.relaisdevenise.com; 10 pm - 11 pm; EC2 closed Sat & Sun; no booking except in Soho.

REUBENS W1

79 BAKER ST   020 7486 0035   2–1A

What a difference three months can make! In August 2019, a quarter of a year after the closure of this well-known, 46-year-old, kosher deli in Marylebone (due to family bereavement) came news that it was to re-open after a big refurb, courtesy of restaurateur Lee Landau. It will still be the same format – deli on the ground floor, a restaurant in the basement. Let's hope the new era will herald better cooking! / W1U 6RG; www.reubensrestaurant.co.uk; 10 pm; closed Fri D & Sat; No Amex.

THE REX WHISTLER RESTAURANT, TATE BRITAIN SW1   £71   3 3 5

MILLBANK   020 7887 8825   2–4C

"Why go? The exceptional wines and the magnificent Whistler mural" provide most of the answer at the Tate's "delightful" dining "oasis": an "unexpected treat" by the standards of gallery venues, dating from 1927. It is true that its British cuisine "doesn't match the liquid refreshment", but it is generally "inviting"; and "the range and depth of wines on offer is reason alone to go", providing "some gems and at fair prices" ("wine is purchased and laid down, more like a St James's Club than a commercial restaurant"). "Satiated by stylish cooking and sensational wines – what better way to kick off a trip around the galleries upstairs…" / SW1P 4RG; www.tate.org.uk/visit/tate-britain/rex-whistler-restaurant; Booking lunch only.

RHYTHM & BREWS W4   3 4 5

22 WALPOLE GARDENS   020 7998 3873   8–2A

"A lovely, local independent coffee shop" on the distant borders of Chiswick and Gunnersbury combining "laid-back music on vinyl (some of which you can buy)" and a "cosy" vibe with "great pastries" and other simple fare, plus some fine brews (using Union coffee). / W4 4HA; rhythmandbrews.co.uk; @InfoBrews.

THE RIB MAN E1   £12   5 3 –

BRICK LANE, BRICK LANE MARKET   NO TEL   13–2C

"Unbelievably good ribs and pulled pork" continue to win top marks for street-food legend Mark Gevaux – even though he "concentrates more on his outrageously hot Holy F**k chilli sauce these days". "The meat is melt-in-the-mouth, superbly cooked and exceptional value" – it's "a pain that you have to wake up early-ish on a Sunday" to scoff a portion on Brick Lane, but the only other option is outside the Boleyn Tavern before West Ham home games. / E1

6HR; www.theribman.co.uk; @theribman; No bookings.

RIB ROOM, JUMEIRAH CARLTON TOWER HOTEL SW1   £100   3 2 3

CADOGAN PL   020 7858 7250   6–1D

Smart and luxurious dining room, off the lobby of a super-swanky five-star hotel bordering Sloane Street, whose focus on traditional meat dishes has been (somewhat) diluted over the years, with the introduction of a wider menu. Even so it's the "melting rib-eye" and other cuts which inspire most praise here, which is most popular as a business haunt: "relaxed, and ideal for talking the deal". / SW1X 9PY; www.theribroom.co.uk; @RibRoomSW1; 9.30 pm, Sat 10 pm.

RICCARDO'S SW3   £51   3 2 2

126 FULHAM RD   020 7370 6656   6–3B

This "great neighbourhood favourite" on a Chelsea corner wins solid marks for its "genuine Italian food", "with Riccardo himself ensuring you're well looked after". It's "cheap 'n' cheerful" with a "lovely informal environment" – "perfect for family Sunday lunch with dog under the table and children throwing pasta over each other". / SW3 6HU; www.riccardos.it; @ricardoslondon; 11.30 pm, Sun 10.30 pm.

RICK STEIN SW14   £66   3 3 4

TIDEWAY YARD, 125 MORTLAKE HIGH ST   020 8878 9462   11–1A

"The food may not live up to the hype, but it's still good, and the overall atmosphere is great", at the Stein empire's two-year-old, near Barnes Bridge. Who knows? If it wasn't named for TV-star Rick, its "decent-but-not-extraordinary fish, simply cooked" might seem more impressive, and might not seem "a little overpriced for what it is". But, just as was the case when this site was previously the Depot (RIP) "what makes the restaurant is the fabulous Thames view". / SW14 8SN; www.rickstein.com/eat-with-us/barnes; @SteinBarnes; 9.30 pm.

RIDING HOUSE CAFÉ W1   £59   2 3 3

43-51 GREAT TITCHFIELD ST   020 7927 0840   3–1C

For "a social start to the day" or to kill off "a boozy afternoon", many recommend this all-day bar/brasserie just north of Oxford Street in Fitzrovia, whose vibey looks and "great brunch menu" have earned it a big fanclub. At other times, some reckon "the food is underwhelming" – a view possibly shared by the management, who shut up shop for ten days in August 2019 to give the interior and general offer a 'facelift'. It now boasts a new long bar and five-course tasting menu. / W1W 7PQ; www.ridinghousecafe.co.uk; 10.30 pm, Fri & Sat 11 pm, Sun 9.30 pm.

THE RISING SUN NW7   £63   3 3 3

137 MARSH LN   020 8959 1357   1–1B

This "picturesque", 17th-century pub (Grade II listed) in Mill Hill attracts a solid following for its "quality British/Italian grub with exceptional service from ever-cheerful brothers Luca and Matteo (Delnevo)". "So different from the chains", it's "reasonably priced" and "there's always a great pasta dish on the menu". / NW7 4EY; www.therisingsunmillhill.com; @therisingsunpub; 10 pm, Fri & Sat 11 pm, Sun 8.30 pm; closed Mon L.

RISTORANTE FRESCOBALDI W1   £84   3 3 2

15 NEW BURLINGTON PL   020 3693 3435   4–2A

"Beautiful cooking and a stunning room" set the scene at this "quiet Mayfair Italian, perfect for business". The heavyweight wine list reflects its ownership by a Tuscan banking and wine dynasty stretching back 30 generations. "Why isn't this restaurant more popular?" – perhaps because: "it's better if you're not paying for yourself – it's pricey!". / W1S 5HX; www.frescobaldirestaurants.com; @frescobaldi_LDN; 11 pm.

THE RITZ, PALM COURT W1   £114   3 4 5

150 PICCADILLY   020 7493 8181   3–4C

"The gold standard" for afternoon tea – this "exquisite room" ("a unique feature of the experience") "is a well-known institution for a reason!". "I've been to more afternoon teas than I can count, and the majority are trying to emulate the Ritz experience". "Book ahead (months ahead, it is notoriously difficult to get a table!) and accept that it's expensive and that it has a dress code. But it's well worth it. A fantastic treat with flawless service and a wonderful, refined, atmosphere. British culture at its best!" / W1J 9BR; www.theritzlondon.com; @theritzlondon; Jacket & tie required.

THE RITZ W1   £129   3 4 5

150 PICCADILLY   020 7493 8181   3–4C

"For a very special occasion, there is nowhere better" than this "beyond-compare" Louis XVI chamber, widely acclaimed as "the most beautiful dining room in London": "it will not only rekindle the romance in your marriage, it's also great for impressing on business". "Not to be totally outdone by the surroundings, staff are friendly and unpretentious, and the classic cuisine under head chef John Willliams is measured and precise (if not exactly cheap… but it's not supposed to be!)". Top Tip – "a lovely fancy place for an epic breakfast"; also "the dinner dance is special and great value". / W1J 9BR; www.theritzlondon.com; @theritzlondon; 10 pm; Jacket & tie required; SRA-Food Made Good – 2 stars.

RIVA SW13 £65 441

169 CHURCH RD 020 8748 0434 11–1A

Loyal regulars (who include numerous fooderati celebs) totally 'get' Andreas Riva's "understated" stalwart, in a row of Barnes shopfronts: a celebrated (to those in-the-know) favourite, where "professional and accomplished staff" deliver "simple", "seasonal and classic" northern Italian dishes, which are "perfectly prepared" and "exquisite tasting": they say it's "an authentic experience, without any airs". Even fans admit the interior is "squashed" and "dowdy", however, and that prices are very "hefty". / SW13 9HR; 10.30 pm, Sun 9 pm; closed Sat L.

THE RIVER CAFÉ W6 £104 333

THAMES WHARF, RAINVILLE RD 020 7386 4200 8–2C

Ruth Rogers' "thrilling" canteen, in an "out-of-the-way" Hammersmith backstreet (originally founded to serve husband, Richard's, architectural practice) has won global renown on the back of "perfectly seasoned" Italian dishes "of such bare simplicity the quality of the phenomenal ingredients truly sing". "On a hot day, there's no better spot in London" than its "delightful" outside terrace near the Thames; and in cooler weather, its "faithfully preserved 1990s-chic" interior, though "tightly packed", mostly gets the thumbs-up too – "bathed in light at lunch, or with a certain buzzing energy in the evening". It's the "ferocious prices", though, which bitterly divide reporters, and which yet again win it No. 1 billing in our list of Most Overpriced restaurants. To its more ardent fans, the situation is clearcut: "forget the haters" – "if you think it's overpriced, you simply don't understand food!" Very many other diners, however, are badly torn: "I know, I know, I know: it's an institution, a pioneer, an icon! And I value it hugely for its contribution to the London scene. The room is still one of my favourites. The food is delectable. But let's be honest: we have many excellent Mediterranean restaurants all across town nowadays, and a grilled piece of fish, a slice of lemon tart, and a glass of Vermentino isn't really worth half-a-week's wages!!" / W6 9HA; www.rivercafe.co.uk; @RiverCafeLondon; 9 pm, Sat 9.15 pm; closed Sun D.

RIVINGTON GRILL SE10 £60 222

178 GREENWICH HIGH RD 020 8293 9270 1–3D

A "usually reliable choice in Greenwich" (where there is little by way of competition) – this Caprice Group venue is the sole surviving offshoot of Mark Hix's original Shoreditch grill, which closed in 2017. But while it's generally "acceptable", the harsh would say that equally there's "nothing noteworthy" either. / SE10 8NN; www.rivingtongreenwich.co.uk; 11 pm, Sun 10 pm; closed Mon, Tue L & Wed L.

ROAST £71 324

GREAT PORTLAND STREET, W1 020 3006 6111 3–1C STONEY ST, SE1 0845 034 7300 10–4C

"Nice views of Borough Market, if you get a window seat" ("watch out for the trains on the adjoining viaduct that appear to be coming towards you") add to the considerable appeal of this "light and airy dining space" (which atmospherically incorporates a converted glazed portico, originally part of the Royal Opera House). Specialising in British cuisine – particularly roast meats – most reports say the food is "brilliant", but there remains a sceptical view that it's "less-than-good home cooking". Top Menu Tip – breakfast and brunch have long been a very reliable experience here. / www.roast-restaurant.com; @RoastRestaurant.

ROBATA W1 £46

56 OLD COMPTON STREET 020 7287 5766 5–3A

Izakaya-style Soho newcomer, which opened in Spring 2019, making a feature of the robata skewers for which it is named, and whose other attractions include bao buns, sushi and cocktails. It opened too late to inspire much in the way of survey feedback, but the general social media buzz about the place is upbeat. / W1D 4UE; www.robata.co.uk.

ROCCA DI PAPA £41 334

73 OLD BROMPTON RD, SW7 020 7225 3413 6–2B 75-79 DULWICH VILLAGE, SE21 020 8299 6333 1–4D

"There's a friendly buzz" at this pair of "good-value neighbourhood Italians" in South Kensington and Dulwich Village, which are handy for most occasions: "reliable for an informal business lunch", but equally "very child-friendly" and "perfect for a family meal with half portions of everything for kids". On top of that, the "food is actually not bad at all – better pizzas than the chains and decent enough fresh pasta". / www.roccarestaurants.com; SW7 11.30 pm; SE21 11 pm.

ROCHELLE CANTEEN E2 £64 333

16 PLAYGROUND GARDENS 020 7729 5677 13–1C

Margot Henderson (wife of St John's Fergus) and Melanie Arnold's "charming" converted school bike shed near Spitalfields elicits lyrical praise from fans of their "great" British cooking – even if some reporters flinch at the "exorbitant wine list". Ratings have rebounded after last year's dip, possibly caused by the pair's takeover of the ICA's catering. "My last meal would be Rochelle Canteen's mince on dripping toast with horseradish and watercress, and a magnificent bottle of wine". Top Tip – "pleasant garden in good weather". / E2 7ES; www.arnoldandhenderson.com; 4.30 pm, Thu-Sat 9 pm; L only, Thu-Sat L & D.

ROCHELLE CANTEEN AT THE ICA SW1 £50 442

THE MALL 020 7930 8619 2–3C

"Margot and Melanie, we love you and your earthbound but fine cooking: gutsy, simple and defiantly based on flavour!". This "bright, if utilitarian, space looking out onto The Mall" is a takeover of a longstanding arts centre café, near Admiralty Arch; a year-old spin-off from Melanie Arnold and Margot Henderson's quirky Spitalfields original: "the seasonal-and-often-unusual ingredients married to straightforward, accurate cooking have transferred successfully from the hipsterland of the East End". "Wines are also good and unusual" (although one or two reporters consider them "toppy pricewise for this kind of set-up"). / SW1Y 5AH; www.ica.art/rochelle-canteen; 11 pm.

ROE SW9 £54

UNIT S38 POP BRIXTON, 29 BRIXTON STATION ROAD 07535 269098 11–1D

Occupying one of Pop Brixton's shipping containers (and with a little terrace, too), Irish chef Simon Whiteside (from Hook in Camden) is serving up fish and seafood cuisine with inspiration from his homeland. Feedback is too thin for a rating but praises its "beautiful, very fresh fish", suggesting it's worth a visit. / SW9 8PQ; www.roebrixton.com; @roebrixton.

ROGANIC W1 £93 542

5-7 BLANDFORD ST 020 337 06260 2–1A

"The closest you can get to L'Enclume without travelling to the lakes" – Simon Rogan delivers "stunning concoctions (your imagination can really run riot)" at his year-old Fitzrovian, which offers either a seven-course or ten-course evening tasting menu (or, at lunchtime, a three-course option). "Although not as glitzy as his stint at Fera at Claridges, the food is just as good". But "if the cuisine is undoubtedly Michelin-quality, the venue is less so" – the former premises of L'Autre Pied, which remain "rather bland" and "cramped". Top Tip – "the utterly divine Tunworth cheese (cake) and caviar dessert (which sounds wrong, but which actually works)". / W1U 3DB; www.simonrogan.co.uk; @roganic; 9.15 pm; closed Mon & Sun.

ROKA £81 544

30 NORTH AUDLEY ST, W1 020 7305 5644 3–2A 37 CHARLOTTE ST, W1 020 7580 6464 2–1C ALDWYCH HOUSE, 71-91 ALDWYCH, WC2 020 7294 7636 2–2D UNIT 4, PARK PAVILION, 40 CANADA SQ, E14 020 7636 5228 12–1C

"I've never had a bad meal at Roka, and I've eaten there many, many times" – Arjun Waney and Rainer Becker's small modern Japanese group delivers an "exceptional", "all-round" package of clean-tasting fusion food served in stylish and "buzzy" contemporary surroundings. Dishes are "beautifully presented

Le Pont de la Tour SE1

but also amazingly well-flavoured" – be it "fantastic black cod", "fabulous sushi" or grilled tapas-y bites from the robata grill. Top Tip – in E14, the "weekend brunch menu is splendid value for money: especially the children's menu". / www.rokarestaurant.com; 11.30 pm, Sun 10.30 pm; E14 11pm, Sun 8.30 pm; WC2 11 pm, Sun 8 pm; booking: max 5 online.

ROMULO CAFÉ W8 £62 `343`

343 KENSINGTON HIGH STREET
020 3141 6390   8–1D

"Beating Jollibee if you want to try decent, quality Filipino food" – this London outlet of a Philippines-based chain (owned by the grandchildren of a famous general) operates on a different level than its fast-food rival in nearby Earl's Court (see also Jollibee). Offering "very fresh" and interesting dishes (for newbies, "there's a strong whiff of Thai cuisine"), "enthusiasm is key, and the food is presented with great bravura". / W8 6NW; www.romulocafe.co.uk; @romulolondon; 10 pm.

ROSA'S £42 `322`

The "lovely Thai food" at these reliable cafés is "impressively authentic given that they are a chain" – "excellent value" and "fast", if occasionally let down by "iffy service". Founded in 2008 by Saiphin and Alex Moore, who inherited the name of their first East End site, the group has 15 branches in London and expanded to Liverpool and Leeds this year following the sale of a majority stake to US investors. The couple also have two spin-offs, Lao Café in Covent Garden and the new Chinese noodle bar Hoh Sek in St Katharine Docks. / rosasthaicafe.com; @RosasThaiCafe; 10 - 10.30 pm; E15 9 pm, Sat 10 pm, Sun 6 pm; E1, SW1 & SW9 6+ to book, W1 4+ to book.

THE ROSENDALE SE21 £50 `333`

65 ROSENDALE RD   020 8761 9008   1–4D

This "lovely, relaxed" Victorian coaching inn in West Dulwich is "great with the kids – and the dog!". The food is simple but consistent – "never had a bad meal there". / SE21 8EZ;

www.therosendale.co.uk; @threecheerspubs; 10 pm, Sat 9.30 pm, Sun 9 pm; No Amex.

ROS SOPOMODORO £49 `222`

JOHN LEWIS, 300 OXFORD ST, W1
020 7495 8409   3–1B
50-52 MONMOUTH ST, WC2 020 7240 9095
5–3B
214 FULHAM RD, SW10 020 7352 7677
6–3B
1 RUFUS ST, N1 020 7739 1899 13–1B
10 JAMESTOWN RD, NW1 020 7424 9900
9–3B
46 GARRETT LN, SW18 020 8877 9903
11–2B

"Neapolitan influences are evident in the choice of ingredients, and the wood-burning oven makes for good, chewy, charred crusts, unlike most high-street pizzas" – so say fans of this global chain, whose HQ is indeed in Naples. Not everyone is impressed, though, and ratings are dragged down by those who feel it's merely an "everyday" choice: "OK for a bog-standard group, but not great". / www.rossopomodoro.co.uk; 11 pm, Fri & Sat 11.30 pm, Sun 10 pm.

ROTI CHAI W1 £46 `433`

3 PORTMAN MEWS SOUTH   020 7408 0101
3–1A

Inspired by street and railway station snacks on the subcontinent, this "large modern Indian", a short stroll from Selfridges, has built a big fanclub thanks to its "marvellous" and "authentic" bites that are "full of interesting flavours". But while reporters agree on the high quality of the food, they are divided about where is best to sit – is it the "good-value" upstairs café, or "classy" basement restaurant? / W1H 6AY; www.rotichai.com; @rotichai; 10.30 pm; booking D only.

ROTI KING NW1 £28 `521`

40 DORIC WAY   020 7387 2518   9–3C

"Worth the queue and the terrible decor" – this "crowded" basement dive near Euston has been around in various locations for yonks, but, with the rise of street food as a genre, has become more 'discovered' in recent times. "Exciting roti" ("with mutton curry, is ridiculously good") that are "cheap and authentically delicious" are the pay-off for braving its decidedly "down-to-earth" quarters. / NW1 1LH; rotiking.info; No bookings.

ROTUNDA BAR & RESTAURANT, KINGS PLACE N1 £56 `334`

90 YORK WAY   020 7014 2840   9–3C

A "great setting" next to the Regent's Canal, with a large and attractive terrace that comes into its own during the summer months, isn't the only feature that raises this bar/dining room to being a destination rather than merely an arts-centre amenity – "its farm-to-plate ethos is something special" too, with a dedicated Northumberland farm providing all beef and lamb (hung onsite in their own

hanging room, and with an in-house butcher). A recent refurb has added an open kitchen and large meat-aging cabinets on view. / N1 9AG; www.rotundabarandrestaurant.co.uk; @rotundalondon; 10.30 pm, Sun 6.30 pm; closed Sun.

ROUX AT PARLIAMENT SQUARE, RICS SW1 £95 `443`

12 GREAT GEORGE ST   020 7334 3737
2–3C

"Never had a bad meal, and the food can be outstanding" – this Roux-branded operation near Parliament Square offers accomplished cuisine overseen by Steve Groves (winner of MasterChef: The Professionals in 2009) in an "impressive" (if, by the nature of the building, slightly institutional) setting. It's typically "backed up by well-judged, discreet service" (although one or two meals were "slow" here this year). Top Tip – "the excellent and well-priced set lunch menu is a bargain for the area". / SW1P 3AD; www.rouxatparliamentsquare.co.uk; @RouxAPS; 9 pm; closed Sat & Sun; No trainers.

ROUX AT THE LANDAU, THE LANGHAM W1 £93 `454`

1C PORTLAND PL   020 7965 0165   2–1B

"Smooth-running and elegant" – the recently-adopted, more modern and svelte style of operation (no tablecloths, and a new central bar for counter-style dining) is suiting this Roux-branded dining room: part of a luxurious five-star hotel, opposite Broadcasting House. Despite the harder-edged look, the ambience remains "delightful" and the cuisine is "first class", with the option of eating à la carte, or from the six-course tasting menu. "Spot-on service", in particular, featured in numerous reports this year. / W1B 1JA; www.rouxatthelandau.com; @Langham_London; 10.30 pm; closed Sat L & Sun; No trainers.

ROVI W1 £65 `544`

59-65 WELLS STREET   020 3963 8270
3–1D

"An impressive step-up for Ottolenghi, and with all the elements that make his food unique": Yotam Ottolenghi's "just brilliant", veg-centric yearling in Fitzrovia provides "some of the most innovative food in town" – "very clever" and "exciting" sharing-plates with "intense flavours" and "exceptional presentation" – and "even though there's meat on the menu, it could turn the most ardent carnivore vegetarian!". With service that's "exemplary" and "committed" and "a really delightful atmosphere (buzzing but not noisy) it's all-in-all a memorable experience". / W1A 3AE; www.ottolenghi.co.uk/rovi; @rovi_restaurant.

ROWLEY'S SW1 £80 `223`

113 JERMYN ST   020 7930 2707   4–4D

"Very English steak and chips" – this classic St James's outfit from the 1970s (occupying Wall's sausages' early-Victorian premises) is, say fans, "one of those places you need to visit" thanks to its "amazing Chateaubriand" and the entrecôte steak, served on a table burner with the signature "delicious Roquefort butter sauce and unlimited fries – what more could one ask for?". Ratings, however, seldom hit the heights here: especially given the 'Welcome to Tourist London' prices, it can seem "disappointing". / SW1Y 6HJ; www.rowleys.co.uk; @Rowleys_steak; 10.30 pm.

ROYAL CHINA £52 312

24-26 BAKER ST, W1 020 7487 4688 *2–1A*
805 FULHAM RD, SW6 020 7731 0081 11–*1B*
13 QUEENSWAY, W2 020 7221 2535 *7–2C*
30 WESTFERRY CIRCUS, E14 020 7719 0888
12–*1B*

"As far as dim sum goes – the go-to place" – these famous Cantonese fixtures are "not unlike ones you could find in Hong Kong". "No-one comes for the cuddly service" ("don't expect any smiles from the staff"), nor the ambience ("proper Chinese chaos") of the group's 1980s-tastic black-and-gold lacquered branches, but they "predictably deliver good food every time you visit" in the manner of an "industrial assembly-line"; and "kids love it". / www.royalchinagroup.co.uk; 11 pm, Sun 10 pm; W1 Fri & Sat 11.30 pm.

ROYAL CHINA CLUB
W1 £70 433

38-42 BAKER ST 020 7486 3898 *2–1A*

Some of the "best Chinese food in London" is on the menu at the Marylebone flagship of the Royal China group, including "fine quality" Cantonese classics and dim sum. It's certainly "not cheap", but a four-month refurb last year seems to have addressed the concerns expressed by reporters in previous years: marks for service and ambience are both up in the latest survey. / W1U 7AJ; www.royalchinagroup.co.uk; @RoyalChinaGroup; 11 pm, Sun 10.30 pm; booking weekdays only.

RUCOLETTA EC2 £49 422

6 FOSTER LANE 020 7600 7776 10–*2B*

"Excellent, simple Italian food for a good price" is a rarity in the City, so it's well worth knowing about this no-nonsense trattoria near St Paul's: "it's cramped, but your wallet feels OK!" / EC2V 6HH; www.rucoletta.co.uk; 9.30 pm, Thu & Fri 10 pm; closed Sat D & Sun; No Amex.

RULES WC2 £77 335

35 MAIDEN LN 020 7836 5314 *5–3D*

"If one wants to wow a visitor to London" then this superbly atmospheric Covent Garden "old timer" – the capital's oldest restaurant to operate continuously on the same site (since 1798) – is just the ticket. The "amazing", "traditional" panelled interior is "very impressive"; and although the "classic British cooking" (rib of beef, game in season, steak 'n' kidney) is decidedly "not cheap" and doesn't please everyone, it mostly makes a decent fist of flying the native culinary flag. Given its prime location, it can inevitably be "overrun with tourists" at times, but it's still a big hit with

many locals too. / WC2E 7LB; www.rules.co.uk; @RulesRestaurant; 11.45 pm, Sun 10.45 pm; No shorts.

RUYA W1 £94 333

30 UPPER GROSVENOR STREET
020 3848 6710 *3–3A*

"Absolutely delicious, fine-dining Turkish-inspired cuisine (another sharing plate concept)" is to be found at this big, fancy-schmancy Park Lane yearling: part of a Dubai-based restaurant empire. "It is, shall we say, a little bit toppy" when it comes to the prices (oh boy, it is), but all reports agree this is "great, great food". / W1K 7PH; ruyalondon.com.

SABOR W1 £63 544

35 HEDDON ST 020 3319 8130 *4–3A*

"Just thinking about it is making my mouth water!" – Nieves Barragan and José Etura's "bustling, casual and friendly" two-year-old, tucked off Regent Street, is establishing itself as one of the West End's brightest stars: "a guaranteed first-class food experience with a lot of fun thrown in". "The downstairs bar serves modern tapas, including the beloved carabineros and croquetas. Upstairs at the communal tables, you'll feast on traditional dishes like suckling pig, cooked in an Asador (wood-fired oven)". Both locations score a big thumbs up: "not cheap, but what an utter treat to have well-executed, passionate, uncomplicated cooking of Spanish classics in the middle of London". / W1B 4BP; www.saborrestaurants.co.uk; @sabor_ldn.

LE SACRÉ-COEUR
N1 £47 323

18 THEBERTON ST 020 7354 2618 *9–3D*

Searching for that classic, "romantic", "cheap 'n' cheerful" bistro of legend? Try this "relatively inexpensive French local" off Islington's Upper Street: "the food's very good considering the price, and portions are generous". / N1 0QX; www.lesacrecoeur.co.uk; @LeSacreCoeurUK; 11 pm, Fri & Sat 11.30 pm, Sun 10.30 pm.

SACRO CUORE £39 432

10 CROUCH END HILL, N8 020 8348 8487
1–*1C*
45 CHAMBERLAYNE RD, NW10
020 8960 8558 *1–***2B*

"Real-deal, crisp bases – like in Italy"; this Kensal Rise and Crouch End duo cook some of "the best Neapolitan pizzas in town", and they're "excellent value". Top Tip – "the Nutella pizza (for dessert) is a must-try". / www.sacrocuore.co.uk; @SacroCuorePizza.

SAGAR £35 332

17A PERCY ST, W1 020 7631 3319 *3–1D*
31 CATHERINE ST, WC2 020 7836 6377
5–*3D*
157 KING ST, W6 020 8741 8563 *8–2C*

This long-running South Indian trio (with an outpost in Harrow) offers a "great selection of

really tasty vegetarian and vegan dishes" that can accommodate specific diets such as 'no onions'. They're "cheap 'n' cheerful but the food is so good" ("seriously, the breads, curries and their lentil pizza thingy is so delish!!!"). / www.sagarveg.co.uk; 10 pm - 11 pm.

SAIGON SAIGON
W6 £36 323

313-317 KING ST 020 8748 6887 *8–2B*

"Reliable and always packed" – this good-value Vietnamese is a stalwart of Hammersmith's restaurant row. Its ratings this year were not on a high, with the odd gripe that it's "not as good as it used to be", but most reporters continue to recommend the place. / W6 9NH; www.saigon-saigon.co.uk; @saigonsaigonuk; 10.30 pm, Fri & Sun 11 pm.

ST JOHN BREAD & WINE
E1 £66 323

94-96 COMMERCIAL ST 020 7251 0848
13–*2C*

Home of "possibly the best bacon sandwich in London amongst all the faddishness and superficiality of modern Spitalfields" – this "carnivore heaven" is "more accessible and less full-on than the original (and still best) St John", but still serves "excellent nose-to-tail food" from breakfast to dinner. Its white-walled, canteen-like quarters are echoey and not especially comfortable, but somehow avoid seeming as grimly utilitarian as they otherwise might. Top Tip – the baking is gorgeous: "an Eccles cake here will offer all the benefits of a warm hug". / E1 6LZ; www.stjohngroup.uk.com/spitalfields; @sjrestaurant; 10.30 pm, Mon 8 pm.

ST JOHN SMITHFIELD
EC1 £68 543

26 ST JOHN ST 020 7251 0848 10–*1B*

"The original nose-to-tail flag-bearer, and still a joy!" – Trevor Gulliver and Fergus Henderson's "stark" ex-smokehouse in Smithfield has won fame with "top quality, distinctive British cuisine" ("using unusual cuts", most famously offal), and "although they might have started the trend, they still lead from the front with exciting, innovative and surprisingly delicious food". It's "honest, skilful cooking that puts the produce front and centre" on "an uncompromising and sometimes challenging menu"; and the "hearty-yet-nuanced" results are a case of "simple things done well"… "perfect". With its brutally "simple and stylish", "whitewash-walled" interior ("deafeningly loud" at times) and "relaxed but attentive service", it remains "a must-go" ("what a place to take visitors to show off London's restaurant scene"). Top Tip – "Eccles Cake with Lancashire Cheese is outstanding". / EC1M 4AY; stjohnrestaurant.com; @SJRestaurant; 11 pm, Sun 4 pm; closed Sat L & Sun D.

ST JOHNS N19 £56 323

91 JUNCTION RD 020 7272 1587 *9–1C*

Handsome Archway tavern that's "hard to beat when on form" and is one of north London's

Charlie's W1

best-known gastropubs, accommodating a large volume of diners throughout, and in the large ex-ballroom space at the rear of the pub. It appeared "more variable this year" in general however; in particular the fact that it can be "extremely noisy when full" bothered more reporters, detracting from what's otherwise a characterful experience. Top Tip – "quieter in the bar", where you can eat a tidy range of tapas. / N19 5QU; www.stjohnstavern.com; @stjohnstavern; 10 pm, Tue-Sat 11 pm, Sun 9 pm; Mon-Thu D only, Fri-Sun open L & D; No Amex; booking max 12 may apply.

ST MORITZ W1　£57　3 4 4

161 WARDOUR STREET　020 7734 3324　4–1C

"Part time-travel, part being transported to actual Switzerland", this chalet-style Soho veteran (est. 1974) is a perennial hit for its "authentic" Alpine cuisine. "What could be more romantic than sharing a bubbling pot of melted cheese in a cosy Swiss chalet?" / W1F 8WJ; www.stmoritz-restaurant.co.uk; 11.30 pm, Sun 10.30 pm.

SAKAGURA W1　£67　3 3 2

8 HEDDON STREET　020 3405 7230　4–3B

This upmarket steak and sake bar is a co-production from the people behind the Araki and Japan Centre, and offers a "wide range and good choice of Japanese food" – "some dishes are more flavoursome than others" but all are "well executed"; and there's "an amazing choice of sake". / W1B 4BU; www.sakaguralondon.com; @sakaguraldn; 10.30 pm, Thu-Sat 11.30 pm, Sun 10 pm.

SAKE NO HANA SW1　£82　4 3 3

23 ST JAMES'S ST　020 7925 8988　3–4D

"Beautiful food in a stunning location" – a Modernist building next to The Economist in St James's – again wins high ratings for this long-running Japanese outfit in the Hakkasan Group. It's never really made its mark, however, and continues to inspire little feedback, but such as there is brims with enthusiasm nowadays for the "always-great meals". And if you support sustainability, you'll want to know that Sake No Hana is, as of September 2019, the first restaurant in the UK to sell fully farmed Bluefin tuna rather than the endangered variety. / SW1A 1HA; www.sakenohana.com; @sakenohanalondon; 11 pm, Fri & Sat 11.30 pm; closed Sun.

SAKONIS　£29　3 2 1

127-129 EALING RD, HA0　020 8903 9610　1–1A

330 UXBRIDGE ROAD, HA5　020 8903 9610　1–1A

Stalwart Indian veggie in Wembley, which has developed over 35 years from a family fruit 'n' veg stall to a full-fledged restaurant (with branches in Hounslow and Hatch End). There's a "really good variety of cuisine, with Indo-Chinese on the side", with "something to suit everyone… except carnivores". Opinions

differ on whether the buffet option or main menu is the best way to go: either way it's cheap as chips.

SALAAM NAMASTE WC1　£47　3 3 2

68 MILLMAN STREET　020 7405 3697　2–1D

"The tastes of freshly ground spices" infuse the interesting modern regional cuisine at chef-patron Sabbir Karim's affordably priced Bloomsbury Indian, close to Russell Square tube. "Boy, does it get busy – and I can see why!". / WC1N 3EF; www.salaam-namaste.co.uk; @SalaamNamasteUK; 11.30 pm, Sun 11 pm.

SALE E PEPE SW1　£67　3 4 3

9-15 PAVILION ROAD　020 7235 0098　6–1D

"Unchanged for donkey's years!" – a "noisy and crowded", old-school trattoria, near the rear entrance to Harrods, whose "at times flamboyant service" provides a heartily "friendly welcome", plus traditional Italian cuisine, which loyal regulars declare "always reliable". / SW1X 0HD; www.saleepepe.co.uk; @salepepe_it.

SALLOOS SW1　£67　3 2 3

62-64 KINNERTON ST　020 7235 4444　6–1D

Posh Pakistani, hidden away in a Belgravia mews townhouse for more than 40 years: some may find it "stuffy", while others praise the "great ambience". It's certainly "not the cheapest", but it's survived on its "stalwart, authentic, fantastic food" (particularly lamb chops). / SW1X 8ER; www.salloos.co.uk; 11 pm; closed Sun; May need 5+ to book.

SALON BRIXTON SW9　£56　4 4 3

18 MARKET ROW　020 7501 9152　11–2D

"Ambitious modern British cuisine" – an "interesting" menu of "trendy but unfussy dishes that are well-prepared" – plus a good list of natural wines with consistent high praise for Nicholas Balfe's "buzzy spot in Brixton market", although "it can get a bit manic". The team has opened a second venue, Levan in Peckham (see also). / SW9 8LD; www.salonbrixton.co.uk; @Salon_Brixton; 10 pm.

LE SALON PRIVÉ TW1　£48　3 3 3

43 CROWN RD　020 8892 0602　1–4A

"Excellent French food prepared by an Italian chef" – Gianluca di Monaco, who trained under the great Pierre Koffmann – wins solid ratings for this "very pretty" St Margaret's bistro. Its prix-fixe menu offers "excellent value and choices", ensuring it is "always busy". Top Tip – "good venue before the rugby at nearby Twickenham". / TW1 3EJ; lesalonprive.net; @lesalon_tweet; 10.30 pm.

SALT YARD W1　£54　4 4 3

54 GOODGE ST　020 7637 0657　2–1B

This pioneer of Spanish and Italian small-plates dining near Goodge Street station is "still going strong after so many years for a very good reason" – "interesting and yummy dishes plus good wine". Ratings have remained solid since the whole group (including siblings Dehesa, Opera Tavern and Ember Yard) was taken over late last year by Urban Pubs & Bars from Simon Mullins and Sanja Moy, who opened Salt Yard in 2005. There's even been a "big improvement in the ambience of the basement". Top Menu Tip – "deep fried courgette flowers with honey: the cheesy goodness within marries perfectly with the honey sweetness drizzled over… just wow!" / W1T 4NA; www.saltyard.co.uk; @SaltYardGroup; 10.45 pm, Sun 9.45 pm; ; booking max 8 may apply.

SALUT N1　£71　4 3 3

412 ESSEX ROAD　020 3441 8808　9–3D

Tiny Canonbury fixture, with "a small but perfectly formed menu" of ambitious modern European dishes, prepared in an open kitchen – "wonderful, well-flavoured, light cooking", from "the amazing roast potatoes to the soups and everything in between". / N1 3PJ; www.salut-london.co.uk; @Salut_London; 11 pm, Sun 10 pm.

SAM'S RIVERSIDE W6

RIVERSIDE STUDIOS, 101 QUEEN CAROLINE STREET　8–2C

Facing the Thames with views of (currently closed and hence very tranquil) Hammersmith Bridge, this October 2019 opening provides an all-day, 90-cover brasserie locals hope will prove a long-needed cheaper alternative to another river café five minutes walk away. It's the brainchild of Sam Harrison, who for years ran long-RIP Chiswick favourite, Sam's Brasserie. / W6 9BN; samsriverside.co.uk; @samsriversideW6.

SAMBAL SHIOK N7　£38　3 3 1

171 HOLLOWAY ROAD　020 7619 9888　9–2D

"Fantastic new arrival in N7" – Mandy Yin's "always crowded, really buzzy" laksa bar (her progression from street-food markets) has ridden a wave of good reviews; fans say, "if you like laksa, chilli and spice, you won't find anywhere better for this type of money". That's the majority view anyway, although there is a minority who feel "it's not worth the time queueing", citing "hype" and clumsy cooking ("either they changed chef, or they're too busy"). There's also some disagreement over the booking slots policy: supporters say "the 90 minute time allocated for the meal is plenty because the service is so fast", but others feel "very rushed given the fixed arrival and departure points". / N7 8LX; www.sambalshiok.co.uk; @SambalShiok; Mon closed; Tue - Sat 9.30 pm; Sun closed.

SAN CARLO SW1   £66   3 4 4

2 REGENT STREET SAINT JAMES'S
020 3778 0768   4–4D

'Affordable glam' is a defining feature of the national San Carlo group, and its large St James's yearling on the lower half of Regent Street carries the classy, comfortable design of its nationwide siblings. "Efficient staff" and "excellent food" complete an all-round good-quality package. / SW1Y 4AU; sancarlo.co.uk/restaurants/san-carlo-london; @SanCarlo_Group.

SAN CARLO CICCHETTI   £56   3 3 4

215 PICCADILLY, W1 020 7494 9435   4–4C
30 WELLINGTON ST, WC2 020 7240 6339
5–3D

"Don't be fooled by its prominent location, just off Piccadilly Circus, that it's just one for the tourists" – this "bustling, noisy and so-atmospheric" Venetian brasserie (which also has a similar sibling, more tucked away in Covent Garden) "looks like a tourist trap, but offers an authentic culinary experience" with its "delicious small plates" (cicchetti) – "a format that caters to all appetites", all at "reasonable prices". Staff are "enthusiastic and professional" and "feed off the buzz of the place", which "feels smart, even if tables are very close together". / www.sancarlocicchetti.co.uk; @SanCarlo_Group; W1 11.30 pm; WC2 midnight; M1 11 pm, Sun 10 pm.

SAN PIETRO W8   £50   3 2 2

7 STRATFORD ROAD   020 7938 1805   6–1A

"Expertly prepared fresh fish" ("magnificent scallops, large and with the coral attached: so rare!") makes it worth truffling out this "slightly expensive but useful local" – the Italian successor to the quiet Kensington site that was for aeons Chez Patrick (RIP), and which nowadays is in a more stylish guise, with the main dining room upstairs, and a counter downstairs. / W8 6RF; www.san-pietro.co.uk.

THE SANDS END SW6   £51   3 3 4

135 STEPHENDALE ROAD   020 7731 7823
11–1B

This unobtrusive-looking gastroboozer in a Fulham backstreet came to prominence for its highly-rated grub and off-duty visits from Prince Harry, a pal of the former owner. It changed hands last year and Harry got hitched, so he's not expected back, but marks have held up for what is still a "great local" – "not so cheap but definitely cheerful". / SW6 2PR; www.thesandsend.co.uk; @thesandsend; 10 pm, Sun 9 pm.

SANTA MARIA   £42   4 3 3

160 NEW CAVENDISH ST, W1   2–1B
15 ST MARY'S RD, W5 020 8579 1462   1–3A
92-94 WATERFORD ROAD, SW6
020 7384 2844   6–4A

"Consistently fantastic pizza, with interesting toppings and a nicely textured base" have created a major buzz around this independent Neapolitan trio, which started out in Ealing before opening off Fulham Broadway and in Fitzrovia. It's still the W5 original that incites most fuss – "a small cafe/bistro, it's always crowded you can end up sitting in a rather tight, alley-like room" although in recent times they've also colonised the Red Lion next door so you can "set yourself down at the pub and tuck in with more space and vibe". / www.santamariapizzeria.com; @SantaMariaPizza.

SANTA MARIA DEL SUR SW8   £54   3 4 3

129 QUEENSTOWN RD   020 7622 2088
11–1C

Since 2006, this out-of-the-way Argentinian has won a strong Battersea following, particularly with its selection of succulent steaks (flown in from Latin America) and "lovely" staff. If you have veggie friends, don't despair: they do now have the odd vegan option. / SW8 3RH; www.santamariadelsur.co.uk; @StaMariadelSur; 10 pm.

SANTINI SW1   £80   2 3 3

29 EBURY ST   020 7730 4094   2–4B

There's "still a sense of occasion when you dine" at this "very smart and fashionable" Belgravia Italian, which remains in the same family after 35 years and is nowadays run by Laura, daughter of founder Gino. It's "very business-y" though, and having hosted Frank Sinatra and the Clintons back in the day, it's fair to say it is "past its glory years". / SW1W 0NZ; www.santini-restaurant.com; @santinirest; 10.45 pm.

SANTO REMEDIO SE1   £63   3 3 3

152 TOOLEY STREET   020 7403 3021 10–4D

This "authentic, up-beat" cantina "lifts the reputation of Mexican cuisine in London" with its "delicious food" and colourful atmosphere. Founders Edson Diaz-Fuentes (ex-Wahaca) and his wife Natalie brought it to Bermondsey via pop-ups, supper clubs and a short-lived Shoreditch venture. A minority of reporters complain of "inconsistency", with dishes veering between "excellent" and "flavourless". / SE1 2TU; www.santoremedio.co.uk; @santoremediouk; 10 pm, Sat 11 pm.

SANTORE EC1   £52   3 2 2

59-61 EXMOUTH MKT   020 7812 1488 10–1A

"Cheerful local Italian" in Exmouth Market that excels in the "delivery of classic dishes by staff who clearly enjoy working here and interacting with customers" – "it's always good to hear Italian spoken in the background". / EC1R 4QL; www.santorerestaurant.london; @Santore_london; 11 pm.

SANXIA RENJIA   £38   3 2 2

29 GOODGE STREET, W1 020 7636 5886
2–1B
36 DEPTFORD BROADWAY, SE8
020 8692 9633   1–3D

"Great food at a good price" continues to win acclaim for the Deptford branch of this Sichuanese duo, whose chilli-hot and numbing cuisine makes it one of SE8's brighter culinary sparks. No feedback this year on its less noteworthy Goodge Street branch.

SAPORI SARDI SW6   £57   3 3 2

786 FULHAM RD   020 7731 0755 11–1B

Limited but all-round positive feedback again on this family-run Sardinian – one of the few bright culinary sparks in the area near the western end of the Fulham Road. / SW6 5SL; @Saporisardi; 10.30 pm; No Amex.

SARAVANAA BHAVAN HA0   £42   4 3 2

531-533 HIGH RD   020 8900 8526   1–1A

The Wembley branch of an international South Indian veggie chain, which has eight venues in Greater London, serves, according to fans, "the best tiffins (light day-time meals) ever". Fascinating fact: P Rajagopal, the 'dosa king' who founded the group in 1981, died of heart failure in June at the age of 71, one week into a life sentence for the murder of an employee whose wife he wanted to marry. / HA0 2DJ; www.saravanbhavanlondon.com; Mon - Thurs 10.30pm, Fri-Sun 11pm.

SARDINE N1   £59   4 3 3

15 MICAWBER STREET   020 7490 0144
13–1A

"Intriguing southern French-inspired food", "simply cooked from fresh ingredients", is the draw at former Rotorino chef Alex Jackson's three-year-old in "an off-the-beaten-track area" near Silicon Roundabout. "Stripped-down décor" and "great natural and low-intervention wines" help set the "very casual" tone. / N1 7TB; www.sardine.london; @sardinelondon; 10 pm.

SARTORIA W1   £77   3 3 3

20 SAVILE ROW   020 7534 7000   4–3A

This "formal" Mayfair Italian is "one of the best D&D London venues", in a "beautiful, discreet and spacious setting", with "expert service" and an "excellent kitchen" nowadays directed by ex-L'Anima chef Francesco Mazzei. All this comes at a price, of course, so while the formula might "work well for business-lunchers", it can appear "expensive" to other diners. / W1S 3PR; www.sartoria-restaurant.co.uk; @SartoriaRest; 10.45 pm; closed Sat L & Sun.

THE SAVANNAH NW1   £54

81-103 EUSTON STREET   020 7691 8588
9–4C

Limited-but-upbeat feedback on this new hotel dining room: "an oasis of calm near

Euston station (an area short of nice places to eat!)". Ethical sourcing and African influences in dishes – as well as Asian ones – help take it slightly out of the mainstream, and one or two early reports say it's "a hidden gem". / NW1 2EZ; www.thesavannah.co.uk; @TheSavannahLDN; 10 pm.

SAVOIR FAIRE WC1 £47 343

42 NEW OXFORD ST 020 7436 0707 5–1C

"Images redolent of 'Le Gai Paris' (the naked bottoms went perfectly with my slow roasted pork belly!)" grace the muralled walls of this "friendly and efficient" Gallic corner bistro, near the British Museum: "a reliable and enjoyable choice", serving affordable classic French dishes. / WC1A 1EP; www.savoir.co.uk; 10 pm.

THE SAVOY HOTEL, SAVOY GRILL WC2 £105 233

STRAND 020 7592 1600 5–3D

"One of London's iconic dining rooms": this panelled chamber – just off the foyer of The Strand's famous Art Deco landmark – still exudes "old-school elegance", and, even if it's not quite the pre-eminent power dining scene that it was in Thatcher's day, it's still popular with expense-accounters, who particularly appreciate its "comprehensive wine list". Under the stewardship of the Gordon Ramsay group, its "classic (old-fashioned even) menu" is "pricey but fabulous" to fans, but a wider view is that it's "moderately average and not cheap": "nothing wrong but no sparkle". / WC2R 0EU; www.gordonramsayrestaurants.com; @savoygrill; 11 pm, Sun 10.30 pm.

THE SAVOY HOTEL, THAMES FOYER WC2 £97 234

THE SAVOY, THE STRAND 020 7420 2111 5–3D

For a "lovely afternoon tea" and "a truly elegant experience" there's much to recommend the light-filled foyer of this posh hotel lounge (set beneath a glass dome). "The price is eye-watering but seconds are regularly provided, so it's actually good value for the amazing experience". Breakfast here is also "a gorgeous start to the day". / WC2R 0ER; www.fairmont.com/savoy-london; @TheSavoyLondon; 11 pm.

SCALINI SW3 £88 233

1-3 WALTON ST 020 7225 2301 6–2C

"The diner is transported straight back to the 1960s, not least because of the breadsticks and very old-fashioned service" at this traditional Italian, close to Harrods. "No doubt because of the location, it's not exactly a bargain" – the "pricey food, although good, does not quite live up to expectations" – but it's popular (opening a branch in Dubai last year), and "when busy, it's pretty much shoulder-to-shoulder". / SW3 2JD; www.scalinilondon.co.uk; 11 pm; No shorts.

SCOTT'S W1 £86 444

20 MOUNT ST 020 7495 7309 3–3A

"Pure glamour" attaches to Richard Caring "really classy" and "sophisticated" Mayfair A-lister – 007's favourite lunch spot – which is "an ideal place to go celeb spotting… if you're into that kind of thing". Culinarily speaking, it's famous for its "spanking fresh" fish and seafood (and vies with its stablemate J Sheekey as the capital's top venue for such specialities) although it also offers "enough meat choices to keep the carnivores happy". In terms of style, it's "smart" and quite "formal", which – together with its "silky smooth service" and "well-spaced tables" – makes it an "impressive" choice for entertaining and "clients love it" (although, by the same token, "the room can be overrun with business suits", especially at lunch, robbing it of some of its habitual sparkle). Top Tip – "the terrace tables are great, weather permitting!" / W1K 2HE; www.scotts-restaurant.com; 10.30 pm, Sun 10 pm; booking max 6 may apply.

SCULLY SW1 £62 543

ST JAMES'S MARKET 020 3911 6840 4–4D

"Mind-blowing food" that's "hard to classify" – "a true pot pourri of tastes from around the world using a cascade of daringly combined ingredients to create a theatrical experience for the eyes, and a surprising explosion for the taste buds" – is carving ever-wider culinary renown for Ramael Scully's "exceptionally interesting" two-year-old in St James's Market, whose kitchen is "really pushing the boundaries". The room is "classy" too, and staff are "so extremely knowledgeable and helpful". "The only downside is a crowd that's a bit St James-y". Top Tip – "sit at the counter, where talking to the chefs is a bonus". / SW1Y 4QU; www.scullyrestaurant.com; @scully_ldn.

SEA CONTAINERS, MONDRIAN LONDON SE1 £71 233

20 UPPER GROUND 020 3747 1000 10–3A

Views of the Thames and a chic interior combine to create a lovely setting for this well-groomed South Bank destination: on the ground floor of a swish hotel near Blackfriars Bridge. It escaped the harsh criticisms of past years in the most recent survey feedback: in particular its "super buffet brunch" with bottomless Prosecco is a top feature. / SE1 9PD; www.seacontainerslondon.com; @SeaContainers_; 11 pm.

SEA GARDEN & GRILL SW17 £46 444

99-101 BROADWAY MARKET, 29 TOOTING HIGH STREET 020 8682 2995 11–2C

Helping make Tooting's Broadway Market a foodie destination, this "very affordable" two-year-old seafood specialist wins praise for its "fabulous food, great service and big smiles". The "really inventive" approach extends to drinks, which include an "amazing

The Ritz W1

gin cocktail" flavoured with oysters. Antiques trade veteran Jimmy Luttman is an "excellent" host. / SW17 0RJ; www.seagardenandgrill.co.uk; @theseagardenuk .

THE SEA, THE SEA SW3 £64 444

174 PAVILION ROAD 020 7824 8090 6–2D

"Fish shop by day and seafood restaurant by night", this "cutely-situated", mid-2019 newcomer, in an über-chichi enclave off Sloane Street, comes from the same stable as Bonnie Gull, and has won instant acclaim as a "great entrant to the London seafood scene". "Minimalist decor" sets a tone where the focus is on pristine ingredients zhooshed up with a bit of culinary magic by chef Leandro Carreria: beautiful, if "very expensive". You can also eat there at lunch, but with "no mains, desserts or coffee". / SW3 2TJ; www.theseathesea.net.

SEABIRD SE1

THE HOXTON, 40 BLACKFRIARS ROAD 020 7903 3000 10–4A

The 14th floor rooftop of the new Hoxton hotel – this time confusingly located in Southwark, despite the name – is home to a fish and seafood restaurant from the team behind Brooklyn's Maison Premiere. It opened in September 2019, with a raw bar, a wide range of oysters – and 'the fresh flavours of southern Europe'. Oh, and great views. / SE1 8NY; thehoxton.com/london/southwark/hotels.

SEAFRESH SW1 £51 322

80-81 WILTON RD 020 7828 0747 2–4B

Marios Leonidou runs this well-established Pimlico veteran, originally founded by his dad, and celebrating 55 years in 2020. For a (slightly) posher-than-usual fish 'n' chip experience, it's something of a classic choice, and the menu runs far beyond cod to scallops, oak-smoked salmon and Dover sole. / SW1V 1DL; www.seafresh-dining.com; @SeafreshLondon; 10.30 pm; closed Sun.

SEARCYS ST PANCRAS GRAND NW1 £59 123

THE CONCOURSE 020 7870 9900 9–3C

"If one arrives early for the train to Paris", this "beautiful, grand space in an historic setting" is, say fans, "not a bad place to while away the time". But a large majority of reporters agree, "it could and should be better" – "I was hoping for the sort of vibe experienced at Grand Central Station in New York but it didn't have the same panache" and "the food can be a let-down for the price". / NW1 2QP; www.searcys.co.uk; @SearcyStPancras; 10.30 pm, Sun 8 pm.

THE SEA SHELL NW1 £51 322

49 LISSON GROVE 020 7224 9000 9–4A

"Great traditional fish and chips" – "still done very well" – have made this chippy a "cabbies' favourite" for decades. Strangely, though, for an institution tracing its origins back almost a century, the interior of its Lisson Grove is dull and "without atmosphere". / NW1 6UH; www.seashellrestaurant.co.uk; @SeashellRestaur; 10.30 pm; closed Sun.

SEN VIET WC1 £29 342

119 KING'S CROSS ROAD 020 7278 2881 9–3D

"Not the most attractive area" – the traffic arteries south of King's Cross station – "but the food in this outwardly fairly nondescript-looking restaurant is fabulous", and this makes a very handy and good value Vietnamese refuelling spot. / WC1X 9NH; senviet.uk.

SEÑOR CEVICHE W1 £51 332

KINGLY CT 020 7842 8540 4–2B

This "buzzy Peruvian in Kingly Court" provides consistently "good, super-tasty food and a warm ambience". A second branch has followed in Charlotte Street. / W1B 5PW; www.senor-ceviche.com; @SenorCevicheLDN; 11.30 pm, Sat midnight, Sun 10.30 pm; booking max 6 may apply.

SETTE SW1 £92

BULGARI HOTEL, 4 KNIGHTSBRIDGE GREEN 020 7151 1025 6–1D

The replacement for Alain Ducasse's Bulgari (RIP) – the first London sibling to famous NYC restaurant Scarpetta opened in Knightsbridge's Bulgari Hotel in June 2019, serving Italian classics. The seventh location for the group, this one is named Sette for "lucky number seven", apparently. It opened too late for survey feedback, but received a major panning from Sunday Times critic, Marina O'Loughlin for pasta "sauced in the American rather than Italian way: drowned rather than dressed…" / SW1X 7QL; www.settelondon.co.uk.

SEVEN PARK PLACE SW1 £111 443

7-8 PARK PL 020 7316 1620 3–4C

"Consistently lovely food" over the past 10 years has earned an ecstatic, if limited, foodie following for low-key chef William Drabble, who "remains a hit in the kitchen rather than on the TV screen". The "cosy" and "romantic"

dining room of this hideaway luxury hotel in St James's also benefits from "cute, quirky decor and friendly, helpful staff". / SW1A 1LS; www.stjameshotelandclub.com; @SevenParkPlace; 10 pm; closed Mon & Sun; No trainers.

7 SAINTS W11 £56 444

7 ALL SAINTS ROAD 020 7460 8566 7–1B

On the site that was Ripe Tomato (RIP), John Gummer's (former maître d' at The Wolseley) popular yearling is praised as "a neighbourhood spot that has it all": a "monthly changing", "short-but-impossible-to-choose-from menu" and an ambience "like going to a friend's house and being left to do what you want in the privacy of your own table". / W11 1HA; 7saints.co.uk.

SEXY FISH W1 £100 122

1-4 BERKELEY SQ 020 3764 2000 3–3B

"Let your friends know you've been, and they'll ask about the food before wanting to know about the food…" – Richard Caring's notorious, LA-style, bling-fest in Mayfair (which reportedly cost £15m to fit out) is most "definitely a place for those eager to see and be seen". Fans also believe its luxurious menu of Asian-inspired fish and seafood (heavy on funky sushi, tempura, and gyoza) is plain "awesome" too. But to a large proportion of reporters, it's "awful – just awful" – exacting "extortionate" prices to deliver "some weird-and-not-always-felicitous flavour combinations" to "a horrific stew of Mayfair types". / W1J 6BR; www.sexyfish.com; @sexyfishlondon; 11 pm, Sun 10.30 pm; booking max 6 may apply.

SHACKFUYU W1 £46 433

14A, OLD COMPTON ST 020 3019 3492 5–2A

"Some amazingly tasty dishes" – of a funky, western-influenced Japanese genre – again earn high ratings for this "really delightful" Soho outfit (the brainchild of Australian chef, Ross Shonhan, creator of the Bone Daddies group). "It may not quite count as cheap 'n' cheerful, but the tasting menu is a bargain for £30" – in fact, it may be a better choice than going off-piste, where "the bills rack up quickly". Top Tip – "deliciously indulgent green tea ice cream dessert". / W1D 4TJ; www.bonedaddies.com/restaurant/shackfuyu; @shackfuyu; 11 pm, Mon & Tue 10 pm, Sun 9 pm; no booking.

SHAHI PAKWAAN N2 £32 443

25 AYLMER PARADEAYLMER ROAD 020 834 11111 1–1B

This "fabulous" two-year-old Indian in East Finchley punches well above its weight with "top-class, authentic food" based on the royal cuisine of Hyderabad. Its reputation for "high-quality cooking" is attracting attention from beyond the immediate locality, despite the "obscure location" in a converted shop – and there's "easy parking". / N2 0PE; www.shahipakwaan.co.uk.

SHAKE SHACK £30 322

NOVA, 172 VICTORIA ST, SW1 01923 555188 2–4B
80 NEW OXFORD ST, WC1 01925 555171 5–1B
24 THE MARKET, WC2 020 3598 1360 5–3D
BOXPARK WEMBLEY, OLYMPIC WAY, HA9 1–1A
THE STREET, WESTFIELD STRATFORD, E20 01923 555167 14–1D
45 CANNON STREET, EC4 10–3B

In less than 20 years, Danny Meyer has transformed his New York City hot-dog cart into a global fast-food brand giant with eight outlets in London – including a Covent Garden flagship that was revamped earlier this year. Ratings remain remarkably solid for "a chain that does what it's supposed to do". / WC2 & E14 11 pm, Sun 9 pm-10.30 pm; E20 9.30 pm, Fri & Sat 11 pm; no bookings.

SHAMPERS W1 £47 344

4 KINGLY ST 020 7437 1692 4–2B

"With lashings of individuality", this unreconstructed Soho wine bar from 1977 stands out for its "old-fashioned style and service" – "the owner, Simon, and his crew simply deliver!" – and "is still going strong with a traditional menu" of "classic French bistro food" (gravadlax, calf's liver, steak…). There's also a "most interesting wine list that has great depth at good prices, rather than too many wines at very high prices". It can, though, "become a little overcrowded (due to its seeming popularity with the Chartered Surveyors' Tribe)". / W1B 5PE; www.shampers.net; @shampers_soho; 11 pm; closed Sun; No bookings.

SHANGHAI MODERN WC2 322

CENTRAL CROSS, 12 NEWPORT PLACE 020 7734 6137 5–3B

In Chinatown's shiny, new, Central Cross development, this "functional but bright and clean" 150-seater opened in spring 2019, and early days feedback says it's a good, modern addition to the area. "My wife and I know Shanghai food from both Hong Kong and Shanghai – this is good, with generous portions at good-value prices". "Staff, despite being rushed off their feet, were pleasant and helpful, though few spoke English". / WC2H 7JP.

THE SHED W8 £54 333

122 PALACE GARDENS TER 020 7229 4024 7–2B

"Lovely food and a great casual atmosphere" draw a buzzy crowd to this quirky, small Notting Hill site (which old-timers recall as The Ark). It was the first of the Gladwin bros' shabby-chic venues in London (see also Rabbit and Nutbourne) and their Sussex-farm-to-metropolitan-fork concept provides an "interesting English variation on the tapas theme"; on the downside, some find the rustic furniture "very uncomfortable". / W8 4RT; www.theshed-restaurant.com; @theshed_resto; 11 pm; closed Mon L & Sun.

J SHEEKEY WC2 £81 4 4 4

28-34 ST MARTIN'S CT 020 7240 2565
5–3B

"Unfailing, first class, and in the heart of Theatreland" – Richard Caring's "wonderfully old-school" icon (est. 1896) has long been the survey's No. 1 most talked-about destination as well as its top choice for fish and seafood. Tucked away, down an alley just off St Martin's Lane, you navigate your way in past a uniformed doorman. The tantalisingly-translucent frontage only gives hints of the "classic" interior beyond with its "feeling of bygone glamour": a series of "compact" panelled rooms , which "feature wood, brass, glass, and vintage photos of stage stars", all presided over by "very professional" staff. The effect is "intimate" ("albeit a bit cramped") and the atmosphere is "always buzzing" (if, occasionally, "to the wrong side of hectic"). The "traditional", "comfort-fish" cuisine is "not inventive nor innovative", "but always of the highest quality". "New ingredients like harissa enliven an otherwise static menu, but if the formula works, why change it?" "The fish pie and and seafood platter remain classics", while "Dover sole is served in umpteen different ways with on/off bone options". Despite expansion (with the addition of the neighbouring Atlantic Bar), "it has maintained remarkable standards for years and years". / WC2N 4AL; www.j-sheekey.co.uk; @JSheekeyRest; 11.30 pm, Sun 10 pm; booking max 6 may apply.

J SHEEKEY ATLANTIC BAR WC2 £74 3 3 4

28-34 ST MARTIN'S CT 020 7240 2565
5–3B

"So cool eating at the bar" – this "enjoyably bustling" spin-off from the neighbouring Theatreland classic has "very good, 1930s-style decor" (even though it was only created about 10 years ago). Compared with the main restaurant it's "perhaps a bit more about the ambience versus the food" here, and – "with the menu opting for the small-plates approach – costs can mount up". But, results are "predictably good", and the operation's "slick" style and "flexible" format suits it to many different occasions: it's particularly "great for lunch sitting at the bar, or an early pre-theatre dinner at one of the tables". / WC2N 4AL; www.j-sheekey.co.uk; @JSheekeyRest; 11.30 pm, Sun 10.30 pm; booking max 3 may apply.

SHIKUMEN, DORSETT HOTEL W12 £57 4 2 2

58 SHEPHERD'S BUSH GRN 020 8749 9978
8–1C

"Excellent upmarket Chinese food" and "great dim sum" may seem out of place on grungy Shepherd's Bush Green, but this joint "can claim to be one of London's top Oriental restaurants – it's where I take my Singaporean friends when they visit". The venue – a plush modern hotel, part of a Hong Kong-owned group – makes for a rather "cold ambience" by some standards, but there are no complaints about the scran. / W12 5AA;

www.shikumen.co.uk; @ShikumenUK; 10.30 pm, Sun 10 pm.

SHILPA W6 £36 5 3 1

206 KING ST 020 8741 3127 8–2B

In an anonymous-looking Hammsersmith parade of shops, this Keralan café is a particularly notable "hidden gem" – "when it comes to authentic, deft, southern Indian cooking for a minimal bill, Shilpa sure hits the spot" and is "unbelievable value". A word of caution: "it's anything but an exciting place": it's all about the "genuine cooking". / W6 0RA; www.shilparestaurant.co.uk; 11 pm, Thu-Sat midnight.

SHORYU RAMEN £49 3 2 2

9 REGENT ST, SW1 NO TEL 4–4D
3 DENMAN ST, W1 NO TEL 4–3C
5 KINGLY CT, W1 NO TEL 4–2B
84 NEW OXFORD STREET, WC1 5–1B
35 GREAT QUEEN STREET, WC2 5–1D
45 GREAT EASTERN STREET, EC2 13–1B
BROADGATE CIRCLE, EC2 NO TEL 13–2B

"Hard-to-beat ramen" – "the tonkotsu pork broth has amazing depth of flavour" – make Japan Centre owner Tak Tokumine's "relatively authentic" West End duo (in Soho's Kingly Court and on Regent Street) "preferred noodle-stops in a very competitive market". / 11 pm-midnight, Sun 9.30 pm-10 pm; E14 9 pm, Sun 6 pm; no booking (except Kingly Ct).

THE SICHUAN EC1 £49 3 3 2

14 CITY ROAD 020 7588 5489 13–2A

"Delicious dumplings" and other "fine" dishes from southwestern China make this nondescript looking three-year-old "a real find on the western edge of the City, near Bunhill Fields". "I even ate their tofu with great enjoyment, which was a revelation". / EC1Y 2AA; www.thesichuan.co.uk; 11 pm.

SICHUAN FOLK E1 £45 4 2 2

32 HANBURY ST 020 7247 4735 13–2C

The "strongly authentic Sichuan food" at this "fairly basic" Brick Lane venue "may not be the best in London, but nonetheless offers a properly 'ma la' (numbingly spicy) experience". It's particularly "good value for lunch". / E1 6QR; www.sichuan-folk.co.uk; 10.30 pm; No Amex.

SIGNOR SASSI SW1 £65 3 3 3

14 KNIGHTSBRIDGE GREEN 020 7584 2277
6–1D

"Always a treat", this old-school trattoria near Harrods is "just the place for traditional Italian hospitality". Launched 35 years ago, it is now part of the upmarket San Carlo group and has branched out in recent years into the Middle East. / SW1X 7QL; www.signorsassi.co.uk; @SignorSassi; 11.30 pm.

SILK ROAD SE5 £23 5 2 2

49 CAMBERWELL CHURCH ST
020 7703 4832 1–3C

"Xinjiang/Uighur flavours that make few excuses for local palates", with "big portions and small prices" have combined to win a cult following for this outpost of north west China in deepest Camberwell. Expect "great food in a basic setting" along with "a wait – it gets seriously busy". Top Tip – hand-made noodles and "lamb fat skewers are divine". / SE5 8TR; 10.30 pm; closed Sat L & Sun L; Cash only; No bookings.

SILO E9

THE WHITE BUILDING, UNIT 7 QUEENS YARD, WHITE POST LANE 14–1C

Due to land in October, Brighton's zero-waste restaurant Silo is coming to London after a half-million-pound crowdfund by chef Doug McMaster. With a similar eco-gourmet formula to the original, it's going to occupy the first floor of Crate, Hackney Wick's grungily-groovy pizza-and-microbrewery haunt, near the Olympic Park. / E9 5EN; silolondon.com; @SiloBrighton.

SIMPSON'S IN THE STRAND WC2 £82 2 2 3

100 STRAND 020 7420 2111 5–3D

"Quintessentially British cuisine in very generous portions" is the raison d'être of this historic, panelled dining room, which has its bicentenary in sight; and where "a recent revamp seems to have done some good – it's still old-fashioned, but in a good way". But when it comes to the quality of the cooking, it's still not a safe bet – there are regulars who feel "its roast beef and Yorkshire pudding never disappoints", but there remains a sizeable contingent, who rate the beef "below average" and the accompanying veg "school dinner standard" – "such a shame for a wonderful old establishment". Top Tip – a Full English here is a good way to start the day. / WC2R 0EW; www.simpsonsinthestrand.co.uk; @simpsons1828; No trainers.

SIMPSON'S TAVERN EC3 £45 3 3 4

38 1/2 BALL CT, CORNHILL 020 7626 9985
10–2C

"Like stepping back in time" – this "prehistoric eatery in the City" (est 1757) has "an incredible atmosphere" and is "old-fashioned in a way we can rejoice in". The Dickensian menu of "traditional English" chops and roasts, steak 'n' kidney pies and 'stewed cheese' wins solid ratings this year – and is "not for those with a small appetite". Top Tip – "this ancient spot dishes up a top Full English". / EC3V 9DR; www.simpsonstavern.co.uk; @SimpsonsTavern; 3.30 pm; L only, closed Sat & Sun.

SINABRO SW11 £69 3 3 3

28 BATTERSEA RISE 020 3302 3120 11–2C

"You need to sit at the bar to watch the cooking and food preparation" according to fans of this 20-seater in Battersea, that fans say is "delightful in every way" not least its "super quality" modern British cuisine, available either à la carte, or from the five-course tasting menu. / SW11 1EE; www.sinabro.co.uk; @SinabroLondon; 10 pm, Fri & Sat 10.30 pm.

SINGAPORE GARDEN NW6 £50 4 4 2

83A FAIRFAX RD 020 7624 8233 9–2A

"Consistently excellent food with friendly service" – all "at reasonable prices" – ensures that this cramped, pan-Asian veteran, tucked away in a parade of shops near Swiss Cottage, is "always busy". Giles Coren of The Times claims to have eaten here more than a thousand times, drawn back by the Malaysian and Singaporean specialties. / NW6 4DY; www.singaporegarden.co.uk; @SingaporeGarden.

SINGBURI ROYAL THAI CAFÉ E11 £23 4 3 3

593 LEYTONSTONE HIGH RD 020 8281 4801 1–1D

As accolades go, the 'best restaurant in Leytonstone' is a bit of a two-edged sword, but this small Thai local is worth remembering for its "cheap 'n' cheerful" chow; and you can BYO. / E11 4PA; @SingburiThaiCaf; 10.30 pm; D only; Cash only.

SIREN SW1 £106

15 BEESTON PLACE 020 7769 4485 2–4B

Occupying a newly-built pavilion designed by Russell Sage Studios, in the lush garden of the ever-more 'with it' Goring Hotel, this collaboration with über-chef Nathan Outlaw, opened in June 2019, focused on showcasing the Cornish fish and seafood for which Outlaw is famous. Its arrival was too late for survey feedback, but an early review from the Evening Standard's Fay Maschler was most unimpressed. Others, since, have been kinder. / SW1W 0JW; www.thegoring.com/food-drink/siren/ @TheGoring.

SIX PORTLAND ROAD W11 £63 4 4 3

6 PORTLAND ROAD 020 7229 3130 7–2A

"Understated Holland Park local" worth discovering on account of its "consistently delicious and always changing British food" – an "inventive menu providing enough diversity to make it a place to return to on a regular basis". It's "cosy" too, with "charming, quirky service" and an "excellent, interesting and different wine list"; in short, a "perfect neighbourhood bistro". / W11 4LA; www.sixportlandroad.com; @SixPortlandRoad; 10 pm; closed Mon & Sun D.

J Sheekey WC2

SKETCH, LECTURE ROOM AT LIBRARY W1 £151 3 3 4

9 CONDUIT ST 020 7659 4500 4–2A

Up the sweeping staircase of this vast Mayfair palace, this "spectacular, grand, imposing and romantic" dining room certainly looks the part for a fairytale date (hint: "it might be a bit OTT for some tastes"). Star chef Pierre Gagnaire's "creative" and complex menu features some "really quirky and delicious touches" and for most reporters "its two Michelin stars are well-deserved". Even some fans, though, feel the wine list in particular is "stupidly overpriced" and there is a school of thought that, although "the tasting menu is all very nice, dishes don't really hang together too well"; or that you plain just "shouldn't waste your money here". "A selfie in the crystal-lined loos is a must though". / W1S 2XG; www.sketch.uk.com; @sketchlondon; 10.30 pm; closed Mon, Sat L & Sun; No trainers; Booking max 6 may apply.

SKETCH, GALLERY W1 £90 1 2 3

9 CONDUIT ST 020 7659 4500 4–2A

Part of Mourad Mazouz's lavish Mayfair palazzo, this OTT favourite (the 'cheap' dining option here – see also Sketch, Lecture Room) is a perennial hit with a Zoolander-esque crowd keener on looking 'really, really, really ridiculously good looking' than on the eclectic cuisine, which is very expensive, and can seem like a case of "Emperor's new clothes". Who cares though? – with David Shrigley's pinker-than-pink design-scheme it's "an Instagrammer's dream", and who doesn't want to have paid at least one visit to the egg-shaped loos? / W1S 2XG; www.sketch.uk.com; @sketchlondon.

SKEWD KITCHEN EN4 £47 4 3 3

12 COCKFOSTERS PARADE 020 8449 7771 1–1C

This "fun, friendly and welcoming Turk" at the northern end of the Piccadilly line in Cockfosters is reinventing the Anatolian grill 'with attitude'. It's a big hit with locals, who say "they're always updating their menu with fantastic specials". / EN4 0BX; www.skewdkitchen.com; @SkewdKitchen; 11 pm.

SKYLON, SOUTH BANK CENTRE SE1 £73 2 3 4

BELVEDERE RD 020 7654 7800 2–3D

"Still one of the best views in London" – this vast chamber was built, back in this South Bank arts centre's, 1950s, Festival-of-Britain prime, as 'The People's Palace' and it remains "a great-looking venue with an enviable location overlooking the Thames" through gigantic picture windows. All reporters would agree that it's a "brilliant spot for watching the world and river go by, and the cocktails are great", but too many find the cooking either "expensive" or "disappointing", or both. Top Tip – "worth visiting for the 'Saxy Saturday Brunch' featuring a nice but limited set menu but also bottomless Prosecco which helps draw in a crowd". / SE1 8XX; www.skylon-restaurant.co.uk; @skylonsouthbank; closed Sun D; No trainers.

SLOANE STREET DELI SW1

162 SLOANE STREET 6–2D

With views of Cadogan Place Gardens, this new Caprice Holdings sibling adjacent to the Cadogan Hotel is in the same mould as Richard Caring's now-defunct Mount Street Deli, and opened in mid-2019. Initially opening is till late-afternoon, but ultimately a wine bar style operation is planned in the evenings. / SW1X 9BS.

SMITH & WOLLENSKY WC2 £103 2 3 2

THE ADELPHI BUILDING, 1-11 JOHN ADAM ST 020 7321 6007 5–4D

NYC's famous, steakhouse chain opened this über-swanky offshoot three years ago at the foot of the Adelphi Building, just off The Strand, but it's never made waves this side of 'The Pond', written off from day one by the cognoscenti due to its "outrageous prices": a complaint that persists in a significant number of reports to this day. But its "amazing steaks" – the best USDA dry-aged cuts, and prime meat from the British Isles too – also help win it good-to-outstanding ratings in practically all feedback; and, especially if you have company plastic to burn, it can cater well for a business occasion in particular. / WC2N 6HT; www.smithandwollensky.co.uk; @sandwollenskyuk; 10.30 pm, Fri & Sat 11 pm; No trainers.

SMITH'S WAPPING
E1 £71 445

**22 WAPPING HIGH ST 020 7488 3456
12–1A**

"Panoramas over the Thames" and "an excellent view of Tower Bridge" provide extra incentive to discover this popular fish brasserie, at the foot of a Wapping development (sibling to a long-standing original, in Ongar). It offers a "well-put-together" all-round experience, incorporating "professional" service that "goes the extra mile", with "well-cooked and presented" fish and seafood. / E1W 1NJ; www.smithsrestaurants.com; @smithswapping; lunch last orders 2.30pm, sunday 3.30pm. Dinner mo; closed Sun D; No trainers.

SMITHS OF SMITHFIELD, TOP FLOOR EC1 £77 324

**67-77 CHARTERHOUSE ST 020 7251 7950
10–1A**

A "lovely location" with "great views" across the meat market to the City is reason enough to visit this top-floor venue, with a menu that focuses unsurprisingly on red meat. There's a "good atmosphere, with tables not too close together", which makes it a top choice for City-fringe business lunches. The "fixed-price steak and Malbec is great value for money". / EC1M 6HJ; www.smithsofsmithfield.co.uk; @thisissmiths; 10.45 pm; closed Sat L & Sun; booking max 10 may apply.

SMOKE & SALT
SW9 £46 543

**53 BRIXTON STATION RD 07421 327 556
11–1D**

"It's a slightly mad room in a shipping container" – well, that's Pop Brixton for you – but this "relaxed and friendly" 20-seater offers "the epitome of modern dining" with its "super-tasty and interesting" dishes: 'on-trend small plates created using British ingredients and the ancient techniques of smoking, curing and preserving'. / SW9 8PQ; www.smokeandsalt.com; @SmokeandSaltLDN; 10 pm Sun 6 pm; May need 4+ to book.

SMOKEHOUSE ISLINGTON
N1 £57 333

**63-69 CANONBURY RD 020 7354 1144
9–2D**

This "very busy (booking is essential)" gastropub in Canonbury is "great for roast meat" – but the starters and desserts also win plaudits, and "there are so many beers on tap (20) to work your way through". "Terrific quick meal before a gig, and I didn't even get to try their signature smoked meat!". / N1 2RG; www.smokehouseislington.co.uk; @smokehouseN1; 10 pm, Sun 9 pm; closed weekday L.

SMOKESTAK E1 £50 533

35 SCLATER STREET 020 3873 1733 13–1C

Some of "the best smoked meat in London" (including "excellent brisket") is prepared on the charcoal in front of you, alongside "some fantastic sides" at David Carter's rugged, southern US-style grill-house, just off Brick Lane. Just one complaint: "the room is nice, but smokey". / E1 6LB; www.smokestak.co.uk; @smokestakUK.

SMOKING GOAT
E1 £51 544

**64 SHOREDITCH HIGH STREET NO TEL
13–1B**

"Better Thai food than Thailand!" – Ben Chapman's hip Shoreditch BBQ goes from strength to strength, with its "perfect and spicy" dishes; and a "slightly haphazard, rock 'n' roll atmosphere when it's busy" (i.e. mostly). "It's a perfect place to celebrate with friends, as the food's handy for sharing, staff are super friendly and there are great local craft beers on tap". Top Menu Tip – "Sometimes the chilli can be a bit heavy handed, but those crunchy, fish sauce chicken wings are like catnip: utterly addictive". / E1 6JJ; www.smokinggoatsoho.com; @SmokingGoatBar.

SMOKOLOKO E1 53

**OLD SPITALFIELDS MARKET, BETHNAL
GREEN ROAD 07508 675363 13–2B**

It's a dead cinch to spot Cleo Vizioli's street market stall at Spitalfields Market: it's the one with the old train locomotive! This is the only permanent site, although there are three other locos in the pipeline to serve events and markets around town. The USP is its "amazing smoked meats": "there's always a queue, but the meat-loaded rolls are divine". / E1 6GY; smokoloko.com; @smokolokoBBQ.

SNACKBAR E8

FARM:SHOP, 20 DALSTON LANE 14–1A

'Pickled' author Freddie Janssen launched a Kickstarter campaign for this new, August 2019 venture in hip Dalston – an all-day café sitting alongside a co-working space and urban farm, and delivering a funky-sounding menu which reads like a 'pick 'n' mix' of global inspiration. / E8 3AZ; snackbarlondon.com.

SNAPS & RYE W10 £59 443

93 GOLBORNE RD 020 8964 3004 7–1A

"Simple Scandi café" and take-away in North Kensington, at the north end of Portobello market, owned by husband-and-wife team, Kell and Jacqueline Skott, that wins rave reviews from its local fanclub for its straightforwardly delicious, Danish-infuenced dishes. Breakfast and brunch are a big deal here with smørrebrød (open sarnies), kedgeree and other light bites: in the evenings they serve a limited, somewhat more substantial menu (meatballs, pan-fried fish, sharing-plates…) / W10 5NL; www.snapsandrye.com; @snapsandrye; 10 pm; L only, Fri open L & D, closed Mon.

SNOOTY FOX N5 £41 323

75 GROSVENOR AVENUE 9–2D

Jolly Canonbury boozer decorated with pictures of 60s icons. There's also a jukebox – so it "can get very noisy". On the menu: "honest pub grub", including "the best burgers" and spit-roast chicken. / N5 2NN; www.snootyfoxlondon.co.uk; @Snootyfoxlondon.

SOANE'S KITCHEN
W5 £47 223

**PITZHANGER MANOR, WALPOLE PARK
020 8579 2685 1–3A**

"A lovely room and outside garden area" – "great on a sunny day" – makes this "a brilliant addition to the west London scene": the new café in the garden adjacent to Pitzhanger Manor (owned, in days past, by the renowned architect Sir John Soane). But while there's a "good-value set menu" and an à la carte with something for everyone ("covering veggie/ vegan/flexi/typical diets"), some dishes are "expensive and poor". / W5 5EQ; soaneskitchen. co.uk.

SOCIAL EATING HOUSE
W1 £80 224

58-59 POLAND ST 020 7993 3251 4–1C

Ratings dropped for the second year running at Jason Atherton's casual Soho venture, amid gripes from reporters confused by the "pub setting with proper restaurant prices" or having to "wade through four menus". Some say the food is still "consistently brilliant". Others were "left wondering what all the hype is for" – "dishes lacked any wow factor" and are "certainly not worth the high price tag". / W1F 7NR; www.socialeatinghouse.com; @socialeathouse; 2.45pm;10.45 pm; closed Sun.

SOIF SW11 £59 333

27 BATTERSEA RISE 020 7223 1112 11–2C

"Easy-yet-delicious French bistro" option, offering the combination of gutsy Gallic small plates and an interesting wine list that's become the hallmark of outlets run by natural and organic wine pioneer Les Caves de Pyrène. / SW11 1HG; www.soif.co; @Soif_SW11; 10 pm, Sun 4 pm; closed Mon L & Sun D.

SOM SAA E1 £52 323

**43A COMMERCIAL ST 020 7324 7790
13–2C**

"Possibly the most authentic Thai cooking in town" ("fresh", "fragrant" and focused on fiery, north-eastern-Thai cuisine), plus some "delicious cocktails" have carved a major culinary reputation for this trendy three-year-old, in a converted factory south of Spitalfields Market. Its ratings are dragged down this year though by a few less rapturous reports: "perfectly good, but not the outstanding blow-out we expected from some reviews". / E1 6BD; www.somsaa.com; @somsaa_london; 11.30 pm, Sat midnight, Sun 10.30 pm.

Marcus, The Berkeley SW1

SÔNG QUÊ E2 £39 3 3 2

134 KINGSLAND RD 020 7613 3222 14–2A

"Very basic", but zippy, Vietnamese chow ("soft shell crab, YOM!") has made this busy dive one of the better known in Shoreditch's 'Little Vietnam' on the Kingsland Road. "Sometimes service is a little bit attitude-y, but you're not going for that; and it's crowded, but the food's the focus". / E2 8DY; www.songque.co.uk; 11 pm, Sun 10.30 pm; No Amex.

SOPHIE'S STEAKHOUSE £62 2 2 3

42-44 GREAT WINDMILL ST, W1 AWAITING TEL 4–3D

311-313 FULHAM RD, SW10 020 7352 0088 6–3B

"Decent burgers and reliable steaks" are highlights of the menu at this pair of "family- and group-friendly" steakhouses in the Fulham Road and Soho – useful ports of call before a match at Stamford Bridge or a night out in the West End. Overall, the level culinary performance is rated somewhere between "solid" and "pretty average". / www.sophiessteakhouse.com; SW10 11pm, Fri & Sat midnight, Sun-Mon 10 pm, W1D 11 pm, Fri & Sat midnight, Sun 10 pm; no booking.

SORELLA SW4 £55 4 3 4

148 CLAPHAM MANOR STREET 020 7720 4662 11–1D

"A great local addition that's worth travelling to": Robin Gill's small, neighbourhood two-year-old, near his Clapham HQ, The Dairy, takes its inspiration from the Amalfi coast, and its traditionally presented Italian dishes (cicchetti, antipasti, primi, secondi and dolci) are consistently "wonderful"; and it's "good fun" too. / SW4 6BX; www.sorellarestaurant.co.uk; @SorellaClapham.

SOUTINE NW8 £59 3 3 4

60 ST JOHN'S WOOD HIGH STREET 020 3926 8448 9–3A

"It's early days, but all the signs are good for Corbin & King's new venture" in St John's Wood (on the site of a defunct branch of Carluccio's) – "a big hit in an area where, surprisingly, there are few really good places to eat" (and "streets-ahead of the nearby Ivy Café"). The faux-French styling is laid on with a bit of a trowel, but the end-result is enveloping and very "stylish"; while the mostly-French brasserie fare steers the typical C&K line between being very acceptable and merely acceptable. "Terrible acoustics" is an issue raised in some feedback ("excessively noisy for the elderly St John's Wood clientele", according to one septuagenarian reporter). / NW8 7SH; soutine.co.uk; @SoutineStJohn.

SPARROW SE13 £47 3 3 2

RENNELL STREET 020 8318 6941 1–4D

"The best restaurant in Lewisham might sound like damning it with faint praise", but this two-year-old indie is a "convivial neighbourhood spot" that fits the bill without too much irony. The first venture from husband-and-wife team Terry Blake and Yohini Nandakumar, it has a "very varied menu" ("mostly small plates") that "divides into dishes with a Sri Lankan heritage and others with a strong 'St John' vibe (but without too much fusion-crossover going on"). "It can get a bit cramped, and hot with its big front windows facing a traffic-clogged and rather unlovely roundabout (currently being redeveloped with new housing/cinema/retail, etc)". / SE13 7HD; sparrowlondon.co.uk; @sparrowlondon.

SPIRITLAND £58 3 3 5

9 - 10 STABLE STREET, N1 9–3C
ROYAL FESTIVAL HALL, BELVEDERE ROAD, SE1 020 3146 1980 2–3D

For the "mind-blowing sound system", or as "a great place to grab a drink and a bite with your mates", this "groovy", music-led three-year-old, near Granary Square has won quite a following. (It was founded by music consultant Paul Noble, who has worked with Monocle and the Beeb; and Canteen founders Patrick Clayton-Malone and Dominic Lake). "The new, handy Festival Hall branch has the same vibe as the King's Cross original, and here they offer really well-prepared cooking to match the cool sounds, laid-back atmosphere and enthusiastic service... it deserves to thrive." / spiritland.com; @spiritland.

THE SPREAD EAGLE E9 £40 3 4 4

224 HOMERTON HIGH STREET 020 8985 0400 14–1C

"Top vegan food in town, courtesy of Club Mexicana" is to be found at this "cool" east Homerton hostelry: London's first 100% vegan pub. Even those who feel it's "hyped" and only "OK if you're in the area" say "they must be doing something right as it's packed". / E9 6AS; www.thespreadeaglelondon.co.uk; @SpreadEagleLDN.

SPRING RESTAURANT WC2 £85 3 4 5

NEW WING, LANCASTER PL 020 3011 0115 2–2D

"A lovely use of a beautiful space" – "with delicate light flowing in, and a cream-focused colour scheme" – this "open and airy room", within magnificent Somerset House, properly "lives up to its name", and "is the perfect setting for the light, fresh and wonderful dishes" created by Skye Gyngell from her "fine, seasonal" menu. That it's "not cheap" is noted, but seldom with rancour. "Courteous service" completes a "superb" and "romantic" experience. / WC2R 1LA; www.springrestaurant.co.uk; @Spring_Rest; 10.30 pm; closed Sun D; credit card required to book.

THE SQUARE W1 £128 3 3 2

6-10 BRUTON ST 020 7495 7100 3–2C

"A bit starchy, but hard to fault" – Clément Leroy continues to prepare "near-faultless" modern French cuisine at Marlon Abela's celebrated Mayfair temple of gastronomy, whose other major culinary feature is one of the capital's more formidable wine lists. Ambience-wise, it's never exactly been a riotous venue – even during its higher profile Phil Howard days – and now, as it was then, is still most often nominated as an expense-accounter favourite, notwithstanding a "refurbished dining room that's more industrial-chic than stylish-comfort". / W1J 6PU; www.squarerestaurant.com; @square_rest; 10.15 pm, Fri & Sat 10.45 pm; closed Sun L; booking max 8 may apply.

SRI SUWOON SW1 £35 4 4 3

44 HUGH STREET 020 7828 0321 2–4B

This "fantastic neighbourhood Thai" is a "local gem (very much part of the Pimlico renaissance)": "the room is delightful", and "the food is exceptional and very good value" from a kitchen that "goes from strength to strength". / SW1V 4EP; www.srisuwoon.com; @sri_suwoon.

ST LEONARD'S EC2 £70 1 2 2

70 LEONARD STREET 020 7613 5346 13–1B

This potentially "very interesting newcomer" in Shoreditch (on the site long famous as Eyre Brothers, RIP) with a 'fire and ice' theme – a combination of open-hearth, roast dishes with a raw seafood bar – failed to ignite passions amongst our reporters in its first 12 months, despite some adulatory press reviews. Some fans did proclaim its "amazing" dishes, but others said "how I hate this place" citing "terrible food and snotty service". Perhaps the management just didn't gel, as Jackson Boxer unexpectedly severed his ties with the place in August 2019, leaving Andrew Clarke to soldier on solo. / EC2A 4QX; stleonards.london; @stleonardsEC2.

ST MARTIN'S LANE KITCHEN WC2 £64

ST MARTIN'S LANE HOTEL, 45 ST MARTIN'S LANE 020 7300 5588 5–4B

Spring 2019 temporary replacement for the once-achingly-hip Asia de Cuba (RIP) – the main dining room at one of London's early-wave, boutique hotels (which was opened in 1999 by NYC-supremo Ian Schrager in partnership with designer Philippe Starck). Initial feedback suggests its new Pan-Asian offering is "more neutral" than its previous wacky sharing-plate menu, but that, while it's "lost some of its appeal", it can still be a useful option in the area. A full-time successor is mooted, but no timetable has been announced thus far. / WC2N 4HX; www.morganshotelgroup.com/originals/originals-st-martins-lane-london/eat-drink/st-martins-lane-kitchen; @StMartinsLDN.

STECCA SW10 £76 2 2 2

14 HOLLYWOOD RD 020 7460 2322 6–3B

Hit and miss feedback on this Italian two-year-old, in a posh side street opposite the entrance to the Chelsea & Westminster hospital. On the plus side, all reports rate the cooking as good or better. But it can also seem pricey for what it is, and meals don't always run like clockwork: "the management and the regular clientele were treating the place as the most remarkable restaurant in this part of the world, but our service was very up and down, to the extent they gave us free puddings". / SW10 9HY; www.stecca.co.uk; 10 pm.

STEM & GLORY EC1   £52   3|2|2

60 BARTHOLOMEW CLOSE   020 3969 9392   10–2B

"Striking the right balance between recreating 'meaty' dishes and classic vegetarian cooking" – this new, all-day vegan near Barts (offshoot of a Cambridge-based business), scores solid marks for its imaginative, meat-free food in early-days reports. The effect of its contemporary white-and-cream design is somewhere between sparkly-fresh and icily-sparse. / EC1A 7BF; www.stemandglory.uk; @stemandglory.

STICK & BOWL W8   £26   3|2|1

31 KENSINGTON HIGH STREET   020 7937 2778   6–1A

"No-fuss" Chinese dive in posh Kensington that's "filled with surprising high-end customers, particularly given its shared table design" and beyond-retro 1950s decor. "The cheap food's always the same: consistently delicious and freshly cooked – long may it continue in this expensive area". / W8 5NP; 10.45 pm; Cash only; no booking.

STICKS'N'SUSHI   £63   3|3|3

3 SIR SIMON MILTON SQ, VICTORIA ST, SW1 020 3141 8810   2–4B
11 HENRIETTA ST, WC2 020 3141 8810 5–3D
113-115 KING'S ROAD, SW3 020 3141 8181 6–3C
NELSON RD, SE10 020 3141 8220   1–3D
58 WIMBLEDON HILL RD, SW19 020 3141 8800 11–2B
CROSSRAIL PL, E14 020 3141 8230 12–1C

"Not Japanese nor pretending to be" – this Danish fusion-chain offers a suspicious-sounding-but-successful mix of "fancy sushi" with "plenty of other stuff on skewers" (i.e. yakitori 'sticks'). "Some of the non-traditional additions don't quite work, but those that do are lovely"; and as a group, "where so many others fail, it delivers well on consistency". Its "big and spacious", Scandi-style branches create a "vibrant and exciting" environment too, "but, oh my word, the prices…" / www.sticksnsushi.com; @sticksnsushi_UK; 10 pm, Wed-Sat 11 pm.

STICKY MANGO AT RSJ SE1   £52   2|2|2

33 COIN STREET   020 7928 4554 10–4A

Having the "same staff as RSJ" (its predecessor on the site, now RIP) preserves some continuity at this 30-year stalwart, near the Festival Hall, whose "brave move to Thai food from classic French" a couple of years ago has split opinion:

"zingy and fresh" to fans, but to critics, "entirely unremarkable". Its famous cellar of Loire wine has also been transferred to the new venture: "still the best wine list I know of, but it goes less well with the Asian food now on offer". The ambience of the room – whose Reinforced Steel Joist inspired the name of the former operation – has never been a major plus. / SE1 9NR; www.stickymango.co.uk; @stickymangoldn; 10.30 pm.

STOCKWELL CONTINENTAL SW8   £43   3|4|3

169 SOUTH LAMBETH ROAD 020 3019 0757 11–1D

"An excellent addition to Vauxhall" – this hip, all-day, café/bar was a new departure last year for the team behind Anchor & Hope (who run the nearby Canton Arms, and who have hitherto concentrated purely on gastropubs). It occupies the characterful site that was once Rebato's (RIP), with coffee and snacks served in the café at the front (the former tapas bar) and a dining room to the rear, majoring in pizza alongside other Mediterranean dishes (and there's "a great selection of classic cocktails" too). It's regularly "busy and packed with regulars" and solidly rated all-round, but yet to enjoy the major love inspired by its stablemates. / SW8 1XW; www.stockwellcontinental.com.

THE STONHOUSE SW4   £46   3|3|3

165 STONHOUSE ST   020 7819 9312 11–1D

"Bright and airy", traditional-ish gastroboozer (plus garden), off Clapham High Street, "reliably serving good food" (if not of a particularly 'gourmet' variety). / SW4 6BJ; www.thestonhouse.co.uk; @threecheerspubs; 10.30 pm, Sun 9 pm.

STORY SE1   £122   3|3|3

199 TOOLEY ST   020 7183 2117 10–4D

"Take your taste buds on a stimulating journey" when you sample the "truly memorable, eight-course or ten-course tasting menu spanning three to four hours" at Tom Sellers' "extraordinary" venture, near Tower Bridge; where reporters are "blown away" by the "sensationally presented cuisine prepared with exceptional care and perfect flavours… it's hard to find enough superlatives". "Somehow the staff find a way to do fine gastronomy with the fun but without the pomp" contributing to an all-round "quite magical experience". That's the majority view anyhow, but ratings are again dragged into the middle ground by a determined minority of refuseniks who find it "an overhyped concept"; "ill-judged and wildly expensive". STOP PRESS: throughout August and September 2019, Tom and team decamped from London to Cornwall to run 'Story by the Sea'. At the time of this review, the presumption is that after their return, it's then back to business as usual in SE1. / SE1 2UE; www.restaurantstory.co.uk; @Rest_Story; 9.15 pm; closed Mon & Sun.

STREETXO W1   £98   4|3|4

15 OLD BURLINGTON ST   020 3096 7555 4–3A

"Delicious, different and interesting" – Dabiz Muñoz's "funky" and "very fun" Mayfair three-year-old inspired much more feedback this year, practically all of it adulatory. From the OTT cocktails in the bar, to the full-on, Hispanic-Asian fusion-cuisine emanating from the restaurant's open kitchen, it's a maximalist experience, but one that comes off much more often than not nowadays. Perhaps it's time for the fooderati, who gave it a rough time on its launch, to re-evaluate the place. Top Tip – dip your toe in the water with the £30 express lunch menu. / W1S 2JR; www.streetxo.com; @StreetXO_London; Mon - Fri 11pm, Sat 12, Sun 9.30; No bookings at lunch.

SUB CULT EC2   £14

CONTAINER, FINSBURY AVENUE SQ 13–2A

This June 2019 newcomer opened too late for any survey feedback, although Ben Chancellor and Gaz Phillip's brand is well known to street-food aficionados for its brilliant US deli-style rolls, having operated out of various locations over the last five years. Its first forever-home is in the City, a short walk from Mansion House tube. / EC2M 2PP; www.sub-cult.co.uk; @SubCultSubs.

SUKHO FINE THAI CUISINE SW6   £52   5|5|3

855 FULHAM RD   020 7371 7600 11–1B

"Carefully prepared cuisine is served with charm and experience" at this accomplished dining room: West London's top-scoring Thai and, oft-tipped by its fans (from as far afield as Cornwall) as "the best Thai in town", full stop. It occupies a shop conversion deep in Fulham that's attractive but tightly packed. / SW6 5HJ; www.sukhogroups.com; 11 pm.

SUKSAN SW10   £49   3|3|2

7 PARK WALK   020 7351 9881   6–3B

This "charming neighbourhood Thai" in Chelsea serves "food equal to the best in town" according to its fans (although its scores lag behind its smarter sibling, Sukho in Fulham). / SW10 0AJ; www.sukhogroups.com; 10.45 pm, Sun 9.45 pm.

SUMAK N8   £40   4|4|2

141 TOTTENHAM LANE   020 8341 6261 1–1C

"Continuing its reign as the best Turkish restaurant in Crouch End, Hornsey and Harringay, beating all opposition in nearby Green Lanes": the "fantastic food" comes with "unlimited, sumac-spiced breads and delicious salads". It "even looks a bit more stylish" since the installation of wall hangings and better lighting. / N8 9BJ; www.sumakrestaurants.co.uk.

THE SUMMERHOUSE W9 £65 `2` `3` `5`

60 BLOMFIELD RD   020 7286 6752   9–4A

"The perfect summer canalside fish restaurant" – this Little Venice charmer makes the best of "a delightful waterside setting", with "well-spaced tables and a calm atmosphere". The cooking is barely mentioned by reporters, although there are no complaints beyond the suggestion that it's "a bit overpriced". / W9 2PA; www.thesummerhouse.co; @FRGSummerhouse; No Amex.

SUMOSAN TWIGA SW1 £69 `2` `2` `2`

165 SLOANE STREET   020 3096 0222   6–1D

"It's eye-wateringly expensive, but the clientele are so rich that it doesn't matter!" at this deluxe Belgravia outpost of the 20-year-old, Moscow-based Sumosan empire, which shifted a couple of years ago from Mayfair to the stretch of Sloane Street south of Harvey Nicks, seemingly patronised solely by 'citizens of nowhere'. Foodwise, an innovative menu of Italian and Japanese dishes are presented side-by-side (prepared by a chef dedicated to each cuisine): "lovely… I wasn't paying…" / SW1X 9QB; www.sumosan.com; @sumosantwiga.

SUNDAY N1 £31 `4` `3` `3`

169 HEMINGFORD RD   020 7607 3868 9–2D

"Dream of a local gem" on the fringes of Islington, with "wonderful food and warm, welcoming service". "No bookings at the weekend, so be prepared to queue for your brunch: accept it, deal with it, and enjoy your table when you get it…" / N1 1DA; @sundaybarnsbury; 10.30 pm; closed Mon, Tue D, Wed D & Sun D; No Amex.

SUPAWAN N1 £48 `4` `3` `2`

38 CALEDONIAN ROAD   020 7278 2888 9–3D

"Superb, zesty southern Thai food" has won a sizeable fanclub for this "cramped canteen" in King's Cross and as a result it's "frequently full". It may be "a bit pricier than many such places in London, but that is reflected in the top-notch quality of the food". / N1 9DT; www.supawan.co.uk.

SUPER TUSCAN E1 £56 `3` `4` `3`

8A ARTILLERY PASSAGE   020 7247 8717 13–2B

"A little bit of proper, authentic Italy near the City" – this audaciously named trattoria tucked away down a little lane near Spitalfields has won a steady following for its "original" approach. Importing specialist ingredients directly from Italy means it's "not cheap", although fans reckon it "offers very good value for money". / E1 7LJ; www.supertuscan.co.uk; @TheSuperTuscan; 10 pm; closed Sat & Sun.

SUSHI ATELIER W1 £33 `5` `4` `3`

114 GREAT PORTLAND STREET 020 7636 4455   2–1B

"Really great sushi with a fusion feel" makes this modern Japanese, just north of Oxford Circus, from the Chisou group "a great place to become acquainted with Japanese food". Sky-high ratings improved further in its second year – a good indication that the "friendly staff" are not resting on their laurels. / W1W 6PH; www.sushiatelier.co.uk; @sushiatelierlondon; 11 pm.

SUSHI MASA NW2 £41 `3` `3` `2`

33B WALM LANE   020 8459 2971   1–1A

"The best place to eat in NW2… keeping up with Sushi Say": its predecessor on this site was a hard act to follow after over twenty years in Willesden Green, and – on limited feedback – this neighbourhood Japanese is a worthy occupant of the site it vacated a couple of years back. / NW2 5SH; 10 pm.

SUSHI TETSU EC1 £90 `5` `5` `3`

12 JERUSALEM PAS   020 3217 0090 10–1A

"Prefer it to The Araki…", "the best sushi I've had outside of Tokyo…", "superb…" – Toru Takahashi's Clerkenwell venture is "beyond reproach": "a true neighbourhood sushiya" that rivals London's best-known names, at a fraction of the price, and delivers "astonishing flavours" and the "intimate" experience you'd expect of somewhere with just 7 seats, minded over by "delightful" staff. One perennial complaint though – "the whole dreary booking process". / EC1V 4JP; www.sushitetsu.co.uk; @SushiTetsuUK; 7.45 pm, Thu-Fri 8 pm, Sat 7 pm; closed Mon & Sun.

SUSHISAMBA £89 `3` `2` `3`

OPERA TERRACE, 35 THE MARKET, WC2 020 3053 0000   5–3D
HERON TOWER, 110 BISHOPSGATE, EC2 020 3640 7330 10–2D

"The lift ride up to the 39th floor is part of the fun", when you visit the "amazing" City branch, in the Heron Tower, of this US-based chain (with siblings in Vegas and Miami): a Hollywood-esque scene, complete with a ritzy cocktail bar; vertigo-inducing outside terrace; and svelte dining room boasting "incredible views". But while it can offer an all-round "great experience" – not least "fabulous" funky, fusion fare – its "pretty-looking" dishes come at extragalactic prices and sceptics feel that "you can eat this style of cuisine better elsewhere" nowadays. (Gripes of an overly "sweet note" to dishes also crept in this year). Its year-old WC2 sibling likewise has a superb setting on top of Covent Garden Market, overlooking the back of the Royal Opera House. But while it, too, is "all very slick and fashionable", it, too, charges "obscene prices albeit for decent food" – lacking the high-rise glam of the Square Mile – can seem more "clinical" and "pleased with itself". / sushisamba.com; 1.30 am, Wed-Sat 2 am.

SUZI TROS W8 £61

18 HILLGATE STREET   7–2B

Husband-and-wife team, Adrien Carre and Christina Mouratoglou (of Mazi, just up the road) launched this new bistro and cocktail bar, off Notting Hill Gate, in June 2019: too late for any survey feedback. Named for a cult 1960s Greek film, the venture serves small plates taking their inspiration from northern Greece; plus an exclusively Greek selection of wines and beers. / W8 7SR; www.suzitros.com.

THE SWAN W4 £53 `3` `3` `4`

1 EVERSHED WALK,119 ACTON LN 020 8994 8262   8–1A

Slightly "hard to find" on the Chiswick/Acton border, this "lovely" panelled pub serves "surprisingly good", "ambitious", yet "unfussy" food with a distinct Mediterranean accent. Service is "friendly", and there's an "amazing garden" for the summer months. / W4 5HH; www.theswanchiswick.co.uk; @SwanPubChiswick; 9 pm, Fri & Sat 10 pm, Sun 9 pm; closed weekday L.

THE SWAN AT THE GLOBE SE1 £64 `3` `3` `4`

21 NEW GLOBE WALK   020 7928 9444 10–3B

"A great view of the river and very competent cuisine" makes this would-be Elizabethan tavern – on the first floor of Shakespeare's Globe theatre – "a delightful find on the tourist trail". Chef Allan Pickett sticks sensibly to modern British rather than cod-historical cooking. / SE1 9DT; www.swanlondon.co.uk; @swanabout; 10.30 pm, Sun 5.30 pm.

SWEET THURSDAY N1 £43 `3` `2` `2`

95 SOUTHGATE RD   020 7226 1727 14–1A

This "good local pizza place" in De Beauvoir Town "continues to be very popular". There's an "interesting variety of toppings (and bases) and gluten-free/dairy-free options", as well as alternatives such as fish stew. "They also have prosecco on tap" and a smart little bottle shop. / N1 3JS; www.sweetthursday.co.uk; @Pizza_and_Wine; 10 pm, Fri & Sat 10 pm, Sun 9 pm.

SWEETINGS EC4 £76 `3` `3` `4`

39 QUEEN VICTORIA ST   020 7248 3062 10–3B

"It feels as if one has been decanted into the 1920s but I never fail to enjoy my visits!" – "This unique City institution has a charm and authenticity that can't be imitated" – a "joyous throwback" (founded, on a different site, in 1830) which offers "simple, well-executed British seafood classics" (followed by steamed puddings) at lunchtimes only, to a largely besuited crowd. The "eclectic seating arrangements" can "be a surprise to newbies" – you either perch at "makeshift bar-tops", or cram into the rear dining room where "service is hindered by the lack of room, but everyone mucks in and plates get passed around". "The waiters are nearly as old as the building, but that just adds to its appeal…". "Black Velvet is served in pewter tankards, and a 'bill of fare' serves instead of a menu". The experience comes at "ridiculous prices", but most reckon they're worth paying… "and the place does now take cards". / EC4N 4SA; www.sweetingsrestaurant.co.uk; @SweetingsLondon; 3 pm; L only, closed Sat & Sun; no booking.

TAB X TAB W2 £25 5|4|4

WESTBOURNE HOUSE, 14-16 WESTBOURNE GROVE   020 7792 3445 7–1B

"The best coffee in town" is the claim made by fans of Mathew and Charmaine Tabatabai's year-old Bayswater brew-stop, which – with Mavam espresso machine, BOCCA beans, partnership with Ozone coffee roasters, hand-made artisanal cups, yada, yada – is a perfect pitstop for caffeine junkies. It's "a great hang out" too, though, serving simple salads, pancakes, eggs on toast… / W2 4UJ; tabxtab. com; @TABxTABLondon.

TABERNA ETRUSCA EC4 £58 2|2|2

9 -11 BOW CHURCHYARD   020 7248 5552 10–2C

"A cramped City Italian with good food", this traditional venue off Bow churchyard "generally performs well" and is "packed at lunchtime – particularly at the tables outside, when weather permits". "Portions are huge" and there's "a fantastic list of regional Italian wines, some of which you might not find elsewhere". Ratings dropped this year, though, with the odd 'off' report. / EC4M 9DQ; www.etruscarestaurants.com; 9.30 pm; closed Sat & Sun.

THE TABLE SE1 £46 3|3|2

83 SOUTHWARK ST   020 7401 2760 10–4B

"A firm favourite for breakfast and brunch in Southwark" – this café-style fixture a short stroll from Tate Modern serves "a great menu to suit all tastes", and fans say it's "unbeatable". / SE1 0HX; www.thetablecafe.com; @thetablecafe; 10.30 pm; closed Mon D, Sat D & Sun D; booking weekdays only.

TABLE DU MARCHE N2 £53 3|3|2

111 HIGH ROAD   020 8883 5750 1–1B

"Delicious, reasonably priced food" has won over the East Finchley crowd at this three-year-old bistro in what is otherwise a "culinary wasteland". As a bonus, it's "very French, and therefore romantic". / N2 8AG; www.tabledumarche.co.uk; @TableDuMarche; 11 pm.

TAKAHASHI SW19 £50 5|5|3

228 MERTON RD   020 8540 3041 11–2B

"Some of the best Japanese food in London, at half the price you'd spend in Zone One", is found at this tiny, "surprisingly calming" outfit, in a parade of shops "on a busy road", near South Wimbledon tube station. "Superb fresh sushi" is prepared on site by chef-proprietor Taka, formerly of Nobu, with service by his "charming wife", Yuko. "I've eaten sushi three to four times in Japan – and this is better!". Booking recommended. / SW19; www.takahashi-restaurant.co.uk; @takahashi_sw19; 10 pm, Fri & Sat 10.30 pm, Sun 9 pm.

TAMARIND W1 £75 3|4|2

20 QUEEN ST   020 7629 3561 3–3B

"The food speaks volumes" – "sensational grills, exquisite curries and traditional biryanis" – for most (if not all) who report on this pioneering Mayfair venture, which helped validate the whole concept of posh Indian restaurants in the UK. It's "a pity about the basement location" though, and the 2018 refurb designed to give a "light and airy modern" interior has proved "OK, but not really an improvement… if anything noise levels are higher". / W1J 5PR; www.tamarindrestaurant.com; @TamarindMayfair; 10.45 pm, Sun 10.30 pm; closed Sat L; No trainers.

TAMARIND KITCHEN W1 £62 3|3|3

167-169 WARDOUR ST   020 7287 4243 4–1C

"A hidden pearl in the heart of Soho", this "smart-casual" spin-off from Mayfair's Tamarind has a "lovely, buzzy vibe"; and serves "really impressive and refined modern Indian cooking" – "with a fresh-tasting twist to the traditional dishes" – from "a short menu that changes regularly. / W1F 8WR; tamarindkitchen. co.uk; @tamarindkitchen.

TAMP COFFEE W4 £23 3|3|3

1 DEVONSHIRE ROAD   NO TEL 8–2A

"A caffeine hit and empañadas, obvs" – that's the deal at this well-liked small coffee bar, off Chiswick's main drag, which, as well as its trademark Latino bites, serves a selection of baps, pastries and other brunch-ish fare from early morning till afternoon. / W4; www.tampcoffee.co.uk; @Tampcoffee; 6 pm; L only; booking max 6 may apply.

TANDOOR CHOP HOUSE WC2 £51 4|3|3

ADELAIDE STREET   020 3096 0359 5–4C

A "different take on Indian favourites, which you can watch being made in the open kitchen" combines with "retro glamour" styling to good effect at this two-year-old behind St Martin-in-the-Fields: an "excellent concept", "almost like a copy-cat of Dishoom, but way more relaxed". / WC2N 4HW; tandoorchophouse.com; @tandoorchop; 10 pm, Sun 9 pm; booking max 6 may apply.

TAPAS BRINDISA £60 3|2|2

46 BROADWICK ST, W1   020 7534 1690 4–2B
18-20 SOUTHWARK ST, SE1   020 7357 8880 10–4C

"Authentic and delicious tapas… if you can get a table" has made the bustling, original branch of this Hispanic food importer's chain a well-known feature of Borough Market, and "at busy times, it feels rushed". It has spawned a number of spin-offs over the years, which are generally high quality, if not as vibey as the original: most recently opening in October 2018 in the new Battersea Power Station development. / www.brindisakitchens.com; @Brindisa; 11 pm-11.30 pm, EC2 12.30 am; SE1 no booking.

TAQUERIA W11 £40 3|2|3

141-145 WESTBOURNE GROVE 020 7229 4734 7–1B

A pioneer of the London taco boom – this Mexican cantina on the Notting Hill and Bayswater border is "good value for money" and "an excellent choice for lunch". After 15 years, however, its menu seems "less interesting than it used to be" – perhaps standards elsewhere have risen. "But the mojitos are as good as ever". (Oldies may recall that this was the joint David Cameron used to be conscientiously spotted in, to show how chilled he was.) / W11 2RS; www.taqueria.co.uk; @TaqueriaUK; 11 pm, Fri & Sat 11.30 pm, Sun 10.30 pm; No Amex.

TARANTELLA RISTORANTE PIZZERIA W4 £53 3|3|3

4 ELLIOT RD   020 8987 8877 8–2A

"Minuscule" – "but perfectly formed" – this "utterly southern Italian local with a regularly changing menu" is a big "favourite" near Turnham Green. Top Tip – "try the specials straight from Puglia, like ox cheek with turnip tops – amazing". / W4 1PE; www.latarantella. london/chiswick.

TARO £34 3|2|2

61 BREWER ST, W1   020 7734 5826 4–3C
193 BALHAM HIGH RD, SW12   020 8675 5187 11–2C
44A CANNON ST, EC4   020 7236 0399 10–3B

Bustling "no-frills" Japanese canteens that serve "great value" noodles and sushi at an efficient pace. The 20-year-old Soho original has now been joined by branches in the City, Balham and most recently Kennington (which is a little more spacious). / www.tarorestaurants.co.uk; W1F 10.30 pm, Fri & Sat 11 pm, Sun 9.30 pm; W1D 10.30 pm, Fri & Sat 10.45 pm, Sun 9.30 pm, Mon 10 pm; no Amex; Brewer St only small bookings.

TAS £47 2|2|2

"They've become a bit boring and rote over the years", but these popular, "cheap 'n' cheerful" Turkish cafés are very affordably priced, and even those who see them as "workaday", can feel they still "have a place as a reasonable-enough option" – especially in a big group, or with the kids – and they also offer "lots of choice for vegetarians". Venues are "well-located for combining with cultural visits" – especially on the South Bank, where Tas originated 20 years ago on The Cut, opposite the Young Vic Theatre. There's also a popular branch, Tas Pide (see also), next door to Shakespeare's Globe. / www.tasrestaurant.com; 11.30 pm, Sun 10.30 pm; EC4 Sat 5 pm; 72 Borough High St 6 pm, Sat & Sun 4 pm; EC4 closed Sat D & Sun, cafe SE1 closed Sun.

TAS PIDE SE1 £40 2 3 4

20-22 NEW GLOBE WALK   020 7928 3300 10–3B

"You can't fault the service or location" at this "reasonably priced" offshoot of useful Turkish chain Tas, next to Shakespeare's Globe, whose cosy, distinctive decor follows an Anatolian theme. 'Pide' is the Turkish equivalent to pizza, the branch speciality. / SE1 9DR; www.tasrestaurants.co.uk; @TasRestaurants; 11.30 pm, Sun 10.30 pm.

TATE MODERN, KITCHEN & BAR, LEVEL 6 SE1 £43 2 2 4

LEVEL 6 BOILER HOUSE, BANKSIDE 0207 401 5108 10–3B

"Beautiful views – adequate but unexciting food": that's the perennial trade-off at Tate Modern's original, elevated dining room – a simple space, but with a stunning vantagepoint for viewing The Thames, St Paul's and the City. It aims to be a showcase for top British ingredients and drinks but results can border on the mundane. / SE1 9TG; www.tate.org.uk; @TateFood; 9 pm; Sun-Thu L only, Fri & Sat open L & D.

TAYYABS E1 £30 4 2 2

83 FIELDGATE ST   020 7247 6400 10–2D

"Queues are mad!" at this "always crazy" and "fantastically good-value" 500-seater, Punjabi BYO in the East End, which is "busy even into the late hours", and a serious rival to the older Lahore five minutes' walk away. Everything is "simply delicious", with "the real highlights being the sizzling and smoking tandoori plates": lamb chops in particular "always hit the mark", but "everything is so fresh". / E1 1JU; www.tayyabs.co.uk; @1tayyabs; 11.30 pm.

TELL YOUR FRIENDS SW6 £47 3 3 4

175 NEW KING'S ROAD   020 7731 6404 11–1B

TYF is the year-old café-style creation of Made in Chelsea sisters Lucy and Tiffany Watson, which brings vegan living to Parsons Green: feedback is still limited, but skips cynicism to laud a "lovely" place with "wonderful", healthy dishes. / SW6 4SW; www.tellyourfriendsldn.com.

TEMPER £49 3 3 4

25 BROADWICK STREET, W1 020 3879 3834 4–1C
5 MERCERS WALK, WC2 020 3004 6669 5–2C
ANGEL COURT, EC2 020 3004 6984 10–2C

"Huge cuts of carefully sourced meat, such as great Barnsley chops, are expertly cooked over wood" at Neil Rankin's "loud and atmospheric" Soho basement with a 6-metre fire pit, which nowadays also has two similar satellites in Covent Garden and near Bank: the set-up – "an open kitchen", "with all the meat on display" creates "some real theatre and buzz". And in WC2, the venue's wood-fired oven is also pressed into service to deliver some "incredible deep-dish pizza". There remain one or two reporters who consider the experience "totally overhyped", but the general impression is of "a time to remember" and with "a surprisingly reasonable bill for such big hunks of meat". / temperrestaurant.com; @temperldn.

THE 10 CASES WC2 £60 3 4 3

16 ENDELL ST   020 7836 6801 5–2C

"A real find so close to the Opera House", this independent Covent Garden wine bar/bistro offers a "sometimes brilliant but always good – eccentric and eclectic – wine list", which is "ever changing" as only 10 cases of each wine are stocked at any point in time. "Friendly and knowledgeable staff" are on hand to advise on your choice and to present a short menu of "beautifully crafted small plates and charcuterie", with "particularly enticing blackboard specials". / WC2H 9BD; www.the10cases.co.uk; @10cases; 11 pm; closed Sun.

10 GREEK STREET W1 £62 4 3 2

10 GREEK ST   020 7734 4677 5–2A

A "great (and ever-changing) range of fairly priced wines", together with a handwritten 'Black Book' of fine wines at low mark-ups, make this "fun and friendly" – but also "crowded" and "noisy" – modern Soho wine bar a regular haunt for wine trade insiders. The food is also "great", "reliably delicious, and avoids cliches", which makes it an ideal spot to "enjoy a long, relaxed, indulgent lunch". A number of fans caution though that "prices seem to be creeping higher…" / W1D 4DH; www.10greekstreet.com; @10GreekStreet; 10 pm; closed Sun; booking L only.

10 HEDDON STREET W1

10 HEDDON STREET 4–3B

In Crown Estates's little restaurant enclave, just off Regent Street, the site that was Magpie (RIP) was relaunched in summer 2019 under an 'agile approach' that envisages 'the ability to invite more creative partners on a short-term basis to add fresh, exciting ideas to London's dining scene'. We think that may mean a series of pop-ups. First up: Chris Leach (Pitt Cue, Kitty Fishers et al) and David Carter (of

Smokestak), whose menu will feature various hand-made salumi and hand-rolled pasta dishes. / W1B 4BX; 10heddonst.co.uk.

TENDIDO CERO SW5 £55 3 3 4

174 OLD BROMPTON ROAD   020 7370 3685 6–2B

"Some of the most reliably good tapas in London" – "delicious and perfectly executed" – plus "an interesting, if pricey wine list" can be found at this "vibrant", black-and-red liveried offshoot of Cambio de Tercio, the South Ken fixture, directly opposite. "Constant innovation" in the kitchen means there's "always something different and appetising" on the menu. / SW5 0BA; www.cambiodetercio.co.uk; @CambiodTercio; 11 pm.

TERRA ROSSA N1 £58 3 4 2

139 UPPER STREET   020 7226 2244 9–3D

"There's no better choice if you're going to Islington's Almeida Theatre" than this "cheerful Puglian" nearby, which serves "way better food than its touristy appearance suggests": "simple, flavourful Italian dishes" washed down with "sensibly-priced, rustic, southern Italian wines". "The atmosphere is unfussy, friendly and easygoing: you get a great meal and a very reasonable bill". / N1 1QP; terrarossa-restaurant.co.uk.

TERROIRS £54 2 2 3

5 WILLIAM IV ST, WC2 020 7036 0660 5–4C
38 LORDSHIP LANE, SE22 1–4D

"Tucked away off Trafalgar Square, you'd need to know about this very buzzy wine bar to find it… but sadly many people do as it's normally packed out". Ten years ago, when it opened, it was a major sensation thanks to its then-novel combination of "really adaptable", gutsy, Gallic tapas ("plates of meat, cheese, paté, etc") washed down with "a superb (if somewhat baffling and esoteric) wine selection, featuring some very interesting natural wines" (it's actually owned by wine importers, Les Caves de Pyrenes). Nowadays the prevailing view is that it's "good but very expensive for what is in effect an uncomfortable and noisy café". / terroirswinebar.com; @TerroirsWineBar.

TEXTURE W1 £122 5 4 3

34 PORTMAN ST   020 7224 0028 2–2A

Aggi Sverrisson's "sublime", Icelandic-inspired cuisine – in particular "a refreshing and very imaginative twist on fish" – again wins one of the survey's highest food-ratings for his well-established flagship, just off Portman Square. To the odd reporter, the low-key space (actually part of a hotel, although you only find out when you look for the WC) can seem "dull and cold", but most reporters like the fact that "there's something a bit different about the style of the place". "Very warm and welcoming" service only adds to its refreshingly un-poncy approach. / W1H 7BY; www.texture-restaurant.co.uk; @TextureLondon; 10.30 pm; closed Mon & Sun.

THALI SW5 £47 4|3|2

166 OLD BROMPTON RD   020 7373 2626
6–2B

"Subtle, aromatic and utterly delicious food" based around "family recipes" are on the menu at this unusual, family-run Indian café decked out with vintage Bollywood posters, on the outer fringe of South Kensington. "I just don't understand how this place isn't better known", it's a "real gem". / SW5 0BA; @thaliLondon; 11.30 pm, Sun 10.30 pm.

THE BUXTON E1 £47

42 OSBORN STREET   AWAITING TEL
13–2C

From the team behind the nearby Culpeper, this new (June 2019) gastroboozer occupies a cleverly rebuilt seven-storey site near the foot of Brick Lane, whose redevelopment has allowed the addition of 15 bedrooms. It opened too late for survey feedback: The Standard's David Sexton found the ground floor bar a little "cramped" and "not for lingering", but a good value, if "lonely pioneer of bourgeois taste" in this grungy 'hood. / E1 6TD; www.thebuxton.co.uk.

THE CHIPPING FORECAST £47 3|3|3

58 GREEK STREET, W1   5–2A
29 ALL SAINTS ROAD, W11   020 7460 2745
7–1B

"Reliable fish 'n' chips – and fun hosts" – earn solid ratings for this new-wave Notting Hill chippy, where the sustainable seafood is sourced directly from Cornish fishermen. A Soho sibling opened in 2018, close to the business's origin as a stall in Berwick Market.

THE CROWN W4 £59 3|3|4

210 CHISWICK HIGH ROAD   020 3330 7131
8–2A

With its "lovely sunny courtyard" and gracious interior, Harcourt Inns' Chiswick yearling represents a successful realisation of the potential of this big, very characterful building (formerly Carvosso's RIP, and originally Chiswick's Victorian police station) as a chichi neighbourhood gastropub. But while the food's consistently well-rated, anyone expecting to experience the magic of the place's much PR'd associations with Harcourt's chef-director Henry Harris (erstwhile patron of Knightsbridge's legendary, but long-defunct, Racine) will likely leave disappointed by food that's creditable pub grub for W4, but nowt more. / W4 1PD; thecrownchiswick.co.uk.

THE GOOD EGG £58 4|3|4

UNIT G9 KINGLY COURT, W1   4–2B
93 CHURCH ST, N16   020 7682 2120   1–1C

"Utterly magic shakshuka served with chunks of roasted sourdough…", "stand-out salt beef bagels…", "incredible coffee with a selection of babka sweet breads (in different flavours!)…", "ZFC – 'za'atar fried chicken' – to die for!…" – these "bustling" Israeli delis

---

in Stoke Newington and Soho's Kingly Court create queues (especially at brunch) with their "quite exceptional and startlingly fresh Middle-Eastern-cum-north-American food. They also make a worthwhile destination at dinner, when the pace is more sedate, the natural wines are flowing and you can actually book a table". "Casual and relaxed", they look "gorgeous" too. / thegoodeggn16.com; @TheGoodEgg_.

THE PETERSHAM RESTAURANT TW10 £66 2|3|5

NIGHTINGALE LANE   020 8003 3602   1–4A

"Brilliant views over the Thames at the window tables", from a "unique" vantagepoint overlooking Petersham Meadows, add to the "tranquil" atmosphere at this impressive-looking hotel (built in 1865 by the same architect as Portland Place's Langham Hotel). On most accounts, "decent" cooking creates "a real experience" (if in a rather old-fashioned mould), but there's also the odd report of "perfunctory" standards. Top Tip – "a fantastic location for a relaxed afternoon tea". / TW10 6UZ; petershamhotel.co.uk/restaurant; @thepetersham; 9.45 pm.

THE RESTAURANT AT THE CAPITAL SW3 £91

22-24 BASIL ST   020 7591 1202   6–1D

Following the departure of Nathan Outlaw, Adam Simmonds is to take over the stoves in the dining room of this luxury hotel, a short walk from the back of Harrods. The new venture will open in autumn 2019. Simmonds's pedigree is good, and he's the latest in a succession of star names to hold the position in the hotel. The main limitation on enjoyment here has historically been the dimensions of the dining room itself: it's a small space, where it's hard to generate much in the way of spark. / SW3 1AT; www.capitalhotel.co.uk; @hotelcapital; 10 pm; closed Sun.

THE YARD, GREAT SCOTLAND YARD HOTEL SW1

GREAT SCOTLAND YARD   020 7925 4700
2–3C

Chef and Restaurateur Robin Gill (The Dairy, Sorella, Darby's) will oversee this new dining room – one of four F&B outlets he will help manage (along with partner Alex Harper) within the Great Scotland Yard Hotel built on the site of the Met's original HQ, just off Trafalgar Square; it's due to open in late 2019. As well as two bars, there is also 'The Parlour', which will be big on afternoon tea. / SW1A 2HN; www.hyatt.com/en-US/hotel/united-kingdom/great-scotland-yard/lhrub.

THEO RANDALL W1 £78 4|4|2

INTERCONTINENTAL HOTEL, 1 HAMILTON PL   020 7318 8747   3–4A

"Exemplary Italian ingredients cooked to perfection" and "served impeccably by delightful people" has earned a glowing

---

reputation for the English-born former River Café chef, whose dining room off the foyer of the 1970s-built Intercontinental Hotel tower near Hyde Park Corner provides some of London's best Italian cuisine. The "soulless setting" always attracts adverse comment, although it is "much improved" since its renovation a few years back. / W1J 7QY; www.theorandall.com; @theorandall; 11 pm, Sun 10.30 pm; closed Sat L & Sun.

THEO'S SE5 £41 4|4|2

2 GROVE LN   020 3026 4224   1–3C

"Lovely pizzas with great crusty bases" have won a thumbs-up from aficionados for this independent pizzeria in Camberwell (which also has a much less commented-on outpost in Elephant and Castle). They also serve panuozzo, or wood-fired sandwiches, at lunchtime. / SE5; www.theospizzeria.com; @theospizzaldn; 10.30 pm, Fri & Sat 11 pm, Sun 10 pm ; No Amex; May need 6+ to book.

34 MAYFAIR W1 £94 3|3|3

34 GROSVENOR SQ   020 3350 3434   3–3A

This swish New York-style grill, appropriately round the corner from the ex-US Embassy in Mayfair, has a lower profile than its siblings in Richard Caring's stable, remaining "so under the radar" for almost a decade. The "safe and easy menu" is "a little uninspiring and expensive, which is unsurprising given the location", but its "unobtrusively attentive service" helps make it a "dependable" all-rounder. / W1K 2HD; www.34-restaurant.co.uk; @34_restaurant; 11 pm, Sun 10 pm.

THE THOMAS CUBITT SW1 £68 3|3|3

44 ELIZABETH ST   020 7730 6060   2–4A

On Belgravia's smart Elizabeth Street, this "bright and airy" destination is "more decent-restaurant than good-gastropub" with its "accomplished cooking" and "light" first-floor dining room. / SW1W 9PA; www.thethomascubitt.co.uk; @TheThomasCubitt; 10 pm, Sun 9.30 pm.

TIBITS £43 3|2|3

12-14 HEDDON ST, W1   020 7758 4110   4–3B
124 SOUTHWARK ST, SE1   10–4B

"For a perfect vegetarian food experience at a fair price, look no further" than this increasingly popular, Swiss-owned, self-service operation, with branches off Regent Street and on Bankside. There's "an amazing choice" of "very fresh food that changes daily", run under an "unusual system whereby you serve yourself from buffet (aka 'the food boat') and pay by weight". The Bankside branch, near Tate Modern, has been revamped to offer a range of seating, from high bar stools or conventional tables to comfy armchairs. / www.tibits.co.uk; @tibits_uk.

TING SE1 £103 2|2|4

LEVEL 35, 31 ST THOMAS ST
020 7234 8108 10–4C

"The view's the thing" at this 35th-floor all-day restaurant and lounge in The Shard, with 360-degree vistas over London and the Home Counties – "including from the loos!". Some reporters also rate the "well-presented and thoughtful menu", which they say contributes to "a fantastic experience". Sceptics, though, reckon the "food is so-so, service patronising, the bill eye-watering: strictly for well-heeled tourists!". / SE1 9RY; www.ting-shangri-la.com; @ShangriLaShard; 11 pm; No trainers; credit card required to book.

TISH NW3 £73 3|4|4

196 HAVERSTOCK HILL   020 7431 3828
9–2A

"Unusually smart for a kosher restaurant" – this yearling in Belsize Park, from property developer David Levin, has "real aspirations". A large and impressively kitted-out all-day brasserie, it still attracts the odd gripe that "the food doesn't live up to the setting", but most reports say it's "improved and hitting its stride". / NW3 2AG; www.tish.london; @tish_london.

TITU W1 £55 4|5|4

1A SHEPHERD STREET   020 7493 8746
3–4B

"Possibly the smallest restaurant I've ever been in but BIG on flavours and service" – this "wonderful" Japanese-inspired, 15-seater yearling in Mayfair's pretty Shepherd Market is piloted by Kiwi chef Jeff Tyler (ex-Novikov), and specialises in luxury gyoza dumplings, stuffed with foie gras and wagyu beef. "It's like being back in Tokyo". Top Tip – "Book – it's tiny". / W1J 7HJ; www.titurestaurant.com; @titulondon.

TOFF'S N10 £39 3|3|2

38 MUSWELL HILL BROADWAY
020 8883 8656   1–1B

"Popular, and sometimes crowded institution, in the culinary wilderness of Muswell Hill", well known as one of north London's best "good, old-fashioned" chippies. Run by brothers George and Costas Georgiou: "their fish is always fresh, and perfectly cooked, and the chips are good too". / N10 3RT; www.toffsfish.co.uk; @toffsfish; 10 pm; closed Sun.

TOKIMEITE W1 £116 3|2|2

23 CONDUIT ST   020 3826 4411   3–2C

Owned by Zen-Noh, Japan's agricultural cooperative, and specialising in high-grade Japanese wagyu, alongside sushi, sashimi, tempura and other more creative fare, this Mayfair three-year-old is centred around an open counter kitchen, controlled by chef Daisuke Hayashi. Fans are "keen for it to be better known" saying its ownership "really shows up in the superb food", but it still has a surprisingly tiny following, perhaps because it's "very expensive (probably too expensive)". /

W1S 2XS; www.tokimeite.com; @tokimeitelondon; 10.30 pm.

TOKYO DINER WC2 £27 3|3|3

2 NEWPORT PLACE   020 7287 8777   5–3B

"I just love it: it's so cheap 'n' cheerful" chorus the many fans of this down-to-earth Japanese canteen in Chinatown, which has been for yonks "a great place for the freshest sushi and yummy tofu". / WC2H 7JJ; www.tokyodiner.com; 11.30 pm; No Amex; No bookings.

TOM SIMMONS SE1 £64 3|3|2

2 STILL WALK   020 3848 2100 10–4D

"Solid cooking" of some ambition – with "clean and distinct flavours" – helps inspire good reports on this Welsh chef's South Bank venue, most particularly as "a handy option for a high-quality meal prior to heading for the Bridge Theatre". "The experience can sometimes feel no more than functional", however, as "the modern setting does not contribute much character", but "friendly service" is some compensation. / SE1 2UP; tom-simmons.co.uk; @TomSimmons_TB; 11 pm, Sun 6 pm; closed Sun D.

TOM'S KITCHEN £61 2|2|3

27 CALE ST, SW3 020 7349 0202   6–2C

Last year's makeover has failed to transform Tom Aikens's casual dining venture in a Chelsea backstreet, which remains a handy amenity for breakfast or a bite in the area, but is "not what it used to be" as a destination (and inspires modest feedback nowadays). Meanwhile, its sister venues in Canary Wharf and Somerset House have closed down, amid little sign of the standards that made Aikens the youngest British chef to earn two Michelin stars at 26. / www.tomskitchen.co.uk; @TomsKitchens; SW3 10.30 pm, Sun 9.30 pm; WC2 10 pm; E14 9.30 pm; SE1 6 pm; B1 10.30 pm, Sun 5 pm; WC2, E14, B1 closed Sun D.

TOMMI'S BURGER JOINT £30 3|4|3

30 THAYER ST, W1 020 7224 3828   3–1A
37 BERWICK STREET, W1 020 7494 9086
4–2D

"His simple burgers are perfect", say fans of Tómas Tómasson, who has been grilling over charcoal in his native Iceland since 1981. His "straightforward" outlets in Soho and Marylebone are now part of a European and Scandi chain spanning from Iceland to Italy. / www.burgerjoint.co.uk; @BurgerJointUk; 10.30 pm, Sun 9 pm; booking: min 5.

TOMOE SW15 £37 4|3|1

292 UPPER RICHMOND ROAD
020 3730 7884 11–2B

"Teeming with Japanese customers and Putney locals in the know", this "great little sushi bar", presided over by its "eagle-eyed chef/owner" ("sit up at the sushi bar to see the main man

St Leonard's EC2

calmly in action") is "just like being in Tokyo". Results are "fabulous": there are "not many places in London where the fish on the sushi is actually thicker than the rice!". Another indie Japanese, Cho-San (RIP) was on the same site, and the "rather tired" interior either "works against it" or adds authenticity, depending on your viewpoint. / SW15; 9.30 pm.

TONKOTSU £44 3|3|2

SELFRIDGES, 400 OXFORD ST, W1
020 7437 0071   3–1A
63 DEAN ST, W1 020 7437 0071   5–2A
7 BLENHEIM CR, W11 020 7221 8300   7–1A
14 NEW BROADWAY, W5 020 8810 1414
1–3A
4 CANVEY ST, SE1 020 7928 2228 10–4B
ARCH 755, BATTERSEA POWER STATION
ARCHES, SW8 11–1C
UNIT 1, ENDEAVOUR SQUARE, E20
020 8534 6809 14–1D
382 MARE ST, E8 020 8533 1840 14–1B
ARCH 334, 1A DUNSTON ST, E8
020 7254 2478 14–2A

"Healthy ramen bowls" and "the best karaage fried chicken in town" are the secrets behind the rapid growth of the cramped Japanese pitstops, of which there are now 10 in London – the most recent openings, in Shoreditch and Peckham, having followed a £5million investment in 2019. They provide "a meal that could fill you up for a day", with "excellent service from a really friendly team who go the extra mile". / www.tonkotsu.co.uk; @TonkotsuSoho; 10 pm - 11 pm, Sun earlier some branches; SW11 closed Mon; no bookings.

TOP CUVEE N5 £57 4|4|3

177B BLACKSTOCK ROAD   020 3294 1665
9–1D

"A brilliant addition to Norf Landon": this "buzzy" and "notably hip" new Highgate wine bar and bistro offers a fashionable formula, combining a curt menu of "lovely small plates" – showing "real depth of flavour" – with an "excellent wine list, which may tend a tad to the 'natural', but which offers plenty of choice". "Knowledgeable and enthusiastic staff" add to the picture. "Only slight issue is acoustics: this is a hard-walled box, so noise-sensitive folk may want to pass... but I'm looking forward to returning soon". / N5 2LL; www.topcuvee.com.

TOZI SW1 £49 333

8 GILLINGHAM ST   020 7769 9771   2–4B

"Delicious food just keeps coming" at this rather "unique" Venetian cicchetti (small-plates) outfit, attached to a hotel near Victoria station, whose "fun" style has helped it acquire a major following. There's "charming service from a close-knit Italian team" who treat children with "welcoming joy". / SW1V 1HN; www.tozirestaurant.co.uk; @ToziRestaurant; 10 pm.

THE TRAMSHED EC2 £57 324

32 RIVINGTON ST   020 7749 0478   13–1B

"Not that cheap but pretty cheerful": Mark Hix's converted Victorian tramshed in Shoreditch is an atmospheric high-ceilinged space, dominated by a stuffed Damien Hirst cow in a tank, presumably meant to symbolise a menu which majors in steak and chicken – "simple dishes, cooked to perfection". / EC2A 3LX; www.hixrestaurants.co.uk/restaurant/tramshed; @the_tramshed; 11 pm, Wed-Sat midnight, Sun 9.30 pm.

TRANGALLAN N16 £48 443

61 NEWINGTON GRN   020 7359 4988   1–1C

"Lovely, rich, authentic Spanish fare (octopus to die for)" with Galician specialities, again wins praise for this "somewhat shabby-chic" tapas haunt in Newington Green: "it can get refreshingly noisy!" / N16 9PX; www.trangallan.com; @trangallan_n16; 10.30 pm; closed Mon; No Amex; No trainers.

TREDWELL'S WC2 £66 333

4 UPPER ST MARTIN'S LN   020 3764 0840   5–3B

With its "dark" decor, there's an "NYC-diner feel" to Marcus Wareing's quirky, Theatreland venue, whose "lively and buzzy" (if sometimes "noisy") style and "friendly and welcoming" staff helped improve its ratings this year. For somewhere in the beating heart of the touristy West End, there's a dizzying range of culinary options created by Kiwi chef Chantelle Nicholson (an offbeat mix of ambitious tasting menus and more down-to-earth dishes, like steaks or roasts); and although there are disappointments, a majority this year do extol its "fantastic culinary creations". / WC2H 9NY; www.tredwells.com; @tredwells; 10 pm, Fri & Sat 11 pm.

TRINITY SW4 £76 554

4 THE POLYGON   020 7622 1199   11–2D

Adam Byatt's "classy" Clapham star is "at the top of its game" and there are only a few restaurants south of the river that give it a run for its money: "a trip always feels special, no matter what the occasion". "Outstanding", contemporary cuisine (from a three-course, or four-course menu) is at the heart of a "wonderful", straightforward formula incorporating "service that's always

on point", plus the "relaxing atmosphere" of a room whose "exterior view is much improved now the public WC has been demolished and the area landscaped!". "Really good cocktails" and a "diverse and interesting wine list" complete the picture – look out for vintages marked 'Chef's Cellar'. See also Trinity Upstairs and Charlie's at Browns. / SW4 0JG; www.trinityrestaurant.co.uk; @TrinityLondon; 10 pm, Sun 9 pm; closed Mon L & Sun D.

TRINITY UPSTAIRS SW4 £62 544

4 THE POLYGON   020 3745 7227   11–2D

The "buzzy, relaxed sibling of the fancier place downstairs"; some fans of chef Adam Byatt's modern British cuisine may even prefer Upstairs for its "informal atmosphere" and "keen prices", which means they can visit more often than down below. There are "delightful small plates to share" with "food of the same quality as the main restaurant", along with "the same wine list". Byatt is very much a man of the moment, having added the role of chef-director at Brown's Hotel in Mayfair in September 2019 (see also). / SW4 0JG; www.trinity-upstairs.co.uk; @trinityupstairs ; 10 pm.

TRISHNA W1 £88 433

15-17 BLANDFORD ST   020 7935 5624   2–1A

"Original, flavour-packed and utterly delicious" – the cuisine at Karam Sethi's original Marylebone venture (the first in the JKS stable) is a fine homage to the Mumbai venue from which it takes its name, and even if "sister-restaurant Gymkhana has the edge" nowadays, it remains one of the capital's top Indian destinations. It's "really buzzy when full" (to an extent one or two reporters find "disturbing" of enjoyment). / W1U 3DG; www.trishnalondon.com; @TrishnaLondon; 10.30 pm, Sun 9.45 pm.

TRIVET SE1

36 SNOWSFIELDS, MELIOR STREET   10–4C

Former Fat Duck duo – head chef Jonny Lake and sommelier Isa Bal, who worked together for 12 years – will open this restaurant and wine bar in Bermondsey later in 2019, in the new Snowsfields Yard development (and the former site of Londrino, RIP). Bal said of the opening, 'The design and experience of the restaurant will also be inspired from our travels, juxtaposing Nordic functionality with the warmth of the Mediterranean and a dose of fun'. / SE1 3QQ.

LA TROMPETTE W4 £85 543

5-7 DEVONSHIRE RD   020 8747 1836   8–2A

"We schlep across town from E18 two or three times a year and we always have a wonderful experience!" – this "consistently fabulous" destination occupies a low-profile location in a Chiswick sidestreet, but remains the "go-to-choice in West London" for many reporters and "rivals many more high-profile West End

temples of gastronomy". Like its even-more-famous stablemate, Chez Bruce, its "bright", neighbourhood-style interior is smart but far from flash – the "spoiling experience" it delivers derives from its "seriously imaginative and beautifully executed" modern cuisine and its "seamless and charming" service. And it offers "very good value", too: "this is exactly what every restaurant at this price point should aspire to". On the downside, the table layout can seem "too crowded", and there were also very occasional good-but-not-great meals reported this year: "are they a bit stretched since they added more covers?" / W4 2EU; www.latrompette.co.uk; @LaTrompetteUK; 10.30 pm, Sun 9.30 pm.

TRULLO N1 £64 333

300-302 ST PAUL'S RD   020 7226 2733   9–2D

"A gem, well worth a visit to darkest Highbury Corner": as it enters its 10th year, Tim Siadatan and Jordan Frieda's "great neighbourhood Italian" remains the survey's most-mentioned destination in north London, buoyed by its "excellent, simple fare" and "efficient service", served in a "compact" but romantic setting that "exudes a tremendous warmth" ("want a first date in a light airy space? Book upstairs, especially in summer; want a sexy tryst? Book a booth downstairs, especially in winter"). On the downside, some former fans feel it's "dropped to middling" of late: "a local place, but with a centre-of-town bill". / N1 2LH; www.trullorestaurant.com; @Trullo_LDN; 10.15 pm; closed Sun D; No Amex.

TSUNAMI SW4 £48 533

5-7 VOLTAIRE RD   020 7978 1610   11–1D

"Exquisite Japanese fusion food as well as fabulously creative cocktails" have made this slick Clapham operation "a perennial favourite" for two decades; and it still gives West End names a run for their money. Top Tip – "gin dara – black cod with sweet miso. I know it's a Nobu original but this is the best version in town". / SW4 6DQ; www.tsunamirestaurant.co.uk; @TsunamiRest; 11 pm, Fri-Sun midnight; closed Sat L & Sun; No Amex.

1251 N1 £46 333

107 UPPER STREET   07934 202269   9–3D

"A much-needed alternative to the usual Upper Street fare" – James Cochran's ambitious yearling is a ray of sunshine in N1, and even the less impressed minority who feel "it's not quite up to the celebrity chef hype" generally feel "it's nice to have something a bit different in the local area". Quibbles also include the "cramped", "corridor-like" space and service that can sometimes seem like "amateur's hour", but at its best this part-Scottish, part-Jamaican chef provides "exceptional dishes, with cleverly combined ingredients and subtle spicing". Top Tip – "The £15 lunch deal is the gastronomic bargain of the year": "extraordinary food, lovingly crafted, and at silly prices". / N1 1QN; www.1251.co.uk; @cochran_ja.

28 CHURCH ROW NW3 £56 4|4|4

28 CHURCH ROW 020 7993 2062 9–2A

A "revelation" – well, by the standards of Hampstead anyhow – this cute basement tapas bar with an open kitchen occupies a cellar space, near the church of St John-at-Hampstead, and has taken the area by storm with its "constantly changing menu, intriguing wine list and very friendly service". There's no booking, but they'll phone you if you wait in the pub opposite. / NW3 6UP; www.28churchrow.com; @28churchrow.com; 10.30 pm, Sun 9.30 pm.

28-50 W1 £74 3|2|2

15-17 MARYLEBONE LN 020 7486 7922 3–1A

"Useful pre-Wigmore Hall" – this Marylebone original is now the sole surviving branch of what for a few years become a chain, but which retrenched last year. The space – with large windows and dominated by the bar – "doesn't encourage you to linger", but the "simple dishes are well executed, at a good price". Really, though, it's "all about the wines by the glass" (15 reds and 15 whites), plus a 'Collector's List' of rare vintages by the bottle. / W1U 2NE; www.2850.co.uk; @2850restaurant.

24 THE OVAL SW9 £46 4|3|3

24 CLAPHAM ROAD 0207 735 6111 11–1D

"Finally a great neighbourhood restaurant in Oval!" – "a parched part of London where average offerings abound" – this bistro yearling comes courtesy of Matt Wells (co-owner of The Dairy, Clapham) and Andrew Bradford (from SW4 steakhouse, Knife). A modern bistro-type place, with the benefit of an outside terrace, it provides an "exciting" modern British menu and there's a "committed team making it all happen". / SW9 0JG; www.24theoval.co.uk; @24theoval.

TWIST W1 £67 5|4|3

42 CRAWFORD ST 020 7723 3377 2–1A

"Very surprisingly delicious, every mouthful – way beyond expectations" – Eduardo Tuccillo's tucked-away Marylebone venture (on the site that ages ago was Garbo's, RIP) is arguably "very underrated due to its location" in a "so-loud, as it's so-small" two-floor space. But while it feels "too casual to be a very special night out, the food and service can't be beaten": "a different approach with tapas that aren't just Spanish" delivering "some inspired food combinations". "On the pricey side, but consistently well worth it." / W1H 1JW; www.twistkitchen.co.uk; @twistkitchen; closed Sun.

TWO BROTHERS N3 £32 3|2|2

297-303 REGENT'S PARK RD 020 8346 0469 1–1B

This "reliable local favourite" has "prepared fish freshly to order" at a consistent level for more than a quarter of a century, while the site itself has hosted a traditional fish 'n' chippy for 60 years or so. / N3 1DP; www.twobrothers.co.uk; 10 pm; closed Mon.

TWO LIGHTS E2 £63 3|4|3

28-30 KINGSLAND ROAD 020 3976 0076 13–1B

If it wasn't backed by the Clove Club, it's hard to know how much buzz this rather functional, Shoreditch-vibe newcomer (on the busy Kingsland Road) would otherwise have generated. The website describes the cooking as 'modern American', in line with the starry NYC-focused CV of chef Chase Lovecky, but if the words 'modern European' were substituted, probably no-one would ever notice the difference. Terminology aside: feedback on the deliciousness of the resulting small plates themselves – while surprisingly limited – has all been upbeat, but, to be harsh, only middling judged by the red-hot standards for this kind of dining in the area generally. / E2 8DA; www.twolights.restaurant.

222 VEGGIE VEGAN W14 £46 4|3|2

222 NORTH END RD 020 7381 2322 8–2D

"Don't wait for Veganuary or your vegan friend to visit!" – hurry along now to this "little, unpretentious gem": a "fairly functional" café that's a well-established fixture on the edge of West Kensington (just north of the gyratory where the Lillie Road and North End Road cross). "There's a vast array of beautifully fresh dishes that are vibrant, tasty and wholesome, and it's brilliant value for money". / W14 9NU; www.222vegan.com; @222VeganCuisine.

2 VENETI W1 £52 3|3|2

10 WIGMORE STREET 020 7637 0789 3–1B

For those who say it's "handy for the Wigmore Hall", this well-established Italian is "a good staple", with "professional service" that helps overcome its "lack of atmosphere", and "offering typical Italian fare". Become a regular, though, and the more you appreciate "an absolute gem", with "incredibly attentive" staff, and the more you value its Venetian cuisine ("specialities like bigoli con acciughe, fegato ...all delicious"). / W1U 2RD; www.2veneti.com; @2Veneti; 10.30 pm, Sat 11 pm; closed Sat L & Sun.

ULI W11 £61 3|3|4

5 LADBROKE ROAD 020 3141 5878 7–2B

This "popular and unpretentious" Singaporean/pan-Asian near Notting Hill Gate has earned a very solid local following in its 22 years – boss Michael Lim "makes it special". The original All Saints Road site closed down in 2015, but the venture was resurrected three years later in this "cool new setting". / W11 3PA; www.ulilondon.com; @ulilondon; 11.45 pm; D only, closed Sun.

UMU W1 £120 4|4|4

14-16 BRUTON PL 020 7499 8881 3–2C

"Yoshinori Ishii is the perfect chef and artist... unique" and goes from strength to strength at this fairly small, hidden-away Japanese – in a quirky Mayfair mews, with little exterior signage – where he's been head chef since 2010. Traditional gripes about the larcenous pricing are notable by their absence this year: instead, feedback could not be more positive about his Kyoto-style kaiseki cuisine, placing it firmly in contention amongst London's top Japanese destinations. Owned by Marlon Abela's M.A.R.C. group – this is head-and-shoulders his best property. / W1J 6LX; www.umurestaurant.com; 10.30 pm; closed Sat L & Sun; No trainers; booking max 14 may apply.

UNION STREET CAFÉ SE1 £65 2|2|2

47-51 GREAT SUFFOLK ST 020 7592 7977 10–4B

Gordon Ramsay's "Italian-leaning" warehouse conversion in Southwark, with an indoor 'olive grove' complete with trees, pleases some with its "giant portions of great food" and "fantastic cocktails". Far too many reporters this year, though, complain of a "sterile" aspect to its "industrial" decor, and dismiss the fare as mightily "uninspired". / SE1 0BS; www.gordonramsayrestaurants.com/union-street-cafe; @unionstreetcafe; 10.45 pm; closed Sun D.

UNWINED SW17 £29 3|4|4

21-23 TOOTING HIGH STREET 02035839136 11–2C

"Little wine bar and kitchen, with a great vibe in Tooting Market" – "a consistently delightful gem" with "regularly changing guest chefs" and "a fun and quirky wine list to accompany whatever's on the menu". (There's a spin-off wine bar in a shipping container by Waterloo station.) / SW17 0SN; www.unwinedbars.co.uk/tooting; @UnwinedSW17.

LE VACHERIN W4 £65 3|3|3

76-77 SOUTH PARADE 020 8742 2121 8–1A

"Consistently good food" and a "lovely French atmosphere" earn solid ratings for this long-running bistro – an unusually "authentic Gallic experience" by Acton Green. It's "excellent value", too, "if you choose carefully". / W4 5LF; www.levacherin.co.uk; @Le_Vacherin; 10.30 pm, Sun 9 pm; closed Mon L.

VAGABOND WINES £42 2|3|3

UNIT 77, NOVA BUILDING, 77 BUCKINGHAM PALACE ROAD, SW1 020 7630 7693 2–4B
25 CHARLOTTE STREET, W1 020 3441 9210 2–1C
4 NORTHCOTE ROAD, SW11 020 7738 0540 11–2C
18-22 VANSTON PLACE, SW6 020 7381 1717 6–4A

A "wealth of wines by the glass" and "tasty nibbles", help make this growing group of

Maggie Jones W8

self-service wine bars a "fun way to try a selection of vintages from a multitude of small producers". At the Battersea Power Station branch's school you can educate your palate towards Wine & Spirit Education Trust certification and watch wine being made from grapes grown in Oxfordshire and Surrey. / www.vagabondwines.co.uk; @VagabondWines.

VANILLA BLACK EC4 £77 433

17-18 TOOKS CT 020 7242 2622 10–2A

"Who needs meat when you can eat like this?" – You don't have to "be in touch with your green tea side" to be "seriously seduced by the grown-up vibe" and "exciting cooking" at this "sophisticated" and ambitious meat-free operation, "tucked away in a corner just outside the City". "I'm a meat-eater and always thought vegetarian meals were about lentils and beans, but the food here is delicious, creative and elegant without being pretentious or fussy". / EC4A 1LB; www.vanillablack.co.uk; @vanillablack1; 10 pm; closed Sun; No Amex.

VARDO SW3

9 DUKE OF YORK SQUARE 6–2D

From the team behind Caravan, this autumn 2019 newcomer (the name comes from Romany travelling wagons) is set to open in a striking, purpose-built, new cylindrical building, on Duke of York Square off the King's Road, with a public roof garden and a fully retractable glass wall (the UK's first apparently). The food – described as top British ingredients prepared using 'low and slow' cooking techniques – looks set to echo the wild-and-wacky global style of its older stablemates. / SW3 4LY; www.caravanrestaurants.co.uk/vardo.html.

VASCO & PIERO'S PAVILION W1 £65 332

15 POLAND ST 020 7437 8774 4–1C

"Pleasingly old-fashioned in style and cooking", this long-serving traditional Soho Italian keeps its many regulars happy with "a simple Umbrian menu, done well", including "excellent home-made pasta". There's a "comfortable and friendly ambience, and the occasional luvvie dining before his/her show". Top Tip – "the chef will do zabaglione at the end if the kitchen isn't too busy – a treat!". / W1F 8QE; www.vascosfood.com; @Vasco_and_Piero; 9.30 pm; closed Sat L & Sun.

VEERASWAMY W1 £86 333

VICTORY HS, 99-101 REGENT ST 020 7734 1401 4–4B

Despite a vintage stretching back to 1926, London's oldest Indian (part of the same group as Chutney Mary) doesn't merely trade on its guidebook potential, with "subtle" and "original" cuisine, "dedicated" service, and a first-floor setting, whose agreeable looks are thoroughly modern. It seems to have become "a wee bit pricey" of late, though, "but it is in the heart of the West End, so perhaps not excessively so". / W1B 4RS;

www.veeraswamy.com; @theveeraswamy; 10.45 pm, Sun 10:15 pm; booking max 12 may apply.

VERDI'S E1 £52 344

237 MILE END RD 020 7423 9563 14–2B

"A relaxing, high-class restaurant in an area offering mostly junk food and takeaways"; white tablecloths help set a 'proper' tone at this Stepney Green trattoria of about five years' standing, which serves genuine Italian food – a particular shout-out to the pizzas. / E1 4AA; www.verdislondon.com; @verdislondon.

VERMUTERIA N1 £48 223

COAL DROPS YARD 020 3479 1777 9–3C

"An exemplary range of vermouths" and "a very approachable style by the rather strained hipster standards of Coal Drops Yard" help win praise for Anthony Demetre's all-day bar/café in the new development, where his stated aim is to ape the best points of his favourite bars in Italy, France and Spain; and where "the food is standard modern small plates fare, decently done". The odd all-round disastrous report, however, somewhat takes the gloss off its ratings. / N1C 4AB; vermuteria.cc.

VIA EMILIA N1 £37 322

37A HOXTON SQUARE 020 7613 0508 13–1B

"Delicious filled pasta" made exclusively with ingredients from Emilia-Romagna in northern Italy: that's the proposition at this "tiny, Spartan place just off Hoxton Square", which has earned solid ratings in its first year. It has also introduced the region's fried bread, gnocco fritto, to London, apparently. Sister establishment Parma in Fitzrovia focuses on cheese, charcuterie and Lambrusco wine. / N1 6NN; www.via--emilia.com.

IL VICOLO SW1 £55 333

3-4 CROWN PASSAGE 020 7839 3960 3–4D

Among the plutocrats' dining rooms of St James's, this "consistently good and friendly family-restaurant", tucked away down an alley, stands out as a "reliable Italian local" with earth-bound prices. / SW1Y 6PP; www.ilvicolorestaurant.co.uk; 10 pm; closed Sat L & Sun.

THE VICTORIA SW14 £55 223

10 WEST TEMPLE SHEEN 020 8876 4238 11–2A

A ten-minute stroll from the Sheen Gate entrance to Richmond Park, this "pleasant gastropub" with a massive dining conservatory is ideal for a family meal, and "its USP is the small but useful outdoor play area for younger sprogs". The food is generally of "good quality", but there's some dispute as to whether it's "losing its spark" or "recovering having gone downhill". / SW14 7RT; victoriasheen.co.uk; @TheVictoria_Pub; 10 pm, Sun 9 pm; No Amex.

VIET FOOD W1 £38 332

34-36 WARDOUR ST 020 7494 4555 5–3A

"Amazing Vietnamese street food", courtesy of ex-Hakkasan chef Jeff Tan, is "swiftly and efficiently served" at this spacious Chinatown operation. It can get "hectic… just like Vietnam". / W1D 6QT; www.vietnamfood.co.uk; @vietfoodlondon; 10.30 pm, Fri & Sat 11 pm.

VIJAY NW6 £36 431

49 WILLESDEN LN 020 7328 1087 1–1B

"Delicious South Indian food at bargain prices", including "lovely, tasty vegetarian dishes", has, for decades, drawn a devoted following to this Kilburn institution, which claims to have been Britain's first Keralan restaurant when it opened in 1964. Little has changed since then, lending it a "greasy spoon atmosphere", but nobody's fussed. BYO recommended. / NW6 7RF; www.vijayrestaurant.co.uk; 10.45 pm, Fri & Sat 11.45 pm; no booking.

VILLA BIANCA NW3 £69 222

1 PERRINS CT 020 7435 3131 9–2A

This "very traditional Italian" in a prime Hampstead spot "hasn't changed much (except the prices)" for the past 30 years. Its enviable location, tucked away off the main drag, explains much of its appeal, as does a "formal but un-snooty" style that's not to all tastes, but helps attract "lots of buzz (and some celebs!)". Some fans applaud the fare as "well-cooked in generous portions", others say it's merely "fair". / NW3 1QS; villabiancagroup.com/villabianca; @VillaBiancaNW3; 11.30 pm, Sun 10.30 pm.

VILLA DI GEGGIANO W4 £79 344

66-68 CHISWICK HIGH ROAD 020 3384 9442 8–2B

"A taste of the real Tuscany in W4" can be "a just fantastic experience" at this "lovely Chiswick local". Named after the ancestral home near Siena of the owners, a 500-year-old Chianti dynasty who wanted a London showcase, its strengths are a "warm welcome", "some real ambience" and – as you might expect – "a great wine list". / W4 1SY; www.villadigeggiano.co.uk; @VilladiGeggiano; 10 pm; closed Mon.

THE VINCENT ROOMS, WESTMINSTER KINGSWAY COLLEGE SW1 £42 332

76 VINCENT SQ 020 7802 8391 2–4C

"London's best-kept secret" offers cut-price haute cuisine prepared by "the stars of the future" – student chefs and waiters at Kingsway College in Westminster. "The food is always great value, and can be excellent", while "watching people being put through their paces and learning the trade is a fun way to spend an evening". "The main room could be a bit less municipal – maybe get some design students

Texture W1

in!". / SW1P 2PD; www.thevincentrooms.co.uk; @thevincentrooms; 7 pm; closed Mon D, Tue D, Fri D, Sat & Sun; No Amex.

VINEGAR YARD SE1

SAINT THOMAS STREET 10–4C

A new 'eating, drinking, shopping and art space' from the founders of Flat Iron Square, also not far from London Bridge, with vintage shops, street food stalls and bars in shipping containers and a large garden. Million Pound Menu stars Baba G's have a stall here, selling their naanwiches and Indian burgers. / SE1 3QU; www.vinegaryard.london; @vinegaryardldn.

VINOTECA £61 2̶2̶2̶

15 SEYMOUR PL, W1 020 7724 7288 2–2A
18 DEVONSHIRE RD, W4 020 3701 8822 8–2A
ONE PANCRAS SQ, N1 020 3793 7210 9–3C
7 ST JOHN ST, EC1 020 7253 8786 10–1B
BLOOMBERG ARCADE, QUEEN VICTORIA STREET, EC2 AWAITING TEL 10–3C

"The wine list's brilliant" at these modern-industrial bars: "a huge range" that's "regularly added to, with some unusual vintages", "plenty at affordable prices" and "excellent options by the glass". And this "wine focus attracts a more interesting crowd than some other chains", all making the group "the perfect standby any night of the week". "All branches are recommended", with the one that's super-handy for King's Cross perhaps the most popular (though, being "always busy", it can seem "squashed and hurried", and booking is advisable). Perhaps the "food's a bit average", but practically all feedback actually focuses on its success as a "tasty" complement to the vino. Top Tip – "even better on a Sunday or Monday, when the wine's sold close to retail price". / www.vinoteca.co.uk; 11 pm, W1H & W4 Sun 4 pm; W1F 10.45 pm, Sun 9.30 pm; EC1 and W1H closed Sun.

VIVAT BACCHUS £60 3̶3̶2̶

4 HAY'S LN, SE1 020 7234 0891 10–4C
47 FARRINGDON ST, EC4 020 7353 2648 10–2A

"There's no better place to try South African wine – from cheap 'n' cheerful to exceptional vintages" – than at this duo of SA-owned City wine bars, with walk-in cellars for your deliberation. The Saffa-inspired food is "fairly hearty" (steaks are a good bet), with a shout-out to the "brilliant cheese room" in each venue. / www.vivatbacchus.co.uk; 10.30 pm; closed Sun.

VQ £45 2̶3̶3̶

ST GILES HOTEL, GREAT RUSSELL ST, WC1 020 7636 5888 5–1A
325 FULHAM RD, SW10 020 7376 7224 6–3B
24 PEMBRIDGE ROAD, W11 020 3745 7224 7–2B
152-156 NORTH GOWER STREET, NW1 020 3301 1224 9–4C
122 CLAPHAM HIGH STREET, SW4 020 3096 5956 11–2D
9 ALDGATE HIGH ST, EC3 020 3301 7224 10–2D

"Handy… especially when other places are shut!" – these "round-the-clock" diners have grown from their SW10 base (which has been around for yonks) to bring their late-night formula of "decent food, a good vibe, friendly service and dependable value" to ever-more 'hoods: recent additions include sites in Euston and Clapham. Only Chelsea, Bloomsbury and Aldgate are actually 24/7. / www.vingtquatre.co.uk; @Vqrestaurants; Mon-Sun 2 am; booking: max 6 online.

VRISAKI N22 £43 3̶3̶2̶

73 MIDDLETON RD 020 8889 8760 1–1C

This Greek-Cypriot taverna in Bounds Green is "famous across North London for the ridiculous size of its mezze". The food, from Andreas and Anthony Antoniou, "is reasonably tasty, service is pleasant enough and the decor plain and uninspiring" – but "all this pales into insignificance if you go very hungry!". / N22 8LZ; vrisakirestaurant.com; @vrisakiuk; 11.30 pm, Sun 9 pm; closed Mon; No Amex.

WAGAMAMA £43 2̶2̶2̶

"Our cheap, go-to choice when out and about" – this famous noodle chain's ratings picked up this year after its October 2018 acquisition by The Restaurant Group, who seem to be re-establishing its core virtues as "an OK place to eat in a hurry", with a "solid and reliable bowl of ramen" that "fills a hole", in a "collective" and "busy" canteen setting, all at a "reasonable price". They're particularly "a firm family-favourite" – "kids love the experience, the service is quick, and it's nice for them to have something that's more exciting than a pizza/pasta/burger". The branch by the Royal Festival Hall is notably handy – "a great option on the South Bank". / www.wagamama.com; 10 pm - 11.30 pm; EC2 Sat 9 pm; EC4 closed Sat & Sun; EC2 closed Sun; no bookings.

WAHACA £37 3̶3̶3̶

"An ever-evolving, fun take on Mexican street food offering zingy flavours (plus a damn fine margarita)" all "efficiently served" in a "bright and buzzy" environment seems to have protected Thomasina Miers's popular chain from much of the casual dining fall-out of recent times; and it remains "the most dependable of fast(ish) food chains" for many reporters. In particular, it's "perfect for kids", and families appreciate that "you fill up well for the price". / www.wahaca.com; 11 pm, Sun 10.30 pm; W12, Charlotte St, SW19 Sun 10 pm; no booking or need 6+ to book.

THE WALLACE, THE WALLACE COLLECTION W1 £59 2̶3̶5̶

HERTFORD HS, MANCHESTER SQ 020 7563 9505 3–1A

A "real hidden gem" – the spectacular glass-ceilinged atrium at the Wallace Collection is a "great place to bring visitors to London", just off Oxford Street; and serves breakfast, coffee and lunch every day, plus dinner on Fridays and Saturdays. For a full-blown meal, its "unhurried" service can grate, as can cooking that's only "so so". But where it undoubtedly scores is as a "lovely setting for a classic relaxed afternoon tea" – "all very nice and proper" – "with an excellent museum attached…" / W1U 3BN; www.peytonandbyrne.co.uk; @peytonandbyrne; 9.30 pm; Sun-Thu closed D; No Amex; booking max 10 may apply.

WANDER N16 £48 4̶4̶3̶

214 STOKE NEWINGTON HIGH STREET 020 7249 7283 1–1C

"The perfect neighbourhood restaurant", say fans of this Stoke Newington yearling, where "a daily/weekly-changing seasonal menu of Italian-influenced food with, say, a Portuguese twist and an Australian sensibility, is provided courtesy of Aussie chef-proprietor, Alexis Noble". "Wines are unusual, cleverly chosen, and invariably delicious. Service is sweet and helpful. A delight." / N16 7HU; www.wanderrestaurant.com.

THE WATCH HOUSE SE1 £9 4̶2̶4̶

199 BERMONDSEY ST 020 7407 6431 10–4D

"A wonderful location off Bermondsey Street" – a "quirky", ancient, tiny shelter originally built for watchmen guarding the graves of nearby St Mary Magdalene Church – helps win fans for this small coffee house (which has since spawned a couple of spin-offs at Tower Bridge and Fetter Lane). It wins many nominations for its "top coffee" too (supplied by Shoreditch roasters, Ozone) and "delicious food". One quibble: service can be "so laid back, it's almost horizontal". / SE1 3UW; www.thewatchhouse.com; @thewatchhouseUK.

THE WELLS TAVERN
NW3 £58 334
30 WELL WALK   020 7794 3785   9–1A

"Ultra reliable" cooking "a notch above usual gastropub fare" and "very friendly staff" have long made this handsome, dog-friendly Grade II listed tavern a Hampstead favourite. "The food is far from groundbreaking – but that is part of the classic appeal" – "been going for years and never had a bad meal". It's run by Beth Coventry, sister of veteran restaurant critic Fay Maschler (as you'll know if you read her pieces, as she's always giving it a plug!). / NW3 1BX; thewellshampstead.london; @WellsHampstead; 10 pm, Sun 9.30 pm.

WESTERNS LAUNDRY
N5 £56 322
34 DRAYTON PARK   020 7700 3700   9–2D

"Innovative food" in a "hard and echoey" space still packs in the crowds at this hipster hit of a couple of years ago, just off the Holloway Road, which fans feel has a "great vibe" (even despite the fact that "when the place is full, conversation can be close to impossible"). The venue has always had its detractors, though, and there were more vocal complaints this year that the whole approach is "a little too cool for its own good" (i.e. "pleased with itself" and "disappearing up its own fundament"); which results in food that's "not bad but underwhelming, so hard to see what all the fuss is about". Also the natural wine list, "while pleasingly ambitious and different, has a high percentage of misses" (to the extent it can seem "plain daft"). / N5 1PB; www.westernslaundry.com; @WesternsLaundry; 10.30 pm, Sun 5 pm.

THE WET FISH CAFÉ
NW6 £54 334
242 WEST END LANE   020 7443 9222   1–1B

"A West Hampstead standard bearer": this converted 1930s fishmonger is not, despite its name, a fish restaurant – it operates as an all-day bistro, and fans say it's "hit the spot for the last 15 years, with the high-quality food, great ambience and friendly service you'd hope for from a great local"; or that it's "busy most of the time, especially at weekend brunch" when "you may need to queue". The critiques of last year weren't repeated this time: the worst anyone says is that it's "nothing special but OK". / NW6 1LG; www.thewetfishcafe.co.uk; @thewetfishcafe; 10 pm; No Amex; Booking evening only.

THE WHITE ONION
SW19 £62 342
67 HIGH ST   020 8947 8278   11–2B

This spin-off from Eric and Sarah Guignard's redoubtable French Table in Surbiton can offer "first-class" cuisine with "professional and attentive service", and – about to enter its fifth year – practically all reports agree that it's been a "very welcome addition to the SW London restaurant scene". It does take some flak, though, for "cooking that's hit and miss – some dishes distinctly mediocre, but others excellent". / SW19 5EE; www.thewhiteonion.co.uk; @thewhiteonionSW; 10.30 pm; closed Mon, Tue L, Wed L & Thu L.

THE WIGMORE, THE LANGHAM W1
£50 445
15 LANGHAM PLACE, REGENT STREET 020 7965 0198   2–1B

"Setting the standards for a central London bar" – Michel Roux's two-year-old near Oxford Circus "has found a real niche" as a top West End rendezvous ("almost too successful for its own good" during peak times,

when it risks becoming too thronging and loud). "You wouldn't know that it is part of a hotel" (it's actually carved out from – and a partnership with – the neighbouring five-star hotel, The Langham) and the unusually "classy" conversion of the space "burnishes the large, pub-style setting". "Its food is stretching the concept of gastropub food" in terms of ambition, but "definitely worth the money". / W1B 3DE; www.the-wigmore.co.uk; @Wigmore_London; Mon - Wed Midnight, Thurs - Sat 1am.

WILD FOOD CAFE
WC2 £46 322
FIRST FLOOR, 14 NEAL'S YARD 020 7419 2014   5–2C

"An ageless vegetarian": if you haven't been to this "no bookings and shared tables" café – tucked away on the first-floor of quaint Neal's Yard – in the last three years, you might easily miss the fact that it's changed its name and gone veggie (it was fka the World Food Café). For a snack near Covent Garden, it provides a smallish menu of "lovely genuine organic salads, veg burgers" and other fare. It also has a less commented-on Islington spin-off, with a good proportion of seating at the open kitchen counter, which features a dedicated brunch menu and a small selection of pizzas. / WC2H 9DP; www.wildfoodcafe.com; @WildFoodCafe.

WILD HONEY ST JAMES
SW1 £79
SOFITEL, 8 PALL MALL   020 7758 9160 3–2C

Anthony Demetre upped sticks and re-located his well-liked Mayfair establishment into the Sofitel, just off Trafalgar Square, taking over the attractive space that was formerly Balcon (RIP). It opened in August 2019, too late for survey feedback, but he's a deft and very accomplished chef, and his presence at this very handily situated venue seems likely to deepen its longstanding appeal as a quality rendezvous just away from the bustle of the West End. Fay Maschler's early days review was rapturous. / SW1Y 5NG; www.wildhoneyrestaurant.co.uk; @WildHoneySJ; 10.30 pm; closed Sun.

WILD RICE & MAMASAN
W1 £50 343
28 BREWER STREET   020 7434 3777   4–2D

Pan Serirak and Mike Asavarut created this duo of Thai-influenced, late-2018 newcomers in Soho: Wild Rice is on the ground floor, and focuses on small plates to share (Thai flavours with seasonal British ingredients). Mamasan is the basement restaurant, offering street food dishes. Early feedback suggests it's finding its feet, but worth a go: "we went and it was empty – I'm not sure why it wasn't packed as it deserved to be". / W1F 0SR; www.wildricelondon.com.

The Wigmore, The Langham W1

THE WILMINGTON
EC1 £55 333

69 ROSEBERY AVENUE   020 7837 1384
10–1A

"Our local – we're so lucky!" Near the foodie mecca of Exmouth Market, this "busy" Clerkenwell corner-boozer receives a consistent thumbs-up in reports: "the standard of the food is high". / EC1R 4RL; www.wilmingtonclerkenwell.com; @wilmingtonec1; 10pm, Fri & Sat 10.30pm , Sun 9pm.

WILTONS SW1 £98 454

55 JERMYN ST   020 7629 9955   3–3C

"The Best of British" – London's oldest restaurant (founded 1742, but not on this site) feels – with its "muffled conversations and refined decor mixing deep reds, browns and greens" – "akin to a compact version of an old-fashioned club"; and its St James's quarters provide a "top drawer", "old-school" experience for those of an "old-fashioned" disposition ("jackets are required for men"). "Acoustics are civilised" and "tables are very discreet, so it's perfect for business lunches or dinners"; while service operates "with class and efficiency", yet "without being unctuous". "If you want first-class, traditional cuisine", in particular fish and seafood (also game in season), this is the place for you – "sublime ingredients" are "presented impeccably, but without frills". Do try to ensure you are there at the invitation of your tax advisor or art dealer, however: "the bill is always brutal". / SW1Y 6LX; www.wiltons.co.uk; @wiltons1742; 10.15 pm; closed Sat L & Sun.

THE WINDMILL W1 £56 333

6-8 MILL ST   020 7491 8050   4–2A

"Excellent home-made pies" make this "always enjoyable" classic pub in Mayfair "worth a visit". They're backed up by a "super selection of ales, craft beers and wine", a "gin terrace" and a "great pubby atmosphere" – "what more could you ask for?" / W1S 2AZ; www.windmillmayfair.co.uk; @windmillpubW1; 10 pm, Sun 5 pm; closed Sat D & Sun.

THE WINE LIBRARY
EC3 £40 235

43 TRINITY SQ   020 7481 0415 10–3D

This ancient cellar near Tower Hill has a "brilliant selection of wines at retail prices", accompanied by charcuterie and cheeses – "basically drinks-party food, but none the worse for that". With its "highly knowledgeable staff", it's a great place for oenophiles to while away an hour or two (if not in huge comfort, given the not-particularly-comfortable seating).

THE WOLSELEY
W1 £68 235

160 PICCADILLY   020 7499 6996   3–3C

"Always buzzing whatever the time of day": Corbin & King's "magnificent" Grand Café near The Ritz remains a linchpin of metropolitan life; the capital's No. 1 venue for a business meal – especially breakfast; and "a must-visit" for anyone getting to know London. "The space always impresses" – a converted Edwardian car-showroom that provides a "uniquely London" take on a "vast Belle-Époch-style brasserie". It has "the right cosmopolitan feel" to lend an air of sophistication to any meal, plus "familiar faces from media and TV" to inject further excitement. "There's a huge menu, so you'll always find something you fancy", but while its "retro", "comfort" cuisine (with a Mittel-European twist) is "served with urbane panache", it is widely acknowledged by regulars that the dishes themselves are "uninspired" and taste "to be honest, average". But who cares? "It is hard not to love this place". Top Tip – "A grand setting for a quintessential and well-priced afternoon tea experience".

WONG KEI W1 £32 311

41-43 WARDOUR ST   020 7437 8408   5–3A

"Go through the doors and instantly get barked at – how many? Then, an instruction is growled: 'Upstairs!'" The ritual of a meal at this famous Chinatown veteran, has elements of self-conscious parody (you can actually buy a T-shirt saying 'upstairs'), but remains relatively 'real': a loose pact between its infamously "rude" and dismissive staff and students, theatre-goers and hungry workers in search of cheap, Chinese chow. "You are unlikely to get any smiles as you find yourself at a shared table, in a crammed-in dining area with plates piled high with deliciously smelly food being slammed onto various tables – they want you to be decisive, eat, and get out as soon as possible" – but it's "a fantastic filler".

WORKSHOP
COFFEE £37 343

**1 BARRETT STREET, ST CHRISTOPHER'S
PLACE, W1 020 7253 5754   3–1B**
**80A MORTIMER ST, W1 020 7253 5754
3–1C**
25 LONDON STREET, W2   7–1D
**GROUND FLOOR, WHITE COLLAR
FACTORY, 1 OLD STREET YARD, EC1
020 7253 5754 13–1A**

"Perfect coffee every time" keeps caffeine fiends crawling back to this small and serious chain. "Baking from Fortitude Bakehouse is a good complement".

WRIGHT
BROTHERS £68 333

13 KINGLY ST, W1 020 7434 3611   4–2B
**56 OLD BROMPTON RD, SW7 020 7581 0131
6–2B**
11 STONEY ST, SE1 020 7403 9554 10–4C
**26 CIRCUS ROAD WEST, SW8 020 7324 7734
11–1C**
8 LAMB ST, E1 020 7377 8706 10–2D

"The best and freshest oysters by far, with seasonal varieties from time to time…"; "superb plateau de fruits de mer"; and "super-fresh fish" from an "ever-changing selection of specials", all make this small group of seafood bistros "easy to love". The style is "busy and jostling" throughout – "be prepared to share your table with other diners" in some locations – in others "some of the tables are so close, you'll make new friends whether you want to or not!". The Borough Market original and South Kensington spin-off attract most (and most favourable) reports – other branches (including at Battersea) can seem "a welcome addition but nothing remarkable".

WULF & LAMB
SW1 £50 422

243 PAVILION ROAD   0203 948 5999   6–2D

"Never thought vegan food could be so guilt-inducing!": this self-consciously decadent plant-based two-year-old – under ex-Vanilla Black chef Franco Casoli in a "lovely" mews off Sloane Square – is "just a damn good restaurant in many ways… unlike many other vegans that seem to equate vegan food with a depressing ambience!". "The only grumble is the need to go downstairs to order".

WUN'S W1 £34

24 GREEK STREET   020 8017 9888   5–2A

The Soho branch of Bun House changed to Wun's in late July 2019 – too late for this year's survey – and, still under the ownership of Z He and Alex Peffly, is now a '1960s-style tea room and late night bar'. Set across two floors in Soho, it aims to mimic the communal, open-air cafes and restaurants in Hong Kong known as 'dai pai dong'.

XI'AN BIANG BIANG
E1 £35 333

**62 WENTWORTH STREET   020 8617 1470
13–2C**

"Oodles of noodles… and fun, too": this "bustling, happy-making eatery" – year-old sibling to Highbury's Xi'an Impression – occupies a canteen-style space in Spitalfields and "specialises in spicy, hand-pulled noodles"; "yum!".

XI'AN IMPRESSION
N7 £33 521

117 BENWELL RD   020 3441 0191   9–2D

"Lip-smackingly good, seriously authentic" dishes from Xi'an in central China, with "a great chilli kick in every mouthful", can be found at this "small and cramped" venue by the Arsenal stadium "with the ambiance of a transport caff". "Some dishes are alien to the European palate", but it's "better – and cheaper – than anywhere in Chinatown", so "always full of Chinese students from the local college, who know a good thing". Top Tip – "scrumptious noodles and dumplings: follow the chef's recommendations".

XIER W1 £121 434

**13-14 THAYER STREET   020 7486 3222
3–1A**

Sharing a building with XR (see also) – the first floor of Carlo Scotto's highly ambitious Marylebone newcomer is much less casual than the ground-floor – a "very elegant room" that's a symphony of whites and neutrals. A ten-course tasting menu is the centrepiece of its evening offer, with British ingredients used to create modern European dishes with Japanese riffs. The odd sceptic feels results are "interesting, but not all of them are delicious", but most diners are total converts, extolling an all-round, exceptional, gastronomic experience.

XR W1 £67 3|3|2

13-14 THAYER STREET 0207 486 3222 3–1A

The ground-floor of Carlo Scotto's Marylebone newcomer (see also Xier) – formerly a branch of PizzaExpress – isn't as warmly greeted as the more ambitious upstairs by reporters. Early days feedback rates the dishes – a more casual version of the fine food above – consistently well, but there's only the odd rave, and the atmosphere here seems more elusive too.

XU W1 £69 4|3|4

30 RUPERT ST 020 3319 8147 4–3D

"Sublime, very different, Taiwanese cuisine" delivering "flavourful and stylish" dishes in a "super-cool setting" (evoking a 1930s tea parlour) makes this "tiny but beautiful" two-year-old on the edge of Chinatown many reporters' "new favourite place for Chinese-style food". Owned by the people behind Bao, its "subtly flavoured delights" include "brilliant tea-based cocktails" and a "lovely selection of the teas themselves".

YALLA YALLA £42 3|2|2

1 GREEN'S CT, W1 020 7287 7663 4–2D
12 WINSLEY ST, W1 020 7637 4748 3–1C

"Cheap 'n' cheerful" Beirut-style street-food duo that offer "a top Lebanese experience" in a hidden Soho alleyway and Fitzrovia. "The food is very good and very good value", with some "unusual and delicious choices – try the mixed fish with za'atar and sumac".

YAMA MOMO SE22 £57 3|2|3

72 LORDSHIP LN 020 8299 1007 1–4D

The "very good cooking at this Japanese fusion place" – an offshoot of stalwart Clapham hotspot, Tsunami – makes it a popular option in East Dulwich. Service, though "sweet", has slipped a notch, though: "they sometimes seem more interested in serving cocktails than getting the food sorted".

YARD SALE PIZZA £42 4|3|2

54 BLACKSTOCK ROAD, N4 020 7226 2651 9–1D
622 HIGH ROAD LEYTONSTONE, E11 020 8539 5333 1–1D
15 HOE STREET, E17 020 8509 0888 1–1D
105 LOWER CLAPTON RD, E5 020 3602 9090 14–1B

"Unusual toppings that actually work" ("BBQ sauce!") and "the best-ever, super-thin crusts" are hallmarks of this "achingly East London trendy" quartet of "excellent" and "inventive" pizza-stops.

YASHIN £98 3|2|2

117-119 OLD BROMPTON RD, SW7 020 7373 3990 6–2B
1A ARGYLL RD, W8 020 7938 1536 6–1A

Backstreet sushi restaurant in High Street Kensington of high ambition which typically elicits high praise, but which curiously inspired practically no feedback this year. By contrast its South Kensington spin-off, which occupies a characterful landmark (formerly Brompton Library) is usually ignored, but inspired a number of reports, mostly adulatory regarding its "exceptionally good" (if pricey) cuisine: "the chef asked us if we wanted him to do something special, he did, and it was the best sushi we have ever had".

YAUATCHA £88 4|2|3

BROADWICK HS, 15-17 BROADWICK ST, W1 020 7494 8888 4–1C
BROADGATE CIRCLE, EC2 020 3817 9888 13–2B

"Silky-fine cheung fun, filled with sweet fresh prawns"… "dumplings wrapped in translucent skins"… "delicious venison puffs"… – "you can't go back to Chinatown dim sum after a trip" to one of these "hip and happening", Chinese-inspired haunts, whose "addictive bites keep reeling you in". The "flash" Soho original, created by Alan Yau, "still feels fresh after all these years" – with its moody basement and lighter ground floor – while the Broadgate spin-off is much larger in scale, more conventionally glam, and with a big cocktail terrace overlooking Broadgate Circle. Any drawbacks? Service is "efficient" but "sometimes brusque". Top Tips – Soho also serves tea, and has a line in "gorgeous, elegant patisserie"; EC2 does "exceptional-value weekend lunches".

THE YELLOW HOUSE SE16 £48 3|4|3

126 LOWER RD 020 7231 8777 12–2A

"We're so lucky this place exists, in SE16 of all places!" – so says a local fan of this oasis in the culinary badlands surrounding Surrey Quays Station. Wood-fired pizza is a highpoint on the wide-ranging and "affordably priced" menu.

YENI W1 £66 4|3|3

55 BEAK STREET 020 3475 1903 4–2C

"As good as that we ate when in the Turkish original" – this stylish-looking Soho newcomer is a London sibling to one of Istanbul's hottest properties, and (at odds with some press reviews) it impresses all early reporters (notwithstanding the odd incident of "shaky service" or "lack of ambience"), with "interesting" cuisine produced by star chef Civan Er.

YI-BAN E16 £59 2|2|2

LONDON REGATTA CENTRE, DOCKSIDE RD, ROYAL ALBERT DOCK 020 7473 6699 12–1D

Watching take-offs and landings at London City Airport provides distraction at this dock-side

Chinese near Royal Albert Dock DLR, which continues to divide opinion between fans who hail its "top dim sum" and sceptics who feel it's merely "average". Sadly, everyone agrees that "neither service, nor other elements of the experience live up to the food".

YIPIN CHINA N1 £50 4|2|1

70-72 LIVERPOOL RD 020 7354 3388 9–3D

"Nobody comes for the decor or service" when choosing this Chinese canteen near Angel, which has "zero charm", to the extent some find it "a strange place". But it's definitely "worth a visit", so long as you "stick to Hunanese and Sichuan dishes in which they specialise – spicy and challenging but very good".

YMING W1 £55 4|4|3

35-36 GREEK ST 020 7734 2721 5–2A

"William (the maitre d') always has a warm welcome" at this "long-term favourite": a Soho "oasis" whose "calm and friendly" atmosphere ("without the feeling we need to rush and free the table") provides a quiet-but-stark contrast with the frenzy of Chinatown a couple of blocks south. Foodwise "it attempts nothing new or extraordinary – just good Chinese cooking that's always wholesome and satisfying", with "decent wine at un-greedy prices".

YOPO W1 £72

20-21 NEWMAN STREET 020 3146 8880 3–1D

With its lush and somewhat 'out-there' styling, Fitzrovia's Mandrake Hotel makes an attractive destination for a meal, but recently closed its former restaurant Serge et Le Phoque (RIP). In its place came this spring 2019 newcomer, hailed as 'modern European with a South American accent' (and named for a powerful hallucinogen). One early report – in keeping with upbeat press reviews from the likes of The Telegraph's William Sitwell – suggests it's well worth a trip.

YORK & ALBANY NW1 £59 2|2|2

127-129 PARKWAY 020 7592 1227 9–3D

Gordon Ramsay's "beautiful" Regency tavern on the Camden Town corner of Regent's Park, is a large venue incorporating both a big bar, plus a sizeable dining area and basement. It doesn't receive a perfect scorecard from reporters, with some feedback describing it as "disappointing" or "overpriced", but its ratings climbed more into the middle-ground this year.

YOSHI SUSHI W6 £45 3|4|2

210 KING ST 020 8748 5058 8–2B

"The best kimchi in London" – apparently "voted by the South Korean Embassy!" – is found at this drab-looking stalwart, near Ravenscourt Park tube. Despite the name, the place is Korean-owned and run – and it's the "fantastic Korean dishes" that garner the plaudits this year: "sweet, savoury, spicy and

Baltic SE1

The Harcourt W1

with generous portions". But the Japanese dishes are also excellent and "service is always personal".

YOSHINO W1 £49 3 3 2
3 PICCADILLY PL 020 7287 6622 4–4C

"Good, simple Japanese food" has drawn a steady crowd to this offbeat, two-storey outfit for 35 years; its trump card is "location, location and location" – a little alleyway between Regent Street and Piccadilly. Cooking standards have "varied over the years", but most reporters still approve the overall experience and "sensible prices for Mayfair".

YUM BUN EC2 £22 5 3 2
DINERAMA, 19 GREAT EASTERN ST 07919 408 221 13–2B

"Perfect fluffy pillows of yumminess" with a range of "classic Asian street-food stuffings" have recruited an army of fans for Lisa Meyer's Chinese-inspired steamed bun stalls in the past 10 years. They can now be found at Spitalfields Market Kitchens and the various Street Feast venues. Top Tip – "do not miss the signature roast pork belly, served with cucumber and a sticky dark sauce exploding with umami".

ZAFFERANO SW1 £99 3 2 2
15 LOWNDES ST 020 7235 5800 6–1D

"Pricey but always 'comme il faut'" sums up the still-accomplished cuisine at this once-famous Belgravian, a short walk from Knightsbridge. That said, 20 years ago under founding chef Giorgio Locatelli, it was "the doyenne of Italian restaurants", while now it's simply "reliable" – if at a high level – and "resting on its laurels".

ZAFFRANI N1 £53 3 3 2
47 CROSS ST 020 7226 5522 9–3D

An "excellent local Indian", close to the Almeida Theatre, that wins consistently solid ratings for its cuisine, and – for non-carnivores – has "enough vegetarian dishes to be interesting".

ZAIBATSU SE10 £32 4 4 2
96 TRAFALGAR RD 020 8858 9317 1–3D

This "buzzy, family-owned Asian" dishes up "really fresh Japanese fusion food" that's "cheap and delicious", including "super-value sushi". It's "basic" and "functional", with "dog-eared menus" and Formica tables, but "service is efficient" and you can BYO.

ZAIKA OF KENSINGTON W8 £71 4 3 3
1 KENSINGTON HIGH STREET 020 7795 6533 6–1A

The forgotten sibling of Mayfair's swanky Tamarind inspires shockingly little feedback nowadays, but all reports continue to applaud this posh nouvelle Indian, which occupies an impressive converted banking hall near Kensington Palace Gardens: "top cuisine, with excellent service, and grand style".

ZELMAN MEATS £64 3 3 3
HARVEY NICHOLS, FIFTH FLOOR, 109-125 KNIGHTSBRIDGE, SW1 020 7201 8625 6–1D
2 ST ANNE'S CT, W1 020 7437 0566 4–1D

"Barbecue perfection!", insist fans of Misha Zelman's "good value" Soho steakhouse (with a Knightsbridge offshoot in Harvey Nichols. The "atmosphere's a bit industrial", but "the cocktails are good" and the "meat fantastic" – "I prefer the steak to Hawksmoor's and Goodman's despite it being reliably half the price".

ZERET SE5 £34 4 4 3
216-218 CAMBERWELL ROAD 020 7701 8587 1–3C

"You get to practically eat the plate (as the food is served on a large injera flatbread)" when you sample the cooking at this "lovely local Ethiopian" in Camberwell. Don't miss out on the coffee ceremony at the end of the meal.

ZERO DEGREES SE3 £47 3 3 3
29-31 MONTPELIER VALE 020 8852 5619 1–4D

"Amazing pizzas" are a culinary highlight on the sizeable menu (moules, salads, pasta…) at this early-wave microbrewery in Blackheath which is celebrating its 20th year in 2020, and where you can also sample, of course, a wide variety of brews fermented in the adjoining stainless steel tanks. Over the years it's spawned spin-offs in Cardiff, Reading and Bristol.

ZHENG SW3 £65 4 3 2
4 SYDNEY ST 020 7352 9890 6–2C

"Great but under-rated Malaysian/Singaporean food", "executed with real style", has earned consistently high marks for this sleek sibling of a successful Oxford venue, since it took over the Chelsea site of Brasserie Gustave (RIP) two years ago.

ZIA LUCIA £36 4 4 3
61 BLYTHE ROAD, W14 8–1C
157 HOLLOWAY ROAD, N7 020 7700 3708 9–2D

"The queuing is now almost part of the trip" to the "frenetic-but-we-love-it" Holloway original: "a terrific local pizzeria that's always packed" thanks to its "inventive, delicious chewy bases (including charcoal dough), generously finished off with a variety of flavoursome toppings", and washed down with "great local beers". Its sibling, north of Brook Green, is in a much less happening location, but already winning feedback as "a great addition to the area, with friendly staff; and where everything on the menu is fresh, and portions are generous".

ZIANI'S SW3 £63 2 3 2
45 RADNOR WALK 020 7351 5297 6–3C

Squashed trattoria off the King's Road that's long been a staple of the Chelsea crowd, who find it fun packing in like sardines next to their neighbours. In the year that saw the death of founder and long-term owner, Roberto Colussi, feedback has become a little more mixed than once it was, but it's still tipped by fans as a "favourite", especially by those with kids in tow.

ZOBLER'S, THE NED EC2 2 3 3
27 POULTRY 020 3828 2000 10–2C

"A great choice for a quick catch-up in the City" – this NYC-style Jewish deli operation vies with Cecconi's within The Ned's humongous food court as its most popular destination, and grabbing a dog, Reuben or burger here is also popular for a casual business meal (although conditions can be "extremely noisy"). Some of the dishes can be "ordinary" – its best feature is actually breakfast: "good coffee" (with unlimited refills) and lots of yummy options ("the Challah French toast is fantastic!") / EC2R 8AJ; www.thened.com; @TheNedLondon.

ZOILO W1 £64 4 4 3
9 DUKE ST 020 7486 9699 3–1A

"Much underrated", this Argentinian tapas and wine bar behind Oxford Street is the perfect place to sample "steaks from the Pampas, cooked to perfection". "Lunchtime specials are terrific value", and the "mini beef burgers dripping with homemade chimichurri are worth a journey".

ZUMA SW7 £82 5 3 5
5 RAPHAEL ST 020 7584 1010 6–1C

Arjun Waney and Rainer Becker's "well-oiled" glamour-magnet, just off Knightsbridge, "has kept its high standards for more than 15 years now" (it opened in 2002, nowadays with spin-offs around the globe). "The cocktail bar is a bit of a zoo", but that just adds energy to its "buzzy" ("so noisy!"), "casual and comfortable" overall style; and even if Japanese-fusion cuisine doesn't today seem like quite the genius-magic it did on opening, the "sublime" dishes here still feel as fresh as a daisy: "wonderous bites" of sushi, black cod and other "supreme" creations.

Charlie's, London

CENTRAL

SOHO, COVENT GARDEN & BLOOMSBURY (PARTS OF W1, ALL WC2 AND WC1)

Price	Restaurant	Cuisine	Rating
£190+	Aulis London	British, Modern	5 5 4
£120+	Maison Bab & Kebab Queen	Turkish	5 4 3
£100+	The Northall	British, Modern	3 2 3
	The Savoy Hotel	British, Traditional	2 3 3
	Smith & Wollensky	Steaks & grills	2 3 2
£90+	The Baptist Grill	British, Modern	3 4 4
	Bob Bob Ricard	"	2 3 5
	The Petersham	"	2 1 4
	Kaspar's Seafood and Grill	Fish & seafood	3 4 4
	The Savoy Hotel	Afternoon tea	2 3 4
£80+	Christopher's	American	2 2 3
	The Ivy	British, Modern	2 2 3
	Social Eating House	"	2 2 4
	Spring Restaurant	"	3 4 5
	Simpson's in the Strand	British, Traditional	2 2 3
	Neptune	Fish & seafood	2 2 2
	J Sheekey	"	4 4 4
	Clos Maggiore	French	3 4 5
	Frenchie	"	3 2 2
	Sushisamba	Fusion	3 2 3
	Evelyn's Table	International	4 5 3
	Cakes and Bubbles	Spanish	3 4 4
	Hawksmoor	Steaks & grills	4 3 3
	Oscar Wilde Lounge	Afternoon tea	3 4 5
	Cecconi's Pizza Bar	Pizza	2 2 4
	Yauatcha	Chinese	4 2 3
	aqua kyoto	Japanese	2 2 4
	Roka	"	5 4 4
£70+	Balthazar	British, Modern	2 2 4
	Frog by Adam Handling	"	5 5 3
	Garden Room	"	2 2 3
	Hix	"	1 2 2
	The Portrait	"	2 3 4
	Holborn Dining Room	British, Traditional	3 2 3
	Rules	"	3 3 5
	J Sheekey Atlantic Bar	Fish & seafood	3 3 4
	Gauthier Soho	French	4 4 3
	Otto's	"	4 4 3
	Gezellig	International	4 3 2
	Laurent at Cafe Royal	"	- - -
	Nopi	Mediterranean	4 3 2
	Eneko Basque Kitchen & Bar	Spanish	4 4 3
	Heritage	Swiss	- - -
	Dalloway Terrace	Afternoon tea	3 2 4
	Lima Floral	Peruvian	3 3 2
£60+	Big Easy	American	3 2 3
	Hubbard & Bell	"	3 3 3
	Andrew Edmunds	British, Modern	3 3 5
	Bryn Williams	"	3 3 3
	Cora Pearl	"	3 2 3
	Dean Street Townhouse	"	2 3 5
	Ducksoup	"	4 3 4
	The French House	"	3 4 5
	Ham Yard Restaurant	"	2 3 4
	Heliot Steak House	"	3 3 3
	The Ivy Market Grill	"	2 2 4
	Quo Vadis	"	3 3 5
	10 Greek Street	"	4 3 2
	Tredwell's	"	3 3 3
	George in the Strand	British, Traditional	3 3 3
	The Ivy Soho Brasserie	"	2 2 4
	The Delaunay East & Cent.	European	2 4 4
	Fishworks	Fish & seafood	3 2 2
	The Oystermen	"	4 3 3
	Parsons	"	4 3 2
	Randall & Aubin	"	4 3 5
	Wright Brothers	"	3 3 3
	Cigalon	French	4 4 4
	L'Escargot	"	3 2 4
	The 10 Cases	International	3 4 3
	Bocca Di Lupo	Italian	5 4 3
	Café Murano	"	2 2 2
	Luce e Limoni	"	4 4 3
	Margot	"	2 4 3
	Vasco & Piero's Pavilion	"	3 3 2
	Cigala	Spanish	2 2 1
	Tapas Brindisa Soho	"	3 2 2
	Sophie's Steakhouse	Steaks & grills	2 2 3
	Zelman Meats	"	3 3 3
	Burger & Lobster	Burgers, etc	3 2 3
	Cantina Laredo	Mexican/TexMex	2 2 2
	Ceviche Soho	Peruvian	3 3 4
	The Palomar	Middle Eastern	4 3 4
	Yeni	Turkish	4 3 3
	The Duck & Rice	Chinese	3 2 3
	Tamarind Kitchen	Indian	3 3 3
	Sticks'n'Sushi	Japanese	3 3 3
	Jinjuu	Korean	4 4 3
	St Martin's Lane Kitchen	Pan-Asian	- - -
	Patara Soho	Thai	3 4 3
	XU	Taiwanese	4 3 4
£50+	Joe Allen	American	2 2 3
	Coopers Restaurant & Bar	British, Modern	3 4 3
	Noble Rot	"	3 4 4
	The Norfolk Arms	"	3 3 3
	Terroirs	"	2 2 3
	Cork & Bottle	British, Traditional	2 2 4
	Bonnie Gull Seafood Shack	Fish & seafood	5 3 3
	Blanchette	French	4 2 3
	Bon Vivant	"	3 2 3
	Le Garrick	"	3 3 4
	Henrietta Bistro	"	3 3 3
	Mon Plaisir Restaurant	"	3 3 4
	The Good Egg	Fusion	4 3 4

Name	Cuisine			
Boulevard	International	2	3	3
Da Mario	Italian	2	3	3
Dehesa	"	2	2	3
Fumo	"	3	3	3
La Goccia	"	2	2	4
Mele e Pere	"	3	3	3
Polpo	"	1	2	2
San Carlo Cicchetti	"	3	3	4
Barrafina	Spanish	5	5	5
Ember Yard	"	3	3	4
Opera Tavern	"	4	4	3
St Moritz	Swiss	3	4	4
Casita Andina	Peruvian	4	3	3
Señor Ceviche	"	3	3	2
The Barbary	North African	5	5	4
Berenjak	Persian	4	4	4
Red Farm	Chinese	3	2	3
Yming	"	4	4	3
Dum Biryani	Indian	3	2	2
Fatt Pundit	"	3	3	2
Kricket	"	4	4	4
Little Kolkata	"	4	3	2
Tandoor Chop House	"	4	3	3
Chotto Matte	Japanese	4	3	4
Flesh and Buns	"	2	3	3
Inko Nito	"	3	3	4
Wild Rice & Mamasan	Thai	3	4	3

£40+

Name	Cuisine			
Hoppers	Sri Lankan	4	3	3
Bodean's	American	2	2	2
Breakfast Club	"	3	3	3
Shampers	British, Modern	3	4	4
VQ	"	2	3	3
Brasserie Zédel	French	2	3	5
Café Monico	"	2	2	4
Prix Fixe	"	3	2	2
Relais de Venise L'Entrecôte	"	3	3	3
Savoir Faire	"	3	4	3
La Fromagerie Bloomsbury	International	3	4	3
Bancone	Italian	5	4	3
Casa Tua	"	4	3	3
Ciao Bella	"	3	4	4
Pastaio	"	3	3	2
Blacklock	Steaks & grills	3	4	4
Macellaio RC	"	4	3	3
Mildreds	Vegetarian	3	3	3
Wild Food Cafe	"	3	2	2
Haché	Burgers, etc	3	4	2
The Chipping Forecast	Fish & chips	3	3	3
North Sea Fish	"	3	4	2
Poppies	"	3	3	3
Pizza Pilgrims	Pizza	4	3	3
Rossopomodoro	"	2	2	2
temper Covent Garden	"	3	3	4
Chick 'n' Sours	Chicken	4	3	3
Bodean's	BBQ	2	2	2
temper Soho	"	3	3	4
Corazón	"	3	4	3
Yalla Yalla	Lebanese	3	2	2
Le Bab	Turkish	4	2	3
Barshu	Chinese	4	2	2

Name	Cuisine			
Four Seasons	"	4	1	1
Golden Dragon	"	3	2	2
Joy King Lau	"	3	3	2
Cinnamon Bazaar	Indian	3	3	3
Darjeeling Express	"	4	3	3
Dishoom	"	3	4	5
Gopal's of Soho	"	3	3	2
Malabar Junction	"	3	3	3
Punjab	"	3	4	3
Salaam Namaste	"	3	3	2
Bone Daddies	Japanese	3	3	3
Ichi Buns	"	2	2	3
Ippudo London	"	3	3	3
Jugemu	"	5	2	3
Oka	"	4	3	2
Robata	"	-	-	-
Shackfuyu	"	4	3	3
Shoryu Ramen	"	3	2	2
Tonkotsu	"	3	3	2
Freak Scene	Pan-Asian	5	4	4
Cay Tre	Vietnamese	3	3	2

£35+

Name	Cuisine			
Gordon's Wine Bar	International	2	2	5
Lina Stores	Italian	4	4	4
Princi	"	3	2	3
MEATliquor	Burgers, etc	3	3	3
Homeslice	Pizza	4	3	3
Ceru	Middle Eastern	4	3	4
Chilli Cool	Chinese	4	2	1
Sagar	Indian	3	3	2
Kanada-Ya	Japanese	5	3	2
Koya-Bar	"	4	4	3
Kulu Kulu	"	3	2	1
On The Bab	Korean	3	3	2
Hare & Tortoise	Pan-Asian	3	3	2
Kiln	Thai	5	4	4
Lao Cafe	"	3	2	2
Viet Food	Vietnamese	3	3	2
Bao	Taiwanese	4	3	3

£30+

Name	Cuisine			
Café in the Crypt	British, Traditional	2	1	4
Bar Italia	Italian	2	3	5
Flat Iron	Steaks & grills	4	4	4
Shake Shack	Burgers, etc	3	2	2
Tommi's Burger Joint	"	3	4	3
50 Kalò di Ciro Salvo	Pizza	4	3	2
Wong Kei	Chinese	3	1	1
Wun's	"	-	-	-
Eat Tokyo	Japanese	3	2	2
Taro	"	3	2	2
Bibimbap Soho	Korean	3	3	2
C&R Café	Malaysian	4	2	2

£25+

Name	Cuisine			
Jacob the Angel	British, Modern	3	3	3
Patty and Bun Soho	Burgers, etc	4	3	3
Coqfighter	Chicken	5	3	2
India Club	Indian	2	2	2
Sen Viet	Japanese	3	4	2
Tokyo Diner	"	3	3	3

£20+	Master Wei	Chinese	4	3	2
	The Kati Roll Company	Indian	4	2	2
	Jidori	Japanese	4	3	2
£15+	The Halal Guys	American	3	3	2
	Curry House Coco Ichibanya	Japanese	-	-	-
£10+	Nordic Bakery	Scandinavian	3	2	2
	Bageriet	Sandwiches, cakes, etc	4	3	3
	Flat White	"	4	4	3
	Bun House	Chinese	4	3	3
£5+	Maison Bertaux	Afternoon tea	4	4	5
	Monmouth Coffee Company	Sandwiches, cakes, etc	3	5	4

MAYFAIR & ST JAMES'S (PARTS OF W1 AND SW1)

£360+	The Araki	Japanese	5	3	2
£150+	Hélène Darroze	French	3	4	4
	Sketch	"	3	3	4
£140+	Hide	British, Modern	3	5	4
	Le Gavroche	French	4	5	4
	The Greenhouse	"	3	3	3
£130+	Alain Ducasse	French	2	3	3
	The Promenade	Afternoon tea	2	4	4
	Park Chinois	Chinese	2	2	3
£120+	The Ritz	British, Traditional	3	4	5
	Galvin at Windows	French	3	3	5
	The Square	"	3	3	2
	Cut	Steaks & grills	3	2	2
	Kai Mayfair	Chinese	3	2	2
	Umu	Japanese	4	4	4
£110+	Pollen Street Social	British, Modern	3	3	3
	La Petite Maison	French	4	3	4
	Seven Park Place	"	4	4	3
	The Ritz	Afternoon tea	3	4	5
	Tokimeite	Japanese	3	2	2
	Jean-Georges	Pan-Asian	2	3	3
£100+	Alyn Williams	British, Modern	4	5	3
	Dorchester Grill	"	3	4	4
	Ormer Mayfair	"	4	4	2
	Corrigan's Mayfair	British, Traditional	3	3	3
	Sexy Fish	Fish & seafood	1	2	2
	Bocconcino Restaurant	Italian	2	2	2
	Novikov (Italian restaurant)	"	2	2	2
	Ikoyi West	African	4	2	2
	China Tang	Chinese	3	3	4
	Hakkasan Mayfair	"	4	2	3
	Benares	Indian	2	2	2
	Nobu	Japanese	3	2	2
	Nobu Berkeley	"	3	2	2
	Novikov (Asian restaurant)	Pan-Asian	3	2	4

£90+	Hush	British, Modern	2	2	3
	The Game Bird	British, Traditional	3	5	3
	Wiltons	"	4	5	4
	Bentley's	Fish & seafood	3	3	3
	Estiatorio Milos	"	3	2	4
	Sketch	French	1	2	3
	StreetXO	International	4	3	4
	Murano	Italian	4	5	3
	Goodman	Steaks & grills	4	3	3
	34 Mayfair	"	3	3	3
	Ruya	Turkish	3	3	3
	Ginza Onodera	Japanese	3	3	2
£80+	Colony Grill Room	American	2	2	3
	Gridiron	British, Modern	-	-	-
	Hide Ground	"	3	4	4
	Scott's	Fish & seafood	4	4	4
	Onima	Fusion	3	3	4
	The American Bar	International	2	4	3
	Cecconi's	Italian	2	2	4
	Chucs Dover Street	"	2	3	3
	Ristorante Frescobaldi	"	3	3	2
	Aquavit	Scandinavian	3	2	3
	Hawksmoor	Steaks & grills	4	3	3
	Rowley's	"	2	2	3
	Ella Canta	Mexican/TexMex	3	3	3
	Coya	Peruvian	4	3	4
	Indian Accent	Indian	5	4	2
	Jamavar	"	3	3	3
	Veeraswamy	"	3	3	3
	Roka	Japanese	5	4	4
	Sake No Hana	"	4	3	3
£70+	Le Caprice	British, Modern	2	4	4
	Galvin at the Athenaeum	"	1	2	2
	Kitty Fisher's	"	3	3	3
	Langan's Brasserie	"	2	2	4
	No. 5 Social	"	-	-	-
	Quaglino's	"	2	3	5
	Brown's Hotel	British, Traditional	3	4	4
	Black Roe	Fish & seafood	3	3	3
	Boudin Blanc	French	3	3	4
	Boulestin	"	2	2	2
	Emilia	Italian	4	4	3
	Sartoria	"	3	3	3
	Theo Randall	"	4	4	2
	The Guinea Grill	Steaks & grills	3	3	3
	Fortnum & Mason	Afternoon tea	3	4	4
	Momo	Moroccan	4	3	4
	Bombay Bustle	Indian	4	3	3
	Gymkhana	"	5	4	4
	Tamarind	"	3	4	2
	Lucky Cat	Pan-Asian	-	-	-
£60+	Bellamy's	British, Modern	3	4	4
	The Keeper's House	"	2	2	3
	The Punchbowl	"	3	3	4
	The Wolseley	"	2	3	5
	Fishworks	Fish & seafood	3	2	2
	Les Platanes	French	-	-	-

Café Murano	*Italian*	2 2 2
Franco's	*"*	3 4 4
Pucci Mayfair	*Mediterranean*	3 3 3
Sabor	*Spanish*	5 4 4
Burger & Lobster	*Burgers, etc*	3 2 3
Chisou	*Japanese*	4 4 2
Sakagura	*"*	3 3 2
Patara Mayfair	*Thai*	3 4 3

£50+	The Avenue	*American*	3 3 3
	The Windmill	*British, Traditional*	3 3 3
	Al Duca	*Italian*	2 2 2
	Il Vicolo		3 3 3
	maze Grill	*Steaks & grills*	2 2 2
	Delfino	*Pizza*	3 3 2
	Lucknow 49	*Indian*	4 4 3
	Titu	*Pan-Asian*	4 5 4
£40+	El Pirata	*Spanish*	2 3 3
	tibits	*Vegetarian*	3 2 3
	Shoryu Ramen	*Japanese*	3 2 2
	Yoshino	*"*	3 3 2
£35+	Rasa	*Indian, Southern*	3 4 2

FITZROVIA & MARYLEBONE (PART OF W1)

£170+	Bubbledogs, Kitchen Table	*British, Modern*	4 4 4
£120+	Xier	*British, Modern*	4 3 4
	Texture	*Scandinavian*	5 4 3
£100+	The Chiltern Firehouse	*American*	1 1 3
	Pied À Terre	*French*	4 4 4
	Beast	*Steaks & grills*	2 2 2
	Hakkasan	*Chinese*	4 2 3
£90+	The Berners Tavern	*British, Modern*	2 1 4
	Roganic	*"*	5 4 2
	Roux at the Landau	*"*	4 5 4
	Locanda Locatelli	*Italian*	4 4 3
£80+	AOK Kitchen	*British, Modern*	2 2 4
	Portland	*"*	4 4 2
	Mere East & Cent.	*European*	4 5 4
	Clarette	*French*	3 3 3
	Les 110 de Taillevent	*"*	2 3 3
	Orrery	*"*	3 3 3
	Arros QD	*Spanish*	4 4 4
	Trishna	*Indian*	4 3 3
	Defune	*Japanese*	4 3 2
	Roka	*"*	5 4 4
£70+	Clipstone	*British, Modern*	4 4 3
	Roast	*"*	3 2 4
	Noizé	*French*	4 5 4
	28-50	*"*	3 2 2
	Yopo	*Fusion*	- - -

Caffè Caldesi	*Italian*	3 2 3
The Ninth London	*Mediterranean*	5 4 3
Palm Court	*Afternoon tea*	3 3 4
Lima	*Peruvian*	3 3 2
The Bright Courtyard	*Chinese*	3 2 2
Royal China Club	*"*	4 3 3
Jikoni	*Indian*	3 3 4
OOTY	*Indian, Southern*	5 4 3
Dinings	*Japanese*	5 4 2

£60+	Brasserie of Light	*British, Modern*	2 2 4
	Vinoteca Seymour Place	*"*	2 2 2
	XR	*"*	3 3 2
	Fischer's East & Cent.	*European*	2 2 4
	Fancy Crab	*Fish & seafood*	3 3 2
	Fishworks	*"*	3 2 2
	Twist	*Fusion*	5 4 3
	Meraki	*Greek*	4 4 4
	Bernardi's	*Italian*	3 4 3
	Fucina	*"*	- - -
	Harry's Bar	*"*	2 2 3
	Blandford Comptoir	*Mediterranean*	3 3 3
	Mortimer House Kitchen	*"*	3 3 4
	ROVI	*"*	5 4 4
	The Harcourt	*Scandinavian*	3 4 4
	Lurra	*Spanish*	3 3 4
	Burger & Lobster	*Burgers, etc*	3 2 3
	Daylesford Organic	*Sandwiches, cakes, etc*	3 1 2
	Zoilo	*Argentinian*	4 4 3
	Pisqu	*Peruvian*	3 3 2
	Honey & Co	*Middle Eastern*	5 3 3
	The Greyhound Cafe	*Thai*	3 2 3
£50+	Bubbledogs	*American*	3 4 4
	Caravan	*British, Modern*	2 2 3
	The Ivy Café	*"*	1 1 3
	The Lore of the Land	*"*	3 3 4
	The Wigmore	*British, Traditional*	4 4 5
	Bonnie Gull	*Fish & seafood*	5 3 3
	The Wallace	*French*	2 3 5
	Carousel	*Fusion*	4 4 3
	Opso	*Greek*	3 3 3
	Foley's	*International*	4 4 2
	Briciole	*Italian*	3 3 2
	2 Veneti	*"*	3 3 2
	Riding House Café	*Mediterranean*	2 3 3
	Mac & Wild	*Scottish*	3 3 3
	Barrica	*Spanish*	3 3 3
	Donostia	*"*	4 4 3
	Ibérica	*"*	3 2 3
	Salt Yard	*"*	4 4 3
	Boxcar Butcher & Grill	*Steaks & grills*	4 4 3
	The Gate	*Vegetarian*	4 2 2
	Maroush	*Lebanese*	3 2 2
	Honey & Smoke	*Middle Eastern*	4 3 2
	Ishtar	*Turkish*	3 3 2
	Royal China	*Chinese*	3 2 1
	Flesh and Buns Fitzrovia	*Japanese*	2 3 3
	Laksamania	*Malaysian*	3 2 2
	Cocochan	*Pan-Asian*	3 2 2

£40+			
Hoppers	Sri Lankan	4 3 3
Passyunk Avenue	American	4 4 3
Lantana Café	Australian	3 3 3
The Long Bar	British, Modern	2 4 4
La Fromagerie Café	International	3 4 3
Circolo Popolare	Italian	- - -
Made in Italy James St	"	4 2 3
Rossopomodoro	"	2 2 2
Vagabond Wines	Mediterranean	2 3 3
Le Relais de Venise	Steaks & grills	3 3 3
Santa Maria	Pizza	4 3 3
Yalla Yalla	Lebanese	3 2 2
Delamina	Middle Eastern	4 4 2
Chettinad	Indian	4 3 2
Roti Chai	"	4 3 3
Bone Daddies	Japanese	3 3 3
Sushiology by Atari-Ya	"	4 2 1
Tonkotsu	"	3 3 2
Bao & Bing	Taiwanese	3 3 4
£35+		
MEATLiquor	Burgers, etc	3 3 3
Golden Hind	Fish & chips	3 2 2
Homeslice	Pizza	4 3 3
Workshop Coffee	Sandwiches, cakes, etc	3 4 3
Sanxia Renjia	Chinese	3 2 2
Ragam	Indian	4 4 2
Sagar	"	3 3 2
Bao Fitzrovia	Taiwanese	4 3 3
£30+		
Ethos	Vegetarian	4 2 3
Tommi's Burger Joint	Burgers, etc	3 4 3
Sushi Atelier	Japanese	5 4 3
Bibimbap Soho	Korean	3 3 2
£25+		
Patty and Bun	Burgers, etc	4 3 3
£15+		
Icco Pizza	Italian	4 2 1
Kaffeine	Sandwiches, cakes, etc	3 5 4
Patogh	Middle Eastern	4 3 2

BELGRAVIA, PIMLICO, VICTORIA & WESTMINSTER (SW1, EXCEPT ST JAMES'S)

£130+			
Celeste at The Lanesborough	French	2 2 4
£120+		
Marcus	British, Modern	3 3 3
Dinner	British, Traditional	2 2 2
£110+		
Pétrus	French	3 4 3
£100+		
Siren	Fish & seafood	- - -
Rib Room	Steaks & grills	3 2 3
Imperial Treasure	Chinese	2 2 2
£90+		
Kerridge's Bar & Grill	British, Modern	3 3 4
Roux at Parliament Square	"	4 4 3
The Dining Room	British, Traditional	3 5 4

Sette	Italian	- - -
Zafferano	"	3 2 2
The Collins Room	Afternoon tea	2 3 4
Hunan	Chinese	4 2 1
The Cinnamon Club	Indian	4 2 3
£80+		
Enoteca Turi	Italian	3 4 2
Olivocarne	"	3 2 2
Santini	"	2 3 3
Ametsa	Spanish	3 3 2
The Crystal Moon Lounge	Afternoon tea	2 4 4
Mr Chow	Chinese	2 1 2
Amaya	Indian	5 3 3
Chutney Mary	"	4 4 3
£70+		
45 Jermyn Street	British, Modern	3 3 4
Hans' Bar & Grill	"	2 3 3
The Rex Whistler Restaurant	"	3 3 5
Wild Honey St James	"	- - -
Olivomare	Fish & seafood	3 3 2
Bar Boulud	French	3 3 3
Colbert	"	2 2 4
Olivo	Italian	3 3 2
Boisdale of Belgravia	Scottish	3 2 3
M Restaurant Victoria Street	Steaks & grills	2 2 2
Drawing Room, Dukes	Afternoon tea	- - -
Kahani	Indian	5 4 3
Quilon	Indian, Southern	5 5 2
£60+		
The Alfred Tennyson	British, Modern	3 3 3
Aster Restaurant	"	2 2 2
Daylesford Organic	"	3 2 1
Lorne	"	5 5 3
The Orange	"	3 2 3
Rail House Café	"	2 2 2
Scully	"	5 4 3
The Thomas Cubitt	"	3 3 3
La Poule au Pot	French	3 3 5
Cambridge Street	International	3 3 4
Caraffini	Italian	3 5 4
Il Convivio	"	3 4 3
Hai Cenato	"	3 2 2
Osteria Dell'Angolo	"	3 3 2
Quirinale	"	3 4 3
Sale e Pepe	"	3 4 3
San Carlo	"	3 4 4
Signor Sassi	"	3 3 3
Zelman Meats	Steaks & grills	3 3 3
Burger & Lobster	Burgers, etc	3 2 3
Oliveto	Pizza	4 3 2
Abd El Wahab	Lebanese	3 3 2
Ken Lo's Memories	Chinese	3 2 2
Sticks'n'Sushi	Japanese	3 3 3
Sumosan Twiga	"	2 2 2
Salloos	Pakistani	3 2 3
£50+		
Granger & Co	Australian	3 2 3
The Botanist	British, Modern	2 2 2
The Other Naughty Piglet	"	4 3 2

	Rochelle Canteen at the ICA	"	442
	Ottolenghi	Mediterranean	322
	About Thyme	Spanish	343
	Ibérica	Spanish	323
	Wulf & Lamb	Vegetarian	422
	Seafresh	Fish & chips	322
	O'ver	Pizza	433
	Kazan	Turkish	332
	AWong	Chinese	553
	Farzi Cafe	Indian	444
£40+	The Jones Family Kitchen	British, Modern	433
	The Vincent Rooms	"	332
	Grumbles	International	334
	Gustoso	Italian	333
	Tozi	"	333
	Vagabond Wines	Mediterranean	233

	Goya	Spanish	323
	Cyprus Mangal	Turkish	432
	Bone Daddies	Japanese	333
	Machiya	"	322
£35+	Market Hall Victoria	International	422
	Kanada-Ya	Japanese	532
	Sri Suwoon	Thai	443
£30+	Shake Shack	Burgers, etc	322
£20+	Bleecker Burger	Burgers, etc	521
£15+	Regency Cafe	British, Traditional	335

WEST

CHELSEA, SOUTH KENSINGTON, KENSINGTON, EARL'S COURT & FULHAM (SW3, SW5, SW6, SW7, SW10 & W8)

£160+	Gordon Ramsay	French	332
£130+	Bibendum	French	334
£110+	The Five Fields	British, Modern	554
£90+	Restaurant at The Capital	Fish & seafood	- - -
	Yashin Ocean House	Japanese	322
£80+	Bluebird	British, Modern	234
	Elystan Street	"	553
	Launceston Place	"	444
	No. Fifty Cheyne	"	344
	Le Colombier	French	343
	Chucs	Italian	233
	Scalini	"	233
	Hawksmoor Knightsbridge	Steaks & grills	433
	Min Jiang	Chinese	335
	Akira at Japan House	Japanese	233
	Koji	"	334
	Zuma	"	535
£70+	Clarke's	British, Modern	454
	Harwood Arms	"	433
	Kitchen W8	"	443
	Medlar	"	443
	Belvedere Restaurant	French	245
	Daphne's	Italian	234
	Frantoio	"	344
	Lucio	"	332
	Manicomio	"	323
	Stecca	"	222

	Bombay Brasserie	Indian	332
	Zaika of Kensington	Indian, Southern	433
	Dinings	Japanese	542
£60+	Big Easy	American	323
	Brinkley's	British, Modern	223
	Daylesford Organic	"	321
	The Enterprise	"	234
	Harlequin	"	444
	The Ivy Chelsea Garden	"	224
	Park Terrace Restaurant	"	233
	Tom's Kitchen	"	223
	Maggie Jones's	British, Traditional	234
	The Sea	Fish & seafood	444
	Wright Brothers	"	333
	Mazi	Greek	443
	Suzi Tros	"	- - -
	Gallery Mess	International	233
	The Kensington Wine Rooms	"	233
	Enoteca Rosso	Italian	223
	La Famiglia	"	234
	Harry's Dolce Vita	"	335
	La Mia Mamma	"	333
	Il Portico	"	354
	Ziani's	"	232
	Cambio de Tercio	Spanish	433
	Sophie's Steakhouse	Steaks & grills	223
	Geales	Fish & chips	222
	Chicama	Peruvian	424
	Good Earth	Chinese	332
	Romulo Café	Filipino	343
	Kutir	Indian	544
	Chisou	Japanese	442
	Sticks 'n' Sushi	"	333
	Zheng	Malaysian	432
	Patara	Thai	343
£50+	The Abingdon	British, Modern	334

Price	Name	Cuisine	Rating
	Brook House	"	3 2 4
	The Builders Arms	"	- - -
	The Cross Keys	"	3 4 4
	maze Grill	"	2 2 2
	Rabbit	"	3 2 3
	The Sands End	"	3 3 4
	The Shed	"	3 3 3
	Bumpkin	British, Traditional	2 2 3
	Bibendum Oyster Bar	Fish & seafood	3 3 4
	Bistro Mirey	Fusion	4 3 3
	The Admiral Codrington	International	3 3 3
	maze Grill	"	2 2 2
	Polpo	Italian	1 2 2
	Riccardo's	"	3 2 2
	San Pietro	"	3 2 2
	Daquise	Polish	2 2 2
	Ognisko Restaurant	"	3 4 5
	Casa Brindisa	Spanish	3 3 4
	Tendido Cero	"	3 3 4
	Pizzicotto	Pizza	4 5 3
	Maroush	Lebanese	3 2 2
	Royal China	Chinese	3 2 1
	Pure Indian Cooking	Indian	3 4 2
	E&O Chelsea	Pan-Asian	3 3 3
	Sukho Fine Thai Cuisine	Thai	5 5 3
	Go-Viet	Vietnamese	4 3 2
£40+	Bodean's	American	2 2 2
	VQ	British, Modern	2 3 3
	Aglio e Olio	Italian	3 3 2
	Chelsea Cellar	"	4 4 4
	Da Mario	"	3 3 3
	Made in Italy	"	4 2 3
	Nuovi Sapori	"	3 3 3
	The Atlas	Mediterranean	4 4 4
	Haché	Steaks & grills	3 4 2
	Macellaio RC	"	4 3 3
	Rocca Di Papa	Pizza	3 3 4
	Rossopomodoro	"	2 2 2
	Lupita West	Mexican/TexMex	3 2 2
	Melabes	Middle Eastern	3 2 2
	Best Mangal	Turkish	4 3 2
	Dishoom	Indian	3 4 5
	Flora Indica	"	4 4 4
	Malabar	"	3 3 2
	Noor Jahan	"	3 4 3
	Thali	"	4 3 2
	Bone Daddies	Japanese	3 3 3
	Oka	"	4 3 2
	Suksan	Thai	3 3 2
£35+	Churchill Arms	British, Traditional	3 2 5
	Mona Lisa	International	3 3 2
	Pappa Ciccia	Italian	3 3 2
	Ceru	Middle Eastern	4 3 4
	Addie's Thai Café	Thai	4 3 2
£30+	Eat Tokyo	Japanese	3 2 2
	Phat Phuc	Vietnamese	3 3 2

Price	Name	Cuisine	Rating
£25+	Stick & Bowl	Chinese	3 2 1
£10+	Jollibee	Chicken	1 2 1

NOTTING HILL, HOLLAND PARK, BAYSWATER, NORTH KENSINGTON & MAIDA VALE (W2,W9,W10,W11)

Price	Name	Cuisine	Rating
£150+	The Ledbury	British, Modern	5 5 4
£120+	Core by Clare Smyth	British, Modern	5 4 4
£80+	104 Restaurant	British, Modern	4 3 3
	Chucs Westbourne Grove	Italian	2 3 3
	Caractère	Mediterranean	5 5 4
£70+	108 Garage	British, Modern	4 3 2
	London Shell Co.	Fish & seafood	3 3 5
	Angelus	French	3 4 2
£60+	Daylesford Organic	British, Modern	3 2 1
	The Frontline Club	"	2 2 4
	Gold	"	- - -
	The Hero of Maida	"	2 2 3
	The Ladbroke Arms	"	3 3 3
	Six Portland Road	"	4 4 3
	The Summerhouse	Fish & seafood	2 3 5
	Cepages	French	4 3 4
	The Cow	Irish	3 3 4
	Assaggi	Italian	3 3 1
	Assaggi Bar & Pizzeria	"	3 3 3
	Edera	"	3 3 3
	Mediterraneo	"	3 2 3
	The Oak W2	"	3 3 4
	Osteria Basilico	"	4 3 2
	Farmacy	Vegetarian	4 4 3
	Flat Three	Japanese	3 3 3
	Maguro	"	4 3 2
	Uli	Pan-Asian	3 3 4
£50+	Electric Diner	American	2 2 3
	Granger & Co	Australian	3 2 3
	Julie's	British, Modern	- - -
	Paradise, Kensal Green	"	2 2 5
	Pomona's	"	3 4 4
	7 Saints	"	4 4 4
	Hereford Road	British, Traditional	4 4 3
	Snaps & Rye	Danish	4 4 3
	Bucket	Fish & seafood	3 4 3
	Ida	Italian	3 4 3
	Polpo	"	1 2 2
	Portobello Ristorante	"	3 3 3
	Ottolenghi	Mediterranean	3 2 2
	Orasay	Scottish	4 4 4
	Lockhouse	Burgers, etc	3 3 3
	Pizza East Portobello	Pizza	3 2 4
	Andina Picanteria	Peruvian	4 3 3
	Maroush	Lebanese	3 2 2

	Name	Cuisine	Ratings
	Kateh	Persian	4 3 2
	Pearl Liang	Chinese	4 2 2
	Royal China	"	3 2 1
	E&O	Pan-Asian	3 3 3
£40+	VQ	British, Modern	2 3 3
	The Chipping Forecast	Fish & seafood	3 3 3
	Raoul's Café	Mediterranean	3 2 4
	Taqueria	Mexican/TexMex	3 2 3
	The Cedar Restaurant	Lebanese	3 3 2
	Four Seasons	Chinese	4 1 1
	Mandarin Kitchen	"	4 3 1
	Bombay Palace	Indian	5 4 3
	Noor Jahan	"	3 4 3
	Tonkotsu	Japanese	3 3 2
	The Heron	Thai	4 3 1
	MAM	Vietnamese	4 4 3
£35+	MEATliquor	Burgers, etc	3 3 3
	Workshop Coffee	Sandwiches, cakes, etc	3 4 3
£30+	Gold Mine	Chinese	4 2 2
£25+	Tab X Tab	British, Modern	5 4 4
	Patty and Bun	Burgers, etc	4 3 3
	Fez Mangal	Turkish	5 4 3
£10+	Lisboa Pâtisserie	Sandwiches, cakes, etc	3 2 3

HAMMERSMITH, SHEPHERD'S BUSH, OLYMPIA, CHISWICK, BRENTFORD & EALING (W4,W5,W6,W12,W13,W14,TW8)

	Name	Cuisine	Ratings
£180+	Endo at Rotunda	Japanese	5 5 4
£100+	The River Café	Italian	3 3 3
£80+	La Trompette	French	5 4 3
£70+	Villa Di Geggiano	Italian	3 4 4
£60+	The Anglesea Arms	British, Modern	4 4 4
	Duke of Sussex	"	2 2 3
	Vinoteca	"	2 2 2
	Michael Nadra	French	4 3 2
	Le Vacherin	"	3 3 3
	Cibo	Italian	4 5 3
	The Oak W12	"	3 3 4
	Popeseye	Steaks & grills	4 3 2
	Little Bird Chiswick	Pan-Asian	3 3 4
£50+	Brackenbury Wine Rooms	British, Modern	2 3 3
	The Carpenter's Arms	"	3 3 3
	Charlotte's W4	"	3 2 3
	City Barge	"	3 3 3
	The Colton Arms	"	2 3 4
	The Dartmouth Castle	"	3 4 4
	Eat 17 Hammersmith	"	3 3 3
	The Havelock Tavern	"	3 2 3

	Name	Cuisine	Ratings
	The Princess Victoria	"	3 3 3
	The Hampshire Hog	British, Traditional	2 3 3
	Albertine	French	3 3 5
	Annie's	International	3 4 4
	L'Amorosa	Italian	4 4 3
	Pentolina	"	4 5 3
	Tarantella Ristorante Pizzeria	"	3 3 3
	Cumberland Arms	Mediterranean	3 3 3
	The Swan	"	3 3 4
	The Crown	"	3 3 4
	The Gate	Vegetarian	4 2 2
	The Bird in Hand	Pizza	4 3 4
	Shikumen	Chinese	4 2 2
	Indian Zing	Indian	4 3 2
£40+	222 Veggie Vegan	Vegan	4 3 2
	High Road Brasserie	British, Modern	2 3 3
	The Pear Tree	"	3 4 4
	Soane's Kitchen	"	2 2 3
	Le Petit Citron	French	3 2 3
	The Andover Arms	International	3 4 4
	Pasta Remoli	Italian	3 3 3
	Santa Maria	Pizza	4 3 3
	Angie's Little Food Shop	Sandwiches, cakes, etc	3 2 2
	Best Mangal	Turkish	4 3 2
	North China	Chinese	4 3 3
	Potli	Indian	4 4 3
	Atari-Ya	Japanese	4 2 1
	Kiraku	"	4 3 2
	Tonkotsu	"	3 3 2
	Yoshi Sushi	"	3 4 2
£35+	Homeslice	Pizza	4 3 3
	Oro Di Napoli	"	4 4 3
	Zia Lucia	"	4 4 3
	Sagar	Indian	3 3 2
	Shilpa	Indian, Southern	5 3 1
	Hare & Tortoise	Pan-Asian	3 3 2
	101 Thai Kitchen	Thai	5 2 2
	Saigon Saigon	Vietnamese	3 2 3
£30+	Adams Café	Moroccan	3 5 3
	Abu Zaad	Syrian	3 3 2
	Anarkali	Indian	3 2 2
	Eat Tokyo	Japanese	3 2 2
£25+	Kerbisher & Malt	Fish & chips	3 2 2
	Alounak	Persian	3 3 3
£20+	Tamp Coffee	Sandwiches, cakes, etc	3 3 3
£5+	Bears Ice Cream	Ice cream	– – –

HAMPSTEAD, WEST HAMPSTEAD, ST JOHN'S WOOD, REGENT'S PARK, KILBURN & CAMDEN TOWN (NW POSTCODES)

Price	Name	Cuisine			
£80+	The Landmark	British, Modern	2	3	5
£70+	The Booking Office	British, Modern	2	1	4
	The Gilbert Scott	British, Traditional	3	2	4
	L'Aventure	French	3	4	5
	Tish	Kosher	3	4	4
	Kaifeng	Chinese	3	2	2
£60+	Bradley's	British, Modern	2	2	2
	Odette's	"	4	4	3
	Michael Nadra	French	4	3	2
	Oslo Court	"	3	5	4
	Bull & Last	International	3	3	3
	Morso	Italian	3	4	3
	The Rising Sun	"	3	3	3
	Villa Bianca	"	2	2	2
	Delicatessen	Middle Eastern	3	2	2
	Good Earth	Chinese	3	3	2
	Phoenix Palace	"	3	2	2
	Patara	Thai	3	4	3
£50+	The Clifton	British, Modern	3	4	4
	Ham	"	3	2	3
	The Ivy Café	"	1	1	3
	Parlour Kensal	"	3	4	4
	Searcys St Pancras Grand	"	1	2	3
	The Wells Tavern	"	3	3	4
	The Wet Fish Café	"	3	3	4
	Holly Bush	British, Traditional	2	2	3
	York & Albany	"	2	2	2
	Lemonia	Greek	1	4	4
	The Savannah	International	–	–	–
	Soutine	"	3	3	4
	La Collina	Italian	2	3	2
	28 Church Row	Spanish	4	4	4
	The Gate	Vegetarian	4	2	2
	Manna	"	2	2	2
	The Sea Shell	Fish & chips	3	2	2
	Pizza East	Pizza	3	2	4
	Crocker's Folly	Lebanese	3	3	4
	Bonoo	Indian	4	4	3
	Singapore Garden	Malaysian	4	4	2
£40+	VQ Euston	British, Modern	2	3	3
	Lure	Fish & seafood	3	4	3
	Authentique Epicerie & Bar	French	3	4	3
	La Ferme	"	3	3	3
	Anima e Cuore	Italian	5	5	2
	L'Artista	"	3	3	3
	Giacomo's	"	3	3	2
	Quartieri	"	4	3	3
	El Parador	Spanish	3	3	3
	Haché	"	3	4	2
	Mildreds	Vegetarian	3	3	3
	Purezza	"	4	3	3
	Harry Morgan's	Burgers, etc	3	3	3
	Poppies Camden	Fish & chips	3	3	3
	L' Antica Pizzeria	Pizza	4	4	3
	L'Antica Pizzeria da Michele	"	3	2	3
	Rossopomodoro	"	2	2	2
	Greenberry Café	Sandwiches, cakes, etc	3	3	4
	The Cedar Restaurant	Lebanese	3	3	2
	Skewd Kitchen	Turkish	4	3	3
	Great Nepalese	Indian	3	3	2
	KoolCha	"	–	–	–
	Paradise Hampstead	"	4	5	4
	Saravanaa Bhavan	"	4	3	2
	Atari-Ya	Japanese	4	2	1
	Jin Kichi	"	5	4	3
	Oka	"	4	3	2
	Sushi Masa	"	3	3	2
	The Petite Coree	Korean	4	3	2
	Bang Bang Oriental	Pan-Asian	2	2	3
£35+	Fiddie's Italian Kitchen	Italian	3	3	2
	Nautilus	Fish & chips	4	4	1
	Sacro Cuore	Pizza	4	3	2
	Kuku Riku	Chicken	–	–	–
	Guglee	Indian	3	3	2
	Vijay	"	4	3	1
	Anjanaas	Indian, Southern	4	2	2
£30+	Shake Shack	Burgers, etc	3	2	2
	Ravi Shankar	Indian	3	2	2
	Asakusa	Japanese	5	2	2
	Eat Tokyo	"	3	2	2
£25+	Ali Baba	Egyptian	3	2	2
	Ariana II	Afghani	3	3	2
	Diwana Bhel-Poori House	Indian	3	2	1
	Sakonis	"	3	2	1
	Roti King	Malaysian	5	2	1
£20+	Balady	Middle Eastern	3	4	2
	Chutneys	Indian	3	2	2
£15+	Icco Pizza	Pizza	4	2	1
	E Mono	Turkish	4	2	1
£10+	Ginger & White Hampstead	Sandwiches, cakes, etc	3	3	3

HOXTON, ISLINGTON, HIGHGATE, CROUCH END, STOKE NEWINGTON, FINSBURY PARK, MUSWELL HILL & FINCHLEY (N POSTCODES)

Price	Restaurant	Cuisine			
£90+	Cub	British, Modern	4	4	3
£70+	The Frog Hoxton	British, Modern	5	5	3
	Plum + Spilt Milk	"	2	3	3
	German Gymnasium	German	2	2	4
	Salut	International	4	3	3
£60+	Frederick's	British, Modern	3	4	5
	Jolene	"	3	2	3
	The Lighterman	"	3	2	4
	Perilla	"	4	4	3
	Prawn on the Lawn	Fish & seafood	4	3	2
	Bistro Aix	French	2	2	3
	Radici	Italian	2	2	2
	Trullo	"	3	3	3
	Vinoteca	Mediterranean	2	2	2
	Parrillan	Spanish	3	4	4
	Casa Pastór & Plaza Pastór	Mexican/TexMex	3	2	3
£50+	Granger & Co	Australian	3	2	3
	The Bull	British, Modern	3	4	3
	Caravan King's Cross	"	2	2	3
	The Drapers Arms	"	3	3	4
	Granary Square Brasserie	"	2	1	3
	Humble Grape	"	3	4	3
	Jones & Sons	"	3	4	3
	Moio	"	3	3	3
	Oldroyd	"	4	3	2
	Pig & Butcher	"	3	4	3
	The Red Lion & Sun	"	3	3	3
	Rotunda Bar & Restaurant	"	3	3	4
	Spiritland	"	3	3	5
	Top Cuvee	"	4	4	3
	Westerns Laundry	"	3	2	2
	St Johns	British, Traditional	3	2	3
	Petit Pois Bistro	French	4	3	3
	Sardine	"	4	3	3
	Table Du Marche	"	3	3	2
	The Good Egg	Fusion	4	3	4
	Banners	International	2	3	4
	Primeur	"	3	3	3
	Il Guscio	Italian	3	4	3
	Osteria Tufo	"	4	3	2
	Terra Rossa	"	3	4	2
	Coal Office	Mediterranean	3	4	4
	Ottolenghi	"	3	2	2
	Bar Esteban	Spanish	3	4	3
	Barrafina	"	5	5	5
	Camino King's Cross	"	2	2	2
	La Lluna	"	3	3	2
	Smokehouse Islington	Steaks & grills	3	3	3
	Black Axe Mangal	Turkish	4	3	3
	Yipin China	Chinese	4	2	1
	Zaffrani	Indian	3	3	2
£40+	Breakfast Club Hoxton	American	3	3	3
	Wander	Australian	4	4	3
	Chriskitch	British, Modern	4	3	3
	Hicce	"	2	3	4
	Linden Stores	"	3	3	2
	1251	"	3	3	3
	Snooty Fox	British, Traditional	3	2	3
	Kipferl East & Cent.	European	3	2	3
	Le Sacré-Coeur	French	3	2	3
	Vrisaki	Greek	3	3	2
	Aleion	International	3	3	3
	La Fromagerie	"	3	4	3
	500	Italian	3	3	3
	Pasta Remoli	"	3	3	3
	Lady Mildmay	Mediterranean	3	3	3
	Café del Parc	Spanish	5	5	3
	Trangallan	"	4	4	3
	Vermuteria	"	2	2	3
	Beef & Brew	Steaks & grills	3	4	3
	Mildreds	Vegetarian	3	3	3
	Rossopomodoro	Pizza	2	2	2
	Sweet Thursday	"	3	2	2
	Yard Sale Pizza	"	4	3	2
	Chick 'n' Sours	Chicken	4	3	3
	Plaquemine Lock	Cajun/creole	2	4	3
	Gallipoli	Turkish	2	3	3
	Sumak	"	4	4	2
	Kaki	Chinese	3	2	1
	Dishoom	Indian	3	4	5
	Farang	Thai	4	4	2
	Supawan	"	4	3	2
£35+	Lina Stores	Italian	4	4	4
	Passione e Tradizione	"	3	2	2
	Pizzeria Pappagone	"	3	3	3
	Via Emilia	"	3	2	2
	Cut + Grind	Burgers, etc	3	3	3
	MEATLiquor Islington	"	3	3	3
	Olympus Fish	Fish & chips	3	3	2
	Toff's	"	3	3	2
	Sacro Cuore	Pizza	4	3	2
	Zia Lucia	"	4	4	3
	Fink's Salt and Sweet	Sandwiches, cakes, etc	3	4	3
	Max's Sandwich Shop	"	5	4	3
	Gem	Turkish	3	3	2
	Indian Rasoi	Indian	3	2	2
	Jashan	"	4	4	2
	Rasa	Indian, Southern	3	4	2
	Kanada-Ya	Japanese	5	3	2
	Dotori	Korean	4	3	2
	Sambal Shiok	Malaysian	3	3	1
	CôBa	Vietnamese	4	3	2
£30+	Sunday	British, Modern	4	3	3
	Two Brothers	Fish & seafood	3	2	2
	Le Mercury	French	2	2	3
	Flat Iron	Steaks & grills	4	4	4
	MEATmission	Burgers, etc	3	3	4
	BabaBoom	Middle Eastern	3	2	2
	Gökyüzü	Turkish	2	2	2

Xi'an Impression	Chinese		5 2 1
Shahi Pakwaan	Indian		4 4 3
£25+ EartH Kitchen	British, Modern		3 2 2
Afghan Kitchen	Afghani		3 3 2
Delhi Grill	Indian		3 3 2
£20+ Piebury Corner	British, Traditional		3 2 2

SOUTH

SOUTH BANK (SE1)

£120+	Story	British, Modern	3 3 3
£110+	Aqua Shard	British, Modern	1 1 4
£100+	Oblix	British, Modern	2 2 4
	Oxo Tower	"	1 1 1
	TING	International	2 2 4
	Hutong	Chinese	2 2 5
£80+	Hawksmoor	Steaks & grills	4 3 3
£70+	Oxo Tower	British, Modern	1 1 3
	Sea Containers	"	2 3 3
	Skylon	"	2 3 4
	Butlers Wharf Chop House	British, Traditional	3 3 4
	Roast	"	3 2 4
	Le Pont de la Tour	French	2 2 3
£60+	Blueprint Café	British, Modern	3 3 4
	The Ivy Tower Bridge	"	2 2 4
	The Swan at the Globe	"	3 3 4
	Tom Simmons	"	3 3 2
	Union Street Café	"	2 2 2
	Applebee's Fish	Fish & seafood	4 2 2
	fish!	"	4 2 2
	Wright Brothers	"	3 3 3
	Vivat Bacchus	International	3 3 2
	La Barca	Italian	3 3 3
	Baltic	Polish	3 3 4
	LOBOS Meat & Tapas	Spanish	4 3 3
	Pizarro	"	4 3 3
	Tapas Brindisa	"	3 2 2
	Pique Nique	Chicken	3 2 3
	Santo Remedio	Mexican/TexMex	3 3 3
	Rabot 1745	Afro-Caribbean	2 3 2
	Bala Baya	Middle Eastern	3 2 2
£50+	The Anchor & Hope	British, Modern	4 3 2
	Caravan Bankside	"	2 2 3
	Elliot's Café	"	4 4 4
	40 Maltby Street	"	4 4 4
	The Garrison	"	3 3 3
	House Restaurant	"	2 3 2
	Lupins	"	4 3 2
	Menier Chocolate Factory	"	2 2 3
	Native	"	3 3 2
	Casse-Croute	French	4 4 4
	Spiritland	Fusion	3 3 5

	Arthur Hooper's	International	3 3 3
	Bar Douro	Portuguese	4 4 4
	Camino Bankside	Spanish	2 2 2
	José	"	5 4 5
	Meson don Felipe	"	2 2 3
	Mimo	"	- - -
	The Coal Shed	Steaks & grills	3 3 3
	O'ver	Pizza	4 3 3
	London Grind	Sandwiches, cakes, etc	3 4 4
	Paladar South	American	4 3 3
	Arabica Bar and Kitchen	Lebanese	3 4 3
	Sticky Mango at RSJ	Pan-Asian	2 2 2
	Champor-Champor	Thai	3 3 2
£40+	Lantana London Bridge	Australian	3 3 3
	The Garden Cafe	British, Modern	3 2 3
	The Green Room	"	2 2 2
	Hello Darling	"	2 3 3
	The Table	"	3 3 2
	Tate Modern	"	2 2 4
	Boro Bistro	French	2 3 3
	Flour & Grape	Italian	4 3 3
	Macellaio RC	"	4 3 3
	Casa do Frango	Portuguese	3 4 4
	Mar I Terra	Spanish	2 3 3
	tibits	Vegetarian	3 2 3
	El Pastór	Mexican/TexMex	4 3 4
	Tas Pide	Turkish	2 3 4
	Est India	Indian	3 3 3
	Gunpowder	"	4 3 3
	Tonkotsu Bankside	Japanese	3 3 2
	Kin and Deum	Thai	5 2 3
£35+	BOB's Lobster	Fish & seafood	3 4 3
	Bao Borough	Taiwanese	4 3 3
£30+	Flat Iron	Steaks & grills	4 4 4
£25+	Mercato Metropolitano	Italian	4 2 3
	Padella	"	5 4 3
	Patty and Bun	Burgers, etc	4 3 3
	Masters Super Fish	Fish & chips	3 2 1
£5+	Monmouth Coffee Company	Sandwiches, cakes, etc	3 5 4
	The Watch House	"	4 2 4

GREENWICH, LEWISHAM, DULWICH & BLACKHEATH (ALL SE POSTCODES, EXCEPT SE1)

£60+	Craft London	British, Modern	443
	Llewelyn's	"	322
	Rivington Grill	"	222
	Brasserie Toulouse-Lautrec	French	- - -
	Sticks'n'Sushi	Japanese	333
£50+	The Camberwell Arms	British, Modern	533
	The Crooked Well	"	333
	Levan	"	554
	Louie Louie	"	323
	The Rosendale	"	333
	Terroirs	"	223
	Peckham Bazaar	Greek	333
	Con Gusto	Italian	344
	Forza Win	"	443
	Luciano's	"	432
	Coal Rooms	Steaks & grills	443
	Kudu South	African	444
	Babur	Indian	554
	Kennington Tandoori	"	343
	Yama Momo	Japanese	323
£40+	Babette	British, Modern	333
	Black Prince	"	332
	Catford Constitutional Club	"	334
	The Guildford Arms	"	343
	Sparrow	"	332
	Next Door	Fish & seafood	432
	Brookmill	International	233
	The Yellow House	"	343
	Artusi	Italian	432
	Marcella	"	333
	Le Querce	"	433
	Mamma Dough	Pizza	333
	Rocca Di Papa	"	334
	Theo's	"	442
	Zero Degrees	"	333
	Dragon Castle	Chinese	433
	Ganapati	Indian	443
	Bone Daddies	Japanese	333
	The Begging Bowl	Thai	432
	Bánh Bánh	Vietnamese	332
£35+	MEATliquor ED	Burgers, etc	333
	Olley's	Fish & chips	332
	FM Mangal	Turkish	342
	Sanxia Renjia	Chinese	322
	Everest Inn	Indian	333
	Mr Bao	Taiwanese	533
£30+	500 Degrees	Pizza	322
	Zeret	Ethiopian	443
	Zaibatsu	Japanese	442
£25+	The Lido Café	British, Modern	334
	Goddards At Greenwich	British, Traditional	343

	400 Rabbits	Pizza	432
	Café East	Vietnamese	522
£20+	Silk Road	Chinese	522
	Paranhodu	Korean	342
£15+	Peckham Levels	International	- - -
£5+	Kappacasein	Sandwiches, cakes, etc	432

BATTERSEA, BRIXTON, CLAPHAM, WANDSWORTH BARNES, PUTNEY & WIMBLEDON (ALL SW POSTCODES SOUTH OF THE RIVER)

£80+	Chez Bruce	British, Modern	554
£70+	Hatched	British, Modern	542
	Trinity	"	554
	Darby's	Irish	444
£60+	Black Radish	British, Modern	443
	Brunswick House Café	"	325
	Cannizaro House	"	113
	Home SW15	"	332
	The Oak SW11	"	334
	Trinity Upstairs	"	544
	Fox & Grapes	British, Traditional	324
	Rick Stein	Fish & seafood	334
	Wright Brothers	"	333
	Bistro Vadouvan	French	443
	Sinabro	"	333
	The White Onion	"	342
	London House	International	222
	Fiume	Italian	224
	Riva	"	441
	Good Earth	Chinese	332
	Sticks'n'Sushi	Japanese	333
	Little Bird Battersea	Pan-Asian	334
	Patara	Thai	343
£50+	The Avalon	British, Modern	344
	Bistro Union	"	322
	The Brown Dog	"	333
	The Dairy	"	545
	Earl Spencer	"	323
	Hood	"	433
	Humble Grape	"	343
	The Ivy Café	"	113
	Lamberts	"	454
	Manuka Kitchen	"	333
	Nutbourne	"	223
	Olympic	"	223
	Salon Brixton	"	443
	The Victoria	"	223
	Canton Arms	British, Traditional	434
	Roe	Fish & seafood	- - -
	Augustine Kitchen	French	443
	Gazette	"	333
	Soif	"	333

Cent Anni	*Italian*	3 3 3
Maremma	"	– – –
Osteria Antica Bologna	"	3 2 2
Sapori Sardi	"	3 3 2
Sorella	"	4 3 4
Boqueria	*Spanish*	4 3 3
Knife	*Steaks & grills*	4 4 3
Naughty Piglets	"	5 5 3
Addomme	*Pizza*	4 3 3
Santa Maria del Sur	*Argentinian*	3 4 3
Chokhi Dhani London	*Indian*	3 4 3
Cinnamon Kitchen Battersea	"	4 3 3
Takahashi	*Japanese*	5 5 3

£40+

Bodean's	*American*	2 2 2
The Abbeville	*British, Modern*	3 3 3
Counter Culture	"	4 4 2
Plot	"	4 3 3
Smoke & Salt	"	5 4 3
24 The Oval	"	4 3 3
VQ Clapham	"	2 3 3
Sea Garden & Grill	*Fish & seafood*	4 4 4
The Light House	*International*	3 3 3
The Plough	"	2 2 4
The Stonhouse	"	3 3 3
Italo	*Italian*	4 3 4
Made in Italy	"	4 2 3
Pizza Metro	"	4 3 3
Stockwell Continental	"	3 4 3
Vagabond Wines	*Mediterranean*	2 3 3
Little Taperia	*Spanish*	3 3 3
Arlo's	*Steaks & grills*	3 3 3
Macellaio RC	"	4 3 3
Tell Your Friends	*Vegetarian*	3 3 4
Haché	*Burgers, etc*	3 4 2
Al Forno	*Pizza*	3 4 4
Dynamo	"	4 3 3
Mamma Dough	"	3 3 3
Mother	"	3 3 4
Pizza da Valter	"	3 2 2
Rossopomodoro	"	2 2 2
Santa Maria	"	4 3 3
Indian Moment	*Indian*	3 2 2
Kashmir	"	3 3 2
Ma Goa	"	3 4 3
Hashi	*Japanese*	3 4 2
Oka	"	4 3 2
Tonkotsu Battersea	"	3 3 2
Tsunami	"	5 3 3
Bánh Bánh	*Vietnamese*	3 3 2

£35+

Flotsam and Jetsam	*Australian*	3 3 3
Fish in a Tie	*Mediterranean*	3 3 3
MEATliquor	*Burgers, etc*	3 3 3
Eco	*Pizza*	3 3 3
Orange Pekoe	*Sandwiches, cakes, etc*	3 3 4
Chit Chaat Chai	*Indian*	4 4 3
Tomoe	*Japanese*	4 3 1
Hare & Tortoise	*Pan-Asian*	3 3 2
Mien Tay	*Vietnamese*	3 2 2

£30+

Amrutha	*Vegan*	4 4 2
Dip & Flip	*Burgers, etc*	3 2 2
Dirty Burger	"	3 3 2
Chicken Shop & Dirty Burger	*Chicken*	3 3 2
Meza	*Lebanese*	3 2 2
BabaBoom	*Middle Eastern*	3 2 2
Indian Ocean	*Indian*	3 4 3
Taro	*Japanese*	3 2 2
Awesome Thai	*Thai*	3 4 2
Daddy Bao	*Taiwanese*	4 3 3

£25+

Unwined	*Chinese*	3 4 4
Hot Stuff	*Indian*	3 4 2
Munal Tandoori	"	4 4 2
Jaffna House	*Indian, Southern*	3 2 2
Mirch Masala	*Pakistani*	4 2 2
Kaosarn	*Thai*	4 2 3

£15+

Joe Public	*Pizza*	4 3 2
Milk	*Sandwiches, cakes, etc*	3 2 3

OUTER WESTERN SUBURBS
KEW, RICHMOND, TWICKENHAM, TEDDINGTON

£80+

The Glasshouse	*British, Modern*	4 3 3
Petersham Nurseries Cafe	"	2 2 5

£70+

The Dysart Petersham	*British, Modern*	3 4 4
M Bar & Grill Twickenham	*Steaks & grills*	2 2 2

£60+

The Bingham	*British, Modern*	3 4 5
The Petersham Restaurant	"	2 3 5
Al Boccon di'vino	*Italian*	4 4 5

£50+

Black Dog Beer House	*British, Modern*	4 3 3
The Ivy Café	"	1 1 3
Petit Ma Cuisine	*French*	3 3 3
A Cena	*Italian*	3 4 3
Bacco	"	3 3 2

£40+

Le Salon Privé	*French*	3 3 3
Matsuba	*Japanese*	4 3 2

£35+

Dastaan	*Indian*	5 4 3
Moksha	"	4 4 3

EAST

SMITHFIELD & FARRINGDON (EC1)

£180+	The Clove Club	British, Modern	3 3 2
£100+	Club Gascon	French	4 4 3
£90+	Sushi Tetsu	Japanese	5 5 3
£80+	Luca	Italian	3 3 4
£70+	Anglo	British, Modern	5 3 2
	The Quality Chop House	British, Traditional	4 4 4
	Bleeding Heart Restaurant	French	3 3 4
	The Drunken Butler	"	4 4 4
	Smiths of Smithfield	Steaks & grills	3 2 4
£60+	The Coach	British, Modern	4 2 3
	The Jugged Hare	"	3 2 2
	The Modern Pantry	"	2 2 2
	Vinoteca	"	2 2 2
	St John Smithfield	British, Traditional	5 4 3
	Palatino	Italian	4 3 2
	Moro	Spanish	3 3 2
	Hix Oyster & Chop House	Steaks & grills	2 2 2
	Burger & Lobster	Burgers, etc	3 2 3
	Ceviche Old St	Peruvian	3 3 4
£50+	Stem & Glory	Vegan	3 2 2
	Granger & Co	Australian	3 2 3
	Bourne and Hollingsworth	British, Modern	3 2 4
	Caravan	"	2 2 3
	Lino	"	3 4 2
	The Wilmington	"	3 3 3
	Café du Marché	French	3 3 5
	Comptoir Gascon	"	3 2 3
	Bowling Bird	International	4 4 3
	Niche	"	3 3 2
	Apulia	Italian	3 3 2
	Da Giua	"	3 4 2
	Polpo	"	1 2 2
	Santore	"	3 2 2
	Fare	Mediterranean	3 3 4
	Ibérica	Spanish	3 2 3
	The Gate	Vegetarian	4 2 2
	Berber & Q Shawarma Bar	Middle Eastern	4 4 4
£40+	Bodean's	American	2 2 2
	Lantana Café	Australian	3 3 3
	La Ferme London	French	3 3 3
	Monsieur Le Duck	"	4 3 3
	Macellaio RC	Italian	4 3 3
	The Eagle	Mediterranean	4 3 3
	Morito	Spanish	4 3 3
	Pizza Pilgrims	Pizza	4 3 3
	Breddos Tacos	Mexican/TexMex	4 2 3
	The Sichuan	Chinese	3 3 2
	Bone Daddies	Japanese	3 3 3
	Pham Sushi	"	4 3 3
	Cây Tre	Vietnamese	3 3 2
£35+	Fish Central	Fish & seafood	3 4 3
	Le Cellar	French	3 4 3
	Homeslice	Pizza	4 3 3
	Workshop Coffee	Sandwiches, cakes, etc	3 4 3
	On The Bab	Korean	3 3 2
£10+	Department of Coffee	Sandwiches, cakes, etc	3 4 3
	Prufrock Coffee	"	3 3 2

THE CITY (EC2, EC3, EC4)

£120+	La Dame de Pic London	French	4 4 3
£110+	Mei Ume	Japanese	3 3 3
	Nobu Shoreditch	"	2 2 2
£90+	City Social	British, Modern	3 3 3
	Fenchurch Restaurant	"	4 3 4
	Angler	Fish & seafood	4 3 3
	Goodman City	Steaks & grills	4 3 3
	Lutyens Grill	"	3 3 3
£80+	Duck & Waffle	British, Modern	2 2 4
	Helix	"	2 3 5
	1 Lombard Street	"	2 2 2
	Bob Bob Cité	French	- - -
	Coq d'Argent	"	2 3 4
	Cecconi's	International	2 2 4
	Hawksmoor	Steaks & grills	4 3 3
	Coya	Peruvian	4 3 4
	Yauatcha City	Chinese	4 2 3
	Sushisamba	Japanese	3 2 3
£70+	Bread Street Kitchen	British, Modern	2 2 3
	Darwin Brasserie	"	2 2 5
	St Leonard's	"	1 2 2
	Fish Market	Fish & seafood	2 2 2
	Sweetings	"	3 3 4
	Cabotte	French	4 5 4
	Manicomio	Italian	3 2 3
	Boisdale of Bishopsgate	Scottish	3 2 2
	M Restaurant	Steaks & grills	2 2 2
	Vanilla Black	Vegetarian	4 3 3
	Mint Leaf Lounge	Indian	3 3 4
£60+	The Don	British, Modern	3 3 3
	Fortnum's Bar & Restaurant	"	2 3 3
	High Timber	"	3 3 3
	The Ivy City Garden	"	2 2 4
	The Mercer	"	3 2 2
	Merchants Tavern	"	2 2 3
	Vinoteca City	"	2 2 2

Paternoster Chop House	British, Traditional	2 2 2
Vivat Bacchus	International	3 3 2
Caravaggio	Italian	3 2 2
Hispania	Spanish	3 3 3
José Pizarro	"	4 3 2
Aviary	Steaks & grills	2 2 3
Burger & Lobster	Burgers, etc	3 2 3
Red Rooster	Chicken	2 2 3
Nanashi	Japanese	3 2 2

£50+

The Anthologist	British, Modern	2 2 2
The Botanist	"	2 2 2
Caravan	"	2 2 3
Humble Grape	"	3 4 3
Leroy	"	3 4 3
Northbank	"	2 2 3
Gloria	Italian	3 3 4
Osteria	"	3 3 2
Popolo	"	5 4 3
Taberna Etrusca	"	2 2 2
Ekte Nordic Kitchen	Scandinavian	3 2 2
Mac & Wild	Scottish	3 3 3
Camino Shoreditch	Spanish	2 2 2
The Jones Family Project	Steaks & grills	3 3 4
The Tramshed	"	3 2 4
Haz	Turkish	2 2 2
Oklava	"	4 4 3
Kym's by Andrew Wong	Chinese	4 3 3
Brigadiers	Indian	5 4 4
Cinnamon Kitchen	"	4 3 3

£40+

Bodean's	American	2 2 2
Coppa Club Tower Bridge	British, Modern	2 3 5
VQ	"	2 3 3
Simpson's Tavern	British, Traditional	3 3 4
The Wine Library	International	2 3 5
Rucoletta	Italian	4 2 2
Blacklock	Steaks & grills	3 4 4
Relais de Venise L'Entrecôte	"	3 3 3
Haché	Burgers, etc	3 4 2
Pizza Pilgrims	Pizza	4 3 3
Ozone Coffee Roasters	Sandwiches, cakes, etc	3 3 4
temper City	BBQ	3 3 4
Shoryu Ramen	Japanese	3 2 2

£35+

Café Below	British, Modern	3 3 3
Homeslice	Pizza	4 3 3
Koya	Japanese	4 4 3
On The Bab	Korean	3 3 2
Hare & Tortoise	Pan-Asian	3 3 2

£30+

Flat Iron	Steaks & grills	4 4 4
Shake Shack	Burgers, etc	3 2 2
K10	Japanese	3 2 2
Taro	"	3 2 2
Bibimbap	Korean	3 3 2

£25+

Patty and Bun	Burgers, etc	4 3 3

£20+

Bleecker Burger	Burgers, etc	5 2 1
Yum Bun	Japanese	5 3 2

£10+

Sub Cult	Sandwiches, cakes, etc	– – –

EAST END & DOCKLANDS
(ALL E POSTCODES)

£180+

Mãos	Portuguese	5 5 4

£90+

Lyle's	British, Modern	4 3 2
Galvin La Chapelle	French	4 4 5
Goodman	Steaks & grills	4 3 3

£80+

Cecconi's Shoreditch	Italian	2 2 4
Hawksmoor	Steaks & grills	4 3 3
Roka	Japanese	5 4 4

£70+

Bright	British, Modern	5 4 3
Galvin HOP	"	3 3 3
Pidgin	"	5 3 2
Smith's Wapping	"	4 4 5

£60+

Big Easy	American	3 2 3
Bistrotheque	British, Modern	3 2 4
The Culpeper	"	3 2 4
The Gun	"	2 2 4
The Narrow	"	1 2 3
Rochelle Canteen	"	3 3 3
Two Lights	"	3 4 3
The Marksman	British, Traditional	4 3 3
St John Bread & Wine	"	3 2 3
Cornerstone	Fish & seafood	5 4 4
Wright Brothers	"	3 3 3
Plateau	French	3 3 3
Brat	Fusion	5 5 4
Canto Corvino	Italian	3 2 3
Brawn	Mediterranean	5 3 4
Boisdale of Canary Wharf	Scottish	2 3 4
Burger & Lobster	Burgers, etc	3 2 3
Buen Ayre	Argentinian	4 3 2
Café Spice Namaste	Indian	5 4 3
Sticks'n'Sushi	Japanese	3 3 3

£50+

Corner Room	British, Modern	3 2 3
Duke of Richmond	"	3 2 3
Eat 17	"	3 3 3
The Empress	"	3 4 3
Humble Grape	"	3 4 3
Madame Pigg	"	3 4 4
Mare Street Market	"	3 2 5
Bumpkin	British, Traditional	2 2 3
Forman's	Fish & seafood	4 3 3
Blanchette East	French	4 2 3
Chez Elles	"	4 4 4
Angelina	Fusion	5 4 3
Blixen	International	2 2 3
Casa Fofó	"	5 3 3
Dokke	"	3 4 3
Eat 17	"	3 3 3

Lagom	"	4	3	3
The Laughing Heart	"	2	3	3
Il Bordello	Italian	3	3	3
Capeesh	"	3	3	3
Lardo	"	3	2	2
Super Tuscan	"	3	4	3
Verdi's	"	3	4	4
Ottolenghi	Mediterranean	3	2	2
Ibérica	Spanish	3	2	3
Burger & Beyond	Burgers, etc	5	3	3
Pizza East	Pizza	3	2	4
Smokestak	BBQ	5	3	3
Andina	Peruvian	4	3	3
Berber & Q	Middle Eastern	4	4	4
Haz	Turkish	2	2	2
Lahpet	Burmese	3	2	3
Royal China	Chinese	3	2	1
Yi-Ban	"	2	2	2
Grand Trunk Road	Indian	4	3	2
Smoking Goat	Thai	5	4	4
Som Saa	"	3	2	3

£40+

Breakfast Club	American	3	3	3
P Franco	British, Modern	4	2	3
The Buxton	"	–	–	–
Provender	French	3	3	3
Campania & Jones	Italian	4	4	3
Emilia's Crafted Pasta	"	4	4	3
Pasta Remoli	"	3	3	3
Morito	Spanish	4	3	3
Mao Chow	Vegetarian	–	–	–
Mildreds	"	3	3	3
The Spread Eagle	"	3	4	4
Ark Fish	Fish & chips	3	4	2
Poppies	"	3	3	3
Pizza Pilgrims	Pizza	4	3	3
Yard Sale Pizza	"	4	3	2
Chick 'n' Sours	Chicken	4	3	3
Lupita	Mexican/TexMex	3	2	2
Delamina East	Middle Eastern	4	4	2
Sichuan Folk	Chinese	4	2	2
Dishoom	Indian	3	4	5
Gunpowder	"	4	3	3
Ippudo London	Japanese	3	3	3
Tonkotsu	"	3	3	2

£35+

Xi'an Biang Biang	Chinese	3	3	3
Mien Tay	Vietnamese	3	2	2
Sông Quê	"	3	3	2
Bao Bar	Taiwanese	4	3	3

£30+

Da Terra	Fusion	5	4	4
Flat Iron	Steaks & grills	4	4	4
Dirty Burger Shoreditch	Burgers, etc	3	3	2
Shake Shack	"	3	2	2
Crate Brewery and Pizzeria	Pizza	4	3	4
Gökyuzu	Turkish	2	2	2
Lahore Kebab House	Pakistani	5	2	2
Tayyabs	"	4	2	2

£25+

E Pellicci	Italian	3	5	5
Patty and Bun	Burgers, etc	4	3	3
Mangal 1	Turkish	5	2	2
Needoo	Pakistani	4	3	2

£20+

Bleecker Burger	Burgers, etc	5	2	1
Jidori	Japanese	4	3	2
Singburi Royal Thai Café	Thai	4	3	3

£15+

The Duck Truck	Burgers, etc	5	3	3

£10+

Black Bear Burger	Burgers, etc	5	3	–
The Rib Man	"	5	3	–
Pavilion Cafe & Bakery	Sandwiches, cakes, etc	4	2	4

£5+

Brick Lane Beigel Bake	Sandwiches, cakes, etc	4	1	1

Coal Office, London

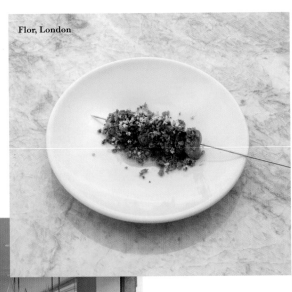

Flor, London

Hide, London

Core by Clare Smyth, London

MAP 1 – LONDON OVERVIEW

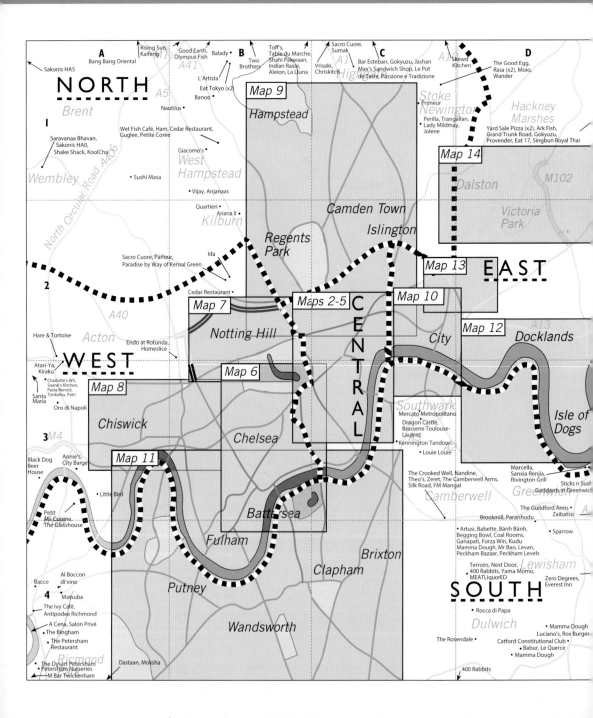

A

Sakonis HA5

Bang Bang Oriental

Rising Sun, Kaifeng

NORTH

Brent

Nautilus

Wet Fish Café, Ham, Cedar Restaurant, Guglee, Petite Corée

Saravanaa Bhavan, Sakonis HA0, Shake Shack, KoolCha

Wembley

Giacomo's

West Hampstead

Sushi Masa

Vijay, Anjanaas

Quartieri

Ariana II

Kilburn

Sacro Cuore, Parlour, Paradise by Way of Kensal Green

Ida

Cedar Restaurant

Map 7

A40

Acton

Hare & Tortoise

Endo at Rotunda, Homeslice

Atari-Ya, Kiraku

WEST

Charlotte's W5, Soane's Kitchen, Pasta Remoli, Tonkotsu, Patri

Santa Maria

Oro di Napoli

Map 8

Chiswick

M4

Black Dog Beer House

Annie's, City Barge

Map 11

Little Bird

Petit Ma Cuisine, The Glasshouse

Al Boccon di'vino

Bacco

Matsuba

The Ivy Café, Antipodea Richmond

A Cena, Salon Privé

The Bingham

The Petersham Restaurant

The Dysart Petersham

Petersham Nurseries

M Bár Twickenham

Richmond

Dastaan, Moksha

B

Good Earth, Olympus Fish

Balady

L'Artista

Eat Tokyo (x2)

Banoo

A41

Two Brothers

Toff's, Table du Marche, Shahi Pakwaan, Indian Rasoi, Aleion, La Lluna

Map 9

Hampstead

West Hampstead

Regents Park

Maps 2-5

Map 6

Notting Hill

Chelsea

Battersea

Fulham

Putney

Wandsworth

C

Sacro Cuore, Sumak

Vrisaki, Chriskitch

A1

High...

Bar Esteban, Gokyuzu, Jashan Max's Sandwich Shop, Le Pot de Terre, Passione e Tradizione

Primeur

Perilla, Trangallan, Lady Mildmay, Jolene

Camden Town

Islington

Map 13

Map 10

C E N T R A L

City

Mercato Metropolitano

Dragon Castle, Brasserie Toulouse-Lautrec

Kennington Tandoori

Louie Louie

Southwark

The Crooked Well, Nandine, Theo's, Zeret, The Camberwell Arms, Silk Road, FM Mangal

Camberwell

Artusi, Babette, Bánh Bánh, Begging Bowl, Coal Rooms, Ganapati, Forza Win, Kudu Mamma Dough, Mr Bao, Levan, Peckham Bazaar, Peckham Levels

Terroirs, Next Door, 400 Rabbits, Yama Momo, MEATLiquorED

Brixton

Clapham

Rocca di Papa

Dulwich

The Rosendale

Catford Constitutional Club

Babur, Le Querce

Mamma Dough

400 Rabbits

D

A1...

Skewd Kitchen

The Good Egg, Rasa (x2), Moio, Wander

Hackney Marshes

Yard Sale Pizza (x2), Ark Fish, Grand Trunk Road, Gokyuzu, Provender, Eat 17, Singburi Royal Thai

Map 14

Dalston

M102

Victoria Park

E A S T

Map 12

Docklands

Isle of Dogs

A13

Marcella, Sanxia Renjia, Rivington Grill

Sticks n Sush

Goddards at Greenwich

Greenwich

The Guildford Arms

Zaibatsu

Brookmill, Paranhodu

Sparrow

Lewisham

Zero Degrees, Everest Inn

SOUTH

Mamma Dough Luciano's, Rox Burger

MAP 2 – WEST END OVERVIEW

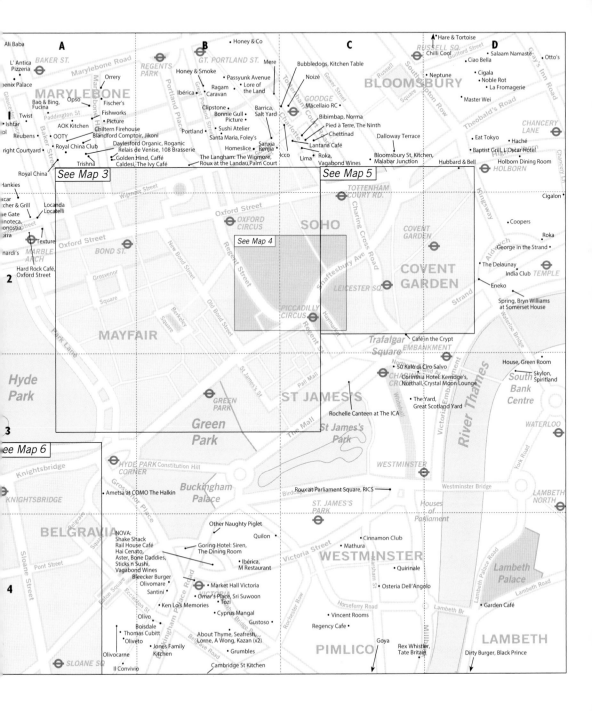

MAP 3 – MAYFAIR, ST. JAMES'S & WEST SOHO

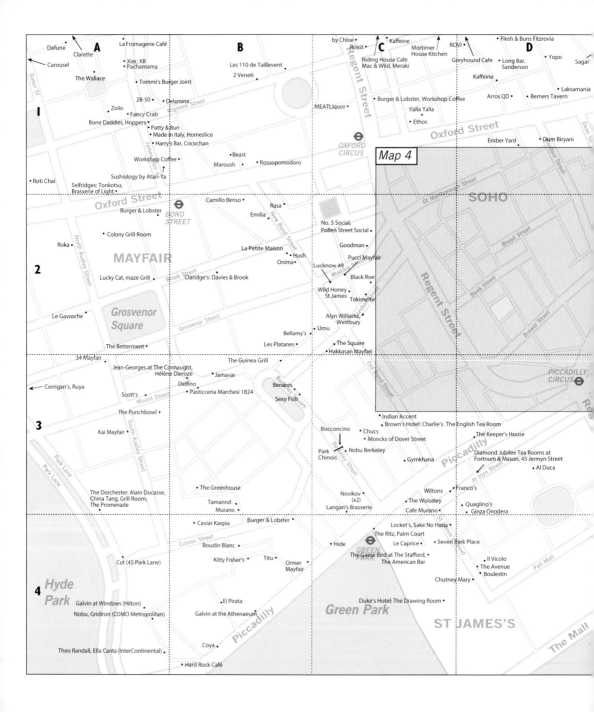

A

Defune
Clarette
Carousel
La Fromagerie Café
Xier, XR
Pachamama
The Wallace
Tommi's Burger Joint
28-50
Delamina
Zoilo
Fancy Crab
Bone Daddies, Hoppers
Patty & Bun
Made in Italy, Homeslice
Harry's Bar, Cocochan
Workshop Coffee
Sushiology by Atari-Ya
Roti Chai
Selfridges: Tonkotsu, Brasserie of Light

B

Les 110 de Taillevent
2 Veneti
MEATLiquor
Camillo Benso
Rasa
Emilia
La Petite Maison
Hush
Onima
Beast
Maroush
Rossopomodoro
Claridge's: Davies & Brook

C

by Chloe
Roast
Kaffeine
Riding House Cafe
Mac & Wild, Meraki
Mortimer
House Kitchen
Burger & Lobster, Workshop Coffee
Yalla Yalla
Ethos

D

Flesh & Buns Fitzrovia
ROVI
Yopo
Greyhound Cafe
Long Bar, Sanderson
Sagar
Kaffeine
Laksamania
Arros QD
Berners Tavern
Ember Yard
Dum Biryani

OXFORD CIRCUS

Oxford Street

SOHO

Map 4

1

2

Oxford Street
Burger & Lobster
BOND STREET
Colony Grill Room
Roka
MAYFAIR
Lucky Cat, maze Grill
Le Gavroche
Grosvenor Square
The Betterment

No. 5 Social, Pollen Street Social
Goodman
Pucci Mayfair
Lucknow 49
Black Roe
Wild Honey St James
Tokimeite
Alyn Williams, Westbury
Bellamy's
Umu
Les Platanes
The Square
Hakkasan Mayfair

Gt Marlborough Street
Broad Street
Regent Street
Beak Street
Brewer Street

3

34 Mayfair
Jean-Georges at The Connaught, Hélène Darroze
Jamavar
Delfino
Pasticceria Marchesi 1824
Scott's
The Punchbowl
Kai Mayfair
The Guinea Grill
Benares
Sexy Fish
Indian Accent
Brown's Hotel: Charlie's, The English Tea Room
Bocconcino
Chucs
Moncks of Dover Street
The Keeper's House
Park Chinois
Nobu Berkeley
Gymkhana
Diamond Jubilee Tea Rooms at Fortnum & Mason, 45 Jermyn Street
Al Duca
Wiltons
Franco's
Novikov (x2)
Langan's Brasserie
The Wolseley
Cafe Murano
Quaglino's
Ginza Onodera

PICCADILLY CIRCUS

4

Corrigan's, Ruya
The Dorchester: Alain Ducasse, China Tang, Grill Room, The Promenade
The Greenhouse
Tamarind
Murano
Caviar Kaspia
Burger & Lobster
Cut (45 Park Lane)
Boudin Blanc
Kitty Fisher's
Titu
Ormer Mayfair
Hide
Locket's, Sake No Hana
The Ritz, Palm Court
Le Caprice
Seven Park Place
The Game Bird at The Stafford, The American Bar
Il Vicolo
The Avenue
Boulestin
Chutney Mary
Hyde Park
Galvin at Windows (Hilton)
Nobu, Gridiron (COMO Metropolitan)
El Pirata
Galvin at the Athenaeum
Duke's Hotel: The Drawing Room
Green Park
ST JAMES'S
Theo Randall, Ella Canta (InterContinental)
Coya
Hard Rock Café
Piccadilly
The Mall

MAP 4 – WEST SOHO & PICCADILLY

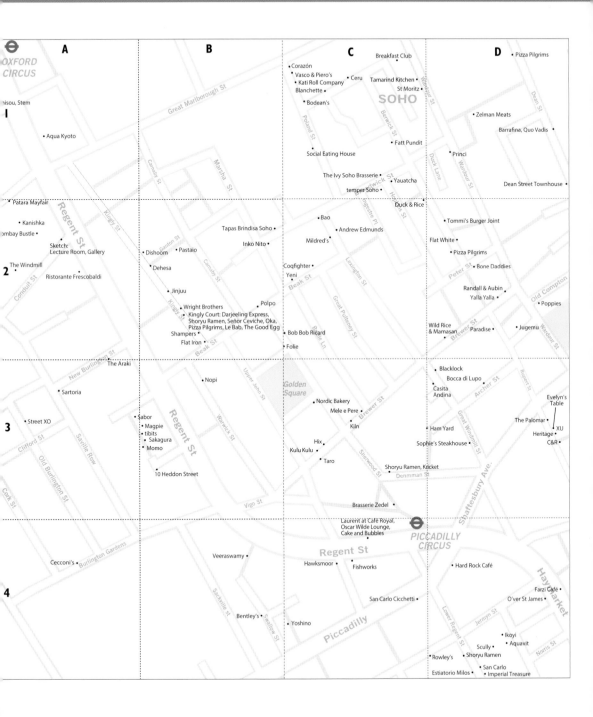

A

B

C

D

OXFORD
CIRCUS

SOHO

Breakfast Club

• Corazón
• Vasco & Piero's
• Kati Roll Company   • Ceru   Tamarind Kitchen
Blanchette •   St Moritz

• Bodean's

• Zelman Meats

Barrafina, Quo Vadis •

hisou, Stem

• Aqua Kyoto

• Fatt Pundit

Social Eating House

• Princi

The Ivy Soho Brasserie •
• Yauatcha
temper Soho •

Dean Street Townhouse •

• Patara Mayfair

Duck & Rice

• Tommi's Burger Joint

• Kanishka

• Bao
• Andrew Edmunds

Flat White •

ombay Bustle •

Tapas Brindisa Soho •

Mildred's •

• Pizza Pilgrims

Sketch:
Lecture Room, Gallery

Inko Nito •

• Dishoom   • Pastaio

• Bone Daddies

• Dehesa

Coqfighter •
Yeni •

Randall & Aubin •
Yalla Yalla •

The Windmill •

Ristorante Frescobaldi •

• Jinjuu

• Polpo

Wild Rice
& Mamasan •   Paradise •   • Jugemu

• Wright Brothers
• Kingly Court: Darjeeling Express,
Shoryu Ramen, Señor Ceviche, Oka,
Pizza Pilgrims, Le Bab, The Good Egg
Shampers •
• Flat Iron

Bob Bob Ricard •

• Folie

The Araki •

• Nopi

Golden
Square

• Blacklock
Bocca di Lupo •

Casita •
Andina

• Sartoria

Nordic Bakery •
Mele e Pere •
Kiln •

Evelyn's
Table

• Street XO

• Sabor
• Magpie
• tibits
• Sakagura
• Momo

Hix •
Kulu Kulu •

• Taro

• Ham Yard

Sophie's Steakhouse •

The Palomar •
• XU
Heritage •
C&R •

10 Heddon Street

Shoryu Ramen, Kricket •

Brasserie Zedel •

• Cecconi's

Laurent at Café Royal,
Oscar Wilde Lounge,
Cake and Bubbles

Regent St

PICCADILLY
CIRCUS

Veeraswamy •

Hawksmoor •   • Fishworks

• Hard Rock Café

Farzi Café •

O'ver St James •

San Carlo Cicchetti •

Bentley's •

• Yoshino

Piccadilly

• Ikoyi
• Aquavit
Scully •
• Shoryu Ramen
• Rowley's
• San Carlo
Estiatorio Milos •   • Imperial Treasure

MAP 5 – EAST SOHO, CHINATOWN & COVENT GARDEN

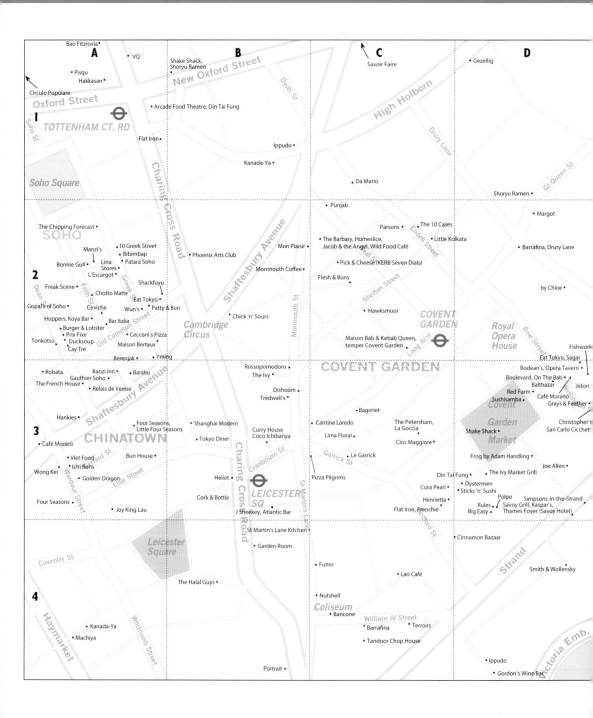

A

• Bao Fitzrovia

• VQ

• Pisqu
Hakkasan •

Circulo Popolare

Oxford Street

1

TOTTENHAM CT. RD

Soho Square

Flat Iron •

The Chipping Forecast •

SOHO

Manzi's •
• 10 Greek Street
• Bibimbap
Bonnie Gull • Lina   • Patara Soho
L'Escargot • Stores •

2

Freak Scene • •
• Chotto Matte
Gopal's of Soho • • Ceviche • Shackfuyu
Wun's • • Eat Tokyo
Hoppers, Koya Bar • • Patty & Bun
• Burger & Lobster
• Prix Fixe Bar Italia •
Tonkotsu • • Ducksoup • Cecconi's Pizza
Cay Tre • Maison Bertaux •
Berenjak • • Yming

• Robata Baozi Inn • • Barshu
Gauthier Soho •
The French House • • Relais de Venise

Hankies •

3

• Café Monico

CHINATOWN

• Viet Food
• Ichi Buns
Wong Kei • • Golden Dragon
Four Seasons •
• Joy King Lau

4

• Kanada-Ya
• Machiya

Haymarket

B

Shake Shack,
Shoryu Ramen

New Oxford Street

• Arcade Food Theatre, Din Tai Fung

Charing Cross Road

Ippudo •

Kanada-Ya •

Shaftesbury Avenue

Mon Plaisir •
• Phoenix Arts Club
Monmouth Coffee •

Cambridge
Circus

Shanghai Modern •

Rossopomodoro •
The Ivy •

Dishoom •
Tredwell's •

• Four Seasons,
Little Four Seasons
• Tokyo Diner

Curry House
Coco Ichibanya

Bun House •

Charing Cross Road

Heliot •

Cork & Bottle

J Sheekey, Atlantic Bar

St Martin's Lane Kitchen

• Garden Room

The Halal Guys •

Portrait •

Monmouth St

Cranbourn St

Chick 'n' Sours •

LEICESTER
SQ

Leicester
Square

St Martin's Lane

Coventry St

Whitcomb Street

C

Savoir Faire

High Holborn

• Da Mario

• Punjab

Parsons •
• The Barbary, Homeslice,
Jacob & the Angel, Wild Food Café
• Pick & Cheese (KERB Seven Dials)
Flesh & Buns •

Drury Lane

Endell Street

Shelton Street

The 10 Cases :
• Little Kolkata

• Hawksmoor

COVENT
GARDEN

Maison Bab & Kebab Queen,
temper Covent Garden

Long Acre

COVENT GARDEN

• Bageriet

• Cantina Laredo

Lima Floral •

Garrick St

• Le Garrick

Pizza Pilgrims

The Petersham,
La Goccia

Clos Maggiore •

Bedford St

• Fumo

• Lao Café

Coliseum
• Bancone

William IV Street

• Barbara • Terroirs

• Tandoor Chop House

D

• Gezellig

Gt Queen St

Shoryu Ramen •

• Margot

• Barrafina, Drury Lane

by Chloe •

Royal
Opera
House

Bow Street

Fishwork
Eat Tokyo, Sagar
Bodean's, Opera Tavern •
Boulevard, On The Bab •
Balthazar • Jidori
Red Farm • Café Murano •
Sushisamba • Grays & Feather •

Covent
Garden
Market

Christopher's
San Carlo Cicchet
Shake Shack •

Frog by Adam Handling •
Joe Allen •
Din Tai Fung • • The Ivy Market Grill
Cora Pearl • • Oystermen
• Sticks 'n' Sushi
Henrietta • Polpo Simpsons-in-the-Strand
Rules • Savoy Grill, Kaspar's,
Flat Iron, Frenchie Big Easy • Thames Foyer (Savoy Hotel)

• Cinnamon Bazaar

Strand

• Smith & Wollensky

• Ippudo

• Gordon's Wine Bar

Victoria Emb.

MAP 6 – KNIGHTSBRIDGE, CHELSEA & SOUTH KENSINGTON

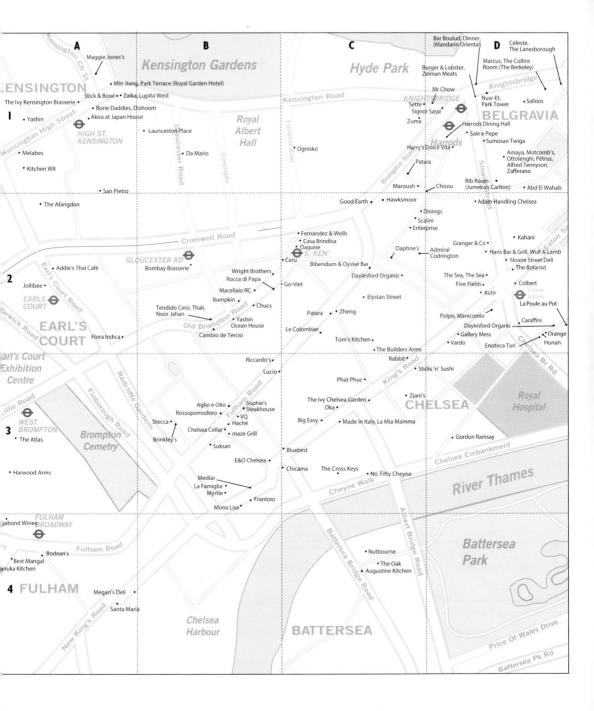

MAP 7 – NOTTING HILL & BAYSWATER

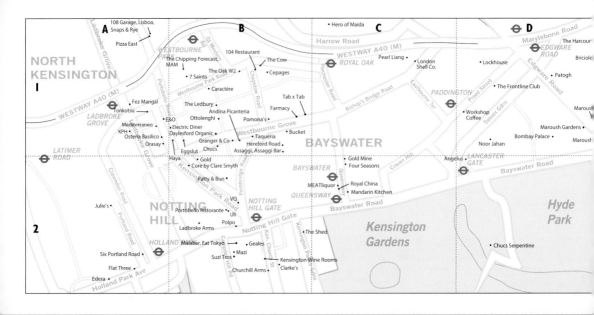

NORTH KENSINGTON

BAYSWATER

NOTTING HILL

NOTTING HILL GATE

QUEENSWAY

PADDINGTON

ROYAL OAK

LANCASTER GATE

Hyde Park

Kensington Gardens

108 Garage, Lisboa, Snaps & Rye · Pizza East · Hero of Maida · The Harcour · Briciole · Patogh · Maroush · The Chipping Forecast, MAM · 104 Restaurant · The Cow · Pearl Liang · London Shell Co. · Lockhouse · The Oak W2 · Cepages · 7 Saints · The Frontline Club · Caractère · Tab x Tab · Fez Mangal · Workshop Coffee · Maroush Gardens · Tonkotsu · The Ledbury · Andina Picanteria · Farmacy · Bombay Palace · Maroush · E&O · Ottolenghi · Pomona's · Noor Jahan · Mediterraneo · Electric Diner · Bucket · KPH · Daylesford Organic · Taqueria · Osteria Basilico · Granger & Co · Hereford Road · Orasay · Eggslut · Chucs · Assaggi, Assaggi Bar · Haya · Gold · Core by Clare Smyth · Gold Mine · Four Seasons · Angelus · Patty & Bun · MEATliquor · Royal China · Julie's · VQ · Mandarin Kitchen · Portobello Ristorante · Uli · Polpo · Ladbroke Arms · The Shed · Malabar, Eat Tokyo · Geales · Chucs Serpentine · Six Portland Road · Mazi · Suzi Tros · Flat Three · Kensington Wine Rooms · Edera · Churchill Arms · Clarke's

MAP 8 – HAMMERSMITH & CHISWICK

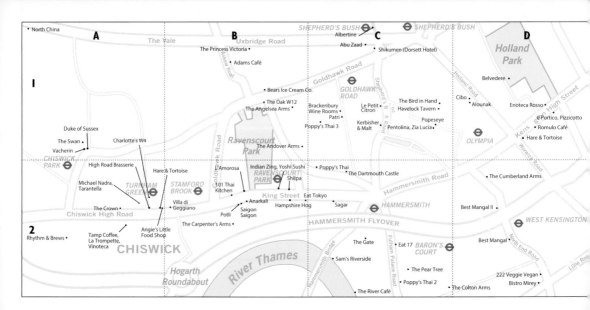

CHISWICK

Holland Park

OLYMPIA

HAMMERSMITH

WEST KENSINGTON

BARON'S COURT

Ravenscourt Park

Hogarth Roundabout

River Thames

North China · Albertine · Abu Zaad · Shikumen (Dorsett Hotel) · The Princess Victoria · Adams Café · Belvedere · Bears Ice Cream Co. · Cibo · Alounak · Enoteca Rosso · The Oak W12 · Brackenbury Wine Rooms · Le Petit Citron · The Bird in Hand · Il Portico, Pizzicotto · The Angelsea Arms · Patri · Havelock Tavern · Romulo Café · Poppy's Thai 3 · Kerbisher & Malt · Popeseye · Hare & Tortoise · Duke of Sussex · Pentolina, Zia Lucia · The Swan · Charlotte's W4 · The Andover Arms · Vacherin · Hare & Tortoise · High Road Brasserie · L'Amorosa · Indian Zing, Yoshi Sushi · Poppy's Thai · The Cumberland Arms · Michael Nadra, Tarantella · 101 Thai Kitchen · Shilpa · The Dartmouth Castle · The Crown · Villa di Geggiano · Anarkali · Eat Tokyo · Best Mangal II · Potli · Hampshire Hog · Sagar · The Carpenter's Arms · Saigon Saigon · Angie's Little Food Shop · Tamp Coffee, La Trompette, Vinoteca · Rhythm & Brews · The Gate · Eat 17 · Best Mangal · Sam's Riverside · The Pear Tree · 222 Veggie Vegan · Poppy's Thai 2 · Bistro Mirey · The Colton Arms · The River Café

170

MAP 9 – HAMPSTEAD, CAMDEN TOWN & ISLINGTON

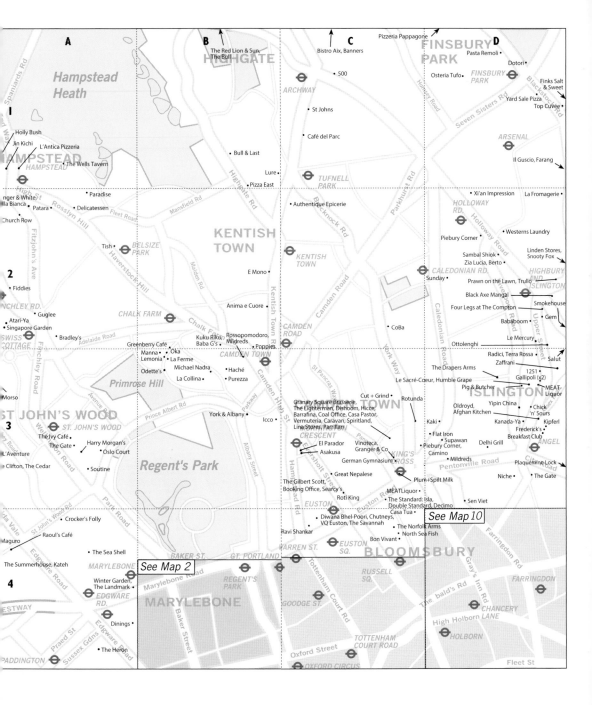

MAP 10 – THE CITY

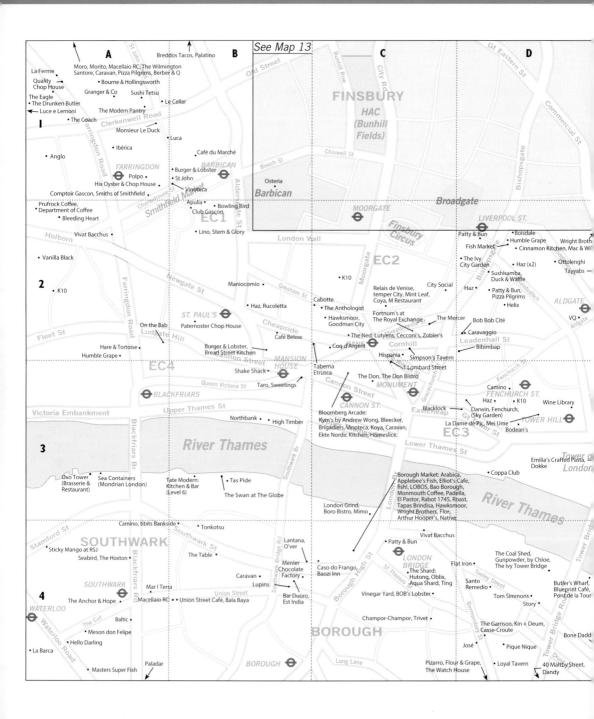

A   B   See Map 13   C   D

La Ferme
Quality Chop House
The Eagle
The Drunken Butler
Luce e Lemoni
Moro, Morito, Macellaio RC, The Wilmington
Santore, Caravan, Pizza Pilgrims, Berber & Q
Bourne & Hollingsworth
Granger & Co
Sushi Tetsu
The Modern Pantry
The Coach
Monsieur Le Duck
Ibérica
Anglo

Breddos Tacos, Palatino

Le Cellar

Luca

Café du Marché

FINSBURY
HAC
(Bunhill
Fields)

Chiswell St

FARRINGDON
Hix Oyster & Chop House
Comptoir Gascon, Smiths of Smithfield
Prufrock Coffee,
Department of Coffee
Bleeding Heart
Vivat Bacchus
Vanilla Black
K10
On the Bab
Hare & Tortoise
Humble Grape

Polpo
Burger & Lobster
St John
Vinoteca
Apulia
Club Gascon
Lino, Stem & Glory

BARBICAN

Beech St

Osteria

Barbican

Broadgate

MOORGATE

LIVERPOOL ST.

Bowling Bird

London Wall

EC1

Holborn

Newgate St

Maniocomio
Gresham St

Cabotte
Haz, Rucoletta

ST. PAUL'S
Paternoster Chop House
Ludgate Hill
Fleet St

Burger & Lobster,
Bread Street Kitchen
Cheapside
Café Below
Coq d'Argent

The Anthologist
Hawksmoor,
Goodman City
Fortnum's at
The Royal Exchange

EC2

Finsbury
Circus

K10

Relais de Venise,
temper City, Mint Leaf,
Coya, M Restaurant

City Social

Cornhill

The Ned: Lutyens, Cecconi's, Zobler's
The Mercer
Bob Bob Cité
Caravaggio
Bibimbap

Patty & Bun
Fish Market
The Ivy
City Garden

Haz

Boisdale
Humble Grape
Cinnamon Kitchen, Mac & Wi
Wright Broth

Sushisamba,
Duck & Waffle
Haz (x2)
Ottolenghi
Tayyabs
Patty & Bun,
Pizza Pilgrims
Helix

ALDGATE
VQ

Leadenhall St

EC4
Shake Shack
Taro, Sweetings

BLACKFRIARS

Victoria Embankment

Queen Victoria St

Upper Thames St

MANSION
HOUSE

Hispania
Taberna
Etrusca
1 Lombard Street
The Don, The Don Bistro

MONUMENT

Simpson's Tavern

CANNON ST.

Camino
Haz
Darwin, Fenchurch,
(Sky Garden)
La Dame de Pic, Mei Ume
Bodean's

FENCHURCH ST.
K10
Wine Library

TOWER HILL

Cannon Street
Eastcheap

Blacklock

EC3

Northbank
High Timber

River Thames

Southwark Br

Bloomberg Arcade:
Kym's by Andrew Wong, Bleecker,
Brigadiers, Vinoteca, Koya, Caravan,
Ekte Nordic Kitchen, Homeslice,

Lower Thames St

Emilia's Crafted Pasta,
Dokke
London

Oxo Tower
(Brasserie &
Restaurant)
Sea Containers
(Mondrian London)
Tate Modern:
Kitchen & Bar
(Level 6)
Tas Pide
The Swan at The Globe

Borough Market: Arabica,
Applebee's Fish, Elliot's;Cafe,
fish!, LOBOS, Bao Borough,
Monmouth Coffee, Padella,
El Pastor, Rabot 1745, Roast,
Tapas Brindisa, Hawksmoor,
Wright Brothers, Flor,
Arthur Hooper's, Native

London Grind,
Boro Bistro, Mimo

Coppa Club

River Thames

Camino, tibits Bankside
Sticky Mango at RSJ
Seabird, The Hoxton

SOUTHWARK
Southwark St
The Table

Tonkotsu

Lantana,
O'ver

Patty & Bun

Vivat Bacchus

The Coal Shed,
Gunpowder, by Chloe,
The Ivy Tower Bridge

SOUTHWARK
Mar I Terra
The Anchor & Hope

WATERLOO

Caravan
Lupins
Union Street
Macellaio RC   Union Street Café, Bala Baya

Menier
Chocolate
Factory

Bar Duoro,
Est India

Caso do Frango,
Baozi Inn

LONDON
BRIDGE

The Shard:
Hutong, Oblix,
Aqua Shard, Ting

Flat Iron

Santo
Remedio
Tom Simmons
Story

Butler's Wharf,
Blueprint Café,
Pont de la Tour

Baltic
Meson don Felipe
Hello Darling
La Barca
Masters Super Fish

Paladar

Vinegar Yard, BOB's Lobster

Champor-Champor, Trivet

BOROUGH

Long Lane

José

The Garrison, Kin + Deum,
Casse-Croute

Pique Nique

Bone Dadd

Pizarro, Flour & Grape,
The Watch House

Loyal Tavern

40 Maltby Street,
Dandy

MAP 11 – SOUTH LONDON (& FULHAM)

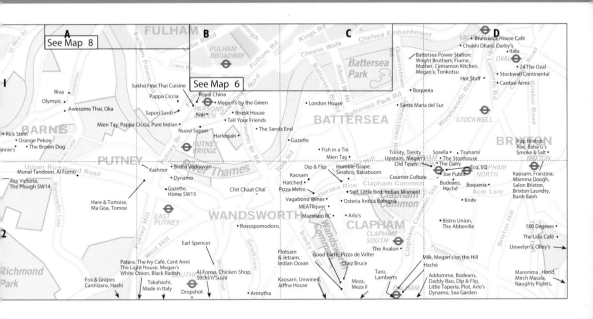

MAP 12 – EAST END & DOCKLANDS

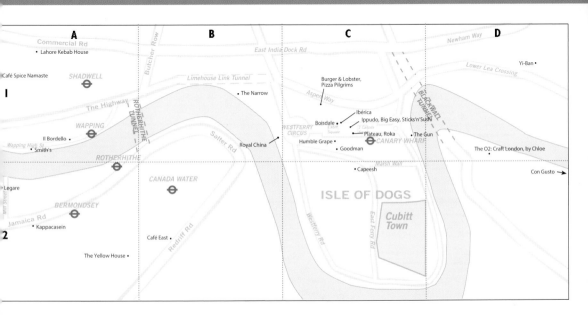

MAP 13 – SHOREDITCH & BETHNAL GREEN

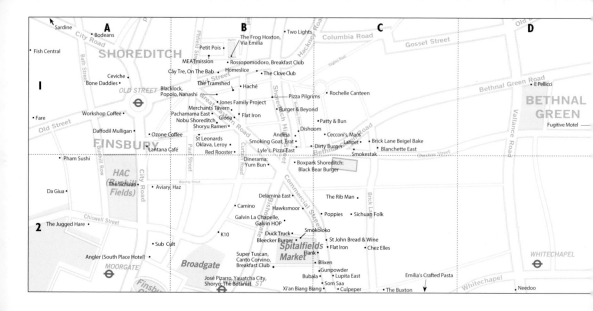

MAP 14 – EAST LONDON

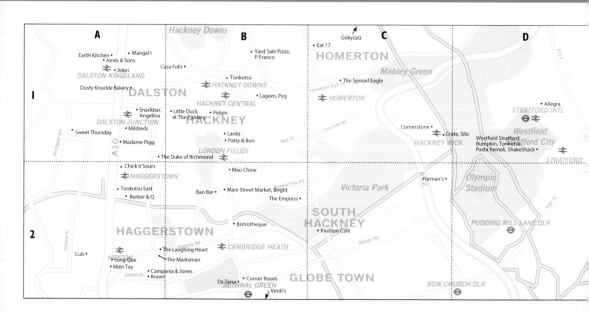

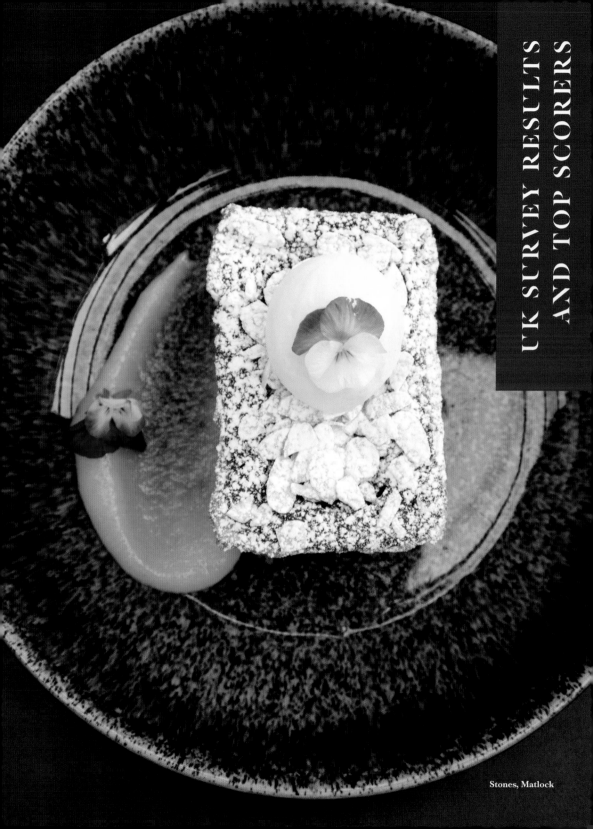

Stones, Matlock

Aulis at L'Enclume, Cartmel

Belmond Le Manoir aux Quat' Saisons, Great Milton

The Barn at Moor Hall, Aughton

Gidleigh Park, Chagford

Waterside Inn, Bray

TOP SCORERS

All restaurants whose food ratings is **5**; plus restaurants whose formula price is £60+ with a food rating of **4**.

£260	Aulis at L'Enclume *(Cartmel)*	4 4 4
£240	Belmond Le Manoir aux Quat' Saisons *(Great Milton)*	5 5 5
£210	Raby Hunt *(Summerhouse)*	4 3 2
£190	Gidleigh Park *(Chagford)*	4 4 4
£180	L'Enclume *(Cartmel)*	5 5 5
	Lympstone Manor *(Exmouth)*	5 4 3
£170	Restaurant Nathan Outlaw *(Port Isaac)*	5 5 4
	Ynyshir Restaurant and Rooms *(Eglwys Fach)*	4 4 3
£160	Mana *(Manchester)*	5 5 4
	Midsummer House *(Cambridge)*	4 4 3
£150	Andrew Fairlie, Gleneagles Hotel *(Auchterarder)*	5 4 4
	The Dining Room, Whatley Manor *(Easton Grey)*	4 3 3
£140	Waterside Inn *(Bray)*	5 4 5
	Casamia *(Bristol)*	5 5 4
£130	Restaurant Sat Bains *(Nottingham)*	5 4 3
	The Wilderness *(Birmingham)*	5 4 3
£120	House of Tides *(Newcastle upon Tyne)*	5 4 4
	Restaurant Martin Wishart *(Edinburgh)*	5 4 4
	The Three Chimneys *(Dunvegan)*	5 4 4
	Sonder *(Edinburgh)*	5 3 4
	Carters of Moseley *(Birmingham)*	5 5 3
	Sosban And The Old Butcher's *(Menai Bridge)*	5 4 3
	Black Swan *(Oldstead)*	4 3 4
£110	Hambleton Hall *(Hambleton)*	5 5 5
	Morston Hall *(Morston)*	5 4 5
	Number One, Balmoral Hotel *(Edinburgh)*	5 4 4
	Adam Reid at The French *(Manchester)*	5 4 3
	Fraiche *(Oxton)*	5 4 3
	Lake Road Kitchen *(Ambleside)*	5 4 3
	Le Cochon Aveugle *(York)*	5 4 3
	The Whitebrook, Restaurant with Rooms *(Whitebrook)*	5 4 3
	The Latymer, Pennyhill Park Hotel *(Bagshot)*	4 3 5
	Where The Light Gets In *(Stockport)*	4 5 4
	Kinloch Lodge *(Sleat)*	4 4 4

£100	Moor Hall *(Aughton)*	5 5 5
	Winteringham Fields *(Winteringham)*	5 4 4
	Roski *(Liverpool)*	5 4 3
	Cotto *(Cambridge)*	5 4 2
	Lucknam Park *(Colerne)*	4 4 5
	Gravetye Manor *(East Grinstead)*	4 3 5
	21212 *(Edinburgh)*	4 4 4
	Pale Hall Hotel Restaurant *(Bala)*	4 4 4
	Simon Radley, The Chester Grosvenor *(Chester)*	4 4 4
	The Burlington at The Devonshire Arms *(Skipton)*	4 4 4
	The Samling *(Windermere)*	4 4 4
	The Kitchin *(Edinburgh)*	4 3 4
	The Orangery, Rockliffe Hall *(Darlington)*	4 3 4
	Grain *(Colchester)*	4 4 3
	The Pass Restaurant, South Lodge Hotel *(Lower Beeding)*	4 4 3
£90	Paris House *(Woburn)*	5 4 5
	Adam's *(Birmingham)*	5 5 4
	Northcote *(Langho)*	5 5 4
	Artichoke *(Amersham)*	5 4 4
	Coombeshead Farm *(Lewannick)*	5 4 4
	Longueville Manor *(Jersey)*	5 4 4
	Monachyle Mhor *(Balquhidder)*	5 4 4
	Restaurant MCR *(Manchester)*	5 4 4
	Sorrel *(Dorking)*	5 4 4
	The Box Tree *(Ilkley)*	5 4 4
	Hipping Hall *(Kirkby Lonsdale)*	5 3 4
	Little Fish Market *(Brighton)*	5 5 3
	Lumière *(Cheltenham)*	5 5 3
	Purnells *(Birmingham)*	5 5 3
	Etch *(Brighton)*	5 4 3
	Orwells *(Shiplake)*	5 4 3
	Tyddyn Llan *(Llandrillo)*	4 4 5
	Buckland Manor *(Buckland)*	4 4 4
	L'Ortolan *(Shinfield)*	4 4 4
	The Forest Side *(Grasmere)*	4 4 4
	The Harrow at Little Bedwyn *(Marlborough)*	4 4 4
	The Oxford Blue *(Old Windsor)*	4 4 4
	Bybrook Restaurant, Manor House Hotel *(Castle Combe)*	4 3 4
	Simpsons *(Birmingham)*	4 3 4
	The Art School *(Liverpool)*	4 3 4
	The Pompadour *(Edinburgh)*	4 3 4
	Fischers at Baslow Hall *(Baslow)*	4 4 3
	The Boat Inn *(Lichfield)*	4 3 3
	Bohemia *(Jersey)*	4 4 2
	Le Champignon Sauvage *(Cheltenham)*	4 4 2
£80	The Neptune *(Old Hunstanton)*	5 5 4
	Mash Inn *(Radnage)*	5 4 4

Ox (Belfast)	5	4	4
Paul Ainsworth at No. 6 (Padstow)	5	4	4
Stark (Broadstairs)	5	4	4
The Cellar (Anstruther)	5	4	4
The Clock House (Ripley)	5	4	4
The Peat Inn (Cupar)	5	4	4
Condita (Edinburgh)	5	4	3
HRiSHi, Gilpin Lodge (Windermere)	5	4	3
John's House (Mountsorrel)	5	4	3
The Blackbird (Bagnor)	5	4	3
The Old Inn (Drewsteignton)	5	4	3
The Small Holding (Goudhurst)	5	4	3
Harry's Place (Great Gonerby)	5	5	2
Aizle (Edinburgh)	5	4	2
Dan Moon at The Gainsborough (Bath)	4	4	4
Llangoed Hall (Llyswen)	4	3	4
The Torridon Restaurant (Annat)	4	3	4
Restaurant James Sommerin (Penarth)	4	2	4
Restaurant Tristan (Horsham)	4	4	3
Lawns Restaurant, Thornton Hall Hotel & Spa (Thornton Hough)	4	3	3
Yorebridge House (Bainbridge)	4	3	3
The Olive Tree, Queensberry Hotel (Bath)	4	3	2

£70

The Fordwich Arms (Fordwich)	5	5	4
Roger Hickman's (Norwich)	5	4	4
Vanderlyle (Cambridge)	5	4	4
Freemasons at Wiswell (Wiswell)	5	3	4
Timberyard (Edinburgh)	5	3	4
Henry & Joe's (Newbury)	5	5	3
Restaurant Twenty Two (Cambridge)	5	4	3
The Moorcock Inn (Sowerby Bridge)	5	4	3
The Muddlers Club (Belfast)	5	4	3
Folium (Birmingham)	5	3	3
Joro (Sheffield)	5	3	3
Haywards Restaurant (Epping)	5	4	2
Menu Gordon Jones (Bath)	5	4	2
Thomas Carr @ The Olive Room (Ilfracombe)	5	4	2
Askham Hall (Penrith)	4	4	5
Jew's House Restaurant (Lincoln)	4	4	4
Little Barwick House (Barwick)	4	4	4
The Barn at Moor Hall (Aughton)	4	4	4
The Hind's Head (Bray)	4	4	4
Thompson's (Newport)	4	4	4
Peace & Loaf (Newcastle upon Tyne)	4	3	4
The Sir Charles Napier (Chinnor)	4	3	4
The Star Inn (Harome)	4	3	4
The Hare Inn Restaurant (Scawton)	4	5	3
Edinburgh Food Studio (Edinburgh)	4	4	3
La Chouette (Dinton)	4	4	3
Le Roi Fou (Edinburgh)	4	4	3
Stovell's (Chobham)	4	4	3
The Tudor Room, Great Fosters Hotel (Egham)	4	4	3
Whites (Beverley)	4	4	3
Old Downton Lodge (Ludlow)	4	3	3
Red Lion Freehouse (East Chisenbury)	4	3	3

Sindhu (Marlow)	4	3	3
The Mason's Arms (Knowstone)	4	3	3
The Walnut Tree (Llandewi Skirrid)	4	3	3
Thompson (St Albans)	4	3	3
Restaurant Roots (Southbourne)	4	2	3
The Salutation Hotel & Restaurant (Sandwich)	4	2	3
Arras (York)	4	4	2
The Honours (Edinburgh)	4	4	2
5 North Street (Winchcombe)	4	3	2

£60

The Sportsman (Seasalter)	5	5	5
Beach House (Oxwich)	5	4	4
Braidwoods (Dalry)	5	4	4
Loch Bay Restaurant (Stein)	5	4	4
Maison Bleue (Bury St Edmunds)	5	4	4
Mono (Edinburgh)	5	4	4
Pensons at Netherwood Estate (Stoke Bliss)	5	4	4
The Seahorse (Dartmouth)	5	4	4
The Angel Inn (Hetton)	5	3	4
Bulrush (Bristol)	5	4	3
Cail Bruich (Glasgow)	5	4	3
Gilpin Spice, Gilpin Lodge (Windermere)	5	4	3
Prithvi (Cheltenham)	5	4	3
The Cross at Kenilworth (Kenilworth)	5	4	3
The French Table (Surbiton)	5	4	3
Verveine Fishmarket Restaurant (Milford-on-Sea)	5	4	3
Old Stamp House (Ambleside)	5	3	3
The Vanilla Pod (Marlow)	5	3	3
Pierhouse Hotel (Port Appin)	4	4	5
Penrose Kitchen (Truro)	4	3	5
Ubiquitous Chip (Glasgow)	4	3	5
Rafters (Sheffield)	4	5	4
Douneside House (Tarland)	4	4	4
Gingerman (Brighton)	4	4	4
Hawksmoor (Manchester)	4	4	4
Jeremy's at Borde Hill (Haywards Heath)	4	4	4
Nutter's (Norden)	4	4	4
Randall & Aubin (Manchester)	4	4	4
Restaurant 27 (Southsea)	4	4	4
Sticky Walnut (Chester)	4	4	4
The Dining Room (Edinburgh)	4	4	4
The Pipe & Glass (Beverley)	4	4	4
The Royal Oak (Littlefield Green)	4	4	4
The Woodspeen (Newbury)	4	4	4
Wild Flor (Brighton)	4	4	4
Friends (Pinner)	4	3	4
The Black Rat (Winchester)	4	3	4
The Lookout by Gardener's Cottage (Edinburgh)	4	3	4
Buoy & Oyster (Margate)	4	4	3
Coast (Saundersfoot)	4	4	3
Docket No.33 (Whitchurch)	4	4	3
Drakes of Brighton (Brighton)	4	4	3
Isaac@ (Brighton)	4	4	3
La Rock (Sandiacre)	4	4	3
Mark Jordan at the Beach (Jersey)	4	4	3
New Chapter (Edinburgh)	4	4	3
The Castle Bow Restaurant (Taunton)	4	4	3

The Park - by Adam Jackson (York)		4 4 3
The Patricia (Newcastle upon Tyne)		4 4 3
The Royal Oak (Shipston-on-Stour)		4 4 3
The West House Restaurant with Rooms (Biddenden)		4 4 3
Vero Gusto (Sheffield)		4 4 3
Wedgwood (Edinburgh)		4 4 3
Whits of Walmer (Deal)		4 4 3
Eric's (Huddersfield)		4 3 3
Etive (Oban)		4 3 3
Henry's Restaurant (Bath)		4 3 3
Kota (Porthleven)		4 3 3
Ondine (Edinburgh)		4 3 3
Pompette (Oxford)		4 3 3
The Beehive (White Waltham)		4 3 3
The Newport (Newport On Tay)		4 3 3
The Salt Room (Brighton)		4 3 3
The Set (Brighton)		4 3 3
The Wensleydale Heifer (West Witton)		4 3 3
Venture In (Ombersley)		4 3 3
Bottle and Glass Inn (Binfield Heath)		4 4 2
Gamba (Glasgow)		4 4 2
The Flitch of Bacon (Dunmow)		4 2 2
£50	Inver Restaurant (Strachur)	5 5 4
	Roots (York)	5 5 4
	Hawksmoor (Edinburgh)	5 4 4
	Mr Pook's Kitchen (Castle Douglas)	5 4 4
	Opheem (Birmingham)	5 4 4
	Outlaw's Fish Kitchen (Port Isaac)	5 4 4
	Pea Porridge (Bury St Edmunds)	5 4 4
	Crab House Cafe (Weymouth)	5 3 4
	Levanter (Ramsbottom)	5 3 4
	1921 Angel Hill (Bury St Edmunds)	5 4 3
	Angela's (Margate)	5 4 3
	Ben's Cornish Kitchen (Marazion)	5 4 3
	Elderflower (Lymington)	5 4 3
	Jon & Fernanda's (Auchterarder)	5 4 3
	Noble (Holywood)	5 4 3
	North Street Bistro (Burnham Market)	5 4 3
	Ox and Finch (Glasgow)	5 4 3
	Prawn on the Lawn (Padstow)	5 4 3
	Rock Salt (Plymouth)	5 4 3
	Terre Ã Terre (Brighton)	5 4 3
	Wilson's (Bristol)	5 4 3
	Eusebi Deli (Glasgow)	5 3 3
	Indian Essence (Petts Wood)	5 3 3
	Sugo (Altrincham)	5 3 3
	The Coach House Norbury (Bishops Castle)	5 3 3
	The Shore (Penzance)	5 3 3
	Purslane (Edinburgh)	5 3 2
	Sugo (Manchester)	5 3 2
£40	Harborne Kitchen (Birmingham)	5 4 4
	The Parkers Arms (Newton-in-Bowland)	5 4 4
	Riverford Field Kitchen (Buckfastleigh)	5 3 4
	Applecross Inn (Applecross)	5 2 4

No 7 Fish Bistro (Torquay)		5 4 3
Paco Tapas (Bristol)		5 4 3
Skosh (York)		5 4 3
Wheelers Oyster Bar (Whitstable)		5 4 3
White Swan at Fence (Fence)		5 4 3
Saffron Summer (Chessington)		5 3 3
Ebi Sushi (Derby)		5 4 2
Mrs Miller's (Culgaith)		5 4 2
Tharavadu (Leeds)		5 4 2
Butley Orford Oysterage (Orford)		5 3 2
Xian (Orpington)		5 3 2
£30	Alchemilla (Nottingham)	5 3 4
	Trongs (Ipswich)	5 5 3
	Magpie Café (Whitby)	5 4 3
	Oli's Thai (Oxford)	5 4 3
	Alchemilla (Glasgow)	5 3 3
	Rudys Pizza (Manchester)	5 3 3
	The Company Shed (West Mersea)	5 2 3
	Clam & Cork (Doncaster)	5 4 2
	Colmans (South Shields)	5 4 2
	McDermotts Fish & Chips (Croydon)	5 4 2
£25	Paesano Pizza (Glasgow)	5 3 3
	The Oban Fish & Chip Shop (Oban)	5 3 2
£20	Julie's Kopitiam (Glasgow)	5 3 2
£15	Burger Brothers (Brighton)	5 4 2

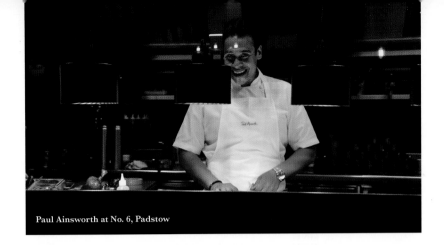

Paul Ainsworth at No. 6, Padstow

Heaney's, Cardiff

The Forest Side, Grasmere

The Angel Inn, Hetton

UK DIRECTORY

ABERAERON, CEREDIGION   4–3C

HARBOURMASTER £54   3 3 4

2 QUAY PDE SA46 0BT 01545 570755

"The absolutely stunning setting" – "at the end of the quay with a lovely view over the harbour in picturesque Aberaeron" – "is matched by above-average food and excellent friendly service" at this brasserie-with-rooms. Local seafood is the mainstay of the menu. / www.harbour-master.com; @hmaberaeron; No Amex; Take bookings all week via phone and/or online.

ABERDEEN, ABERDEENSHIRE   9–2D

SILVER DARLING £56   3 4 4

NORTH PIER HOUSE, POCRA QUAY AB11 5DQ 01224 576229

"Innovative seafood" coupled with "fantastic views from an upper floor over Aberdeen harbour watching the boats go by" are the key ingredients of what is often tipped as "the best restaurant in the city". The dining room is a glass-encased roof-top addition to the old customs building – hence the sensational sea vistas. / www.thesilverdarling.co.uk; @darling_silver; Mon-Sat 8.30 pm, Sun 8 pm; children: +16 after 8 pm.

ABERDOUR, FIFE   9–4C

ROOM WITH A VIEW, FORTH VIEW HOTEL £42   3 4 3

HAWKCRAIG POINT KY3 0TZ 01383 860 402

"An 'interesting' journey – you either drive down a 45-degree slope, or tackle the short walk from the village of Aberdour" – is the prelude to a visit to this tucked-away fish restaurant, with a "fabulous view across the Forth to Edinburgh". "The husband-and-wife team cook/serve up interesting ways of cooking with fish" – "intriguing, light combinations of flavours" – alongside a "basic but adequate wine list". / www.roomwithaviewrestaurant.co.uk/; Mon-Sat 10 pm, Sun 9 pm; Take bookings all week via phone and/or online.

ABERGAVENNY, MONMOUTHSHIRE 2–1A

THE ANGEL HOTEL £48   3 3 3

15 CROSS ST NP7 5EN 01873 857121

Close to the English border, this attractive hotel – sibling to the well-known Walnut Tree – is a versatile spot, where chef Wesley Hammond turns out high-quality food (including a "great choice for veggies and vegans") in the clubby Foxhunter Bar or more

elegant Oak Room. Head to the Wedgwood Room for their "amazing", award-winning afternoon teas featuring "exceptional gluten-free savoury pastries" ("liked the doggy bag for the extra cakes later"). / www.angelabergavenny.com/dining; @lovetheangel; Sun-Thu 11 pm, Fri & Sat 11.30 pm.

THE HARDWICK £54   3 2 3

OLD RAGLAN RD NP7 9AA 01873 854220

"High-quality ingredients, deftly cooked to delicious effect" is typical of the high praise often evident in feedback on Stephen Terry's restaurant-with-rooms: a stop-off, en route to the Brecon Beacons. More sceptical reports, though, feel the food is merely "OK", and there's also the odd gripe about "chaotic" service. / www.thehardwick.co.uk; @The_Hardwick; No Amex.

ABERYSTWYTH, POWYS   4–3C

GWESTY CYMRU £49   3 3 3

19 MARINE TERRACE SY23 2AZ 01970 612252

"Proper Welsh cooking" takes pride of place at this "really enjoyable" restaurant in a smart little hotel overlooking Cardigan Bay from the Victorian promenade. / www.gwestycymru.com; @gwestyc; Mon, Wed-Sun, Tue 9 pm; No Amex; children: 5+.

PYSGOTY £46   4 4 3

THE HARBOUR, SOUTH PROMENADE SY23 01970 624611

"A revelation – what a wonderful find": this "ridiculously small" seaside restaurant ("book well ahead") delivers "excellent fresh fish". "I felt I was on the coast in New England…" rather than in converted toilets (albeit glam Art Deco ones) in mid-Wales! / pysgoty.co.uk/home/; @Pysgoty; Wed-Sat 9 pm, Tue 2.30 pm; No bookings.

ULTRACOMIDA £37   4 3 2

31 PIER ST SY23 2LN 01970 630686

It's "a bit cramped", admittedly – you sit on stools or round a shared table in the rear of a deli – "but the food is always reliably good and the wine list both excellent and reasonably priced" at this tapas joint and Spanish wine merchant. The owners have two other outposts: a Narberth spin-off, and Basque café/bar, Curado Bar, in Cardiff city-centre. / www.ultracomida.com; @ultracomida; Take bookings all week via phone and/or online.

ALBOURNE, WEST SUSSEX   3–4A

THE GINGER FOX £56   3 3 3

MUDDLESWOOD ROAD BN6 9EA 01273 857 888

"Exceptional food and service" in a "lovely location in the Sussex countryside" – this "great rural pub" "stands out within an accomplished group" – Brighton's Gingerman operation. / thegingerfox.com/; @GingerfoxDish; Sun, Mon 9 pm, Tue-Thu 2.30 pm, Fri & Sat 10 pm; Take bookings all week via phone and/or online.

ALDEBURGH, SUFFOLK   3–1D

ALDEBURGH FISH AND CHIPS £15   3 2 2

226 HIGH ST IP15 5DB 01728 454685

Over 50 years in the business, the Cooney family's beloved local institution is "still of a high standard" by common accord, and you'll still have to wait patiently in line for its superior fish 'n' chips – then protect them from the gulls on the beach (if you'd rather sit, try their spin-off, the Golden Galleon). / www.aldeburghfishandchips.co.uk; @aldefishnchips; Tue, Wed 2 pm, Thu-Sat 9 pm, Sun 2.30 pm; Cash only.

THE LIGHTHOUSE £45   3 4 4

77 HIGH STREET IP15 5AU 01728 453377

"Long a local favourite" with a big and loyal fan club, which "maintains standards effortlessly, or so it seems" – be it for the "terrific fish" ("from boat to restaurant in 100 metres") or the "always-great welcome" from owner Sam Hayes, "an absolute master of the art". / www.lighthouserestaurant.co.uk; @AldeLighthouse; Take bookings all week via phone and/or online.

REGATTA £38   3 3 2

171 HIGH STREET IP15 5AN 01728 452011

"Been there for years" and "always reliable" – a "cheery" sea-view restaurant where "the fish is always fresh and beautifully cooked"; "when in Aldeburgh go there!" / www.regattaaldeburgh.com; @AldeburghR; Wed-Fri 8 pm, Sat 8.30 pm, Sun 6.30 pm; Take bookings all week via phone and/or online.

SEA SPICE, THE WHITE LION HOTEL £52   3 3 2

MARKET CROSS PLACE IP15 5BU 01728 451 800

"Seriously good Indian food in an otherwise limited area" is the hallmark of this three-year-old – the first ever subcontinental in these parts. On the downside the contemporary-hotel setting doesn't add much: "it's just not Indian enough!" / seaspice.co.uk; @SeaSpiceAlde; Take bookings all week via phone and/or online.

ALDFORD, CHESHIRE   5–3A

THE GROSVENOR ARMS   £42 3 4 4
CHESTER RD CH3 6HJ 01244 620228

The original branch of the now-sprawling Brunning & Price empire – an imposing and very character Victorian pub owned by the Duke of Westminster on the edge of his Cheshire estate. Besides pleasant gardens, it has "everything that you'd want in a country gastro pub: a good menu and wine, great bar stocked with special gins and guest beers, but most of all a fab atmosphere". / www.grosvenorarms-aldford.co.uk; @GrosArmsAldford; Mon-Sat 9.30 pm, Sun 9 pm; No Amex; Take bookings all week via phone and/or online.

ALKHAM, KENT   3–3D

THE MARQUIS   £50 3 3 4
ALKHAM VALLEY RD CT15 7DF 01304 873410

"Great food" and "a beautiful setting with stunning views" are found at this 200-year-old former village pub, converted 10 years ago into a boutique hotel. Now under the same ownership as the nearby Hythe Imperial, it has reverted to its original name – and "the food and service have got better". / www.themarquisatalkham.co.uk; @marquisalkham; Mon-Fri 9 pm, Sat 9.30 pm, Sun 5 pm; children: 8+ at D.

ALRESFORD, HAMPSHIRE   2–3D

CARACOLI   £22 3 3 2
15 BROAD ST SO24 9AR 01962 738730

An "excellent coffee and cake selection" (verging on the "healthy" side), supported by "interesting" snack lunches underpin the allure of this town-centre café – and "in summer you can retire to the courtyard or sit out front to watch the world go by"; "unfortunately the branch in Winchester has now closed". / www.caracoli.co.uk; @Caracolistore; Mon-Sun 5 pm; No Amex; No bookings.

ALSTONEFIELD, DERBYSHIRE   5–3C

THE GEORGE   £51 3 4 4
DE6 2FX 01335 310205

A new regime has done nothing to dent the charms of this "fantastic gastropub in the middle of nowhere" – it's "just as beautiful as ever" while still being "a real pub", and "the food, always good, has got better if anything". Top Tip – "they now run good value set-menu tasting evenings; huge credit to anywhere brave enough to run an all-vegetarian evening in the beautiful depths of rural Staffordshire!" / www.thegeorgeatalstonefield.com; @Thegeorge1710; Mon-Fri 8.30 pm, Sat 9 pm,

Sun 4 pm; Take bookings all week via phone and/or online.

ALTRINCHAM, GREATER MANCHESTER   5–2B

ALTRINCHAM MARKET   £35 4 3 4
GREENWOOD STREET WA14 1SA

A rare beacon amid tales of the death of the high street, the "vibrant" regeneration of Alti's covered market – which dates back to 1290, and has been reinvented in recent years by local lad Nick Johnson – is heartening indeed. It's now "a very exciting place to eat", with a "massive choice of different food" under its Victorian roof – including noted sourdough pizza purveyors Honest Crust, who occupy Market House, the new market's centrepiece. / www.altrinchammarket.co.uk; @altrinchammkt; Tue, Fri-Sun 4 pm, Thu 3 pm.

HONEST CRUST, MARKET HOUSE ALTRINCHAM   £18 4 3 3
26 MARKET STREET WA14 1PF

This sourdough pizzeria at "buzzy" Altrincham Market (and now Manchester's Mackie Mayor) is by well-earned repute "significantly better than anything else in the area". It's "still belting out some amazing food, but don't get too pricey guys – remember, it's a marketplace and we sit on hard benches". / @Honest_Crust; Tue-Sat 9.30 pm, Sun 5.30 pm.

SUGO   £50 5 3 3
22 SHAW'S RD, ALTRINCHAM WA14 1QU 0161 929 7706

"Home-style Italian dishes that are plentiful and utterly delicious" ("they regularly change the menu") have carved a major name for this small, family-run venture near Altrincham Market, which also benefits from its "chatty and informed served". "They have not got too big and arrogant – even though they have expanded to two sites now they have kept the quality, and I know as it's two minutes from my house!" / www.sugopastakitchen.co.uk; @Sugo_Pasta; Tue-Sat 11 pm, Sun 9 pm; Take bookings all week via phone and/or online.

ALVESTON, WARWICKSHIRE   2–1C

BARASET BARN, 40   £52 3 4 4
PIMLICO LANE CV37 01789 295510

This "exceptional" venue – part 200-year-old country pub, part contemporary brasserie – has an eclectic menu of global dishes and is "always super value for a leisurely lunch". It "now has very good rooms for overnighters". / www.barasetbarn.co.uk; Mon-Sat 11 pm, Sun 5 pm; lunch noon - 2.30 pm, dinner 6.30 pm - 9.30 pm; 1; *; children: Highchair, Portions,.

AMBERLEY, WEST SUSSEX   3–4A

AMBERLEY CASTLE   £97 3 2 5
BN18 9LT 01798 831992

"A romantic and beautiful ruined medieval castle" – dating from the era when bishops required a fortified residence – makes a "stunning location" for a Brownsword hotel. The food served in the first-floor dining room, under a 12th-century barrel-vaulted ceiling, is generally felt to be "pretty good", although it (and the service) is "not quite up to a level that matches the setting". "Afternoon tea served on tiered cake stands in the gardens (complete with a noisy white peacock named Bob)" is a very safe bet. / www.amberleycastle.co.uk; @amberleycastle; No jeans; Booking max 6 may apply; children: 8.

AMBLE, NORTHUMBERLAND   8–1B

THE OLD BOAT HOUSE AMBLE   £49 3 4 2
LEAZES STREET NE65 0AA 01665 711 232

In summer 2019, this once-basic fish hut reopened after a £210K refurb doubling capacity and adding a new café/bar (the owners cut ties to two other venues on the Northumberland coast but kept on the neighbouring Fish Shack). Its formula has by-and-large remained intact, namely a "great setting by the harbour in Amble with river views towards a distant Warkworth Castle" ("sometimes a seal appears") and the provision of "generous seafood platters" from an "excellent selection" (and also sourdough pizza). / boathousefoodgroup.co.uk/theoldboathouse-amble.html; @TOBHFoodGroup.

AMBLESIDE, CUMBRIA   7–3D

DRUNKEN DUCK   £67 3 3 4
BARNGATES LA22 0NG 01539 436347

"Idyllic Lake District country pub" – "the food is great too, and surprisingly inventive" at this perennially popular inn on an old Lakeland sheep-driving route, run by owner Steph Barton for 42 years. / www.drunkenduckinn.co.uk; @DrunkenDuckInn; Mon-Sat 11 pm, Sun 10.30 pm; No Amex; Booking evening only.

FELLINI'S   £48 3 4 3
CHURCH ST LA22 0BT 01539 432487

This "buzzing vegetarian restaurant" attached to a cinema features an "interesting menu and high-quality cooking". "Fairly old-school Italian in feel", it has been "inventively adapted" to be meat-free and – given its location – is "the perfect pre-film venue". / www.fellinisambleside.com; No Amex; Take bookings all week via phone and/or online.

The Barn at Moor Hall, Aughton

LAKE ROAD KITCHEN
£117 5 4 3

3 SUSSEX HOUSE, LAKE ROAD LA22 0AD
015394 22012

"The aesthetic is paired back and the entire focus is on the food" at this small venue headed up by ex-Noma chef James Cross, which – in keeping with a modern Scandi vibe – has "an intensely local and seasonal focus, with a strong emphasis on foraged ingredients": "exceptional dishes... and you get to chat to the chef while he works on it". "There is a real passion about the produce (we listened to James explain the provenance of the beef for about ten minutes to our neighbouring table)", so "the meal is both interesting as well as absolutely delicious." / www.lakeroadkitchen.co.uk; @LakeRoadKitchen.

OLD STAMP HOUSE **£61** 5 3 3

CHURCH ST LA22 0BU 01539432775

"An outstanding meal showcasing the very best Cumbrian ingredients can offer" is to be found at Ryan Blackburn's "quirky, small and friendly" operation, which occupies an old cellar with "modern décor" and thick, painted stone walls in the town centre. Choose from the à la carte, or there's a seven-course tasting menu for £70. / www.oldstamphouse.com; @oldstamphouse; No Amex; Take bookings all week via phone and/or online.

ZEFFIRELLI'S
£42 3 3 3

COMPSTON RD LA22 9AD 01539 433845

"Get a movie and dinner deal, which is great value for money" at this veteran veggie and pizza-stop attached to a cinema and jazz bar, "in the heart of the town". "Meat eaters need not worry, you will be charmed and seduced by the interesting menu" – and the ambience, which is "not hippy or with 'vibes'", thankfully, but actually rather "sophisticated". / www.zeffirellis.com; @ZeffsFellinis; No Amex; Take bookings all week via phone and/or online.

AMERSHAM, BUCKINGHAMSHIRE 3–2A

ARTICHOKE
£93 5 4 4

9 MARKET SQ HP7 0DF 01494 726611

"Laurie Gear and his team never fail to delight in this French fine dining establishment": a "small and intimate" haunt in a characterful part of Old Amersham, where "the best seats are downstairs by the kitchen where you can witness how hard and skilfully the chefs work".

For many years now, the opinion has been widespread that its "impeccable" cuisine and "warm and welcoming" service were being inexplicably ignored by the tyre men, but in October 2019 Michelin finally gave way and gave it its long overdue recognition with the award of a star. / www.artichokerestaurant.co.uk; @ArtichokeChef; Tue-Thu 11 pm, Fri & Sat 11.30 pm; No shorts; Take bookings all week via phone and/or online.

GILBEY'S
£63 3 4 3

1 MARKET SQ HP7 0DF 01494 727242

Part of the Gilbey gin empire, a "very cosy", "slightly old-fashioned" bistro "with lots of nooks and crannies", making it a "great choice for a catch-up with a friend or a romantic meal". The menu offers "lots of English specialities" and – while critics say it's "no longer seems to rise above average" – even they say it is rarely less than "solid". The "interesting wine list" includes bottles from nearby Hambleden. / www.gilbeygroup.com/restaurants/gilbeys-old; @GilbeysAmersham; Mon-Sat 9.30 pm, Sun 3 pm; Take bookings all week via phone and/or online.

THE GREEN GROCER
£12 3 3 3

91 HIGH STREET HP7 0DT 01494 724581

"A great little café" in Amersham Old Town, with "fabulous salads and cakes" and other dishes that are "authentic and well-priced". It recently went vegan, and is one of a small group with three outlets locally (you can still eat meat at 15 The Broadway) and there's also a branch in Gerrards Cross. / www.thegrocershops.co.uk; @thegrocershops; Mon-Fri 4.30 pm, Sat 5 pm, Sun 4 pm; No bookings.

HAWKYNS BY ATUL KOCHHAR, THE CROWN INN
£56 3 2 4

16 HIGH STREET HP7 0DH 01494 721541

"Outstanding food in a lovely setting" again wins praise for celeb chef, Atul Kochhar's Indian take on British food at this ancient, beamed Elizabethan coaching inn on the high street (which was one of the locations in 'Four Weddings'). But once again, its ratings are held back by the odd reporter who's unconvinced: "after several attempts wanting to believe, we've concluded it falls short overall". / www.hawkynsrestaurant.co.uk;

@Hawkynsamersham; Mon-Thu 9.30 pm, Fri & Sat 10 pm, Sun 1.

TOM YUM
£41 3 3 4

101 SYCAMORE ROAD HP6 5EJ
01494 728806

Homely Thai delivering solid, good-value noodles and curries – and which is thus well-loved locally, so you'll need to book ahead for Friday and Saturday nights. / www.tomyum.net; Tue-Thu 10 pm, Fri & Sat 10.30 pm, Sun 9 pm.

ANGMERING, WEST SUSSEX 3–4A

THE LAMB AT ANGMERING
£42 3 4 4

THE SQUARE BN16 4EQ 01903 774300

"Wonderful fresh produce and stunning dishes" win fans for the Norbury family's "fantastic gastropub", handily placed for the South Downs and coast, and there's a "great atmosphere" to boot. / www.thelamb-angmering.com; @LambAngmering; Mon-Sat 9 pm, Sun 8 pm; Take bookings all week via phone and/or online.

ANNAT, WESTER ROSS 9–2B

THE TORRIDON RESTAURANT
£87 4 3 4

THE TORRIDON IV22 2EY 01445 791242

"Very good Highlands food is served in a grand ex-hunting lodge" – and supervised for the past few years by Ross Stovold, previously of Isle of Eriska – at this refined albeit off-piste lochside hotel, and there's an "excellent gin and whisky bar to relax in afterwards"... hoorah! / www.thetorridon.com; @thetorridon.

ANSTRUTHER, FIFE 9–4D

ANSTRUTHER FISH BAR
£28 4 3 2

42-44 SHORE ST KY10 3AQ
01333 310518

Famous for its "top-quality", "astoundingly cheap" fish – this harbourside chippy has been owned since 2003 by Robert Smith, from a local fishing dynasty that stretches back to the 1700s. He set up supply specialist Argofish in nearby St Monans with his wife Alison in 1980. / www.anstrutherfishbar.co.uk; @ansterfishbar; Sun-Thu 9 pm, Fri & Sat 9.30 pm; No Amex; No bookings.

THE CELLAR
£88 5 4 4

24 EAST GREEN KY10 3AA
01333 310378

"Excellent Scottish produce (much foraged) is creatively presented" and showcased through nine-course tasting menus at Billy Boyter's subtly luxurious outfit, a former smokehouse. Bearer of a Michelin star since 2015, it previously served as a fish restaurant for three decades under Scottish food icon Peter Jukes. / www.thecellaranstruther.co.uk; @The_Cellar_Fife; Thu-Sun, Wed 9 pm; No Amex; Take bookings all week via phone and/or online.

APPLECROSS, HIGHLAND 9–2B

APPLECROSS INN £40 5 2 4

SHORE ST IV54 8LR 01520 744262

"A mission to get to but oh so worth it!" – this "busy inn on the Applecross peninsula" is "an amazing spot with a great welcome" serving "dependably top-notch fresh seafood". Our worst report this year? – "the food's perfectly acceptable and the service and atmosphere made for an enjoyable evening". / www.applecross.uk.com/inn/; No Amex; May need 6+ to book.

APPLEDORE, DEVON 1–2C

THE COFFEE CABIN £16 3 3 3

22 THE QUAY EX39 1QS 01237 475843

"Amazing breakfasts" and "great coffee" (plus cream teas, cakes and crab sarnies) win fans for this small and smartly decorated five-year-old operation, which overlooks an estuary, and is "always good while in Exeter". / No Amex; No bookings.

ARLINGHAM, GLOUCESTERSHIRE 2–2B

THE OLD PASSAGE INN £62 3 3 3

PASSAGE ROAD GL2 7JR 01452 740547

"A long way from anywhere but worth the drive", say fans of this "lovely spot beside the River Severn", who hail its "reliably good cooking of high-end fish". Its ratings were dragged down this year, though, by a couple of mediocre reports: "after several visits I'm baffled by the sky-high score: the food is pleasant enough but not exceptional". / www.theoldpassage.com; @OldPassageInn; Tue-Sat 9 pm, Sun 2.30 pm; Take bookings all week via phone and/or online.

ARMSCOTE, WARWICKSHIRE 2–1C

THE FUZZY DUCK £54 3 3 3

ILMINGTON ROAD CV37 8DD 01608 682293

Cosy, modernised pub, near Stratford-upon-Avon, that's consistently well-rated (if on limited feedback) for its 'Contemporary Cotswolds' cooking: traditional pub dishes like chicken 'n' chips, complemented by slightly more ambitious seasonal items. / www.fuzzyduckarmscote.com; @fuzzyduckpub; Tue-Thu 9 pm, Fri & Sat 9.30 pm, Sun 5 pm; No Amex; Booking max 10 may apply.

ARUNDEL, WEST SUSSEX 3–4A

MOTTE AND BAILEY CAFE £34 3 4 3

BN18 9AG 01903883813

Chef-owner Michael Etherington's "relaxed and good-value" operation has a double identity – by day, it's a café serving breakfast, brunch and toasties, but on Wednesday to Saturday nights it looks south to serve "great tapas" and other Spanish/Moroccan dishes. /

www.motteandbaileycafe.com/; Mon & Tue, Sun 5 pm, Wed & Thu 10.30 pm, Fri & Sat 11 pm.

THE PARSONS TABLE £59 4 4 3

2 & 8 CASTLE MEWS, TARRANT STREET BN18 9DG 01903 883477

"Deservedly popular, local chef-run place in the middle of town" – a simply but effectively decorated operation run by Lee & Liz Parsons, which won very consistently high ratings all-round this year for its "thoughtful and relaxed service" and "wonderful" cooking that "makes brilliant use of local produce" to create "fantastic flavours": "the bread alone tells you the place knows its stuff!" A meal comes "at a realistic price" too. / theparsonstable.co.uk; @tpt_restaurant; Take bookings all week via phone and/or online.

THE TOWN HOUSE £49 4 4 3

65 HIGH STREET BN18 9AJ 01903 883 847

"Utterly consistent and fabulous" – chef Lee Williams "never lets you down" at his restaurant-with-rooms in a Regency house looking out over Arundel Castle. Its talking-point is the "beautiful gold-leaf ceiling" in the dining room, which was made in Florence in the sixteenth century. Local seafood is the star on a "delicious" menu ("especially when fresh lobster is in season"). / www.thetownhouse.co.uk; @thetownhousearundel; Wed-Sat 9.30 pm; No Amex; Take bookings all week via phone and/or online.

ASCOT, BERKSHIRE 3–3A

RESTAURANT COWORTH PARK, COWORTH PARK £99 3 4 4

BLACKNEST RD SL5 7SE 01344 876 600

For "elegance and luxury", the Dorchester Collection's spectacular mansion near Ascot, on a sizeable estate complete with polo pitches, certainly fits the bill. When it comes to the dining room and Adam Smith's "first class cuisine", "it's maybe not the most creative, and would struggle to top the value-for-money rankings, but is certainly a safe bet for a fabulous meal". / www.dorchestercollection.com; @CoworthParkUK; Fri & Sat, Wed & Thu 9.30 pm, Sun 2.30 pm; No trainers; Take bookings all week via phone and/or online; children: 9.

ASCOTT-UNDER-WYCHWOOD, OXFORDSHIRE 2–1C

THE SWAN INN £62

4 SHIPTON ROAD OX7 6AY 01993 832332

The co-founders of group that owns The Chequers in the Cotswolds and The Talbot in North Yorkshire have added another historic venue to their collection: a 16th century inn, complete with a 100-cover dining room and seven guest bedrooms. No survey feedback as yet, but press reviews are very upbeat. / www.countrycreatures.com/the-swan; Tue-Sat 9 pm, Sun 2.30 pm.

ASENBY, NORTH YORKSHIRE 8–4C

CRAB & LOBSTER £69 3 4 4

DISHFORTH RD YO7 3QL 01845 577286

Just off Junction 49 of the A1(M), and with a fish-centric menu belying its landlocked locale, this "eclectic" thatched pub has been doing the business for years: the flag-festooned interior is "cosy and intimate", while it is "gorgeous in summer to sit outside" – and it's also well worth an overnight to enjoy the "quirky" themed bedrooms. Its rating for food is becoming ever-more borderline though, with critics saying that "while prices soar ever skywards, quality doesn't". Overall though, this is still assessed (just) as "good pub cooking" with "wonderful seafood". / www.crabandlobster.co.uk; @crabandlobster.

ASHBOURNE, DERBYSHIRE 5–3C

JACK RABBITS £22 3 3 3

10 SAINT JOHN STREET DE6 1GH 01335 342285

Good all-round, if limited, feedback on this trendily designed 'café and kitchen' at the back of The Greenman complex, which serves an all-day 'brunch & lunch' menu. / www.jackrabbitskitchen.com/locations/ashbourne; @_JackRabbits; Mon-Fri 5 pm, Sun 4 pm, Sat 6 pm.

ASHTON-UNDER-LYNE, GREATER MANCHESTER 5–2B

LILY'S INDIAN VEGETARIAN CUISINE £21 3 3 3

85 OLDHAM RD OL6 7DF 0161 339 4774

As of January 2019, this unexpected gem – a café in the shadow of a vast IKEA – has "moved to new premises across the road from the terrific Indian wholesale supermarket they are connected to, and everything is a bit snazzier", bedecked in bells, kite spools and bangles. These days "you could go for supper rather than just catching a quick nosh" and while "the range of sweetmeats looks bigger, everything else is the same" (namely a huge variety of veggie fare "from street snacks to fusion to more familiar Indian meals"… "hoorah!"). / lilys-indian-vegetarian-cusine.business.site; Wed & Thu 8 pm, Fri & Sat 9 pm, Mon 2 pm, Sun 5 pm.

AUCHTERARDER, PERTH AND KINROSS 9–3C

ANDREW FAIRLIE, GLENEAGLES HOTEL £156 5 4 4

PH3 1NF 01764 694267

"Andrew is no longer with us… but the tasting menu is still perfect!!". Head chef Stephen McLaughlin and general manager Dale Desbury have given their now-departed boss the best send-off they could by maintaining the "truly amazing food of the highest order and faultless service at this beautiful restaurant, whose incredibly good 'Degustation' menu is an excellent exhibition of skill and creativity" (eight courses for £155). The Michelin man agrees and in October 2019, maintained this famous (if windowless) chamber as Scotland's only two star. (For afternoon tea, "there's a lovely new venue in the Glendevon Room – where the G8 summit meeting was held many years ago – beautiful views across to the Ochil Hills. Expensive but delicious!") / www.andrewfairlie.co.uk; @AndrewFairlie1; children: 12+.

JON & FERNANDA'S £55 5 4 3

34 HIGH STREET PH3 1DB 01764 662442

"Just down the road from Gleneagles Hotel" – and in its own mould "able to hold its own" with its more famous neighbour (where the proprietors used to work) – this "cosy" high street restaurant "ticks all the right boxes", and is a big hit with all those who comment on it. It helps that it's a fraction of the cost: the table d'hote menu offers a choice of six dishes for each course: two courses for £29.95 and three for £37.95. / www.jonandfernandas.co.uk; No Amex; children: 10+.

THE BARN AT MOOR HALL £75 4 4 4

PRESCOT RD L39 6RT 01695 572511

The "wonderfully converted barn" has an "excellent design" – complete with heavy beams and bare brick walls – and is the casual dining, "sister outlet to the two-Michelin star main operation Moor Hall". It's not quite as exceptional as the main dining room, but its "inventive" take on posh-brasserie dishes (roasted turbot, 40-day aged sirloin, soft herb gnocchi…) is very highly rated in all reports, and you can still "expect quite a glitzy crowd at the weekend, with live piano on Friday and Saturday nights". / moorhall.com/the-barn/about/; @restmoorhall; Wed-Sun 11 pm.

MOOR HALL £100 5 5 5

PRESCOT RD L39 6RT 01695 572511

"A beautiful building in a beautiful setting with a beautiful kitchen garden, and beautiful food… just fabulous!". Mark Birchall's "outstanding" two-year-old occupies a "mediaeval manor house adapted for the 21st Century" to the north of Liverpool and is "excellent in every way, from start to finish". After the approach down a long driveway, "an ancient stone arch holds a door of ecclesiastical proportions, leading onto to a panelled reception. From here you are led into the lounge (proper fire places, more intricate carvings and Latin inscriptions) to be served from the charcuterie bar as you wait (black pudding parcel; smoked eel basket with edible flowers; cod's roe mousse with caviar and the most beautiful crackers ever…)". Once in the dining room proper (a very modern space), "everything coming out of the kitchen is exquisite": thoroughly "deserving of its two stars" and oft-compared with L'Enclume (even if the food's "not quite as cheffy and messed about with"). "What Mark Birchall can do with carrots and turnips is just remarkable"

and "symptomatic of the ethos: fresh, simple ingredients taken to a higher level by the chef's craft". "Integral to the experience" is a "front of house team fully on the top of its game; and a team of sommeliers passionate about their work, all dedicated to creating the ultimate dining experience". It doesn't all take itself too seriously either: the vibe is "fun and convivial". Top Tip – don't miss a jaunt to the cheese room, and take a stroll around the gardens if you have the time. / www.moorhall.com; @restmoorhall; Wed-Sun 9 pm; Take bookings all week via phone and/or online; children: 12.

THE TRADDOCK HOTEL £39 4 3 4

LA2 8BY 01524 251224

'A comfortable 'Dales' hotel with exceptional comfort, eminently suitable for exploring and close to the three peaks and cave systems and the Ingleton Waterfalls'. Feedback on its (recently extended) dining room suggests a meal here is very good value. / www.thetraddock.co.uk; @thetraddock; Mon-Sun 8.30 pm.

RIVER COTTAGE CANTEEN £53

TRINITY SQUARE EX13 5AN 01297 631 715

Hugh Fearnley-Whittingstall's TV tie-in kitchen – serving sharing boards and veggie tapas alongside more conventional starters and mains – is celebrating its twentieth anniversary, but feedback on it has seldom matched the hype, and is too limited this year for a rating. Such as we have says it's OK value, but variable in performance. / www.rivercottage.net; @rivercottage; Mon-Sat 9 pm, Sun 4 pm.

HARTWELL HOUSE £83 2 2 5

OXFORD ROAD HP17 8NR 01296 747444

"A fantastic location with old-fashioned silver service" – this Grade I-listed Jacobean/Georgian mansion is the perfect place to experience stately-home hospitality, complete with waiters in tailcoats. The food may "not be quite up to the mark for the price", but all feedback is basically upbeat, with no harsh critiques for the dining room's standards. Now leased to the National Trust and celebrating its 30th anniversary as a grand spa hotel, Hartwell hosted exiled King Louis XVIII after the French Revolution. / www.hartwell-house.com/wine-and-dine/; @hartwellhouse; No jeans; children: 4+.

THE BLACKBIRD £85 5 4 3

HIGH STREET RG20 8AQ 01635 40005

"An absolutely stand-out meal in what initially looked like a bland country pub" – Dom Robinson's CV is a glittering one and his "top-level cuisine" at this cosy pub "in a charming

village location" has won it a big culinary reputation. There is a 'Dégustation' menu, but – as with the à la carte and menu du jour – the cuisine is very grounded and un-poncy: "I dream about the butternut squash soup, which sounds so ordinary but is SO much more!" / www.theblackbird.co.uk; @BlackbirdBagnor; Tue-Thu 11 pm, Fri & Sat midnight; Take bookings all week via phone and/or online.

THE LATYMER, PENNYHILL PARK HOTEL £110 4 3 5

LONDON ROAD GU19 5EU 01276 486150

"Everything is hushed and cushioned, dark and cocooning" in the luxurious and much-accoladed dining room of this well-known country house hotel. Matt Worswick offers both five-course (£69) and seven-course (£95) tasting menu options which are rated good or better in all reports. The experience is "VERY expensive" and there is a sceptical view that "while the food is pretty good, it's the place that is just lovely". / www.exclusive.co.uk; @PennyHillPark; Wed-Sun 9 pm; Booking max 8 may apply; children: 12+.

YOREBRIDGE HOUSE £89 4 3 3

DL8 3EE 019 6965 2060

This "fabulous hotel with food to match" has developed into a North Yorkshire boutique powerhouse since Dave & Charlotte Reilly opened it in a converted Wensleydale school in 2007. Chef Dan Shotton has led the kitchen for six years, and a new kitchen garden was added in 2017, followed by a basement tasting room in the old cellar last year. / www.yorebridgehouse.co.uk; @yorebridgehouse.

PIEDANIELS £53 4 4 2

BATH ST DE45 1BX 01629 812687

"Still here (since 1994) and busier than ever", this "family-run home to solid if unshowy French cooking" "stands out for excellence in an otherwise mediocre region". "Great value", too – "particularly mid week & lunch". / www.piedaniels-restaurant.com.

PALE HALL HOTEL RESTAURANT £100 4 4 4

PALE ESTATE, LLANDDERFEL, LL23 7PS 01678 530 285

There's no overlooking the gorgeous setting of this lavish Dee valley Relais & Chateaux country house hotel – owned by the UK's richest man, the Duke of Westminster in the 1950s and 1960s. Chef Gareth Stevenson produces a short à la carte alongside some "exceptional" tasting menus (five courses for £70, eight for £90), all with very careful sourcing and "the impression of impressive

Adam's, New Oxford House, Birmingham

attention to detail". / www.palehall.co.uk; @palehallhotel; No trainers; Take bookings all week via phone and/or online.

BALQUHIDDER, PERTH AND KINROSS 9–3C

MONACHYLE MHOR £91 544

FK19 8PQ 01877 384622

A perennial favourite since the 1990s – Tom Lewis's boutique hotel near Rob Roy's grave in the Trossachs wins rave reviews for the "delightful" meals prepared with produce grown or foraged on the property. Marysia Paszkowska heads the kitchen, while the Lewises also run a local bakery, a motel and a chippie under the Mhor banner. / www.mhor.net; @MhorHotel.

BAMBURGH, NORTHUMBERLAND 8–1B

THE POTTED LOBSTER £47 333

3 LUCKER ROAD NE69 7BS 01668 214088

"A real winner" – "fresh fish" benefit from "careful treatment" and customers from "smiling staff" at Richard Sim's appealing seafood bistro in "a beautiful location in the shadows of Bamburgh Castle". / www. thepottedlobsterbamburgh.co.uk.

BAMPTON, DEVON 1–4A

THE SWAN £42 323

STATION RD EX16 9NG 01398 332 248

"Steaks are particularly praiseworthy" at chef-owners Donna & Paul Berry's "attractive pub in a pretty Devon village", which serves "a good menu, with tasty, well-presented dishes". They strengthened the team last year with the addition of head chef Olivier Certain, ahead of the opening of a second venue, Spelt, a neighbourhood sharing-plates outfit in Bampton's old village bakery in September 2019. / www.theswan.co; @theswanbampton; Mon-Thu 11 pm, Fri & Sat midnight, Sun 10.30 pm; Take bookings all week via phone and/or online.

BARLOW, CAMBRIDGESHIRE 3–1B

THE THREE HILLS, BARTLOW £59 323

DEAN ROAD CB21 4PW 01223 890500

"Smart gastropub" – twenty minutes drive from Cambridge – a seventeenth century building extensively refurbished in late 2017 and with six bedrooms: "good food, with nice combinations and they do a great – and I mean great! – Sunday lunch" ("the black treacle roasted beef is an especially delicious option"). A gripe? – "staff are pleasant and friendly" but a couple of reports suggest that "more training is needed". / www.thethreehills.co.uk; @TheThreeHills2.

BARNET, HERTFORDSHIRE 3–2B

SAVORO £51 332

206 HIGH STREET EN5 5SZ 020 8449 9888

A former boathouse on the high street, turned hotel and dining room, that remains of note for its "delightful food impeccably served in a not overcrowded restaurant" – though you'll need to book ahead on weekends, when they also lay on a "good Sunday lunch". / www.savoro.co.uk; Mon-Sat 10 pm, Sun 7 pm; Take bookings all week via phone and/or online.

BARNSLEY, GLOUCESTERSHIRE 2–2C

BARNSLEY HOUSE £59 223

GL7 5EE 01285 740000

Owned by the same folk as The Village Pub, just across the road, this "very fancy" boutique hotel turns out "solid cooking with bold flavours", and uses "a lot of produce straight from the garden". / www.barnsleyhouse.com; @Barnsley_House; Sun, Thu-Sat 5 pm; children: 14+ after 7.30 pm.

BARRASFORD, NORTHUMBERLAND 8–2A

BARRASFORD ARMS £44 343

NE48 4AA 01434 681237

Michael and Victoria Eames took over this pub overlooking Houghton Castle in 2017 and their "very friendly" team contribute to its "relaxed atmosphere", serving traditional-ish, very affordable cooking that's consistently well-rated: "we locals want to support them because they are doing a good job". / www.barrasfordarms.co.uk; @barrasfordarms; Tue-Sat 8.30 pm, Sun 2.30 pm; No Amex; children: 18 + in bar after 9.30pm.

BARTON-ON-SEA, HAMPSHIRE 2–4C

PEBBLE BEACH £60 444

MARINE DRIVE BH25 7DZ 01425 627777

"Lovely views from the terrace over to the Needles" ("try to grab an outside table on those rare sunny days") elevate a trip to this "light, airy establishment", and by all accounts Karl Wiggins – who took the helm from longtime chef Pierre Chevillard in 2018 – has more than risen to the challenge, with "delicious",

"straightforward" seafood remaining a particular highlight. / www.pebblebeach-uk.com; @pebblebeachUK; Mon-Sat 11 pm, Sun 10.30 pm; Take bookings all week via phone and/or online.

BARWICK, SOMERSET 2–3B

LITTLE BARWICK HOUSE £78 444

BA22 9TD 01935 423902

With its "classical cooking in a traditional and comfortable country-house setting", Emma & Tim Ford's "welcoming and elegant" restaurant-with-rooms near Yeovil is "difficult to beat" – and it "always seems even better than last time". "Emma keeps a very good wine list, full of interesting things at reasonable prices – and there's always a nice selection of pinot noir from the New World". / www.littlebarwickhouse.co.uk; @LittleBarwick; Tue-Sat 9 pm; children: 5+.

BASLOW, DERBYSHIRE 5–2C

FISCHERS AT BASLOW HALL £98 443

CALVER RD DE45 1RR 01246 583259

"In the Peak District, close to Chatsworth House, Baslow Hall is much more modern than it at first appears up its little hill from the road and – surrounded by a vibrant kitchen garden – it provides a very romantic destination". Rupert Rowley, chef of 17 years' standing, upped sticks in early 2019, leaving sous chef James Payne to step into his shoes. Michelin removed their star on the back of the change, but we've maintained the survey's very good ratings, and will reassess next year if necessary. / www.fischers-baslowhall.co.uk; @FischersBaslow; No trainers; Take bookings all week via phone and/ or online.

BATH, SOMERSET 2–2B

ACORN VEGETARIAN KITCHEN £55 433

2 NORTH PARADE PASSAGE BA1 1NX 01225 446059

"Now fully vegan, but you wouldn't know – everything is so brilliantly created": this upmarket venture, super-cutely located in the city-centre, remains one of the UK's top non-meat destinations and is "worth a special trip" for its "exquisite" and "innovative" cooking (not least the "sublime" five-course tasting menu). / www.acornvegetariankitchen.co.uk; @AcornVegetarian.

THE BATH PRIORY £125 344

WESTON RD BA1 2XT 01225 331922

"Wonderful food is amply delivered" at this posh country house hotel, riding high after the arrival of Michael Nizzero in January 2017, and where "a tour of the ("fab") grounds by the head gardener following a meal makes for a perfect celebration and reason to return"; casual sister restaurant The Pantry is also worth a look. / www.thebathpriory.co.uk; @Thebathpriory; No jeans; children: 5+ L, 12+ D.

THE BECKFORD BOTTLE SHOP £56 223

5-8 SAVILLE ROW BA1 2QP 01225 809302

"A new addition to Bath's wine bar and food scene" (and sibling to the Tisbury original) which opened in late 2018, and serves "interesting small plates" – modern British fare, plus cheese and charcuterie – alongside a "great wine selection" including over 250 bottles. / www.beckfordbottleshop.com; Mon-Sat 11 pm, Sun 10.30 pm.

CHEZ DOMINIQUE £60 433

15 ARGYLE STREET BA2 4BQ 01225 463482

Just over Pulteney Bridge (and with views of the weir from one of the dining rooms), this three-year-old venue is attracting ever more support as a favourite amongst the locals: "wonderful French food in the heart of the city", with both steak and fish options being well-reviewed. / www.chezdominique.co.uk; @ChezDomBath; Wed-Fri 4 pm, Sat & Sun 5 pm.

THE CIRCUS £49 443

34 BROCK ST BA1 2LN 01225 466020

"In a tourist town littered with chain restaurants", this "lovely neighbourhood spot" is "one of the more reliable choices" locally (especially for fish) – and it's "surprisingly affordable given its prestigious location next to the famous circus". / www.thecircusrestaurant.co.uk; @CircusBath; Take bookings all week via phone and/or online; children: 7.

CLAYTON'S KITCHEN £65 333

15A GEORGE ST BA1 2EN 01225 585 100

This "busy restaurant in the heart of this Georgian city" provides an attractive "combination of great cooking with good flavours, smart presentation and a relaxed, easy-going atmosphere" (even if the setting is "a little tightly packed"). "Wasn't this the site of the legendary 'Hole in the Wall' run by George Perry-Smith from the 1950s? Clearly his spirit benevolently haunts this fine establishment!" / www.claytonskitchen.com/; @PorterBath; Sun-Thu 9.30 pm, Fri & Sat 10 pm; Take bookings all week via phone and/or online.

COLONNA & SMALLS £11 444

6 CHAPEL ROW BA1 1HN 07766 808067

"Caffeine for connoisseurs served by enthusiastic baristas" – this Queen's Square coffee shop from three-times UK barista champion Maxwell Colonna-Dashwood is a must for the aficionado. "Best coffee in Bath and so cool!" / www.colonnaandsmalls.co.uk; @colonnaandsmalls; Mon-Sat 5.30 pm, Sun 4 pm; No Amex; Booking max 6 may apply.

CORKAGE (WALCOT STREET) £40 333

132A WALCOT STREET BA1 5BG 01225 422577

The successor on the site that was, for yonks, Beaujolais may be "quirky" – a wine bar/bottle shop/small plates venue with no wine list and only minimal ingredient-led entries for food items (waiters explain the rest), but the results are "totally professional" and "always great"; "the garden is a nice place to relax in summer" – and there are also fans of the spin-off on Chapel Row. / corkagebath.com; @corkagebath; Tue-Fri 11 pm, Sat 11.30 pm; Take bookings all week via phone and/or online.

DAN MOON AT THE GAINSBOROUGH, THE GAINSBOROUGH HOTEL £84 444

BEAU STREET BA1 1QY 01225 358 888

"Dan Moon's cooking is consistently top-class as is the unstuffy service at this city-centre luxury hotel, converted in 2015 from a former hospital". Reporters all raved about the "very contemporary dining room" this year, be it for business or its "amazingly good value" midweek lunch deal – and its spa (the only one in Bath with access to the local thermal waters) is among the UK's finest. / www.thegainsboroughbathspa.co.uk/pages/dining.html; @GainsBathSpa; Mon-Sat 9.30 pm, Sun 10 pm; Take bookings all week via phone and/or online.

DOUGH £50 333

14-16 THE CORRIDOR BA1 5AP 01225 443686

The USP of this "very relaxed" yet "lively" Bath pizzeria is the ability to choose your dough as well as the topping on your pizza; not just regular and gluten-free, they also offer hemp, seaweed, black rice and turmeric bases, plus distinctly adventurous toppings ("who knew pistachios on a pizza could be so amazing?!"). A Bristol branch opened in March 2019. / www.doughpizzarestaurant.co.uk; @doughpizza_; Sun-Thu 10 pm, Fri & Sat 11 pm.

EIGHT £44 443

3 NORTH PARADE PASSAGE BA1 1NX 01225 724111

On one of the super-cutest pedestrian cut-throughs of this gorgeous town (near Sally Lunn's), this "lovely" new townhouse hotel (named for its eight bedrooms) opened in August 2018, and has been one of the most talked-about arrivals of the year in these parts. Chef Fred Lavault offers "very enjoyable modern cuisine in a small plates format" from a "simple 8-8-8 menu that's excellent and well-presented". / eightinbath.co.uk; Tue-Thu, Sun 9.30 pm, Fri & Sat 10 pm.

HENRY'S RESTAURANT £62 433

4 SAVILLE ROW BA1 2QP 01225 780055

Following on from Casanis (RIP) was no mean feat but, since taking over this Georgian townhouse venue in 2016, chef Henry Scott (ex-of Claude Bosi's now defunct Hibiscus) has more than risen to the challenge, and his French-led cuisine is uniformly well-rated. Top Tip – "they do an excellent (weekday) set lunch, not advertised on the website". / www.henrysrestaurantbath.com.

INDIAN TEMPTATION £33 422

09-10 HIGH STREET (CHEAP STREET) BA1 5AQ 01225464631

While readers might not agree that this abbey-view venture is the 'number one Indian in the UK' as its website claims – before promising 'a journey of infusion, innovation and illicit flavours' – it's nonetheless "different and well worth a visit", with "delicious veggie curries", dosas and so on (from a menu spanning North and South Indian specialities). / www.indiantemptation.com/; Mon-Fri 10.30 pm, Sat & Sun 11 pm; Take bookings all week via phone and/or online.

THE IVY BATH BRASSERIE £57 224

39 MILSOM ST BA1 1DS 01225 307 100

"There is something striking about the design" of this former NatWest bank: one of the more "elegant and spacious" spin-offs from the London celeb haunt. It's "food to a formula", of course ("best stick to old favourites, like steak 'n' chips") but all in all this two-year-old establishment is "a dependable example of the ever-expanding chain". / theivybathbrasserie.com; @ivybathbrass; Mon-Sun 12.30 am.

KOFFMANN & MR WHITE'S, ABBEY HOTEL £56 122

NORTH PARADE BA1 1LF 01225 461603

Despite its puzzling backing by two of the UK's most famous culinary names – Pierre Koffmann and Marco Pierre White – this casual, all-day hotel brasserie has utterly failed to make waves. Feedback is limited, and though not all is terrible ("really enjoyed this friendly recent opening"), sufficient is mediocre or even "appalling" that it's hard to believe there's much genuine input from either name over the door. / www.mpwrestaurants.co.uk/our-brands/koffmann-and-mr-whites/bath; @KW_Bath; Mon-Fri 10 pm, Sat 10.30 pm, Sun 9.30 pm.

MENU GORDON JONES £79 542

2 WELLSWAY BA2 3AQ 01225 480871

"Gordon Jones is expert in the flavours he can coax out of sometimes-modest ingredients" and his 'surprise', no-choice tasting menu of "well-coordinated and

Sugo, Altrincham

beautifully presented" dishes makes his "small but sweet" venue (in a somewhat "ordinary location", just outside the town centre) into "a foodie's temple of joy!". "Quirky but worth a detour". / www.menugordonjones.co.uk; @MenuGordonJones; Mon-Sat 11 pm, Sun 10.30 pm; No Amex.

NOYA'S KITCHEN £55 442

7 SAINT JAMES'S PARADE BA1 1UL 01225 684439

"What a find!" – "stunning Vietnamese food" with "really exciting and fresh flavours" is "introduced with charm, energy and humour by Noya herself" to make a meal here "a really special experience". Noya Pawlyn opened her supper club/cookery school/café in the heart of Bath two years ago; she left Vietnam aged seven and cooked for her family in a Hong Kong refugee camp. / www.noyaskitchen.co.uk; @NoyasKitchen; Tue, Thu 3 pm, Fri & Sat 10.30 pm, Wed 9 pm.

THE OLIVE TREE, QUEENSBERRY HOTEL £84 432

RUSSELL ST BA1 2QF 01225447928

Chris Cleghorn's "very classy and well-composed" cuisine maintains this well-known basement dining room as the town's most accolated foodie hotspot (it's the only restaurant in town with a Michelin star) and he offers a variety of menus (with vegan and vegetarian options) focused in the evenings on tasting menu formats, although – unusually – they allow you to pick out individual dishes from them if you don't want 'the full monty' and to pay per plate. The dining room itself is well-appointed and pleasant, but the constraints of this basement space are griped about even in the most favourable of reports ("tables close together…", "room is a bit spartan for food of this quality…"). / www.thequeensberry.co.uk; @OliveTreeBath; Tue-Sun 9 pm; No Amex; No shorts; Take bookings all week via phone and/or online.

THE PUMP ROOM £52 225

STALL ST BA1 1LZ 01225 444477

One of the UK's quintessential afternoon tea experiences: the Georgian chamber next to the famous Roman baths. There are better cakes, sarnies and cups of tea to be had elsewhere to be sure, but few in quite such stately and suitable surroundings. / www.searcys.co.uk; @searcysbars; Mon-Sun 9 pm; Booking weekdays only.

SCALLOP SHELL £46 323

22 MONMOUTH PLACE BA1 2AY 01225 420928

"Beautiful fresh fish cooked to perfection every time" hits the seafood sweet spot at this modern update of the traditional fish-and-chip restaurant, set across two floors in the town centre. The visual pun of a fresh fish display in an old Victorian bath dominates the dining room. / www.thescallopshell.co.uk;

@thescallopshell; Mon-Sat 9.30 pm, Sun 4 pm; No bookings.

THE WHITE HART INN £44 343

WIDCOMBE HILL BA2 6AA 01225 338053

"Bath's best-kept secret" – this gastropub-with-rooms (great value) and a sheltered garden wins consistently strong ratings for its hearty good food. / www.whitehartbath.co.uk; @WhiteHartBath; Mon & Tue 9 pm, Wed-Sat 10 pm, Sun 2.30 pm; No Amex.

BAUGHURST, HAMPSHIRE 2-3D

THE WELLINGTON ARMS £60 434

BAUGHURST RD RG26 5LP 0118 982 0110

"A wonderful find in the middle of nowhere" on the Hants-Berks border: chef Jason King and front-of-house Simon Page's "exceptional" venture "reflects the very best of an English pub" – "a beautifully simple and fresh set lunch represented rural hospitality at a very high level". / www.thewellingtonarms.com; @WellingtonArms; Mon-Thu 8.30 pm, Fri & Sat 9 pm, Sun 3 pm; No Amex.

BEACONSFIELD, BUCKINGHAMSHIRE 3-3A

THE CAPE GRAND CAFE & RESTAURANT £51 334

6A, BURKES PARADE HP9 1NN 01494 681137

This Saffa-owned café, handy for the station, is "a firm favourite", where the "freshly made quiches and salads are a highlight" – though they also serve the "best coffee in Beaconsfield" and reporters "like the varied South African dishes on the menu" too. / www.thecapeonline.com; @capegrandcafe; Sun-Wed 4 pm, Fri & Sat 11 pm, Thu 5 pm; No Amex; Take bookings all week via phone and/or online.

BEAMINSTER, DORSET 2-4B

BRASSICA £55 342

4 THE SQUARE DT8 3AS 01308 538 100

In a "nice location overlooking the village square", Cass Titcombe turns out "some unusual seasonal food, much foraged" at this indie café, praised for its "consistently high standards" (partner Louise is behind the stylish décor). / www.brassicarestaurant.co.uk; @brassica_food; Wed-Sat 9.30 pm, Sun 2.30 pm.

THE OLLEROD £64 323

3 PROUT HILL DT8 3AY 01308 862200

"So lucky to have such a venue locally!" Formerly, The Bridge House Hotel, this 13th century restaurant-with-rooms (and a secret walled garden) was taken over by Chris Staines (ex-Foliage) and Silvana Bandini (ex-The Pig hotels) in early 2018 and it's a spot that's "particularly delightful in summer with its large outside area and conservatory". Dorset produce

is used to realise a high quality, eclectic menu of small plates – "delicious", but the experience is sometimes let down by "staff lacking training". / theollerod.co.uk; @TheOllerod.

BEARSTED, KENT 3-3C

FISH ON THE GREEN £63 332

CHURCH LN ME14 4EJ 01622 738 300

"Definitely a go-to restaurant in this neck of the woods" – this "lovely" fish spot is "a small, cosy" room in the converted stable block of a coaching inn on the village green. Prices are reasonable, and the fish and seafood are "very good quality". / www.fishonthegreen.com; Tue-Thu 11 pm, Fri & Sat 11.30 pm, Sun 6.30 pm; No Amex.

BEAULIEU, HAMPSHIRE 2-4D

THE TERRACE, MONTAGU ARMS HOTEL £86 343

SO42 7ZL 01590 612324

"You won't be disappointed" by this pretty Arts and Crafts hotel which, say fans, remains "excellent in all areas". New chef Matthew Whitfield arrived in 2019 fresh from a stint at Eleven Madison Park in New York, and delivers "very good" cuisine, much sourced from the organic kitchen garden. / www.montaguarmshotel.co.uk; @themontaguarms; No jeans; children: 11+ D.

BECKENHAM, GREATER LONDON 3-3B

CHAI NAASTO £42 333

2 - 4 FAIRFIELD ROAD BR3 3LD 020 3750 0888

"Interesting small plate Indian food is served in a space laid out somewhat like a railway carriage" at this colourful tapas spot in the 'burbs. / www.chai-naasto.co.uk; @ChaiNaasto.

BEELEY, DERBYSHIRE 5-2C

DEVONSHIRE ARMS AT BEELEY, ON THE CHATSWORTH ESTATE £56 333

DEVONSHIRE SQUARE DE4 2NR 01629 733259

"Recently refitted", the contemporary interiors of this Chatsworth Estate pub is at odds with its period, stone-clad exterior. All reports say the food – which is served from breakfast onwards, from a range of menus – is of dependably high quality. Top Tip – attractive garden terrace for the summer months. / www.devonshirebeeley.co.uk; @DevArmsBeeley; Mon-Sun 9 pm; Take bookings all week via phone and/or online.

EDO £43 434

3 CAPITAL HOUSE, UNIT 2 UPPER QUEEN STREET BT1 6FB 028 9031 3054

A "bustling" operation from Johnny Elliott, who learnt the ropes with Gordon Ramsay and Gary Rhodes, before setting up on his own in the city-centre two years back; choose between "brilliant tapas" or meaty dishes cooked on the rare Bertha oven, which uses apple and pear wood for a smoky flavour. / www.edorestaurant.co.uk; @edobelfast.

HOWARD STREET £48 322

56 HOWARD STREET BT1 6PG 02890 248 362

Marty Murphy's well-liked, industrially styled brasserie (est 2013, and recently revamped, adding to its appeal) may not gain any particular raves, but is a decidedly "decent" spot by all accounts – and, even on a "very busy Saturday night, it still produces good solid cooking". / www.howardstbelfast.com; @howardstbelfast; Mon-Sat 9.30 pm.

JAMES STREET £59 333

19-21 JAMES STREET SOUTH BT2 7GA 028 95 600 700

Solidly good marks this year for Niall and Joanne McKenna's "understated and classy" venue, which last year incorporated its neighbouring 'bar and grill' and fine dining operations into a single more brasserie-style set-up, complete with cocktail bar: many of the dishes, including steaks, come from the charcoal grill. / www.jamesst.co.uk; @jamesSt_; Take bookings all week via phone and/or online.

MOURNE SEAFOOD BAR £53 333

34 - 36 BANK STREET BT1 1HL 028 9024 8544

"Good fish in down-to-earth surroundings" has won renown for this simple haunt (which has an offshoot in Dundrum) serving its own shellfish direct from the owners' beds. / www.mourneseafood.com; @msbbelfast; Mon-Thu 9.30 pm, Fri & Sat 10 pm, Sun 9 pm; No bookings at lunch.

THE MUDDLERS CLUB £75 543

1 WAREHOUSE LANE BT1 2DX 028 9031 3199

"Amazing food" and "prestige wines" are "delivered with a bit of 'craic'" at former Ox chef Gareth McCaughey's increasingly well-known open-kitchen venue in the Cathedral Quarter, named after a revolutionary secret society in the 1790s, which is celebrating its fifth year of operation this year. "The surprise tasting menu always feels like a real treat" and delivers "outstanding" results. / www.themuddlersclubbelfast.com; @TheMuddlersClub; Tue-Thu 9 pm, Fri & Sat 10 pm.

OX £86 544

1 OXFORD ST BT1 3LA 028 9031 4121

"The heavenly tasting menu is the way to go" at chef Stephen Toman's understated riverside operation, which focuses on seasonal food, and which in March 2019 the Irish Times hailed as the best on the island of Ireland. The adjacent Ox Cave is also "a thoroughly genuine wine bar", combining "excellent charcuterie and cheeses and a full selection of wine by the glass". / www.oxbelfast.com; @oxbelfast; Mon-Sat 11 pm, Sun 9 pm.

THE GATSBY £59 323

97 HIGH ST HP4 2DG 01442 870403

"Well cooked and presented meals" – and "good value", too – are served at this unusual venue in the foyer of the beautifully preserved 1930s Rex cinema. There's also a cocktail bar with live pianist – and a particularly strong lunch and pre-film menu. / www.thegatsby.net; @thegatsbyathome; Mon-Thu 11 pm, Fri & Sat 12.30 am, Sun 10.30 pm; No Amex; Booking max 10 may apply.

ZAZA £46 332

21-23 LOWER KINGS ROAD HP4 2AB 01442 767 055

"A loyal following – due no doubt to their discount programme for regulars – ensures that this Italian-style place (part of a solid local chain, and set around a 200-year-old olive tree) is buzzing every evening". "Birthday celebrators can make it overly noisy, but a visit in the summer to the little garden solves that issue!" / www.zaza.co.uk; @ZAZAItalian; Mon-Sat 10.30 pm, Sun 10 pm.

OGINO £54 443

1ST FLOOR BEAVER HOUSE, BUTCHER ROW HU17 0AA 01482 679500

"Authentic" cooking and presentation win consistent high ratings for Julian and Rieko Ogino-Stamford's "fantastic Japanese restaurant, which are few and far between in this neck of the woods!". The sushi, tempura and other dishes served in the first-floor dining room present "a value-for-money experience not to be missed". / ogino.co.uk/; @OGINOJAPANESE; Tue-Sun 11 pm; Take bookings all week via phone and/or online.

THE PIPE & GLASS £62 444

WEST END HU17 7PN 01430 810246

"It looks like a pretty country pub, but the quality of the cooking once inside is spot-on, putting many other Michelin starred restaurants to shame" – James & Kate Mackenzie's "classy" destination "perfectly situated, off the beaten track, deep in the countryside" of East Yorkshire is still a 'proper' inn, with open fire, real ale… but also superb food!": "not quite as inventive as some similar level establishments with exciting tasting menus, but good value

and very sound". / www.pipeandglass.co.uk; @pipeandglass; Tue-Sat 11 pm, Sun 4 pm; Take bookings all week via phone and/or online.

THE WESTWOOD RESTAURANT £65 333

NEW WALK HU17 7AE 01482 881999

"Excellent" modern brasserie in a listed Georgian courthouse that's prospered in its ten years under twins Michele & Matt Barker, who grew up in their parents' gastropubs. "The menu changes seasonally so you don't get bored" according to its strong local fan club, who feel it "always delivers". / www.thewestwood.co.uk; @The_Westwood; Tue-Sat 9.30 pm, Sun 3 pm; No Amex; Take bookings all week via phone and/or online.

WHITES £72 443

12-12A NORTH BAR WITHOUT HU17 7AB 01482 866121

For a decade, local boy John Robinson's restaurant-with-rooms has bought a touch of gastronomic excellence to this market town, turning out "excellent" tasting menus (four- or nine-course only, depending on which day you visit). Reporters this year appreciated the "good atmosphere" and "very personal touch" Robinson provides. / www.whitesrestaurant.co.uk; @Whitesbeverley; Tue-Sat 8 pm; No Amex; Take bookings all week via phone and/or online.

KENTISH HARE £61 343

95 BIDBOROUGH RIDGE TN3 0XB 01892 525709

"Well-executed food from the Tanner Bros of Saturday Kitchen fame" is the order of the day at this "very useful and enjoyable" gastropub… "worth a detour if in the area". / www.thekentishhare.com; @TheKentishHare; Tue-Sat 9.30 pm, Sun 3.30 pm.

THE WEST HOUSE RESTAURANT WITH ROOMS £68 443

28 HIGH ST TN27 8AH 01580 291341

In a tiny village, Graham Garrett and his family's sixteenth-century cottage (complete with wattle and daub) has, since it opened in 2002, won fame thanks to its "consistently excellent" cuisine: more offbeat items like ceviche or tacos are mixed in with much more "classic" fare on its taster menu, while the à la carte is all a little more conventional. With the summer departure of chef Tony Parkin, Michelin removed its long-held star this year, but we've maintained our survey rating for the time being. / www.thewesthouserestaurant.co.uk; @grahamgarrett; Wed-Sat 9.30 pm, Sun 2 pm; No Amex; Booking max 8 may apply.

The Muddlers Club, Belfast

THE OYSTER SHACK   £55   3 3 5

MILLBURN ORCHARD FARM, STAKES HILLS TQ7 4BE   01548 810876

It's not much more than a bright blue hut with a covered terrace, but the seafood on offer at this offbeat former oyster farm, set on the Avon estuary, has made it a known stop-off in this part of the world. Since the departure of longtime owner Chris Yandell in 2018, feedback on it has dwindled noticeably, but such as we have says it remains "consistently good", with added marks for being "dog, child and everything friendly!" / www.oystershack.co.uk; @theoystershack.

THE BILDESTON CROWN   £53   3 3 4

104 HIGH ST IP7 7EB   01449 740510

"Beautiful and atmospheric, with lovely décor" – Chis Haley's fifteenth century wood-framed inn pleases all who comment on it, with its "beautifully presented" local grub. "Was it worth the 125 mile round trip? Oh yes!" / www.thebildestoncrown.com; @BildestonCrown.

THE MAGIC MUSHROOM   £59   4 3 2

BARLEYLANDS ROAD CM11 2UD 01268 289963

"Clever, careful cuisine" earns consistently high ratings for Darren Bennett's "friendly" venue, popular for weddings and celebrations as well as smaller parties for more than 20 years. / www.magicmushroomrestaurant.co.uk; Tue-Sat 9.30 pm, Sun 4 pm.

BOTTLE AND GLASS INN   £64   4 4 2

BONES LANE RG9 4JT   01491 412 625

A "lovely" thatched pub serving a "short but excellent menu" of food "up to the standards of a London restaurant" – owners Alex Sergeant and David Holloway, graduates of stellar Fulham gastroboozer the Harwood Arms, have put their know-how to excellent effect in south Oxfordshire. "It manages to retain the atmosphere of a village pub while offering very high-quality dining" – "locals still use it for a drink". Two years down the track, the pair have opened their second venue, Hart Street Tavern, in nearby Henley-on-Thames. Top Tip – "wonderful garden serving great pizzas from a huge pizza oven and drinks from a horsebox". / www.bottleandglassinn.co.uk; @btlandglassinn; Mon-Sat 9.30 pm, Sun 4.30 pm.

ADAM'S, NEW OXFORD HOUSE   £99   5 5 4

16 WATERLOO ST B2 5UG   0121 643 3745

"No need to go to London restaurants that so often disappoint!" – Adam & Natasha Stoke's "beautiful restaurant with a lovely bar and intimate dining area is in a central location that has parking outside". Its food score remains the highest in Brum (by a very narrow whisker from Purnells) with practically all feedback describing "fine dining at its best" – "no over the top scientific nonsense", just "food that continues to be innovative, beautifully prepared and presented" and service that's "professional, never pompous and which knows how to connect without intruding". "Enjoying the tasting menu downstairs at the chef's table is a great experience." / www.adamsrestaurant.co.uk; @RestaurantAdams; Booking max 10 may apply.

ASHA'S INDIAN BAR AND RESTAURANT   £53   3 4 2

12-22 NEWHALL ST B3 3LX 0121 200 2767

This city-centre venue with a focus on delicious kebabs and other dishes from the subcontinent's Northwest Frontier is part of an international empire set up by Asha Bhosle, the prolific Bollywood singer, which also has branches in Manchester and Solihull. Now 86, Bhosle is credited as the most recorded artist in music history, and insists she would have been a cook if her singing career had not taken off. Fun fact: Cornershop's 1997 hit single Brimful of Asha was a tribute to Bhosle. / ashasbirmingham.co.uk/; @ashasbirmingham; Sat, Thu & Fri 11 pm, Mon-Wed 10.30 pm, Sun 10 pm; Take bookings all week via phone and/or online.

CARTERS OF MOSELEY   £124   5 5 3

2C WAKE GREEN RD B13 9EZ 0121 449 8885

"Passion for food and drink" is much in evidence, "along with a really warm welcome" at Brad Carter's "smart casual" fixture, which again scores top marks for his "fantastic" and "inventive" cuisine, from an eight-course tasting menu (for £90), or, if you go earlier in the week, four-course and six-course options. Added attractions include a "really imaginative vegetarian option" and a "passionate wine supremo" who also has some "really interesting alternatives to wine" up his sleeve ("quirky beers, plum sake, natural cider…"). / www.cartersofmoseley.co.uk; @cartersmoseley; Fri & Sat, Tue-Thu 9 pm; children: 8+.

CHAKANA   £50

140 ALCESTER ROAD B13 8HS 0121 448 9880

Robert Ortiz, ex-head chef at London's acclaimed Lima, is set to open Brum's first Peruvian venture inside handsome former bank premises in Moseley village, in late 2019. Will the locals take to ceviche and Pisco sour… it seems like a fair bet. / www.chakana-restaurant.co.uk; @Chakana_moseley; Tue-Thu 10.30 pm, Fri & Sat 11 pm, Sun 8.30 pm.

DAMASCENA   £22   4 3 3

133 ALCESTER ROAD B13 8JP 0121 449 9245

"Very authentic" and "always busy" Middle Eastern café (this, the Moseley branch, was the first of three local addresses to open) offering a "fresh, exquisitely spiced feast for the eyes and heart" (including "always fabulous mint tea and pastries"). / damascena.co.uk; @Damascena_UK; Mon-Thu 9 pm, Fri & Sat 10 pm, Sun 6 pm.

FAZENDA   £57   3 3 3

55 COLMORE ROW, BARWICK STREET ENTRANCE B3 2AA   0121 728 5656

"Latino steak restaurant in the heart of Birmingham city centre" – this well-appointed new branch of the expanding Brazilian chain offers its trademark "generous meat and buffet" formula. It's tipped by one or two reporters as "good for business meals". / fazenda.co.uk; @fazendagroup; Mon-Sat 10 pm, Sun 9 pm.

FOLIUM   £78   5 3 3

8 CAROLINE STREET B3 1TR 0121 638 0100

You choose between five-course and seven-course tasting menus at Ben Tesh and Lucy Hanlon's 28-seat pop-up turned permanent in the Jewellery Quarter, which opened in November 2017. "It must be close to a Michelin star" say fans, who feel the food is "outstanding" and the whole enterprise "beautifully run". Portion size and wine matches were two areas where one or two reporters felt it fell short, but most reports are full-on raves. / restaurantfolium.com; @foliumrest; Wed-Sat 9 pm, Sun 2.30 pm.

HARBORNE KITCHEN   £49   5 4 4

B17 9QE   01214399150

Jamie Desogus has created a "vibrant, relaxed, open-plan environment" at the former butcher's shop that he opened in 2016, and all reports are full of praise for his "exceptional" modern cuisine, available from a three-course à la carte ('choice') menu early week, or at weekends from six-course or eight-course ('chosen') menus. / www.harbornekitchen.com; @HarborneKitchen; Tue-Sat 11 pm; Take bookings all week via phone and/or online.

THE IVY TEMPLE ROW BIRMINGHAM £57 234

67-71 TEMPLE ROW B2 5LS
0121 725 2110

"I guess the place to be seen 2018-19" – this famous brasserie chain hit Brum in April 2018, and feedback on it divides along familiar lines between those who see it as "always a pleasant experience whatever the time of day" to those who find the food "disappointing" or "OK but nothing special". / theivybirmingham.com; Wed-Fri 4 pm, Sat & Sun 5 pm.

JYOTI'S VEGETARIAN £21 432

1045 STRATFORD ROAD B28 8AS
0121 778 5501

For "cheap and reliably high-standard South Indian cuisine", there's no beating this modestly styled Hall Green veggie. / www.jyotis.co.uk; Wed-Sat 10 pm, Sun 7 pm; No Amex.

THE KARCZMA, POLISH MILLENNIUM HOUSE £43

BORDESLEY ST B5 5PH 0121 448 0017

10/10 for effort on the décor at this kitschy classic five minutes from the Bull Ring, but decorated like an old Pollish cottage. Too limited reports this year for a proper rating of the hearty east European scoff, but all feedback is positive. / www.thekarczma.co.uk; @thekarczma; Tue-Sat 11 pm, Sun 9 pm; Take bookings all week via phone and/or online.

LASAN £60 443

3-4 DAKOTA BUILDINGS, JAMES STREET B3 1SD 0121 212 3664

This "upmarket Indian in the Jewellery quarter" has pioneered a fine-dining approach as an alternative to the classic UK curry house for almost two decades. Ratings continue to impress under founder Jabbar Khan following the 2018 departure of high-profile chef-director Aktar Islam (see Opheem). / www.lasan.co.uk; @lasan; Tue-Fri, Mon 10 pm, Sat 11 pm, Sun 9 pm; No trainers; Take bookings all week via phone and/or online.

LEGNA £58 223

ISLINGTON GATES, 8 FLEET STREET B3 1JH 0121 201 3525

"Good… but is it good enough for the prices they're charging" is a key question regarding Opheem owner Aktar Islam's new Italian in Summer Row. If you like a swish setting though, its interior is well worth experiencing. / legnarestaurant.com; @LegnaRestaurant; Tue-Sat 9.30 pm, Sun 6 pm.

MARIBEL £54

6 BRINDLEY PLACE B1 2JB
0121 633 4944

On the Brindleyplace site that was once Edmunds (RIP), this April 2018 newcomer attracted some brilliant reviews in this year's survey for Richard Turner's accomplished cuisine. He departed, though, in mid May 2019, just before our current survey closed, to be replaced by Harvey Perttola: formerly a sous chef at Lichfield's Swinfen Hall. The move seems to herald a desire for a 'more relaxed' (less ambitious) style of dining than previously and in the circumstances it seems sensible to leave a re-rating till next year. / www.maribelrestaurant.co.uk; @Maribel_bham; Tue-Sat 10 pm; No trainers.

OPHEEM £55 544

65 SUMMER ROW B3 1JJ 0121 201 3377

"Aktar Islam (ex-Lasan) is doing a fabulous job in his new venue" – a "super-stylishy", 70-cover venture that's immediately hailed as "Birmingham's best Indian", with "dedicated" staff delivering an "equisite" and "exciting" modern twist on Indian cuisine. "It's is a little off the beaten track from the city-centre but well worth seeking out". In October 2019, Michelin – unusually for a regional Indian – awarded it a star. / www.opheem.com; @opheemtweets; Tue-Thu 9.30 pm, Fri & Sat 10 pm, Sun 7.30 pm; Take bookings all week via phone and/or online.

OPUS RESTAURANT £59 343

54 CORNWALL STREET B3 2DE
0121 200 2323

Located in the Colmore District, this "warm" brasserie garners nominations both for a top culinary experience and also for being "good for business": winning features include accomplished modern cuisine with well-priced wine flights and a "good ambience without pretension". / www.opusrestaurant.co.uk; @opuscornwallst; Mon-Thu 8.30 pm, Fri 9 pm, Sat 9.30 pm.

ORIGINAL PATTY MEN £35 433

9 SHAW'S PASSAGE B5 0121 643 2546

The "top burgers – oh yes, plus excellent ales to quaff" (from locals Siren Craft Brews) set this "cool" joint apart. In April 2018 they added a Scandi-style bar, Kilder, which serves to take up the overspill – but not just, having its own distinct drinks list plus a menu of British produce and grilled cheese. / www.originalpattymen.com; @OriginalPattyM; Wed-Sat 11 pm, Sun 8 pm; No bookings.

PINT SHOP £39 334

38 BENNETTS HILL B3 2AA
0121 236 9039

"Modern in décor but traditional in feel" – this new offshoot from the Cambridge original occupies a Grade II listed townhouse in the city-centre, converted last year into a hipster-ish pub. "The flatbread kebabs are a winner on the menu of pub staples and bar food (which is small compared to the list of gins and beers)". / pintshop.co.uk; @pintshopbrum; Sun-Thu 10 pm, Fri 10.30 pm, Sat midnight.

PLOUGH £48 333

21 HIGH STREET B17 9NT 0121 427 3678

Yummy brunches, fine coffee and stone-baked pizza are the top attractions at this funkily decorated pub, on the high street (which has a good garden for the summer months). / www.theploughharborne.co.uk; @PloughHarborne; Mon-Sun 9.30 pm; Take bookings all week via phone and/or online.

PURNELL'S BISTRO £44 324

11 NEWHALL STREET B3 3NY
0121 200 1588

"High quality cooking and well trained staff" help win fans for TV-chef Glynn Purnell's modern bistro/brasserie in the business district. Some reports, though, are more middling: "OK, but not a patch on his proper restaurant nearby!". Top Tip – "it does some great offers – get on their mailing list!" / purnellsbistro-gingers. com; @PurnellsBistro; Mon-Sat 9.30 pm, Sun 3.30 pm.

PURNELLS £96 553

55 CORNWALL ST B3 2DH 0121 212 9799

TV-chef Glynn Purnell's swish HQ in the business quarter was Birmingham's most-mentioned restaurant in the survey this year and is often recommended as "Brum's best" (with ratings on almost exactly level pegging with rivals Adam's and Opheem). Criticism is most notable by its absence, with nothing but rapturous reviews for his "technically accomplished cuisine, with well-executed creative dishes" and "interested, attentive and well-paced service". / www.purnellsrestaurant.com; @purnellsrest; children: 6+.

SAN CARLO £55 343

4 TEMPLE STREET B2 5BN
0121 633 0251

The very first outpost of the glam Italian chain (est 1992), with "super stylish décor (albeit quite retro), slick service, an extensive menu and a relaxed atmosphere. The food doesn't always live up to expectations", but it can, at times, be "excellent". / sancarlo.co.uk/restaurants/birmingham/; @SanCarlo_Group; Take bookings all week via phone and/or online.

SIMPSONS £98 434

20 HIGHFIELD ROAD B15 3DU
0121 454 3434

"Totally worth the trip… and also great value for money" – this "magnificent" Edwardian villa of over a quarter century's standing is one of Birmingham's most firmly rooted culinary attractions. One or two sceptics feel that "it is still recovering from its decision to adopt a more casual-dining look" ("I would have expected proper table linen for the very high prices"), but there's been no change in the scale of ambition of the cuisine – be it from the three-course menu for £75, or eight-course taster menu for £95 – and overall it maintains its ratings as one of the city's top dining destinations. / www.simpsonsrestaurant.co.uk; @simpsons_rest; Tue-Sat 9 pm, Sun 3 pm.

TATTU £53
**18 BARWICK STREET B3 2NT
0121 236 5556**

"Arresting" design is a big feature of Adam and Drew Jones's stunning-looking Chinese-themed newcomer: the city's biggest basement bar and restaurant situated in the recently reopened Grand hotel (built in 1879, and refurbished after over a decade's closure). Too few reports for a rating as yet: its menu contains a "theatrically presented combination of small bites and larger dishes". The next stop after this is Edinburgh, opening late 2019. / tattu.co.uk/birmingham/; @TattuRestaurant.

THE WILDERNESS £130 5 4 3
**27 WARSTONE LANE B18 6JQ
0121 233 9425**

With its black-painted walls and punchy sound track, Alex Claridge's decidedly rock 'n' roll Jewellery Quarter three-year-old has courted attention over the years with ants on the menu (and this year a social media campaign involving fake guns). There's serious intent in the open kitchen here, though – "something quite unique happens, with a tasting menu that blows you away" and "beautifully crafted" drinks to go with it; "more restaurants should aim for an '80s soundtrack too!" / wearethewilderness.co.uk; @thewildernessb5; Wed-Sat 8.30 pm; Credit card deposit required to book; children: 12.

BISHOPS CASTLE, SHROPSHIRE   5–4A

THE COACH HOUSE NORBURY £54 5 3 3
NORBURY SY9 5DX   01588 650846

Twenty-two-year-old chef, Harry Bullock, is producing some "superb" cuisine from a short (four choices at each course), imaginative, and very competitively priced menu – at this "lovely and intimate" restaurant-with-rooms: which occupies a former pub in the South Shropshire Hills AONB. / www.coachhousenorbury.com; @norburycoach; Wed-Sat 8.30 pm.

BISHOPS TACHBROOK, WARWICKSHIRE   5–4C

MALLORY COURT, MALLORY COURT HOTEL £92 3 3 3
**HARBURY LANE CV33 9QB
01926 330214**

"A bastion of culinary good sense and refinement", the formal dining room at this Lutyens-style Relais & Châteaux spa hotel is the sort of place where "little changes" – although chef Paul Evans's menus show evidence of his experience in progressive kitchens including L'Enclume. / www.mallory.co.uk; @mallorycourt; Mon-Sun 9.30 pm; No trainers.

BLAIRGOWRIE, PERTH AND KINROSS   9–3C

KINLOCH HOUSE £86 3 4 4
PH10 6SG   01250 884 732

"With Dundee on the doorstep and the new V&A to visit", this "perfect" country house hotel benefits from an "exceptional restaurant, service and comfort" too. The cooking, featuring fruit from nearby Blairgowrie and game from resident shooting parties, "shows flair and immaculate presentation", while hotel manager "Paul, a man of skill and humour, always makes a stay special". / www.kinlochhouse.com; No Amex; Jacket required; children: 6 for dinner.

BLAKENEY, NORFOLK   6–3C

THE MOORINGS £48 4 3 2
HIGH STREET NR25 7NA   01263 740 054

"Consistently good fresh food" has been on the menu at this "unpretentious" family-run operation for 20 years – "how they can cook fish so well always amazes me, given the numbers they cater for". Along with the seafood, there's local game and meat, and vegetables from their own garden. / www.blakeney-moorings.co.uk; No Amex.

BOLLINGTON, CHESHIRE   5–2B

THE LIME TREE £38 3 4 4
**18-20 HIGH STREET SK10 5PH
01625 578182**

It's not as well-known as its famous Didsbury sibling, but Patrick Hannity's "excellent" brasserie is "just as good" according to its local fans, with "fantastic" and "consistent" cooking. / www.limetreebollington.co.uk; @thelimetreeres; Tue-Thu 10 pm, Fri & Sat 11 pm, Sun 6 pm; Take bookings all week via phone and/or online.

BOLNHURST, BEDFORDSHIRE   3–1A

THE PLOUGH AT BOLNHURST £57 3 3 4
MK44 2EX   01234 376274

A "wonderful gastropub in the depths of rural Bedfordshire", dating back to Tudor times, and full of "beams and interesting nooks and crannies" – plus a "cosy bar for winter" and "gorgeous garden for summer"; the "short but interesting seasonal menu" results in "assured" cooking, with "some stand-out dishes". / www.bolnhurst.com; @atBolnhurst; No Amex.

BOLTON ABBEY, NORTH YORKSHIRE   8–4B

THE DEVONSHIRE BRASSERIE, THE DEVONSHIRE ARMS, THE DEVONSHIRE ARMS £49 3 3 3
BD23 6AJ   01756 718100

The less formal option at this grand ducal hotel also benefits from a terrace on sunny days with sweeping views of the Dales. Limited but good feedback this year on its wide-ranging and affordable brasserie menus: fairly standard fare, bolstered by a range of steaks and above-par cheeses. There's a cut-down wine list, but the full selection is also available if the occasion demands it! / thedevonshirearms.co.uk/contact.shtml; @Dev_Hotels; Mon-Sat 9.30 pm, Sun 9 pm.

BOREHAM, ESSEX   3–2C

THE LION INN £48 3 3 4
MAIN RD CM3 3JA   01245 394900

"A short drive from Chelmsford" in "the heart of Essex" – this "highly recommended" inn is large enough to host weddings and conferences, with a spacious Victorian-style conservatory for dining that has a "real vibrant buzz", along with "decent good-value food and very friendly service". / www.lioninnhotel.co.uk; @lioninnboreham; Mon-Sat 9 pm; No Amex.

BOUGHTON LEES, KENT   3–3C

THE MANOR RESTAURANT, EASTWELL MANOR £77 2 2 5
EASTWELL PK TN25 4HR   01233 213000

Afternoon tea at this deluxe Elizabethan country house hotel can be a "great experience in beautiful surroundings". Other aspects of the trip, however, "don't always live up to the ambience". / www.eastwellmanor.co.uk; @EastwellManor; No jeans; Booking max 8 may apply.

BOURNEMOUTH, DORSET   2–4C

ARBOR RESTAURANT, THE GREEN HOUSE HOTEL £59 3 3 3
4 GROVE RD BH1 3AX   01202 498900

This all-day and affordable hotel restaurant was nominated by numerous reporters this year as a favourite destination in the area. In particular, it's a champion of sustainability, with an emphasis on local, organic, fairtrade and farm assured produce. / www.arbor-restaurant.co.uk; @arborrest.

CHEZ FRED £32 4 4 2
10 SEAMOOR RD BH4 9AN   01202 761023

"Traditionally good" chips and catch "with mushy peas and a cuppa" (and a side of "unadorned British seaside memories") do the trick at Fred Capel's local luminary – "better than any London chippy", say out-of-towners.

Opheem, Birmingham

Top Tip – "if you don't fancy the wait they also do daily specials in the takeaway which can be really good value". / www.chezfred.co.uk; @ChezFredUK; Mon-Sun 9.30 pm; No Amex; No bookings.

WESTBEACH   £57   3|2|3

PIER APPROACH BH2 5AA 01202 587785

"A perfect breakfast stop with a fabulous view of the beach" (and outside seating in warm weather) – this seaside café, a short drive from central Bournemouth, has a wider culinary reputation too, for its cooking of fish and seafood in particular. Service can lag, though. / www.west-beach.co.uk; @WestBeachBmouth; Sun & Mon 5 pm, Tue-Sat 11 pm; Take bookings all week via phone and/or online.

HORSE & GROOM   £48   3|2|3

GL56 9AQ 01386 700413

Classic, "lovely" Cotswolds inn, with rooms, that's well-reviewed in all feedback for its "good pub food". Even those who find it dependable, however, can feel that the menu "could use some more interesting dishes". / www.horseandgroom.info; @thehorsengroom; Mon-Sat 11 pm; No Amex; Take bookings all week via phone and/or online.

BORAGE   £59   4|4|3

7 VALE VIEW, VICARAGE LANE WA14 3BD 0161 929 4775

This "excellent neighbourhood bistro" – "but with much better food than the 'bistro' moniker would lead one to expect" – is a "very good addition to the limited restaurant scene to the south of Manchester" (and so "very convenient for the airport"). Chef Mariusz Dobies was exec chef at Michael Caines Manchester. / www.boragebowdon.co.uk; @BorageBowdon; Wed-Sat 9 pm, Sun 8 pm.

BILLYS ON THE BEACH   £44   3|3|4

BRACKLESHAM LANE PO20 01243 670373

A candy-striped shack in a "super spot right on the beach" at Bracklesham Bay, with "a good selection of food plus wine & beer" – "with a strong emphasis as you'd expect on seafood". Facing southwest, the bay is a perfect place to watch sunsets and kite-surfers. / www.billysonthebeach.co.uk; @BillysontheBeach; Sun-Wed 5 pm, Thu-Sat 9 pm; Take bookings all week via phone and/or online.

AKBAR'S   £33   4|2|3

1276 LEEDS RD BD3 8LF 01274 773311

"The food is superb" at the "always full" flagship of Shabir Hussain's northern curry house group. "If you like a buzzy setting with

'all human life' bustling around – this is for you". / www.akbars.co.uk; @OfficialAkbars; Mon-Sat midnight, Sun 11.30 pm.

MUMTAZ   £33   4|3|2

386-410 GREAT HORTON RD BD7 3HS 01274 571861

This Kashmiri institution started life 40 years back as a street stall but nowadays is a proper brand with its own line in ready meals. The secret of their success? "They have a magic formula and it's all to do with the herbs and spices they use to produce such excellent dishes". / www.mumtaz.com; @Mumtaz; Sun-Thu midnight, Fri & Sat 1 am.

THE SAMUEL FOX COUNTRY INN   £54   4|3|3

STRETFIELD RD S33 9JT 01433 621 562

James Duckett's "tastefully decorated" inn is set in the Peak District National Park with wonderful views of the Hope Valley. It offers a wide variety of dining options – from bargain early evening menus to tasting menu options – "top notch" fairly traditional cooking provided by "friendly and efficient staff". Top Menu Tip – "legendary sticky toffee pudding". / www.samuelfox.co.uk; @SamuelFoxInn; Wed-Sat 11 pm, Sun 5.30 pm; Take bookings all week via phone and/or online.

THE CLUNIE DINING ROOM, THE FIFE ARMS   £63   3|2|5

MAR ROAD AB35 5YN 01339 720200

Named for the river running past this newly refurbished old coaching inn and hotel, The Clunie serves seasonal Scottish produce (much of it seafood and game) sourced from local suppliers, gamekeepers and farmers, and cooked over a wood fire. "The décor is wonderful" by all accounts, and early feedback (though limited) applauds the cuisine too. There's also a public bar, The Flying Stag, with bar meals and a vast range of whiskies. / thefifearms.com; Mon-Sat 9.30 pm, Sun 4 pm.

THE WHITE HORSE £56   3|4|4

MAIN RD PE31 8BY 01485 210262

"Impeccably fresh and delicious fish, especially the oysters and mussels – and a great view to match" sums up the appeal of a coastal pub that's "so different from most, with a real Norfolk twist". "What could be better on a summer's evening than supper here, sitting outside on the terrace?". / www.whitehorsebrancaster.co.uk; @whitehorsebranc; Take bookings all week via phone and/or online.

CALDESI IN CAMPAGNA   £79   3|4|4

OLD MILL LN SL6 2BG 01628 788500

There's an "idyllic experience" to be had at Giancarlo & Katie Caldesi's "outstanding Italian", which was significantly spruced up two years back – especially out on the sunny patio come summer. Add in "impeccably charming service" and it makes a "delightful location for that 'special meal'". / www.caldesi.com; @CaldesiCampagna; Tue-Sat 11.30 am, Sun 3.30 pm; No trainers.

THE FAT DUCK   £396   2|3|2

HIGH ST SL6 2AQ 01628 580333

Is Heston Blumenthal's world-famous HQ starting to look "a bit old hat"? Or is it just "too bloody expensive"? What's for sure is that over half of reporters commenting on this renowned ex-pub now nominate it as their most overpriced meal of the year, while only a quarter say it was their best. Truly, it's "a unique gastronomic experience, unlike any other": "more of an event than a meal" ("it's a long evening"), with a series of courses "very theatrically presented" based on your past experiences (as researched at the time of booking). To a majority, it's "Alice in Wonderland on steroids" and in a good way – "yes, absurdly expensive" ("half the price would be too much!"), but not the disappointment we had feared: "joyful, engaging and oddly emotional…", with "exquisite tastes and textures, extraordinary flavours and surprising sensory phenomena…", "…in short we loved it; a bravura performance all round". But even those who "fared very well on the food" can feel that "it would not be for everyone, as the approach is somewhat a production line, with neighbouring tables either behind or ahead in their journey to Cornwall or wherever". And "the dining room is very stark which detracts from the ambience". And then there are the few folk who plain loathe the whole set-up. "This place is a performance art commentary on capitalism. If you've ever read '120 Days of Sodom' and want to eat something that gives you the same feeling as that book, come here!". / www.thefatduck.co.uk; @Whatley_Manor.

THE HIND'S HEAD £77   4|4|4

HIGH STREET SL6 2AB 01628 626151

"Still a fabulous gastropub… even if prices are a little on the high side" – Heston Blumenthal's "very relaxing" hostelry takes a bit more flak nowadays for being expensive, but for the most part remains very highly rated by the survey. "Classic, very English pub dishes are interpreted with creative flair" and "washed down with imaginative cocktails (and mocktails)" as well as good ales and wines. / www.hindsheadbray.com; Mon-Sat 11 pm, Sun 6.30 pm; Take bookings all week via phone and/or online.

WATERSIDE INN £148 5 4 5

FERRY RD SL6 2AT 01628 620691

"From the moment you arrive, and someone comes to take your car away, you don't have to think" at Alain Roux's legendary destination (est 1972), which remains one of the most commented-on restaurants in the UK (and one of the few that has regularly been graced by Her Majesty over the years). It enjoys an "idyllic", supremely "romantic" location on the Thames, with the option of drinks on the terrace in fine weather, or a quick tootle in the restaurant's private launch before you eat. With large windows facing the water, the dining room itself is very comfortable, and most reporters adore its "old-fashioned" style (although it's undeniably a little bit of a "time warp"). The "impeccable", slightly "formal" service is in keeping with the setting, although – while it's still extremely highly rated – has perhaps lost a hint of its sparkle since the retirement last year of long-term maitre d', Diego Masciaga. "Classic" Gallic gastronomy comes "with a subtle modern twist" and on practically all accounts is "exceptional from start to finish". But it also comes at "crazy prices" naturellement, and – in the relatively few cases that reports fall short of rapture – the gripe is typically that the "eye-watering bill and very old-school approach make it hard to understand the fuss" (but then, complaints like this have been knocking about for the last 30 years…) / www.waterside-inn.co.uk; @rouxwaterside; No jeans; Booking max 10 may apply; children: 9.

BRECON, POWYS 2–1A

THE FELIN FACH GRIFFIN £42 4 3 4

FELIN FACH LD3 0UB 01874 620111

"London food at Welsh prices" and a "great ambiance" (it's set in a former cider mill) are the main draws to this veteran gastroboozer, praised for maintaining "consistently high standards year in, year out". / www.eatdrinksleep.ltd.uk; @felinfachgriff; Take bookings all week via phone and/or online.

BRENTWOOD, ESSEX 3–2B

ALEC'S £66 3 3 3

NAVESTOCK SIDE CM14 5SD 01277 375 696

This "glitzy and glamorous" smartened-up pub is perhaps a little TOWIE and inspires the odd complaint about its prices, but, nevertheless, it's fish and seafood cuisine won consistently decent ratings this year, and fans say the place is "excellent for a special occasion". / www.alecsrestaurant.co.uk; @Alecsrestaurant; Wed-Sat, Tue midnight, Sun 7 pm; No Amex; Credit card deposit required to book; children: 12+.

BRIDPORT, DORSET 2–4B

DORSHI £46 4 4 4

6 CHANCERY LANE DT6 3PX 01308 423221

Mix 'DOR'set with su'SHI', and you end up with this well-known, hipster-ish destination down a narrow alley, where "local ingredients are given an Asian twist" – "always a great meal" with "delightful" service. / dorshi.co.uk; @eatdorshi

BRIGHTON, EAST SUSSEX 3–4B

BASKETMAKERS ARMS £39 3 2 3

12 GLOUCESTER RD BN1 4AD 01273 689 006

"Exactly want you want in a pub", this "snug" Victorian in the North Laine area is "reliable, affordable and friendly", with "good pub grub". "There's always a great mix of people here – old men, fresh-faced students and ultra-cool hipsters collide and this gives the place a really welcoming feel" – "even when it's rammed on weekends". / www.basket-makers-brighton.co.uk/; @thebasketmakers; Sun-Thu 11 pm, Fri & Sat midnight; No bookings.

BINCHO YAKITORI £37 4 3 3

63 PRESTON STREET BN1 2HE 01273 779021

"Still below the radar for outsiders" – David Miney's squeezed izakaya serves a wide range of Japanese dishes, including sushi and yakitori, and – though feedback was more limited this year – fans still say it's outstanding. / www.binchoyakitori.com; @BinchoYakitori; Tue-Thu, Sun 10 pm, Fri & Sat 10.30 pm.

BURGER BROTHERS £15 5 4 2

97 NORTH RD BN1 1YE 01273 706980

"It doesn't look like much from the outside", and there are only a handful of seats, but step into this "tiny burger heaven" and you'll be rewarded with "the best burger you will ever eat"; "no fries, but who cares – it means you can have another burger!". / @BurgerBrethren; No bookings.

THE CHILLI PICKLE £49 4 3 3

17 JUBILEE ST BN1 1GE 01273 900 383

"Everyone's favourite Indian in Brighton" – practically all reports acclaim the "modern, lively and always enjoyable" (if "rather noisy") style of this Arts Quarter fixture; and its "lovey choice" of dishes that "elevate the CP above your standard curry house fare". / www.thechillipickle.com; @TheChilliPickle; Wed-Sat 10.30 pm, Mon & Tue 10 pm, Sun 9.30 pm; Take bookings all week via phone and/or online.

CIN CIN £50 4 4 3

WESTERN ROAD BN3 1JD 01273 726 047

"Brighton & Hove's top Italian" – David Toscano's larger (35-seat) Hove spin-off is in a similar vein to his Brighton original, but generates a shade more enthusiasm. "Inventive and delicious dishes on an Italian theme are made from local produce" and are matched with some good wines. / www.cincin.co.uk; @CinCinUK; Tue-Sat 11 pm, Sun 6 pm.

CIN CIN £48 4 4 3

13-16 VINE ST BN1 4AG 01273 698813

In 2016, David Toscano turned his series of pop-ups into this tiny, 20-seater converted from a garage, and with much of the seating around the u-shaped bar. Its lack of frills and comfort makes it a turn-off to some folks, but most rate it very highly: "super for a perfect plate of pasta, and really great fresh Italian food". / www.cincin.co.uk; @CinCinUK; Take bookings all week via phone and/or online.

THE COAL SHED £61 3 3 3

8 BOYCES ST BN1 1AN 01273 322998

"Top quality grilled meats and a lively atmosphere" help score good all-round ratings for Dave Mothershill's stylish grill (which has a London offshoot near Tower Bridge). / www.coalshed-restaurant.co.uk; @thecoalshed1; Sun-Thu 10 pm, Fri & Sat 10.30 pm; Take bookings all week via phone and/or online.

CURRY LEAF CAFE £46 3 4 3

60 SHIP ST BN1 1AE 01273 207070

Albeit "casual" and "relaxed", this "shabby chic" South Indian in the Lanes (with offshoots in Kemptown and at the station) is a "great find", and the "award-winning selection of craft beer and great array of alcohol-free brews for drivers is a great bonus". / www.curryleafcafe.com; @curryleafcaff; Mon-Thu 10 pm, Fri & Sat 10.30 pm, Sun 9 pm; Take bookings all week via phone and/or online.

DONATELLO £38 3 3 3

1-3 BRIGHTON PL BN1 1HJ 01273 775477

A "big, bustling Italian" with a "fun atmosphere" in the Lanes, "where genuine Italian staff serve huge portions of tasty pasta and pizza" – it's an "outstanding cheap 'n' cheerful choice" and "the kids love it, too". / www.donatello.co.uk; @donatello__; No Amex; Take bookings all week via phone and/or online.

DRAKES OF BRIGHTON, DRAKES HOTEL £67 4 4 3

43 - 44 MARINE PARADE BN2 1PE 01273 696934

It's 15 years since this basement in a Kemptown boutique hotel helped raise the excitement level about Brighton's eateries, and it remains one of the city's better dining destinations to this day. One repeat visitor was "disappointed on a return-visit after many years", but most reporters still rate the cuisine here very highly and the only other gripe we received this year was "pity it doesn't have a sea view…" / drakesofbrighton.com/restaurant; @drakeshotel; No trainers; Take bookings all week via phone and/or online; children: 8.

ENGLISH'S £50 344

29-31 EAST ST BN1 1HL 01273 327980

One of England's oldest restaurants: the Leigh-Jones family's seafood period-piece, in the Lanes – run by the clan since 1945, but established in the 1890s – has a "huge number of things to recommend", not least its "lovely fresh local oysters and mussels" and an outside terrace for sunny days. / www.englishs.co.uk; @englishsoB; Take bookings all week via phone and/or online.

ETCH £95 543

216 CHURCH RD BN3 2DJ 01273 227485

"Fine dining experience without a fine dining ambience" – MasterChef: The Professionals winner Steven Edwards continues to cook up a major storm in his converted bank in Hove, which offers a choice of five-, seven- or nine-course menus. Reporters are wowed by the "attention to detail, with a personal touch" resulting in food with "depth of flavour and delicacy that's a level up from most other such places". Top Tip – "juice flight for the non-alcoholic drinkers". / www.etchfood.co.uk; @EtchFood; Thu-Sat, Wed 8.30 pm; Take bookings all week via phone and/or online.

FATTO A MANO £40 322

01273 600621

"No need to go to Naples!" – "for an exceptional pizza in Brighton", head to one of the three branches of this "top chain" which, as well as this location, operates in North Laine and Hove; "the huge and delicious pizzas arrive fast and are fresh-tasting and reasonably priced (with a good vegan choice too)". Top Tip – "great for kids, who eat for free with an adult". / www.fattoamanopizza.com/; @fattoamanopizza; Mon-Thu 10 pm, Fri & Sat 10.30 pm, Sun 9 pm; May need 6+ to book.

FLINT HOUSE £50 344

13 HANNINGTON'S LANE BN1 1GS 01273 916333

"A great addition to central Brighton, but totally different to other Ginger places: almost like an English Barrafina" – the fifth opening from Pamela and Ben McKellar occupies a new-build site that has a 50-cover eatery with open kitchen and counter, complete with a "pleasant upstairs bar and roof terrace". Not everyone's totally converted though: "the food choices are OK, but I found the limited small plates menu made it difficult to construct a great meal". / www.flinthousebrighton.com; @flinthousebtn.

FOOD FOR FRIENDS £43 332

17-18 PRINCE ALBERT ST BN1 1HF 01273 202310

"A mainstay within the ever-changing Brighton scene" – this "simply decorated" Lanes fixture of four decades' standing is "a favourite amongst the city's many vegetarian restaurants". "It can feel a bit squashed sometimes as tables are close together, but it's always worth a visit" thanks to its "absolutely gorgeous, stunning, colourful food". / foodforfriends.com; @FoodforFriends; Mon-Thu 10 pm, Fri-Sun 10.30 pm; no booking, Sat L & Sun L.

THE GINGER DOG £55 333

12 COLLEGE PL BN2 1HN 01273 620 990

"More 'pubby' than The Gingerman" – the namesake group's original site and flagship, opened in 1998 – "but more relaxing" too, this dog-friendly Kemptown spot is a solid performer which "cannot be beaten for family get-togethers"; the newest ginger, The Flint House, mixing tapas, cocktails and a roof terrace, opened in central Brighton in spring 2019. / www.gingermanrestaurants.com; @GingerDogDish; Mon-Sun 10 pm; Take bookings all week via phone and/or online.

THE GINGER PIG £59 343

3 HOVE ST BN3 2TR 01273 736123

This "Hove stalwart" (part of the local Gingerman group) scores well for its "great atmosphere, dependably good food and attentive staff" – locals reckon "the Pig can hold its own against some of Brighton's more hyped recent openings". The recent addition of boutique hotel-style bedrooms makes it useful for an overnight break. / www.thegingerpigpub.com; @gingerpigdish; Tue-Sat 10.30 pm, Sun 10 pm; No trainers.

GINGERMAN £62 444

21A NORFOLK SQ BN1 2PD 01273 326688

"The tiny backstreet original of the Ginger empire" – near the front – Ben & Pamela McKellar's stalwart favourite has earned itself a sizeable and enduring fan club over two decades with its "intimate" style, "attentive but unobtrusive service" and, most importantly, its "wonderfully consistent, accomplished, fresh and tasty dishes". "The true king of Brighton's food scene!" / www.gingermanrestaurant.com; @thegingerchef; Mon & Tue 10 pm, Wed-Sat 11 pm, Sun 9.30 pm; Take bookings all week via phone and/or online.

INDIAN SUMMER £53 342

69 EAST ST BN1 1HQ 01273 711001

"Fresh-tasting and unusual Indian food is served by welcoming staff" at this Lanes subcontinental which has a sizeable and dedicated local following. "It can confuse visitors as it's not your standard curry house" ("I've seen groups come in, look at the menu and leave, which is a shame as they are missing a wonderful

experience"). / www.indiansummerbrighton.co.uk; @indiansummer108; Mon-Sat 10.30 pm, Sun 10 pm; Take bookings all week via phone and/or online.

ISAAC@ £62 443

2 GLOUCESTER STREET BN1 4EW 07765 934740

Localism is taken to new extremes at Isaac Bartlett-Copeland's tiny North Laine "gem", where "imaginative cooking and interesting presentation" win high ratings for a "young and enthusiastic staff" (Isaac and his team are all in their early-mid 20s) "who work hard to make an evening here a special experience". Not only is the "great food sourced from local producers" – you'd be hard-pressed to find a wine from beyond the Sussex borders on the all-British drinks list. / www.isaac-at.com; @Isaac_at; Tue-Sat 10.30 pm; Take bookings all week via phone and/or online.

IYDEA £21 322

17 KENSINGTON GARDENS BN1 4AL 01273 667 992

"Nostalgia for the long term vegetarian" is to be found at this North Laine café which provides "huge platefuls of scrummy veggie and vegan food" ("fairly trad fare") and "lovely service". / www.iydea.co.uk; @iydea; Mon-Sat 10 pm, Sun 5.30 pm; No Amex.

LITTLE FISH MARKET £96 553

10 UPPER MARKET ST BN3 1AS 01273 722213

"Just off the front in a charming maze of streets in Hove", Duncan Ray's small 20-seater is "a cute spot with no fine dining trappings to make you feel awkward". He is at the stoves alone, creating an ever-changing five-course menu of sustainable seafood: "just gorgeous fish cookery from raw to grilled – not hugely fancy, just brilliantly conceived and executed". / www.thelittlefishmarket.co.uk; @LittleFishHove; Tue-Sat 10.30 pm.

MURMUR £50 334

91-96 KINGS ROAD ARCHES BN1 1NB 01273 711 900

"Within a hop, skip and jump of the i360", but with a "great setting right on the seafront" (and al fresco seating), this "casual, laidback" venture turns out "excellent seasonal produce" (predominantly fish) from a "small but perfectly formed menu". Owner "Michael Bremner deserves to be as successful with Murmur as he has been with 64 Degrees". / murmur-restaurant.co.uk/; @Murmur_Beach; Mon-Sat 9 pm, Sun 6 pm.

PETIT POIS £39 344

70 SHIP STREET BN1 1AE 01273 911211

A "lovely, bustling and buzzy little bistro that serves up generously sized plates" at "great value" prices in the Brighton backstreets; there are "great French standards on the menu and

then great specials on the blackboard" too. /
petitpoisbrighton.co.uk; Mon, Wed-Sun 10 pm.

PLATEAU   £53   ███

**1 BARTHOLOMEWS BN1 1HG
01273 733 085**

"A shabby-chic bistro with pleasant staff and
interesting small plates" – fish-centric – plus
"natural wines to complement the seasonal
organic food". / www.plateaubrighton.co.uk; Sun-
Wed 10 pm, Thu-Sat 10.30 pm; Take bookings all
week via phone and/or online.

POLPO   £43   ███

20 NEW RD BN1 1UF   01273 697 361

A "very convivial" London-on-Sea outpost of
Russell Norman's hit Venetian bacaro (Italian
small plates) spot; while it is doing better than
its Bristol and Exeter siblings – both now
closed – and avoids any harsh critiques, some
reports speak of a "drop-off in quality" of late,
or food that's "average to good, but nothing to
be delighted about". / www.polpo.co.uk; @Polpo;
Take bookings all week via phone and/or online.

THE REGENCY
RESTAURANT   £39   ███

131 KINGS RD BN1 2HH   01273 325014

With its "basic, unpretentious interior and
bustle", this "traditional chippie in a seafront
setting" serves "still probably the best fish 'n'
chips in town" of the conventional, un-gastro
variety. Both hot and cold seafood come
on "exceptionally large platters", and "it's
the perfect place for a Sunday lunch on a
stormy day looking out over the Channel". /
www.theregencyrestaurant.co.uk; Take bookings all
week via phone and/or online.

RIDDLE & FINNS   £59   ███

**12B MEETING HOUSE LN BN1 1HB
01273 721667**

"Overall just a fantastic experience" – a
Lanes oyster bar, with a spinoff on the
promenade ("both are very popular"), which
wins numerous raves for "the most amazing
seafood", combined with "brilliant" service
and a pleasingly "informal" set-up (communal
tables) whereby "you might easily find
yourself sharing a tall table with strangers".
/ www.riddleandfinns.co.uk; @RiddleandFinns1;
Sun-Fri 10 pm, Sat 11 pm; No bookings.

RIDDLE & FINNS ON
THE BEACH   £59   ███

**139 KINGS ROAD ARCHES BN1 2FN
01273 721667**

An "excellent location (under the arches on
Brighton beach) to soak up the sun on the
terrace or watch it set from a window seat on
the first floor" – this offshoot of the well-
known Lanes oyster bar makes for the "perfect
end to a day at the seaside", not least thanks
to its "amazingly fresh" fish and seafood. /
www.riddleandfinns.co.uk; @riddleandfinns1; Sun-
Fri 10 pm, Sat 11 pm; Take bookings all week via
phone and/or online.

Little Fish Market, Brighton

THE SALT ROOM   £65   ███

**106 KINGS ROAD BN1 2FA
01273 929 488**

"It's all about the fish" ("amazing" albeit "very
expensive") at this "great seafood brasserie
in a lovely location on Brighton seafront" –
although they also turn out "brilliant quality
steaks" (with "sharing plates for two – fish
or meat – a particular feature"). The venue
elicits reams of feedback – amongst the
highest quantity of any venue in town – all
highly positive. / www.saltroom-restaurant.co.uk;
@TheSaltRoomUK; Mon-Sun 10 pm; Take
bookings all week via phone and/or online.

64 DEGREES   £53   ███

**53 MEETING HOUSE LANE BN1 1HB
01273 770 115**

"Wonderful, very quirky choices cooked to
order" inspire an ongoing outpouring of love
for this "casual" small-plates venue, owned
by Great British Menu 2017 winner, Michael
Bremner. Consequently, it's "a little crowded"
but "good fun", with "slick and quick service" –
"a vibrant spot where you can sit very squashed
on a stool at the bar watching the kitchen cook
and serve great food!" / www.64degrees.co.uk; @
chef64degrees.

SMALL BATCH
COFFEE   £14   ███

17 JUBILEE ST BN1 1GE   01273 697597

"Lovely strong coffee" (from flat whites to
snobbier single origin brews) is the secret
behind the success of this beloved local
chain – now with six branches, plus carts at
Hove and Brighton stations and, as of 2016,
a Worthing outpost. This venue, in a former
bank, has outdoor seating and a barista lab
for those seeking to perfect their latte art. /
www.smallbatchcoffee.co.uk; @SmallBatchCR;
Mon-Sat 7 pm, Sun 6 pm; No bookings.

TERRE Ã TERRE   £53   ███

71 EAST ST BN1 1HQ   01273 729051

"Who needs meat?" – This Lanes icon is "still
the finest veggie around": indisputably "the
best in Brighton" and many reporters feel
"unquestionably the best veggie in Britain"
too. Its "adventurous and fun menu" ("some
absolute stormers!") is reliably "exciting" and

"has every angle covered if your tendencies
splash over into the domains of veganism
or gluten free diets, plus a good worldwide
selection of organic wines (red and white) along
with some pretty unusual sparkling ones".
"Definitely well worth a visit even if you are a
dedicated carnivore". / www.terreaterre.co.uk;
@TerreaTerre; Booking max 8 may apply.

THE SET, UNIQUE
HOTEL   £65   ███

**33 REGENCY SQUARE BN1 2GG
01273 855572**

Eat from a "tempting short menu" ("there's
no longer just a set menu") at Dan Kenny's
funky former pop-up that's now permanently
parked in a "relaxed and quiet" location,
within a trendy boutique hotel. "How can
kale taste like heaven? How can sultanas make
such an intense jam? How can rhubarb zing
in an eclair? Go visit The Set and discover
for yourself!" / www.thesetrestaurant.com;
@TheSet_Brighton; Take bookings all week via
phone and/or online.

URCHIN   £46   ███

**15-17 BELFAST ST BN3 3YS
01273 241881**

"Fabulous, reasonably priced seafood" is the
focus at this smart corner gastroboozer with
stripped wooden floors. A "great range of
beers" (some brewed on-site) complements
"always innovative shellfish dishes and specials".
/ www.urchinpub.co.uk; @urchinpub; Tue-Fri 9.30
pm, Sat 10 pm, Sun 8 pm; Take bookings all week
via phone and/or online.

WILD FLOR   £61   ███

**42 CHURCH ROAD BN3 2FN
01273 329111**

"A great new opening in Hove, with
experienced staff from Ginger group": this new
bistro (from Robert Maynard, Faye Hudson
and James Thomson, together with chef Oliver
Derby) only opened in April 2019 (in the
middle of our survey) but is already inspiring
enthusiastic reviews from reporters, who say
it's "a perfect local" with "friendly and efficient
service as you would expect of such a team,
but also really good food" and – last but not
least – a "brilliant wine list" (there are 120 bins
to choose from). / wildflor.com; @wildflorhove;
Mon, Thu-Sat, Wed 9.30 pm, Sun 7.30 pm.

THE POINTER £73

27 CHURCH ST HP18 9RT 01844 238339

With its oak beams, rustic décor and roaring fire, this rural pub with rooms – pub up front, dining room in a converted 19th century barn to the rear – has proved an asset to this lovely Bucks village. In September 2019, though, it closed for a major revamp until we receive feedback on the new set-up we've removed ratings for the time being. / www.thepointerbrill.co.uk; Tue-Thu 11 pm, Fri & Sat midnight, Sun 9 pm.

ADELINA YARD £56 442

QUEEN QUAY, WELSH BACK BS1 4SL 0117 911 2112

Jamie Randall and Olivia Barry's "slightly sparse and understated", "bare-walled" venue near the docks and Old Town is in its fourth year now, but support shows no sign of slacking off. Its imaginative tasting menus deliver "very interesting blends of tastes and textures" and results are "excellent". / www.adelinayard.com; @AdelinaYard; Sun-Thu 9 pm, Fri & Sat 9.30 pm.

BAR 44 £79 333

18 - 20 REGENT STREET BS8 4HG 03333 44 40 49 OPTION 4

"Proper jamon, a good selection of small plates, and an excellent Spanish wine list with a wide range of good sherries" – "a great drinks list with something for everyone" – help inspire positive reviews on this Hispanic newcomer – "a great new addition to Bristol" and the first English branch of a small minichain originating near Cardiff. / www.bar44.co.uk/bristol; @bar44bristol; Take bookings all week via phone and/or online.

BIANCHI'S £43

1-3 YORK ROAD BS6 5QB 0117 3294100

Taking over the Montpelier premises that for over 40 years housed the much-loved Bell's Diner (RIP), this summer-2019 Italian newcomer is from the team behind local hits Pasta Loco, Pasta Ripiena, and La Sorella. Top Tip – very competitively priced lunch deal. / bianchisrestaurant.co.uk; Mon-Sat 10 pm.

BIRCH £48 343

47 RALEIGH RD BS3 1QS 01179 028 326

"An excellent small independent restaurant in an increasingly trendy part of Bristol" (Southville), which rose to success under former owners Sam Leech & Beccy Massy; now run by (FOH) Tom Masters, who imparts a "lovely warm welcoming feel to the place", it "offers a varied, innovative, largely vegetarian menu" and the former small plates ethos has remained intact. / www.birchbristol.co; @birch_bristol; Tue-Sat 10 pm, Sun 4 pm; Take bookings all week via phone and/or online.

BOSCO PIZZERIA £45 344

96 WHITELADIES RD BS8 2QX 01179 737 978

"Really great pizza and small plates" ensure that this Neapolitan-style outfit (also with a Clifton Village sibling) is "always buzzing"; it's "particularly great in the summer when the windows are open to the pavement on a sunny evening". / www.boscopizzeria.co.uk; @boscopizzeria; May need + to book.

BRAVAS £38 344

7 COTHAM HILL BS6 6LD 0117 329 6887

Fans "love this place" – a softly-lit tapas joint, in Cotham Hill, which has made a name for its "small plates and Spanish sandwiches done right"; if there's a caveat it's that "too many covers squashed into a tiny space" can spell noise and a "rapid turnover". Owners Kieran & Imogen Waite – also behind Bakers & Co (Gloucester Road) and Cargo Cantina/Gambas (Wapping Wharf) – launched new Mexican eatery, Masa + Mescal, in Stokes Croft, in March 2019. / www.bravas.co.uk; @bravasbristol; Mon-Wed 11 pm, Thu-Sat midnight; Take bookings all week via phone and/or online.

BULRUSH £61 543

21 COTHAM ROAD SOUTH BS6 5TZ 0117 329 0990

Chef-owner George Livesey's "very adventurous tasting menus" – full of "unusual ingredients and foraged items" – have made this modest-looking, former greengrocers a top star of the Bristol dining scene. Some reporters reckon it's "a bit of a Marmite restaurant – love it or hate it", but all are converted by the time they leave, and if some dishes "don't look appealing on the menu or on the black plates, they certainly taste good". Service is "friendly and well-informed", and there's an "interesting, mainly organic wine list". / www.bulrushrestaurant.co.uk; @bulrushbs6; Thu-Sat, Tue, Wed 8.30 pm; Take bookings all week via phone and/or online.

CASAMIA, THE GENERAL £149 554

THE GENERAL, LOWER GUINEA ST BS1 6FU 0117 959 2884

"WOW!" – "every mouthful is wonderful and foodgasmic" at the Sanchez-Iglesias family's "sensational" HQ: that has regularly won a place at the top of our list of the UK's top 100 restaurants. It marries a "stunning, stone-walled venue" on the ground floor of the city-centre's former General Hospital with "sublime" dishes from a twelve-course tasting menu, with the option of "perfectly matched wine flights". Getting a reservation is no mean feat though: availability is released on the first Tuesday of each month at noon (UK time) for the period four months in advance! And even fans "dislike being required to pay (non-refundable) in advance at the time of booking". / www.casamiarestaurant.co.uk; @Casamia_; Wed-Fri 8.15 pm, Sat 9.30 pm, Sun 1.30 pm.

CLIFTON SAUSAGE £47 333

7 PORTLAND ST BS8 4JA 0117 9731192

"Remaining very popular with locals", 'the Sausage' – a contemporary café serving various types of banger and other meaty British fare – "offers a good selection of food and (in an area where there are not as many good pubs as in the past) has become a haunt for a glass of wine too". Its Bath sibling shut up shop in late 2018. / www.cliftonsausage.co.uk; @cliftonsausage; Take bookings all week via phone and/or online.

FLOUR & ASH £42 432

230B CHELTENHAM RD BS6 5QX 0117 908 3228

"Delicious pizzas" cooked in a wood-fired oven (plus eccentric ice-creams) win fans for this "basic room on the main road north of the city centre". / www.flourandash.co.uk; @flourandash; Mon-Wed 9.30 pm, Thu-Sat 10 pm, Sun 9 pm; Take bookings all week via phone and/or online.

GAMBAS £37

UNIT 15 CARGO 2, WAPPING WHARF BS1 6WD 0117 329 6887

Taking over the former site of Russell Norman's Spuntino in Bristol's Cargo shipping container development (also home to Box-E), a new tapas joint from husband and wife team Kieran and Imogen Waite, who also run the fantastic Bravas in Cotham Hill and Wapping Wharf's Cargo Cantina. Good initial feedback, but too limited for a rating. / www.gambasbristol.co.uk; @GambasTapasBar; Mon-Sat 11 pm, Sun 5 pm.

THE IVY CLIFTON BRASSERIE £56 233

42-44 CALEDONIA PLACE BS8 4DN 0117 203 4555

The glitzy London chain's West Country offshoot occupies a former bank in chichi Clifton Village, and – though food can be a bit up and down – reporters "still love the location", and award it respectable marks in the main. Even so, perhaps because Bristol boasts such a thriving culinary culture, this particular branch seems to have made less of an impact on the local market than it has in most other locales countrywide. / theivycliftonbrasserie.com; @ivycliftonbrass; Mon-Sun 12.30 am.

LIDO £53 335

OAKFIELD PLACE BS8 2BJ 0117 933 9533

A "quirky", even "crazy place for a meal" – a "Victorian lido where you sit and watch Bristolians swim lengths in the open air" while you eat behind glass in the former viewing gallery. This "unexpected venue has even more unexpected culinary standards, serving "rather interesting food with distinctive Mediterranean elements" – a legacy of former Moro chef Freddy Bird, who ran the kitchen here for 10 years – "and service that is friendly rather than professional. The pool and the building are the real stars, though". / www.lidobristol.com;

@lidobristol; No Amex; Take bookings all week via phone and/or online.

LOCKSIDE £41 3 2 2

NO.1 BRUNEL LOCK ROAD BS1 0117 9255 800

Sid's Cafe in 'Only Fools & Horses' is, in reality, this ex-transport caff with a large outside area on the waterfront on the edge of the Avon Gorge, with great views of the Clifton Suspension Bridge. Its aspirations go a bit beyond that of a greasy spoon nowadays, but it's still as a top breakfast venue that it receives the most nominations. / www.lockside.net; Mon-Sun 4 pm; Take bookings all week via phone and/or online.

MARMO £47

31 BALDWIN STREET BS1 1RG 0117 316 4987

Bar Buvette (RIP) has been taken over by (chef) Cosmo and (ex-lawyer, nowadays front of house) Lily Sterck, who met at Bristol Uni and whose CVs include well-known London restaurants, St John and Luca. Local press reports say it's agreeable, white painted looks and short menu of straightforward Mediterranean-influenced cooking (including pasta, charcuterie and ice cream made on the premises) make it one of the best local openings of the year. / www.marmo.restaurant; Tue-Sat 9.30 pm.

THE MINT ROOM £59 4 3 3

12-16 CLIFTON RD BS8 1AF 01173 291 300

"No flock wallpaper here", but a "classy" and "tastefully decorated" spot in Clifton. The food is also "like a work of art" and "tastes as good as it looks" – "spicy, interesting and not too hot". (It also has a branch in Bath). / www.themintroom.co.uk/bristol; @TheMintRoom; Mon-Sat 11 pm, Sun 9 pm; Take bookings all week via phone and/or online.

OTIRA & CHANDOS SOCIAL £58 4 4 3

5-7 CHANDOS ROAD BS6 6PG 0117 973 3669

"You can choose between full meal or tapas" at this white-walled (slightly "stark") yearling run by Kiwi Stephen Gilchrist and Devon-born Kathryn Curtis, which is split between a NZ-inspired restaurant and 'Argentinian Tapas Bar' (Chandos Social @ Otira). The smaller plates are "highly original and so delicious" and the well-rated more adventurous fare features "interesting combinations of sometimes-foraged food, from a limited but frequently changing menu". "Friendly and efficient" service completes the picture. / www.otira.co.uk; @Chandos_Social; Tue-Sat 10 pm.

PACO TAPAS, THE GENERAL £47 5 4 3

LOWER GUINEA ST BS1 6SY 0117 925 7021

Near the docks, Peter Sanchez-Iglesias's aim is to 'transport you to Andalusia' (well that's what the website says) at his casual tapas haunt (named after his dad). As a concept, it's "absolutely spot on" and "tapas of the highest quality, with every dish a delight", alongside a decent list of wines and sherries. "Try to get a seat at the counter for top banter with the chefs and great views as they toss stuff into the open fire". / www.pacotapas.co.uk; @PacoTapas_; Tue-Sat 10 pm; Take bookings all week via phone and/or online.

PASTA LOCO £59 4 4 3

37A COTHAM HILL BS6 6JY 0117 973 3000

This "magical" pasta specialist has in three short years launched cousins Ben Harvey & Dominic Borel as key Bristol restaurateurs. "Authentic-sounding but unusual and delicious pasta sauces" contribute to the "wonderful gastronomic experience" at this "laid-back and intimate" venue. See also Pasta Ripiena, La Sorella and Bianchi's (named after their Italian grandfather Aldo Bianchi). / www.pastaloco.co.uk; @pasta_loco/; Mon-Sat 10 pm; Take bookings all week via phone and/or online.

PASTA RIPIENA £45 4 2 2

33 SAINT STEPHEN'S STREET BS1 1JX 0117 329 3131

It's not fancy (wood banquettes and orange school chairs), but this small new Redcliffe Italian turns out "wonderful" fresh stuffed pasta – a USP in this country – that's full of "interesting seasonal flavours". The owners, behind Pasta Loco, are fast building a local empire, having opened a deli/café, La Sorella, two doors down from the premises in May 2019, followed by trattoria Bianchi in the old Bell's Diner (RIP). / pastaripiena.co.uk; @PastaRipiena; Mon-Sat 10 pm.

PASTURE £48 4 4 3

2 PORTWALL LANE BS1 6NB 07741 193445

'Fire, meat, music' is the mantra at this atmospheric converted warehouse in Redcliffe, dedicated to cooking over fire, complete with open kitchen and meat hanging in chiller cabinets. One of the hottest places in town right now, according to the locals – "the food is simple but very tasty, and the team really care". / www.pasturerestaurant.com; @pasture_bristol; Mon-Sat 10.30 pm, Sun 4 pm.

PREGO £43

7 NORTH VIEW BS6 7PT 0117 973 0496

On the border of Westbury Park and Henleaze, this new neighbourhood spot (started by a pair of floorlayers who gave up their day jobs to become self-taught chefs

and restaurateurs) is already inspiring very positive reports as an excellent new favourite (but too limited feedback for a rating as yet). / www.pregobar.co.uk; @FaielloJulian; Tue-Thu 9.30 pm, Fri & Sat 10 pm, Mon 9 pm.

RIVER COTTAGE CANTEEN £55 3 3 3

ST JOHNS CT, WHITELADIES RD BS8 2QY 0117 973 2458

Hugh Fearnley-Whittingstall's "attractive" converted church escaped the critiques of last year in the current survey, with praise for its "friendly" staff and approachable menu featuring plenty of options for brunch and also "now including interesting vegetarian and vegan choices". / www.rivercottage.net/canteens; @plymouthcanteen; Mon-Sat 10 pm, Sun 5 pm; Take bookings all week via phone and/or online.

RIVERSTATION £52 2 3 4

THE GROVE BS1 4RB 0117 914 4434

"A privileged location" on the harbour is part of the draw at this "modern but mature" operation in a striking looking former river police station (nowadays owned by Youngs). As of a big 2018 refit, "its Pontoon Bar, with its lovely view of the docks, has become a brunch/lunch favourite" owing to its "good choice of food" (and somewhat atoning for the loss of Bordeaux Quay, RIP). Upstairs, in the airy restaurant (with balcony), the performance is "pleasant but unexciting". / www.riverstation.co.uk; @riverstation_; Mon-Sat 11 pm, Sun 10 pm; No Amex; Take bookings all week via phone and/or online.

ROOT £52 4 3 3

WAPPING WHARF BS1 6WP 0117 930 0260

"A harbourside container in the docks" makes for a suitably hipster location for Rob Howell and his partner Megan Oakley's "unpretentious and fun" two-year-old. It serves a small plates menu that's "heavily veg-based" and dishes are "interesting and delicious… without being ridiculous". / www.eatdrinkbristolfashion.co.uk/root; @RootBristol; Mon-Sat 9 pm; No Amex; Take bookings all week via phone and/or online.

SAN CARLO £51 3 3 3

44 CORN STREET BS1 1HQ 0117 922 6586

"Never had a poor meal" – this smart but low-key branch of the slick national group founded by Sicilian-born Carlo Distefano delivers "lovely cooking, attentive and well-trained staff, and there's always a good atmosphere" – "a tried and tested favourite for all special occasions". / www.sancarlo.co.uk; @SanCarlo_Group; Take bookings all week via phone and/or online.

1766 BAR & KITCHEN, BRISTOL OLD VIC £89 3|2|3

KING STREET BS1 4ED 0117 907 2682

"Better food than expected" is to be discovered in this striking, light-filled (perhaps "noisy") space – part of the recent £25m renovation of the UK's oldest theatre, dating back to, er, see if you can guess. Open all day until an hour after the last evening performance, it aims to be a community hub, serving a menu devised by head chef Coco Barone (ex-Glassboat and Rosemarino). There are also pre-theatre deals, obvs. / bristololdvic.org.uk/food-drink/bar-kitchen; @bristololdvic; Mon-Sat 11 pm, Sun 5 pm.

SOUK KITCHEN £46 3|2|2

277 NORTH ST BS3 1JP 0117 966 6880

"Vibrant stuff!" – the Lovells' "buzzy" Middle Eastern venue (there's also a sibling in Clifton) turns out an impeccable array of shakshuka, mezze and hummus and is particularly of note for its "very enjoyable brunch"; a location opposite the Tobacco Factory makes it ideal for pre-theatre dining. / www.soukitchen.co.uk; @soukkitchenbris; Mon-Sat 9.30 pm, Sun 2.30 pm; Take bookings all week via phone and/or online.

SPINY LOBSTER £55 4|4|3

128-130 WHITELADIES ROAD BS8 2RS 0117 9737384

"Still the best fish/seafood in Bristol", say fans of this long running operation (fka Rockfish Grill) from Mitch Tonks of The Seahorse in Dartmouth. "If we were confined to one restaurant forever, this would be it" – "excellent, very fresh fish", "reliable cooking, good service and comfortable". / www.thespinylobster.co.uk; @_SpinyLobster; Mon-Sat 11 pm, Sun 10.30 pm; Take bookings all week via phone and/or online.

WILKS £80

1 CHANDOS RD BS6 6PG 0117 9737 999

"Elegant and imaginative cuisine" and an excellent standard of service again won nothing but rave reviews for James Wilkins & Christine Vayssade's small restaurant in a Redland sidestreet, whose ambiance was "greatly improved" a couple of years ago "with a new feature street-art wall and intimate décor". But in October 2019, the pair put it up for sale in order to pursue an opportunity overseas: hence we've removed the rating for now. / www.wilksrestaurant.co.uk/; @wilksrestaurant; Fri-Sun, Wed & Thu 9 pm; No Amex; Credit card deposit required to book.

WILSON'S £50 5|4|3

24 CHANDOS RD BS6 6PF 0117 973 4157

"The most innovative, original and seasonal food in Bristol at the moment" is the claim made by fans of Jan Ostle and Mary Wilson's Redlands bistro – "a very small place" offering a "reassuringly limited choice of very well-sourced dishes (magnolia blossom and mackerel a surprise and a success) with service that's charming, enthusiastic and helpful". At the end of October 2019, the couple announced

a further step towards hyper-locality, with new menus incorporating ever-more produce from their own expanding farm. / wilsonsrestaurant.co.uk; @JanWilsons; Tue-Sat 10 pm.

WOKY KO CARGO £27 3|3|3

UNIT 7, CARGO, WAPPING WHARF, GAOL FERRY STEPS BS1 6WP

Masterchef finalist, Larkin Cen's original venture is housed in a converted shipping container in Wapping Wharf, serving Asian street food featuring bao, xiao sharing plates, noodle and rice dishes (and a salted caramel ice cream bao dessert that's gone down a storm locally). He also has a number of 'Woky Ko' spin offs, including a new 'Jing Xu' branch in Clifton, which – in September 2019 – replaced his 'Kauto' branch. The new business is based on Siu Lap Dong (BBQ meats). / www.wokyko.com/cargo; @WokyKo; Mon-Wed 9 pm, Thu & Fri 10.30 pm, Sat 9.30 pm, Sun 8 pm.

BRITWELL SALOME, OXFORDSHIRE 2–2D

OLIVIER AT THE RED LION £46 4|4|3

OX49 5LG 01491 613140

"Rustic French food in the heart of the Chilterns" wins high ratings for this old village pub, "a lovely venue for lunch or dinner". Chef-patron Olivier Bouet's "reliably interesting cooking" has earned him quite a following in the area, after 12 years at The Sweet Olive (RIP) in nearby Aston Tirrold. / www.theredlionbritwellsalome.co.uk; Wed-Sat 9 pm, Sun 2.30 pm; Take bookings all week via phone and/or online.

BROADSTAIRS, KENT 3–3D

STARK £85 5|4|4

1 OSCAR ROAD CT10 1QJ 01843 579786

"Utterly triumphant" food "which surprises and delights" again inspires only adulation for Ben & Sophie Crittenden's tiny converted sandwich shop. "It's a privilege to see a chef working on the pass on his own – a real feat!" – and with "one person front of house and ten covers", the overall impression given by this "small, stylish and sexy venue", which only serves a no-choice tasting menu, is "phenomenal". Now three years old, it was blessed with a star by the Michelin man in October 2019. / www.starkfood.co.uk.

WYATT & JONES £56 2|3|3

23-27 HARBOUR ST CT10 1EU 01843 865126

"Ask for a window table overlooking the harbour, but wherever you sit, you'll not be disappointed", say fans of this tastefully decorated and "lively" bar/restaurant. Its ratings are constrained by a couple of reporters who found it pricey or disappointing, but most feedback relates of "careful cooking", with fish dishes particularly recommended. Top Tip – "a quality breakfast near the sea". /

www.wyattandjones.co.uk; Wed & Thu 9 pm, Fri & Sat 10 pm, Sun 4 pm.

BROADWAY, WORCESTERSHIRE 2–1C

THE LYGON ARMS £56 2|4|4

HIGH ST WR12 7DU 01386 852255

It's "always a delight to eat in the beautiful dining room" of this famous Cotswolds institution, a Tudor coaching inn where both Charles I and Oliver Cromwell stayed during the Civil War. Now in the same stable as Cliveden and Chewton Glen, its owners clearly plan to rebuild its place on the map as a luxury country hotel (after some years in the wilderness after it was sold out of the Savoy Group). Historically this barrel-vaulted chamber has attracted celeb chefs such as Gary Rhodes back in the day: now the style is 'Bar & Grill' – results seem "fine but nothing outstanding". / www.lygonarmshotel.co.uk; @The_LygonArms; No jeans; Booking max 8 may apply.

RUSSELL'S OF BROADWAY £66 3|3|3

20 HIGH STREET WR12 7DT 01386 853555

In British furniture designer Gordon Russell's old workshop, this modern British venture is a "well loved local" offering "great-quality ingredients" to "generally good" effect. The owner also runs the adjoining chippie: "top fish 'n' chips with gluten free option". / russellsofbroadway.co.uk; @RussellsRandR; Tue-Sat 9.30 pm, Sun 3.30 pm.

BROCKENHURST, HAMPSHIRE 2–4D

THE PIG £52 3|3|5

BEAULIEU ROAD SO42 7QL 01590 622354

The original and some say "the best" of the six country-house hotels in the 'Pig' litter put together by Robin Hutson, the founder of Hotel du Vin. The "laid-back atmosphere" and "shabby-chic look" have won over a legion of fans, who say it's "good for a date-night and a stay-over" as well as "great for kids, who can run around outside between courses while you chat". The dining room – a "glorious orangerie looking out over the gardens" – reflects the sustainable, home-grown ethos of the kitchen, although the cooking divides opinion: some reporters have enjoyed "fantastic food"; others describe an "interesting but very limited menu that won't appeal to everyone's tastes" and is "overpriced for the quality". / www.thepighotel.com; @The_Pig_Hotel; Mon-Sun 9.30 pm; Take bookings all week via phone and/or online.

BROCKHAM, SURREY 3–3A

THE GRUMPY MOLE £49 3|3|3

BROCKHAM GREEN RH3 7JS 01737 845 101

"Just love it!" – a "consistently enjoyable" destination with "very good-value, reasonably gastronomic food" from a "small but super pub-restaurant chain in Surrey". / www.thegrumpymole.co.uk; Mon-Sat 9.30 pm, Sun 9 pm; No Amex; No bookings.

BROMESWELL, SUFFOLK   3–1D

THE UNRULY PIG   £46   2 1 4

ORFORD RD   IP12 2PU   01394 460 310

This "attractive" sixteenth century inn is a very well-known Suffolk destination that fans say is "well worth the detour off the A12", praising its "excellent" locally sourced food. It inspired uneven reviews this year though: even fans feel it's "somewhat pricey for a meal en route" – and more critical souls "don't understand why it's so popular" given food they feel is "a bit mixed" and incidents of "poor" service. / www.theunrulypig.co.uk; @unrulypig; Mon-Thu 9 pm, Fri & Sat 9.30 pm, Sun 8 pm; Take bookings all week via phone and/or online.

BROUGHTON, LANCASHIRE   5–1A

ITALIAN ORCHARD, SAN MARCO GROUP   £52   3 3 4

96 WHITTINGHAM LANE   PR3 5DB 01772 861240

"Expanding again to highlight how popular it is" – "this already vast Britalian restaurant on the outskirts of Preston has just added an enormous extension (primarily a bar) into which you could probably fit The Ritz's dining room" – and "the whole operation is remarkable given its size". It's the "very good and reasonably priced food" that draws the crowds ("your favourite pizzas and pastas") "but it's the specials menu where the most interest lies", plus "stuff they don't cook" – ie oysters and "Italian charcuterie imported direct from the owning Bragagnini family's homeland in Friuli, as is much of the wine". / www.italianorchard.com; @San_marco_group; Mon-Sun 10.30 pm; Take bookings all week via phone and/or online.

BROUGHTON, NORTH YORKSHIRE   8–4B

BULL AT BROUGHTON   £48   4 4 4

BD23 3AE   01756 792065

Passed from Northcote's Ribble Valley Inns group to Brunning & Price in 2018 (and promptly refurbed), this poshified gastroboozer is a "lovely place to visit" for its "agreeable surroundings with nooks and crannies" and "excellent food and service". / www.thebullatbroughton.com; @Bull_Broughton; Sun-Thu 9 pm, Fri & Sat 9.30 pm; No bookings.

BRUTON, SOMERSET   2–3B

AT THE CHAPEL   £47   3 3 3

28 HIGH ST   BA10 0AE   01749 814070

"It caters for anything – coffee, brunch, lunch, dinner, casual or formal event" – say the many fans of this "clever conversion of a chapel" which is "worth a visit just for the amazing space, windows and views". Top of its repertoire: the wood-fired "pizza is the best for miles" and "they have a great bakery too, but you need to get there early to get anything". /

www.atthechapel.co.uk; @at_the_chapel; Mon-Sat 9 pm, Sun 8 pm; Take bookings all week via phone and/or online.

ROTH BAR & GRILL £58   3 2 4

DURSLADE FARM, DROPPING LN   BA10 0NL   01749 814060

Swiss art behemoths Hauser & Wirth's "sophisticated" Somerset spin-off – with Piet Oudolf-designed gardens and a "wacky" ex-cowshed bar/grill – delivers a "delightful" taste of "urbe in rus". A "really buzzy and vibrant setting" that's "great for cocktails" and with some very solid cooking – in particular "lovely meat" ("outstanding" burgers and "amazing steaks aged in their own salt room"). / www.rothbarandgrill.co.uk; @rothbarandgrill; Tue-Thu, Sun 5 pm, Fri & Sat 11 pm; Take bookings all week via phone and/or online.

BUCKFASTLEIGH, DEVON   1–3D

RIVERFORD FIELD KITCHEN   £44   5 3 4

WASH BARN   TQ11 0JU   01803 762074

"Incredibly tasty", "healthy, hearty organic food" wins universal high praise for this "custom-built hangar" at the HQ of the organic veggie box company. The "wonderful meals" – "not strictly vegetarian but giving full emphasis to the vegetables!" – are "served on large refectory tables", "by informed and friendly staff". "The formula works, and I continue to be impressed". / www.riverford.co.uk; @RiverfordFK; Mon-Sat 10 pm, Sun 7 pm; Booking lunch only.

BUCKLAND, OXFORDSHIRE   2–2C

MOLLIE'S MOTEL & DINER   £29   2 2 3

SHIVENHAM ROAD   SN7 8PY 01367 707777

With blazing neon signage, Soho House have branched out with this new motel concept, now open on the Oxford-Swindon road, with a general store and affordable rooms for overnight stays. A modern take on the "classic US diner": early reports say it's "very smart and cool" but that – in keeping with the brand's DNA – the atmosphere's rated higher than the cooking. Particularly tipped for breakfast; and if you're on the road, you can eat Drive Thru. / www.molliesmotel.com; @molliesmotelUK

BUCKLAND, WORCESTERSHIRE   2–1C

BUCKLAND MANOR £99   4 4 4

WR12 7LY   01386 852626

"A first class experience from the warm welcome on arrival" – this Relais & Châteaux country house hotel is the epitome of a traditional Cotswolds destination and "very efficiently run, but in a very charming and stylish way". William Guthrie and his team deliver "wonderful" updated cuisine, be it from the three-course menu for £70, or the hardly more expensive seven-course taster option for £80. This is also a splendid choice for afternoon tea: "a little piece of calm luxury".

/ www.bucklandmanor.co.uk; @Buckland_Manor; Jacket & tie required; Booking max 8 may apply; children: 12+.

BURCOT, OXFORDSHIRE   2–2D

THE CHEQUERS   £55   3 3 3

ABINGDON ROAD   OX14 3DP 01865 407771

Steven Sanderson's "welcoming" modernised thatched pub in a Thames-side village majors in grass-fed British steak from Sussex, alongside a variety of pub classics. / www.thechequers-burcot.co.uk; @stevesanderson4; Tue-Sat 11 pm, Sun 6 pm.

BURNHAM MARKET, NORFOLK   6–3C

NORTH STREET BISTRO   £54   5 4 3

20 NORTH STREET   PE31 8HG 01328 730330

In March 2017, this converted chapel was morphed into a "lovely local bistro, with excellent food and service from the couple who run it, Holly and Dan (the former, a grad of Gary Rhodes and the Galvin bros, is chef, she is FOH). The French-accented fare, from a shortish menu, is "well above the local standard" – for a "cheap and cheerful" culinary hit, it's "faultless". / www.20northstreet.co.uk; Wed-Fri 4 pm, Sat & Sun 5 pm.

BURTON BRADSTOCK, DORSET   2–4B

HIVE BEACH CAFE   £53   4 2 4

BEACH ROAD   DT6 4RF   01308 897 070

"A lovely place for a seaside lunch", this café has a "nice beach vibe and great seafood" – from "the best fish 'n' chips" to "whole fish and lobster or crab platters". "No reservations and it can get busy, but it's worth the wait every time, with the sands to wander on afterwards". / www.hivebeachcafe.co.uk; @HiveBeachCafe; Sun-Thu 5 pm, Fri & Sat 7 pm; No bookings.

THE SEASIDE BOARDING HOUSE HOTEL   £55   4 3 4

CLIFF ROAD   DT6 4RB   01308 897 205

This "magical cliff-top haven" on Dorset's 'Jurassic Coast' combines the attractions of "superb views" with "exciting but traditional dishes" using "excellent locally sourced ingredients". It offers a "slightly more refined experience than the neighbouring (and highly rated) Hive Beach Café". / www.theseasideboardinghouse.com; @SeasideBH; May need + to book.

BURTON ON TRENT, STAFFORDSHIRE   5–3C

PASCAL AT THE OLD VICARAGE   £47   4 4 4

2 MAIN STREET   DE14 3EX   01283 533222

"A real find in the area – they clearly know what they are doing and have been doing it over many years" at this "longtime favourite", a red brick Georgian outfit where there may be the odd blip on the (French-slanted British fine dining) food front, but it's usually "heaving early on a Monday evening – that says it all". / www.pascalattheoldvicarage.co.uk/; @PascalArnoux; Mon-Thu 9 pm, Fri & Sat 10 pm, Sun 3 pm; Take bookings all week via phone and/or online.

BURY ST EDMUNDS, SUFFOLK   3–1C

MAISON BLEUE   £62   5 4 4

30-31 CHURCHGATE ST   IP33 1RG
01284 760 623

"Fantastique!" – Pascal & Karine Canavet's "little piece of France in Suffolk" goes "from strength to strength", providing "an absolutely first rate" combination of "fabulous and exquisitely presented" Gallic fare, "charming" and "so professional" service and "elegant surroundings". In particular the "super fish dishes always hit the mark". "We usually visit at lunchtime and have to drive through two counties to get there!!" / www.maisonbleue.co.uk; @Maison_Bleue.

1921 ANGEL HILL   £54   5 4 3

19-21 ANGEL HILL   IP33 1UZ
01284 704870

"The influence of a committed chef-patron is obvious" at this "fab old building" – a "lovely old house just off Angel Hill", modernised with a "smart interior": Zack Deakins's "phenomenal" food is "ambitious yet well-executed" ("I was genuinely left speechless it was so good!") and delivered by "a well-led front of house" who provide "slick, discreet service". "Do try the canapes, but get your own set or you will fight over them!". / nineteen-twentyone.co.uk; @1921AH; No bookings.

THE ONE BULL   £49   3 3 3

25 ANGEL HILL   IP33 1UZ   01284 848220

"A great family atmosphere" buoyed by "cheery, well-informed staff" adds to the appeal of this very modern pub – part of the small stable run by the local Brewshed brewery. As well as their own good brews, they serve 40 wines by the glass. / www.theonebull.co.uk; @theonebullbury; Mon-Thu 11 pm, Fri & Sat midnight, Sun 6 pm; Take bookings all week via phone and/or online.

PEA PORRIDGE   £50   5 4 4

28-29 CANNON ST   IP33 1JR
01284 700200

One of the most popular and highly rated neighbourhood restaurants in the country – Justin & Jurga Sharp's "delightful" bistro occupies a "tucked-away" townhouse in the heart of the town and "though a little off-the-beaten track is worth seeking out". "Often combining quirky ingredients", the "exciting" cuisine is "unusual, hearty" and "brilliantly realised" and supported by a "very interesting wine list": "of diverse inspiration, with lots of natural wines and perfectly complementing the food". Service, meanwhile "could not be more welcoming or accommodating." / www.peaporridge.co.uk; @peaporridge; Thu-Sat 9.30 pm, Tue, Wed 9 pm; No Amex; No bookings.

THE NORTHGATE   £52   3 3 4

NORTHGATE STREET   P33 1HP
01284 339604

"For that romantic meal close to the town centre within super gardens and with a great terrace", this elegant restaurant with rooms provides a "gorgeous" setting and "delicious cooking". At lunch, there's a cheaper set menu (as well as the option of sandwiches and salads). / www.thenorthgate.com; @northgatebury; Mon-Fri 9.30 pm, Sat & Sun 11 pm.

BUSHEY, HERTFORDSHIRE   3–2A

ST JAMES   £56   3 3 2

30 HIGH ST   WD23 3HL   020 8950 2480

A "stalwart modern British venue in Bushey High Street, in the otherwise culinary wastelands of Watford", whose "very good, straightforward" cuisine makes it something of a "local gem" – another plus being the warm welcome from "affable" proprietor Alonso. / www.stjamesrestaurant.co.uk; No Amex; Take bookings all week via phone and/or online.

BUSHMILLS, COUNTY LONDONDERRY   10–1D

THE FRENCH ROOMS   £43   3 3 3

45 MAIN STREET   BT57 8QA
028 2073 0033

"Food and décor have a genuinely French feel" as befits the name of this all-day restaurant, whose hearty, slightly old-fashioned fare again wins a thumbs up in (albeit limited) local feedback. The property is currently undergoing an upgrade with six bedrooms due to open in 2020. / www.thefrenchrooms.com; @TheFrenchRooms; Wed & Thu 4 pm, Fri & Sat 11 pm.

BUXTON, DERBYSHIRE   5–2B

SIMPLY THAI   £42   3 3 2

2-3 CAVENDISH CIRCUS   SK17 6AT
01298 24471

"A must if you visit Buxton", serving "authentic, freshly cooked Thai food in the heart of the Peak District" – albeit "toned down for Western tastes". "Useful to combine a meal and performance at the Buxton Opera House". / www.simplythaibuxton.co.uk; @Simplythai_Thai.

CAMBER, EAST SUSSEX   3–4C

THE GALLIVANT   £54   3 3 3

NEW LYDD RD   TN31 7RB   01797 225 057

"A wonderful beachside location" is a key selling point at this former 1960s motel: nowadays a hip B&B serving an "intelligent" menu of locally sourced fare. The September 2019 arrival of chef Jamie Guy may see it develop further. / www.thegallivant.co.uk; @thegallivant; Take bookings all week via phone and/or online; children: under 12s 8.30.

CAMBRIDGE, CAMBRIDGESHIRE   3–1B

AMELIE FLAMMEKUECHE   £23   4 3 2

GRAFTON CENTRE   CB1 1PS
07585 427545

Look out for the bright yellow Citroën van, if you want to try veteran restaurateur Regis Crépy's latest venture, selling Alsatian pizza-type Flammekueche in a Cambridge food court. For a tasty, cheap 'n' cheerful snack that's a little out of the ordinary, these "light", "fresh-tasting" and "reasonably priced" wafers of bread dough complete with toppings are just the job. / www.amelierestaurants.co.uk; @amelie_rest; Mon-Thu 8 pm, Fri & Sat 9 pm, Sun 5 pm.

COTTO   £102   5 4 2

GONVILLE HOTEL, CB1 1LY
01223 302010

For "understated excellence in all categories", Hans Schweitzer's accomplished outfit – which relocated to the Gonville Hotel in 2017 – is "always a must"; "if there is a downside it's the relatively few choices available" on the menu, but beyond that everything is "absolutely exquisite" (and of a classical bent). / www.cottocambridge.co.uk; @cottocambridge; No Amex; need + to book.

THE IVY CAMBRIDGE BRASSERIE   £56   2 2 4

16 TRINITY STREET   CB2 1TB
01223 344044

"An attractive brasserie, professionally staffed and competently run" – "and the food is perfectly fine" at the Cambridge branch of Richard Caring's national roll-out. "The problem with the Ivy Brasseries is that there are too many of them and you can forget which town you're in as they even look the same". "There's nothing really to complain about, they're just a bit formulaic – like an upmarket Côte!". / www.theivycambridgebrasserie.com; Mon-Sun 12.30 am.

MIDSUMMER HOUSE   £165   4 4 3

MIDSUMMER COMMON   CB4 1HA
01223 369299

"Amazing… every time" is still the most typical assessment of this acclaimed Victorian villa – one of the UK's most renowned eateries – which is very picturesquely situated across the Cam from the Varsity's boat houses and bordering Midsummer Common. Daniel Clifford and his team deliver "a superb overall dining experience: the number and quality of amuse-bouches, the sourdough bread, each individual course… the service… all of the highest order". Even many fans feel that the "exuberant bill is hard to justify", however, and to its critics the "staggering costs" are plain OTT, with toppish wine prices a particular gripe ("some more reasonable 'house' options would be welcome"). /

Heaney's, Cardiff

www.midsummerhouse.co.uk; @Midsummerhouse;
Take bookings all week via phone and/or online.

MILLWORKS £52 323

**THE WATERMILL, NEWNHAM ROAD CB3
9EY   01223 367507**

This "meaty joint" occupies an attractive
converted mill, complete with working
water wheel. It "continues to please students
and locals in its airy space overlooking
river and millpond (I saw a kingfisher!)". /
www.themillworks.co.uk; @Cambscuisine; Mon-
Thu 10 pm, Fri & Sat 10.30 pm, Sun 9.30 pm.

NAVADHANYA
CAMBRIDGE £52 433

**73 NEWMARKET RD CB5 8EG
01223 300583**

"Wonderfully subtle-tasting Indian food"
("go for their tasting menu…so good") is
now the order of the day at this former pub
turned dining room; it's "not the cheapest
but the menu is always interesting". /
www.navadhanya.co.uk; @navadhanyauk; Mon-Sat
11 pm, Sun 9 pm.

OAK BISTRO £61 243

**6 LENSFIELD ROAD CB2 1EG
01223 323 361**

A "good local bistro" that's "always very busy"
owing to its solid, reasonably priced Anglo/
European food and a "very visible" owner
who "obviously cares very much about the
business"; "lovely courtyard in summer" too.
/ www.theoakbistro.co.uk; @theoakbistro; No
bookings.

PARKER'S TAVERN £56 224

**1 PARK TERRACE CB1 1JH
01223 606266**

The formerly creaky old University Arms Hotel
has been expensively transformed, and this – it's
new 'pub' – is a "wonderful room in Parisian
brasserie style with high ceilings and mirrors",

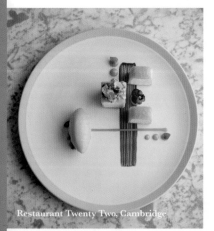

Restaurant Twenty Two, Cambridge

and "with a brilliant view over Parker's Piece".
Tristan Welch (once of Launceston Place) is at
the stoves and has won some stellar newspaper
reviews for his "high-end brasserie food." But
while survey feedback on it is mostly OK,
it's also pretty middling: "nice but not 100%
perfect…"; "pleasantly consistent but a bit
underachieving…"; "nowhere near as good as
initial reviews suggested – shame as the setting's
great". Still, it's "well-placed to up its game in a
city short of options". / www.parkerstavern.com;
@Parkers_Tavern; Sun-Thu 10.30 pm, Fri & Sat
11 pm.

PINT SHOP £44 333

10 PEAS HILL CB2 3PN   01223 352 293

"Tasty, simple, British bistro fare" washed
down by a "great selection of craft beers" plus
a "brilliant range of gins" is the formula at this
"great traditional pub with a twist", launched
five years ago. There's a second branch in
Birmingham, but a spinoff in Oxford closed
down. / www.pintshop.co.uk; @PintShop; Sun-
Wed 10 pm, Thu-Sat 10.30 pm; No bookings.

RESTAURANT TWENTY
TWO £73 543

**22 CHESTERTON ROAD CB4 3AX
01223 351880**

A "top foodie spot in Cambridge" that's going
places – in early 2018, Gordon Ramsay protégé
Sam Carter and his wife Alexandra (FOH) took
over this long-established Victorian townhouse
restaurant on the fringes of the town centre,
and the "new chef has revitalised the site" to
the extent one or two local foodies prefer it to
nearby Midsummer House. Even those who
poke fun at its "modish rough, scratchy, plates"
say its "fabulous and imaginative, local and
seasonal set menu" (from three to seven courses
as well as the à la carte) is "excellent and comes
at a good price". / www.restaurant22.co.uk; Thu-
Sat, Tue, Wed 8.30 pm; Take bookings all week via
phone and/or online; children: 12.

THE ST JOHN'S CHOP
HOUSE £62 333

**21-24 NORTHAMPTON ST CB3 0AD
01223 353 110**

Solid marks again for this sibling to the
Cambridge Chop House, in a cute, two-
floor seventeenth-century house behind
St John's College, and similarly majoring
in meaty mains with ales and wines to
wash a meal down. Top Tip – worth
heading here for their set lunch menu. /
www.cambscuisine.com/st-johns-chop-house;
@cambscuisine; Mon-Sat 9 pm, Sun 2 pm; Take
bookings all week via phone and/or online.

STEAK & HONOUR £13 322

**4 WHEELER STREET, CAMBRIDGE, CB2
3QB CB2 3QB   07766 568430**

"Top-quality burgers either from their
vans (Citroën, you can't miss them) or this
permanent home by the market square", have
built up a firm following for this local brand.
/ www.steakandhonour.co.uk; @steakandhonour;

Mon-Fri 9.30 pm, Sat 10 pm, Sun 5 pm; No
bookings.

STEM & GLORY
CAFE £49 333

13 KING STREET CB1 1LH   01223 314331

The top vegan in town – "a rather small
café but with great ambience and service"
tucked away in the city-centre. Now also with
a London offshoot near Barts (see also). /
www.stemandglory.uk; @stemandglory.

TRINITY £56 343

**15 TRINITY STREET CB2 1TB
01223 322130**

"Definitely above average for a touristy part
of Cambridge" – it's set opposite the Great
Gate of the namesake college – this "lovely
little" establishment has worked up a loyal
following since opening a few years back, and
is a top tip for a "good-value early dinner". /
www.trinitycambridge.co.uk; Mon-Fri 10 pm.

VANDERLYLE £78 544

38 MILL ROAD CB1 2AD

In April 2019, former MasterChef finalist Alex
Rushmer, who closed his Cambridge restaurant
Hole in the Wall in 2017, took over a former
Subway shop a little outside the city centre,
with his former sous chef, Lawrence Butler.
Focusing on local, ethical food, it offers a fixed
five-course vegetarian menu which changes
daily and features a chef's table where diners
sit at a countertop pass for four with views over
the open kitchen. Its fanclub is still small as
things stand but couldn't rate it more highly,
saying its "very inventive non-meat cuisine" is
"well-sourced and just perfect". Don't plan on
dropping in though: bookings are released on
the first Thursday of the month, two months
in advance! / www.vanderlyle-restaurant.com; @
VanderlyleR.

CANTERBURY, KENT   3–3D

THE AMBRETTE
CANTERBURY £52 433

**14 - 15 BEER CART LANE CT1 2NY
01227 200 777**

Dev Biswal's roomy converted pub continues
to do a swift trade in "Indian cuisine with a
twist" (including trademark pyramid-shaped
dosa). As of October 2019, Biswal has mooted
closing his Sussex branch, The Devil in Rye,
to focus on a new Margate spin-off, opened in
2018, as well as here in Canterbury, where he
is reportedly seeking out a second venue for
more casual dining. / www.theambrette.co.uk;
@The_Ambrette; Mon-Thu 9.30 pm, Fri-Sun 10
pm.

CAFÉ DES AMIS £39 334

**95 ST DUNSTAN'S ST CT2 8AA
01227 464390**

"A restaurant to lift the spirits" – this "very
lively" and "very popular" Westgate Mexican
has been turning out "enjoyable" and "fresh-
tasting" fajitas etc for three decades now and

happily there's "lots of choice for non meat-eaters too". / www.cafedez.com; Booking max 6 may apply.

CAFE MAURESQUE £42 [3][2][3]

8 BUTCHERY LN CT1 2JR 01227 464300

"Quirky – but does it for us", this atmospheric cellar close to the cathedral has long been popular for its "good quality, authentic Moroccan food" and Moorish décor, complemented by Andalusian tapas (classified as 'light', 'medium' or 'rich') and paella. / www.cafemauresque.com; @CafeMauresque; Mon & Tue, Thu-Sun 10 pm; Take bookings all week via phone and/or online.

GOODS SHED £48 [3][2][4]

STATION ROAD WEST CT2 8AN 01227 459153

"Located in Canterbury's permanent farmers' market, so it's really buzzing at lunchtimes", this informal spot has had a strong local following across two decades. "It's not elaborate food – the ingredients are sourced from the market and left to speak for themselves" – but it's backed up by a "good-value wine list". A word of warning for winter: "the food's good, but you're sitting in a converted goods shed and boy it's cold. We kept our coats on for the whole meal". / www.thegoodsshed.co.uk; @The_Goods_Shed; Mon-Sat 10.30 pm, Sun 10.15 pm.

CARDIFF, CARDIFF 2–2A

ASADOR 44 £46 [3][3][3]

14 - 15 QUAY STREET CF10 1EA 029 2002 0039

An "almost entirely Spanish drinks list" deconstructed by an "excellent sommelier" sets the tone at Tom & Owen Morgan's – of '44' group fame – two-year-old flagship, with its own dedicated wine cave. "A wonderful experience from beginning to end", the food is consistently highly rated, with Spanish and Welsh produce singed on the parilla grill over different sorts of wood (think 70-day dry-aged Rubia Gallega chuletón steaks). / asador44.co.uk/; @asador44; Mon-Thu 11 pm, Fri & Sat 11.30 pm; Take bookings all week via phone and/or online.

BAR 44 CARDIFF £39 [3][3][3]

15-23 WESTGATE STREET CF10 1DD 03333 44 40 49

"Very popular (but consequently sometimes very noisy)" city-centre Spaniard, part of a local chain (which now extends to Bristol), that wins praise for its "top tapas" and wide selection of wines and sherries. On the downside, some reporters "prefer the Cowbridge original". / www.bar44.co.uk; @bar44cardiff; Sun-Thu 11 pm, Fri & Sat midnight; Take bookings all week via phone and/or online.

CAFE CITTA £39 [3][4][3]

4 CHURCH ST CF10 1BG 029 2022 4040

"A real gem", this low-key but popular city centre venue provides "hearty Italian family fare" – mainly pasta and pizza – backed up by "great service". / www.cafecitta.com; Take bookings all week via phone and/or online.

CASANOVA £52 [3][3][2]

13 QUAY ST CF10 1EA 029 2034 4044

Opened in 2005 by three Italian amici, this "very friendly" outfit features a seasonal, purposefully not extensive menu that "uses a lot of authentic Italian produce" (though arguably "it's actually more Sicilian" in result); while "not cheap", the victuals are "really good" by all accounts. / www.casanovacardiff.co.uk; @CasanovaCardiff.

DUSTY KNUCKLE £40 [4][3][3]

THE PRINTHAUS, 70A LLANDAFF ROAD CF11 9NL 07396 354824

Husband-and-wife team Phil and Deb Lewis run this cool pop-up-gone-permanent pizzeria in Canton – "I felt more on trend just by being there". A crowdfunded sibling was scheduled to open in the restored Warden's House on the edge of Bute Park in 2019. / www.dustyknuckle.co.uk; @dusty_knuckle.

HEANEY'S £48 [4][4][3]

6-10 ROMILLY CRESCENT CF11 9NR 029 2034 1264?

Chef Tommy Heaney, from Great British Menu, moved from the Great House hotel in Bridgend in October 2018 to open his own project in Pontcanna, on a well-known site that's hosted Arbennig and Le Gallois in their day (both now RIP). Serving a variety of small plates, plus various other menus (including vegan and vegetarian options) , fans have immediately hailed it as "Cardiff's best" – it would have scored even higher were it not for the odd 'off' report. / heaneyscardiff.co.uk; @CardiffHeaneys; Tue-Thu 11 pm, Fri & Sat midnight, Sun 6 pm.

MILKWOOD £46 [3][3][2]

83 PONTCANNA STREET CF11 9HS 029 2023 2226

This "friendly and interesting" Pontcanna two-year-old serves up "outstanding" modern Welsh fare. Chef-owners Tom Furlong and Gwyn Myring met while working on the premises 15 years when it was an Italian restaurant, Cibo. / milkwoodcardiff.com; @Milkwoodcdf; Tue-Sat 10 pm, Sun 4 pm.

MINT AND MUSTARD £36 [4][3][3]

134 WHITCHURCH ROAD CF14 3LZ 02920 620333

"South Indian heaven" awaits in the unlikely setting of Cardiff at this, the original of a regional mini-chain – "full of a lively crowd reflecting the academic community around the nearby university"; its "interesting and unusual menu" focuses on seafood, and "pleases the entire family – rare!" / www.mintandmustard.com; @mintandmustard; Mon-Sun 11 pm; No shorts.

PURPLE POPPADOM £49 [4][3][2]

185A, COWBRIDGE ROAD EAST CF11 9AJ 029 2022 0026

"Superb Keralan food from chef Anand George" – formerly of Mint and Mustard – is to be found "in a surprisingly upmarket setting for a grotty Cardiff suburb". The cooking is "refined and elegant, with delicate sauces", and constitutes "a real gastronomic experience" – "without doubt some of the best food in town". / purplepoppadom.com; @Purple_Poppadom; Tue-Sat 11 pm, Sun 9 pm; Take bookings all week via phone and/or online.

VEGETARIAN FOOD STUDIO £24 [3][3][2]

115-117 PENARTH RD CF11 6JU 029 2023 8222

"A Cardiff favourite", this 15-year-old family-run Gujerati BYO is "very much a student hangout – but the vegan/vegetarian food is always excellent". / www.vegetarianfoodstudio.co.uk; @VegFoodStudio; Tue-Sat 10 pm, Sun 8 pm; No Amex; Take bookings all week via phone and/or online.

CARLISLE, CUMBRIA 7–2D

ALEXANDROS GREEK RESTAURANT AND DELI £39 [3][4][3]

68 WARWICK ROAD CA1 1DR 01228 592227

"A buzzy restaurant – a real family affair, with brother in law the chef, his wife helping front of house and now two of their sons joined them" – where the owner Aris is truly committed to making sure you enjoy his food! "The menu features Greek dishes as well as charcoal grilled meat and fish" – lamb chops and octopus get top billing. / www.thegreek.co.uk.

CARTMEL, CUMBRIA 7–4D

AULIS AT L'ENCLUME £260 [4][4][4]

CAVENDISH ST LA11 6PZ

"A personal dining experience of excellence and artistry" – you eat perched on one of six stools at the 'chef's table' / development kitchen experience at this famous Lakeland destination, which offers an alternative to the main restaurant for those spending a couple of nights in the village. Unsurprisingly, it only generates limited feedback, but the picture emerges that – even if "the dishes aren't quite at the standard of those in the restaurant, they are under development so that's fine!" – and it's "an unforgettable evening and privilege to see such culinary magic!" / www.lenclume.co.uk/aulis; @AulisSimonRogan; book online only.

L'ENCLUME £189 555

CAVENDISH ST LA11 6PZ 01539 536362

"Phenomenal… superb… food, wine, service: everything was magical. Please go!". Simon Rogan's "Fat Duck of the North" inspired stunningly consistent reports this year, practically all of them unadulterated hymns of praise, and collectively confirming its position as one of the country's very top gastronomic destinations. A converted smithy in an out-of-the-way village, it has such a "cute" and "beautiful" location and a "very romantic" interior to match. Superlatives abound in descriptions of its "engaging and surprising" tasting menus: "sixteen courses providing incredible mouthfuls of pure culinary bliss with every element utterly excellent". "Highly recommended if you're in the Lakes… or not!" / www.lenclume.co.uk; @lenclume.

ROGAN & CO £65 343

DEVONSHIRE SQUARE LA11 6QD 01539 535917

"Friendly" bistro-style fixture that's the little sister of nearby L'Enclume, and with a similarly picturesque Lakeland setting. Despite its possession of a Michelin star, and reports of some "fantastic" meals here, it's not aiming for culinary pyrotechnics in the same way as its stablemate, and its relatively conventional offering "suits any occasion", most particularly a "romantic" dinner. / www.roganandcompany.co.uk; @simon_rogan; No Amex; Credit card deposit required to book.

CASTLE COMBE, WILTSHIRE 2–2B

BYBROOK RESTAURANT, MANOR HOUSE HOTEL £94 434

SN14 7HR 01249 782206

Rob Potter's "excellent" modern British cuisine is sampled either from a six-course tasting menu (£95) or a three-course à la carte (£75) with a small selection of dishes for each course at this plush five-star hotel in the Cotswolds. Perhaps unsurprisingly, there's the odd gripe about "London prices" but most reports here remain hymns of praise. / www.exclusive.co.uk/the-manor-house/restaurants-bars/the-bybrook/; @themanorhouse; Sun, Mon-Thu 9 pm, Fri & Sat 9.30 pm; No jeans; children: 11+.

CASTLE DOUGLAS, DUMFRIES AND GALLOWAY 7–2B

MR POOK'S KITCHEN £55 544

THE OLD BANK, 38 KING STREET DG7 1AD 01556 504000

"Surprisingly exceptional" – this recent newcomer occupies a converted old bank on the high street that's been stylishly refurbished and where Ed Pook "specialises in using local produce and foraging for ingredients" to provide a very high quality offering, with prime steak something of a speciality (but by no means the defining factor). "The addition of a wine store allows them to stock a long list of wines by the glass". "Excellent – worth a visit". / www.mrpooks.co.uk; Mon-Sat 11 pm, Sun 10 pm.

CAVENDISH, SUFFOLK 3–1C

THE GEORGE £47 333

THE GREEN CO10 8BA 01787 280248

"A lovely timber-beamed building in a charming pretty village" houses this sixteenth-century inn, by the green: "more a restaurant than a pub really but locals still pop in after work for a quick snifter!". Its rated on limited feedback this year, but all very complimentary about its modern British fare either from the à la carte or good value set menus. / www.thecavendishgeorge.co.uk; @TheGeorgecav; Sun-Fri 9.30 pm, Sat 10 pm; Take bookings all week via phone and/or online.

CHADDESLEY CORBETT, WORCESTERSHIRE 5–4B

BROCKENCOTE HALL £88 323

DY10 4PY 01562 777876

A "beautiful setting" adds wow factor to the Eden Collection's Victorian country manor, graced with 70 acres of parkland. "The restaurant excels in all areas, and is best appreciated as part of a package giving access to one of their wonderful choice of rooms". / www.brockencotehall.com; Sun-Fri & Sat 9.30 pm; No trainers.

CHAGFORD, DEVON 1–3D

GIDLEIGH PARK £193 444

TQ13 8HH 01647 432367

Possibly "not as good as in the days of Michael Caines… but still a joy to behold". It's SatNavs at the ready, as you charge down single-track lanes on the fringes of Dartmoor to discover this plush gourmet Shangri-la, set in 100 acres of picturesque grounds. Andrew Brownsword's famous Tudorbethan manor house has long been one of the UK's foremost culinary destinations, but has not hit a proper stride since Michael Caines left (after 21 years) in 2016. Since that time, the hotel has seen a steady succession of new chefs. Michael Wignall came and went. Then Chris Simpson, lasted a year but he moved on in January 2019. Then, in October 2019, the establishment lost the second of the two Michelin stars it formerly held. The upheavals of this period have notably decreased the volume of survey feedback we receive, and there is also the odd disappointing report, too. What's more eye-catching, however, is the resilient quality of the team, and the relative consistency of both ratings and commentary we receive (for example – "we got there and the executive chef had left two weeks before. The head chef had taken over and still did a brilliant job, the sommelier also did a stunningly good job; I am not always the best customer as I like to ask questions, but the service was absolutely excellent throughout"). In September 2019, Chris Eden joined from Cornwall's Driftwood – perhaps he's the man finally to capitalise on the enduring potential and appeal here? / www.gidleigh.co.uk; @Gidleighhotel; No jeans; children: 8.

CHANDLER'S CROSS, HERTFORDSHIRE 3–2A

THE GLASSHOUSE, THE GROVE £71 323

WD3 4TG 01923 296015

"Just reopened and even better than before", this ultra-lux country-house hotel has an unusual 'high-concept' buffet-style dining room inspired by Asian food halls, with chefs cooking at eight 'live action food stations' (robata grill, seafood, tandoor oven et al), from which guests choose as much as they want. It's not fine dining, but it is good-value in its way and it's something-for-everyone style suits entertaining or a family get-together. / www.thegrove.co.uk; @thegrovehotel; Mon-Thu 9 pm, Fri & Sat 9.30 pm.

PRIME STEAK & GRILL, THE CLARENDON £70 333

REDHALL LANE WD3 4LU 01923 264 580

"Friendly staff and one hell of a steak" earn solid praise for this converted pub with a focus on Scottish Highlands beef – part of a group with smaller branches in St Albans and Chandler's Cross. It's "not economical but great for a celebration" – and has a private dining room for parties. / www.primesteakandgrill.com/chandlers-cross; @SteakPrime.

CHELTENHAM, GLOUCESTERSHIRE 2–1C

L'ARTISAN £56 343

30 CLARENCE ST GL50 3NX 01242 571257

"Quaint" and "very French" ("in a non-posey sort of way", i.e. "like being in a really good quality restaurant in provincial France"), the Ogrodzki family's diminutive Gallic haunt was "thoroughly enjoyed" by reporters again this year thanks to its "beautifully presented and perfectly cooked" traditional fare. / www.lartisan-restaurant.com.

BHOOMI £55 443

52 SUFFOLK RD GL50 2AQ 01242 222 010

After six years in business this popular Indian closed its doors in August 2018… only to relaunch with a new Indian BBQ and South Indian plates concept (plus thali deal) just weeks later. On early reports, it's "another great addition to the surfeit of excellent locals", delivering "sublime food and exotic tastes". / www.bhoomi.co.uk; @bhoomichelt.

LE CHAMPIGNON SAUVAGE £94 442

24-28 SUFFOLK RD GL50 2AQ 01242 573449

"Shame on the inspector who was responsible for removing one of this outstanding restaurant's stars" – fans are still scratching

Stovells, Chobham

their heads about Michelin's October 2018 decision to demote David & Helen Everitt-Matthias's famous venue to a single gong. To be fair, the "somewhat suburban" décor has always grated with some diners here, as have odd incidents of "stuffy service". And our own survey has seen a rise in minority reports of "well-cooked but unexceptional" cuisine (with a slight hit to its ratings as a result). And yet, for the most part, feedback on this "calm" and "low key" dining room just outside the city centre – where David is, famously, always at the stoves, with Helen front of house – remains a rhapsody of praise: "a one-off passion project from husband and wife team demonstrated in every superb and gimmick-free dish" – "a masterclass in 'fine' dining with very precise preparation, presentation and exciting flavours" that's "expertly and efficiently run both front of house and in the kitchens". ("It is the yardstick against which we measure everything else: we visit four or five times a year despite it being a six-hour round trip – it's worth the price, and why they lost a star is a total mystery!") / www.lechampignonsauvage.co.uk; @lechampsauvage; Take bookings all week via phone and/or online.

THE COCONUT TREE £34 333

59 SAINT PAUL'S ROAD GL50 4JA 01242 465758

Not a huge volume of feedback, but good ratings all-round from those who do comment on this cheap 'n' cheerful, modern Sri Lankan street food café: the original of a now five-strong mini-chain stretching from Oxford to Cardiff. / www.thecoconut-tree.com; @CoconutTreeUK; Sun-Wed 11 pm, Fri & Sat 1 am, Thu midnight.

THE IVY MONTPELLIER BRASSERIE £57 224

ROTUNDA TERRACE, MONTPELLIER STREET GL50 1SH 01242 894 200

"The fabulous décor in this converted bank and former ballroom with a grand circular bar" is the prime selling point at this branch of Richard Caring's national chain. Ratings have edged up in the last year, but the "lovely building" can't mask the feeling that "the menu choices are more like a Café Rouge", while "the food is OK, but doesn't match the ambience". / www.theivycheltenhambrasserie.com; @ivtcheltenham; Mon-Sun 12.30 am.

KOJ £45 333

3 REGENT STREET GL50 1HE 01242 580455

"Fantastic small plates of Japanese food" win solid ratings for MasterChef finalist Andrew Kojima's "great place – right in the city centre". There's a "changing menu" of izakaya-style dishes, including a beer drinkers' menu – but a 'no sushi' policy as Koj strives to extend understanding of Japanese cuisine. / kojcheltenham.co.uk; @KojCheltenham; Wed-Sat, Tue 9.30 pm.

LUMIÈRE £96 553

CLARENCE PARADE GL50 3PA 01242 222200

"On our foodie tour of the area's culinary heavy hitters (four in four nights) Lumière was by far the best in every way! – the food itself, the artistry and invention of the cooking, the front of house…!" Jon & Helen Howe's small (just 24 covers) venture "benefits from a feeling of intimacy and calm" and scored the top ratings in town this year. Jon Howe's food is "out of this world" with "some very good flavour combinations, some very clever and precise cooking" – all "without pretentious twiddles". Dishes are delivered by the "serene and endlessly helpful Helen in charge of a small team" and "you are made to feel your dining experience is uppermost in their minds rather than your visit being an opportunity for them to 'showcase'". "We liked it so much that we went back to Cheltenham just to eat there again!" (STOP PRESS, the restaurant closed for eight weeks in summer 2019 after Jon Howe broke his ankle walking, but is now up and running again). / www.lumiere.cc; @LumiereChelt; Fri & Sat, Wed & Thu 8.30 pm; children: 8.

NO 131 £69 223

131 PROMENADE GL50 1NW 01242 822939

A "beautiful, stylish hotel and restaurant in a prime town-centre location" (the Prom), whose parent group 'The Lucky Onion', is run by Superdry founder Julian Dunkerton (who is set to open a sixth link – the 300-year-old The Crown pub, in Minchinhampton – in November 2019). On balance, reports are positive, but all come with a catch: "elegant, but ultimately style over substance…", "well-prepared food, service can be haphazard…", "everything was delicious (and priced accordingly!)…" / www.no131.com; @131TheProm; Take bookings all week via phone and/or online.

PRITHVI £64 543

37 BATH ROAD GL53 7HG 01242 226229

"Clever, well-imagined" and "delicately spiced food, unlike any normal Indian restaurant" distinguishes this "superb" venue, named after the Skanskrit for 'Mother Earth'. Opened in 2012, it has now moved house into a "much more elegant setting" opposite Pittville Park. Top Tip: "a relative bargain for lunch". /

www.prithvirestaurant.com; @37Prithvi; Tue-Sat 9.30 pm; No Amex.

PURSLANE £65 333

16 RODNEY RD GL50 1JJ 01242 321639

"A real gem", Gareth Fulford's "friendly" backstreet outfit is "far better than the rather unprepossessing exterior suggests", with "very well cooked fish" the star of a menu that's "creative" – with "exquisite flavour combinations" – if a little too "cheffy" for some tastes. It took some flak for seeming "a little overpriced" this year, and an interior that's "buzzy" and "very relaxing" to fans is, to sceptics, "dreary". / www.purslane-restaurant.co.uk; @eatatpurslane; No Amex; Take bookings all week via phone and/or online.

CHESSINGTON, SURREY 3–3A

SAFFRON SUMMER £45 533

4 ACE PARADE KT9 1DR 020 8391 4477

"A brilliant part of the Surrey dining scene" – Awanish Roy's "contemporary" Indian sits just off the A3, and wins uniform praise in numerous reports for its "classic Indian dishes" ("such as an authentic wild boar vindaloo" and other game, such as guinea fowl) "with a modern fine dining twist", and all "at suburban prices". / www.saffronsummer.co.uk; @SaffronSummer_; Wed-Fri 4 pm, Sat & Sun 5 pm.

CHESTER, CHESHIRE 5–2A

LA BRASSERIE, CHESTER GROSVENOR, CHESTER GROSVENOR £66 223

EASTGATE CH1 1LT 01244 324024

"Hotel brasseries don't usually hold much appeal", but this "big, slightly blingy, and certainly buzzing" operation provides an unusually high level of polish for a venue in a small provincial city. The food? – from a "fairly standard" menu some reporters feel results are "terrific", but others say "while prices weren't awful, I expected more from the place, so the bill felt like it was heavy without delivering". Top Tip – "fabulous afternoon tea in beautiful surroundings". / www.chestergrosvenor.com; @TheGrosvenor; Mon-Sun 9 pm; Take bookings all week via phone and/or online.

THE CHEF'S TABLE £58 453

4 MUSIC HALL PAS CH1 2EU
01244403040

"Small but perfectly formed" – this "tiny place with an open-plan kitchen" tucked away off Northgate Street serves "wonderful food" with "great depth of flavour" and "you're really well looked after" too. / www.chefstablechester.co.uk; @ChefsTableCH1; Take bookings all week via phone and/or online.

CORNICHON £45 334

71 HIGH STREET CH3 8JA 01829 741391

Just a short drive outside Chester, a smartly appointed "bar and bistro in an old family grocers shop retaining much of the original features and fittings of the Georgian building" (The Gunnery). "A straightforward menu is well realised" and weekend brunch is a feature. / www.cornichonrestaurant.co.uk; @CornichonFood; Wed & Thu 10.30 pm, Fri & Sat 11 pm, Sun 5.30 pm.

1539 £53 334

THE RACECOURSE CH1 2LY
01244 304 611

"With stunning views over Chester Racecourse" ("book early to be sure of a window table"), this well-established venue marries "fine wines and food" and, so long as you "don't go on race days", there are "usually quiet areas for those important business meetings". / www.restaurant1539.co.uk; @Restaurant1539; Mon-Thu 11 pm, Fri & Sat 1 am, Sun 9 pm; No bookings.

JOSEPH BENJAMIN £50 333

140 NORTHGATE STREET CH1 2HT
01244 344295

Joe & Ben Wright's "reliable" bistro, close to the city walls, is noted for its "good pre-dinner drinks list (several different gins which slip down well)" and "warm and friendly" service. The pair also run a tapas bar next-door, Porta, which has spin-offs in Altrincham and, as of 2018, Salford. / www.josephbenjamin.co.uk; @joseph_benjamin; Tue, Wed, Sun 5 pm, Thu-Sat midnight; Take bookings all week via phone and/or online.

MOULES A GO GO £49 334

6-12 CUPPIN STREET CH1 2LE
01244 348818

"A long-term favourite which has been going for decades" – in recent times now decamped to La Tasca's old digs from its original home in The Rows – it boasts "plush and trendy" décor; "the moules marinières are wonderful and there are nights dedicated to surf and turf or lobster". / www.moulesagogo.co.uk; @MoulesaGoGo; Sun-Thu 9 pm, Fri & Sat 10 pm; Take bookings all week via phone and/or online.

SIMON RADLEY, THE CHESTER GROSVENOR £101 444

56-58 EASTGATE STREET CH1 1LT
01244 324 024

Acclaimed by some conservative types as "the best dining experience in the north-west of England" – this much-accoladed dining room sits in the heart of an unusually grand city-centre hotel (well, it is owned by one of the UK's wealthiest men, the Duke of Westminster) right next to Chester's iconic Eastgate clock. Simon Radley has held a Michelin star here nigh-on since he joined in 1998, and his "awesome" cuisine, the "wonderful service" and the duke's impressive cellar (with 700 bins) maintains this as one of the region's culinary 'heavy hitters' if you are seeking an experience of traditional luxury and sophistication. "Huge bill" though. The hotel also provides "the best afternoon tea for miles" in its Arkle Bar & Lounge. / www.chestergrosvenor.com; @TheGrosvenor; No trainers; children: 12+.

STICKY WALNUT £64 444

11 CHARLES ST CH2 3AZ 01244 400400

Gary Usher's increasingly famous Elite Bistros chain started with this "lovely neighbourhood bistro" in Hoole – although it's "only small", and it's in what might seem like "an unlikely location", being a low-key residential suburb of Chester, whose main claim to fame is that it's not far from the railway station. The venue bears all the all-round formula that's driven Gary's success though: an "intimate" yet "bustling and lively" atmosphere; "warm, humorous service"; and "generous portions of very well-cooked food" from a "slightly unusual" menu that's "very reasonably priced". / www.stickywalnut.com; @stickywalnut; Sun-Thu 9 pm, Fri & Sat 10 pm; Credit card deposit required to book.

UPSTAIRS AT THE GRILL £52 333

70 WATERGATE ST CH1 2LA
01244 344883

Good all-round ratings again (if on limited feedback) for this swish steakhouse and cocktail bar in the city-centre. It offers an unusually comprehensive range of cuts, with a variety of Aberdeen Angus and USDA options, plus a big selection of sides. / www.upstairsatthegrill.co.uk; @UpstairsatGrill; Mon-Sat 10.30 pm, Sun 9.30 pm; Take bookings all week via phone and/or online.

CHEW MAGNA, SOMERSET 2–2B

THE PONY & TRAP £71 333

BS40 8TQ 01275 332 627

"Incredible food" in "a lovely countryside setting" (complete with garden, and views over the Chew Valley) has carved a major culinary reputation for Josh & Holly (brother and sister) Eggleton's converted pub (more of a restaurant nowadays). But even reporters who acknowledge the quality of the "beautifully prepared dishes, with great combinations of texture and flavour" can still find it notably "overpriced" ("decent but not worth the high cost"). / www.theponyandtrap.co.uk; @theponyandtrap; Tue-Sat 9 pm, Sun 6 pm; No Amex.

CHICHESTER, WEST SUSSEX 3–4A

FARMER, BUTCHER, CHEF, THE GOODWOOD HOTEL £62 322

GOODWOOD ESTATE PO18 0PX
01243 755070

By most, if not quite all, accounts a "lovely place to visit on the east side of the Goodwood Estate", which was set up a few years back to purvey Lord March's glamorous sporting venue's organic, homegrown lamb, pork and "great butcher's board beef". / www.goodwood.com/estate/farmer-butcher-chef; @FBCrestaurant; Take bookings all week via phone and/or online.

FIELD & FORK £51 333

4 GUILDHALL ST PO19 1NJ
01243 789915

Sam & Janet Mahoney's "super" city-centre venue – with "open fires in winter and conservatory in summer" – "seems to improve with every visit and the set lunches are remarkable value" (as are the "excellent pre-theatre deals" before a trip to the Festival Theatre). The "emphasis is on locally sourced food", with "fish a speciality and always cooked in an interesting manner". / www.fieldandfork.co.uk; @samsfork.

PALLANT RESTAURANT AND CAFE £53 323

EAST PALLANT PO19 1TJ 01243 770827

"Great for lunch while visiting the small but fantastic namesake gallery" – this light-filled café turns out straightforward but satisfying seasonal plates (they also do steak nights and monthly pop-ups) and "the courtyard in particular is delightful in the summer". / www.pallantrestaurantandcafe.co.uk; @EatAtPallant; Tue, Wed, Fri-Sun 5 pm, Thu 11 pm; Take bookings all week via phone and/or online.

THE RICHMOND ARMS £52 333

MILL ROAD, WEST ASHLING PO18 8EA
01243 572046

"A definite must-visit" – "an amazing small gastropub next to a beautiful pond", on the Goodwood Estate, and with a line in "tasty and flavoursome" victuals (including game). / www.therichmondarms.co.uk; Wed-Sat 9 pm, Sun 3 pm; Take bookings all week via phone and/or online.

OLD HALL INN £44 **333**

WHITEHOUGH SK23 6EJ 01663 750529

This atmospheric sixteenth-century inn serves "good quality pub food for a small village" in a remote part of the Peak District. It's under the same ownership as the Paper Mill Inn opposite (which serves pizzas) – and guests are welcome to carry their drinks from one to the other. They also offer accommodation. / www.old-hall-inn.co.uk; @oldhallinn; Mon-Thu 9 pm, Fri & Sat 9.30 pm, Sun 7.30 pm.

THE SIR CHARLES NAPIER £71 **434**

SPRIGGS ALLEY OX39 4BX 01494 483011

"Always worth the slightly tortuous drive to the 'back of beyond'", Julie Griffith's Chilterns gastropub "hasn't really changed much (other than the sofa cushions) in over 25 years", but when that means "beautiful food in beautiful surroundings" ("lovely cosy log fires in winter, wonderful garden for outdoor dining in the summer") no one seems to mind. / www.sircharlesnapier.co.uk; @SirCNapier; Tue-Sat 9.30 pm, Sun 3.30 pm.

BANK HOUSE WINE BAR & KITCHEN £38

11 HIGH STREET BR7 5AB 020 8249 0461

This September 2019 newcomer in the heart of the town (occupying a former NatWest bank, hence the name) is notable for its owner: Stuart Gillies is the former CEO of Gordon Ramsay's restaurant group, and has launched this venture with the help of wife Cecilia. Previously a chef, Gillies has devised a 'European small plates' menu for the two-floor wine bar. / bankhousechislehurst.com; @BankhouseBR7; Tue-Sat 11 pm, Sun 6 pm.

STOVELL'S £74 **443**

125 WINDSOR ROAD GU24 8QS 01276 858000

Fernando & Kristy Stovell's beamed Tudor farmhouse helps put Chobham on the foodie map with its "amazing" and ambitious cuisine, prepared on a wood-fired grill and with a 'Taste of Mexico' tasting menu, nodding to the chef's own roots. Practically all reports this year rate the food extremely highly, and it's a "romantic" spot too. / www.stovells.com; @Stovells; Mon-Wed 11 pm, Thu & Fri midnight, Sat 10 pm, Sun 5 pm.

CAPTAIN'S CLUB HOTEL & SPA £62 **333**

WICK FERRY, WICK LANE BH23 1HU 01202 475111

"A fantastic riverside location" is the prime attraction at this glass-fronted modern hotel overlooking the Stour estuary, but its food offering is consistently well-rated too: "as regular visitors, we're never disappointed and the all-day menu's great for casual drop-ins". / www.captainsclubhotel.com; @TheOfficialCCH.

THE JETTY, CHRISTCHURCH HARBOUR HOTEL & SPA £62 **344**

95 MUDEFORD BH23 3NT 01202 400950

"On the edge of delightful Christchurch, with lovely views over Mudeford" – Alex Aitken's well-known venture is "a great spot in the grounds of the Christchurch Harbour Hotel" ("especially on a sunny day when you can also sit outside"); and being "here as the sun sets, gazing through the sky-high windows across the gently lapping waters, brings a feeling of calm, even after the toughest of weeks at work". "London prices make it a special occasion destination", with predominantly fish dishes that are generally "first class" ("if a little patchy at times"). Top Tip – "parking is woefully insufficient, so allow time to sort that out". / www.thejetty.co.uk; @alexatthejetty; Mon-Sat 10 pm, Sun 8 pm; Take bookings all week via phone and/or online.

MADE BY BOB, THE CORNHALL £47 **433**

THE CORNHALL 26 MARKET PL GL7 2NY 01285 641818

Cooking of "exceptional quality" ensures that this long-established open kitchen/deli venue in the town centre is "always busy, with a vibrant atmosphere". It's "great" for breakfast and lunches, with dinner served on Fridays and Saturdays. / www.foodmadebybob.com; @MadeByBob; Mon-Thu 5 pm, Fri & Sat 10.30 pm, Sun 4 pm.

TIERRA & MAR £49 **343**

29 SHEEP STREET GL7 1QW 01285 642777

"Very good Mediterranean cooking at a reasonable price" and "an incredibly friendly team to look after you" both win praise for this two-year-old, whose sharing plates approach is "somewhere between fine dining and relaxed bistro". "It serves tapas in two sizes, often quite original (slow-cooked rabbit terrine with macadamia nuts, chocolate-coated venison with Jerusalem artichoke puree, etc)" and is "a welcoming place, with widely spaced tables". / www.tierraandmar.co.uk; @TierraandMar; Take bookings all week via phone and/or online.

LOCH FYNE RESTAURANT AND OYSTER BAR £50

LOCH FYNE PA26 8BL 01499 600482

It spawned a national chain, but there's curiously little feedback this year on this popular stop-off on the A83. Originally little more than a shed (started in the 1970s), it has been refurbished in recent times to provide a more comfortable bistro-style experience, with views of the loch, but the focus remains on simple fish and seafood, much of it from its in-house smokery. / www.lochfyne.com; @lochfyneoysters.

THE FENWICK ARMS £45 **333**

LANCASTER RD LA2 9LA 01524 221250

"A gastropub favourite" – this 250-year-old inn, part of the regional Seafood Pub Company group, is "a top choice for fish in north Lancashire/southeast Cumbria", "even if you just want fish 'n' chips superbly cooked and presented". "The meat is not bad too", while its "excellent rooms" make it a perfect stop en route to the Lake District. / www.fenwickarms.co.uk; @FenwickArms; Sun-Thu 9 pm, Fri & Sat 10 pm; Take bookings all week via phone and/or online.

THE CRICKETERS £51 **333**

WICKEN RD CB11 4QT 01799 550442

Trevor & Sally Oliver have run this village pub for 43 years – they moved in when their nowadays-world-famous son Jamie was a baby, and he helped out in the kitchen as a teenager. Its pub-grub avoids fancy fireworks, but is consistently well-rated. Like his son, Trevor grew up in an Essex pub, training as a chef and becoming a licensee at the tender age of 19, and was a pioneer of the notion that pubs could serve really good food. / www.thecricketers.co.uk; @CricketersThe; Mon-Sat 9.30 pm, Sun 8 pm; No Amex; Take bookings all week via phone and/or online.

THE SWAN INN £52 **443**

2 HARE LANE KT10 9BS 01372 462 582

"Esher needed a really good restaurant and this is it!" – star Spanish chef José Pizarro took over this "very smart pub" near Esher Common in March 2019, purchasing it from Bibendum's Claude Bosi, and replaced its menu of pub classics with "wonderful, new Spanish tapas fare", plus some Hispanified British dishes. For parties of 8 or more, you can order a 'feast' of suckling pig or turbot. / www.theswanesher.co.uk; @jose_pizarro; Mon-Wed 9.30 pm, Thu & Fri 10 pm, Sun 8.30 pm.

GEORGE & DRAGON £52 **3**|**3**|**3**

CA10 2ER   01768 865381

This "cosy and relaxed gastropub" near Penrith serves "reliably good" food "using produce from their own farm and garden". With its "simple rooms and reasonable breakfast", it makes "a great overnight stopping-point just off the M6" – and dogs are welcome, too. / www.georgeanddragonclifton.co.uk; @GeorgeDragonCli; No bookings.

BAILIFFSCOURT HOTEL £77 **3**|**4**|**4**

CLIMPING ST   BN17 5RW   01903 723511

A plush spa-hotel, medieval in style, but actually built in the 1920s for a Guinness scion, and located a short stroll through woodland to the Climping coastline (Arundel castle is also within easy reach); the dining room, with its tapestry-adorned walls and mullioned windows, was consistently highly rated this year (if on limited feedback). / www.hshotels.co.uk; Mon-Sun 11 pm; Booking max 8 may apply; children: 7+.

THE OLIVE BRANCH £47 **4**|**4**|**4**

MAIN ST   LE15 7SH   01780 410355

"A great village asset" – Ben Jones & Sean Hope's "intimate old pub" of two decades' standing was one of the country's early wave of rural gastropub, and has – with the help latterly of chef Nick Evans – "maintained high standards" over many years: "it's the best affordable restaurant for miles around" turning out reasonably priced, locally sourced food, alongside an "interesting and eclectic wine list"; "comfortable, well-appointed accommodation available in a separate house over the road", too. / www.theolivebranchpub.com; @theolivebranch; Mon-Sat 9.30 pm, Sun 9 pm; No Amex; Take bookings all week via phone and/ or online.

THE ASSHETON ARMS £43 **3**|**2**|**4**

BB7 4BJ   01200 441227

This "lovely gastropub in the pretty village of Downham, under the shadow of Pendle Hill" is part of Jocelyn Neve's Seafood Pub Company – the interior has been "completely renovated", but retains a proper atmosphere with its "roaring fires". Views on its performance diverged a little this year: most reports suggest the "excellent fish and seafood is definitely worth going for", but a couple of mixed reports ("good but not as good as it was"; "trying hard but no organisation") sound a warning note. / seafoodpubcompany.com/the-assheton-arms/; @SeafoodPubCo; Sun-Fri 11 pm, Sat midnight.

FOREST OF BOWLAND   BB7 3AT   01200 448222

This famous, "charmingly old-fashioned" eighteenth-century inn has been run by the Bowman family for three generations and is set in the stunning landscape of the Forest of Bowland – bang in the middle of what the Office of National Statistics says is the happiest place to live in Britain. All reports give a solid thumbs-up to its traditional cooking and high quality cellar, but it somewhat lacks the profile of yesteryear. / www.innatwhitewell.com/; @innatwhitewell; Take bookings all week via phone and/or online.

THE CRICKETERS £52 **3**|**3**|**4**

DOWNSIDE COMMON   KT11 3NX   01932 862 105

This big, "wonderfully positioned" inn, on Downside Common offers "a great formula which feels truly local, despite being part of a growing chain" (Raymond Blanc's White Brasserie Co.). Service is "friendly and efficient" and provides "a great combination of high-quality traditional pub food" and some "good-value brasserie-style items". / www.cricketerscobham.com; @white_brasserie; Mon-Sat 11 pm, Sun 10 pm; Take bookings all week via phone and/or online.

THE IVY COBHAM BRASSERIE £56 **2**|**2**|**4**

48 HIGH ST   KT11 3EF   01932 901777

"The food may be lacklustre but it's adequate – we go for the warm and rich ambience, and the lovely garden": a good summary of the appeal of this very popular Surrey branch of the upmarket Ivy brand. "Of course it lacks originality" but most reporters are forgive this and also the fact that it gets "noisy and busy". Top Tip – "great place for brunch". / theivycobhambrasserie.com; @IvyCobhamBrass; Mon-Sun 12.30 am.

THE PLOUGH INN £58 **3**|**4**|**3**

PLOUGH LANE   KT11 3LT   01932 589790

Celebrating its fifth year this year, this comfortable gastropub just outside Cobham in the village of Downside attracts very solid scores all-round thanks to its "better-than-average pub food", "friendly front of house team and a relaxed atmosphere" ("love that you can just pop in for a pint"). "Delightful outdoor eating area in summer" too. / www.theploughinncobham.co.uk; Mon-Thu 9.30 pm, Fri & Sat 10 pm, Sun 7.30 pm.

GRAIN £108 **4**|**4**|**3**

11A NORTH HILL   CO1 1DZ   01206 570005

"Some of the best food in Essex" risks being a double-handed compliment, but this trendy three-year-old is winning ever-more awards and accreditations. The food (chosen from a menu with five sections, 'garden', 'water', 'land', 'cheese' and 'sweet') provides "a wonderful combination of flavours and the concept here of small plates works really well". / www.grain-colchester.co.uk; @grainrest; Wed-Sat 9.30 pm, Tue 9 pm; Take bookings all week via phone and/or online.

LUCKNAM PARK, LUCKHAM PARK HOTEL £104 **4**|**4**|**5**

SN14 8AZ   01225 742777

Stunning Palladian mansion, whose sweeping tree-lined driveway and ornate regalia is tailor-made for a special occasion, complete with "lovely view and garden" and impressive, formal dining room. Longtime chef Hywel Jones continues to produce "superb" cuisine here: "the seven-course tasting menu is a must", say fans, but there's also a three-course à la carte (for £87). / www.lucknampark.co.uk; @LucknamPark; Wed-Sat 10.30 pm, Sun 10 pm; Jacket required; children: 5+ D & Sun L.

BANNY'S RESTAURANT £30 **4**|**4**|**3**

1 VIVARY WAY   BB8 9NW   01282 856220

This nautically styled old Harry Ramsden's remains "very popular with Boundary Mill shoppers" owing to its "great fish 'n' chips and service" (not to forget the textbook mushy peas. / www.bannys.co.uk; @Bannys; No Amex.

THE HUT £53 **4**|**3**|**3**

COLWELL CHINE ROAD   PO40 9NP   01983 898 637

"Always a goody and great fun" – a summer-only beach shack with "phenomenal sea views, a brilliant atmosphere, and some surprisingly serious, even refined cooking" (of fish, but also burgers and tacos); reporters "can't wait to come back!" / www.thehutcolwell.co.uk; Take bookings all week via phone and/or online.

BRYN WILLIAMS AT PORTH EIRIAS £51 **3**|**2**|**3**

THE PROMENADE, LL29 8HH   01492 577 525

"Fish is the thing at Bryn Williams's contemporary, casual cafe on the shore at Rhos on Sea" in a landmark development central to the new promenade, and with "amazing views". Overall there's "nothing revolutionary or over-luxurious here, but rather bistro comfort and good cooking". / www.portheirias.com; @brynportheirias; Wed-Sat 9 pm, Mon & Tue, Sun 4 pm; Take bookings all week via phone and/or online.

Number One, Balmoral Hotel, Edinburgh

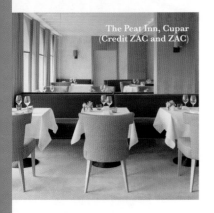
The Peat Inn, Cupar
(Credit ZAC and ZAC)

CONGLETON, CHESHIRE   5–2B

PECKS   £65   2 2 4

NEWCASTLE RD CW12 4SB
01260 275 161

A "unique theatrical atmosphere" helps distinguish this long-established local destination – founded in 1984 and given an overhaul in autumn 2018. 'Dinner at 8' is the main event: a five-course (seven at weekends) blow-out that makes for quite an occasion (with a more conventional format for lunch and afternoon tea). Rated on limited feedback this year. / www.pecksrest.co.uk; @pecksrest; Tue-Sat 10.30 pm, Sun 3 pm; Take bookings all week via phone and/or online.

COOKHAM, BERKSHIRE   3–3A

MALIKS   £45   4 3 3

HIGH ST SL6 9SF   01628 520085

"In the lovely setting of a half-timbered house in Cookham high street" – and "beautifully restored after a fire" two years back – this "good-quality" Indian "offers far more varied dishes than are available on the average high street", and its "fantastic value Sunday buffet" remains of particular note. / www.maliks.co.uk; Mon-Sat 11 pm, Sun 10 pm; Take bookings all week via phone and/or online.

THE WHITE OAK   £42   2 3 2

THE POUND SL6 9QE   01628 523043

"Imaginative combinations and good service" have earned a "well-deserved" reputation over a dozen years for what is "more a restaurant with a bar than the other way round". This was not a vintage year for feedback, however, with some reporters feeling its performance "only just scraped by". / www.thewhiteoak.co.uk; @thewhiteoakcoo; Mon-Sat 11 pm, Sun 6 pm; No Amex.

COPSTER GREEN, LANCASHIRE   5–1B

YU   £58   4 4 3

500 LONGSIGHT RD BB1 9EU
01254 240665

"Not by any stretch of the imagination your average Chinese", beginning with the odd

setting in an unglamorous-looking former pub, right on the A59, and continuing inside, which "comes across as a bit blingy". "Fortunately the food really is excellent, especially from a Western point of view" – "even simple dishes are fresh-tasting and cleanly fried – not at all masked by gloopy sauces". / @yuandyou; Take bookings all week via phone and/or online.

CORSE LAWN, GLOUCESTERSHIRE   2–1B

CORSE LAWN HOTEL   £58

GL19 4LZ   01452 780771

The Hine family's long-established country house hotel has a scenic location, occupying a rural Queen Anne house next to a duck pond. Baba Hine, la patronne of 40 years standing, still cooks breakfast and her son Giles nowadays presides over the cellar established by her late husband Denis. The restaurant is old-fashioned in design, although its traditional cooking (with Chris Exley nowadays at the stoves) has somewhat moved with the times. Feedback was limited this year, and hence we've held off on a rating. / www.corselawn.com; @corselawn; Sun-Thu 10 pm, Fri & Sat 10.30 pm.

COWBRIDGE, VALE OF GLAMORGAN   1–1D

BAR 44   £39   3 3 3

44C HIGH ST CF71 7AG   03333 44 40 49

Still good marks, if on limited feedback, for this upbeat, simply decorated modern bar, serving high quality Spanish tapas and a wide range of wines and sherries. It's the original of the Morgan family's small group – founded 17 years ago – which is now four-strong and has recently moved into Bristol. / www.bar44.co.uk; @bar44cowbridge; Fri & Sat midnight, Tue-Thu 11 pm, Sun, Mon 5 pm; No Amex; Take bookings all week via phone and/or online.

HARE AND HOUNDS   £43   4 4 4

ABERTHIN CF71 7LG   01446 774892

"Wonderful seasonal local food, a great wine list and lovely, knowledgeable staff" are an attractive mix at this "terrific" 300-year-old pub in the Vale of Glamorgan. Chef Tom Watts-Jones grew up in the village and trained in top London kitchens including St John and the Anchor & Hope. / www.hareandhoundsaberthin.com; @Hare__Hounds; Wed-Sat 9 pm, Sun 4 pm; Take bookings all week via phone and/or online.

CRASTER, NORTHUMBERLAND   8–1B

JOLLY FISHERMAN   £43   3 3 4

HAVEN HILL NE66 3TR   01665 576461

A "lovely-looking pub in a beautiful location", next to a harbour on the spirit-raising mid-Northumberland coastline, and opposite the iconic L Robson & Sons 'Craster Kipper' smokehouse; "wonderful" fish is the order of the day, unsurprisingly, with both smoked versions and salmon sarnies exemplary. / www.thejollyfishermancraster.co.uk;

@TheJollyCraster; Mon-Sun 11 pm; No Amex; No bookings.

CRATHORNE, NORTH YORKSHIRE   8–3C

CRATHORNE ARMS   £55   3 3 4

TS15 0BA   01642 961402

"Now in its sixth year, this country pub run by Eugene and Barbara McCoy (of the Cleveland Tontine fame) offers everything from a wonderful restaurant to bar meals, fine wines and ales" and "you are always made to feel welcome by an excellent team" (whether you're a farmer or a footie star, who have been known to drop in while detouring off the A19). / thecrathornearms.co.uk; Tue-Sat 9.30 pm, Sun 3.30 pm; No bookings.

CRAWLEY, HAMPSHIRE   3–4B

THE FOX   £56   2 3 4

PEACH HILL LANE SO21 2PR
01962 461302

This 1780s pub in a village near Winchester reopened in late 2018 after an 18-month refurb that saw it "transformed" – with a "sophisticated dining room (now by far the largest section of the establishment)" offering "well-made modern pub classics". The owners (who also run The Bugle at Twyford) have installed five B&B suites upstairs. / the-fox.pub; Wed-Fri 4 pm, Sat & Sun 5 pm.

CROMARTY, HIGHLAND   9–1B

SUTOR CREEK   £48   3 3 2

21 BANK ST IV11 8YE   01381 600855

Graham & Phoebe Fox's funky harbourside venue in a well-preserved seventeenth-century east Highlands town earns solid ratings for its crowd-pleasing combination of "tasty" local seafood, produce from its Black Isle hinterland and wood-fired pizza. / www.sutorcreek.co.uk; No Amex; Take bookings all week via phone and/or online.

CROMER, NORFOLK   6–3C

NO. 1   £34   3 3 2

1 NEW ST NR27 9HP   01263 515983

"A delish menu of seafood (and other dishes) in the upstairs restaurant" is matched by "excellent fish 'n' chips downstairs" at this "terrific" outfit "owned by Galton Blackiston of Morston Hall fame". "Upstairs is really inventive, with tapas-style small plates as well as conventional main courses". There are "great views" and "nothing is too much trouble". / www.no1cromer.com; @no1cromer; Wed & Thu, Sun 8 pm, Fri & Sat 9 pm; Take bookings all week via phone and/or online.

CROSTHWAITE, CUMBRIA   7–4D

THE PUNCH BOWL INN   £54   4 4 4

LA8 8HR   01539 568237

"This is how you do great pub food" – "full of flavour", using seasonal ingredients from the owner's farm and with "generous helpings as befits as a gastropub". "They don't try to be too clever but they are still a step above everyone else nearby", hence their "excellent" local reputation. / www.the-punchbowl.co.uk; @PunchbowlInn; Take bookings all week via phone and/or online.

CROYDON, SURREY — 3–3B

MCDERMOTTS FISH & CHIPS £30 542

5-7 THE FORESTDALE SHOPPING CENTRE FEATHERBED LN CR0 9AS 020 8651 1440

Tony & Sean McDermott "deserve all their awards" at this "great fish 'n' chippie (est 1987), on the outskirts of Croydon", but "worth going miles out of your way" for; it's "always packed", so expect to queue. / www.mcdermottsfishandchips.co.uk; Tue-Fri 9.30 pm, Sat 9 pm; Take bookings all week via phone and/or online.

CRUDWELL, WILTSHIRE — 2–2C

THE POTTING SHED £50 333

THE ST SN16 9EW 01666 577833

"A superb pub, part of the Rectory Hotel" opposite, and likewise revamped by music biz owner Alex Payne a few years back. Whether it's for the "first-class Sunday lunch (if you can get in)" or the "cosy" ambiance it's "well worth a visit" by (nearly) all accounts. / www.thepottingshedpub.com; @pottingshedpub; No Amex; No bookings.

CRUNDALE, KENT — 3–3D

THE COMPASSES INN £57 333

SOLE ST CT4 7ES 01227 700 300

A "proper rural pub" with "exceptional food" – Rob and Donna Taylor's rural inn is in "beautiful walking country" between Canterbury and Ashford and makes the most of its "lovely location and delightful interior". It manages to be "relaxed but very focused" – and is fast "gaining popularity". (For some walkers, "the only downside is that they no longer allow dogs in the restaurant" – although you can eat with the pack outside when weather permits). / www.thecompassescrundale.co.uk; @compasses_inn; Wed-Sat 11 pm, Sun 6 pm.

CUCKFIELD, WEST SUSSEX — 3–4B

ROSE AND CROWN £49 333

LONDON ROAD, RH17 5BS 01444 414217

"High-quality ingredients are cooked well and provided by welcoming staff" at this West Sussex gastropub, run for six years by the family team of Mark Dennis, a food-loving former accountant, and his son Simon, a professional chef. / www.roseandcrowncuckfield.co.uk; Mon-Fri 9 pm, Sat 10 pm, Sun 3.30 pm; Take bookings all week via phone and/or online.

CULGAITH, CUMBRIA — 7–3D

MRS MILLER'S £41 542

HAZEL DENE GARDEN CENTRE CA10 1QF 01768 882520

"Continuing to turn out some really quality cooking at remarkably low prices" – this surprise find is to be discovered behind a garden centre in the Eden Valley. "Inflation has reached the tiny village of Culgaith and the two-course set lunch (say parsnip soup and a mighty good looking fish 'n' chips) is now a whole £9! That doesn't even get you a starter most places. Service superficially seems a bit tea-shoppy, but is efficient and well trained. The décor isn't going to win any restaurant design awards, but the loos provide some excellent reading matter, as they are papered with menus from a number of illustrious restaurants". / www.mrsmillersculgaith.co.uk; @MrsMillers; Sun-Thu 3 pm, Fri & Sat 9 pm; Take bookings all week via phone and/or online.

CUPAR, FIFE — 9–3D

THE PEAT INN £85 544

KY15 5LH 01334 840206

"Superb food, wonderful service and a perfect atmosphere… what more could one ask for?" – Geoffrey & Katherine Smeddle's famous country inn sits a short drive out of St Andrews and would be "a hidden gem" had it not been so famous for so many years now: on all accounts "it never fails to impress" with its fairly traditional cuisine and "A+ wine list". "I've been coming here regularly for almost 50 years, since David Wilson set out to create a French-style country restaurant in the middle of rural Fife. I have never been disappointed and the Smeddles have carried on David's dream superbly. Having a place like this on your doorstep is just so good". Top Tip – "unbelievable three-course lunch for £25, including an amuse bouche and 3 petit fours each". / www.thepeatinn.co.uk; @thepeatinn; Take bookings all week via phone and/or online.

DALRY, NORTH AYRSHIRE — 9–4B

BRAIDWOODS £69 544

DRUMASTLE MILL COTTAGE KA24 4LN 01294 833544

"Simply the best – year after year Keith & Nicola deliver consistently the best there is to offer using the finest Scottish produce" at this "beautiful relaxed farmhouse" in remote surroundings. And the duo are always so "warm and welcoming" too. / www.braidwoods.co.uk; Wed-Sat, Tue 9 pm; children: 12+ at D.

DANEHILL, EAST SUSSEX — 3–4B

COACH AND HORSES £48 333

SCHOOL LN RH17 7JF 01825 740369

This "delightful pub with an excellent garden" on the edge of Ashdown Forest wins solid ratings for an inviting menu of locally sourced dishes. A family-run freehouse, it also has a strong list of local beers, wines and ciders. /

www.coachandhorses.co; Mon-Thu 9 pm, Fri & Sat 9.30 pm, Sun 3 pm; Take bookings all week via phone and/or online.

DARLINGTON, COUNTY DURHAM — 8–3B

THE ORANGERY, ROCKLIFFE HALL £106 434

DL2 2DU 01325 729999

Limited but all-round very good feedback this year on this glass-roofed dining room – the top eating option at this five-star retreat, near the North Yorks border, set in over 365 acres. Richard Allen's cuisine makes use of local ingredients – many foraged or grown on the property – to present the choice of either the three-course menu (£55) or spend an extra tenner and you can go for the six-course tasting option. / www.rockliffehall.com; @rockliffehall; Jacket required; Take bookings all week via phone and/or online.

DARSHAM, SUFFOLK — 6–4D

DARSHAM NURSERIES £50 433

MAIN RD IP17 3PW 01728 667022

This barn conversion "offers something rare for Suffolk – vegetable-led seasonal food" (much "grown on site") that's "innovative and creative" to boot. The "Friday night set menu is always a surprise and delight", while "the bar team are always whipping up interesting preserves and shrubs to recommend". "Much better than the 'usual suspects' down in Aldeburgh". / www.darshamnurseries.co.uk; @DarshamNurserie; Mon-Sat 10 pm, Sun 5 pm; Take bookings all week via phone and/or online.

DARTMOUTH, DEVON — 1–4D

ROCKFISH £47 333

8 SOUTH EMBANKMENT TQ6 9BH 01803 832800

"The original Rockfish and still the best" – serving up the "freshest fish and scallops to die for" – and it's also "nice to see unusual fish on the menu". "The day's catch is always worth having and the different soles grilled are delicious". / www.therockfish.co.uk/; @therockfishuk; Take bookings all week via phone and/or online.

THE SEAHORSE £64 544

5 SOUTH EMBANKMENT TQ6 9BH 01803 835147

"British seafood at its best" is "worth a detour" at Mitch Tonks's "buzzy" (if "rather cramped") flagship. The "unfussy cooking" and "respect shown to the super-fresh produce always leaves you happy"; and it's "a perfect little spot to hunker down over a long lunch, before walking it all off along the waterfront". / www.seahorserestaurant.co.uk; @SeahorseDevon; Tue-Sat 9.30 pm, Sun 3 pm.

THE TILBURY   £57   334

WATTON RD SG3 6TB   01438 815 550

Brothers James & Tom Bainbridge are behind this popular pitstop, on the village green, where the "food is above average for Hertfordshire gastropubs", being split between relaxed pub classics and more adventurous British cuisine; the "ambience outside is particularly great", and you can have "a lovely meal on a hot summer evening under the pergola". / www.thetilbury.co.uk; @the_tilbury; Mon-Thu 3 pm, Fri & Sat 9.30 pm, Sun 3.30 pm; No bookings.

FROG & SCOT   £47   433

86 HIGH STREET CT14 6EG   01304 379444

This "very good bistro" serves "metropolitan-quality cooking of local and seasonal ingredients (especially seafood)" – "on the high street of a charming (and currently chic) seaside town". It's "light and spacious", with "friendly and efficient service" and a "good-value lunch menu". Owners Benoit and Sarah – embodying the 'Auld Alliance' of France and Scotland – also run Le Pinardier wine bar almost next door, which explains the "original list" of classics and natural/bio wines. / www.frogandscot.co.uk; @frogandscot; Tue-Thu 5 pm, Fri & Sat 11 pm, Sun 4 pm; No bookings.

WHITS OF WALMER £66   443

61 THE STRAND CT14 7DP   01304 368881

"Beautiful fish and amazing oysters" top the bill at this cute seaside spot – while "wonderful soufflés" show its French classical pedigree. Steve and Eva Whitney met at Anton Mossiman's private dining club in Belgravia, where he was executive chef and she was general manager. / www.whits.co.uk; @Whitsrestaurant; Thu-Sat 9 pm, Sun 3.30 pm.

MILSOMS   £48   333

STRATFORD RD CO7 6HW   01206 322 795

This "popular" ivy-clad Constable country hotel is a rangy place whose menu might scare the indecisive, running as it does from mezze to 28-day dry-aged steaks; notwithstanding the odd gripe, it put in a very decent performance overall in the survey, and was tipped for its good value. / www.milsomhotels.com; @milsomhotels; Mon-Fri 9.30 pm, Sat & Sun 10 pm; No bookings.

THE SUN INN   £49   334

HIGH ST CO7 6DF   01206 564325

"A proper pub with roaring fires, dogs and good beer on tap", and where the food is "a notch above your average boozer", whether you opt for the bar food or a more formal meal in the restaurant. Add in "comfortable" rooms and a "stunning, thoughtfully decorated" building and it's a "great place for a long weekend". / www.thesuninndedham.com; @SunInnDedham;

No Amex; Take bookings all week via phone and/or online.

LE TALBOOTH   £84   335

GUN HILL CO7 6HP   01206 323150

The "superb setting" – a picturesque, half-timbered building by the River Stour complete with riverside terrace, which features in paintings by Constable – helps maintain the allure of this classic, famously romantic destination. However, its large loyal following from Essex and beyond also award its updated traditional cuisine consistently high ratings. / www.milsomhotels.com; @milsomhotels; Mon-Sat 9.30 pm, Sun 3 pm; No jeans.

THE SWAN INN   £54   333

VILLAGE ROAD UB9 5BH   01895 832085

Looking for a pub meal to escape from London? Head to this atmospheric and tastefully renovated Georgian gastropub, just off J1 of the M40, in the cutest of cute Home Counties villages (complete with small outside terrace garden in summer). The straightforward food is not aiming to 'push the envelope' but it's dependably well-realised. Top Tip – grab any parking space you can find: finding a spot a nightmare. / www.swaninndenham.co.uk; @swaninnub9; Mon-Thu 9 pm, Fri & Sat 9.30 pm, Sun 8 pm.

DARLEYS   £70   333

DARLEY ABBEY MILL DE22 1DZ   01332 364987

This "old mill overlooking the river and weir" – part of the Darley Abbey Mills World Heritage site on the Derwent – has an "interesting menu and consistently high-quality cooking". "Lunch here is always a pleasure, thanks to its setting, space and service as much as its food". / www.darleys.com; @DarleysDerby; No Amex; Take bookings all week via phone and/or online; children: 10.

EBI SUSHI   £42   542

59 ABBEY ST DE22 3SJ   01332 265656

"Exceptional quality" Japanese fare has long drawn workers from the Toyota factory down the road to this dinky outfit, and while its appearance is "slightly at the café end of the spectrum, when the food's this good who cares?" / ebisushi.co.uk; No Amex; Take bookings all week via phone and/or online.

LA CHOUETTE   £74   443

WESTLINGTON GRN HP17 8UW   01296 747422

"A visit to (chef/owner/waiter) Frederic's is always an experience – his forthright views on just about anything complement his efforts in the kitchen!", which revolve around Belgian cuisine and are supplemented by wildlife photography on the walls (by Frederic lui-même

of course). / www.lachouette.co.uk; Mon-Sat 9 pm; No Amex.

CLAM & CORK   £33   542

2 FISH MARKET DN1 1NJ   07912 687581

"Sitting up at a bar in Doncaster Fish Market may not sound like the last word in fun", but this brave yearling "is the kind of place that is usual in Barcelona and Lisbon, but a wonderful gift to my part of the world", with its zingy small plates of fish curries and top quality seafood; "let's have some more like this!" / clam-cork.business.site/; Tue, Thu-Sat, Wed 4 pm.

THE FORESTER INN   £50   343

LOWER STREET SP7 9EE   01747 828038

A thatched fifteenth century pub with "lovely landlords", a "great ambience" and ambitious (for these parts) grub, sourced everywhere from a local rare-breed cattle farm to Rungis market in Paris. / www.theforesterdonheadstandrew.co.uk; @ForesterNews; Tue-Sat 9 pm, Sun 2 pm; Take bookings all week via phone and/or online.

SIENNA   £52   442

36 HIGH WEST STREET DT1 1UP   01305 250022

MasterChef finalist Marcus Wilcox's modern British cuisine takes in a "great tasting menu (four, six or eight courses, and there's also a set option) with perfectly matched wines"; it seats just 16, adding to the "quiet" intimacy of a meal here. / www.siennadorchester.co.uk; @siennadorset; Wed-Sat, Tue 9 pm, Sun 2 pm; No Amex; children: 12+.

SORREL   £92   544

77 SOUTH STREET RH4 2JU   01306 889 414

"You begin to wish you could dine on the amuse-bouches alone they are so good, and then along comes a stunning meal and contentment reigns!" – Steve Drake's "brilliantly presented and superbly tasty cuisine" delivers consistently "wonderful and creative dishes" at his "lovely if slightly formal" 40-seater, with fans crossing the county to get here. Now two years old, it still feels like a relatively new arrival here since he relocated from Ripley. "Staff are invested in the place" too – "they have a detailed knowledge of the plates, are helpful and engaging without being fussy and intrusive". / www.sorrelrestaurant.co.uk; @SteveDrakeFood; Credit card deposit required to book.

DOUGLAS, ISLE OF MAN — 7–4B

TANROAGAN — £57 — 3 3 3
9 RIDGEWAY ST IM1 1EW 01624 612355

A "small, family-run fish restaurant in the old part of Douglas", with a spin-off – The Boatyard, in Peel – delivering "simple dishes but with very fresh fish and interesting twists"; add in appealingly rustic décor and "excellent value for money". / tanroagan.co.uk; Take bookings all week via phone and/or online.

DREWSTEIGNTON, DEVON — 1–3D

THE OLD INN — £83 — 5 4 3
EX6 6QR 01647 281 276

Ex-Gidleigh Park chef Duncan Walker continues to win stellar marks for his food at this appealingly cosy, low-key seventeenth century village inn, on the edge of Dartmoor, and run together with Anthea Christmas; if you stay over in one of the three comfortable rooms "breakfast is also excellent". / www.old-inn.co.uk; @duncansoldinn; No Amex; Take bookings all week via phone and/or online; children: 12.

DUNBAR, EAST LOTHIAN — 9–4C

THE CREEL — £45 — 3 3 3
25 LAMER STREET EH42 1HJ
01368 863279

"Always a treat" – a tiny, informal seafood bistro, in a "lovely location" near the harbour, whose creative cooking – from a limited menu – is a real find in these parts and where they send out interesting little bites (a Virgin Mary or rhubarb smoothie, say) to refresh the palate between courses. / creelrestaurant.co.uk; Wed-Sat 9 pm, Sun 2 pm.

DUNFERMLINE, WEST LOTHIAN — 9–4C

DHOOM
19-21 NEW ROW KY12 7EA 01383 223340

A bright Indian street food design is laid on strong at this large newcomer, serving a variety of boldly flavoured bites. One or two encouraging early reports of "amazing flavours" win it an inclusion, but too few reports for a rating as yet. / dhoomuk.co.uk; @DStreetery; Wed-Fri 4 pm, Sat & Sun 5 pm.

DUNMOW, ESSEX — 3–2C

THE FLITCH OF BACON — £67 — 4 2 2
THE ST CM6 3HT 01371 821 660

"It was excellent when it was Daniel Clifford's alone, but under Tim Allen... it is perhaps even better!" – The general view on this gentrified pub, where the latter's "incredibly deft touch" results in "superb" cooking ("the signature maple bacon with scallops is one of the best things I've ever tasted!"). It would be rated higher if a couple of reporters had not found it "disappointing after the high hopes when it opened". But a better overall summary of feedback? – "at last: somewhere to eat in Essex!" / www.flitchofbacon.co.uk;

@flitchofbaconld; Wed-Sat 9 pm, Tue 6 pm, Sun 3.30 pm; Credit card deposit required to book.

DUNVEGAN, HIGHLAND — 9–2A

THE THREE CHIMNEYS — £123 — 5 4 4
COLBOST IV55 8ZT 01470 511258

"Worth the scenic drive to get there and highly recommended" – this former crofter's cottage has been a gastronomic feature of the inner Hebrides since it opened in 1985. It's all change this year, though, as – after 34 years – Shirley & Eddie Spears have retired: selling the business to well-known hotelier Gordon Campbell Gray, who is himself returning to his native Scotland and establishing his new 'Wee Hotel Company'. We've rated the restaurant on the basis that he knows what he's doing, that the Spears remain somewhat involved, and that the "amazing" Scottish cuisine focused on fish and seafood for which the place has become internationally famous will endure. / www.threechimneys.co.uk; @3_chimneys; children: 8+.

DYFED, PEMBROKESHIRE — 4–4B

THE GROVE OF NARBERTH — £89 — 3 3 4
MOLLESTON SA67 8BX 01834 860915

"Imaginative and well-presented food" from "inventive taster menus" in "a wonderful setting" – dining at this lavishly restored 17th-century mansion overlooking the Preseli Hills is "an amazing experience from start to finish". Neil and Zoe Kedward, who rescued the property from dereliction a dozen years ago, also own Coast at Saundersfoot and the Beach House on the Gower. / www.thegrove-narberth.co.uk; @GroveNarberth; Take bookings all week via phone and/or online.

EAST CHISENBURY, WILTSHIRE — 2–3C

RED LION FREEHOUSE — £70 — 4 3 3
SN9 6AQ 01980 671124

"Almost the perfect village pub, but to a foodie, far more…" – this acclaimed free house, not far from Stonhenge, offers "an eclectic mix of highly skilled and imaginative cooking, plus friendly individual service in an atmosphere that veers from cosy inn to new annexe in feel, depending on your table". / www.redlionfreehouse.com; @redlionfreehse; Thu-Sat 9 pm, Sun 2 pm; No Amex; No bookings.

EAST DEAN, WEST SUSSEX — 3–4A

THE STAR & GARTER — £40 — 3 3 3
PO18 0JG 01243 811318

"The surroundings are stunning on the South Downs" at this "relaxed pub" at the heart of the Goodwood Estate, which has "great views if you can sit at the back". It serves "good straightforward food, with no pretensions". / www.thestarandgarter.co.uk; @StarandGarterED; Mon-Sat 9.30 pm, Sun 6 pm; No Amex; Take bookings all week via phone and/or online.

EAST GRINSTEAD, WEST SUSSEX — 3–4B

GRAVETYE MANOR — £107 — 4 3 5
VOWELS LANE RH19 4LJ 01342 810567

"George Blogg's plot-to-plate food is just superb" at this famous Elizabethan manor, where a major investment in a new "stunning glass-fronted dining room" provides "both warmth and class" and is emblematic of its reemergence as a seriously good dining destination. "Set amidst a stunning, natural garden" – created in the 1880s and of significant importance if you're into horticultural history – "lovely leafy walks are thrown in". It's very much not a cheap experience, but the equation stacks up for most (if not quite all) reporters: "it broke the bank… but we'll be back!" / www.gravetyemanor.co.uk; @GravetyeManor; Booking max 8 may apply; children: 7+.

EAST MOLESEY, SURREY — 3–3A

MEZZET — £50 — 4 4 3
43 BRIDGE RD KT8 9ER 020 89794088

"A lovely local restaurant" serving "fresh well-cooked Lebanese food at sensible prices", and whose owner "always remembers your name"; spin-off Mezzet Dar, blending Spanish and Lebanese tapas, is nearby. / www.mezzet.co.uk; @Mezzet; Mon-Sat 10 pm, Sun 9 pm; Take bookings all week via phone and/or online.

EAST WITTON, NORTH YORKSHIRE — 8–4B

THE BLUE LION — £60 — 3 2 3
DL8 4SN 01969 624273

"The Blue Lion experience is always really very good" – whether you're a celeb patron such as Prince Charles or just a regular diner, and "whether you want light food or a full meal, it fits the bill"; "they are excellent at game cooking and in the bar in winter with the log-fire going, it is a wonderfully cosy place". / www.thebluelion.co.uk; @bluelioninn

EASTBOURNE, EAST SUSSEX — 3–4B

THE MIRABELLE, THE GRAND HOTEL — £72 — 2 3 3
KING EDWARDS PARADE BN21 4EQ
01323 412345

"Old-style in the nicest way" – this white-linen dining room in a grand old seaside hotel can still be a "lovely spot for dinner when taking a trip to the coast". It has, though, become a battleground between traditionalists and modernisers following the 2017 appointment of Stephanie Malvoisin to head the kitchen and moves to update the 30-year-old interior. For some, the process has not gone nearly far enough: "what an antediluvian and over-rated place!", whose, "refurbishment was a terrible waste of time and money". For others "things seems to be picking up a little under the new lady chef (but while acceptable, it's in no way memorable)". And at best, "a really pleasant surprise!" / www.grandeastbourne.com;

@Grandeastbourne; Jacket required; Take bookings all week via phone and/or online.

EASTON GREY, WILTSHIRE 2–2C

THE DINING ROOM, WHATLEY MANOR £156 433

SN16 0RB 01666 822888

Niall Keating put this Cotswold manor house (which, the history books tell us, was originally named 'Twatley Manor') ever-more firmly on the culinary map in October 2019, when it became one of 23 restaurants in the country with two Michelin Stars. All survey feedback on his eclectically inspired twelve-course tasting menu rates it between "very good" and "outstanding", and this beautiful spot is a "great place for a romantic weekend away". / www.whatleymanor.com; @Whatley_Manor; Thu, Sun, Fri & Sat 10 pm; No jeans; children: 12+.

EDGEHILL, WARWICKSHIRE 2–2D

THE CASTLE AT EDGEHILL £46 244

MAIN STREET OX15 6DJ 01295 670255

"Fantastic views" over the Warwickshire countryside (and a famous battleground from the English Civil War) from an "interesting building" are an immediate draw at this cosy, picture-book castle – a pub since 1822 and built 100 years earlier. Service is "friendly" and the "competent" gastropub menu majors in a selection of steaks and burgers. / castleatedgehill. co.uk; @CastleEdgehill; Mon-Fri 9 pm, Sat & Sun 9.30 pm.

EDINBURGH, CITY OF EDINBURGH 9–4C

AIZLE £81 542

107-109 ST. LEONARD'S STREET EH8 9QY 0131 662 9349

"Stunningly good food" – "consistently ambitious, intriguing and successful in its execution of superb ingredients" – is on the daily, no-choice, six-course menu at this dynamic Newington fixture, where everything is baked, fermented and otherwise created in-house. "All the food is good but the fish is really outstanding". (The name rhymes with hazel, and is Scots for a glowing hot ember). / www.aizle.co.uk; @Aizle_Edinburgh; Wed-Fri 11 pm, Sun 2 pm.

ANGELS WITH BAGPIPES £57 333

343 HIGH ST, ROYAL MILE EH1 1PW 0131 2201111

Owned by the Crolla family (who started Valvona & Crolla, Scotland's oldest deli and Italian wine merchant – see also), this sixteenth century fine dining spot is a beacon on the otherwise touristy Royal Mile owing to its "well-cooked and well-seasoned" Scottish fare and "good value Sunday lunch"; for a truly intimate dining experience, try 'Halo', upstairs, which seats just four. / www.angelswithbagpipes.co.uk; @angelsfood.

BELL'S DINER £43 333

7 ST STEPHEN ST EH3 5EN 0131 225 8116

"A great wee place", this Stockbridge institution is "still good and reliable" – and a reminder that burgers have been fashionable for almost 50 years. "Fond memories – we took our children, and they're now wanting to take their children". / www.bellsdineredinburgh.co.uk; Mon-Sat 10 pm, Sun 3 pm; No Amex.

BERTIE'S £40 333

9 VICTORIA STREET EH1 2JL 0131 322 1000

"Another venture from the Valvona family, in the premises that used to house Khushi's (RIP)". Tony Crolla has transformed this former Old Town church into a "large and buzzy" £3 million fish 'n' chip restaurant (Scotland's largest). Early feedback cites "very good fish 'n' chips and friendly, prompt service". Top Menu Tip – deep-fried Mars Bar! / www.bertiesfishandchips.com; Sun-Thu 10 pm, Fri & Sat 11 pm.

BIA BISTROT £42 444

19 COLINTON RD EH10 5DP 0131 452 8453

"A very decent choice in the posh neighbourhood of Morningside" – Roisin & Matthias Llorente's "very friendly" and "always reliable" bistro has a strong fanclub, both amongst the locals and visitors who have truffled it out, some of whom would say it's "Edinburgh's top dining option" thanks its "exceptionally well-prepared" and reasonably priced modern Scottish dishes and "personal" service. / www.biabistrot.co.uk.

CAFÉ MARLAYNE £45 323

1 THISTLE STREET EH2 1EN 0131 226 2230

This "consistently entertaining" and "very French bistro (better than many in France nowadays!)" is a "reliable" source of reasonably priced classic dishes, with "friendly" (if "slightly chaotic) service". The Antigua Street branch closed down a couple of years ago. / www.cafemarlayne.com/thistle-street; Sun-Fri & Sat 10 pm; No Amex; Take bookings all week via phone and/or online.

THE CAFÉ ROYAL BAR £53 334

19 WEST REGISTER ST EH2 2AA 0131 556 1884

For "great seafood", "right in the centre of town", you could do worse than this "easygoing", well-preserved Victorian emporium with gilt-and-glass interiors – though you'll find it "quieter and more civilised at lunchtime". / www.caferoyaledinburgh.co.uk/; Mon-Wed 11 pm, Thu, Sun midnight, Fri & Sat 1 am; Take bookings all week via phone and/or online; children: 5.

CAFÉ ST-HONORÉ £62 333

34 NW THISTLE STREET LN EH2 1EA 0131 226 2211

"French romantic at its best… I felt transported 500 miles south" – Neil Forbes's "intimate brasserie" is a long-term fixture of the New Town, and wins glowing all-round praise for its "lovely cosy atmosphere" and "delicious" food that's "always consistent", too. / www.cafesthonore.com; @CafeStHonore; Mon-Fri 10 pm, Sat & Sun 10.30 pm; Take bookings all week via phone and/or online.

THE CASTLE TERRACE £109 333

33-35 CASTLE TER EH1 2EL 0131 229 1222

Tom Kitchin's second venture opened in 2010 with Dominic Jack as chef-patron and this chic Gallo-Scottish outfit is, say fans, a "joy to be at", turning out "fantastic food" in a "lovely atmosphere". There remains, however, a vocal minority of sceptics, for whom it's "a bit gimmicky", "not cheap" and occasionally "misconceived" ("had the surprise menu… the surprise was how bad it was!"). / www.castleterracerestaurant.com; @dominicjack; Tue-Sat 10 pm.

CHAOPHRAYA £46 324

33 CASTLE ST EH2 3DN 01312 267614

"Excellent views from the conservatory" – including possibly "the best view of the castle, if you get the right table" – are incentive enough to visit this branch of an eight-strong Thai chain. It also delivers "surprisingly good and inexpensive food". / www.chaophraya.co.uk; @ChaophrayaThai; Sun-Wed 10 pm, Thu-Sat 10.30 pm; Take bookings all week via phone and/or online.

CONDITA £85 543

15 SALISBURY PLACE EH9 1SL 0131 667 5777

"An exquisite five or eight course surprise tasting menu is sure to tantalise your tastebuds and create a truly unique dining experience!" – so say fans of Conor Toomey and Mark Slaney's spacious (just six tables) and elegant newcomer. Rated on still-limited early feedback, it's certainly "a welcome addition to the ever-expanding Edinburgh dining scene" and Scotsman restaurant critic Joanna Blythman left 'utterly enchanted' by the cuisine here. To book, you email in advance. / www.condita.co.uk.

CONTINI GEORGE STREET £157 344

103 GEORGE STREET EH2 3ES 0131 225 1550

A converted banking hall provides the "amazing setting" for Victor and Carina Contini's relanched venture, which now puts small plates centre stage. Reporters praise the "good Italian food with very fresh ingredients" but "friendly and professional staff" also play a big part in "making this place a pleasure".

The Seahorse, Dartmouth

/ www.contini.com/contini-george-street;
@continibites; Sun-Fri 10 pm, Sat 10.30 pm;
Booking weekends only.

THE DINING ROOM £69 | 4 4 4

28 QUEEN ST EH2 1JX 0131 220 2044

More praise this year for the Scotch Malt
Whisky Society's dining room, on the first floor
of a Georgian townhouse in the city-centre,
which serves a choice of menus (including a
veggie option). "Despite being a huge whisky
fan, my husband was unsure about going for the
five-course tasting menu with matched whiskies
but he was glad he did: flavour combinations
worked really well – smoky whisky with smoked
haddock, sweeter whisky with rabbit and carrot,
and a honeyed whisky to go with dessert (to
name but a few – all cask strength too!)". /
www.thediningroomedinburgh.co.uk/booking;
@TheDiningRoomEd; Take bookings all week via
phone and/or online.

DISHOOM EDINBURGH £36 | 4 3 3

**3A ST ANDREW SQUARE EH2 2BD
01312 026 406**

"Fan-bloody-tastic!" – for "sumptuous" tapas
dishes or a "different type of breakfast" (a
top tip here), in a "fun, buzzy atmosphere",
this "very welcome addition to the Edinburgh
dining scene" (the first offshoot of the
celebrated Parsi chain outside the Big Smoke) is
just the ticket. / www.dishoom.com; @Dishoom;
Sun-Thu 11 pm, Fri & Sat midnight.

DIVINO ENOTECA £57 | 3 4 5

**5 MERCHANT ST EH1 2QD
0131 225 1770**

This "stylish and relaxed" Italian wine bar
and restaurant occupies a basement in the
Old Town, and provides a "guaranteed night
out" with "high-class food" and in particular
an "excellent wine list" – "under the masterly
direction of maître d' Silvio Praino". Part of
the Vittoria group owned by a branch of the
Italo-Scottish Crolla clan, it celebrates its 10th
anniversary this year. / www.vittoriagroup.co.uk;
@divinoed; Mon-Thu midnight, Fri 1 am.

DUMPLINGS OF CHINA £27 | 4 3 3

**60 HOME STREET EH3 9NA
0131 624 0056**

The clue is in the name at this bright, white-
walled 2019 newcomer. It opened late in the
day for the survey, but initial feedback says it's
a "very good, cheap 'n' cheerful option": well
worth a trip. / www.dumplingsofchina.co.uk/;
Sun-Thu 10.30 pm, Fri & Sat 11 pm.

EDINBURGH FOOD STUDIO £70 | 4 4 3

**158 DALKEITH ROAD EH16 5DX
0131 258 0758**

"In a slightly odd location and format… but
always interesting!" – Ben Reade and Sashana
Souza Zanella opened this crowdfunded
venture a little way out of the city-centre in
late 2015, with a view to 'combine eating
and drinking with arts, sciences, fun times
and banter'. "Each evening seems different,
with an approach like a research kitchen, and
while fun combinations prevail, they are not
as bonkers as you might fear". "You feel that
the whole place is totally infused with care
and love for the ingredients and what they
are doing – a passion you can sense, without
being endlessly told about the 'concept' behind
the restaurant". "I'm still not entirely sold on
multiple courses that I find over-punctuate the
meal and interrupt conversation. But I'm really
glad to have been". / edinburghfoodstudio.com;
@EdFoodStudio.

EDUCATED FLEA £47 | 3 3 2

**32B BROUGHTON ST EH1 3SB
01315568092**

"Unusual dishes" using bold flavours from a
diverse set of cuisines again wins fans for this
dinky diner – a spin-off of Three Birds and
Apiary; flexibly served wines are appreciated
too: in 500ml or 1l carafes as well as the usual
options. / educatedflea.co.uk/; @edfleaedinburgh;
Mon-Sat 9 pm, Sun 3 pm; Take bookings all week
via phone and/or online.

EL CARTEL £31 | 4 3 4

64 THISTLE ST EH2 1EN 0131226 7171

"Cool", if "cramped" – this "fab wee place"
in the New Town serves "fresh and deliciously
different Mexican food" from a "short menu",
although "some customers may find the

music not to be to their vibe". (The Thistle
Street original has a no-reservations policy,
but "they take your name and call you when
a table is ready"; the newer Teviot Place
branch near the university takes bookings.) /
www.elcartelmexicana.co.uk; @elcartelmexican;
Sun-Thu 10 pm, Fri & Sat 2 am; No bookings.

L'ESCARGOT BLEU £52 | 3 2 3

**56 BROUGHTON ST EH1 3SA
0131 557 1600**

"The French bistro food always hits the mark"
at this "friendly" 10-year-old West End outfit
with a "lively and convincingly authentic
atmosphere". Chef-patron Fred Berkmiller,
from the Loire Valley, also owns L'Escargot
Blanc nearby. / www.lescargotbleu.co.uk;
@Lescargot_edin; Mon-Thu 10 pm, Fri & Sat
10.30 pm; No Amex; Take bookings all week via
phone and/or online.

FAVORITA £51 | 3 2 3

325 LEITH WALK EH6 8SA 0131 554 2430

In Leith Walk, this "family-orientated"
staple can be relied upon for "superb"
wood-fired pizzas, pastas and so
forth in a "buzzing atmosphere".
/ www.vittoriagroup.co.uk/lafavorita;
@LaFavoritaEd; Take bookings all week via phone
and/or online.

FHIOR £64 | 2 3 3

**36 BROUGHTON STREET EH1 3SB
0131 477 5000**

This yearling from ambitious chef Scott Smith
and his wife Laura follows the closure of well-
regarded Norn in Leith, and presents his take
on modern Scottish cuisine in a minimalist
city-centre setting – the name derives from the
Gaelic for 'true'. Feedback has been limited
so far, and splits between praise for "a really
interesting tasting menu" and dismissal of
an experience that's "just unmemorable…
apart from the bill!" / www.fhior.com;
@FhiorRestaurant; Wed-Sat midnight; Take
bookings all week via phone and/or online.

FIELD £47 | 3 3 2

**41 WEST NICOLSON ST EH8 9DB
01316 677010**

"Jovial staff compensate for cramped
surroundings" at this "unpretentious"
Southside establishment, turning out Scottish
food with "unusual flavour combinations that
really work well" and are "good value too".
/ www.fieldrestaurant.co.uk; @Field_Edinburgh;
Mon-Sat 11 pm, Sun 10 pm; Take bookings all
week via phone and/or online.

FISHERS IN THE CITY £55 | 3 3 3

58 THISTLE ST EH2 1EN 0131 225 5109

"Wonderful fresh seafood and fish is
imaginatively presented and served
unpretentiously at a very reasonable price"
at this relaxed bistro, handy for the National
Gallery (and a spin-off of a veteran Leith

venture). / www.fishersrestaurants.co.uk; @FishersLeith; Take bookings all week via phone and/or online.

FISHERS LEITH £56 3|3|4

1 THE SHORE EH6 6QW 0131 554 5666

"Properly fresh fish with no fuss but lots of care" (plus delectable puds) continues to explain the success of this two-decades-old haunt in a historic Leith harbour watchtower. Their sibling venue The Shore, next door, serves British grub, and there's also a city-centre spin-off, the literally titled 'Fishers In the City'. / www.fishersrestaurants.co.uk; @FishersLeith; Mon-Sun 10 pm; Take bookings all week via phone and/or online.

FISHMARKET £43 3|3|3

23A PIER PLACE EH6 4LP 0131 552 8262

"Top-notch seafood – down by the Newhaven jetty!" is making a name for this modern chippy and fish restaurant in the docks, where – as well as fish 'n' chips (including to take away), there's a wider menu of posher seafood dishes. / www.thefishmarketnewhaven.co.uk; @TheFishmarketNH.

GARDENER'S COTTAGE £64 3|3|4

1 ROYAL TERRACE GARDENS, LONDON ROAD EH7 5DX 0131 558 1221

"The menu is fixed and you sit at one of three large tables with others" at this quirky venture, which occupies a stone cottage in Royal Terrace Gardens. You get what you're given from a mystery tasting menu on which sustainability is to the fore, with many of the ingredients grown by Charlie the gardener. On practically all reports the food is well-rated, and they must be doing something right having this year now opened The Lookout (see also). / www.thegardenerscottage.co; @gardenersctg; Mon-Sun 9.30 pm.

LA GARRIGUE £59 3|3|2

31 JEFFREY ST EH1 1DH 0131 557 3032

"The hearty food and wine of the Languedoc" dominate the menu at Jean-Michel Gauffre's "enjoyable" Old Town stalwart, which celebrates its 20th anniversary next year and remains "a fine place to dine". There's also a "huge wine list, mainly from southern France with many rare and unusual bottles from Languedoc and Roussillon". / www.lagarrigue.co.uk; @lagarrigue; Sun-Fri 9.30 pm, Sat 10 pm; Take bookings all week via phone and/or online.

GRAZING BY MARK GREENAWAY £56

WALDORF ASTORIA EDINBURGH (THE CALEDONIAN), RUTLAND STREET EH1 2AB 0131 222 8857

"The much fanfared Mark Greenaway replacement for the Galvins' casual dining venue at the Caledonian Hotel" opened in April 2019, occupying a plush, contemporary space.

"We're not sure where the 'Grazing' comes from, except in the name", as the focus here is not on small plates but more conventionally-sized ones. Opening late in the day for the survey, such feedback as we have is downbeat, particularly on the eclectic and bold modern cuisine, but press reviewers in both the Scottish and national broadsheets have generally raved. / www.markgreenaway.com; @GrazingByMG; Mon-Fri 9 pm, Sat & Sun 9.30 pm.

HAWKSMOOR £57 5|4|4

23 WEST REGISTER STREET EH2 2AA 0131 526 4790

"New to Edinburgh and certainly living up to its reputation": the "classy" first Scottish outpost of the famous steakhouse chain – housed in the former Bank of Scotland HQ on St Andrew Square – opened in 2018, and it's hard to imagine feedback that's much more positive: all locals extol its "perfect steak"; "friendly" and "well-informed service"; and "great wines". / thehawksmoor.com; @HawksmoorEDI; Mon-Fri 10 pm, Sat 10.30 pm, Sun 9 pm.

HENDERSONS THE SALAD TABLE £38 3|2|2

94 HANOVER ST EH2 1DR 0131 225 2131

Located beneath their own deli/shop, Scotland's oldest vegetarian is a "longstanding Edinburgh favourite where the food is largely unchanged over many decades… and that is one of the attractions!". Head down the road for their vegan spin-off, or to the Holyrood branch, which combines vegan/veggie cuisine. / www.hendersonsofedinburgh.co.uk; @HendersonsofEdi; Mon-Thu 9 pm, Fri & Sat 9.30 pm, Sun 4 pm; No Amex; Take bookings all week via phone and/or online.

THE HONOURS £72 4|4|2

58A, NORTH CASTLE STREET EH2 3LU 0131 220 2513

"An Edinburgh favourite" – star chef, Martin Wishart's New Town brasserie maintains a very solid fan cub thanks to its "delicious brasserie-style cooking". One or two reporters, however, are "not sure about the interior" (is it "slightly unimaginative"?) / www.thehonours.co.uk; @TheHonours; Tue-Sat 9.30 pm; Take bookings all week via phone and/or online.

HOWIES £40 3|2|2

29 WATERLOO PLACE EH1 3BQ 0131 556 5766

David Howie Scott's flagship venue at the foot of Calton Hill celebrates its 30th anniversary this year as a purveyor of inexpensive Scottish classics. The odd reporter feels that it's "nice enough, but not the stand-out it could be", but that's within the context of pretty solid ratings overall. There are two spinoffs in Edinburgh and one in Aberdeen. / www.howies.uk.com; @HowiesScotland; Mon-Sun 10 pm.

THE IVY ON THE SQUARE £61 2|3|4

6 ST ANDREW SQUARE EH2 2BD 0131 526 4777

"Lots of ladies lunching" indicates that this branch of Richard Caring's Ivy roll-out is hitting an important segment of its target market. With its "reliably slick service" and "stylish surroundings", it "doesn't let you down" on keeping up appearances, but there's a familiar feeling that, beneath the gloss, "the food is just ordinary" – and "rather overpriced". / theivyedinburgh.com; @ivyedinburgh; Mon-Sun 12.30 am.

KANPAI £35 4|4|3

8 - 10 GRINDLAY STREET EH3 9AS 0131 228 1602

"Tasty, freshly prepared sushi" and "friendly service" can be found at this "very popular" Japanese: a stylishly minimal operation near the Lyceum Theatre – from the team behind Sushiya. / www.kanpaisushiedinburgh.co.uk/; Tue-Thu 10.30 pm, Fri & Sat 11 pm; Take bookings all week via phone and/or online.

THE KITCHIN £107 4|3|4

78 COMMERCIAL STREET EH6 6LX 0131 555 1755

Tom & Michaela Kitchin's "relaxed and informal" Leith warehouse conversion remains one of Edinburgh's most-mentioned destinations thanks to Tom's "innovative" dishes that are (aside from "the odd minor glitch") "generally very skillfully made". Ratings would be even higher, were it not for one or two reporters who judge it as "overpriced and underwhelming", but this remains a minority verdict. / www.thekitchin.com; @TomKitchin; Tue-Thu 10 pm, Fri & Sat 10.30 pm; Booking max 7 may apply; children: 5+.

THE LITTLE CHARTROOM £55 4|3|3

30 ALBERT PLACE EH7 5HN 0131 556 6600

Ex-Castle Terrace head chef Roberta Hall and restaurant manager Shaun McCarron strike out on their own with a new, little (just 18-covers) French/British-inspired bistro in Leith. Early feedback suggest it's worth a visit: "tiny and hard to get in, but the food is great and front of house spot-on". / www.thelittlechartroom.com; @LittleChartroom; Wed-Sun 9 pm.

LOCANDA DE GUSTI £43 3|3|3

102 DALRY ROAD EH11 2DW 0131 346 8800

'Good food from Naples' is the bold claim on the front of this well-known pizza joint, five minutes walk from Haymarket station, and – though reports were not numerous this year – all feedback is good. / www.locandadegusti.com/; @LocandaDG; Mon-Sat 10 pm; Take bookings all week via phone and/or online.

The Angel Inn, Hetton

THE LOOKOUT BY GARDENER'S COTTAGE £67 4 3 4

CALTON HILL EH7 5AA 0131 322 1246

"The setting is lovely" at this intriguing, all-day newcomer (open from breakfast): a cantilevered structure, partially suspended over Calton Hill, with panoramic views across Edinburgh and the Firth of Forth. It's a partnership between The Gardener's Cottage restaurant and Collective (the organisation that has redeveloped the City Observatory), and all reports say it serves "great" modern bistro fare. / www.thelookoutedinburgh.co; @TheLookoutByGC; Mon-Fri 10 pm, Sat 10.30 pm, Sun 9 pm.

MONO £69 5 4 4

85 SOUTH BRIDGE EH1 1HN 0131 466 4726

"Making other fine dining establishments in town look somewhat staid, out of touch and overpriced" – this April 2018 newcomer is "superb", and some would say "the best restaurant to have opened in Edinburgh in recent times". "A charismatic space" with "splendid service" – "the reference on its website to 'progressive Italian dining' is accurate" and the modern cuisine is "outstanding" – "go downstairs to see the kitchen in action". To match the fine cooking there's "an exceptional, mostly Italian, wine list". / monorestaurant.co.uk; @mono_edinburgh; Tue-Thu 4 pm.

MOTHER INDIA'S CAFE £34 4 3 3

3-5 INFIRMARY ST EH1 1LT 0131 524 9801

"It does exactly what it says on the (tiffin) tin!" – this offshoot of the famous Glasgow curry-tapas haunt has built a solid reputation in its own right for its south Asian small plates: "if you like Indian food, then you've come to the right place". It's very popular, so "booking is essential at busy times". / www.motherindiaglasgow.co.uk; @official_mindia; Sun-Thu 10 pm, Fri & Sat 10.30 pm; No Amex; Take bookings all week via phone and/or online.

NEW CHAPTER £63 4 4 3

18 EYRE PL. EH3 5EP 0131 556 0006

"It's always a pleasure to dine" at this "beautiful restaurant, slightly off the beaten track in glorious Edinburgh" – the "contemporary décor" is matched by "sublime, beautifully cooked" modern European dishes, which benefit from chef Maciej Szymik's "very different presentation". "Staff are welcoming and attentive". There's now a sibling brasserie in the West End, Otro. / www.newchapterrestaurant.co.uk/; @newchapter18; Mon-Fri 9 pm, Sat 10 pm, Sun 9.30 pm; Take bookings all week via phone and/or online.

NOTO £33

47A THISTLE STREET EH2 1DY 0131 241 8518

Stuart Ralston, chef patron of Aizle, has opened this new venture offering a casual dining experience influenced by his time working in New NYC and named after his late friend, food photographer Bob Noto (who, it is said, ate at Spain's famous El Bulli more than any other guest). Early press reviews suggest this is one of the better openings in the City in recent times. / notoedinburgh.co.uk; @EdinburghNoto; Mon-Fri 9 pm, Sat & Sun 10 pm.

NUMBER ONE, BALMORAL HOTEL £118 5 4 4

1 PRINCES STREET EH2 2EQ 0131 557 6727

"Still-fantastic food, service and a very special location" again win powerful support for this landmark hotel's cosseting and sophisticated basement – long one of the city's heaviest culinary hitters. And the arrival of new head chef Mark Donald – still under the hotel's executive chef, Jeff Bland – has caused n'er a ripple in reports. Even a rare reporter who isn't wowed by its luxurious below-ground setting feels "the excellent standards make it a worthwhile destination nonetheless". / www.roccofortehotels.com/hotels-and-resorts/the-balmoral-hotel/restaurants-and-bars/number-one/; @NumberOneEdin; No trainers; Booking max 5 may apply; children: 5.

ONDINE £62 4 3 3

2 GEORGE IV BRIDGE EH1 1AD 0131 2261888

"Fantastic fresh seafood and fish", "beautifully and imaginatively cooked", draw a lively crowd to Roy Brett's "atmospheric and professional" Old Town venue, where guests are greeted by a spectacular array of oysters. "We return year after year – it's simply the best fish restaurant we know". / www.ondinerestaurant.co.uk; @OndineEdin; Booking max 6 may apply.

THE OUTSIDER £41 3 2 3

15 - 16 GEORGE IV BRIDGE EH1 1EE 0131 226 3131

"Get the best seats in the place" (at the back, which offers "beautiful views" of the castle) to make the most of a visit to this city-centre staple, also turning out "enjoyable" cuisine of a modern European bent. / www.theoutsiderrestaurant.com/; No Amex; Booking max 12 may apply.

PIZZERIA 1926 £36 4 3 3

85 DALRY ROAD EH11 2AA 0131 337 5757

"From the owners of nearby Locanda De Gusti" – this two year-old sibling is praised for its "authentic Neapolitan pizza" and at a good price too. / www.pizzeria1926.com; @pizzeria1926; Wed-Fri 4 pm, Sat & Sun 5 pm.

PURSLANE £53 5 3 2

33A ST STEPHEN STREET EH3 5AH 01312 263500

"Tucked away" in a "cosy" Georgian Stockbridge basement, chef Paul Gunning's 'casual fine dining' venue serves "exceptionally delicious" cuisine "at a fraction of the price of other restaurants serving food of this quality". "I'm amazed by how good the menu and dishes are for such a small restaurant". / www.purslanerestaurant.co.uk; @Purslane_1; children: 6+.

THE RABBIT HOLE £53 3 3 3

0131 229 7953

This "lovely neighbourhood restaurant" in Marchmont excels for the "tasty, generous and well-judged" meals prepared by its owner-chefs – a Sicilian-Canadian couple with a passion for French cuisine – and for its "affordable prices". Fish is supplied daily by Eddie's Seafood Market next door, and there's a "well-priced wine list". Top Tip: "excellent-value set lunch" (two courses for £13; three for £16). / www.therabbitholerestaurant.com; Take bookings all week via phone and/or online.

RESTAURANT MARTIN WISHART £124 5 4 4

54 THE SHORE EH6 6RA 0131 553 3557

"Still the best in Edinburgh" – Martin Wishart delivers "a glorious celebration of Scottish fare" at this "slightly formal" operation. "This is serious no-nonsense cooking from the canapés, to the amuse bouche, and you can opt for the tasting menu, à la carte, vegetarian tasting menu and fish tasting menu; plus a fantastic selection of wine and wine flights". Stylewise, it's "a classic modern dining room" in "a nice location by the water in Leith", and "with a level of service akin to that of a top London hotel". "The only quibble is the very limited choice at lunchtime" although the set deal is "overall very good value for the price". / www.martin-wishart.co.uk; @RMWLeith; Tue-Thu 9 pm, Fri & Sat 9.30 pm; No trainers.

RHUBARB, PRESTONFIELD HOTEL £62 3 3 4

PRIESTFIELD RD EH16 5UT 0131 225 1333

With its "rich and opulent" setting, this Georgian former private estate provides a "unique environment" for "high-end" meals that are a feast for the eyes as much as the tastebuds. James Thomson pioneered his borderline kitsch approach to hospitality at his gothic-themed Witchery. / www.prestonfield.com; @PrestonfieldHH; Mon-Sat 10 pm, Sun 3 pm; Booking max 8 may apply; children: 12+ at D, none after 7pm.

LE ROI FOU £74 4 4 3

FORTH STREET EH1 3LE 0131 557 9346

"No pretension here, just good food at the right price" – Jérôme Henry's New Town venture (est 2017) attracts consistently enthusiastic reviews and "it's not to denigrate the talent of the chef (quite the opposite) to say that it's almost akin to a top-class brasserie – it takes wonderful ingredients and puts them on the plate with the minimum of interference". Some diners feel that the "surroundings seem a bit pedestrian" in comparison to the high quality of the cuisine, whereas others feel that "it gets the balance of formality and informality just right". / www.leroifou.com; @LeRoiFouEdin; Tue, Wed 10 pm, Thu-Sat 10.30 pm; Take bookings all week via phone and/or online.

SCRAN & SCALLIE £59 444

1 COMELY BANK RD EH4 1DT
0131 332 6281

"Lives up to the hype, year after year" – fans of Tom Kitchin's Stockbridge gastroboozer insist it serves "hands-down the best pub grub in Edinburgh". "The menu has a Scottish focus and the décor is fairly tartan-heavy, so it's a perfect place to introduce visitors to Scottish pub food". "Charming staff" and "a nice choice of kids' options" add further to the appeal. Even fans, though, acknowledge that it's "not cheap". / scranandscallie.com/; @ScranandScallie; Mon-Sun 10 pm; Take bookings all week via phone and/or online.

SONDER £126 534

74-78 SOUTH CLERK STREET EH8 9PT
0131 667 7032

A globetrotting menu of small plates features at this August 2018 newcomer from events specialist Trisha McCrae, who also owns the Camera Bar below it. Early survey feedback is highly promising: "a fabulous new restaurant and cocktail bar in the Newington area of Edinburgh", with "world class" cooking from chef Paul Graham, whose CV includes No. 1 at the Balmoral. / restaurant-sonder.com; Wed & Thu, Sun 9.30 pm, Fri & Sat 10 pm.

SOUTHSIDE SCRAN £62 333

14-17 BRUNTSFIELD PLACE EH10 4HN
0131 342 3333

Tom Kitchin, with his wife and business partner, ventures into Edinburgh's southside with this Bruntsfield newcomer, and early reports are all positive, if stopping short of out-and-out raves. "More than a neighbourhood bistro, the cooking is very precise and accomplished" (if – some feel – a tad "pricey"). There's "a good variety of dishes catering to all tastes" and an above-average wine selection with good choices by the glass. / southsidescran. com; @SouthsideScran; Mon-Sun 10 pm.

TAISTEAL £55 443

1-3 RAEBURN PLACE EH4 1HU
0131 332 9977

"Expect a twist on the ordinary" at Gordon Craig's "cracking" two-year-old – "a modern space" with greige tongue-and-groove panelling, which has proven "a very welcome addition to the restaurant scene in Stockbridge". "It's difficult to describe the cuisine, but it is deliciously eclectic, with some lovely, unusual flavours": "not always 100% successful but

interesting and for the quality, very good value". / www.taisteal.co.uk; Wed-Fri 4 pm, Sat & Sun 5 pm.

THE POMPADOUR, THE CALEDONIAN £93 434

PRINCES STREET EH1 2AB   01312228857

"The ambience is one to savour for a special occasion" at this pretty and romantic chamber: long one of the city's landmark dining rooms. Just as our survey was underway, in spring 2019, the Galvin brothers severed their ties with it, but chef Dan Ashmore remains at the stoves, so we've maintained its high ratings on our bet that this will be a case of 'plus ça change'. Choose between a three-course à la carte selection for £55, or a seven-course mystery tasting menu at £70. / www.thepompadour.com; @The_Pompadour_; Wed-Sun 9.30 pm.

TIMBERYARD £79 534

10 LADY LAWSON ST EH3 9DS
01312 211222

"I would travel a LONG way for these exceptional, innovative flavours" says a London-based reporter about this Fountainbridge fixture, opened in 2012 in the "charismatic" space of a converted Victorian warehouse, and serving a selection of Ben Radford's Scandi-influenced tasting menus (from four-courses to eight-courses), offset by a "long" wine list of exclusively natural wines from small European producers. / www.timberyard.co; @timberyard10; Booking max 5 may apply.

21212 £101 444

3 ROYAL TER EH7 5AB   0845 222 1212

Paul Kitching's Georgian townhouse – named for the number of options for each section of its five-course tasting menu – celebrated its tenth year in 2019: "it's a small dining room looking through glass onto the kitchen so you can see the large number of chefs working hard". His trademark culinary style is "never dull", although "some dishes have so many distinct flavours it can become confusing". That's always been a part of his gastronomic DNA, however, even when he was at Juniper in Altrincham, so why Michelin chose this year to take his star away is a mystery to us, and for most reporters this remains "a little gem in every way". / www.21212restaurant.co.uk; @paulk21212; Wed & Thu 9 pm, Fri & Sat 9.30 pm; children: 5+.

VALVONA & CROLLA £40 333

19 ELM ROW EH7 4AA   0131 556 6066

The all-day caffè-bar attached to Edinburgh's legendary Italian deli (est. 1934) is most tipped for a quality coffee-stop or light bite. Open later on Friday and Saturday evenings, the big draw is a wine list, which "must be the best Italian-based (and priced) in the UK" – effectively it includes every bottle stocked in the deli's drinks department, for the shop price plus a £5 corkage charge. The accompanying food is "OK… enjoyable" but unlikely to

evoke Tuscan hillsides, the Amalfi coast… / www.valvonacrolla.com; @valvonacrolla; Tue-Thu 7 pm, Fri & Sat 8.30 pm, Mon 5 pm, Sun 4 pm; Take bookings all week via phone and/or online.

THE WALNUT £45 443

9 CROALL PLACE EH7 4LT
0131 281 1236

This "real gem" on the road to Leith – "family-run with flair and passion" – "uses unusual cuts of locally sourced meats and seasonal produce to keep the cost of lunch to £10". It's "intimate and cosy, but on a hot summer's day, sitting outside sipping wine and eating the amazing fresh food the kitchen sends out is a real treat". / Mon, Wed-Fri 9.30 pm, Sat & Sun 10 pm.

WEDGWOOD £64 443

267 CANONGATE EH8 8BQ
0131 558 8737

"Glad we found them before they became so popular and Paul becoming a personality!" – Paul & Lisa Wedgwood's "gem of a restaurant" on the Royal Mile (much of it below ground) wins consistent praise for its "fabulous" modern Scottish cuisine: "very well executed dishes from locally sourced ingredients". / www.wedgwoodtherestaurant.co.uk; @chefwedgwood; Sun-Thu 4.30 pm, Fri & Sat 9.30 pm; Take bookings all week via phone and/or online.

THE WHITE HORSE £43 433

266 CANONGATE EH8 8AA
0131 629 5300

The oldest trad boozer on the Royal Mile (est 1742) has now been reincarnated as an oyster and seafood bar – the name switching connotation from the equine to the maritime. It has won immediate high ratings for its "outstanding" crustacea. / www.whitehorseoysterbar.co.uk; @WhiteHorseEdin.

THE WITCHERY BY THE CASTLE £69 335

CASTLEHILL, THE ROYAL MILE EH1 2NF
0131 225 5613

"Stupidly expensive but bags of fun" – James Thomson opened this "warm, quirky, and brilliant" (if somewhat touristy) sixteenth-century merchant's house very near Edinburgh Castle 40 years ago, and it's undoubtedly "very atmospheric" both in its Gothic oak-panelled dining room or beautiful 'Secret Garden'. The traditional Scottish cuisine is OK, but its main distinguishing culinary feature is "a heavyweight wine list backed up by a strong selection of malt whiskies and other digestifs". Plan on over-indulging? Book one of its glam bedrooms. / www.thewitchery.com; @thewitchery.

THE TUDOR ROOM, GREAT FOSTERS HOTEL   £73   443

STROUDE RD TW20 9UR   01784 433822

"Well worth the journey out from London", this imposing seventeenth century manor house set in extensive formal gardens boasts a very "beautiful setting". Its small (24-cover) dining room achieved consistent ratings this year, although it's been a time of change with Douglas Balish leaving the stoves to be replaced by Tony Parkin. / www.alexanderho tels.co.uk/great-fosters/food-drink/the-tudor-room/; @GreatFosters; Sun-Wed 11.30 pm, Thu & Fri 11 pm.

YNYSHIR RESTAURANT AND ROOMS, YNYSHIR HALL   £172   443

SY20 8TA   01654 781 209

"Most exciting food is served to the beat of The Prodigy and The National" at Gareth Ward's "small but super-comfy country house hotel in the wild, wild west of Wales": "a very different and accomplished" experience, whose many fans say is "well worth the (extensive) detour": "some of the best dishes I have eaten from a tasting menu of 20 plates in a chilled space with great staff, banter, and fun". Prices are high, though, and its funky approach including the "sonic assault" of the soundtrack mean that even those who praise "astonishing and inspired" cuisine can be in two minds about (or occasionally dead set against) it: "I quite like hip hop and do think the servers should have a good time, but this is a bit like having an expensive and romantic meal in a room that has been taken over by teenagers". / www.ynyshir.co.uk; @ynyshirrest; Credit card deposit required to book; children: 9+.

THE BUTCHER'S ARMS   £57   333

LIME ST GL19 4NX   01452 840 381

It's still early days for Grain Store chef, Mark Block, who took over this celebrated county inn in January 2018. While there's the odd complaint – of food that's "competent but has

no zing" – the general sense is that, despite the former regime being "quite a tough act to follow, it's doing nicely under the new ownership": no longer chasing Michelin stars, but "very much a rural pub with good food". / www.thebutchersarms.net; Tue-Sat 11 pm, Sun 3 pm; children: 10+.

THE BAY HORSE   £47   443

BAY HORSE LN LA2 0HR   01524 791204

This "crackingly good country pub" in a hamlet on the edge of the Trough of Bowland has a "fairly short menu of great food – not just pub classics". Ambitious chef Craig Wilkinson, who moved here with his parents 26 years ago, makes good use of the excellent local larder, and his "plate-lickingly-good, brasserie-style food" is "very good value for the quality" – "in an area with a lot of competition, the Bay Horse is our go-to and never disappoints". / www.bayhorseinn.com; @bayhorseinn; Wed-Sat 9 pm, Sun 8 pm; No Amex.

OLD FIRE ENGINE HOUSE   £46   443

25 ST MARY'S ST CB7 4ER 01353 662582

"Beautiful home-cooked food" has been on the menu of this real "long-time favourite" since 1968, when owner Ann Jarman opened an "informal" restaurant and art gallery with two friends in this Georgian house with a large walled garden near the cathedral. ("A diner at a table nearby had ham, jacket potato and salad. The ham looked to be real ham, and he was offered more meat if he wanted it. My husband had an amazing bakewell tart, with very light pastry and a lovely almond flavour"). / www.theoldfireenginehouse.co.uk; Mon-Sat 9 pm; No Amex; Take bookings all week via phone and/or online.

THE DECK   £42   223

EMSWORTH MARINA, THORNEY ROAD PO10 8BP   01243 376161

Taken over – and later expanded – by twenty-something sailor-chef Ed Collison three years ago, this "lovely restaurant in Emsworth yacht

basin" turns out a "great breakfast" but is also a "favourite lunchtime venue on a sunny afternoon (they're open Friday and Saturday evenings too)". / thedeckcafe.co.uk; Sun-Wed 5.30 pm, Thu-Sat 11 pm.

FAT OLIVES   £55   443

30 SOUTH ST PO10 7EH   01243 377914

"Reliably superb, locally sourced" cooking induces many locals to "return regularly" to Lawrence & Julia Murphy's "small and friendly" favourite – a converted cottage on the main road running up from the quay, which is celebrating its twentieth year in 2020. One or two reporters this year, however, couldn't see what the fuss was about. / www.fatolives.co.uk; @fat_olives; Mon-Sat midnight, Sun 11 pm; No Amex; children: 8+, except Sat L.

36 ON THE QUAY   £89   344

47 SOUTH ST PO10 7EG   01243 375592

With "boats bobbing outside", this "lovely small restaurant with rooms on Emsworth harbour" (complete "with a gorgeous sheltered courtyard") "feels like being welcomed into someone's home". A fixture for more than 20 years, it is now run by chef Gary Pearce (who joined the kitchen as a teenager before working at Le Champignon Sauvage) and his wife Martina – under whom ratings have risen for a second successive year. / www.36onthequay.co.uk; Take bookings all week via phone and/or online.

HAYWARDS RESTAURANT   £74   542

111 BELL COMMON CM16 4DZ 01992 577350

"Some of the best fine dining in Essex" – Amanda & Jahdre's "local favourite" is tucked away behind The Forest Gate Inn (owned by Amanda's family). It has a large regular following from across the county for its "continuously excellent" cuisine: "it could rival any top London restaurant any day". / www.haywardsrestaurant.co.uk; @HaywardsRestaur; Wed & Thu 9.30 pm, Fri & Sat 10 pm, Sun 3 pm; Credit card deposit required to book; children: 10.

GOOD EARTH   £58   344

14 - 18 HIGH STREET KT10 9RT 01372 462489

"A huge cut above a regular Chinese" – this "very smart" branch of the family-run London group is "not overly cheap" and also "a bit predictable", but remains "very popular" nonetheless: "we love that we don't have to go into town for excellent Chinese food and lovely service to look after you". / www.goodearthgroup.co.uk; Mon-Sat 10.30 pm, Sun 10.15 pm; Booking max 12 may apply.

Gareth Ward at Ynyshir, Eglwys Fach

THE WHEATSHEAF £50 333

40 ESHER GREEN KT10 8AG
01372 464014

A refurbishment/relaunch a few years ago
added to the charms of this good all-round
boozer, handy pre- or post catching the nags
at Sandown Park, whose food was consistently
well-rated this year. / wheatsheafesher.co.uk; Sun-
Thu 9.30 pm, Fri & Sat 10 pm.

ETON, BERKSHIRE 3–3A

GILBEY'S £58 333

82 - 83 HIGH STREET SL4 6AF
01753 854921

The cuisine is "somewhere between modern
British and French in looks and taste", and
reliably – if not perhaps dazzlingly – executed
at this comfortable stalwart, on the high street
near the bridge. As befits a venue owned by the
gin dynasty, the wine list is worth a look – "if
possible sleep off the after-effects in one of
the super bedrooms above" (which opened a
couple of years ago). / www.gilbeygroup.com;
@GilbeysEton; Sun-Thu 9.30 pm, Fri & Sat 10 pm;
Take bookings all week via phone and/or online.

EVERSHOT, DORSET 2–4B

THE ACORN INN £61 333

28 FORE ST DT2 0JW 01935 83228

This fifteenth-century inn with a skittle alley in
picturesque Hardy country was the model for
the 'Sow & Acorn' in 'Tess of the d'Urbervilles'
and, like the swankier Summer Lodge in the
same village, is part of the Red Carnation hotel
group. Here you get "similar food, but with
simpler presentation" than at its sibling – "an
all-round pleasure". / www.acorn-inn.co.uk; @
Acorn_Inn.

SUMMER LODGE, SUMMER LODGE COUNTRY HOUSE £100 335

DT2 0JR 01935 482000

Under the Relais & Châteaux banner, and
partly designed by Thomas Hardy no less (an
architect before he was an author), this "gem"
of a country hotel is "a little out of the way
but well worth the effort". When it comes to
its "comfortable fine dining" offer, "no doubt
the price reflects the amazing surroundings"
but, given that "everything is beautifully done",
only the odd reporter raises any complaint. /
www.summerlodgehotel.co.uk; @Summer_Lodge;
Mon-Fri 9 pm, Sat & Sun 9.30 pm; No jeans.

EXETER, DEVON 1–3D

RENDEZVOUS WINE BAR £52 333

38-40 SOUTHERNHAY EAST EX1 1PE
01392 270 222

This independent basement wine bar-restaurant
is a "reliable city-centre standby" with a
"lovely atmosphere", plus a "decent menu"
and wines – even a reporter who says "it won't

thrill you" says "it won't let you down either!" /
www.winebar10.co.uk; @RendezvousWBar.

EXMOUTH, DEVON 1–3D

LYMPSTONE MANOR £185 543

COURTLANDS LANE EX8 3NZ
01395 202040

"Gidleigh Park on steroids!". Michael Caines
"has shown exceptional skill" in creating this
hugely ambitious and "luxurious" two-year-
old ("you can see a lot of money has been
pumped in"), which has a "wonderful setting,
now complete with a vineyard"; and "once
the grounds have matured a bit, it will be even
more stunning than it already is", and with
excellent views of the Exe estuary. "Dining is
split between several rooms so you do not feel
you are in a crowd" and the "very confident"
cuisine is "as you would expect of Caines: if
not overly inventive, then classical, delicious
and executed to perfection" from either the à
la carte or the 'Signature' or (in the evenings
only) 'Taste the Estuary' eight-course tasting
menus. For many reporters it's just an all-round
smash hit, and an "unpretentious" one too. But
there are others who qualify their praise. The
"ornate surroundings" ("the pomp factor is
off the scale") can feel "very quiet and refined,
but lacking buzz" and service though generally
"very helpful" and "unobtrusive" is found on
occasion to be a "work in progress" or "stilted".
Top Tip – afternoon tea is another option here:
"the scones and sandwiches are particularly
delicious". / www.lympstonemanor.co.uk;
@Lympstone_Manor; Mon-Thu 9 pm, Fri-Sun
9.30 pm; No shorts; children: 5.

RIVER EXE CAFE £52 334

RIVER EXE ESTUARY 07761 116 103

A "great location" for a meal with a "very
different feel", this 'floating gastro shed' moored
in the Exe is only accessible by boat (water taxi
£5 return from Exmouth harbour). "Delicious
local seafood" is the star of the menu, but
pizzas and burgers are also available. Note:
the six-month season runs from April to late
September, and plan your visit so that the
deadline for the return boat allows sufficient
time for the meal. / www.riverexecafe.com/;
@riverexecafe; Tue-Sat 10.30 pm, Sun 8.30 pm;
Take bookings all week via phone and/or online.

ROCKFISH EXMOUTH £49 333

PIER HEAD EX8 1DU 01395 272100

You'll find a "nice seaside vibe" and "great
fresh fish" at this "fun seafood restaurant on
the mouth of the Exe" – the newest in the West
Country group from Mitch Tonks. It has a
"buzzy cool atmosphere I can't ever remember
from the Exmouth of my childhood". /
www.therockfish.co.uk/restaurants/exmouth;
@therockfishuk; Take bookings all week via phone
and/or online.

EXTON, HAMPSHIRE 2–3D

SHOE INN £43 333

SHOE LN SO32 3NT 01489 877526

A "lovely relaxed pub with friendly service
and excellent food"; "all courses are worth a
try, though be aware the large fish 'n' chips
are indeed very large!" (a boon for hikers
stopping in to this spot on the River Meon
while tackling the South Downs Way). /
www.theshoeexton.co.uk; Mon-Sat 9 pm, Sun 8.30
pm.

EXTON, RUTLAND 5–3D

THE FOX AND HOUNDS HOTEL £53 334

19 THE GREEN LE15 8AP 01572 812 403

This "very smart and much-renovated old
coaching inn" sits on the village green of one of
the settlements bordering Rutland Water, and
serves "high quality" fare in a cosy traditional
setting. / www.afoxinexton.co.uk; @afoxinexton;
Tue-Sat 9 pm, Sun 3.30 pm; Take bookings all week
via phone and/or online.

EYE GREEN, CAMBRIDGESHIRE 6–4A

HOUSE OF FEASTS £60 432

41 CROWLAND ROAD PE6 7TP
01733 221279

"A very decent addition to the scene in
Peterborough" – Damian Wawrzyniak's
two-year-old venture in a village a short drive
outside the city specialises in modern Polish
cuisine, which you can enjoy either via the à
la crate menu or a ten-course tasting menu. /
www.houseoffeasts.co.uk; @HouseOfFeasts; Wed
& Thu 9.30 pm, Fri 10 pm, Sat 10.30 pm, Sun
3.30 pm.

FAIRSTEAD, ESSEX 3–2C

THE SQUARE AND COMPASSES £44 323

FULLER STREET CM3 2BB 01245 361477

"Good cooking, with locally sourced ingredients
that will not break the bank" attracts solid
feedback for this mid-1600s inn, which has
held on to attractive original features and
taps nearby estates for its hearty game-centric
fare (villagers themselves contribute the
vegetables). / www.thesquareandcompasses.co.uk;
@SCFullerStreet; Mon-Fri 11.30 pm, Sat midnight,
Sun 11 pm; Take bookings all week via phone and/
or online.

FALMOUTH, CORNWALL 1–4B

THE COVE RESTAURANT & BAR £44 343

MAENPORTH BEACH TR11 5HN
01326 251136

A "lovely position" with views over Maenporth
Beach – including from the all-weather
'Glassroom' – combines with "very good food"
from Cornish-born chef-patron Arty Williams
at the attractive restaurant he has run for
nearly 20 years. / www.thecovemaenporth.co.uk;

@covemaenporth; Tue-Sat 9.30 pm, Sun 4 pm; Take bookings all week via phone and/or online.

OLIVER'S £53 443

33 HIGH ST TR11 2AD 01326 218138

"A friendly welcome" sets the tone for a visit to this husband-and-wife operation on the high street; "lovely, fresh, vibrant" fish and seafood is the star of the "tiny, changing menu" ("if it was in London at these prices I'd be there weekly!"). / www.oliversfalmouth.com; @oliversfalmouth; No Amex; Take bookings all week via phone and/or online.

RICK STEIN'S FISH & CHIPS £43 322

DISCOVERY QUAY TR11 3XA 01841 532700

There are critics of the TV chef's cavernous (rather corporate) outlet by the Maritime Museum ("in my view only the name brings in the customers"), but on balance it's deemed a "reliable" spot, and its fish 'n' chips are, say fans, "the best for miles and miles". / www.rickstein.com; @TheSeafood; Tue-Sat 11 pm, Sun 10 pm; No Amex; No bookings.

THE WHEEL HOUSE £41 444

UPTON SLIP TR11 3DQ 01326 318050

Admittedly there are "no frills here (kitchen-paper on bare wooden tables)", but other than that the "unpretentious" cash-only spot is "perfect in literally every way", thanks to its "limited menu of fresh shellfish dishes that are simply and perfectly cooked and come at fair prices" too. / Take bookings all week via phone and/or online.

FAVERSHAM, KENT 3–3C

READ'S £90 344

MACKNADE MANOR, CANTERBURY RD ME13 8XE 01795 535344

"High-end dining in a comfortable manor house setting" has been a gastronome's treat at David and Rona Pitchford's stylish operation near the north Kent coast for three decades. "The food may seem slightly old-fashioned" these days, but there's no shame in that – "if you're a traditionalist, rate quality, and place substance over style, then Read's will not disappoint". / www.reads.com; @READSREST; Take bookings all week via phone and/or online.

YARD £14 443

10 JACOB YD, PRESTON ST ME13 8NY 01795 538265

"Amazing breakfast food every time" and "the best coffee and inventive light bites (amazing cakes) in town" help make this "friendly and relaxed" café tucked away in a mews "a really great find". "On their special Thirsty Thursday and Fizzed Up Friday nights", you can also dine in the evening. / @YardFaversham; Mon-Sat 5 pm, Sun 12.30 pm; No bookings.

FENCE, LANCASHIRE 5–1B

WHITE SWAN AT FENCE £47 543

300 WHEATLEY LANE RD BB12 9QA 01282 611773

"Very classy indeed" – Tom Parker's "informal" pub-restaurant "shows no sign of slowing down", having snaffled a star from the tyre men in 2018. A "small menu of great seasonal and local ingredients is cooked and presented beautifully" and, as the only Timothy Taylors pub in Lancashire, there's no cause to complain about the beer. / www.whiteswanatfence.co.uk; Mon-Sat 11 pm, Sun 10.30 pm; Take bookings all week via phone and/or online.

FERRENSBY, NORTH YORKSHIRE 8–4B

GENERAL TARLETON £56 333

BOROUGHBRIDGE RD HG5 0PZ 01423 340284

This "welcoming" and "very reliable" pub-with-rooms has a kitchen that "goes from strength to strength" by most – if not quite all – accounts, and its location, just off the A1 and close to Harrogate, makes it a handy stop-off or rendezvous. / www.generaltarleton.co.uk; @generaltarleton; Mon-Fri 9.30 pm, Sat & Sun 9 pm; Take bookings all week via phone and/or online.

FIONNPHORT, ARGYLL & BUTE 9–3A

THE CREEL £14 433

FIONNPHORT PIER PA66 6BL 07864 605682

"Lovely snacks from this shack, while waiting for the Iona ferry" – ultra-fresh locally caught langoustines, scallops and crabs are served from a tiny wooden hut at the furthest end of the Ross of Mull, from April to September. /

FLAUNDEN, HERTFORDSHIRE 3–2A

THE BRICKLAYERS ARMS £54 323

HOGPITS BOTTOM HP3 0PH 01442 833322

This ivy-clad gastropub, originally a trio of early-18th-century cottages, is popular among both locals and visitors to the nearby Warner Brothers studio for its "good-value pub grub". Chef Claude Paillet trained under the legendary Pierre Gagnaire before switching his focus to heartier fare. / www.bricklayersarms.com; @bricklayerspub; Mon-Sat 9.30 pm, Sun 7 pm; Take bookings all week via phone and/or online.

FLETCHING, EAST SUSSEX 3–4B

THE GRIFFIN INN £51 323

TN22 3SS 01825 722890

A "sublime setting" – especially in summer when "eating outside has marvelous views" over the Ouse Valley – and "superb food using local produce" are the trump cards at this "charming" eighteenth-century inn. Piers Morgan lived here as a child, when his stepdad was the landlord. / www.thegriffininn.co.uk; @GriffinInnPub; Mon-Sat 9.30 pm, Sun 3.30 pm; Take bookings all week via phone and/or online.

FOLKESTONE, KENT 3–4D

THE FOLKESTONE WINE COMPANY £45 322

CHURCH STREET CT20 1SE 01303 249952

Good if still-limited reports on David Hart's no-frills wine bar, bottle shop and 26-seat restaurant, serving mostly French and Italian bottles as well as some local Kent wines and a small menu of simple dishes to keep them company. / www.folkestonewine.com; @folkestonewine; Wed-Fri 10 pm, Sat 11 pm, Sun 4.30 pm.

ROCKSALT £55 445

4-5 FISHMARKET CT19 6AA 01303 212 070

"Amazing food overlooking the harbour" with "a view to die for!" – Mark Sargeant's "elegant" waterside venture is nowadays one of the survey's most popular dining destinations, drawing fans from across Kent and on days out from the capital ("wish we lived closer!"). Particularly prized (as you might expect, given its proximity to the sea) for its "terrific, locally sourced" fish and seafood – it's "ideal for a special occasion, although it is somewhat pricey". / www.rocksaltfolkestone.co.uk; @rocksalt_kent; Mon-Thu 10 pm, Fri & Sat 10.30 pm, Sun 5 pm; Take bookings all week via phone and/or online.

STEEP STREET COFFEE HOUSE £18 344

18-24 THE OLD HIGH STREET CT20 1RL 01303 247819

"Top marks all round for this excellent coffee house that also does great cakes and light lunches", is stuffed with books to read or buy, and is well "worth seeking out" in the newly regenerated Old High Street in Folkestone (now at the heart of the town's 'Creative Quarter'). / www.steepstreet.co.uk; @steep_street; Mon-Sat 6 pm, Sun 5 pm.

FONTHILL GIFFORD, WILTSHIRE 2–3C

BECKFORD ARMS £43 343

SP3 6PX 01747 870 385

"A favourite out-of-town spot" – this spruced-up Georgian coaching inn "right next to beautiful Fonthill Park" offers "a good choice of well-prepared food", although, with its "beautiful dining room", it's really "more a restaurant than a pub". From the same boutique stable as the Lord Poulett Arms and Talbot Inn in Somerset. / www.thebeckfordarms.co.uk; @beckfordarms; No Amex.

WHITE PHEASANT £51 `3` `4` `3`

21 MARKET ST CB7 5LQ 01638 720414

"Modern cuisine using local seasonal produce" wins plaudits for chef-owner Calvin Holland at this upscale village pub. "Surprising and innovative" dishes from the tasting menu sit alongside "simple steak and fish dishes for more traditional diners". "A recent refurb has created a relaxed seating area where you can enjoy a drink before and after eating". / www.whitepheasant.com; @whitepheasant; Tue-Sat 9.30 pm, Sun 2.30 pm.

THE FORDWICH ARMS £79 `5` `5` `4`

KING STREET CT2 0DB 01227 710444

"Not the easiest place to find in what is apparently Britain's smallest town" – Dan Smith (ex Clove Club), Tash Norton and Guy Palmer's venture is barely two years old and "has really hit its stride" as one of the UK's best dining destinations: "high end, but not poncy". Picturesquely located on the river, "when you enter it feels initially more like a pub with food, but my goodness you are soon disavowed of that!". "Every dish is beautifully crafted and presented" – "superbly intelligent combinations, prepared with skill and ambition" – and with "flavours that just hit you". What's more "staff are so attentive and polite and seem genuinely to care!" / www.fordwicharms.co.uk; @FordwichArms; Tue-Sat 11 pm, Sun 6 pm.

CRANNOG £60 `3` `2` `3`

TOWN CENTRE PIER PH33 6DB 01397 705589

"Wonderful seafood straight from the sea under the windows of the restaurant" helps win praise for this well-established fixture, on a pier by Loch Linnhe (with arguably the best location by the water in the town). Feedback is somewhat mixed, though, with sceptics citing "mediocre plating", "slow service" and "enormous" bills. / www.crannog.net; @CrannogHighland; Mon-Fri 1 am, Sat & Sun 2 am; No Amex; Take bookings all week via phone and/or online.

FITZROY £52

2 FORE STREET PL23 1AD 01726 932934

In April 2019, the team behind the Capital's hipster hits Jolene, Primeur and Westerns Laundry struck out far beyond the M25 to open this two-floor newcomer, which occupies a converted old bank building. No survey feedback as yet, but if you're in Cornwall and craving that northeast London vibe with trendy small plates to match, try here. / www.fitzroycornwall.com; Tue-Sun 9 pm.

JOLLY NICE FARM SHOP £16 `4` `3` `3`

THE OLD WHITE HORSE FILLING STATION, CIRENCESTER ROAD GL6 8HZ 01285 760868

"An atmospheric and charming farm shop (in a converted petrol station, on the A419) serving fabulous breakfasts and lunches with very tasty hamburgers from local meat". "It's been great to see JN progress from offering ice cream from an airstream caravan to butcher, deli, burger bar, Xmas tree seller..." (is there anything they can't do?!). / jollynicefarmshop.com; @JollyNice_.

THE FOX & GOOSE £61 `3` `3` `3`

CHURCH RD IP21 5PB 01379 586247

This listed 500-year-old former guildhall with exposed beams is "a top choice in northern Suffolk" under Paul & Sarah Yaxley, who took over more than 10 years ago. There's a clever mix of pub classics and more sophisticated dishes on the menu, and it's "always good, especially for lunch". / www.foxandgoose.net; @Foxygossip; Take bookings all week via phone and/or online; children: 9+ at D.

THE POT KILN £61

RG18 0XX 01635 201366

Reopened in September 2019 after a period of closure – complete with guest rooms, new kitchen, restaurant extension and game cookery school – this well-known pub won renown for its game cooking under former proprietor Michael Robinson. Nowadays run, with much of the same team, by his ex-wife, Katie Robinson, we would hazard a guess that its new incarnation will continue the good points it had of old, including its well-kept beer and beautiful large garden in summer. / www.potkiln.org; Tue-Sat 9.30 pm, Sun 3.30 pm; Take bookings all week via phone and/or online.

THE ALFORD ARMS £47 `3` `3` `4`

HP1 3DD 01442 864480

"What a discovery, hidden away in the beautiful Chilterns!" in "a remote rural setting far from the madding crowd" – this "very characterful family-run pub" is highly rated for its "well-presented and slightly unusual cooking". "You feel like you're a million miles from anywhere, when in reality it's only a 40-minute drive from London". / www.alfordarmsfrithsden.co.uk; @alfordarmshp1; Mon-Sat 11 pm, Sun 10.30 pm; Booking max 12 may apply.

THE PALM £38 `4` `4` `3`

BATH RD SN8 3HT 01672 871 818

It might not look like much from the road – an out-of-town bathroom showroom might be on the mark – and the location on the A4 doesn't help, but brave the underwhelming façade of this outfit and you'll find a "swanky" restaurant turning out "inventive Indian cuisine". / www.thepalmindian.com; Take bookings all week via phone and/or online.

SIX, BALTIC CENTRE FOR CONTEMPORARY ARTS £61 `3` `3` `5`

BALTIC (SIXTH FLOOR), SOUTH SHORE ROAD NE8 3BA 0191 440 4948

"One of the best views in the world" (if you don't mind Newcastle's urban sprawl) elevates a visit to this posh art gallery restaurant. It dodged the usual critiques it has often received this year, and although even some fans concede that "there is better-value food to be had in the city", it was consistently well-rated ("creative without being silly"). / www.sixbaltic.com; @sixbaltic; Tue-Sat 9.30 pm, Sun 4 pm.

TRAKOL £56 `4` `4` `4`

HILLGATE QUAYS NE8 2BH

"Right on the banks of the Tyne, under the iconic Tyne Bridge, with some of the UKs best city views" – these "trendily laid-out, converted shipping containers" have "a fabulous setting" and are "quirky in every way". "Start with a beer: there's around 15 to choose from, many brewed on the premises, served in 1/3 and 2/3 measures (a good plan given the strength range, of 5%-10%)". The food is "cooked in-view" in a 'fiercely seasonal, open-fire kitchen' and the fairly eclectic results are regularly outstanding: "mains were as good a meat as I've had. The Barnsley Chop was gargantuan, cooked with seafood (it works!). The whole lemon sole easily fed two, and was perfect". The odd reporter does strike unlucky, though: "duck predicted as 'tender' wasn't'… steak and bone marrow was very salty yet vegetables were bland". / www.bytheriverbrew.co/trakol/; @BTRBrewCo; Wed-Sat, Mon & Tue 10.30 pm, Sun 6 pm.

MALIKS £43 `4` `4` `3`

14 OAK END WAY SL9 8BR 01753 889634

"Exceptional food and service" distinguish this "excellent Indian", an offshoot of the well-known Cookham original (there's a third branch in Marlow). It "tends to be more expensive than similar places", but it's "not at all your typical curry house" – most reporters are happy to pay a little extra for the "high-end aspirations, traditional-style white tablecloths", and "best authentic kormas around". / www.maliks.co.uk; Mon-Sat 11 pm, Sun 10.30 pm; Take bookings all week via phone and/or online.

THREE OAKS £44 3️⃣3️⃣4️⃣

AUSTENWOOD LN SL9 8NL
01753 899 016

With "good cheerful service" and food that's "great value for money" too, this well-known destination – run by Terry Wogan's daughter and her husband (the pair are also behind Cookham's White Oak) – offers "a gastropub-plus experience" that's consistently well rated, and which draws a large fan club from across the outer fringes of west London. / www.thethreeoaksgx.co.uk; @TheThreeOaksGX; Take bookings all week via phone and/or online.

GISBURN, LANCASHIRE 5–1B

LA LOCANDA £51 4️⃣4️⃣3️⃣

MAIN STREET BB7 4HH   01200 445303

"Possibly the most authentic Italian food in the north of England, and with no compromise to British ideas of what Italian food is" – this converted old cottage on the A59 is "somewhat reminiscent of an agriturismo, but casting its net over Italy, serving various cuisines rather than just one". Maurizio Bocchi is the chef, while his wife Cinzia runs front of house, and "their knowledge of oils and wines is amazing" ("olive oil is a speciality verging on obsession and the all-Italian wine list is full of excellent wines you've never heard of, all at very fair prices"). "The food is hearty enough for a rural Lancastrian appetite" – "pastas, particularly the home made ones, are always excellent, fish is always very good, but meat tends to be overcooked in that curiously Italian manner". / www.lalocanda.co.uk; @LaLocandaCinzia; Mon-Sun 10 pm; Take bookings all week via phone and/or online.

GLASGOW, CITY OF GLASGOW 9–4C

ALCHEMILLA £37 5️⃣3️⃣3️⃣

1126 ARGYLE STREET G3 8TD
0141 337 6060

This three-year-old modern bistro "on Finneston's eating strip" has won renown as one of the city's better dining destinations. All reports are full of the highest praise for "small dishes bursting with flavour" and food that "genuinely melts in the mouth". / www.thisisalchemilla.com.

BATTLEFIELD REST £39 3️⃣4️⃣3️⃣

55 BATTLEFIELD ROAD G42 9JL
0141 636 6955

It is as a family-friendly option that Marco Giannasi's quirky Southside landmark – occupying a 1914 building once described as Scotland's most glamorous tram stop – attracts most nominations; on the large Italian menu: pizza, pasta and a variety of affordable dishes. / www.battlefieldrest.co.uk; Take bookings all week via phone and/or online.

THE BISTRO AT ONE DEVONSHIRE GARDENS £69 3️⃣3️⃣3️⃣

ONE DEVONSHIRE GDNS G12 0UX
0141 339 2001

"Tucked away in a corner of the West End, this top-end venue" is nowadays part of the Hotel du Vin group, but has long been one of the city's famous culinary destinations, with many top chefs having cut their teeth here in years past. Nowadays formatted in less formal style, this wood-panelled bistro is "full of nooks and crannies to dine in", and features some "excellent, exemplary cooking", including a full vegan tasting menu, "and the superb wine list, expertly introduced by the sommelier, is to die for". But in its new guise, it can be "rather too noisy: perhaps tablecloths might help". / www.hotelduvin.com; @HotelduVinBrand/; Mon-Sat 10 pm, Sun 9.30 pm.

BRETT

321 GREAT WESTERN ROAD G4 9HR

Cail Bruich's new sibling occupies narrow premises with a mezzanine in Finnieston. It's a bar as much as it is a place to eat, but has a serious food offering too: sharing plates of locally-supplied meat, fish, vegetables, shellfish, cheese and charcuterie. It opened in July 2019, after the survey had concluded, but critiques in the Scottish press are very upbeat. / www.barbrett.co.uk; @BarBrett1; Mon-Sun 1 am.

CAFÉ GANDOLFI £54 2️⃣3️⃣5️⃣

64 ALBION ST G1 1NY   0141 552 6813

This Merchant City legend, with its custom-made furniture and stained-glass window, still wins a good number of nominations, particularly for brunch, and it's often held out as a "casual and relaxed" landmark of local life with "always reliable" cooking and a "good, somewhat unusual wine list". One sceptical report, though, has some ring of truth to it: "Long held up as a Glasgow highlight, it can now seem a bit dull. The food is absolutely fine, but without any particular interest. But the room, with its wooden furniture seemingly made from driftwood and fallen trees, is great!" / www.cafegandolfi.com; @cafegandolfi; Mon-Sun 10 pm; Booking weekdays only.

CAIL BRUICH £63 5️⃣4️⃣3️⃣

725 GREAT WESTERN RD G12 8QX
01413 346265

"Really carefully thought out and extremely well executed dishes" – "some of the best in Scotland" – "showcase the best of Scottish produce" at Paul & Chris Charalambous's under-the-radar, yet exceptional West End outfit. "Even when a dish is a little challenging – such as a pre-dessert of white asparagus parfait with black olive meringue and marinated strawberries – when eaten the combination was a delicious revelation". "A slight refresh to the décor has worked well, though there's not much they can do about the unprepossessing exterior". / www.cailbruich.co.uk; @CailBruich; Wed-Sat, Mon & Tue 9 pm, Sun 8.30 pm; Take

---

bookings all week via phone and/or online; children: 5.

CRABSHAKK £54 4️⃣3️⃣4️⃣

1114 ARGYLE ST, FINNIESTON G3 8TD
0141 334 6127

It's "very crowded", but there's no knocking the "consistently fabulous fish and seafood" (which comes at "amazing" prices) at this idiosyncratic Finnieston fixture. You eat either counter-style at the front, or at a "closely-packed table" in one of the many nooks at the back or in the small upstairs section. / www.crabshakk.com; @CRABSHAKK; No Amex; Take bookings all week via phone and/or online.

THE DHABBA £41 3️⃣3️⃣2️⃣

44 CANDLERIGGS G1 1LE   0141 553 1249

"Right in the centre of Glasgow", and with "trendy" décor, this Merchant City fixture (est 2002) is beloved for its "different" North Indian dishes, notably "excellent dosas". Usefully, nearby sibling Dakhin is that rare restaurant offering 100% gluten-free Keralan cuisine. / www.thedhabba.com; @thedhabba; Mon-Sun 10.30 pm; Take bookings all week via phone and/ or online.

EUSEBI DELI £56 5️⃣3️⃣3️⃣

152 PARK ROAD G4 9HB   01416489999

Phenomenal small Italian deli of over four decades' standing, a few minutes from Kelvinbridge subway station, which has its "counters of prepared deli produce and cakes and patisserie" but is also a notable destination thanks to its "amazing" cooking – "unfailingly well-prepared pasta in particular", alongside antipasti and more substantial dishes. "Seemingly busy at all times of the day", "staff are always so friendly and happy to explain the menu" but "service seems to suffer a bit from being so popular, particularly on the cramped ground floor (downstairs is a little more sedate and, dare I say, comfortable?)". / eusebideli. com/; @eusebi_deli; Sun-Thu 10 pm, Fri & Sat 2 am; Take bookings all week via phone and/or online.

THE FISH PEOPLE CAFE £53 4️⃣3️⃣3️⃣

350 SCOTLAND STREET G5 8QP
0141 429 8787

"A cosy little restaurant in an odd, but handy, location" (next to the subway on Shields Road) "turning out platefuls of fishy deliciousness for their loyal and local fans". "Despite its small size, the quality surpasses many other more expensive fish places". / www.thefishpeoplecafe.co.uk/; @fishpeople_cafe; Tue-Thu 9 pm, Fri & Sat 10 pm, Sun 4 pm; Take bookings all week via phone and/or online.

GAMBA £66 4️⃣4️⃣2️⃣

225A WEST GEORGE ST G2 2ND
0141 572 0899

"Simply cooked" but "superb" Scottish seafood has long been the hallmark of Derek Marshall's

Cail Bruich, Glasgow

"consistent and wonderful", if fairly low-key basement veteran in the city-centre: one of Glasgow's best destinations for a high quality meal, but one with a "friendly atmosphere and reasonable prices" to boot. / www.gamba.co.uk; @Gamba_Glasgow; Mon-Sat 9.30 pm, Sun 9 pm; Booking max 6 may apply.

THE GANNET £54 443

1155 ARGYLE ST G3 8TB 0141 2042081

Peter McKenna & Ivan Stein's stripped-back Finnieston venture has made waves since opening six years back; "the cooking (modern British) is perhaps more serious here than the bare-brick walls décor suggests" (being "full of interesting small dishes, but not too 'out there'"). In fact, more than one reporter notes "it deserves a Michelin star" such is the quality of the food but – perhaps as prices are not supercheap – stops short of awarding it full marks for value. / www.thegannetgla.com/; @TheGannetGla; Tue-Sun 9.30 pm; Take bookings all week via phone and/or online.

HANOI BIKE SHOP £28 342

8 RUTHVEN LN G12 9BG 0141 334 7165

This rickety and atmospheric three-year-old in the West End has earned a reputation for its "fantastic Viet food", including 'build-your-own pho' with beef, seafood and veggie options, and organic tofu made on the premises. / www.hanoibikeshop.co.uk; @hanoibikeshop; Take bookings all week via phone and/or online.

THE IVY BUCHANAN STREET £63

106 BUCHANAN STREET G1 2NB

Opened in summer 2019 after the survey's conclusion, Glasgow's outpost of the ever-growing brasserie chain (in the works since 2017), is housed in a former Nationwide bank and features over 220 covers, plus two bars, a private dining space and 'Parisian-style outdoor seating'. / theivyglasgow.com; @theivyglasgow.com/menus/#; Mon-Sat midnight, Sun 11.30 pm.

JULIE'S KOPITIAM £22 532

1109 POLLOKSHAWS ROAD G41 3YG 0141 237 9560

"A little jewel" – Masterchef competitor Julie Lin made her debut in Shawlands on the Southside in 2017 with this 16-seater serving fabulous and highly affordable Malaysian scoff. She also now has a pop-up at SWG3's popular Acid Bar diner in Finnieston. / @julielinkitchen; Tue-Sun 11 pm; No bookings.

MOTHER INDIA £43 433

28 WESTMINSTER TER G3 8AD 0141 339 9145

Famous for its "fabulous-quality, carefully seasoned Indian dishes" – this West End institution "can be loud and… well Glaswegian, but the food is delicious". "Prices are modest", too, and there's a "great view of Kelvingrove Museum from the window". / www.motherindiaglasgow.co.uk; @Official_Mindia; Sun-Thu 10 pm, Fri & Sat 10.30 pm; Take bookings all week via phone and/or online.

OX AND FINCH £50 543

920 SAUCHIEHALL ST G3 7TF 0141 339 8627

"Adventurous taste combinations, very consistently delivered" via a good selection of "innovative small plates" score top marks this year for this Finnieston gastropub. Service is "lovely too" and the only gripe is that some seats are "a wee bit cramped". / www.oxandfinch.com; @OxAndFinch; Take bookings all week via phone and/or online.

PAESANO PIZZA £28 533

94 MILLER STREET G1 1DT 0141 258 5565

"I've been back more than 40 times, which says it all!". These "truly excellent" and "really buzzy" pizza-stops in Glasgow's city centre and West End are "really hard to beat" – the dough uses both yeast and sourdough and is proved for 48 hours for maximum Neapolitan-style authenticity. In August 2019 they announced a new sibling, Sugo, to launch in the Charles Rennie Mackintosh Herald Building, specialising in fresh homemade pasta. / paesanopizza.co.uk; @paesano_pizza; Sun-Wed 10.30 pm, Fri & Sat midnight, Thu 11 pm; Take bookings all week via phone and/or online.

ROGANO £66 335

11 EXCHANGE PLACE G1 3AN 0141 248 4055

"Such an institution" and "a true throwback to the 1930s" – even reporters who hadn't visited in a quarter of a century were delighted to find that "little has changed" at this "timeless" dining room, where "the menu is biased towards seafood and, where the genuine Art Deco interior (created in 1935 by the same craftsmen who fitted out the Queen Mary) is a joy to behold". Naturally the big draw is the room itself, but the food is well-rated too. / www.roganoglasgow.com; @roganoglagow.

SINGL END £28 333

265 RENFREW STREET G3 6TT 0141 353 1277

"Raising the standard for breakfast in Glasgow" – this "fantastic indie café" in Garnethill doesn't just serve "excellent coffee" and "great food" with "everything fresh and clearly made on the premises". It also provides "very right-on ethical packaging for take-away with everything biodegradable". There's also a branch in Merchant City at 15 St John Street. / thesingl-end.co.uk/; Take bookings all week via phone and/or online.

STRAVAIGIN £55 334

28 GIBSON ST G12 8NX 0141 334 2665

Now in its 25th year, Colin Clydesdale's well-known local operates on the principle 'think global, eat local', serving an eclectic selection of dishes on world food principles using Scottish ingredients in its basement restaurant. Many regulars just go for a burger or other bar snacks in the popular ground floor bar, however (same kitchen). / www.stravaigin.co.uk; @straivaiging12; No Amex; Take bookings all week via phone and/or online.

TWO FAT LADIES AT THE BUTTERY £61 335

652 ARGYLE ST G3 8UF 0141 221 8188

"In a quiet Glasgow backstreet" (between the M8 and the SECC) and with an "unassuming" exterior, Ryan James's "splendidly preserved institution" is one of the city's oldest venues, complete with an "unexpectedly beautiful interior" (of the tartan-clad, vaguely baronial variety) lined with booths – a "fine destination that has maintained standards for many years" (especially for Scots seafood). / www.twofatladiesrestaurant.com; Mon-Thu 4 pm, Fri-Sun 5 pm; Take bookings all week via phone and/or online.

UBIQUITOUS CHIP £64 435

12 ASHTON LN G12 8SJ 0141 334 5007

"Still with a buzz about it" – this sprawling West End legend is fast approaching its 40th anniversary and still manages to be both "different and classical". Its many fans agree that it's "wonderful for both food and environment", not to mention its bible of a wine list and its "awe-inspiring malt whisky selection" (of which "the staff have a remarkably broad and deep knowledge"). Now run by Colin Clydesdale, son of founder Ronnie, the 'Chip' has a more casual brasserie upstairs. / www.ubiquitouschip.co.uk; @UbiquitousChip.

GLAZEBURY, CHESHIRE 5–2B

THE GLAZEBURY £42

207 WARRINGTON ROAD WA3 5LL 01925 382056

South African-born chef Ernst van Zyl and partner Liz Kellett have taken over (and substantially refurbished) this Warrington pub, which opened at the end of 2018. This new place has 60 covers, five rooms and a huge beer garden. Scant survey feedback as yet, but based on his previous gaff – The Lord Clyde in Kerridge – there's reason to hope for notably accomplished food in this village pub. / www.theglazebury.co.uk; @TheGlazebury; Mon-Thu 8 pm, Fri & Sat 9 pm, Sun 7 pm.

GLINTON, RUTLAND   6–4A

THE BLUE BELL   £46   3 3 3

10 HIGH STREET PE6 7LS   01733 252285

Will and Kelly Frankgate took over this village gastropub in 2013, and have since added a timber-framed garden room extension, which is one of the best of the numerous areas for dining and leads onto its outside dining area for the summer. Rated on more limited feedback this year. / www.thebluebellglinton.co.uk; @bluebellglinton; Mon-Thu 11 pm, Fri & Sat midnight, Sun 8 pm; Take bookings all week via phone and/or online.

GORING-ON-THAMES,
OXFORDSHIRE   2–2D

DON GIOVANNI AT THE
LEATHERNE BOTTEL £67

BRIDLE WAY RG8 0HS   01491 872667

A serene and gorgeous Thames Valley location is the main reason to continue to include this riverside stalwart, which has been through numerous owners in recent times (and which, at the time of writing, is marked as closed on TripAdvisor even though it appears to be open). Previously run as 'Rossini at the Leatherne Bottel', it was relaunched in April 2019 under new owners, but still serving Italian cuisine. / www.leathernebottel.co.uk; @leathernebottel; Mon-Sat 10.30 pm, Sun 3 pm; children: 10+ for D.

THE MILLER OF
MANSFIELD   £60   4 4 3

HIGH ST RG8 0HB   01491 872829

"What a treat" – reporters (and the odd local celeb) "absolutely adore" former Heston staffers Nick & Mary Galer's 18th-century inn; there are shout-outs for the "cosy" fire-lit ambiance, but it's the "exceptional" food which stands apart, be it superior breakfasts, "lovely puds" or "unusual" libations (think Cornish pastis). / www.millerofmansfield.com; Mon-Sat 9 pm, Sun 7 pm; 6 - 9 Sat Lunch: 12 - 2.30, Dinner 6 - 9 Sun 12 - 3, 6 - 8; 0.

GOUDHURST, KENT   3–4B

THE SMALL
HOLDING   £81   5 4 3

**RANTERS LANE, KILNDOWN TN17 2SG
01892 890105**

"The first visit was amazing and I'm looking forward to returning": Will Devlin's "interesting tasting menus" (either the five-course '1/2-acre' menu for £30, or the ten-course 'full acre' menu for £60) have Kent foodies in raptures, and this small, simple year-old venture (founded in April 2018) is the talk of the county. Part of the appeal are the "very generous wine flights

and knowledgeable sommelier" to introduce them. / thesmallholding.restaurant; Wed-Fri 11 pm, Sun 2 pm, Sat 4 pm.

GRASMERE, CUMBRIA   7–3D

THE FOREST SIDE   £92   4 4 4

LA22 9RN   01539 435 250

"Every course leaves you wanting more… even though you knew you shouldn't as there are so many more to come", according to fans of ex-L'Enclume chef Kevin Tickle's "sublime" cuisine at Andrew Wildsmith's swish three-year-old hotel: a "delightful" venue, in beautiful Lakeland setting, just outside Grasmere. The "quirky and interesting set of menus" are "well-realised and quite fun as well", featuring "seasonal food that's either from the garden, local suppliers or foraged". It's not utterly beyond criticism, though. Even fans concede it's "costly" and criticisms include its "manicured style of cooking (I pity the sous chefs with tweezers)" and service that "leaves you feeling a bit giddy with so much coming and going". / www.theforestside.com; @TheForestSide; Mon-Fri 11 pm, Sat 10.30 pm.

THE JUMBLE
ROOM   £54   3 2 3

**LANGDALE ROAD LA22 9SU
01539 435 188**

"An old favourite (est 1996) that's "still as quirky as ever; in the last five years the cuisine has segued towards Asian, whilst the décor has changed little" (vivid walls with an eclectic mix of bright canvases). / www.thejumbleroom.co.uk; Take bookings all week via phone and/or online.

GREAT BEDWYN, WILTSHIRE   2–2C

THREE TUNS
FREEHOUSE   £45   3 3 3

HIGH ST SN8 3NU   01672 870280

"A super pub and family destination, with good food" – James Wilsey's sizeable operation, with beer garden, has a beautiful rural location and is consistently well-rated. / tunsfreehouse.com/; @ThreeTunsBedwyn; Tue-Sat 11 pm, Sun 5 pm.

GREAT GONERBY, LINCOLNSHIRE 5–3D

HARRY'S PLACE   £88   5 5 2

**17 HIGH STREET NG31 8JS
01476 561780**

Harry & Caroline Hallam were way ahead of their time when – over thirty years ago – they launched what's effectively a pop-up supper club in their front room. A handwritten menu offers a limited choice of two dishes for starter, main and pud and Harry's cooking is in fairly traditional style, but – if not exactly 'fine dining' – very highly accomplished. It's not a big space, with only ten seats, so on a quiet night you need to bring your own atmosphere. But no-one commenting gives anything less than full marks: book ahead, or they won't know to buy food for you. / No Amex; children: 5.

GREAT MILTON, OXFORDSHIRE   2–2D

BELMOND LE MANOIR
AUX QUAT' SAISONS,
BELMOND   £248   5 5 5

CHURCH ROAD OX44 7PD   01844 278881

"You feel on Cloud Nine when eating in such incomparable surroundings" as Raymond Blanc's famous Elizabethan manor: the survey's most-mentioned destination outside London, and, "unparalleled for a special occasion", with legions of reports of weddings, landmark anniversaries and birthdays celebrated in its cosseting quarters. It boasts "a gorgeous setting, buried deep in the Oxfordshire countryside", "everything about the place is done with impeccable taste", and no visit is complete without a stroll around its glorious and "well-tended gardens". From the moment you arrive, staff "make you feel special", and you are "whisked through to the cosy lounge to make your menu choice". Most diners are then seated in the dining conservatory: a "wonderful environment" on most accounts (if, arguably, a tiny bit anticlimactic compared with the house proper). "The food tastes like it has come straight from the garden, field or ocean to your plate" and dishes "are not ostentatious: just perfectly-made food, beautifully served". That's by far the majority view anyway, although there is, perennially, a dissenting view that "while classy, the food lacks innovation" (very occasionally laced with cynicism that the whole experience is a luxurious "production line"). For most folks, though, the whole experience is plain "genius! – truly unforgettable!". Ah yes… including the bill! "Your credit card has a severe heart attack, but at least you'll have ticked it off, and enjoyed doing so". Staying the night is also highly popular, although it docs then take the cost to a new, parallel dimension. Justify it to yourself with the thought of breakfast which "is unbelievable in scale, scope and quality!". / www.manoir.com; @lemanoir; Mon-Sun 9.30 pm; Booking max 12 may apply.

GREAT WALTHAM, ESSEX   3–2C

GALVIN GREEN
MAN   £65   3 2 2

HOWE ST CM3 1BG   01245 408 820

The Galvin brothers' "very busy" fourteenth-century pub out in rural Essex – with glazed dining area attached – is particularly "good if the weather's nice and you can sit outside" but inside can become "too noisy due to the lack of sound-deadening furnishings". All reports, though, agree the cooking is "superb". "There is always something going on, and one of their excellent regular events is a monthly food book club, featuring guest chefs". / www.galvingreenman.com; @Galvin_brothers; Mon-Wed 9 pm, Fri & Sat 10.30 pm, Thu 9.30 pm; Take bookings all week via phone and/or online.

GREETHAM, RUTLAND   5–3D

THE WHEATSHEAF £46   3 3 2

STRETTON RD LE15 7NP   01572 812325

This "busy neighbourhood pub-restaurant" has "become an institution in the 10+ years

L'Enclume, Cartmel

it's been open", and wins high praise for its "surprisingly extensive menu (in a land-locked area) of wonderfully fresh fish". "Booking is pretty much essential as the place is usually humming". / www.wheatsheaf-greetham.co.uk; Tue-Sun 11 pm; No Amex; Take bookings all week via phone and/or online.

GRESFORD, WREXHAM 5–3A

PANT-YR-OCHAIN £51 334

OLD WREXHAM ROAD LL12 8TY
01978 853525

"Like having your own country club!" – this handsome sixteenth-century inn with substantial grounds a short drive outside Wrexham is "very comfortable, with friendly staff". Part of the Brunning & Price group, its cooking is generally found "reliable", although a couple of repeat visitors reported disappointing trips this year. / www.brunningandprice.co.uk/pantyrochain; Mon-Sat 9.30 pm, Sun 9 pm; Take bookings all week via phone and/or online.

GUERNSEY, CHANNEL ISLANDS –

LE NAUTIQUE £59 333

GY1 2LE 01481 721714

"Quiet, discreet and very enjoyable", this classy seafood specialist occupying a late-18th-century harbourside warehouse in picturesque St Peter Port has just celebrated its 20th anniversary under chef-patron Günter Botzenhart. / lenautiquerestaurant.co.uk/; Take bookings all week via phone and/or online.

LA REUNION £59 444

COBO COAST ROAD GY5 7HB
01481 255600

"One of the best restaurants on Guernsey" – this beachside venue, complete with large terrace and bar overlooking the bay has gorgeous views and continues to inspire enthusiastic feedback for its contemporary cuisine (mostly fish and seafood, but also with steak). / www.lareunion.gg/; Tue-Sat 9.30 pm, Sun 3 pm; Take bookings all week via phone and/or online.

GUILDFORD, SURREY 3–3A

THE IVY CASTLE VIEW £61 333

TUNSGATE SQUARE, 98-100 HIGH STREET GU1 3HE 01483920100

"One has to ignore the twenty-somethings who spend their entire time selfie-ing themselves here, including in the loos", but otherwise "the setting is excellent" at this castle-view spot, "and having been to The Ivy in London numerous times this is a pretty good knock-off". As per others in the chain, "the food probably needs to be better, but we enjoy it and will certainly go back". Top Tip – "afternoon tea is served in an unhurried way". / www.theivyguildford.com; Mon-Sun 12.30 am.

RUMWONG £41 343

18-20 LONDON RD GU1 2AF
01483 536092

The "lovely" Thai food "never disappoints" at this "perfect local", which has maintained its standards for four decades, remaining "the same as ever with an unchanging menu" of "delicious and authentic" dishes. Diners have the option to eat from low tables in the 'khan tok' room, seated on cushions northern Thai-style. / www.rumwong.co.uk; Take bookings all week via phone and/or online.

THE THAI TERRACE £43 434

CASTLE CAR PK, SYDENHAM RD GU1 3RW 01483 503350

For "fabulous Thai food with an equally fabulous view", this quirky Guildford feature – somewhat bizarrely located over a multi-storey car park – is just the ticket, "especially on a warm evening with a cocktail in hand!" / thaiterrace.co.uk/; No Amex; Take bookings all week via phone and/or online.

GULLANE, EAST LOTHIAN 9–4D

THE BONNIE BADGER £59 334

MAIN STREET EH31 2AA 01626 21111

Tom & Michaela Kitchin have forayed outside of Edinburgh for the first time to this coastal village, heavily refurbishing what was previously the Golf Inn: now a hip restaurant with rooms, where the dining room – with pitched roof – is decked out in a very 'now' design of greige, wood and bare bricks. Most reviews say its modern gastropub fare is as outstanding as its pedigree would suggest, but there's also a minority for whom it's "disappointing given TK's reputation and very overpriced for rather average pub food". / bonniebadger.com; @bonniebadgerg; Mon-Fri 9.30 pm, Sat & Sun 10 pm.

CHEZ ROUX, GREYWALLS HOTEL £80 344

EH31 2EG 01620 842144

The well-established Roux-branded operation at this well-known, Lutyens-designed country house hotel (bordering Muirfield golf course, and looking towards the Firth of Forth) attracted only limited feedback this year, but all was upbeat: "really high class cuisine showing good attention to detail – quite expensive but well worth it!" / www.greywalls.co.uk; @Greywalls_Hotel; Jacket required; Take bookings all week via phone and/or online.

HALE, GREATER MANCHESTER 5–2B

SIGIRIYA £52 433

173 ASHLEY ROAD WA15 9SD
0161 941 3025

For "Sri Lankan food with clean, fresh flavours", this Hale newcomer (est 2017) can't be beat; named after that country's

dramatic UNESCO site, it's owned by industry veteran Don Buddhika, whose CV includes the Jumeirah Beach in Dubai and, more recently, Mughli in Knutsford. / sigiriya.co.uk; @sigiriyahale; Mon & Tue, Sun 10 pm, Wed & Thu 10.30 pm, Fri & Sat 11 pm.

HAMBLETON, RUTLAND 5–4D

FINCH'S ARMS £50 224

OAKHAM RD LE15 8TL 01572 756575

"A good, hearty, meat-rich lunch and a pint by an open fire on a cold November day in the middle of Rutland Water: there are worse places to be…". This "modernised" and extended old inn – "the original bits are by far the best, with open fires in the bar" – has a "brilliant location" with a big garden (and can become "exceptionally busy in the summer months, at which time service gets stretched"). "There are good set lunches and bar fare, but the cooking can be variable, with the occasional strange mix of ingredients leading to a mild note of caution". "An out of season bar lunch though can be a very pleasant experience." / www.finchsarms.co.uk; Wed-Sat 9.30 pm, Sun 3.30 pm; Take bookings all week via phone and/or online.

HAMBLETON HALL £110 555

LE15 8TH 01572 756991

"A perfect country retreat!". The crunch of gravel on the drive and "beautiful views" set the scene at Tim Hart's "beautiful" hotel (a fine mansion once owned by the Hoare banking family, and constructed long before Rutland Water which it nowadays overlooks). It offers a "pampering" experience "which makes no compromises to quality" in a very traditional style that's occasionally thought to be "stiff" but more commonly elicits nothing but rave reviews. Aaron Patterson has overseen the kitchen here since 1992, and his "exceptional classic cuisine" is "beautifully presented with amazing flavours". It's not an inexpensive experience, but no-one considers it overpriced: "we rarely feel we can afford it, but it's always turned out to be a pleasure!" – "a self-indulgent treat that makes one feel good days or even weeks later". / www.hambletonhall.com; @hambleton_hall; Take bookings all week via phone and/or online; children: 5.

HAMPTON POYLE, OXFORDSHIRE 2–1D

THE BELL £56 323

11 OXFORD ROAD OX5 2QD
01865 376242

A "buzzy, busy pub" with nine rooms plus flagstone floors, oak beams and slouchable leather armchairs; while the food is perhaps good rather than stellar, they're "trying hard" and it's handily located if you're en route in or out of Oxford. / www.thebelloxford.co.uk; Fri & Sat 9.30 pm, Sun-Thu 9 pm.

THE PHEASANT HOTEL   £59   343

YO62 5JG   01439 771241

Co-run by Jacquie Pern and head chef Peter Neville, this quintessential English country hotel, overlooking a duck pond, delivers "attractive plates" of "tasty food" that continue to compete ratings-wise with its better-known neighbour (the Star Inn, run by Jacquie's ex-husband Andrew). / www.thepheasanthotel.com; @pheasant_harome; Mon-Sun 9 pm; No Amex; Take bookings all week via phone and/or online.

THE STAR INN   £77   434

HAROME YO62 5JE   01439 770397

Andrew Pern's growing foodie empire started off at this "beautiful", "charming and comfortable", thatched 14th-century inn over two decades ago, and he has successfully maintained its reputation for "wonderful food, with superb flavours". One or two fans tip the "brilliant à la carte" over a tasting menu that can seem "a bit out-there" to more conservative tastes, or "prefer the light and airy modern dining room to the old pub-style one". And on the downside, there remains a minority view that it is "overpriced and living off its kudos". / www.thestaratharome.co.uk; @TheStaratHarome; Mon-Sat 9.30 pm, Sun 6 pm; No Amex.

LUSSMANNS   £48   332

20A LEYTON ROAD AL5 2HU
01582 965393

A "consistently good-quality experience", this two-storey local restaurant has earned improved ratings in the last year. Part of Andrei Lussmann's five-strong Hertfordshire-based group, it is sustainable and Marine Stewardship Council-friendly. / www.lussmanns.com/restaurants/harpenden-restaurants/; @lussmanns; Mon & Tue, Sun 9 pm, Wed & Thu 9.30 pm, Fri & Sat 10.30 pm; Take bookings all week via phone and/or online.

BALTZERSENS   £32   443

HG1 1PU   01423 202363

Paul Rawlinson may have shut down his beloved Norse, but his other local venture, albeit "cramped", remains "way beyond what other numerous high street coffee shops can offer"; "the brews are absolutely delicious" and "the bakes (Scandi buns etc) are brilliant…": "go for the waffles – the big secret is they're gluten-free and you don't even notice it!" / www.baltzersens.co.uk.

BETTYS   £40   345

1 PARLIAMENT STREET HG1 2QU
01423 814070

"Still the most civilised place on Earth" – these archetypal tea rooms have been a "Yorkshire institution" for a century now, founded as they were in 1919. There's "no point wasting calories elsewhere" when here you can enjoy "afternoon tea, exactly as it should be": "surrounded by starched white tablecloths and napkins, plus silver teapots, with a great selection of sandwiches (extra if you want them!) and cakes, plus unlimited tea or coffee served in grand surroundings by lovely staff". "Every town should have one. Why don't they?" / www.bettys.co.uk/cafe-tea-rooms/our-locations/bettys-harrogate; Sun-Fri & Sat 9 pm; No Amex; No bookings.

BETTYS GARDEN CAFÉ, RHS GARDENS HARLOW CARR   £38   444

CRAG LANE, BECKWITHSHAW HG3 1QB
01423 505604

"Overlooking the gardens at RHS Harlow Carr", which considerably add to the charms of this "lovely" branch of the well-known Yorkshire tea room chain. From the "magnificent" coffee to the breakfast and afternoon tea, it's "always busy – with good reason". / www.bettys.co.uk; @Bettys1919; Sun-Fri & Sat 9 pm; Take bookings all week via phone and/or online.

DRUM & MONKEY   £50   433

5 MONTPELLIER GDNS HG1 2TF
01423 502650

"Classy but not stuffy" – this "most agreeable" seafood restaurant has been a Montpelier institution for half a century – William Fuller, who owned it for 25 years and died in 2018, is still missed by regulars. Now run by the Carter family, it retains its old-school atmosphere, while "the seafood on offer is always fresh, appetising and excellent". / www.drumandmonkey.co.uk; @DrumAndMonkey; Mon-Thu 9 pm, Fri & Sat 9.30 pm; No Amex; Booking max 10 may apply.

GRAVELEY'S FISH & CHIP RESTAURANT   £42   332

8-12 CHELTENHAM PARADE HG1 1DB
01423 507 093

"A very traditional Yorkshire chippie" which doesn't offer anything fancy but "just good fish 'n' chips" (the former "huge and well-battered", and "you can go for more exotic if you wish"); "a little tip – avoid early evening when the 'pensioners' special menu' is served – it will be heaving!" / www.graveleysofharrogate.com; @graveleys; Mon-Thu 9 pm, Fri & Sat 10 pm, Sun 8 pm; Take bookings all week via phone and/or online.

THE IVY HARROGATE   £53   223

7-9 PARLIAMENT STREET HG1 2QU
01423 787 100

A "bustling" ambiance that "gives a lift to the spirits" is the chief plus-point of this brasserie offshoot of the ever-expanding London luminary. Even fans concede it's "expensive for what it is", and "could be said to be a little formulaic", while a couple of other reporters noted meals that were positively bad. / www.theivyharrogate.com; @ivyharrogate; Mon-Sun 12.30 am.

ORCHID   £51   443

28 SWAN ROAD HG1 2SE   01423 560 425

"A touch of class… and in a classy area": this "unfailing" Pan-Asian occupies the ground and first floor of the Studley hotel and – "a Harrogate institution" of approaching 20 years' standing – remains the most-mentioned eatery in the area thanks to its "civilised" style and "tremendous" dishes. Top Tip – "Sunday buffet lunch is superb value" and gets "hectic" as a result (at other times the place has a "calm and relaxing ambience"). / www.orchidrestaurant.co.uk; @orchidnstudley; Sun-Fri & Sat 10 pm; Take bookings all week via phone and/or online.

SASSO   £51   443

8-10 PRINCES SQUARE HG1 1LX
01423 508 838

"Italian food as it should be" – Stefano Lancellotti's "good, traditional" operation (established 22 years ago) has maintained "consistent high standards in all areas over the years", and focuses on the Emilia Romagna region, from whence Lancellotti hails. / www.sassorestaurant.co.uk; @sassorestaurant; Mon-Thu 9.30 pm, Fri & Sat 10 pm, Sun 3 pm.

STUZZI   £50   443

46B KINGS ROAD HG1 5JW
01423 705852

There's a "nice buzz" about this "trendy, artisan foodie restaurant with bustling, ever-changing Italian small plates", opposite Harrogate Convention Centre. 'Stuzzichini' are snacks typically served by Venetian osterias – but don't worry about minuscule portions: this is "hugely enjoyable and satisfying food", offered by "knowledgeable staff" alongside "some impressive wines". They recently opened in Leeds too. / @STUZZIHARROGATE; Take bookings all week via phone and/or online.

MAGGIE'S   £25   332

ROCK-A-NORE ROAD TN34 3DW
01424 430205

"You're at the seaside, so it's gotta be fish 'n' chips, and Maggie's has to be the destination"; it may have humble décor (plastic table cloths etc), but the "fabulous view over the Hastings fishing fleet" more than compensates for that, hence its popularity ("advise booking as it's usually full!"). / www.maggiesfishandchips.co.uk; Sun-Thu 3 pm, Fri & Sat 8 pm; Cash only.

ROCK A NORE KITCHEN   £35   433

23A ROCK-A-NORE RD TN34 3DW
01424 433764

"Delicious fresh fish straight off the boat" and "expertly cooked" (not least "great crab and top whitebait") ensure that reporters "can't wait to go back" to this diminutive joint, set right opposite the fishermen's huts. / rockanorekitchen.com/; Thu-Sat 9 pm, Sun 3.30 pm; No bookings.

WEBBE'S ROCK-A-NORE £39 333

1 ROCK-A-NORE ROAD TN34 3DW
01424 721650

A "good location on Hastings seafront" and stellar seafood (plus other local grub) to go with it – the formula behind this consistent offshoot of the Paul Webbe empire, opposite the Jerwood Gallery. / www.webbesrestaurants.co.uk; @WebbesRockaNore; Mon-Thu 9 pm, Fri & Sat 9.30 pm, Sun 8.30 pm; Take bookings all week via phone and/or online.

HATCH END, GREATER LONDON   3–2A

SEA PEBBLES £40 322

348-352 UXBRIDGE RD HA5 4HR
020 8428 0203

"Consistently good fish 'n' chips" (grilled, fried or in matzo meal) is what brings customers back to the Andreou family's recently refurbished fixture, which celebrates its 30th anniversary this year, and nowadays has an offshoot in Bushey Heath. / www.seapebbles.co.uk; Mon-Thu 10 pm, Fri-Sun 11.30 pm; May need 8+ to book.

HATFIELD PEVEREL, ESSEX   3–2C

THE BLUE STRAWBERRY £50

THE STREET CM3 2DW 01245 381333

"I can always guarantee a special occasion that is fabulous and memorable", declared a regular who recently celebrated his 60th birthday at this destination of two decades' standing, just off the A12. Feedback has dwindled in recent times, however, so we've left a new rating till next year. / www.bluestrawberrybistrot.co.uk; @thebluestrawb; Mon-Fri 10 pm, Sat midnight, Sun 4 pm; No Amex; Take bookings all week via phone and/or online.

HAXBY, NORTH YORKSHIRE   5–1D

MILLER'S FISH & CHIPS £25 442

55 THE VILLAGE YO32 2JE
01904 769169

"The jewel in Haxby's crown!" – Nick and David Miller's "unmissable chippy" (est 1940) inspires rave reviews from fans for "out-of-this-world fish 'n' chips" and "marvellous staff". "Eat in!". / www.millershaxby.com; @MillersHaxby; Tue-Thu 8 pm, Mon, Fri & Sat 9 pm; Take bookings all week via phone and/or online.

HAYWARDS HEATH, WEST SUSSEX 3–4B

JEREMY'S AT BORDE HILL £66 444

BORDE HILL, BORDE HILL GARDENS
RH16 1XP 01444 441102

"Just a delight" – set among 200 acres of landscaped gardens, Jeremy & Vera Ashpool's

"overwhelmingly popular venue" has been a "consistent favourite" for many years in a part of Sussex with "little competition". The food is "of a high standard, with an occasional nod to grande cuisine", and "relatively good value", while "the terraced area is particularly pretty on a summer's evening". Be warned, though, it can be "busy with wedding receptions". / www.jeremysrestaurant.com; @Jeremysrest; Tue-Sat 9.30 pm, Sun 3 pm; Take bookings all week via phone and/or online.

HEDLEY ON THE HILL, NORTHUMBERLAND   8–2B

THE FEATHERS INN £49 432

NE43 7SW 01661 843 607

A "very good village pub", but also rather more than that: Rhian Craddock's snug Northumbrian boozer, in an out-of-the-way spot overlooking the Tyne valley, helped to kick off the local/seasonal craze over a decade ago, and continues to turn out top-quality fare, including local game. / www.thefeathers.net; @thefeathersinn; Mon-Sat 4.30 pm, Sun 3.30 pm; No Amex; Take bookings all week via phone and/or online.

HELMSLEY, NORTH YORKSHIRE   8–4C

BLACK SWAN £78 323

MARKET PL YO62 5BJ 01439 770466

This extended fifteenth-century inn (nowadays with nearly fifty bedrooms) sits at the heart of this very attractive market town. Its Gallery Restaurant (named for its dual purpose during the day as an art gallery) has quite a reputation, and – despite sustained gripes over the years that it's rather pricey – all reports rate it good or better. / www.blackswan-helmsley.co.uk.

MANNION & CO £39 433

5 CASTLEGATE YO62 5AB

"Splendid cafe/restaurant in a charming building overlooking Helmsley's picturesque stream that's on another plane altogether from Helmsley's other establishments". Sibling to the York original it serves "delicious, wholesome café food": "the selection, especially from the specials board, is always interesting, and uses lots of local seasonal ingredients". / Mon-Sat 5 pm, Sun 4.30 pm.

HENLEY IN ARDEN, WARWICKSHIRE   5–4C

CHEAL'S OF HENLEY £76 332

64 HIGH ST B95 5BX 01564 793 856

Celebrating its fifth year in 2020, the Cheal family's dining room on the high street attracted somewhat mixed feedback in the latest survey. In all reports, son Matt Cheal's ambitious cuisine attracts ratings that are decent to outstanding, but prices are not bargain basement (the three-course meal in the evening is £55 and six-course tasting menu is £77), and the sceptical view is that it's "rather disappointing" given the expense. / www.chealsofhenley.co.uk; @Chealshenley; Wed-Sat

San Carlo, Manchester

9.30 pm, Sun 3 pm; Take bookings all week via phone and/or online.

HENLEY, WEST SUSSEX   3–4A

THE DUKE OF CUMBERLAND £62 323

GU27 3HQ 01428 652280

"Fabulous country food" (hefty and satisfying) is the order of the day at chef-patron Simon Goodman's hillside sixteenth century boozer, which these days profits from a proper dining area and, as ever, an "amazing garden" overlooking Leith Hill, the highest point in Surrey. / www.thedukeofcumberland.com; @theduke_Henley; Sun-Thu 11.30 pm, Fri & Sat midnight; Take bookings all week via phone and/or online.

HENLEY-ON-THAMES, OXFORDSHIRE   3–3A

BISTRO AT THE BOATHOUSE, THE BOATHOUSE £78 333

THE BOATHOUSE RG9 1AZ
01491 577937

FKA 'Shaun Dickens at The Boathouse' – this riverside operation has split opinion in the past, but seems to be on more solid ground this year, winning nothing but praise for its "imaginative food" and "lovely" Thames-side surroundings. Stop Press – on 31 October 2019, it relaunched and rebranded as 'the Bistro at The Boathouse', promising a more casual spin on its ingredient-led cooking. / www.shaundickens.co.uk; @henleyboathouse; Wed-Sat 9.30 pm, Sun 2.30 pm; Take bookings all week via phone and/or online.

THE GREYHOUND £56 333

GALLOWSTREE RD, PEPPARD COMMON
RG9 5HT 0118 972 2227

"Antony (and Jay) Worral Thompson manage to hit the sweet spot between casual bistro and gourmet dining" at this "lovely" operation, also benefiting from "quirky rooms" – "a treat". / www.awtgreyhound.com/; @TheGreyhoundAWT; Wed & Thu 9.30 pm, Fri & Sat 10 pm, Sun 4 pm; Take bookings all week via phone and/or online.

H CAFÉ

22 MARKET PLACE RG9 2AH

Henley residents can now save on the rail fare to 'The Smoke'. Hot on the heels of opening a luxury food court in Harrods, the famous store's first café outside London is to open in late 2019 on the market place of this chichi town (in what was formerly a branch of Nicolas). We are promised an experience akin to the new food hall approach recently adopted in SW1: 'a menu of dine-in and dine-out options, replicating the current food-to-go and deli offering' in Knightsbridge. / Wed-Sun 11 pm.

LUSCOMBES AT THE GOLDEN BALL £63 `3` `3` `3`

THE GOLDEN BALL, LOWER ASSENDON RG9 6AH 01491 574157

"Reliable", "high-quality food" makes this former pub on the edge of Henley "a safe choice". "The set lunch menu is particularly good value". / www.luscombes.co.uk; Wed-Sat 9.30 pm, Sun 3 pm; No Amex.

VILLA MARINA £49 `3` `3` `3`

18 THAMESIDE RG9 1BH 01491 575262

"Romance and the aroma of Italian food waft through the premises" – an "excellent, authentic" riverside venture (sibling to Marlow's Villa d'Este) whose "outstanding" food ain't cheap, but is largely deemed to be worth it. / www.villamarina-henley.com; @Villa_Marina_; Mon-Thu 10.30 pm, Fri & Sat 11 pm, Sun 9 pm.

HEREFORD, HEREFORDSHIRE   2–1B

A RULE OF TUM BURGER SHOP £20 `4` `3` `3`

32 AUBREY STREET HR4 0BU 01432 351764

"Fab burgers", especially the "exciting range of veggie options" (plus "stellar sweet potato fries on the side") have cemented the reputation of this hangout and Deliveroo hit; "if you don't want a burger they replace the bap with a salad" – although there are probably easier places to carb-avoid. / www.aruleoftum.com/burger-shop; @aruleoftum; Mon-Sat 10 pm, Sun 8 pm.

BEEFY BOYS £26 `4` `4` `3`

HR4 9HU 01432 359209

"One of the best burgers... in the world!"… well, almost, is to be found at this "cheerful and helpful" city-centre pop-up turned permanent, at a unit in the town's old market. / www.thebeefyboys.com; @thebeefyboys.

THE BOOKSHOP £44 `3` `2` `3`

33 AUBREY STREET HR4 0BU 01432 343443

Behind the Green Dragon Hotel, this former bookshop serves up steaks and a mean Sunday lunch, using dry-aged Herefordshire beef. / aruleoftum.com/thebookshop; @bookshophfd; Wed & Thu 10 pm, Fri & Sat 11 pm, Sun 6 pm.

CASTLE HOUSE RESTAURANT, CASTLE HOUSE HOTEL £60 `3` `4` `4`

CASTLE ST HR1 2NW 01432 356321

A "lovely and very friendly" Georgian hotel, overlooking Capability Brown-designed gardens, where chef Claire Nicholls makes the most of the "tasty" vegetables and herbs grown in the kitchen garden, and beef from their own farm, with some very "reliable" cooking. / www.castlehse.co.uk; @castlehsehotel; Take bookings all week via phone and/or online.

HERNE BAY, KENT   3–3D

A CASA MIA £41 `3` `3` `2`

160 HIGH STREET CT6 5AJ 01227 372 947

Neapolitan wannabes may be ten-a-penny in the crowded pizza market, but as the first UK pizzeria to win certification from Naples's Associazione Verace Pizza, you can be sure that the "great pizzas" on offer at this low-key Herne Bay spot are authentic as it gets (at least in these parts). / www.acasamia.co.uk; @AcasamiaHB; Mon-Thu 11 pm, Fri & Sat 11.30 pm, Sun 10 pm.

HESWALL, MERSEYSIDE   5–2A

BURNT TRUFFLE £54 `4` `4` `3`

104-106 TELEGRAPH ROAD CH60 0AQ 0151 342 1111

"A very reliable destination on the Wirral that usually delivers the goods" – Gary Usher's cosy bistro was the first of his crowdfunded sequels to Chester's Sticky Walnut and continues to inspire very high all-round satisfaction with its "consistently wonderful and reasonably priced" cooking, and service that's "cheerful and makes you feel at home". / www.burnttruffle.net; @BuRntTruffle; Tue-Thu 9 pm, Fri & Sat 10 pm, Sun 8 pm.

HETTON, NORTH YORKSHIRE   5–1B

THE ANGEL INN £63 `5` `3` `4`

BD23 6LT 01756 730263

"So nice to see this old friend, smartened up, rejuvenated and walking proud again" – this old Dales inn (made famous in the 1980s by David & Juliet Watkins) was taken over in late 2018 by much-accoladed chef Michael Wignall, who has immediately succeeded in putting it very much back on the culinary map. "As you would expect of a top chef, the food is all faultless beyond criticism – real plates of real food in very satisfying combinations" and it's "good value for money" too. / www.angelhetton.co.uk; @angelinnhetton; Mon-Sat 9 pm, Sun 8 pm; Take bookings all week via phone and/or online.

HEXHAM, NORTHUMBERLAND   8–2A

BOUCHON BISTROT £49 `4` `3` `3`

4-6 GILESGATE NE46 3NJ 01434 609943

A "perfect, archetypally French restaurant, with all the classical touches, from the staff to the ambiance" – Greg Bureau's bistro is "as fun as it is authentic". "After several visits, it's still a surprise to find a place with such a French feel in the heart of a Northumbrian town!". / www.bouchonbistrot.co.uk; @bouchonhexham; Mon-Thu 9 pm, Fri & Sat 9.30 pm; No Amex; Take bookings all week via phone and/or online.

THE RAT INN £41 `4` `3` `5`

ANICK NE46 4LN 014 3460 2814

"Not sure pubs get any better than this?" – this "quintessential country pub" in a hamlet outside Hexham comes complete with "dogs and pints at the bar" and "unsurpassed views" from the "beautiful garden". The cooking is in a traditional vein with "a good choice of local fish/game": it offers "very good-value snacks, or a full-blown restaurant-quality meal should you prefer". / www.theratinn.com; @ratales; Mon-Sat 9 pm, Sun 4 pm; Take bookings all week via phone and/or online.

HINTLESHAM, SUFFOLK   3–1D

HINTLESHAM HALL £61

HINTLESHAM IP8 3NS 01473 652334

"A lovely building" – dating from the reign of Henry IV and most famous to oldies for its associations with 1970s TV-chef Robert Carrier – this imposing country house hotel attracted too few reviews for a rating this year, but was tipped for "delightful afternoon tea in the garden", or one of its stately lounges. / www.hintleshamhall.co.uk/; @hintlesham_hall; Jacket required; children: 12+.

HINTON-ST-GEORGE, SOMERSET   2–3A

LORD POULETT ARMS £50 `3` `3` `3`

TA17 8SE 01460 73149

This "lovely" thatched village pub opened in 1680 as an inn for passing travellers, and still makes a "delightful stopover" just off the A303 near Crewkerne. Ratings for its "high quality", "classical" food have revived in the past 12 months under new owners backed by Nick Jones of Soho House (who also own the Beckford Arms at Tisbury and the Talbot Inn at Mells). Steve Hill and Michelle Payton, who ran it for 15 years, have retired to France. / www.lordpoulettarms.com; @LordPoulettArms; No Amex.

THE FARMHOUSE AT REDCOATS   £53   433

**REDCOATS GREEN SG4 7JR
01438 729500**

Revamped in summer 2018, this fifteenth-century pub-with-rooms nowadays incorporates a stylish dining conservatory, which – notwithstanding the odd downbeat report – scored very highly this year with its earthy, high quality cooking. / www.farmhouseatredcoats.co.uk; @FarmAtRedcoats; Mon-Sat 9.30 pm, Sun 9 pm.

HERMITAGE RD   £52   343

**20-21 HERMITAGE ROAD SG5 1BT
01462 433603**

This former ballroom gains most praise for its "great breakfast/brunch" that makes "a brilliant way to start the weekend, with lots of free top-up coffee and newspapers to read". In addition to "the best brews, home bakes and bagels", there's also a full dinner menu featuring sustainable local produce. / www.hermitagerd.co.uk; @HermitageRd; Mon-Sat 10 pm, Sun 7 pm.

THE VICTORIA AT HOLKHAM, HOLKHAM HALL   £50   324

. NR23 1RG   01328 711008

Halfway between a sandy beach and the parkland surrounding Palladian stately home Holkham Hall, Downton-esque nineteenth century inn 'The Vic' "has gained a consistency in recent years", offering a "warmth of welcome, good hearty cooking ("lots of local game including venison") and plenty of style"; bonus points for the "wonderful estate in which to walk it off!" / www.holkham.co.uk; @VictoriaHolkham; No Amex; Take bookings all week via phone and/or online.

WIVETON HALL CAFE   £46   332

1 MARSH LANE NR25 7TE   01263 740515

Fans are "happy to report the continued success and popularity of owner Desmond's venture on the north Norfolk coast" – lionised in a BBC TV series, and combining "really good freshly cooked" farm food with "lots of outside space to run around in". / www.wivetonhall.co.uk/restaurant-cafe/; @WivetonHall; Booking lunch only.

NOBLE   £54   543

**27A CHURCH RD BT18 9BU
028 9042 5655**

"An amazing local eatery where you can always guarantee to find awesome local food cooked to perfection, and exceptional front of house staff" – so say fans of Pearson Morris and Saul

McConnel's small modern bistro above the Iona health food store. / nobleholywood.com; @nobleholywood; Wed-Sat 10 pm, Sun 7.30 pm.

THE HOLT   £55   332

178 HIGH STREET EX14 1LA   01404 47707

"A friendly, well-run pub" that's "owned by the Otter brewery, so the beer is always well kept". On the food front, it "maintains a steady standard" ("tapas in the downstairs bar are always interesting and the full menu is served upstairs in a non-fancy environment"). / www. theholt-honiton.com.

THE PIG AT COMBE   £63   234

**COMBE HOUSE, GITTISHAM EX14 3AD
01404 540400**

"Have fun pottering around the kitchen garden" at the Pig group's "lovely"-looking Otter Valley outpost, where "you can relax and enjoy provided you're not seated on a wobbly chair – they do like shabby chic!". Even fans concede the culinary performance is "a bit patchy" (sometimes all in one day) and while a good proportion of meals are "cracking" some do fall short: "what's the point of going on about air miles when the food is this bland and expensive!?". / www.combehousedevon.com; @CombeHouseDevon; No Amex; Take bookings all week via phone and/or online.

LOSEHILL HOUSE HOTEL & SPA   £70   334

**LOSEHILL LANE, EDALE ROAD S33 6AF
01433 621 219**

"Beautifully presented, tasty food, excellent service and beautiful views" win praise for this characterful hotel in the Peak District National Park. You can choose between a three-course menu for £50 or go the whole hog and have seven courses for £65. It's also a hit for afternoon tea: "love this place at any time, but you get great vistas from the orangery in the afternoon." / www.losehillhouse.co.uk; @LosehillHouse; Mon-Thu 9 pm, Fri & Sat 9.30 pm, Sun 3 pm.

THE BELL INN   £53   444

HIGH RD SS17 8LD   01375 642463

This fifteenth-century timber-framed favourite has been run by the same family for 80 years, and "really stands out for its service" and "remarkable consistency". "They use local, seasonal ingredients and the menu is different on every visit – love it!". The owners also run The Ostlers, a modern cocktail bar and grill a few doors away. / www.bell-inn.co.uk; @Bellhorndon; Mon-Thu 9 pm, Fri & Sat 9.30 pm, Sun 4 am; Booking max 12 may apply.

RESTAURANT TRISTAN   £80   443

3 STANS WAY RH12 1HU   01403 255688

"A great find out in an area of relative culinary wilderness" – Tristan & Candy Mason's well-established destination occupies a converted sixteenth-century building in the town centre, complete with pitched roof and wood beams. There's a range of fixed menus from three courses for £30 up to eight courses for £90, and the modern British dishes are "beautiful" – "creative (but not gimmicky)". Top Tip – it has a bar where they serve breakfast and brunch. / www.restauranttristan.co.uk; @tristanshorsham; Take bookings all week via phone and/or online.

BROWNLOW ARMS   £42   333

NG32 2AZ   01400 250234

Paul & Lorraine Willoughby's old stone pub with rooms, north of Grantham near the A1, has been revitalised in recent years in tasteful country house style (linen tablecloths etc). Feedback is more limited than we would like, but all reports rate the experience highly, including the fairly traditional British cooking. / www.brownlowarms.co.uk; Mon-Sun 11 pm; No Amex; children: 10+.

LINO'S   £38   443

**122 MARKET STREET CH47 3BH
0151 632 1408**

"Always reliable and enjoyable", this veteran family-run Italian (est. 1983) has recently passed to the next generation, with Enrico Galantini taking over the reins from his parents, Lino & Barbara. It has always "deserved its mention" but such feedback as we have on the generational shift says the cooking has "improved considerably". / www.linosrestaurant.co.uk; Tue-Fri 9 pm, Sat 10 pm; No Amex; Take bookings all week via phone and/or online.

ERIC'S   £64   433

73-75 LIDGET ST HD3 3JP   01484 646416

"A favourite in an area with a dearth of good eateries", this is "a really well-run restaurant, with superb food and a nice location". Chef-owner Eric Paxman worked in London (under MPW) and Australia (under Bill Granger) before returning to his hometown, where he marks his 10th anniversary in business this year. ("Eric has also ventured into PAX, a local burger bar as well – let's hope his undoubted talent is not stretched too thinly"). / www.ericsrestaurant.co.uk; @ericrestaurant; Tue-Sat 10 pm, Sun 4 pm; No Amex; Take bookings all week via phone and/or online.

OLD HOUSE   £62   333

5 SCALE LANE   HU1 1LA   01482 210253

Part of the street food empire established in recent years by well-connected chef Chris Harrison (ex-Fat Duck, Hand & Flowers and Gidleigh Park), this cute old town venue offers "quality food for such a little pub" – and is a place "Hull can be proud of". / www.shootthebull.co.uk/the-old-house; @oldhousehull; Mon-Sun 9.30 pm; Take bookings all week via phone and/or online.

TAPASYA @ MARINA   £49   332

HUMBER DOCK STREET, MARINA, HU1 1TB   01482 242607

An "excellent" and rather classy Indian, with a superb setting on Hull marina, and offering fine dining dishes that are "way above your standard type" of subcontinental; a street-food branch opened in Trinity Market in 2018 and, as of May 2019, they've reinvented their out-of-town HQ on Beverley Road as another casual spin-off, Chowki. / www.tapasyarestaurants.co.uk/marina; @MarinaTapasya; Mon-Fri 10 pm, Sat 10.30 pm, Sun 8 pm; Take bookings all week via phone and/or online.

THIEVING HARRY'S £24   333

73 HUMBER PLACE   HU1 1UD   01482 214141

"Delicious breakfasts and coffee" are the standouts at this "quirky" ("dog-friendly, too") Humber Street café, which also serves burgers until late at the weekend. / thievingharrys.co.uk; @ThievingHarrys; Mon-Thu 4 pm, Fri & Sat 11 pm, Sun 6 pm.

ELIANE OF HUNGERFORD   £25   333

24 HIGH STREET   RG17 0NF   01488 686100

"Really healthy food" (be it gluten-free, veggie, vegan or even more specific – think raw vegan) is the calling card of this bright "cafeteria-style" outfit, which spawned a Sunningdale spin-off in 2017. / elianesmiles.com; Mon-Sat 5 pm, Sun 4 pm.

THE FOX AND HOUNDS RESTAURANT & BAR   £42   323

2 HIGH STREET   SG12 8NH   01279 843 999

"Top-quality food from chef/owner James Rix" has earned a stellar reputation for this village gastropub. The "daily changing menus of mainly English dishes, influenced by rural Italian and French cooking, always have a few delightful surprises" and "although it's a long way from the sea, the freshness of the grilled seafood is a special feature", as is "excellent" steak prepared on the Josper grill. / www.foxandhounds-hunsdon.co.uk; @thefoxhunsdon?lang=en; Tue-Sat 9.30 pm, Sun 3.30 pm; No Amex; Take bookings all week via phone and/or online.

OLD BRIDGE HOTEL   £58   343

1 HIGH ST   PE29 3TQ   01480 424300

"The food is fine, though perhaps not exceptional", at this "very professional hotel restaurant", but "the wine list is incredible" – "selected by proprietor John Hoskins, Master of Wine", who also runs the in-house vintner's: there are "some real gems at very fair prices", along with "a remarkable number of lovely and interesting wines by the glass". / www.huntsbridge.com; @oldbridgehotel; Mon-Thu 9.15 pm, Fri & Sat 10 pm, Sun 9 pm; Take bookings all week via phone and/or online.

HURLEY HOUSE HOTEL   £66   343

HENLEY ROAD   SL6 5LH   01628 568 500

"Part hotel, part roadhouse, part restaurant" – this well-appointed Thames Valley venue with ten bedrooms also has a large garden with heated awnings. It offers a very extensive all-day menu, with the unusual alternative of a full Japanese menu. All reports rate the food good or better. / www.hurleyhouse.co.uk; @HurleyHouseH.

GEORGE & DRAGON   £45   343

THE SQUARE   SP11 0AA   01264 736277

A "high-quality gastropub (with rooms) not too far from Andover", winning increasingly favourable reports for its "interesting food, varied flavours and unusual takes on traditional fare". Add in "obliging service and not too outrageously expensive" prices. / www.georgeanddragon.com; @GeorgeDragonHbT; Mon-Sat 9.30 pm, Sun 8.30 pm.

THE BAY HORSE   £67   333

45 THE GRN   DL2 2AA   01325 720 663

Chef-patron Marcus Bennett's "excellent cooking" has earned solid ratings for this fifteenth-century coaching inn over the past dozen years. Bennett and his business partner, fellow-local Jonathan Hall, now own three other venues on Teesside, the Devonport Hotel and Yarm's Cena and Muse Café. / www.thebayhorsehurworth.com; @thebayhorse_; Mon-Thu 9 pm, Fri & Sat 9.30 pm, Sun 8 pm.

HYTHE BAY SEAFOOD RESTAURANT   £54   333

MARINE PARADE   CT21 6AW   01303 233844

"For those who like fish, this is the place with a lot locally caught" and featuring on an "extensive menu"; "you sit in the restaurant overlooking the bay with ships on the horizon" (make sure to get a "table in the conservatory for the views"). They also have outposts in Dover and Deal. / www.hythebay.co.uk; @hythebay?lang=en.

THE DUKE WILLIAM   £50   333

THE ST   CT3 1QP   01227 721308

Ex-Ramsay chef Mark Sargeant's Farrow-and-Balled village boozer combines "very friendly and engaging service with a well-expected yet deceptively simple menu" – and continues to score solid feedback and the odd out-and-out rave. / www.thedukewilliamickham.com/; @DukeWilliamKent; Mon-Fri 9 pm, Sat 9.30 pm, Sun 5 pm.

THOMAS CARR @ THE OLIVE ROOM   £78   542

56 FORE STREET   EX34 9DJ   01271 555005

Chef Thomas Carr is "exceptionally talented", turning out "perfectly balanced" fish-centric food which "honours the ingredients" at this North Devon five-year-old, boosted last year by a paean from Jay Rayner. Ilfracombe is "a truly tough environment for a high-end restaurant, especially to survive year-round, so hats off to the chef and team". / www.thomascarrdining.co.uk/restaurants/the-olive-room/; @ThomasCarrChef; Mon-Sat 9 pm, Sun 3.30 pm.

BETTYS   £40   345

32 THE GROVE   LS29 9EE   01943 608029

This "bright and welcoming" branch of the legendary Yorkshire tearoom-empire, which has just celebrated its centenary, has a real sense of style. Breakfast is almost as popular as afternoon tea, and "to have their full English with Swiss rosti (a nod to Swiss founder Frederick Belmont) is a very special treat". / www.bettys.co.uk/tea-rooms/locations/ilkle; @bettys; No Amex; No bookings.

THE BOX TREE   £97   544

35-37 CHURCH ST   LS29 9DR   01943 608484

"Why it lost its Michelin star I do not know, it was as good as ever", so it's hard to avoid the conclusion that this Yorkshire institution has been unfairly cursed by the tyre company.

Established in 1962, this "intimate and opulent" venue is Yorkshire's answer to Le Gavroche: "a proper classical restaurant, with all the standards of service, napery, glassware, etc that we're always being told aren't important for the dining public these days". But since the October 2018 demotion by Michelin, change has been been nearly non-stop. The star loss led to the immediate departure of head chef Kieran Smith and appointment of Samira Effa in his stead. Then in April 2019 Michael Carr joined because Samira didn't last. All the while "despite the upheavals, the Box Tree has sailed serenely on: the chintz still looks out over the hushed rooms, Didier da Costa still presides over a great wine list, and there is still soufflé for dessert". And practically all reports still attest to its "impeccable", somewhat classical cuisine and "gentle, low-key hospitality that treats you beautifully". In September 2019 – more change – as Simon and Rena Gueller announced they are selling up, despite significant investment in the property these last two years. Hopefully the next owners will just forget Michelin, and continue to do what the place has been doing so well (and it's rated on that basis). / www.theboxtree.co.uk; @boxtreeilkley; Wed-Sat 9.30 pm, Sun 3 pm; No jeans; children: 10+.

HOST £37 3 4 4

58-60 THE GROVE LS29 9PA
01943 605337

Joel Monkman's "fusion-esque flavours" from a selection of 'eclectic, British seasonal plates' win consistently high approval ratings for this stylishly decorated, December 2018 newcomer. / www.hostilkley.co.uk; @hostilkley?lang=en; Wed-Sat 9 pm, Sun 3.30 pm.

IPSWICH, SUFFOLK 3–1D

1900 MARINERS £53 4 3 4

NEPTUNE QUAY IP4 1AX 01473 289748

"Quirky, quaint and stylish, with excellent food" – Julien & Karine Jourdain took over this antique Belgian gunboat in October 2018 from the Crépy family, and it's "one of the best Ipswich has to offer". Permanently moored in the marina, near the city-centre, its modern European menu options vary by the day. / www.marinersipswich.co.uk; @MarinersIpswich; No Amex.

TRONGS £35 5 5 3

23 ST NICHOLAS ST IP1 1TW
01473 256833

"Still our favourite!" – this beloved Chinese operation remains "just fabulous all round", delivering "exquisite and authentic Asian flavours, paired with great service and years of knowledge" from the Vietnamese owners; "they hardly need reviews as word of mouth seems to always keep them busy, but here is one!" / www.trongschineserestaurant.com/.

JERSEY, CHANNEL ISLANDS –

BOHEMIA, THE CLUB HOTEL & SPA £97 4 4 2

GREEN ST, ST HELIER JE2 4UH
01534 876500

Some of the best dining experiences of the year are reported at this well-known, luxurious Jersey destination, where Stephen Smith's cuisine can produce some "stunning" dishes. Even fans can find the culinary approach a little "over complex" however, and the slightly "gloomy" dining room itself, "tucked away in a corner of the hotel", is increasingly judged "intimate but a little uninspiring". / www.bohemiajersey.com; @Bohemia_Jersey; No trainers.

LONGUEVILLE MANOR £97 5 4 4

LONGUEVILLE RD, ST SAVIOUR JE2 7WF
01534 725501

"Top-notch", "consistently excellent" cuisine from chef Andrew Baird distinguishes this "very comfortable" and slightly old-fashioned Relais & Chateaux establishment: a fourteenth-century manor house with landscaped grounds which has been run as a hotel since 1949 by three generations of the Lewis family. Particular strengths include "wonderful Jersey seafood", "the best Sunday roasts" and a "brilliant wine list". / www.longuevillemanor.com; @longuevillemanor; No jeans.

MARK JORDAN AT THE BEACH £61 4 4 3

LA PLAGE, LA ROUTE DE LA HAULE, ST PETER JE3 7YD 01534 780180

Co-run by the owners of The Atlantic Hotel – and helmed by Mark Jordan, who held a star at the hotel's Ocean Restaurant for over a decade – this smart, beachside bistro wins uniformly stellar marks for its fishy cuisine, not least a "lovely lobster Thermidor". / www.markjordanatthebeach.com.

THE OYSTER BOX £57 3 3 4

ST BRELADE'S BAY JE3 8EF
01534 850 888

A chic venue in a "glorious beachside surrounding", in St Brelade's Bay, with a terrace and gallery-style windows to let the light pour in; "on the whole it hits the spot and when it's on form it delivers the highest quality food". / www.oysterbox.co.uk; @JPRests; Mon-Thu 9 pm, Fri & Sat 9.30 pm, Sun 2.30 pm; No Amex; Take bookings all week via phone and/or online.

KENILWORTH, WARWICKSHIRE 5–4C

THE CROSS AT KENILWORTH £68 5 4 3

16 NEW ST CV8 2EZ 01926 853840

"Although it looks just like a village pub from the outside" and has an agreeably "unassuming" approach, Andreas Antona's well-accoladed venture "maintains extremely high standards" – "way better than just posh pub food". "Chef Adam Bennett and his very able staff do not put a single foot wrong" and this "is a fine restaurant" with "some exquisite cooking and presentation" and "an Interesting wine list with a wide range including some top vintages available by the glass". "After 94 (and counting) visits, it's a great place to have just up the road and a real joy to visit!" / www.thecrosskenilworth.co.uk; @TheCrossKen; Tue-Sat 9.30 pm, Sun 3.30 pm.

KENTISBURY, DEVON 1–2D

KENTISBURY GRANGE HOTEL £72 3 3 4

EX31 4NL 01271 882 295

A seventeenth-century former coaching house attached to a luxury hotel, where "very attentive service and comfortable surrounds make a superb environment for tasty and very well-presented dishes". Cynics feel the "high price point is no doubt for the privilege of having Michael Caines's name above the door", but the general consensus is that it's "worthy of its high AA rating" (three rosettes) and lunch, by contrast, is "a lovely affordable treat". / www.kentisburygrange.com/; @KentisburyG; Take bookings all week via phone and/or online.

KESWICK, CUMBRIA 7–3D

FELLPACK £46 3 4 3

19 LAKE ROAD CA12 5BS 01768 771177

Positive feedback again – if still quite limited – for this all day deli/café strong on coffee, light bites and brunches, and which moonlights as a restaurant when a more eclectic, 'world food' type menu is served (from baked camembert to Louisiana Jambalaya, via potted shrimp). They must be doing something right, as in March 2019 they acquired a second site in this north Lakes town. / www.fellpack.co.uk.

LYZZICK HALL COUNTRY HOUSE HOTEL £55 3 4 3

UNDERSKIDDAW CA12 4PY 017687 72277

The Fernandez family's comfortable Victorian country house, set down a sweeping driveway, is still going strong after three decades, serving "consistently good" British food with a twist (including, latterly a monthly changing tasting menu); be sure to "get plenty of exercise during the day", as portions err on the generous size. / www.lyzzickhall.co.uk; @LyzzixkHall; No Amex.

KETTLESHULME, CHESHIRE 5–2B

THE SWAN INN £48 3 3 3

MACCLESFIELD RD SK23 7QU
01663 732943

A "wonderful old" fifteenth century pub which "retains its age-old atmosphere" and is split between a "popular" bar and "adjacent light and pleasant dining room" delivering "reliably good food, especially fish" ("well-sourced, ultra fresh and complemented by skilled cooking"). / Tue-Sat 8.30 pm, Sun 4 pm; No Amex.

Hambleton Hall, Hambleton

FISH! KITCHEN   £48   3 4 2

56-58 COOMBE ROAD KT2 7AF
020 8546 2886

An "incredible selection of fresh fish" from its in-house fishmonger, Jarvis, next door is the draw to this offshoot of a 20-year-old Borough Market stalwart. "Everything can be grilled for you to order" – and there are "very good specials". / www.fishkitchen.com; @fishkitchenking.

JIN GO GAE   £51   4 2 3

270- 272 BURLINGTON ROAD KT3 4NL
020 8949 2506

"One of the best of New Malden's Koreans (and the only one we've found with charcoal grills)" – "the ambiance has its own pure charm, with smoke in the air from the table-BBQs and queues out the door on weekends". "Service is a bit brusque and chaotic at times, but the flavours cannot be beaten!" / jingogae.wordpress.com/menus; Mon-Sun 11 pm.

ROZ ANA   £39   4 3 2

4-8 KINGSTON HILL KT2 7NH
020 8546 6388

"The food is delicious" at chef-partner Deepinder Sondhi's "superb, modern fusion-Indian", which opened in 2008 on Kingston Hill. "Some say upstairs is better but I disagree – far better being near the bar for lush cocktails with Bollywood classics playing in the background". / www.roz-ana.com; @therozana; Mon-Thu 10.30 pm, Fri & Sat 11.30 pm, Sun 10 pm; No Amex; Take bookings all week via phone and/or online.

THE HALF MOON   £59   3 2 3

GLASSHOUSE LANE RH14 0LT
01403 820223

Celeb MasterChef contestant Jodie Kidd (better known as a 1990s supermodel) has proved the cynics wrong at this fifteenth century venue, which she relaunched in summer 2017; the worst anyone has to say is that it's "nice enough but nothing to rush back for", while fans had a "most enjoyable experience at this village pub". / www.halfmoonkirdford.co.uk; @HalfMoonKird; Wed-Fri 11 pm, Sat 11.30 pm, Sun 8 pm.

HIPPING HALL   £92   5 3 4

COWAN BRIDGE LA6 2JJ   01524 271187

"A splendid addition to the growing Lake District circle of fine restaurants" – the first of the Wildsmith Hotels has a "gorgeous" country setting, but "being south of the main tourist areas makes it more accessible from the major population centres". With its "beautifully decorated and luxurious bedrooms", it's "perfect for a foodies' romantic break", and the highlight is the cooking: "clever and heartfelt

---

THE PHEASANT AT KEYSTON   £54   3 3 3

LOOP RD PE28 0RE   01832 710241

On a high after being named 'Cambridgeshire Dining pub of the Year 2019' by the GPB, this attractive thatched inn combines a nicely old-school bar (beams, open fires) and an airier Garden Room with a patio beyond. Reporters praise its "good food and service" – the former from Simon Cadge, who trained at the Old Bridge at Huntingdon (whose owner, John Hoskins, has long retained ties to this pub). / www.thepheasant-keyston.co.uk; @pheasantkeyston; Tue-Sat 9.30 pm, Sun 3.30 pm; No Amex; Take bookings all week via phone and/or online.

KILBERRY INN   £58   4 4 3

PA29 6YD   01880 770223

On the western edge of Scotland, looking out at the Inner Hebrides, Clare Johnson & David Wilson's inn is "miles from anywhere but worth tracking down" for "the freshest seafood", "brilliant front of house", and a "great atmosphere". Reporters "recommend the breakfasts" too. / www.kilberryinn.com; @Kilberryinn; Tue-Sun 8.30 pm; No Amex.

KINNEUCHAR INN   £54

9-11 MAIN STREET KY9 1LF
01333 340377

This revamped, old Scottish boozer reopened in September 2019 after a two-year refurb. Owned by the nearby Balcaskie Estate, its pedigree is promising, with both chef James Ferguson and front-of-house Alethea Palmer hailing from good positions at Rochelle Canteen. / www.kinneucharinn.com; Wed-Sun 11 pm.

MARKET BISTRO   £57   4 4 3

11 SATURDAY MARKET PL PE30 5DQ
01553 771483

The Goldings' "superb" fine dining spot in the centre of town (they also run a classy pub/deli, Goldings, nearby) has "an emphasis on local produce" and delivers "imaginative dishes" that are particularly "excellent value" at lunchtime. / www.marketbistro.co.uk; @Market_Bistro; Tue-

---

Thu 8.30 pm, Fri & Sat 9 pm; Take bookings all week via phone and/or online.

DAYLESFORD CAFÉ   £56   2 2 4

DAYLESFORD NEAR KINGHAM GL56
NEW08/2389 01608 731700

Lady Bamford's "bouji" farm shop is "still doing exactly what it says on the tin" – the "perfect antidote to country pubs", with its faux-rustic formula of "clean-eating and fresh local produce" consumed amid "posh locals and towny tourists". Caveat? "We try not to look too closely at the bill as it's usually extortionate!" / www.daylesford.com; Mon-Sat 4.30 pm, Sun 3.30 pm; 8am â€© 8pm SUN\; 1.

THE KINGHAM PLOUGH   £58   3 3 3

THE GREEN OX7 6YD   01608 658327

"Quiet and beautiful surroundings" set the tone at ex-Fat Duck chef Emily Watkins and husband Miles Lampson's old inn, in picture-perfect Kingham, opposite the village green; inside marries 'pubby' appeal (including a gastro comfort-food bar menu) with finer British cuisine, often based on old Cotswolds recipes. / www.thekinghamplough.co.uk; @kinghamplough; No Amex.

THE WILD RABBIT   £70   2 2 5

CHURCH ST OX7 6YA   01608 658 389

This country pub-turned-"high-end restaurant" with rooms is part of Lady Bamford's Daylesford project in the Cotswolds, so making it a handy local for the Chipping Norton set – "all the people you see in Notting Hill and Holland park during the week!". The kitchen has lost some of its culinary zip since the departure two years ago of chef Tim Allen, while his successor, Alyn Williams of Mayfair's esteemed Westbury Hotel, lasted less than a year as chef-patron. Feedback this year is dominated by comment on "hyped" and "forgettable" meals while even supporters say it is "very good, but not the best, and we paid an eye-watering price". / www.thewildrabbit.co.uk; @wildrabbitpub; Wed-Fri 9.15pm, Sat 9.30 pm, Sun 9 pm; Take bookings all week via phone and/or online.

---

food, served with care and warmth by Oli Martin and his crew" (from an eleven-course tasting menu, with a vegetarian but not a vegan alternative). / www.hippinghall.com; @hippinghall; No Amex; No trainers; children: 12+.

THE BLACK SWAN   £48   4|3|4

FELL ROAD CA17 4NS 015396 23204

A comfortable stone inn set far from the madding crowds in a picturesque Eden Valley village, handy for the market town of Kirkby Stephen; food is in the safe hands of Scott Fairweather, whose hearty and occasionally inventive cooking makes the most of prime local sourcing (including pheasants from the Helbeck estate down the road). / www.blackswanhotel.com; @BlackSwanEden; Mon-Sun 9 pm.

THE MASON'S ARMS   £73   4|3|3

SOUTH MOLTON EX36 4RY 01398 341231

"The quality and style of the food produced at this Devon country pub" is testament to chef-patron Mark Dodson's 12 years as head chef at the Roux brothers' legendary Waterside Inn. The pub itself is a gorgeous thatched cottage on the edge of Exmoor, dating back to the 13th century. / www.masonsarmsdevon.co.uk; @masonsknowstone; Tue-Sat 9 pm, Sun 2 pm; Booking max 4 may apply; children: 5.

KYLESKU HOTEL   £53   4|4|4

IV27 4HW 01971 502231

This "fantastic small hotel in remote northwest Scotland" serves "fresh fish and seafood to die for from the local waters" – Loch Glendhu is just the other side of the slipway, and there's an "amazing view across the water from the dining room window on a sunny evening". "A great place to stop in an area not over-supplied with good restaurants". / www.kyleskuhotel.co.uk; Take bookings all week via phone and/or online.

FALCONDALE HOTEL   £57   3|3|3

**FALCONDALE DRIVE SA48 7RX
01570 422910**

Tucked away at the top of the Teifi Valley, a mile outside the uni town of Lampeter, this "very friendly" manor house and wedding venue wins praise for its "good honest cooking", making the most of local produce from Ceredigion and surrounding counties, as well as its "terrific view". / www.thefalcondale.co.uk; @thefalcondale; Take bookings all week via phone and/or online.

LANGAR HALL   £79   3|3|5

CHURCH LN NG13 9HG 01949 860559

A Belvoir Valley institution for 30 years, this family home-turned-country-house hotel is "ideal for good, old-fashioned courtship" thanks to its "beautiful grounds" and the "lovely" environment created by founder Imogen Skirving, who, after her inheritance, converted her family seat into a hotel – "it's extra special if you stay over". Four years on from her death, her granddaughter Lila has continued the good work, and even if the odd old-timer feels it's "lost its sparkle since the loss of Imogen", it still inspires little but praise for "first class cuisine delivered with flair". / www.langarhall.com; @Langarhallhotel; Sun-Thu 8.30 pm, Fri & Sat 9 pm; No Amex; No trainers.

THE BELL INN   £48   3|3|3

GL7 3LF 01367 860249

On its relaunch two years ago by chef Tom Noest and manager Peter Creed, this village gastroboozer served The Times reviewer Giles Coren 'the best mouthful' of his life. It seems to have survived the accolade intact, and is still "one of the better pub/restaurants in the Cotswolds". / thebelllangford.com; Mon-Sun 9.30 pm.

NORTHCOTE   £90   5|5|4

NORTHCOTE RD BB6 8BE 01254 240555

One of the "top class gold-standards for restaurants in the North West" – this luxurious country house hotel, just off the A59 near Preston, has risen to ever-greater prominence over the years, and "its new ownership (The Stafford Collection) promises yet-additional investment". "With Lisa Goodwin Allen now established as Executive Head Chef, there's a new vibrancy to the cuisine, with interesting and imaginative new dishes whilst maintaining the best from the past" (established under Nigel Haworth); and "better touching base with its North West roots than it has in recent times". Over the years the property has been lavishly added-to and refurbished with a result that can seem a bit "naff" or "corporate", but which mostly gets the thumbs up for giving a "classy" impression. There's "an exceptionally curated wine list, whose selection is led by MD Craig Bancroft, with plenty of classics but lots of other interesting wines from around the world". "Will they now get the second Michelin star that they so crave?" / www.northcote.com; @NorthcoteUK; No trainers.

THE EARL OF MARCH   £40   3|3|3

LAVANT RD PO18 0BQ 01243 533993

"A great find" – this eighteenth-century coaching inn offers a "true gastronomic experience" under the ownership of Giles Thompson, formerly executive chef at The Ritz. The food is generally "excellent – with particularly fine puddings", although ratings were tempered by a couple of 'off' reports. The spectacular views of the South Downs towards nearby Goodwood are said to have inspired the poet William Blake to write his anthem Jerusalem while staying in 1803. / www.theearlofmarch.com; @theearlofmarch; Mon-Fri 11 pm, Sat 11.30 pm, Sun 10.30 pm.

THE GREAT HOUSE HOTEL & RESTAURANT, LAVENHAM   £56   4|4|5

MARKET PL CO10 9QZ 01787 247431

After 32 years the Crêpy family were a tough act to follow at this "lovely" old (in parts 14th century) inn, on the square of a picturesque town: "a unique, quintessentially English building, whose other defining features are essentially French: this includes the staff, food, wine and especially the cheeseboard!". "There's very little to fault in its classic French cuisine", and although the ratings awarded by its huge and dedicated fan club have slipped a fraction in the transition period, most reporters are optimistic: "since the Crêpys have retired the new owners have tried to keep the Great House just the same, and although it's not 100% as good it's getting there" is a sensible middle view. However you cut it, it's "certainly one of the best East Anglian restaurants". / www.greathouse.co.uk; @GreatHouseHotel; Wed-Fri, Tue 9.30 pm, Sat 10 pm, Sun 2.30 pm; No Amex; Take bookings all week via phone and/or online.

LAVENHAM GREYHOUND   £53

**97 HIGH STREET CO10 9PZ
01787 249553**

With the collapse of former owners, Stuart Inns, this well-known pub in a charming village changed hands in Spring 2019 and now follows a new formula based around Spanish tapas. Not all former fans are delighted by this turn of events, so we've left a rating till next year when the dust has settled. / www.lavenhamgreyhound.com; @LavenhamGH; Take bookings all week via phone and/or online.

NUMBER TEN   £44   3|3|3

10 LADY ST CO10 9RA 01787 249438

A "great place to eat in Lavenham", this wine bar and restaurant-with-rooms in a beautifully converted fifteenth-century brick-and-timber house rates strongly across the board. Hosts Jo Knight and Rod Benson are locals. / www.ten-lavenham.co.uk; Sun-Fri 9 pm; Take bookings all week via phone and/or online.

SWAN HOTEL   £57   2|2|4

HIGH ST CO10 9QA 01787 247477

"The most beautiful old Tudor building" in the stage-set town of Lavenham is "just the place for a special-occasion meal" – whether "an indulgent tea served on old-fashioned trays"

or "a sumptuous dinner in the elegant Gallery restaurant". / www.theswanatlavenham.co.uk; @SwanLavenham; Mon-Wed 11 pm, Thu & Fri midnight, Sat 10 pm, Sun 5 pm; No jeans; Take bookings all week via phone and/or online; children: 12+ at D.

LEAMINGTON SPA, WARWICKSHIRE   5–4C

LA COPPOLA   £48   443

14 THE PARADE CV32 4DW
01926 888 873

This "excellent" – if "slightly camp" – "old-school Italian" moved into ornately decorated new premises in January 2019, with the addition of an oyster bar ("daily seafood displayed on ice tempting you with plump oysters and delicate fizz!"). Regulars reckon it's now "even better than ever" – a "magic little corner of Italy in the heart of Warwickshire". Part of a local group, it has sibling venues in Leamington and Warwick. / www.lacoppola.co.uk; Sun-Thu 10 pm, Fri & Sat 10.30 pm; No Amex.

OSCARS FRENCH BISTRO   £51   333

39 CHANDOS STREET CV32 4RL
01926 452807

"Still reliable, still cramped, still comforting", this is a "bustling French bistro as you might have found in Paris in the 1980s", where "meaty dishes excel" ("who wants to eat cutting edge all the time?"), and where there's a "great ambience" in which to enjoy them. / www.oscarsfrenchbistro.co.uk; @oscars_bistro; Take bookings all week via phone and/or online.

THE TAME HARE   £73   343

97 WARWICK STREET CV32 4RJ
01926 316191

"Pleasant and friendly" venue off the main drag: modern British dishes are "clearly made with both love and knowledge" in the semi-open kitchen, and "it's good to interact with the chefs as they serve a course"; reasonable prices too. / www.thetamehare.co.uk; @thetamehare; Take bookings all week via phone and/or online.

LECHLADE, GLOUCESTERSHIRE   2–2C

THE FIVE ALLS   £55   334

FILKINS GL7 3JQ 01367 860875

"A real pleasure" – takeover by a chain (Cardiff's Barkby Group, at the helm as of 2018) hasn't led to a fall in fortunes for this eighteenth century village boozer; it continues to deliver "very enjoyable", "well-sized and well-priced" grub (including the "perfect Sunday roast") that's "worth travelling some way for" – and, while it "gets pretty packed, it appears the kitchen is used to that and copes admirably". / www.thefiveallsfilkins.co.uk; @fiveallsfilkins; Mon-Thu 9.30 pm, Fri & Sat 10 pm, Sun 3 pm; No Amex; Take bookings all week via phone and/or online.

LEEDS, WEST YORKSHIRE   5–1C

AAGRAH   £36   343

ST PETER'S SQ LS9 8AH 0113 2455667

"Sometimes the old guard can maintain its position – which certainly applies to the Aagrah", a mighty chain whose "consistently high-quality and value-for-money" food features a "Kashmiri bias but includes most standards from the subcontinent". Bonus – it's "ideally located to enjoy Leeds nightlife before or after". / www.aagrah.com; @Aagrahgroup; Mon-Sat 11.30 pm, Sun 10.30 pm.

ART'S   £42   233

42 CALL LANE LS1 6DT 0113 243 8243

In its 25th year, this nineties survivor near the Corn Exchange has weathered various ups-and-downs over the years, and remains one of the town's better-known locations. The odd sceptic feels it's "OK, but nothing special" nowadays, but fans declare it "back on form with a new menu that really hits the spot". / www.artscafebar.com; @artscafeleeds; Mon-Fri 11 pm, Sat midnight, Sun 9 pm.

BUNDOBUST   £27   333

6 MILL HILL LS1 5DQ 0113 243 1248

"Flavours galore and a regularly changing menu means you can fill up on Indian street food without breaking the bank and wash it down with a great range of beers" at this five-year-old haunt, where service uses "environmentally friendly compostable plates and cutlery" on shared benches at communal tables: "cheap, fast and fun"… "just a great place". / www.bundobust.com; @Bundobust; Mon-Thu 9.30 pm, Fri & Sat 10 pm, Sun 8 pm; Booking weekdays only.

CRAFTHOUSE, TRINITY LEEDS   £57   334

LEVEL 5 LS1 6HW 0113 897 0444

From the D&D London group, a "very smart" location in the city-centre "overlooking the rooftops of the city". Its food has tended to polarise opinion in the past, and though it "can be a bit variable", reports were weighted more positively this year, with praise for some "interesting" seasonal dishes. / www.crafthouse-restaurant.com; @CrafthouseLeeds; Mon-Thu 10 pm, Fri & Sat 11 pm; Booking max 8 may apply.

FUJI HIRO   £22   432

45 WADE LN LS2 8NJ 0113 243 9184

This no-nonsense Japanese comfort food canteen in the Merrion Centre enjoys legendary status in Leeds: "why go anywhere else for the best noodles?". It "never fails to satisfy" – although this year has seen a plea to "bring back the original chicken gyoza recipe". / merrioncentre.co.uk/units/fuji-hiro; @merrioncentre; Sat & Sun, Mon-Fri 9 pm; May need 5+ to book.

HOME   £89   334

16/17 KIRKGATE LS1 6BY 0113 430 0161

"Exceptional cooking" and "innovative seasonal dishes" win a lot of ardent fans for Mark Owens (ex-Gavroche and Box Tree) and Elizabeth Cottam's two-year-old, on Leeds's oldest street, which they hail as a "low-key but high-class addition to the local restaurant scene". It doesn't universally impress reporters, however, and there is also a sceptical school of thought that "the food is pretty, but not always big on taste". / www.homeleeds.co.uk; Wed & Thu 8 pm, Fri & Sat 8.30 pm, Sun 3 pm.

IBERICA   £48   334

HEPPER HOUSE, 17A EAST PARADE LS1 2BH 01134 037 007

"Truly Spanish food" (plus sherries and wines) melds with "superb architecture" at this glamorous outpost of the eight-strong, London-centric tapas chain, which occupies a Grade II-listed former auction house now kitted out with "cosy booths and tables" plus a basement wine bar/deli. / www.ibericarestaurants.com/restaurants/iberica-leeds/; @IbericaLondon; Mon-Sat 11 pm, Sun 10 pm.

ISSHO   £62   343

VICTORIA GATE, GEORGE ST LS2 7AU 0113 426 5000

"They have evolved the culinary experience" at D&D London's splashy Japanese two-year-old, atop Trinity shopping centre, and featuring a "superb terrace"; nowadays "the food is just beautiful" (albeit "expensive") and "they also have an amazing cocktail bar". / www.issho-restaurant.com; Mon-Wed 9 pm, Fri & Sat 11 pm, Thu 10 pm, Sun 3 pm.

KENDELLS BISTRO £51   444

ST PETERS SQUARE LS9 8AH 0113 2436553

"Intimate… delightfully eclectic" – there's no shortage of plaudits for this "romantic" fixture, where there's "no menu but all the choices are on a giant blackboard". The overall effect is "just like dining in France…confit of duck, French onion soup, boeuf bourguignon etc.", and the early-evening menu is "amazing value for money" too. / www.kendellsbistro.co.uk; @KendellsBistro; No Amex.

THE MAN BEHIND THE CURTAIN   £119   332

TOP FLOOR FLANNELS, 68-78 VICAR LN LS1 7JH 0113 2432376

"Everything about The Man Behind The Curtain is exciting, delivering star quality without being stuffy and dry!" – Michael O'Hare's "genuinely exceptional and innovative" city-centre venture is "set in a basement, but a really trendy and modern one", and he has carved his major gastronomic reputation with "serious food with a sense of fun and almost ridiculous attention to detail". But whereas most reporters remain dazzled by his culinary pyrotechnics (not to mention the crockery!), ratings are again sapped by a minority for whom the performance is not terrible but "vastly overrated", not helped by prices – in particular for wine – which can be a bit "galling". / www.themanbehindthecurtain.co.uk; @hairmetalchef; Tue-Thu 8.15 pm, Fri & Sat 9.30 pm.

MATT HEALEY X THE FOUNDRY £55 433

1 SAW MILL YD LS11 5WH 0113 245 0390

MasterChef: The Professionals runner-up (2016) Matt Healey is at the stoves of this modern café/brasserie: a bare-brick, restored Victorian industrial space that's been going a little under ten years. The "interesting" menu (some small plates, plus cheese, charcuterie, and sharing options) mixes more familiar items with "quite original" combinations, and feedback on the results is mostly – if not quite universally – very upbeat. / mhfoundry.co.uk; @mhfoundry; Tue-Thu 9.30 pm, Fri & Sat 10 pm, Sun 4 pm; No Amex.

OX CLUB £58 332

19A THE HEADROW LS1 6PU 07470 359961

A "hearty" modern bistro menu majoring in steak from the charcoal grill pleases all diners at this venue in Headrow House, a former textile mill. It was closed for several weeks in late 2019 after a fire. / www.oxclub.co.uk; @OxClubLeeds; Tue-Sat 10 pm, Sun 3 pm; Take bookings all week via phone and/or online.

PATTY SMITHS, BELGRAVE MUSIC HALL £24 433

1 CROSS BELGRAVE ST LS2 8JP 0113 234 6160

"The best place to go to scratch that burger itch", this "funky" operation shares the ground floor of the Belgrave Music Hall venue in the Northern Quarter with another "outstanding" fast-food pitstop, Dough Boys pizza. Bars are on hand to provide libation. / www.belgravemusichall.com; @pattysmithsUK; Take bookings all week via phone and/or online.

PRASHAD £50 432

137 WHITEHALL RD BD11 1AT 0113 285 2037

"Superb Indian vegetarian food" – "spicy but beautifully presented" – has made this family-run Gujarati a West Yorkshire institution since its humble beginnings in 1992. Now run by the second generation under Bobby Patel (brother Mayur founded Bundobust), it's "still going strong" – and the "starters are spectacularly good". / www.prashad.co.uk; @prashad_veggie/; Tue-Sat 11 pm, Sun 10 pm; No Amex; Take bookings all week via phone and/or online.

THE RELIANCE £41 433

76-78 NORTH ST LS2 7PN 0113 295 6060

"You can feel the influence of Fergus Henderson" on Tom Hunter's cuisine at this cavernous and carnivorous venue – also home to a small cinema – serving up "very tasty and interesting pub food and good real ales to go with it". "The ambience is determinedly dressed down, which appeals to its clientele", but it's "far better than its unassuming façade suggests". / www.the-reliance.co.uk; @The_Reliance; Mon-Wed 10 pm, Thu-Sat 10.30 pm, Sun 8.30 pm; No bookings.

SALVO'S £53 443

115 & 107 OTLEY ROAD LS6 3PX 0113 275 2752

The Dammone family's Headingley fixture (est 1976) is "a Leeds institution that maintains its standards and is still evolving", having moved beyond offering first-rate pasta and pizza to add a next-door café/salumeria serving bolder 'alter ego' tasting menus on Fri and Sat nights. / www.salvos.co.uk; @salvosleeds; Sun-Thu 9 pm, Fri & Sat 10 pm; No Amex; Take bookings all week via phone and/or online.

SOUS LE NEZ EN VILLE £52 433

QUEBEC HS, QUEBEC ST LS1 2HA 0113 244 0108

"Good French bourgeois cooking à la Yorkshire (ie big portions)" and a "great wine list" have combined to make this basement a popular city-centre refuge for thirty years. Weekly deliveries from Rungis market in Paris are complemented by more local produce. "A great spot for business" for which it's often and highly recommended in the survey: it's run "with efficient and friendly charm" – although "if you get one of the small alcoves, you may have to hunt for a waiter". / www.souslenez.com; @SousLeNezLeeds; Mon-Fri 9.45 pm, Sat 10.30 pm; Take bookings all week via phone and/or online.

SUKHOTHAI £41 334

15 SOUTH PARADE LS1 5QS 0113 242 2795

"Wonderful, authentic Thai food" wins solid ratings for Thai-born chef-owner Ban Kaewkraikhot, whose original Chapel Allerton restaurant from 2002 has spawned two outposts in Leeds and one in Harrogate. / www.sukhothai.co.uk; @Sukhothai_.

SUKHOTHAI £40 343

8 REGENT ST LS7 4PE 0113 237 0141

Well-known Chapel Allerton Thai (est 2002) with a number of spin-offs, including in the city-centre, which retains a strong reputation in these parts. Feedback was surprisingly thin this year, but good all-round. / www.sukhothai.co.uk; @Sukhothai_; Mon-Sat 11 pm, Sun 10 pm; No Amex; Take bookings all week via phone and/or online.

THE SWINE THAT DINES £67 342

58 NORTH STREET LS2 7BF 0113 244 0387

Popular for its "good value cooking", this "small plates and small dining area" venue has a strong following for its vegetarian options – despite the name. Themed set menus are served in the evenings, and weekends are known for 'Pie Sundays'. / swinethatdines.co.uk; Fri & Sat, Wed & Thu 9 pm.

TATTU £35 334

29 EAST PARADE, MINERVA HOUSE LS1 5PS 0113 245 1080

"Amazing flowering blossom décor" is the undoubted highpoint at this "noisy" Chinese-influenced Asian: part of an expanding glam-Asian national chain. Though not especially foodie, the cooking escaped any criticism this year: "it's fun and you come away having had a good meal". / www.tattu.co.uk; @tatturestaurant; Sun-Thu 1 am, Fri & Sat 2 am.

THARAVADU £43 542

7- 8 MILL HILL LS1 5DQ 0113 244 0500

"If you didn't know it was there, you might just walk past, even though it gets very busy!" – this popular gem "a few minutes walk from Leeds Station" is well worth remembering for its "exemplary" Keralan food: "if you like fish and honest south Indian flavours then this is THE place". / www.tharavadurestaurants.com; @TharavaduRestau; Mon-Thu 10 pm, Fri & Sat 10.30 pm; Take bookings all week via phone and/or online.

ZAAP £31 334

16 GRAND ARCADE LS1 6PG 0113 243 2586

A "great and authentic Thai food experience" awaits at this "street-food spot-turned restaurant" which, despite still "looking and feeling like a pop-up", is by now "a staple part of Leeds life", especially if you're after "something different"; the "buzzy and fun" (kid-friendly) décor involves eating in a tuk-tuk. / www.zaapthai.co.uk/zaap-leeds; @ZaapThai; Sun-Thu 11 pm, Fri & Sat midnight; No bookings.

ZUCCO £45 433

603 MEANWOOD ROAD LS6 4AY 01132 249679

This smart Italian small-plates spot – run by Venetian owners, for added authenticity – is "always a delight to visit" owing to its superior regional dishes and interesting wines. / www.zucco.co.uk; @Zuccouk; Tue-Thu 10 pm, Fri & Sat 10.30 pm, Sun 8.30 pm.

BOBBY'S   £27   3️⃣2️⃣2️⃣

**154-156 BELGRAVE RD LE4 5AT
0116 266 0106**

You "always can depend on excellent vegetarian food" (of a Gujarati bent) at this affordable sweet shop and canteen: a fixture on the Golden Mile since way back in 1976 – though it's somewhat spruced-up these days, and the menu has taken into account modern healthy-eating trends (sadly the founder, Bhagwanji Lakhani, passed away in 2017). / www.eatatbobbys.com; @bobbysleicester; Mon, Wed-Sun 10 pm; No Amex.

KAYAL   £44   4️⃣3️⃣3️⃣

153 GRANBY ST LE1 6FE   0116 255 4667

"Authentic South Asian cooking at its best" – Kayal has blazed a trail for Keralan cuisine in Leicester "with an excellent choice of dosas, fish and vegetarian dishes and a knowledgeable waiter to talk you through the options". Top Tip: "amazing business lunch for £6". / www.kayalrestaurant.com/; @kayalrestaurant; Mon-Sat 11 pm; Take bookings all week via phone and/or online.

TANDEM   £50

**59-59A HIGHCROSS STREET LE1 4PH
01164784974**

Cyrus Todiwala OBE, the acclaimed Bombay-born TV-chef behind London's Café Spice Namaste, has chosen a Grade II listed building in the city-centre for his first restaurant outside London; and will feature five separate areas over two floors, including a bar, casual dining and fine dining room. For the town with the biggest Diwali festival outside India, Leicester has always curiously lacked a go-to Indian dining destination – maybe this is it? / tandemrestaurant.co.uk; @TandemLeicester.

Northcote, Langho

THE STOCKTON CROSS   £44

KIMBOLTON HR6 0HD   01568 612509

Between Ludlow and Leominster, this sixteenth-century, black and white pub was taken over and revamped in spring 2018. Feedback on the new regime is too limited as yet for a full rating, but all of it is upbeat. / www.thestocktoncross.co.uk; Wed-Sat, Tue 9 pm, Sun 4 pm; Take bookings all week via phone and/or online.

COOMBESHEAD FARM   £90   5️⃣4️⃣4️⃣

**COOMBESHEAD FARM PL15 7QQ
01566 782 009**

"Tucked away down Cornish lanes" – "a very innovative menu", "full of new ideas and interesting flavours", awaits at this "inspiring" venture, from chefs April Bloomfield (of New York's Spotted Pig) and Tom Adams (of Pitt Cue in London). A stay on the farm, which produces food for the communal table shared by diners, is a "joyful and relaxed" experience that's "unforgettable" – the "energetic and helpful staff" give guests a "real sense of involvement in the preparation of fine cooking". / www.coombesheadfarm.co.uk; @CoombesheadF; Take bookings all week via phone and/or online.

LIMETREE KITCHEN   £35   3️⃣3️⃣3️⃣

**14 STATION STREET BN7 2DB
01273 478636**

"A great little spot with a fab menu" featuring sharing plates of eclectic inspiration, wins praise for this agreeable modern bistro, with adjacent deli. / www.limetreekitchen.co.uk; @LimetreeKitchen; Wed-Sat 9.30 pm, Sun 2.30 pm.

THE BOAT INN   £94   4️⃣3️⃣3️⃣

WALSALL ROAD WS14 0BU   01543361692

"Still a pub with a decent pint of real ale but with serious ambition to become a fine dining restaurant" – Liam Dillon's year-old pub conversion was Estrella Damm's Newcomer of the Year in its February 2019 Top 50 Gastropub Awards, and manages to steer a course between its pubby origins and "well-prepared and attractively-presented food", be it from the à la carte or ten-course tasting menu. / www.theboatinnlichfield.com; @TheBoatInn_; Wed-Sat 9.30 pm, Sun 4.30 pm.

LICKFOLD INN   £63

HIGHSTEAD LN GU28 9EY   01798 532535

It's all change again at this out-of-the-way old country pub, north of Petworth. DJ Chris Evans owned it about five years ago, then Tom Sellers ran it, but that came to an end this year, and as of August 30 2019, it has a new management team and a less 'fine dining' approach than under the chef of London's Restaurant Story. Reports please! / www.thelickfoldinn.co.uk; @LickfoldInn; Wed-Sat 10 pm, Sun 8 pm; Take bookings all week via phone and/or online.

THE ARUNDELL ARMS HOTEL   £70   3️⃣3️⃣3️⃣

PL16 0AA   01566 784666

This well-run country inn near Dartmoor "never disappoints", with a menu of locally sourced produce that makes much of its delightful setting. With 20 miles of private riverbank for the use of guests, it has been a centre for fly fishing since the 1930s, and in recent years it has developed impressive green credentials – heat and hot water are powered by its own 'eco energy centre', there are charging points for electric cars, and guests who arrive by cycle, bus or electric car earn a 20% discount. / www.arundellarms.com; @TheArundellArms; Mon-Sun 9.30 pm; No Amex; No jeans.

JEW'S HOUSE RESTAURANT   £71   4️⃣4️⃣4️⃣

15 THE STRAIT LN2 1JD   01522 524851

A "wonderful setting in a medieval building" (a twelfth century house that's one of the oldest in town, on 'Steep Hill' leading up to the Cathedral) contributes to the charms of this long-established fixture, which is "still going strong". It's modern British menu delivers "lovely delicate food, with fresh flavours from quality meat and fish". / www.jewshouserestaurant.co.uk; @JewsHouse; No Amex; Take bookings all week via phone and/or online.

CHAMPANY INN   £75   3️⃣3️⃣4️⃣

EH49 7LU   01506 834532

"Steaks to die for" are the USP of the Davidson family's operation, dedicated to the glorification of prime Scottish beef from both the Highlands and the Borders. It's not a place to go when counting the pennies, but has maintained a long-term reputation for quality over a number of decades. / www.champany.com; Mon-Sat 10 pm; No jeans; Take bookings all week via phone and/or online; children: 8+.

THE CARTFORD INN   £56   4 3 3

CARTFORD LANE PR3 0YP
01995 670 166

"What a delightful place" – the Beaumes's "quirky" and extremely popular inn has a "wonderful" setting on the banks of the Wyre, ("where you may see the curious sight of the river changing direction"). The "interesting fare runs from British and French classics to modern creations that work most of the time (e.g. onion churros with baba ganoush)". / www.thecartfordinn.co.uk; @Cartfordinn; Mon-Thu 9 pm, Fri & Sat 10 pm, Sun 8.30 pm; Take bookings all week via phone and/or online.

THE ROYAL OAK   £61   4 4 4

PALEY STREET SL6 3JN   01628 620541

"The epitome of the dining pub" – broadcaster Michael and his son Nick Parkinson's gastroboozer "combines the informality of a genuine working pub with the elegance and comfort of a high-class restaurant". The "delicious, unpretentious food is meticulously prepared and presented", and there's a "fantastic list of interesting wines from around the world". / www.theroyaloakpaleystreet.com; @royaloakpaleystreet; Tue-Thu 9.30 pm, Fri & Sat 10 pm, Sun 3.30 pm; Take bookings all week via phone and/or online; children: 3+.

EAST BEACH CAFE £48   3 3 4

SEA ROAD BN17 5GB   01903 731 903

"The food is decent" (particularly the fish) and the "service friendly" at this driftwood-themed Thomas Heatherwick construction – "but what a location! The children can play outside on the beach while you wait for the grub to arrive, and then you can all stroll by the sea afterwards... just choose a sunny day!". / www.eastbeachcafe.co.uk; @EastBeachCafe; Wed-Sat 9.30 pm, Sun 3.30 pm; Take bookings all week via phone and/or online.

ALBERT'S SCHENKE   £43

16 HANOVER STREET L1 1AA
0151 709 2401

Sibling to Manchester's popular Albert's Schloss, this 'bohemian bier halle and cook haus' replaces The Hub Alehouse. It's unlikely to be a hugely foodie destination, but – if we're reading the runes correctly – it should be a good laugh with hearty scoff (schnitzel, burgers, raclette) to soak up some fine brews. / www.albertsschenke.co.uk; Mon-Sat midnight, Sun 11 pm.

THE ART SCHOOL   £96   4 3 4

SUGNALL ST L7 7DX   0151 230 8600

"Paul Askew's elegant five-year-old, next door to the Liverpool Philharmonic, continues to produce some equally elegant and accomplished cuisine" which makes it one of the city's top dining options. Recognising that not everyone will want something as full-on as the nine-course tasting menu, there are also prix fixe and 'Excellence' menus, also with pescatarian, vegetarian and vegan options. / www.theartschoolrestaurant.co.uk; @ArtSchoolLpool; No trainers; Take bookings all week via phone and/or online.

BELZAN   £38   4 4 3

371 SMITHDOWN ROAD L15 3JJ
0151 733 8595

A "great small spot in resurgent Smithdown Road", which opened in December 2017, and combines "good-quality small plates, and an excellent list of wines from small independent producers, with a sommelier who knows his stuff". "Lovely atmosphere", too – "only issue is that it can be crowded" so you'll "need to book". / belzan.co.uk; @belzan_lpl; Mon-Sat midnight, Sun 11 pm.

EL GATO NEGRO   £90

UNIT 2, WALKER HOUSE, EXCHANGE FLAGS L2 3YL   0151 236 1331

Manchester's tapas smash hit branched out in August 2019, in this large 250-seat opening, in the Exchange Flags development, overlooking Liverpool's fine town hall (which formerly traded as Steven Gerrard's 'The Vincent'). A big and well-stocked bar is also key to the offering. / www.elgatonegrotapas.com/liverpool/; @ElGatoNegroFood.

HANOVER STREET SOCIAL   £43   3 3 3

16-20 HANOVER ST L1 4AA
0151 709 8764

"Consistently good food at a competitive price" plus a "useful central location and a great choice of gins" means this modern brasserie from Merseyside's Red & Blue Restaurants group is "worth a visit". / www.hanoverstreetsocial.co.uk; @hanoversocial; Mon-Sun 10.30 pm; Take bookings all week via phone and/or online.

THE ITALIAN CLUB FISH   £45   4 3 3

128 BOLD ST L1 4JA   0151 707 2110

"Seafood heaven!" – part of an Italian-Scottish family-run group, this "casual" venue "changes from café at lunchtime to packed restaurant at night time" – when "it's worth the crush for the brilliant fish and shellfish". Top Tip: "go early evening for oysters and prosecco". / www.theitalianclubfish.co.uk; @italianclubnews; Mon-Sat 11 pm, Sun 10.30 pm; No Amex; Take bookings all week via phone and/or online.

LUNYA   £44   3 3 3

18-20 COLLEGE LN L1 3DS
0151 706 9770

Going from strength to strength after its 2017 move to bigger premises – in shopping mecca Liverpool ONE – Peter & Elaine Kinsella's "authentic" Catalan tapas spot serves up "mouthwatering dishes full of flavours" (the "churros are a dream"). "An added joy is stopping to make purchases at the deli counter as you leave". Also in the Albert Dock (Lunyalita) and with a branch in Manchester. / www.lunya.co.uk; @lunya; Mon & Tue 9 pm, Wed & Thu 9.30 pm, Fri & Sat 10 pm, Sun 8.30 pm; Take bookings all week via phone and/or online.

MARAY   £43   4 4 4

91 BOLD STREET L14 4HF   0151 709 5820

"Fabulous Maray never disappoints" – whether you head to this "packed" and "buzzing" outpost (est. 2014), or the equally popular offshoots in Allerton and the Royal Albert Dock. Inspired by the kind of food found in the Marais in Paris, it serves "interesting and inspiring" Middle Eastern small plates ("with a focus on vegetarian dishes"), and the end result is "a great experience" according to its army of fans. / www.maray.co.uk; @marayrestaurant; Sun-Thu 10 pm, Fri & Sat 11 pm; Take bookings all week via phone and/or online.

MOWGLI   £43   3 4 4

69 BOLD ST L1 4EZ   0151 708 9356

"Liverpool's answer to London's Dishoom" – Nisha Katona's Indian street-food concept, "in the heart of the city", has really nailed it, delivering "small sharing helpings of Mumbai-style street food", alongside "yumblelicious" cocktails, served "by welcoming and knowledgeable staff" in a "modern and individual setting" (albeit one now being replicated around the country). Top Tip – "the always-good tiffin box option is the best". / www.mowglistreetfood.com; @Mowglistfood; Sun-Wed 9.30 pm, Thu-Sat 10.30 pm; Take bookings all week via phone and/or online.

OKTOPUS   £31   3 3 3

HARDMAN YARD, 24 HARDMAN ST L1 9AX   07565 299879

"The food here is always fascinating", say fans of this Merseyside two-year-old (which, despite its name, is not a seafood specialist). Critics reckon the standards are "mixed", to which comes the riposte that "too many people don't get the concept – it's designed for sharing plates, not separate orders". There's no debating the "good beer selection". / www.oktopus-restaurant.com; @Hello_Oktopus; Mon-Sat 9.45 pm.

PANORAMIC 34, WEST TOWER   £69   3 4 5

BROOK STREET L3 9PJ   0151 236 5534

"The views are just to die for" at the West Tower's 34th floor restaurant – a "great place to bring people", particularly if you opt for the afternoon tea – but it's no one-trick pony, and also pumps out some "gorgeous", more serious cooking. Even the least enthusiastic report (which finds it "overpriced and way too pretentious") says "it has the most amazing setting, and the food's good". / www.panoramic34.com/; @Panoramic34; Tue-Thu 9.30 pm; No Amex; No trainers; Take bookings all week via phone and/or online.

PEN FACTORY £39 333

13 HOPE ST L1 9BQ 0151 709 7887

"As popular as ever" – launched in 2014, this small plates operation (the name spells out the site's former purpose) recreates "Liverpool legend" Paddy Byrne's beloved old Everyman Bistro next door. "Paddy keeps prices fair" and the kitchen has been turning out some "more adventurous" plates of late, much to reporters' content. / www.pen-factory.co.uk/; @ThePenFactory; No Amex; Take bookings all week via phone and/or online.

PILGRIM £128

46 DUKE STREET L1 5AG

BBC2's 'My Million Pound Menu' winners Dave Bone (chef) Jamie Duffield (front of house), and Anthony Power opened this new venture in Duke Street Market (a revamped docklands warehouse) in spring 2019. The food offering is based on dishes found along the Camino de Santiago pilgrimage routes in Spain, France and Portugal, and – though we received no survey feedback – it's receiving a good rep generally (including from Michelin who awarded it a 2020 Bib Gourmand). / pilgrimrestaurant.com; Wed-Fri 11 pm, Sat & Sun 9 pm.

ROSKI £100 543

16 RODNEY STREET L1 2TE 0151 708 8698

This city-centre two-year-old from "incredibly talented chef" Anton Piotrowski, a BBC MasterChef: The Professionals winner, "is really getting it right now – great to see such a risky enterprise doing so well". "What an unexpected delight – just another bistro from the outside, but inside it's quickly clear it's so much more". "The tasting menu includes some very adventurous offerings" and on all accounts the food is "beautifully plated and tastes gorgeous". / www.roskirestaurant.com; @roskirestaurant; Tue-Sat 9.30 pm; Take bookings all week via phone and/or online; children: 8.

SALT HOUSE £47 323

1 HANOVER STREET L1 3DW 0151 706 0092

A stylish tapas joint just round the corner from John Lewis (should you be hungry after shopping for a washing machine) – "very busy, lively and fun, with interesting dishes that are reasonably priced". Top Tip – "a very good value set lunch". / www.salthousetapas.co.uk; @salthousetapas; Take bookings all week via phone and/or online.

SALT HOUSE BACARO £42 333

47 CASTLE ST L2 9UB 01516650047

"Italian small plates (this time)" "from the Salt House tapas stable" – win solid ratings for this "friendly, buzzy restaurant" from the Red & Blue team. It's "great for a larger party", with "seats at the bar good for dates"; "it's crowded so you do get to hear your neighbours' conversations – although in Liverpool that can be theatre". / www.salthousebacaro.co.uk/; @salthousebacaro; Take bookings all week via phone and/or online.

SAN CARLO £61 334

41 CASTLE ST L2 9SH 0151 236 0073

A "really vibrant and buzzing" venture – this branch of Carlo Distefano's stylish Italian group has a business-district location well-suited to entertaining. But it also makes an "ideal spot for a relaxed meal out": "Saturday night and the place is full of life, music, and all types of people – just lovely". / www.sancarlo.co.uk; @SanCarlo_Group.

60 HOPE STREET £63 332

60 HOPE ST L1 9BZ 0151 707 6060

This well-established (est. 1999) and "ever-reliable" contemporary restaurant, in a Grade II-listed house near the Anglican cathedral, still provides a "wide-ranging" and "interesting" menu of modern brasserie fare delivered by "young and friendly" staff. / www.60hopestreet.com; @60HopeSt; Mon-Sat 10.30 pm, Sun 6 pm.

SPIRE £46 332

1 CHURCH ROAD L15 9EA 0151 734 5040

"Consistently good cooking and attentive service" has built a loyal local following over 12 years for brothers Matt & Adam Locke's "great neighbourhood restaurant", around the corner from Penny Lane. Its modern British food is "up there with the best" and the "good-value deals" ensure that it's "busy every day with the local ladies who lunch". / www.spirerestaurant.co.uk; @spirerestaurant; Mon-Fri 9.45 pm, Sat 10.30 pm; Take bookings all week via phone and/or online.

WRECKFISH £48 344

60 SEEL STREET L1 4BE 0151 707 1960

"Another of Gary Usher's fabulous bistros" is a typical take on this "great addition to the city-centre": a stylishly refurbished two-year-old (formerly a derelict workshop), in the city's merchant quarter, that's nowadays the city's most-mentioned eatery. Its gutsy, affordable fare is generally well-rated, but ratings sipped a notch this year on some more middling reports ("good in parts…", "good but expected more…", "prices are slightly high even if everything they do, they do well…") / wreckfish. co; @WreckfishBistro; Mon-Sun 9 pm.

LLANARTHNE, CARMARTHENSHIRE 4–4C

WRIGHTS FOOD EMPORIUM £37 433

GOLDEN GROVE ARMS SA32 8JU 01558 668929

The former chief inspector for the AA, Simon Wright, owns this four-year-old café/deli and wine store. "Something a bit different in this neck of the woods" – "it's the best breakfast, lunch and tea place: in fact, drop in any time and you'll find something to delight you… but it's extremely hard to leave without a slice of one of their fabulous cakes!" / www.wrightsfood.co.uk; @WrightsFood; Sun & Mon 5 pm, Wed & Thu 7 pm, Fri & Sat 9 pm; No bookings.

LLANDEWI SKIRRID, MONMOUTHSHIRE 2–1A

THE WALNUT TREE £75 433

LLANDDEWI SKIRRID NP7 8AW 01873 852797

"Shaun Hill's cookery book is great": "so full of clear sanity and common sense – qualities that shine through in all you are served" at this famous, rural Welsh pub (which was established in the 1970s as a pioneering foodie mecca under former owners, Franco & Ann Taruschio; and which Shaun has run for the last decade). It's "an unfussy but welcoming environment" – "a bustling dining room full of people very happily tucking in, and with nice associated cottages to stay in". Its ratings suffered this year though, with a new theme in reports that it's "still good, but a bit in decline": "no complaints, but it was just not the superb meal we were expecting". / www.thewalnuttreeinn.com; @lovewalnuttree.

LLANDRILLO, DENBIGHSHIRE 4–2D

TYDDYN LLAN £94 445

LL21 0ST 01490 440264

"Welsh country house food, service and ambience at its best" has won many accolades over the years for Bryan & Susan Webb's former hunting lodge, out in the boonies. Its ratings slipped a notch this year, on the back of a couple of iffy reports: meals that were "OK but some distance from expectations". But most reporters' experience of "top ingredients, unfussily cooked" continues to bear out its stellar reputation as an "unfailingly delightful" destination. / www.tyddynllan.co.uk; @BryanWWebb; Wed & Thu 10 pm, Fri-Sun 4 pm; Credit card deposit required to book.

LLANDUDNO, CONWY 4–1D

BODYSGALLEN HALL, DINING ROOM £75 333

THE ROYAL WELSH WAY LL30 1RS 01492 584466

"Delicious" silver service meals live up to their grand setting in this imposing grade II-listed manor house a mile from Llandudno. Owned by the National Trust, it is run as a hotel and spa, and has spectacular grounds and gardens. / www.bodysgallen.com; @BodysgallenHall; Mon-Fri 9 pm, Sat & Sun 9.30 pm; No trainers; children: 6+.

LLANGOLLEN, DENBIGHSHIRE   5–3A

THE CORN MILL   £46   224

DEE LN LL20 8PN   01978 869555

"It is lovely to overlook the tumbling River Dee" and its water wheel while dining on the deck of this unusually attractive Brunning & Price gastroboozer; the food's tolerable but not the main event. / www.brunningandprice.co.uk/cornmill; Mon-Sat 9.30 pm, Sun 9 pm; Take bookings all week via phone and/or online.

LLYSWEN, POWYS   2–1A

LLANGOED HALL   £89   434

LD3 0YP   01874 754525

This "real country house hotel" provides lashings of "old-fashioned romance in a beautiful setting". Long "a lovely place to stay and eat", its culinary reputation has soared in recent years with chef Nick Brodie's "delightful" cooking, enjoyed in the evening from a six-course (£60) or nine-course (£90) tasting menu. / www.llangoedhall.com; @TheLlangoedHall; No Amex; Jacket required.

LOCKSBOTTOM, KENT   3–3B

CHAPTER ONE   £54   443

FARNBOROUGH COMMON BR6 8NF
01689 854848

"Back to its best" – long-time chef Andy McLeish and his business partner purchased this well-known site in late 2017, and have re-established it as one of the major destinations on the fringes of south east London and beyond. "Dishes are beautifully presented and have substance as well as style" and service is "very efficient, slick and unobtrusive". The only hitch used to be the "staid" and "old-fashioned" interior, but early 2019 saw a month-long, six-figure revamp, and early reports say "post-revamp, the dining room is buzzing" with "an atmosphere of contentment". Top Tip: "special lunch menus continue to be a bargain worth travelling for". / www.chaptersrestaurants.com; @chapter1kent; Mon-Thu 10.30 pm, Fri & Sat 11.30 pm, Sun 9 pm; No trainers; Booking max 12 may apply.

LONG CRENDON, BUCKINGHAMSHIRE   2–2D

THE ANGEL   £54   323

47 BICESTER RD HP18 9EE
01844 208268

"Delicious fresh fish" is the star of the "always reliable" menu at this attractive sixteenth-century coaching inn on the Oxon-Bucks border. "Strong wine list", too. / www.angelrestaurant.co.uk; @theangeluk; Mon-Sat 9.30 pm, Sun 3 pm.

LOSTWITHIEL, CORNWALL   1–3B

ASQUITHS   £56   442

19 NORTH STREET PL22 0EF
01208 871714

Chef-patron Graham Cutherbertson cooks "ambitious and imaginative dishes", "using local and seasonal produce" at his restaurant opposite the church in one of Cornwall's less-touristy towns. Local reporters reckon they're "lucky to have such a good spot near us". / asquithsrestaurant.co.uk.

LOUGHBOROUGH, LEICESTERSHIRE   5–3D

THE HAMMER & PINCERS   £46   443

5 EAST RD LE12 6ST   01509 880735

"The food is sublime and the presentation exemplary" at this "exquisite" beamed gastropub, whose considerable charms have, over the past decade and a half, established it as a real foodie haunt. Menu options are numerous: from Sunday lunch to a ten-course grazing option. A collaboration with 'galerie gARTenhaus' means there is regularly changing art on display. / www.hammerandpincers.co.uk; Tue-Sat 9.30 pm, Sun 4 pm; No Amex; Take bookings all week via phone and/or online.

LOWER BEEDING, WEST SUSSEX   3–4A

INTERLUDE

LEONARDSLEE GARDENS, BRIGHTON ROAD RH13 6PP   01403 289490

On the 240 acre estate of Grade I listed Leonardslee Lakes and Gardens (incorporating a vineyard), this year-old venture has yet to generate sufficient feedback for a rating. But its 14-course and 19-course menus from South African chef Jean Delport – using produce from the estate – have immediately caught the attention of the tyre men, who awarded it a Michelin star in October 2019. / www.restaurant-interlude.co.uk; @InterludeSussex; Wed-Fri 4 pm, Sat & Sun 5 pm.

THE PASS RESTAURANT, SOUTH LODGE HOTEL   £101   443

BRIGHTON ROAD RH13 6PS
01403 891711

Run for just a year by chef Tom Kemble, an alumnus of Sweden's famous Fäviken who made his name at Bonhams in Mayfair, this funky venue features 28 covers served from an open kitchen, in an apparently staid country-house hotel: "an enjoyable and well-presented concept" whose "interesting tasting menu" inspires very enthusiastic (albeit nowadays rather limited) feedback. / www.exclusive.co.uk/south-lodge/restaurants-bars/the-pass; @southlodgehotel; Wed-Sun 8.30 pm; children: 12+.

LOWER BOCKHAMPTON, DORSET   2–4B

YALBURY COTTAGE   £60   443

DT2 8PZ   01305 262382

"A real treat for foodies" – this thatched cottage in Thomas Hardy's home village of Bockhampton serves "the best food in the area". "You'll pay London prices, but it's great value for cooking of this standard". / www.yalburycottage.com; @YalburyDorset; No Amex; practically no walk-ins – you must book.

LOWER FROYLE, HAMPSHIRE   2–3D

THE ANCHOR INN   £49   333

GU34 4NA   01420 23261

"So quirky and friendly", "and the food is great too" at this smart pub-with-rooms geared up for huntin', shootin' and fishin' in the Hampshire countryside. Top Tip: "Go for the scrumptious dessert of beer cake and apple ice cream". / www.anchorinnatlowerfroyle.co.uk; @anchorinnfroyle; Mon-Thu 9 pm, Fri & Sat 9.30 pm, Sun 8 pm; Take bookings all week via phone and/or online.

LOWER SLAUGHTER, GLOUCESTERSHIRE   2–1C

THE SLAUGHTERS MANOR HOUSE   £91   333

COPSEHILL RD GL54 2HP   01451 820456

Blessed with a picture-perfect village setting, this well-established hotel restaurant (nowadays under the Brownsword group) is a light, airy space whose fine dining food – afternoon tea to eight-course tasting menus – makes the most of local and foraged ingredients. It attracted limited feedback this year, but all positive. / www.slaughtersmanor.co.uk; @SlaughtersManor; No jeans; children: 8.

LOWER SWELL, SOMERSET   2–3A

THE LANGFORD   £59   444

LANGFORD FIVEHEAD TA3 6PH
01460 282020

Olly & Rebecca Jackson's "beautiful old mansion", in a "secluded location", and with "log fires in winter and aperitifs in the garden come summer"; the kitchen delivers "excellent simple cooking of a high standard" and the whole experience "makes you feel like a house guest in a medieval manor" (which you effectively are). / www.langfordfivehead.co.uk/; @Langford5head; Wed-Fri, Tue, Sat 10.30 pm; Take bookings all week via phone and/or online.

LUDLOW, SHROPSHIRE   5–4A

THE CHARLTON ARMS, CHARLTON ARMS HOTEL   £41   333

LUDFORD BRIDGE SY8 1PJ
01584 872813

Cedric (brother of Claude, who used to run Hibiscus nearby) & Amy Bosi's old stone pub with rooms profits from "superb views over the

River Teme". "The food has its off days, but is generally reliable, and often very good". / www.thecharltonarms.co.uk; @Charlton_Ludlow; Take bookings all week via phone and/or online.

THE CLIFFE AT DINHAM £51 333

6 HALTON LANE SY8 2JE 01584 872063

Just across the River Teme from Ludlow Castle, a short walk from Dinham Bridge, this small hotel incorporates a conservatory restaurant extension with garden views, and terrace for the summer. Reviews of Ian Pugh's modernised but relatively traditional cooking are very positive: "consistently delivering a good quality dining experience, with an imaginatively presented, seasonal menu". / www.thecliffeatdinham.co.uk; @cliffeatdinham.

CSONS AT THE GREEN CAFE £40 334

DINHAM MILLENNIUM GREEN SY8 1EG 01584 879872

"Everything is very fresh and full-flavoured" at this "great riverside venue" run by the four Crouch brothers, overlooking the Teme at Dinham weir, beneath the dramatic walls of Ludlow Castle. It's a "relaxed and friendly" spot, "ideal for meeting friends" for an "excellent breakfast or lunch", with dinner on Fridays and Saturdays. / csons-ludlow.co.uk; @greencafeludlow; Mon-Thu, Sat & Sun 4 pm, Fri 10 pm.

GOLDEN MOMENTS £38 443

50 BROAD STREET SY8 1NH 01584 878 488

"Delicious and authentic-tasting" South Asian cooking has won consistent high praise for this Bengali venue over the last two decades. "You'll find all the old favourites but also some less common dishes" – and "everything is freshly cooked, so the wait is worthwhile". / www.goldenmomentsofludlow.co.uk; Mon, Wed & Thu, Sun 10 pm, Fri & Sat 10.30 pm; Take bookings all week via phone and/or online.

MORTIMERS £74 344

17 CORVE ST SY8 1DA 01584 872 325

"Oak-panelled comfort" with "beautiful décor", plus "charming" and "professional" service set a perfect tone for "delightful" and "inventive" modern cuisine at this well-known foodie address, formerly made famous by Bibendum's Claude Bosi (and nowadays run by his protégé, Wayne Smith). Its ratings waned a little this year, though, on the back of some reviews which were not damning, but "disappointing at the price". / www.mortimersludlow.co.uk; @MortimersLudlow; Wed & Thu 9 pm, Fri & Sat 9.30 pm, Tue 8 pm, Sun 3.30 pm; Take bookings all week via phone and/or online.

OLD DOWNTON LODGE £73 433

DOWNTON ON THE ROCK SY8 2HU 01568 771826

Very attractively converted from an old farm with barns and a mill, this restaurant-with-rooms a short drive from Ludlow has its sights set high when it comes to the high quality of its cuisine, and Karl Martin's cooking – awarded a rare four rosettes by the AA – "shows a high degree of skill without confronting diners with too many tastes". One or two reporters find the experience too costly, but all rate the victuals here as good or better. / www.olddowntonlodge.com; @olddowntonlodge; Wed & Thu 10 pm, Tue, Sun & Mon 8.30 pm, Fri & Sat 11 pm; Take bookings all week via phone and/or online; children: 11.

LUTON, BEDFORDSHIRE 3–2A

LUTON HOO, LUTON HOO HOTEL £70 234

THE MANSION HOUSE, LUTON HOO ESTATE LU1 3TQ 01582 734437

Afternoon tea is "a real treat" in the "wonderful and friendly surroundings" of this country house hotel and spa, whose claim to fame is that it appeared in 'Four Weddings'. Reports of more substantial meals here are more up-and-down. / www.lutonhoo.co.uk; @lutonhoo; Wed-Fri 7 pm, Sat 6.30 pm; Take bookings all week via phone and/or online.

LYME REGIS, DORSET 2–4A

HIX OYSTER & FISH HOUSE £53 334

COBB RD DT7 3JP 01297 446910

"The architecture and position are unbeatable, and the fish is cooked simply, as it should be", according to most reports on Mark Hix's cliff-top venture, which has "great views over Lyme Bay". It has by-and-large been above criticism in recent times, winning renown as some of "the best food on the Jurassic Coast", but complainers were a little more in evidence this year ("another example of a restaurant trading mainly on its location…", "magnificent views didn't stop us feeling that we wouldn't return…") / www.restaurantsetcltd.co.uk; @hixlymeregis.

LYMINGTON, HAMPSHIRE 2–4C

ELDERFLOWER £59 543

QUAY ST SO41 3AS 01590 676908

Former Club Gascon chef, Andrew Du Bourg and wife Marjolaine's "friendly" five-year-old is "well-positioned near the quay" and bills itself as being 'quintessentially British, with a sprinkling of French'. Ratings were very high this year, celebrating "remarkable food cooked with precision and flair": in particular the "excellent taster menu which is modest cost, given the quality" – four-, five- or six-courses for £45, £55 or £65: "lots of different flavours, enticingly presented". / www.elderflowerrestaurant.co.uk;

@TheElderflower1; Wed & Thu 9.30 pm, Fri & Sat 10 pm, Sun 4 pm; Take bookings all week via phone and/or online.

LYMM, CHESHIRE 5–2B

LA BOHEME £52 443

3 MILL LANE WA13 9SD 01925 753657

"Superb... as always" – there's no let-up in standards at Olivier Troalen's classy local fave rave (est. 2000, in a posh suburb, half an hour's drive from Manchester), where the "excellently presented French-style favourites come with a twist". / laboheme.co.uk; Mon-Sat 10 pm, Sun 9 pm; Take bookings all week via phone and/or online.

LYNDHURST, HAMPSHIRE 2–4C

HARTNETT HOLDER & CO, LIME WOOD HOTEL £83 344

BEAULIEU RD SO43 7FZ 02380 287177

The "beautiful dining room" of this stylish New Forest country house retreat sets an upbeat tone for this celeb-chef's out-of-town venture. There's a general acknowledgement, however, that its Italian-style cooking is "pricey", and although fans say it's "well worth every penny", others recommend avoiding the à la carte and timing your visit for the "great set lunch menus". / www.limewoodhotel.co.uk/food/hh-and-co; @limewoodhotel; Mon-Sat midnight, Sun 5 pm; Booking max 4 may apply.

MACCLESFIELD, GREATER MANCHESTER 5–2B

KANDY £46 343

116 MILL STREET SK11 6NR 01625 402495

"I can't vouch for its authenticity as a Sri Lankan experience… but it's a delight to eat!" – so say fans of this family-run two-year-old café. By its nature, a good choice for pescatarians, veggies and vegans. / www.portobellomacc.com.

THE SUTTON GAMEKEEPER £55 433

13 HOLLIN LANE SK11 0HP 01260 252000

"Very good value for money food" is to be had at this village pub: Dining Pub of the Year in the Cheshire Life Food & Drink Awards 2019. Go for the game options if they are on – landlord James Kennedy is a keen huntsman and shoots and butchers much of the food himself. / www.thesuttongamekeeper.co.uk; @suttongkpub; Tue-Fri 9 pm, Sat 9.30 pm, Sun 7 pm.

MAIDENHEAD, BERKSHIRE 3–3A

THE CROWN £53 454

BURCHETTS GREEN SL6 6QZ 01628 824079

Simon Bonwick's acclaimed 20-seater pub is a family-run venture where often all front of house are from the clan: a feature whose

Wood Restaurant, Manchester

"impact is clear from the moment you enter, with the warm and friendly greeting, followed through in terms of attentive service and an atmosphere more like a cosy home than a restaurant". The cuisine takes a classic gastronomic approach, with "a short and punchy menu providing four or five options each for starter, main and dessert". Results are splendid, and even those who feel it's "a touch on the pricey side (with mains around £30)" feel "it's money better spent than other poor meals for half the cost". thecrownburchettsgreen.com; @crownburchetts; Thu-Sat 10.30 pm, Wed 11 pm, Sun 2 pm.

FREDERIC BISTRO £48 3 3 3

**MARKET BUILDINGS, EARL ST ME14 1HP
01622 297414**

"Huge portions" of "good wholesome food" make this "cheap and cheerful" Gallic outfit serving bistro classics "amazing value for money". There's a good selection of "fine wines", but the place is "very noisy indeed". / www.fredericbistro.com; Mon & Tue 4 pm, Wed-Sat midnight; Take bookings all week via phone and/ or online.

ADAM REID AT THE FRENCH, MIDLAND HOTEL £113 5 4 3

PETER ST M60 2DS 01612354780

"Adam has put his stamp on this place now, and it keeps getting better". This grade II listed chamber – somewhat funked up, with yellow leather banquettes and massive lights, within what is, in essence, a very traditional space – has had many culinary ups and downs over the decades, but, after three years at the helm, Adam Reid is now settling into a "fabulous" stride here, with his selection of "totally desirable" four, six or nine-course menus. The cuisine is "not so challenging that you don't want to come!" – "flowing wonderfully and generously, with notably well-executed dishes that simply delight". And you eat to a "terrific soundtrack too (Buddy Holly to Arctic Monkeys to the Beatles)". Until Mana triumphed at this year's Michelin awards, The French was the only Manchester restaurant ever to have held a Michelin star (most recently in 1974) and was a hot tip to be the first to regain the prize for the city. "How other places in the region can have a Michelin star and The French doesn't is utterly inexplicable (apart from Michelin's pig-headedness of course)". / www.the-french.co.uk;

@thefrenchmcr; Tue-Sat 9.30 pm; No trainers; Take bookings all week via phone and/or online; children: 8.

AKBAR'S £33 4 2 2

**73-83 LIVERPOOL RD M3 4NQ
0161 834 8444**

This "crazily busy" branch of Shabir Hussain's Bradford-based group "still delivers great curry and their specialism of over-sized naan". It's one of the few places that lists camel ('on the bone') on its menu. / www.akbars.co.uk; Sun-Thu 11 pm, Fri & Sat 11.30 pm; May need 10+ to book.

ALBERT'S SCHLOSS £51 3 3 5

**27 PETER STREET M2 5QR
0161 833 4040**

"Loud, fun... copious plates of tasty food... great beer" – that's the scene at this "vibrant and friendly" German-themed beer-hall. It's not subtle, but hits the mark for a big night out with its "tempting options of hearty food" – think "pork cheese croquettes, currywurst, trout with spaetzle...". / albertsschloss.co.uk; @AlbertsSchloss; Mon-Sun 2 am.

ALMOST FAMOUS £29 4 3 3

100-102 HIGH ST M4 1HP 0161 244 9422

"Real dirty burgers" – including the dirty vegan (if that's not a contradiction in terms) 'Phok-Meat' – win excellent ratings at the founding branch of what is now a four-strong Northern group. / www.almostfamousburgers.com; @AlmostFamousNQ; Sun-Thu 10 pm, Fri & Sat 11 pm; No bookings.

AUSTRALASIA £63 3 3 4

**1 THE AVENUE SPINNINGFIELDS M3 3AP
0161 831 0288**

"From the same group as Grand Pacific but a major cut above in terms of food quality" – this "superglam" colonial-themed basement venue, off Deansgate, turns out some "scrumptious" Aussie/Asian-fusion sharing plates (plus afternoon teas, etc). "Given its rep as a 'beautiful people' hangout, in an act of inverse snobbery I'd been avoiding it – more fool me!". / www.australasia.uk.com; @AustralasiaMcr.

BAR SAN JUAN £34 4 3 4

56 BEECH RD M21 9EG 0161 881 9259

This "consistently fab, tiny tapas bar" on a Chorlton backstreet provides "a top, authentic Spanish experience" – and "attracts diners from Manchester and beyond". "The long queue to get in is all part of the fun!" / barsanjuan.com; Tue-Thu 11.30 pm, Fri & Sat midnight, Sun 11 pm.

THE BULL & BEAR

STOCK EXCHANGE HOTEL, 4 NORFOLK ST M2 1EW 0161 4703 901

Tom Kerridge will open in the latest incarnation of Manchester's imposing former Stock Exchange (soon to be relaunched as a luxury hotel) in November 2019. Chef Dan Scott will be at the stoves overseeing a menu in TV Tom's trademark style of refined British classics. If you're a Man U fan, though, head over to Old Trafford – to whom he signed up as caterer in October 2019 – and grab one of his pies on match days. / stockexchangehotel.co.uk; @StockExHotel.

BUNDOBUST £27 3 2 2

61 PICCADILLY M1 2AQ 0161 359 6757

"What a feast... you won't even notice it's vegetarian!" – "great street food and a cracking selection of craft beers" have won fame for this "atmospheric, slightly studenty haunt": "essentially a beer hall, but one in a chic post-industrial setting", and with Indian bites to soak up the brews. Mostly it copes well with its phenomenal popularity, but misfires ("looked better than it tasted") were a bit more common this year. / www.bundobust.com; @BundobustMCR; Mon-Thu 9.30 pm, Fri & Sat 10 pm, Sun 8 pm.

CHAOPHRAYA £47 3 3 3

19 CHAPEL WALKS, OFF CROSS STREET M2 1HN 0161 832 8342

This smart operation from the Thai Leisure Group has "returned to the top of the tree among conventional Thais in the city", thanks to some "unusual new dishes". Portions tend to be "generous". / www.chaophraya.co.uk; @ChaophrayaThai; Mon-Thu 10.30 pm, Fri & Sat 11 pm, Sun 9.30 pm.

THE CREAMERIES £39 3 3 2

406 WILBRAHAM ROAD, CHORLTON M21 0SD 0161 312 8328

Former Aumbry owner "Mary Ellen McTague is no longer cooking but she has left the stoves in excellent hands" at this award-winning yearling – a restaurant/wine bar/bottle shop, in an Edwardian creamery, with "basic" school benches. By day, the focus is on cakes, breads etc courtesy of co-owner/baker Sophie Yeoman. Come the evening, "small, light dishes from the minimal menu are cleverly executed" – albeit "not for those expecting a robust plate of food". / www.thecreameries.co.uk; @hellocreameries; Tue, Wed 3 pm, Thu-Sun 11 pm.

CROMA £38 333

1-3 CLARENCE ST M2 4DE
0161 237 9799

The "always reliable" flagship branch of this small Manchester chain in "an airy city-centre location" is "busy at times so you may have to book". Fans say it's "how PizzaExpress would be in a perfect world" (well, it is run by two folks who used to work for PE, and the interior was designed by Enzo Apicella, who created over 80 PizzaExpress outlets in his lifetime). / www.cromapizza.co.uk; @cromapizza; Mon-Sat 10 pm, Sun 9 pm; Take bookings all week via phone and/or online.

DISHOOM £36 435

MANCHESTER HALL, 36 BRIDGE STREET, SPINNINGFIELDS M3 3BT AWAITING TEL

"An outstanding addition to Manchester" – JKS Restaurants and Shamil Thakrar's phenomenal Indian street food chain is creating just as much of a stir up north, as it did in the big smoke, with its "refreshingly different, tasty and interesting" street food and "sumptuous" interior which makes "stylish use of an interesting space" (a grade II listed former Freemasons' lodge). The "very unusual breakfast" goes down well too. / www.dishoom.com; @Dishoom; Sun-Thu 11 pm, Fri & Sat midnight.

EVUNA £44 433

277 - 279 DEANSGATE M3 4EW
0161 819 2752

"Tapas as it should be" still gets a firm nod for this pioneer of Spanish food and wine in Manchester, a fixture on Deansgate for the past two decades. "The perfect setting for a romantic get-together or date", it "gets very busy" at times. A fourth branch opened in Altrincham in early 2019. / www.evuna.com; @evunamanchester; Wed-Sat 9.30 pm, Sun 3.30 pm; Take bookings all week via phone and/or online.

EL GATO NEGRO £46 434

52 KING STREET M2 4LY 0161 694 8585

"Deservedly Manchester's top destination" – this "vibrant" operation (which made the move into town from Ripponden three years ago) delivers a superb all-round experience. "It's the buzzing ambience of this multi-level townhouse and the great cocktails that really seal its appeal" though: "their sherry-tinged takes on an Old Fashioned and Espresso Martini make for a heady evening and the bar operation is slick, further boosting the vibe". Quibbles? – service under pressure can be "slightly chaotic". And although many diners say the tapas "is to die for", one or two reporters feel its repertoire is "classic" rather than utterly inspirational. / www.elgatonegrotapas.com; @ElGatoNegroFood.

GLAMOROUS £39 322

WING YIP BUS' CENTRE, OLDHAM RD M4 5HU 0161 839 3312

"One of the few places left where the dim sum still comes on trolleys", this "buzzing and handy" Cantonese has more than 300 dishes on the menu and is upstairs from the Wing Yip Oriental supermarket. The name strikes an unintentional ironic note – "it'll always be an eating hangar, but the quality seems to have taken an uptick". / www.glamorous-restaurant.co.uk; @glamorous_uk; Mon-Thu 11.30 pm, Fri & Sat midnight, Sun 11 pm; Take bookings all week via phone and/or online.

GREENS £46 333

43 LAPWING LN M20 2NT 0161 434 4259

TV chef Simon Rimmer's polished stalwart remains the "best vegetarian for miles", despite the rise of far more competition since he set up in 1990; the "varied menu" spans classics and more "adventurous" fare, and "homely portions" means you won't leave hungry. / www.greensdidsbury.co.uk; @greensveggie; Sun-Thu 9.30 pm, Fri & Sat 10 pm; No Amex.

HAWKSMOOR £65 444

184-186 DEANSGATE M3 3WB
0161 836 6980

"The stuff meaty dreams are made of!" – this "vibrant yet relaxed" outpost of the hipster steakhouse chain (which opened in 2015) is arguably the classiest all-rounder in Manchester. "The bar area may be a bit overwhelmingly clubby, but the main dining area is – at least at lunchtime – light and airy", occupying an impressively converted Victorian space, and with comfortable seating. Steaks are "amazing", "all the sides are also faultless" (not least "the best chips in the north west!"), and also "what is surprising is the quality of the seafood in what is a carnivore's delight". "Service is always top notch and the wine list is a dream". Sadly, though, the special offer whereby you can buy £4,500 bottles of wine for £300 has now finished! / www.thehawksmoor.com; @HawksmoorMCR; Mon-Sat 10.30 pm, Sun 9.30 pm; Take bookings all week via phone and/or online.

HISPI BISTRO £47 433

1C SCHOOL LANE M20 6RD
0161 445 3996

Celeb restaurateur, Gary Usher's "very reliable" Didsbury operation is nowadays the most commented-on member of his crowdfunded Elite Bistros chain, and one of Manchester's most popular destinations. That it's a bit "loud" is the worst charge anyone has to level at it – most reports merely praise its "brilliant" dishes, "relaxed" style and "very attentive" service. Top Menu Tip – "the custard tart is to die for". / www.hispi.net/; @HispiBistro; Sun-Thu 9 pm, Fri & Sat 10 pm; Take bookings all week via phone and/or online.

HOME £41 323

2 TONY WILSON PLACE M15
0161 212 3500

"Very handy for the cinema" (all five of them) at this art centre – or "for a quick bite" in general – this is a "very welcoming" café, whose pizzas and sharing platters do the trick. But "you'll need to book". / homemcr.org/visit/food-and-drink/; @HOME_mcr; Wed-Sat 8 pm, Sun 3 pm; Take bookings all week via phone and/or online.

IBÉRICA, SPINNINGFIELDS £47 323

14-15 THE AVENUE M3 3HF
01613 581 350

Every dish is "somewhere between good and very good" at the Spinningfields link in an eight-strong national chain that "remains competitive with the other top-end Manchester tapas joints". / www.ibericarestaurants.com; Mon & Tue, Sun 10 pm, Wed-Sat 11 pm.

INDIAN TIFFIN ROOM £45 322

2 ISABELLA BANKS STREET, FIRST STREET, M15 4RL 0161 228 1000

"A large and understandably popular South Indian restaurant, specialising in street food and dishes served in roadside restaurants, all delightfully fresh and cooked to order" – this "buzzy (and noisy)" modern glass-walled outfit in First Street has become a "go-to curry house in Manchester city centre" with its menu of idlis and dosas supplemented with grills and mains from across the subcontinent. The original ITR is in Cheadle, and there's a branch in Leeds. / www.indiantiffinroom.com/restaurants/manchester/; @Indtiffinroom; Mon-Fri 10 pm, Sat 10.30 pm, Sun 9.30 pm; Take bookings all week via phone and/or online.

INDIQUE £40 333

110-112 BURTON ROAD M20 1LP
0161 438 0241

An "exquisite menu" of "subtle and refined" Indian dishes goes down well at this "buzzy" modern outfit in West Didsbury. But perhaps they should "ditch the smoke-filled cloche: good theatre, but not sure what it did for flavour!" / www.indiquerestaurant.co.uk/; @IndiqueDidsbury; Mon-Fri 10.30 pm, Sat 11 pm.

THE IVY ASIA £52 334

THE PAVILION, BYROM STREET M3 3HG
0161 5033222

In a major departure for Richard Caring's Ivy group, the second floor of the new Ivy Spinningfields complex is an Asian formula. True to form, though, opulence is the key word for the décor, which includes a green floor made of semi-precious stone. It is, depending on your point of view, "a glorious, romantic setting for delicious food" or "pretentious and over-the-top"; but the overall ratings are stronger all-round here than at most of the other Ivy spin-offs; and either way, it's "great for people-

Paul Ainsworth at No. 6, Padstow

watching". (A second Ivy Asia is scheduled towards Christmas 2019 on the site of Jamie Oliver's Barbecoa (RIP) at St Paul's in London.) / theivymanchester.com; Mon-Wed midnight, Thu-Sat 3 am, Sun 11.30 pm.

THE IVY SPINNINGFIELDS £60 2 2 4

THE PAVILION, BYROM STREET M3 3HG 0161 5033222

One of the biggest restaurant openings of the year, The Ivy's foray into Manchester has four floors of dining rooms, with a separate pan-Asian operation on the second floor (see Ivy Asia), bar, private dining and roof garden. When it comes to the more conventional ground-floor brasserie, one early report paints a picture now familiar around the country: "If you look beneath the shiny surface, the food is overpriced and fayre average. It's fine so long as expectations aren't high... but they're built up by the glitz. Basically it's like Bill's in an expensive setting with a couple of quid added on to everything". / theivymanchester.com; Mon-Wed 11 pm, Thu-Sat 10.30 pm, Sun 10 pm.

JAMES MARTIN £59 4 4 2

2 WATSON ST M3 4LP 0161 820 9908

The TV host's "quirky" flagship restaurant wins high ratings despite its "interesting" (some would say iffy) location, upstairs at the Manchester235 casino. Head chef, Doug Crampton's cooking here is "a real pleasure" – "all dishes are prepared with great care and are a delight to eat". "Try the afternoon tea they recently introduced, very yummy!". / www.jamesmartinmanchester.co.uk; @JamesMartinMCR; Mon-Thu 10 pm, Fri & Sat 11 pm, Sun 5 pm; Take bookings all week via phone and/or online.

KALA £53 4 4 4

KING STREET M2 7AT 0800 160 1811

"Usher's best yet" say fans of Gary Usher's ambitious crowd-funded opening, which opened in a prominent corner site in the city-centre in May 2019. It beamed down very late for us to receive huge volumes of survey feedback, but such reports as we have say it's already a hit, with "friendly staff and cranking out 'fantastic' modern bistro fare in the trademark, deft 'Elite Bistros' style. / www.kalabistro.co.uk; @kala_manchester; Mon-Sat 10 pm.

KATSOURIS DELI £13 3 3 2

113 DEANSGATE M3 2BQ 0161 937 0010

"Top breakfast butties" are a good reason to head to this "ever busy" fixture, set in a Gothic-style building; others include filling ciabattas, the carvery and "particularly good value" platters. / www.katsourisdeli.co.uk; Mon-Fri 4.30 pm, Sat 4 pm, Sun 12 pm; No Amex.

THE LIME TREE £41 3 4 4

8 LAPWING LN M20 2WS 0161 445 1217

"We have been coming here for years with family members from children to 96 year olds, and have always enjoyed good food with the warmest of welcomes" – Patrick Hannity's appealing modern brasserie in Didsbury has been one of Manchester's top destinations since 1987, and "one word sums the place up: consistency" – "the menu appeals to all tastes", and "the service is class". / www.thelimetreerestaurant.co.uk; @thelimetreeres; Tue-Fri 10 pm, Sat 10.30 pm, Sun 6 pm.

LITTLE YANG SING £37 4 2 2

17 GEORGE ST M1 4HE 0161 228 7722

"Just a great Chinese restaurant (and a Manchester institution)" – this Cantonese basement operation in the heart of Chinatown was the first of the Yang Sing group to open, 40-odd years ago, and still wins good ratings all round, particularly its "tremendous food". / www.littleyangsing.co.uk.

LUNYA £46 3 4 3

BARTON ARCADE, DEANSGATE M3 2BW 0161 413 3317

"Very pleasant staff and an excellent tapas selection" (also parlayed in a well-stocked downstairs deli) are two good reasons to visit this "consistent" branch of a hit Scouse Spanish/Catalan operation, also recommended as a "good choice before or after a theatre visit". / www.lunya.co.uk/manchester; @lunyaMCR; Mon & Tue 9 pm, Wed & Thu 9.30 pm, Fri & Sat 10 pm, Sun 8.30 pm.

MACKIE MAYOR £35 3 3 5

1 EAGLE STREET M4 5JY NO TEL

"THE place to visit in Manchester!" – a grand listed Victorian building in the Northern Quarter, once a derelict meat market, now beautifully restored to host a selection of "very high-quality" street-food stalls. There's a "wonderful, buzzing atmosphere, and an amazing choice of food and drinks". / www.mackiemayor.co.uk; @MackieMayor; Tue-Thu 10 pm, Fri & Sat 11 pm, Sun 6 pm.

MANA £169 5 5 4

SAWMILL COURT M4 6AF 01613927294

"You know as soon as you enter that this is going to be something special"; Simon Martin guaranteed his place in the history books in October 2019 when this dazzling newcomer secured the city's first Michelin star in 40 years. "In part of Ancoats which has risen from waste ground in recent years, Mana looks like an anonymous office from the outside, with double (triple?) height net curtains over the large windows, and almost imperceptible signage". The interior itself is "beautifully designed" (by Chester design practice, James Roberts): "light and modern, with a breathtaking, completely open kitchen – you can actually walk between the work stations as the chefs are plating up". "The chef trained with Rene

Redzepi and brings back to Manchester some of his magic" – "Nordic-style" cuisine from a choice of 15-course or 18-course tasting menus that's "challenging in parts" but little short of "exquisite". "Contrary to fears that everything might be covered in moss, what's striking is how many dishes seem like 'real' food – there's a real flow to the menu, enhanced by excellent service, both from the actual front of house, and the chefs who come forward to serve some dishes". / www.manarestaurant.co.uk; @restaurant_mana; Wed-Sat 11 pm.

MI AND PHO £24 4 3 2

M22 4FZ 0161 312 3290

"A basic set-up", "no-great-shakes exterior" and "odd high street location" would all make this Vietnamese "easy to ignore", but "the stream of people visiting for lunch tells you it's doing something right" – that something being its "delicious" food ("taunted by my sister's tales of the places she'd been eating in around Asia, this made me feel like I was halfway there..."). / www.miandpho.com; @MiandPho; Tue-Fri, Sun 9 pm, Sat 10 pm.

MR COOPER'S, THE MIDLAND HOTEL £56 2 2 3

PETER ST M60 2DS 0161 235 4781

This famous five-star hotel's more casual dining option occupies a distinctively designed and pretty space, complete with indoor tree. It received more muted support this year, though, as a useful amenity for a light bite such as pre-theatre dining: other reports were limited, and more up-and-down. / www.mrcoopers.co.uk; @mrcoopersmcr; Mon-Sat 10 pm, Sun 8 pm; Take bookings all week via phone and/or online.

MUGHLI £32 4 3 4

30 WILMSLOW RD M14 5TQ 0161 248 0900

A veteran on Manchester's Curry Mile (est. 1991) – this "reliable" outfit has a crowd-pleasing menu of Indian/Pakistani street food and charcoal-singed dishes (including "lamb chops to die for"), best washed down either with one of the numerous craft beers or their funky twisted cocktails. / www.mughli.com; @mughli; Mon-Thu midnight, Fri & Sat 12.30 am, Sun 10.30 pm; Take bookings all week via phone and/or online.

PETER STREET KITCHEN, RADISSON BLU £40 3 3 4

FREE TRADE HALL, PETER STREET M2 5GP 0161 835 8941

Part of the Radisson occupying Manchester's iconic Free Trade Hall, this fusion yearling occupies a glossily designed space on the ground floor with floor-to-ceiling windows; and is one of the 'Kitchens' run by London's Edwardian group. Its unusual offer presents Japanese and Mexican small plates on separate menus, but – even if the prices are not bargain basement – all feedback is positive: "the food is so fresh, the tastes are clean and vibrant,

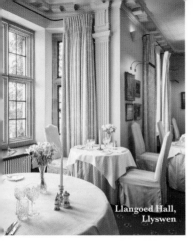

Llangoed Hall, Llyswen

I love it!" / www.peterstreetkitchen.co.uk; @peterst_kitchen; Mon-Sun 10.30 pm.

RANDALL & AUBIN £66 [4][4][4]

64 BRIDGE STREET M3 3BN
0161 711 1007

"Still good despite recent changes": this Spinningfields spin-off from London's foodie hub shares the "metropolitan", "fin de siècle" style of the original – "with high tables and bar stools" – and is still "an 'in' place to eat", having been bought out of administration in 2018 by founders Ed Baines and Jamie Poulton. It's famous for its "brilliant seafood" ("oysters are especially lovely, as are the lobsters") but the "eclectic menu" roams beyond the sea – and "even 'ordinary' dishes are done with flair". / www.randallandaubin.com; @randallandaubinmcr; Mon-Sun 11 pm; Booking lunch only.

RED CHILLI £38 [3][2][2]

70-72 PORTLAND STREET M1 4GU
0161 236 2888

An "adventurous menu" of "authentic, flavoursome and very Chinese food" – best of all Sichuanese dishes with a real kick – makes this Chinatown spot "well worth a visit". It has siblings near the university in Oxford Road, in Leeds and York. / redchillirestaurant.co.uk; Fri & Sat 11.30 pm, Sun-Thu 10.30 pm; Take bookings all week via phone and/or online.

REFUGE BY VOLTA £38 [3][3][4]

OXFORD STREET M60 7HA
0161 223 5151

A "magnificent", interiors-magazine-worthy setting in an old Victorian office block adds to the drama of a visit to this hip enterprise, by Justin Crawford and Luke Cowdrey, aka The Unabombers (also behind Electrik and Volta). The small plates generally hit the mark, the all-day Sunday roasts are "superb" and it's "great fun being able to finish off with a game of table football!". "We were a large motley crew and our waitress did a fantastic job accommodating everyone – from vegans to carnivores, toddlers to octogenarians". / www.refugemcr.co.uk; @TheRefugeMcr; Mon-Wed midnight, Fri & Sat

2 am, Thu 1 am, Sun 11.30 pm; Take bookings all week via phone and/or online.

RESTAURANT MCR £97 [5][4][4]

18-22 BRIDGE ST M3 3BZ 0161 835 2557

"Delighted that Aiden Byrne has re-opened, doing what he does best": this Spinningfields site, accessed via a lift – which formerly traded as Manchester House under Byrne – is at the centre of a revolving doors scenario which first saw the site lose Byrne to 20 Stories, then it closed, only for him next to return here in December 2018 as chef/patron, and relaunch it in its current guise. In the evening, the choice is between a six-course (£50) or nine-course (£75) tasting menu, and early reports say he is producing "exceptional food" in the same "lovely environment" with huge open kitchen as before. Its previous incarnation once looked like Manchester's best bet for a Michelin star in ages; with Mana's success, perhaps it might now be the best bet for a second? / www.restaurantmcr.com; @restaurantMCR; Tue-Thu 9.30 pm, Fri & Sat 10 pm.

ROSSO £76 [3][3][3]

43 SPRING GARDENS M2 2BG 0161 8321400

Going strong for a decade and looking good after a revamp – Rio Ferdinand's glossy Italian restaurant and cocktail bar in a "lovely listed building" with twin domed ceilings is rated well across the board for its "exceptional atmosphere" and "great food". / www.rossorestaurants.com; @rossorestaurants; Sun-Thu 10 pm, Fri & Sat 11 pm.

RUDYS PIZZA £31 [5][3][3]

9 COTTON STREET, ANCOATS, M4
07931 162059

"Taking pizza in the North West up a notch" – this "buzzing" local superstar is "located off a lovely square in trendy Ancoats" and has become a Mancunian foodie legend, thanks to its "simple-but-delicious Neapolitan pizzas": "definitely the best in town, with the dough made and stretched on site, and you can taste how fresh all of their ingredients are". "Be prepared to wait by grabbing a drink in one of the nearby bars and they will text you when your table is ready." There's also a newer, more central, branch on Peter Street. / www.rudyspizza.co.uk; @RudysPizzaMcr; Mon-Thu 10 pm, Fri & Sat 10.30 pm, Sun 9 pm; No bookings.

SALVIS £49 [3][3][3]

UNIT 22B, THE CORN EXCHANGE
0161 222 8021

A "fun and friendly Italian", in the Corn Exchange, featuring family recipes from Naples, with pasta and bread made daily on the premises. "Excellently prepared main courses are supplemented with delicacies available in the shop upstairs". There's also a branch in John Dalton Street. / www.salvismanchester.co.uk/; Take bookings all week via phone and/or online.

SAM'S CHOP HOUSE £51 [3][3][3]

BACK POOL FOLD OFF CROSS STREET M2 1HN 0161 834 3210

"LS Lowry at the bar" in the shape of a life-size bronze statue of Manchester's greatest artist – and "local Lancashire grub: what more is there to say?" This stalwart institution has served up classic dishes and traditional hospitality since 1872. "The beef hash remains one of my favourites and I will have a heart attack halfway through it one day, I'm sure!" / www.samschophouse.com; @chophousesams.

SAN CARLO £55 [3][2][5]

40 KING STREET WEST M3 2WY
0161 834 6226

"A see-and-be-seen venue" – this "vibrant and longstanding Italian" is one of the most successful in the national chain and one of the city-centre's key "glitzy" haunts. But whereas fans praise "great food, it at footballer prices", mere mortals can feel ignored: "staff are disinterested unless your face fits (i.e. you're a footballer or some other celeb!"). / www.sancarlo.co.uk; @SanCarlo_Group; Tue-Thu 10 pm, Fri & Sat 10.30 pm, Mon 9.30 pm, Sun 9 pm; Take bookings all week via phone and/or online.

SAN CARLO CICCHETTI £44 [3][3][4]

42 KING STREET WEST M3 2QG
0161 839 2233

With its menu of quality Venetian tapas, this bright city-centre staple (on the ground floor of Kendal's the department store, but with its own entrance) wins consistently good feedback from reporters. Those who find its glam namesake a bit snotty say "the service especially is miles better here than at its bigger sibling nearby". / www.sancarlocicchetti.co.uk; @SC_Cicchetti; Mon-Sat 11 pm, Sun 10 pm; Booking evening only.

SOLITA £42 [3][2][3]

37 TURNER ST M4 1DW 0161 839 2200

"Good-quality, well-cooked and inventive burgers – and some genius specials" (remember the 'Spam Allardyce'?) draw a steady stream of salivating carnivores to this Northern Quarter joint, "although the trademark barrage of social media seems to have calmed down this year, as has the constant invention/reinvention of new burgers". "The steaks are also some of the best around, and they make a decent bearnaise", as well as four different meat-free burgers. Outposts in Prestwich and Preston have closed down, but there's still one in Didsbury. / www.solita.co.uk; @SolitaNQ; Sun-Thu 10 pm, Fri & Sat 11 pm; Take bookings all week via phone and/or online.

THE SPARROWS £22

**UNIT 3, MIRABEL STREET M3 1PJ
07711 300116**

In a converted railway arch near Victoria Station – opposite the now-sadly-defunct Umezushi – this little 12-seater specialises in different varieties of pasta and dumplings from all over Europe: many of course of Italian inspiration, but including, for example, Polish pierogi. It opened after the survey had started in April 2019 – too late for feedback – but the word on the street is that it's very good. / www.thesparrows.me; Tue-Sat 10 pm, Sun 4 pm.

SUGO £50 5️⃣3️⃣2️⃣

**46 BLOSSOM STREET M4 6BF
0161 236 5264**

"Extremely authentic pasta from Puglia" ("you smell how fantastic it is going to be") has been successfully duplicated from the Altrincham original at this larger Ancoats spin-off, where "the wine is great value, served in painted jugs". "The minus has got to be the huge warehouse-y, new-build space, which is of a type that's abundant in Manchester, but cold and samey". / www.sugopastakitchen.co.uk/manchester; @Sugo_Pasta; Wed-Fri 4 pm, Sat & Sun 5 pm.

TAMPOPO £42 3️⃣2️⃣2️⃣

16 ALBERT SQ M2 5PF 0161 819 1966

This pan-Asian pleases the crowd with everything from Japanese ramen and Singaporean laksa to Thai red curry and Balinese pork belly. The Albert Square original has spawned five other sites across the city. / www.tampopo.co.uk; @TampopoEats; Mon-Wed 10.30 pm, Thu-Sat 11 pm, Sun 10 pm; May need 7+ to book.

TAPEO & WINE £44 3️⃣3️⃣3️⃣

209 DEANSGATE M3 3NW 0161 832 2770

"Delicious tapas but a great wine list as well, with loads by the glass" are the draw to this three-year-old operation, on Deansgate, which lures the local football VIPs (it's run by United's Juan Mata and his padre, Juan Manuel, no less). / tapeoandwine.com; @TapeoandWine; Mon-Sat 11 pm, Sun 10 pm.

TAST CUINA CATALANA £39 3️⃣3️⃣3️⃣

**20-22 KING STREET M2 6AG
0161 806 0547**

"A fantastic addition to Manchester's burgeoning Spanish scene" – chef Paco Perez opened this Catalonian newcomer with a bit of help from Pep Guardiola and other Man City grandees. "It's a few doors down from El Gato Negro and must be giving it a run for its money, although it could certainly be argued that they're so different in both style and food that, apart from both being restaurants, they're hardly direct competitors". Reports mostly are enthusiastic about its "modern and flavoursome" Catalan small plates ('Tastets' – 'more complex than tapas but smaller than a plate'), but also note that they're "not cheap".

There's also an "interesting, if surprisingly brief Catalan wine list, with prices that accelerate nearly as fast as a Manchester City player's Lamborghini!" / www.tastcatala.com; @TastCatala; Tue-Thu midnight, Fri & Sat 1 am, Sun 11 pm.

TATTU £62 2️⃣3️⃣4️⃣

**3 HARDMAN SQ, GARTSIDE ST M3 3EB
0161 819 2060**

"A great see-and-be-seen atmosphere" – Adam and Drew Jones's expanding, Chinese, national chain is characterised by "superb surroundings" and as a result its Manchester branch (the chain's first, which opened in 2015) is "understandably one of the most popular venues in town". But there's a general feeling that "it's nice looking but could do better" – "surroundings set an excellent first impression but I expected more of the food" ("on our visit, we couldn't spot anyone Chinese in the kitchen, and it showed"); "and it's pricey too". "Overall there are better Chinese restaurants in Manchester... they're not as striking though". / www.tattu.co.uk; @tatturestaurant; Mon-Thu 10.30 pm, Fri-Sun 10.45 pm; No trainers; Take bookings all week via phone and/or online.

THIS & THAT £24 4️⃣2️⃣2️⃣

3 SOAP ST M4 1EW 0161 832 4971

"Can't beat it!" for "big platefuls of steaming, flavour-packed curries for not much dosh!" – this brilliantly named curry house ("just point at what's on offer and he dollops it on your plate") has been a Northern Quarter institution for 35 years. Family-run, it's "a model of consistency", and hugely popular for its offer of "rice and three different curries for £6". "There's talk of redevelopment for new offices, but a lot of the office workers in the area will protest loudly!!" / www.thisandthatcafe.co.uk; Mon-Thu 4.30 pm, Fri & Sat 8 pm, Sun 4 pm; Cash only.

TNQ RESTAURANT & BAR £54 3️⃣4️⃣2️⃣

108 HIGH ST M4 1HQ 0161 832 7115

This "excellent, reasonably priced neighbourhood spot in the Northern Quarter always delivers" with its "surprisingly affordable and beautifully presented high-end food" – "everyone should have a reliable, high-quality local like this in their area!" / www.tnq.co.uk; @TNQrestaurant; Mon-Sat 10.30 pm, Sun 7 pm; Take bookings all week via phone and/or online.

20 STORIES £59 2️⃣2️⃣5️⃣

NO 1 SPINNINGFIELDS, 1 HARDMAN SQUARE M3 3JE 0161 204 3333

The rooftop restaurant, bar and terrace at Manchester's new 95-metre 1 Spinningfields Tower has "superb views across the city ... even if much of its immediate location is currently a building site, you can see for miles". The food offering – from D&D London – has struggled to impress, and the departure of highly rated chef Aiden Byrne within a year of launch did not help matters. But "you don't come here for the food (which is significantly overpriced for

what it is). Far better just to go for a drink and take in the fantastic panorama". / 20stories.co.uk; @20StoriesMCR; Sun-Thu midnight, Fri & Sat 2 am.

WHITWORTH ART GALLERY £30 2️⃣2️⃣4️⃣

THE UNIVERSITY OF MANCHESTER, OXFORD RD M15 6ER 0161 275 7511

"You would not realise you are in Moss Side" at the Whitworth's "beautiful" and "family-friendly" glass-walled conservatory, overlooking Whitworth Park. Its location (above all) and victuals make it an "excellent place for lunch", with the "three daily changing salads particularly recommended". / www.whitworth.manchester.ac.uk; @WhitworthArt; Mon-Wed, Fri-Sun 5 pm, Thu 9 pm; Booking evening only.

WING'S £48 4️⃣4️⃣4️⃣

1 LINCOLN SQ M2 5LN 0161 834 9000

"High-end traditional Chinese cuisine at its best" and "exceptional service" win a chorus of praise for Wing Shing Chu's smart city-centre Cantonese, which has welcomed millions of pounds-worth of United and City players, their WAGs and other celebs through its doors over the past two decades. / www.wingsrestaurant.co.uk; Mon-Sat 10.30 pm, Sun 11 pm; children: 11+ after 8 pm Mon-Fri.

WOOD RESTAURANT £56 2️⃣3️⃣3️⃣

**JACK ROSENTHAL STREET M15 4RA
0161 236 5211**

MasterChef winner Simon Wood's debut venture occupies a "loud and buzzy" modern unit, complete with open kitchen; it opened in September 2017, not far from Home Manchester. Fans "love Simon's food – especially the blind tasting menu" (all 10 courses of it), but a fair number of those drawn by his name and early hype felt that "everything was OK, but we were expecting a lot more... especially for the high prices!" / www.woodmanchester.com; @woodrestaurants.

YANG SING £44 4️⃣2️⃣2️⃣

**34 PRINCESS STREET M1 4JY
0161 236 2200**

"Still smashing it after all these years: there's no better dim sum to be had in MCR" – that's the view, particularly of some of our most consistent reporters, on Harry & Bonnie Yeung's famous Chinatown destination: they say it's still "on balance probably the best up-market Chinese restaurant in the north of England and deservedly popular for its dim sum and banquets". And "closer to its roots than Manchester's other 'high end' oriental places – cheaper Chinatown eating houses come close to equalling it, but lack its long-term consistency". So to such supporters "it's a mystery why it seems more quiet nowadays when in the past, you had to queue down the stairs". But undoubtedly it takes more flak these days, from some who comment on its "faded glory" and "rather flat and dull" dishes – negative feedback that pulls it down from the 5/5 food rating that it enjoyed for so long. But we will leave the last word to a lifelong regular: "I have been eating the Yeung family's cooking since they worked for Charlie Chan at the 'San Ho' and while there have been highs, even higher highs, and one or two meals that were merely above-average, I cannot remember anything that was disappointing over the years, except as judged by the very highest standards". Top Menu Tip – "shredded mooli pastries have the lightest flakiest pastry I've ever come across, and how they get such flavour out of mooli is verging on the alchemical". / www.yang-sing.com; @yangsingmcr; Take bookings all week via phone and/or online.

MARAZION, CORNWALL 1–4A

BEN'S CORNISH KITCHEN £50 5|4|3

WEST END TR17 0EL 01736 719200

"Always worth the trip to Marazion for such a treat", Ben & Jayne Prior's "relaxed and simple" seaside bistro serves absolutely "top-notch" food (especially fish) that's "fantastic value". / www.benscornishkitchen.com; @cornishkitchen; Take bookings all week via phone and/or online.

MARGATE, KENT 3–3D

THE AMBRETTE £53 4|4|3

10 FORT HILL CT9 1QE 01843 231 504

"Amazing and very different" Indian "fusion" cuisine (fans say it's "better than Benares in London") inspires nothing but praise for Dev Biswal's "buzzy" Margate HQ, opposite the Turner Gallery – and with outposts in Canterbury and Rye. In 2018 it relocated to the former Hoy pub after eight years at its original King Street site, and the "much more comfortable" surrounds contribute to make a visit a "real joy". / www.theambrette.co.uk; @the_ambrette; Mon-Thu 9.30 pm, Fri & Sat midnight, Sun 10.30 pm; Take bookings all week via phone and/or online.

ANGELA'S £50 5|4|3

21 THE PARADE CT9 1EX 01843 319978

Lee Coad and Charlotte Forsdike's "homely" two-year-old is proving "a great addition to the local food scene": "a tiny (so slightly cramped), bright, café-style resto" (26 covers, plus open kitchen) "near the front in the chic part of hipster Margate". The focus is on fish and "sustainability is at the heart of everything they do"; the end result is food that's "unussy" but "sublime" alongside service that's "warm and friendly" (if "at the limits of what's possible in the space"). "Hard to get into but definitely worth persevering!" / angelasofmargate.com; @angelas_margate; Wed-Sat 9 pm, Sun 3 pm.

BUOY & OYSTER £63 4|4|3

44 HIGH STREET CT9 1DS 01843 446631

"Lifting the area of Margate!" – this family-run bistro boasts large windows with sweeping views over the sands and an outside terrace for sunny days. All reports are of "fantastic" food from the menu which majors in fish and seafood. / www.buoyandoyster.com; @BuoyandOyster.

DORY'S £19

24 HIGH STREET CT9 1DS 01843 520 391

No reservations and counter-stool seating keep things informal at this new spin-off from Angela's: an all-day seafood bar. Too few reports for a rating as yet, but such feedback as we have is very upbeat. / angelasofmargate.com; @angelas_margate.

GB PIZZA £35 4|3|2

14A MARINE DRIVE CT9 1DH 01843 297 700

"Unusual toppings on wafer thin crusts" – the best pizza for many miles around – "compensate for the basic amenities" at this "friendly" sea-front venture, as does its "top seaside view". / www.greatbritishpizza.com; @gbPizzaCo; Take bookings all week via phone and/or online.

HANTVERK & FOUND £44 3|3|3

18 KING STREET CT9 1DA 01843 280 454

Scandi-influenced small eatery and gallery that's become one of the best known in Shoreditch on Sea, thanks to its "friendly service and interesting food" – primarily fish, and also some local cheeses and charcuterie (plus one or two veggie options). Opening in winter 2019, a neighbouring natural wine bar from the same team, so that visiting hipsters feel even more at home, called 'Big Naturals'. / www.hantverk-found.co.uk; @Hantverk_found; Fri & Sat 10 pm, Thu 9.30 pm, Sun 4 pm; Take bookings all week via phone and/or online.

MARKET HARBOROUGH, LEICESTERSHIRE 5–4D

ASCOUGH'S BISTRO £40 3|3|2

24 ST MARY'S ROAD LE16 7DU 01858 466 966

"Everything is cooked well and flavourful" at this modern brasserie in the centre of town. "It may be unfair to label it as cheap 'n' cheerful, but it's certainly very good value". / www.ascoughsbistro.co.uk/; practically no walk-ins – you must book.

MARLBOROUGH, WILTSHIRE 2–2C

THE HARROW AT LITTLE BEDWYN £94 4|4|4

LITTLE BEDWYN SN8 3JP 01672 870871

"An astonishing breadth of wines for a small restaurant" is the key feature at this well-known pub-conversion, set far out in the sticks, and the "extremely knowledgeable staff, including Sue Jones the owner", give "excellent guidance on the list". On all accounts, however, the food is "fantastic" too, and there are "exceptional and imaginative wine pairings with the tasting menu". "Well worth the trek". / www.theharrowatlittlebedwyn.co.uk; @littlebedwyn; No trainers; Credit card deposit required to book.

RICK STEIN £68

LLORAN HOUSE, 42A HIGH STREET SN8 1HQ 01672 233333

"If you like fish, this is the place to be" say fans of the Stein empire's upmarket brasserie, which occupies a fine period building (Lloran House) on the high street. But while favourable feedback still says it's "a very enjoyable experience", it elicited remarkably few reports this year compared to last, so we've left a rating till next year. / www.rickstein.com/eat-with-us/marlborough/; @SteinMarlb; Mon-Sat 10 pm, Sun 9 pm; Take bookings all week via phone and/or online.

MARLOW, BUCKINGHAMSHIRE 3–3A

THE COACH £50 4|4|4

3 WEST STREET SL7 2LS 01628 483013

"Just a delight all round" – seldom is a bad word said about Tom Kerridge's 'other' pub in this Thames valley town: an "extremely crowded and very buzzy" haunt that is also "lovely and chilled". "You don't need to book a table and you can order the plates tapas-style": "the food is so good". / www.thecoachmarlow.co.uk; @TheCoachMarlow; Mon-Sat 9.30 pm, Sun 9 pm; No bookings.

HAND & FLOWERS £115 2|2|2

WEST STREET SL7 2BP 01628 482277

"Tom Kerridge's (wonderful) versions of pub grub" mean there are still many reporters who "can't wait to go back" to his immensely popular and consequently "overcrowded" Thames-valley gastropub, which owes its mighty reputation to Michelin's award of a rare two stars, back in 2012. It was a questionable decision from the start, but could be glossed over at the time by the Hand & Flowers' undeniably crowd-pleasing performance. However, ratings here have been in decline for years now, and it's reaching a point where this down-to-earth hostelry is starting to seem "seriously overhyped". It doesn't help that TV Tom's opened The Coach "literally down the road" which is "more fun" and has better scoff. And with this celebrity chef's multiple other openings in London and Manchester, "Is TK just too stretched to keep control?". (There's also the question of when Michelin will finally stop slumbering and take away one or both stars here). / www.thehandandflowers.co.uk; @HandFMarlow; Mon & Tue, Thu-Sat 9.30 pm, Sun 3.30 pm, Wed midnight; Take bookings all week via phone and/or online.

THE IVY MARLOW GARDEN £56 2|2|4

66-68 HIGH ST SL7 1AH 01628 902 777

While it's generally agreed to be a "good addition to the Marlow scene", with a "nice ambience" and in particular "a beautifully glamorous room" – this Thames Valley link in the national chain Richard Caring has spun out from the 1980s West End celeb haunt attracts familiar criticisms. Too often it's "a bit of a disappointment" – "a little pricey for albeit fancy comfort food" – and just too obviously samey: "couldn't each restaurant have a unique signature dish appropriate to the location?" / www.theivymarlowgarden.com; @iymarlowgarden; Mon-Sun 12.30 am.

SINDHU, MACDONALD COMPLEAT ANGLER HOTEL £75 `4` `3` `3`

THE COMPLEAT ANGLER SL7 1RG 01628 405 405

Atul Kochhar is celebrating his fifth year in this "fabulous riverside location". As experiences go, it's "as refined as curry gets", with "wonderful" modern dishes (if in slightly "small portions") and "beautiful views over the River Thames" from its traditional, leaded windows. "Hotel restaurants are never supposed to be this good in the UK, especially in the home counties!" / www.sindhurestaurant.co.uk; @SindhuMarlow; Mon-Sat 10 pm, Sun 9.30 pm.

THE VANILLA POD £67 `5` `3` `3`

31 WEST ST SL7 2LS 01628 898101

"You are always well looked after" at Michael Macdonald's "tiny" venture – a timbered room in a house once owned by TS Eliot. Many who report on it are regulars: "best value in town…"; "not one but several excellent meals this year…"; "sublime consistent food without a doubt, as I have been about thirty times – just perfect with fish and the only place in the world I eat pudding!" / www.thevanillapod.co.uk.

MARPLE, GREATER MANCHESTER 5–2B

ANGKOR SOUL £32 `3` `3` `2`

12 STOCKPORT RD SK6 6BJ 0161 222 0707

"All the Cambodian food is tasty and authentic", and for lunch they serve "flavoursome" soups, filled baguettes and noodle dishes at this "small and cramped" operation – which (with its spin-offs) is quite possibly the only restaurant of its type in northern England. In the basement they buy and sell second-hand vinyl – hence the name. Branches have now opened in Altrincham and, most recently, Stockport market. / www.angkorsoul.co.uk; @angkor_soul; Wed-Sat 11 pm, Tue 3 pm.

THE FISHERMAN'S TABLE £43 `4` `3` `2`

103 CHURCH LANE SK6 7AR 0161 536 4389

A "new restaurant serving ultra-fresh fish from Fleetwood" (but also Shetland scallops, Irish sea trout and Cornish monkfish), set up by fishmonger Jamie Barrett, who owns the Marple Fish shop round the corner. A former car spares shop, it's now a hybrid country-pub and beach shack, style-wise. / www.thefishermanstable.co.uk; Tue-Sat 10 pm, Sun 8 pm.

Stones, Matlock

MARTLEY, WORCESTERSHIRE 2–1B

THE ADMIRAL RODNEY £45

BERROW GREEN WR6 6PL 01905 886 181

Limited but all-round positive feedback on this relative newcomer – a country inn with rooms, relaunched in mid 2018, and serving a brasserie-style menu majoring in steak (also with lighter options at lunch). / www.admiral-rodney.co.uk/; Mon-Sat 9 pm, Sun 8 pm; Take bookings all week via phone and/or online.

MARTON, CHESHIRE 5–2B

LA POPOTE £67 `3` `4` `3`

CHURCH FARM, MANCHESTER ROAD SK11 9HF 01260 224785

This "lovely, small French restaurant with a delightful garden" wins steady praise from fans for its "unhurried and meticulous service" and "exceptional food", although its ratings were held back this year by those who judge its performance to be more middling. Dutch-born proprietor Victor Janssen celebrated his 55th anniversary as a chef last year, and opened La Popote 10 years ago with his Scottish wife, Lynne, after stints in South Africa and the Scottish Highlands. / la-popote.co.uk; @LaPopoteUK; Wed-Sat 11 pm, Sun 6 pm.

MASHAM, NORTH YORKSHIRE 8–4B

SAMUEL'S, SWINTON PARK HOTEL & SPA £80 `3` `3` `4`

SWINTON PARK HG4 4JH 01765 680900

With its gold-leaf decoration, the stylish dining room of this grand country house hotel and spa provides a traditionally luxurious backdrop to a meal. But ratings have come off the boil a little with personnel changes. Mehdi Amiri – in post since mid-2017 – sometimes gave reporters the impression that "the sheer confidence and assurance typically found here was lacking". He himself then moved on after our survey in summer 2019. We have maintained this year's survey scores on the bet that further changes are more likely to be positive than negative, but further upheavals may be afoot. / www.swintonestate.com/eating; @swintonestate; No jeans; children: 8+ at D.

MATFIELD, KENT 3–4B

THE POET £51 `4` `3` `4`

MAIDSTONE RD TN12 7JH 01892 722416

"A revelation in West Kent which is starved of good quality restaurants" – this seventeenth-century pub is "a gem hidden in a quiet village", where South African Petrus Madutlela and his team deliver an "excellent and varied menu including à la carte, table d'hote and specials – all to a very high standard". Top Tip – Tuesday evening can be "overflowing" for their steak and malbec deal (£44.95 for two). / thepoetatmatfield.co.uk/; @poetatmatfield; Tue-Thu 9 pm, Fri & Sat 9.30 pm, Sun 4 pm; Take bookings all week via phone and/or online.

MATLOCK, DERBYSHIRE 5–2C

STONES £60 `4` `4` `4`

1C DALE RD DE4 3LT 01629 56061

"Excellent in every way" – Kevin Stone's modern British cooking with Mediterranean flourishes is showcased at the pretty restaurant he runs with his wife Jade and sister Katie, perched above the River Derwent (and with a terrace for sunny days). Prices are brilliant for food of this quality, with an eight-course tasting menu at £52. / www.stones-restaurant.co.uk; @stonesmatlock; Wed, Tue, Thu-Sat 8.30 pm; No Amex; No shorts; Take bookings all week via phone and/or online.

MAWGAN PORTH, CORNWALL 1–3B

THE SCARLET HOTEL £73 `3` `2` `4`

TREDRAGON RD TR8 4DQ 01637 861800

Views over gorgeous Mawgan Porth beach help set a very "romantic" tone at this 10-year-old spa hotel, where you can be sure you won't be interrupted by the kids (as the entire property is 'adults-only'). Food is served from breakfast onwards, with a three-course format in the evening: straightforward modern British cuisine that's very "sound". / www.scarlethotel.co.uk.

MAYFIELD, EAST SUSSEX 3–4B

MIDDLE HOUSE £51 `3` `3` `3`

HIGH STREET TN20 6AB 01435 872146

Dominating the high street of the village, this Grade I-listed Elizabethan inn, with its wattle-and-daub infill, was built for financier Sir Thomas Gresham, who kept Elizabeth I's privy purse; the newly extended restaurant and old-world pub offers a large array of fine pubby food from Ploughman's to heartier grub. / www.themiddlehousemayfield.co.uk; Mon-Sat 9.30 pm, Sun 9 pm.

MENAI BRIDGE, GWYNEDD 4–1C

DYLAN'S RESTAURANT £45 3 2 3

ST GEORGE'S ROAD LL59 5EY
01248 716 714

"Excellent views" of the Menai Straits through its large, floor-to-ceiling windows are a defining feature of this modern, timber-clad café by the water (which also has spin-offs in Criccieth and Llandudno). Seafood dishes are served alongside more everyday staples like pizza, but while some reports praise the overall quality of the offering, others are less certain: "is it because everywhere on Anglesey (apart from Sosban) is so mediocre that we all love Dylan's?" / www.dylansrestaurant.co.uk; @dylansNWales; Take bookings all week via phone and/or online.

SOSBAN AND THE OLD BUTCHER'S £120 5 4 3

1 HIGH ST, MENAI BRIDGE LL59 5EE
01248 208 131

Stephen & Bethan Stevens's converted butcher's shop is the "best in North Wales" – (surprise) menus morph daily to take account of supply, so "you get what is on offer – all local and fresh", and uniformly "terrific". Top Tip – "booking is a MUST, as it may be months before a table becomes available". / www.sosbanandtheoldbutchers.com; @The_oldbutchers; Thu-Sat 11 pm; Take bookings all week via phone and/or online.

MIDDLETON TYAS, NORTH YORKSHIRE 8–4B

THE COACH HOUSE £54 3 3 3

MIDDLETON LODGE ESTATE, KNEETON LANE DL10 6NJ 01325 377977

Set in 200 acres of North Yorkshire, this informal bar/brasserie is an "interesting conversion of stables attached to the main house" (there is also a posher dining option here, 'The Forge'). An all-day operation, it offers food that's "reliable and well presented" from a series of menus, including breakfast, afternoon tea and dinner (with the focus on Mediterranean char grills). / www.middletonlodge.co.uk/coach-house-restaurant; @MiddletonLodge.

MIDHURST, HAMPSHIRE 3–4A

LA PIAZZETTA £38 3 3 2

4 WEST STREET GU29 9NQ
01730 817 040

"A snip or three above the best chains: a pretty noisy, but very good, pizza spot in the centre of this old market town" – an "Italian staple" with a "good and fairly priced menu". / www.lapiazzettamidhurst.com.

MILFORD-ON-SEA, HAMPSHIRE 2–4C

VERVEINE FISHMARKET RESTAURANT £64 5 4 3

98 HIGH ST SO41 0QE 01590 642 176

"An unusual concept: you tell the server if there's anything you don't like and how many courses you want and they will concoct a menu around that – mainly fish but with the occasional meat item". That's the deal at David Wykes's "small-but-exciting" ten-year-old where "everything is presented beautifully, the taste is superb and service efficient and friendly". "Go out of your way to visit!" / www.verveine.co.uk; @98verveine; No Amex.

MISTLEY, ESSEX 3–2D

THE MISTLEY THORN RESTAURANT & ROOMS £45 3 3 3

HIGH ST CO11 1HE 01206 392 821

"A lovely little place" with "great seafood" by the river Stour, this early-eighteenth-century inn "keeps high standards", is "always buzzing" and "worth a stay". Californian owner Sherri Singleton has run it and the cookery school next door for 20 years. / www.mistleythorn.com; @mistleythorn; Mon-Sun 9.30 pm; Take bookings all week via phone and/or online.

MOIRA, COUNTY ARMAGH 10–2D

WINE AND BRINE £59 4 4 3

59 MAIN ST BT67 0LQ 028 9261 0500

"The ingredients are fresh, local and put together with verve" at Chris McGowan's four-year-old. The Great British Menu star, who worked for Richard Corrigan and Pierre Koffmann, brought newfound contemporary techniques such as brining and fermenting to small-town Co Down – executed with "exceptional dedication" and "warm and professional service". / www.wineandbrine.co.uk; @wine_brine; Wed-Sat 9.30 pm, Sun 6 pm; Take bookings all week via phone and/or online.

MORECAMBE, LANCASHIRE 5–1A

MIDLAND HOTEL £53 4 4 5

MARINE ROAD WEST LA4 4BU
01524 424000

"The glamour of the building competes with the beauty of the outlook" at this "superb Art Deco hotel with the most beautiful views across Morecambe Bay, which makes this a fabulous location for dinner". "Better still, the food is very good!" – Lancastrian sourced, and in an elegant, modern British style. There's also a "quintessential afternoon tea, with perfect sandwiches, scones and cakes", while "it's worth staying over for the breakfast – and the view of the birdlife on the shore". / www.englishlakes.co.uk; @englishlakes; Mon-Sun 9.30 pm.

MORETON-IN-MARSH, GLOUCESTERSHIRE 2–1C

THE FOX INN £47 3 3 4

LOWER ODDINGTON GL56 0UR
01451 870 555

This gentrified, ivy-covered Cotswolds inn, handily placed for Stow-on-the-Wold and Daylesford Organic, is "excellent in every way": decent real ales, comfortable setting and British cuisine which, while "not cheap", is "very, very good". / thefoxatoddington.com/; @foxinn; Mon-Sat 11 pm, Sun 6 pm; No Amex; Take bookings all week via phone and/or online.

MORSTON, NORFOLK 6–3C

ANCHOR INN £52 4 3 3

THE STREET NR25 7AA 01263 741392

"Relaxed, friendly" and a "brilliant pub", just along the coast from Blakeney, which was taken over by old school friends in 2011, and swiftly given a retro, nautical refurb'; the "delicious menu" takes in local north Norfolk catch and game. / www.morstonanchor.co.uk; @morstonanchor.

MORSTON HALL £118 5 4 5

MAIN COAST RD NR25 7AA
01263 741041

Galton Blackiston's well-known country house establishment has a gorgeous location, near the north Norfolk coast. Long known as a major culinary destination, it inspired no negative commentary this year, but rather very consistent praise for its "faultless" all-round performance. "The nightly menu is never the same but dictated by the available ingredients, and the preparation is exceptional". / www.morstonhall.com; @MorstonHall; Mon-Sat 10.30 pm, Sun ; Take bookings all week via phone and/or online.

MOULTON, CAMBRIDGESHIRE 3–1C

THE PACKHORSE INN £55 3 2 2

BRIDGE ST CB8 8SP 01638 751818

A "smart pub/restaurant" with "old-school furnishings in a lovely country setting"; add in "very friendly staff" and very enjoyable food, and it's a winner all round. / www.thepackhorseinn.com; @Moultopackhorse; Sun-Thu 11 pm, Fri & Sat midnight; Take bookings all week via phone and/or online.

MOUNTSORREL, LEICESTERSHIRE 5–4D

JOHN'S HOUSE £82 5 4 3

139-141 LOUGHBOROUGH ROAD LE12 7AR 01509 415569

"Everything is first class" at chef John Duffin's acclaimed venture set on his family's farm (which provides much of the produce for the menu). His seasonal cuisine (with the option of a seven-course blow-out) delivers a "superb" "taste-sensation" and yet it "does not try too hard". Staff provide an "immediate warm welcome" and "obviously care about what they do". Top Tip – "Set lunch is very good value for such top notch food". / www.johnshouse.co.uk; @JohnsHouseRest; No Amex; Jacket & tie required; Take bookings all week via phone and/or online.

MOUSEHOLE, CORNWALL — 1–4A

THE OLD COASTGUARD £34 [4][3][4]

THE PARADE TR19 6PR 01736 731222

A "perfect setting" looking out to the sea and St Michael's Mount awaits at this "laidback", boutique-ish hotel dining room, where the current regime – shared with the Gurnard's Head – turn out "exceedingly tasty" fish-centric food. STOP PRESS: In June 2019, there was a fire, and until early 2020, the Old Coastguard team will be cooking at The Vault (17-18 Market Pl, Penzance TR18 2JP - tel 01736 733033). / www.oldcoastguardhotel.co.uk; @leroundhouse; Mon-Sun 9 pm; Take bookings all week via phone and/or online.

2 FORE STREET RESTAURANT £46 [4][5][3]

2 FORE ST TR19 6PF 01736 731164

With his "varied and interesting menu" of "delicious local produce", Raymond Blanc-trained chef Joe Wardell knows how to "totally blow you away", say fans of his long-established harbourside cottage. Given the setting, a short walk from the quay, it's no surprise to find "really fresh fish, with inventive things done to it" – and the tarte tatin is pretty special, too. / www.2forestreet.co.uk; @.2forestreet.co.uk; Sun-Thu 11 pm, Fri & Sat 11.30 pm; Take bookings all week via phone and/or online.

MUDEFORD, CORNWALL — 2–4C

NOISY LOBSTER £50 [3][3][3]

BH23 4AN 01425 272162

"They still queue at this popular, all-year-round, beachfront diner, despite having added an extension". Seafood is not surprisingly the main focus, but there are plenty of alternatives for the fish-fearful, while breakfast and brunch are also a big feature. / avon-beach.noisylobster.co.uk; @thenoisylobster; Mon-Sat 11 pm, Sun 5 pm; Take bookings all week via phone and/or online.

MURCOTT, OXFORDSHIRE — 2–1D

THE NUT TREE INN £76 [4][4][3]

MAIN STREET OX5 2RE 01865 331253

The "quality" of the food is exceptional ("soufflés are a must!") at Mike & Imogen North's "pleasant" and "understated", fifteenth-century thatched pub in rural Oxfordshire (which is still a proper pub, despite its vaunted culinary reputation). "The accessible tasting menu sensibly draws from the main menu, offering a genuine tasting experience, with solidly conceived and well-balanced flavours in each dish". / www.nuttreeinn.co.uk; @nuttreeinn/; Tue-Sat 11 pm, Sun 6 pm; Booking max 4 may apply.

MUTHILL, PERTH AND KINROSS — 9–3C

BARLEY BREE £65 [3][4][2]

6 WILLOUGHBY ST PH5 2AB 01764 681451

"Inventive French cuisine with fine Scottish produce", and "wonderful service" too, make it worth taking a detour from Gleneagles (just down the road) to visit Fabrice & Alison Bouteloup's "highly recommended restaurant-with-rooms". / www.barleybree.com; @barleybree6; Wed-Sat 9 pm, Sun 7.30 pm; No Amex; Take bookings all week via phone and/or online.

NAILSWORTH, GLOUCESTERSHIRE — 2–2B

WILD GARLIC £54 [3][3][2]

3 COSSACKS SQ GL6 0DB 01453 832615

Matthew Bearshall's fixture has become a "favourite" in this part of the world, and wins consistent praise for its mix of brunch dishes, sharing plates, steaks and other bistro fare. For more ambitious cooking, nowadays, there is also his nearby venue, Wilder (see also). / www.wild-garlic.co.uk; @TheWildGarlic; Wed-Sat 9.30 pm, Sun 2.30 pm; No Amex.

WILDER £92 [3][3][2]

MARKET STREET GL6 0BX 01453 835483

Sibling to nearby Wild Garlic, Matthew Bearshall's more ambitious venture concentrates on a daily-changing eight-course tasting menu format. All locals agree that results are "skillful" in their realization, but opinions divide on the level of value – "outstanding" to some but "expensive for these parts" to others. / www.wild-garlic.co.uk; @dinewilder; Wed-Fri 4 pm, Sat & Sun 5 pm.

NANTGAREDIG, CARMARTHENSHIRE — 4–4C

Y POLYN £59 [4][3][3]

CAPEL DEWI SA32 7LH 01267 290000

Mark & Sue Manson's rural Welsh pub/restaurant is becoming an "old favourite" in this neck of the woods (it's now twelve years old). Strong points are meat and seasonal fish and they "now also have a range of local-ish gins at the bar as an added inducement" for a visit. "A bit off the beaten track, but very much worth the detour, as they say in the guides". / www.ypolyn.co.uk; @YPolyn; Tue-Thu 9 pm, Fri & Sat 9.30 pm, Sun 2.30 pm; Take bookings all week via phone and/or online.

NETHER BURROW, CUMBRIA — 7–4D

THE HIGHWAYMAN £47 [3][3][3]

BURROW LA6 2RJ 01524 273 338

This "very lively pub" in the gorgeous Lune Valley offers notably "good food and welcoming atmosphere". Its recent acquisition by the growing Brunning & Price empire seems to have "sparked it up" to general satisfaction. / www.brunningandprice .co.uk/highwayman/homepage/; @highwayman_inn; Sun-Thu 9.30 pm, Fri & Sat

10 pm; Take bookings all week via phone and/or online.

NETHER WESTCOTE, OXFORDSHIRE — 2–1C

THE FEATHERED NEST INN £90

OX7 6SD 01993 833 030

"Fantastic views when you can sit outside" and "a beautiful Cotswolds setting" are the constant at this attractively modernised country pub. In other respects, however, it's all change here, as in August 2019 long-term owners Tony and Amanda Timmer retired, and chef for the last decade, Kuba Winkowski, moved on in September 2019. It remains to be seen whether new owner, Adam Taylor, will maintain the stunning standards that have made this such a hot destination, hence we've left it unrated till next survey. / www.thefeatherednestinn.co.uk; @FeatheredNestIn; Thu-Sun 9.30 pm; Take bookings all week via phone and/or online.

NEW MILTON, HAMPSHIRE — 2–4C

CHEWTON GLEN £99 [3][3][3]

CHEWTON GLEN RD BH23 5QL 01425 282212

This famous and "beautifully situated" country hotel provides "a super experience all round", from the grand dining room to the 130 acres of immaculate grounds. Chef Luke Matthews has led the kitchen for many years (he joined as a sous in 1993) and sends out many "gorgeously presented dishes", although arguably "the wine list is the star of the show". Perhaps unsurprisingly, a meal here can seem punishingly "expensive if it's not part of a room-plus offer" – perhaps dip your toe in the water with a "splendid afternoon tea". / www.chewtonglen.com; @chewtonglen; No trainers; Take bookings all week via phone and/or online.

THE KITCHEN AT CHEWTON GLEN £82 [3][4][3]

CHEWTON FARM ROAD BH23 5QL 01425 275341

"I avoided the stuffier looking dining room, and went for the kitchen instead (a good choice)", says one fan of the more relaxed option at this super-swish country house hotel: part of the cookery school. It doesn't seem to be aiming for fireworks, rather "decent food, good value, helpful staff, and a really well-looked-after setting". / www.chewtonglen.com/thekitchen/; @TheKitchenatCG; Mon-Sat 9.30 pm.

NEWBOROUGH, ISLE OF ANGLESEY — 4–1C

THE MARRAM GRASS £49 [3][3][3]

WHITE LODGE LL61 6RS 01248 440 077

"A lovely, warm dining environment and excellent tasting menu" is the main impression given by this well-known, slightly offbeat fixture: a converted shed in a caravan park, which in the evening offers three-course, five-course and seven-course menu options. There was also the odd letdown reported this year, however. / www.themarramgrass.com; @TheMarramGrass; Take bookings all week via phone and/or online.

NEWBURY, BERKSHIRE 2–2D

ARIGATO £47 4 3 3

1 BRIDGE STREET RG14 5BE
01635 580015

"Exciting and modern Japanese cooking, exemplified by the house special tempura sushi roll", and turned out by an ex-Nobu chef, wins stellar feedback for this operation in a Grade II-listed Georgian former bank by the river; new innovations include kids' and vegan menus, and a first-floor 'Music Room' for casual izakaya dining, sushi masterclasses and karaoke. / www.arigatodining.co.uk; @ArigatoDining; Tue-Sat 9.30 pm, Sun 4 pm.

HENRY & JOE'S £75 5 5 3

17 CHEAP STREET RG14 5DD
01635 581751

"A wonderful find in the centre of Newbury": local lads Henry and Joe's "small but perfectly formed gem" (22 covers) has been open a couple of years now and it is winning renown for its "incredible value and great food". "Passionately run" by this "former head chef and head waiter from the Woodspeen" they "started it as a pop-up and it grew from there": "the open kitchen runs like clockwork", service from Joe is "very personalised" and results – either from the à la carte or (if you push the boat out) the seven-course taster menu for £75 – are "truly stunning: every element of each dish is well thought out and blissful flavours dance around in the mouth". / henryandjoes.co.uk; Wed-Fri 4 pm, Sat & Sun 5 pm.

THE WOODSPEEN £63 4 4 4

LAMBOURN RD RG20 8BN
01635 265 070

"Set in rural Berkshire with stunning views", John Campbell's accoladed venue "sounds like it should be a pub, but is in reality a skilled and soignée restaurant": "thoughtfully designed", with an "airy", "modern" interior that "opens onto a large terrace". "The cooking is very good" from an "interesting and changing menu" of "original yet reassuring dishes", "beautifully presented, and skilfully and charmingly served". Top Tip – "good for a sophisticated supper before the theatre at the nearby Watermill". / www.thewoodspeen.com; @thewoodspeen; Mon-Sat 9.45 pm, Sun 4.15pm.

NEWCASTLE UPON TYNE, TYNE AND WEAR 8–2B

ADRIANOS £46 3 3 3

90 HIGH STREET NE3 1HB
0191 284 6464

A high street outfit 'bringing a dash of Sardinian sunshine to Gosforth', as their website proclaims – and which is well-regarded locally; they have now opened up an on-site deli, should you prefer to take away. / www.adrianos.co.uk; Mon-Sat 10 pm, Sun 9 pm.

BLACKFRIARS RESTAURANT £53 3 3 4

FRIARS ST NE1 4XN 0191 261 5945

"The building is so historic" – an "ancient" thirteenth-century friar's rectory that claims to be the UK's oldest dining room – it helps make for a good occasion at Andy and Sam Hook's restaurant, events venue and cookery school. The "reliable, locally sourced" cooking from a bistro/brasserie style menu (from nut-roast to sirloin steak) also rates a favourable mention. / www.blackfriarsrestaurant.co.uk; @BlackfriarsRest; Mon-Sat 10 pm, Sun 4 pm; Take bookings all week via phone and/or online.

BROAD CHARE £48 3 3 3

25 BROAD CHARE NE1 3DQ
019 1211 2144

"A great pub beautifully located on the Newcastle quayside near Live Theatre", with "fantastic bar food, a class above other pubs and a cask beer selection to match" – "the upstairs restaurant is also very popular". This is a "consistently top-notch establishment" which provides a "great all-round drinking and dining experience" – but be warned: it can be "noisy". / www.thebroadchare.co.uk; @_thebroadchare; Mon-Sat 10 pm, Sun 5 pm; No Amex; Take bookings all week via phone and/or online.

CAFÉ ROYAL £47 3 3 3

8 NELSON ST NE1 5AW 0191 231 3000

A "stunning" early 2019 revamp has scrubbed up this elegant continental-style café/bistro that's a classic local rendezvous. Aided by its in-house bakery, it comes into its own for breakfasts or cake-fuelled afternoon teas. More substantial fare sometimes takes flak for being "pricey and average". / www.sjf.co.uk; @caferoyalsjf; Mon-Fri 5 pm, Sat 6 pm, Sun 4 pm.

CAL'S OWN £28 3 3 2

1-2 HOLLY AVENUE WEST NE2 2AR
0191 281 5522

Fans of this puntastic pizzeria may be going OTT when they hail it as "probably the best pizza in the UK". But Jesmond-born former joiner Calvin Kitchin and his brother Kerry take their trade seriously – their "good-value pizzas" are accredited by the Associazione Verace Pizza Napoletana and cooked in a wood-fired Stefano Ferrara oven imported from Naples. / www.calsown.co.uk; @cals_own; Wed & Thu 10.30 pm, Fri & Sat 9.30 pm, Sun 9 pm.

COOK HOUSE £45 4 4 4

FOUNDRY LANE NE6 1LH 0191 276 1093

"A real star amongst Newcastle's growing stable of good eateries" – ex-architect Anna Hedworth's casual, all-day haunt has moved from its original home in a Byker shipping container to a bricks-and-mortar building thanks to a Kickstarter campaign. Serving up accomplished all-day fare and now also dinner: "excellent cocktails to start are followed by great food based on local and seasonal ingredients". /

cookhouse.org; @the_grazer; Tue-Sat 11 pm, Sun 4 am; No bookings.

DABBAWAL £39 4 2 3

69-75 HIGH BRIDGE NE1 6BX
0191 232 5133

"Quality Indian street food" and a "fantastic selection of really unusual small plates" attract the most feedback of any curry house on Tyneside for this 12-year-old near the Theatre Royal (and its Jesmond offshoot). "Our go-to for a very rapid meal in Newcastle", its "innovative menu and fresh cooking" "never disappoint". / www.dabbawal.com; @dabbawal; Fri-Sun-Wed & Thu 10.30 pm; Take bookings all week via phone and/or online.

DABBAWAL £37 4 3 3

1 BRENTWOOD MEWS NE2 3DG
0191 281 3434

"Love this place" – "the Indian street food flavours are wonderful" and "very different" at this Jesmond outfit with bright interiors, an open kitchen and verandah, which compares favourably with the city-centre original. / www.dabbawal.com; @Dabbawal; Mon-Thu, Sat & Sun 10.30 pm.

DOBSON AND PARNELL £55 3 3 4

21 QUEEN ST NE1 3UG 0191 221 0904

Chef Troy Terrington's "refined European food" and a "lovely ambience" win praise for Andy Hook's three-year-old venture on the Quayside (in times gone by, on the site of Café 21 and Pan Haggerty). / www.dobsonandparnell.co.uk; @DobsonParnell; Tue-Sat 9.30 pm, Sun 4 pm; Take bookings all week via phone and/or online.

DOSA KITCHEN £39 4 3 3

7 OSBORNE ROAD (REAR) NE2 2AE

This "almost hidden" yearling serves "great South Indian food" – much of it vegan, following recipes from the state of Tamil Nadu. It's executed a "brilliant" transition to a permanent site in Jesmond after making its name as a "pop-up in an old fire station in West Newcastle". Top Tip: "Sunday sapaad (lunchtime set menu) should be your first port of call". / www.dosakitchen.co.uk; @DosaKitchenUK; Tue-Sun 9.30 pm.

FRANCESCA'S £31 3 4 4

134 MANOR HOUSE RD NE2 2NE
0191 281 6586

A "brilliant traditional Italian", in Jesmond, whose "fabulous" ambience, "cheap but great quality food" and "consistently good service" ensure that, even decades on, it's usually packed to the gills. / No Amex; No bookings.

HOUSE OF TIDES £128 5 4 4

28-30 THE CLOSE NE1 3RN 0191 2303720

Behind "an unassuming but smart exterior", Kenny & Abbie Atkinson's much-accoladed venue was Newcastle's highest-rated this year. Set on the Quayside in a Grade I listed sixteenth-century town house, you enter through the "lovely bar", and climb to the upstairs restaurant, which is warm and vibrant, with "extremely helpful staff". In the evening, the offering is a ten-course tasting menu (for £95) which is almost universally rated as exceptional in its quality. / www.houseoftides.co.uk; @houseoftides; Tue-Fri 8.30 pm, Sat 9 pm; Credit card deposit required to book.

JESMOND DENE HOUSE £81 2 3 4

JESMOND DENE RD NE2 2EY 0191 212 6066

A former stomping ground of overachieving North East chef Terry Laybourne – this "smart" boutique hotel overlooking Jesmond Dene certainly provides a "lovely setting for a special occasion" – most particularly afternoon tea. As of 2018, Danny Parker (ex-of starred Newcastle venue House of Tides) took over chef duties from longtime former incumbent Michael Penaluna, but feedback on more serious fare is still very mixed (eg "food OK, but not value for money"). / www.jesmonddenehouse.co.uk; @jesmonddenehous; Mon-Sun 9.30 pm; Booking max 7 may apply.

PANI'S £34 3 4 5

61-65 HIGH BRIDGE NE1 6BX 0191 232 4366

"Still going strong after all these years"; for "real Italian food" (the "usual suspects" plus "some interesting Sardinian specialities") you "can't beat" brothers Roberto & Walter Pani's recently refurbed "old favourite", launched in the mid nineties. / www.paniscafe.co.uk; @PanisCafe; No Amex; No bookings at lunch.

THE PATRICIA £62 4 4 3

139 JESMOND ROAD NE2 1JY 0191 2814443

"On the coast road through Jesmond not far out of Newcastle's centre", and hiding behind a "shop-front style façade that doesn't really do it justice", Nick Grieve's bistro proves to be a "cosy" and "romantic" spot, with "lots of care taken to source and present quite excellent dishes". "Brilliant Sunday lunch" too – "hooray!" / www.the-patricia.com/; @thepatricianc1; Fri & Sat, Wed & Thu 10 pm, Sun 4 pm; Take bookings all week via phone and/ or online.

PEACE & LOAF £74 4 3 4

217 JESMOND ROAD NE2 1LA 0191 281 5222

Dave Coulson's "grown up" six-year-old in Jesmond is one of the city's best-known and best-liked addresses: "a very pleasant venture with some surprising dishes" either from the à la carte, competitively-priced prix fixe (two courses for £25) or the "fantastic seasonal tasting menu" (£80 – must be ordered in advance). / www.peaceandloaf.co.uk; @peaceandloafjes; Mon-Wed 9 pm, Thu-Sat 9.30 pm, Sun 3.30 pm; Take bookings all week via phone and/or online.

ROUTE £48 4 4 3

35 SIDE NE1 3JE 0191 222 0973

MasterChef: The Professionals finalist John Calton's follow-up to hit North Shields gastropub Staith House took over this former Burger Stop, in central Newcastle's finest medieval street, The Side, in May 2018. Early reports on the "casual" small plates spot are stellar, with "fantastic" dishes featuring "combinations not seen elsewhere" hereabouts. / routenewcastle.co.uk; @routenewcastle; Mon, Wed-Sat 9 pm.

SACHINS £42 3 2 2

FORTH BANKS NE1 3SG 0191 261 9035

A Toon institution for 35 years, this Punjabi curry house behind Central Station has been run since 2000 by chef-owner Bob Arora, and is known for its "consistently amazing food". / www.sachins.co.uk; @Sachins_NCL; Take bookings all week via phone and/or online.

ST VINCENT £47 3 4 4

29 BROAD CHARE NE1 3DQ 0191 232 1331

Terry Laybourne's 21 Group closed the beloved Caffè Vivo in August 2018 to much local ire, but after a remarkably short interregnum, the space was "reinvented as an imaginative, wine-led tapas restaurant" ("still with an Italian slant", and featuring a new bar and metro-chic décor). Reassuringly, head chef Emanuele Lattanzi, a carry-over from the Vivo days, oversees the menu, which dances about all over the place (mac 'n' cheese, black pudding, etc.) but so far it's the "fascinating wine list" which draws all the comments. / www.saintvincentncl.co.uk; @SaintVincentNcl; Wed-Fri 4 pm, Sat & Sun 5 pm.

A TASTE OF PERSIA £29 4 4 3

14 MARLBOROUGH CR NE1 4EE 0191 221 0088

The "excellent Persian food" at this "friendly" Jesmond spot wins high ratings for "one of the cheapest restaurants in Newcastle for cooking of high quality". A more central branch near the station has closed down. / www.atasteofpersia.com; Take bookings all week via phone and/or online.

21 £60 4 4 4

TRINITY GDNS NE1 2HH 0191 222 0755

"Still setting the standard for Newcastle restaurants" – Terry Laybourne's "first class" brasserie remains the city's most-mentioned venue, as it has been for most years in various locations since 1988. "Caring and friendly staff" provide "creative" food and it's recommended for just about any occasion. / www.cafetwentyone.co.uk; @21Newcastle; Mon-Sat 10.30 pm, Sun 8 pm.

TYNESIDE COFFEE ROOMS, TYNESIDE CINEMA £32 3 2 4

10 PILGRIM ST NE1 6QG 0191 227 5520

"A perfect time-warp" – the "Art Deco bar/ cafe" in Newcastle's only surviving independent cinema "hasn't changed in 50 years and more". "My family are into our fourth generation coming here since the 60s and we're still enjoying our coffee, tea, sandwiches, baked potatoes and other light meals" (and "specials sell out quickly for good reason"). Particularly tipped for breakfast, coffee or a light lunch, it's "also a great venue for singles – you won't feel out of place!" / www.tynesidecinema.co.uk; @tynesidecinema; Sun-Fri 7 pm, Sat 9.30 pm; No Amex.

URY £35 4 3 3

27 QUEEN STREET NE1 3UG 0191 232 7799

"Wonderful spices in every dish" are the hallmark of this three-year-old "South Indian development of the old Rasa enterprise, maintaining the high standards of the old regime", and with "lovely staff" an added boon. / www.uryrestaurants.com; @UryRestaurants; Sun-Thu 10.30 pm, Fri & Sat 11 pm; Take bookings all week via phone and/or online.

NEWPORT ON TAY, FIFE 9–3D

THE NEWPORT £61 4 3 3

1 HIGH STREET DD6 8AA 01382 541 449

Jamie Scott's award-winning "low-key" inn enjoys a "wonderful" view across the Tay to the V&A in Dundee; and its level of cuisine is "first-class with a strong emphasis on local produce". Menu options range from an à la carte to a six-course tasting menu: the latter is the only choice available on Friday and Saturday evenings. / www.thenewport.co.uk/; Tue-Sat 11.30 pm, Sun 3.30 pm; Take bookings all week via phone and/or online.

NEWPORT, ISLE OF WIGHT 2–2A

THOMPSON'S £78 4 4 4

11 TOWN LANE PO30 1JU 01983 526118

"A true island favourite" from Robert Thompson – perhaps its most renowned chef: this "romantic" four-year-old occupies a "quirky" listed building, where "tables opposite the open kitchen are in high demand, while upstairs is more intimate". It wins raves for "outstanding" food "inventively using

Joro, Sheffield

the best local/seasonal ingredients" and "there is every chance that one or more of the courses during your meal will be served by a chef". "The personal cutlery drawers are an interesting touch" allowing your own choice of the best utensils at any juncture! / www.robertthompson.co.uk; @RThompsonIOW; Take bookings all week via phone and/or online.

NEWTON ON OUSE, NORTH YORKSHIRE 8–4C

THE DAWNAY ARMS £54 4|4|3

YO30 2BR 01347 848345

Martel Smith's "comfy, beamed old pub" has a "modern, light interior with flagstone and bleached wood" and also benefits from a "back patio overlooking the River Ouse". "Local ingredients wherever possible are prepared in an imaginative way" and it's "a wonderful spot for Sunday lunch". / www.thedawnayatnewton.co.uk; @thedawnayarms; Tue-Sat 9 pm, Sun 4 pm; Take bookings all week via phone and/or online.

NEWTON-IN-BOWLAND, LANCASHIRE 5–1B

THE PARKERS ARMS £48 5|4|4

HALL GATE HILL BB7 3DY 01200 446236

"An exceptional place", whose "glorious" location places it "in the middle of nowhere (or the middle of God's own country, depending on your point of view)". "It's the most welcoming pub you could wish for" with "always a warm welcome from AJ and Ben". Chef Stosie Madi "cooks intelligently and from the heart" displaying "a knowledge and understanding of a wide variety of cuisines, plus classical and non-classical techniques"; and "her food is modern, fresh and bursting with flavour". "When in season there's no better place to enjoy stunning game, fish is perfectly cooked" and "even the simple things like pies are done so well, you end up thinking that this must be what other pies want to be when they grow up". / www.parkersarms.co.uk; Wed-Fri 8 pm, Sat 8.30 pm, Sun 6.30 pm; Take bookings all week via phone and/or online.

NOMANSLAND, WILTSHIRE 2–3C

LES MIRABELLES £54 4|4|4

FOREST EDGE RD SP5 2BN 01794 390205

A "little corner of France in the New Forest" – Claude Laage's "all-time favourite" is known for its "true Gallic charm, fab food, wine and ambience". "Such terrific value", too. / www.lesmirabelles.co.uk; No Amex; Take bookings all week via phone and/or online.

NORDEN, LANCASHIRE 5–1B

NUTTER'S £64 4|4|4

EDENFIELD ROAD OL12 7TT 01706 650167

TV chef Andrew Nutter's manor house dining room provides a "very impressive" setting, ten minutes' drive from Rochdale, and "capable" and "attentive" service. The French-influenced modern British cuisine is acknowledged in practically all reports to be "consistently excellent". Top Tip – "A good value business lunch is available during the week". / www.nuttersrestaurant.com; @nuttersofficial; Tue-Thu 9 pm, Fri & Sat 9.30 pm, Sun 8 pm; Take bookings all week via phone and/or online.

NORTH SHIELDS, TYNE AND WEAR 8–2B

STAITH HOUSE £51 4|2|3

57 LOW LIGHTS NE30 1JA 0191 270 8441

"Very good fresh local fish" tops the menu at this pub-restaurant with a "nautical theme, adjacent to the Fish Quay", but there's "also meat and game in season". Proprietor John Calton, a MasterChef: The Professionals finalist, has also opened a bistro, Route, in Newcastle. / www.thestaithhouse.co.uk; @Thestaithhouse; Mon-Thu 9 pm, Sat, Fri 9.30 pm, Sun 5 pm; Credit card deposit required to book.

NORTHLEACH, GLOUCESTERSHIRE 2–1C

WHEATSHEAF INN £60 3|3|3

WEST END GL54 3EZ 01451 860244

This "country hotel with a warm and welcoming restaurant" is owned by Superdry fashion king Julian Dunkerton, who has smartened it up as part of his Lucky Onion Cotswold group. / www.cotswoldswheatsheaf.com; @wheatsheafgl54; Take bookings all week via phone and/or online.

NORWICH, NORFOLK 6–4C

BENEDICTS £57 4|4|4

9 ST BENEDICTS ST NR2 4PE 01603 926 080

Many "utterly fabulous" meals are again reported at Great British Chef, Richard Bainbridge's Norwich fixture, which is nowadays the most-commented-on dining destination in town. Despite its chilled style, it has a "very accomplished offer", which ranges from a three-course à la carte menu for £39 through to a seven-course taster option for £60. Its ratings were dragged off its former top heights this year, though, by a few locals finding it "hyped" or "disappointing". / www.restaurantbenedicts.com/home; @restbenedicts; Take bookings all week via phone and/or online.

FARMYARD £51 4|4|3

01603 733 188

From Hannah Springham & Andrew Jones, also behind Dial House in Reepham, this

contemporary bistro (est. 2017) is "such a lovely place to come and eat" and stands out even on a "street with many acceptable restaurants"; "the décor is minimalist" (it can be a tad "noisy" as a result) but is atoned for by an "interesting menu making great use of fresh local produce". / www.farmyardrestaurant.com; @FarmyardRestau1; Mon-Thu 9 pm, Fri & Sat 10 pm; Take bookings all week via phone and/or online.

THE GUNTON ARMS £51 3|4|5

CROMER RD, THORPE MKT NR11 8TZ 01263 832010

This "quirky" country pub combines an "old-fashioned" interior with striking artworks by YBAs on the walls, to create the "perfect ambience" and it has won a fair following. Game from the surrounding Gunton Deer Park is a highlight of the menu – most (if not quite all) opinions on the cooking are positive. / www.theguntonarms.co.uk; @theguntonarms; Take bookings all week via phone and/or online.

LAST WINE BAR & RESTAURANT £53 3|4|4

70 - 76 ST GEORGES STREET NR3 1AB 01603 626626

"After nearly 30 years under the same ownership" owner James Sawrey-Cookson retired and this "well-loved Norwich institution" changed hands this year: bought by a number of business-minded regulars. Chef of three years' standing, Iain McCarten is "well into his stride, but what makes this place so popular is the whole atmosphere (there is a real sense of belonging"). "Hopefully the new owners don't ruin the formula" although change is certainly afoot, with a new outside terrace and adjoining brasserie section opening in autumn 2019. / lastwinebar.co.uk; @LastWineBar.

NAMASTE INDIA £34 4|4|3

2A OPIE STREET NR1 3DN 01603 662016

"Exceptional" Indian vegetarian and vegan cooking wins high ratings for this "beautifully decorated" little restaurant on a central Norwich backstreet – a family-run business operated by "people who really care". / namasteindiannorwich.com; @namaste_norwich; Mon-Thu 10.30 pm, Fri & Sat 11 pm.

ROGER HICKMAN'S £77 5|4|4

79 UPPER ST. GILES ST NR2 1AB 01603 633522

"Still the best restaurant in Norwich" say fans of Roger Hickman's long-established fine dining destination, whose fanclub is smaller nowadays than that of nearby Benedicts, but overall scored more highly this year. The level of cost here is a tad higher, and the approach more in the vein of traditional fine dining. "A new private dining room has been opened this year, which is stunning, and such an investment shows a real confidence from Roger H, who pleasingly is pretty much always in evidence at every

UK DIRECTORY

service". / www.rogerhickmansrestaurant.com; @rogerhickmans; Take bookings all week via phone and/or online.

ALCHEMILLA £33 5 3 4

192 DERBY ROAD NG7 1NF 0115 941 3515

"A great addition to the city's food scene, whose food is getting better and better" – Alex Bond's "restored Georgian stables" on the Park Estate (a little way outside the city-centre) opened in summer 2017 and his "amazing and very creative" approach and "modish" design makes it Nottingham's hottest rising culinary star of the moment. You can eat from either a five-, seven- or ten-course tasting menu (everyone at the table should have the same option) and results are "exceptional". / alchemillarestaurant. uk; @alchemillaresto; Tue-Sat 9.30 pm.

ANNIE'S BURGER SHACK £26 3 3 3

5 BROADWAY NG1 1PR 01156849920

The "mind-blowing selection" of "unusual" burger combinations is the trump card of this Lace Market outfit, with "something to please everyone including vegan, gluten-free etc"; add in a "lively" vibe and reporters "love this place"; following a Derby spin-off, they branched out to Worcester in late 2018. / www.anniesburgershack.com; @original_annies; Sun-Thu 11 pm, Fri & Sat midnight; Take bookings all week via phone and/or online.

BARESCA £49 3 3 3

9 BYARD LN NG1 0115 948 3900

"Very reliable and reasonably priced (especially at lunch. or for the popular pre-theatre menú deli dia)" – Escabeche's lively, city-centre spin-off provides "tasty tapas in a utilitarian but appealing setting". On a nice day, nab one of the few tables outside. / www.baresca.co.uk; @barescanotts; Sun & Mon 10.30 pm, Tue-Thu 11 pm, Fri & Sat midnight.

BURRA KHANA £38

20 VICTORIA STREET NG1 2EX 0115 784 4844

Tom Brooke, launched this 70-seater in Nottingham in September 2019 by splitting his existing Red Dog Saloon site (sibling to the well PR'd one in Shoreditch, as well as three others around the country) into two. The all-day format will offer Indian small plates cooked on a charcoal BBQ, with influences from Middle Eastern countries such as Persia, Turkey and Lebanon. / www.burrakhana.co.uk; Mon-Thu 11 pm, Fri & Sat 2 am, Sun 10.30 pm.

CAFE ROYA £43 3 4 3

130 WOLLATON RD NG9 2PE 0115 922 1902

"Exceptional veggie food in the heart of Beeston" ("at lunchtime it's entirely vegan") draws nothing but praise for this two-floor outfit which "excels in taste combinations and spices"

– even "carnivores will not miss the meat!" / caferoya.restaurantwebx.com/; @CafeRoya; Take bookings all week via phone and/or online.

CALCUTTA CLUB £48 4 3 3

8-10 MAID MARIAN WAY NG1 6HS 0115 941 4441

Impressive marks, if on limited feedback, on this gourmet Indian, which set up shop in 2014 on Nottingham's trafficky Maid Marian Way, and has won a firm local following for its decadent, if not too subtle, dishes; off-shoot Maharaja's Retreat opened five doors down, in May 2019, replacing a seafood joint which stayed open for barely a month. / www.calcutta-club.co.uk; @TheCalcuttaClub; Mon-Thu 10.30 pm, Fri & Sat 11 pm, Sun 10 pm.

THE CUMIN £37 4 5 2

62-64 MAID MARIAN WAY NG1 6BQ 0115 941 9941

"Freshly cooked food to a high standard" and "really excellent service from Monika and Sunny" make the Anand family's Punjabi specialist stand out from the crowd on Nottingham's 'Madras Mile' of curryhouses. / www.thecumin.co.uk; @Thecumin; Mon-Thu 11 pm, Fri & Sat 11.30 pm; Take bookings all week via phone and/or online.

FRENCH LIVING £51 3 3 3

27 KING ST NG1 2AY 0115 958 5885

Established in 1994, Corsican Stéphane Luiggi's "authentic" (down to the Gallic staff) homage to La Belle France, spanning a café, deli and shop, remains "the perfect place to relax with good food and wine after a long shop in town"; bien sûr "you have to be a bit of a Francophile to get the most out of it!" / www.frenchliving.co.uk; @FrenchLivingUK; No Amex; Take bookings all week via phone and/or online.

THE FRUSTRATED CHEF £43 4 3 2

90-94 CHILWELL ROAD, BEESTON NG9 1ES 0115 922 8300

An "extensive" and "interesting tapas menu" (plus a "very good-value lunch") is the formula behind this relaxed but reliably busy spot. / thefrustratedchef.co.uk; @TFC_Beeston; Tue, Wed 10 pm, Fri & Sat midnight, Thu 11 pm.

HART'S KITCHEN £70 3 4 2

STANDARD HILL, PARK ROW NG1 6GN 0115 988 1900

"Culinary standards are being maintained, but the smaller new venue is a little less inviting" is the near-universal 'take' on Tim Hart's "downsized" modern brasserie, which has left its seminal 1990s quarters (Jonathan Meades was a big fan, back in the day) to be incorporated into the former bar of his nearby hotel, near the Castle: "the entrance is unprepossessing and surroundings somewhat cramped, but the food's fine". / www.hartsnottingham.co.uk; @HartsNottingham; Mon-Fri 9.30 pm, Sat 10 pm, Sun 9 pm.

IBERICO £47 4 3 4

THE SHIRE HALL, HIGH PAVEMENT NG1 1HN 01159 410410

"Amid the hustle and bustle of Nottingham Lace Market", this "go-to" cellar in a historic building elicits real raves for its "London-quality tapas" and "lively" atmosphere. A "cheaper and cheerful" no-reservation sibling, on Carlton St, is also a hit. / www.ibericotapas.com; @ibericotapas; Tue-Sat 10 pm; Take bookings all week via phone and/or online; children: 12+ D.

MASALA JUNCTION £43 4 3 3

301-303 MANSFIELD ROAD, CARRINGTON NG5 0115 9622366

The "creative and well-cooked food" at the Aziz family's third Nottingham venue is inspired by the flavours of Kashmir and Lahore. A "well-run establishment" in a "beautifully converted former NatWest building", it provides a "great all round experience". Top Tip: "the goat curry is a favourite". / masalajunction.co.uk/; @masalajct; Mon-Thu 10.30 pm, Fri & Sat 11 pm; Take bookings all week via phone and/or online.

MEMSAAB £43 4 3 3

12-14 MAID MARIAN WAY NG1 6HS 0115 957 0009

"Nottingham's best Indian" and the most-commented-on restaurant in the city centre: Amita Sawhney's "buzzy, friendly and efficient" fixture continues to inspire nothing but praise for producing "wonderfully flavoursome, yet refined, dishes time and time again". Is it "the attention to detail and woman's touch seemingly so apparent in the meet and greet, presentation… even down to the Molton Brown in the toilets?". "I've eaten at many Indian restaurants all over the world, including renowned Michelin-starred ones in London. This is right up there, and at a decent price". / www.mem-saab.co.uk; @MemSaabNotts; Mon-Thu 10.30 pm, Fri & Sat 11 pm, Sun 10 pm; No shorts; Take bookings all week via phone and/or online.

RESTAURANT SAT BAINS £134 5 4 3

LENTON LANE NG7 2SA 0115 986 6566

Sat Bains's "special" cuisine "doesn't miss a beat" at his much-acclaimed foodie Xanadu, which remains one of the country's foremost culinary destinations. "Much is made of the bizarre location" – a converted motel amidst flyovers, "on the fringe of an industrial estate at the edge of the city" – "but once inside, you are cocooned in luxury" (including, if you stay, in the "quite reasonably priced bedrooms"). Both seven-course and ten-course tasting options are "hugely inventive and utterly brilliant with a superb matching wine flight". The "chef's table is an exceptional experience" and many regular diners also report "experiential touches like a tour of the busy kitchen after dinner with a signed menu". "Top waiting staff too: friendly and knowledgeable, but more importantly, keen". / www.restaurantsatbains.com; @satbains1; Wed & Thu 9 pm, Fri & Sat 9.30 pm; No Amex;

Take bookings all week via phone and/or online; children: 8+.

SHANGHAI SHANGHAI £38 432

15 GOOSE GATE NG1 1FE 0115 958 4688

"Authentic and very tasty Sichuan cooking" is served "in basic surroundings" at this Lace Market operation, which is reassuringly popular with Chinese (around 80% of the clientele, apparently), as well as students and – better for PR – even the odd Times food critic. / www.shanghai-shanghai.co.uk; @ShanghaiShang; Sun-Thu 10 pm, Fri & Sat 11 pm.

200 DEGREES £12 344

HESTON HS, MEADOW LANE NG2 3HE 0115 837 4849

"Coffee that packs a punch and plenty of good food options" set the tone at this "simply fab" indie coffee shop, now the HQ of a national group with 10 shops and five barista schools in the Midlands, the North and Cardiff. The name derives from the Centigrade temperature at which they roast coffee (slightly lower than most rivals) and the Fahrenheit temperature at which they serve it. / www.200degs.com; @200degreescafe; No bookings.

VICTORIA HOTEL £38 323

DOVECOTE LN NG9 1JG 0115 925 4049

"Splendid, just splendid" – this "crowded", old-school late-Victorian boozer, cited in DH Lawrence's debut novel, is "a nice local with good food and beers" (the former from an "interesting", wide-ranging menu). It might not be a gourmet hotspot but it's "all a pub should be". / www.victoriabeeston.co.uk; @TheVicBeeston; Sun-Thu 11 pm, Fri & Sat midnight; No Amex; Take bookings all week via phone and/or online; children: 18+ after 8 pm.

WORLD SERVICE £58 334

NEWDIGATE HS, CASTLEGATE NG1 6AF 0115 847 5587

"A stalwart of the Nottingham restaurant scene" near the castle, whose "clubby setting" owes much to the intriguing seventeenth century building and courtyard garden which it shares with The Nottingham Club. Its ambitious contemporary cuisine has always tended to divide opinion – exceptional to its fans but "somewhat overpriced and bland" to its foes (with the latter a bit more in evidence this year). / www.worldservicerestaurant.com; @ws_restaurant; Mon-Sat 10.15 pm, Sun 10.30 pm; Take bookings all week via phone and/or online; children: 10+ at D.

ZAAP £35 344

UNIT B, BROMLEY PLACE NG1 6JG 0115 947 0204

"The smells, the sounds, the buzzy atmosphere" that transport you (via tuk-tuk) to Bangkok – "it's all wonderful" at this outpost of a Leeds-based group, and so convincing that "I honestly believe this is how street food is in Thailand". /

www.zaapthai.co.uk; @ZaapNottingham; Sun-Thu 11 pm, Fri & Sat midnight; Take bookings all week via phone and/or online.

OAKHAM, RUTLAND 5–4D

HITCHEN'S BARN £59 443

12 BURLEY ROAD LE15 6DH 01572 722255

"Neil and Louise Hitchen have now left the lovely Berkeley Arms at Wymondham and opened this town-centre bistro, which slightly lacks the ambience of their pub but in every other respect is superb". On the menu, "excellent seasonal food including game", which is "smilingly and delightfully" delivered with "speedy efficiency". "Massively popular in a short time – deservedly": "booking is essential". / www.hitchensbarn.co.uk; Wed-Fri 4 pm, Sat & Sun 5 pm.

OARE, KENT 3–3C

THE THREE MARINERS £45 323

2 CHURCH RD ME13 0QA 01795 533633

"The recent change of hands (as of 2017) has done nothing to spoil" this classic boozer; although it had a brief dip in fortunes, it's once again well-rated by all who report on it: particularly its above average cooking. / www.thethreemarinersoare.co.uk; Mon-Thu 10 pm, Fri & Sat 11 pm, Sun 8 pm; No Amex; Take bookings all week via phone and/or online.

OBAN, ARGYLL AND BUTE 9–3B

EE-USK (SEAFOOD RESTAURANT) £56 433

NORTH PIER PA34 5QD 01631 565666

A fantastically popular "presence on the North Pier at Oban", where it perches in a glass box, this venue is famous for its "superb" fresh fish and seafood (the name is Gaelic for 'fish'). Be warned, though, you may have to "queue even on a Monday night" (and parents take heed, "children under the age of 12 are barred from 5:45 pm onwards"). / www.eeusk.com; @eeuskoban; No Amex; children: 12+ at D.

ETIVE £68 433

43 STEVENSON STREET PA34 5NA 01631 564899

"A fabulous find in Oban" – John McNulty and David Lapsley's venture moved from its former location (of this name) a couple of years ago, and is praised for its very accomplished Scottish cuisine using the best local produce (choose either a 'land' or 'sea' six-course tasting menu for £45) and a "small but thoughtful wine list" (plus the option of matching wine flights) – "highly recommended!" / www.etiverestaurant.co.uk; @EtiveRestaurant; Take bookings all week via phone and/or online.

THE OBAN FISH & CHIP SHOP £25 532

116 GEORGE STREET PA34 5NT 01631 567000

A take-away and 40-seater restaurant lauded by Rick Stein that "goes way beyond what you might expect from a chip shop"; there's "some great cooking on display – no wines but for a first-class fish supper you can't go wrong". / obanfishandchipshop.co.uk.

THE WHITEHOUSE £78

PA34 5XP 01967 421777

Only open in summer into the mid-autumn, this simply decorated restaurant overlooking the Sound of Mull (at the base of Loch Linnhe) serves daily changing menus, from which you can choose from two to six courses at lunch and four to six for dinner. Sustainability is a strong focus of the operation, as is the approach of the 'Slow Food Movement'. It has won a major culinary reputation, with numerous accolades and guide inclusions – all our survey feedback is exceptional, but too limited for a rating. / www.thewhitehouserestaurant.co.uk; @whitehouse_info.

OLD HUNSTANTON, NORFOLK 6–3B

THE NEPTUNE £87 554

85 OLD HUNSTANTON RD PE36 6HZ 01485 532122

"Stunning food, and a true personal touch from owners Jacqui and Kevin Mangeolle" inspires nothing but rapturous reviews for their restaurant-with-rooms occupying a former eighteenth-century coaching inn. "Husband and wife are both still on top of their game": service is "relaxed" and "friendly" and Kevin's cuisine (incorporating locally landed fish and lobster, plus game from local estates) is "understated but just lovely": "a gastronomic delight!" / www.theneptune.co.uk; @NeptuneChef; Tue-Sun 9 pm; May need + to book; children: 10+.

OLD WINDSOR, BERKSHIRE 3–3A

THE OXFORD BLUE £90 444

10 CRIMP HILL SL4 2QY 01753 331080

"In a desert of really good restaurants", Stephen Ellis's game-led 19th century gastroboozer "stands out for brilliant food combinations and really inventive presentation"; part of its repertoire includes the "careful crafting of what could otherwise be basic dishes e.g. scotch egg, pork pie, fruit tart" (Ellis's wife Ami is a formidable pastry chef). / www.oxfordbluepub.co.uk; @OxfordBluePub; Wed-Sat 9.30 pm, Sun 5 pm; Take bookings all week via phone and/or online.

House of Tides, Newcastle upon Tyne

OLDSTEAD, NORTH YORKSHIRE   5–1D

BLACK SWAN   £127   4|3|4

YO61 4BL   01347 868 387

"Every bit as good as the hype… exceptionally clever cooking, lovely staff and a very jolly atmosphere": still the most common verdict on the Banks family's isolated pub, "tucked away in the North Yorkshire countryside" (near the family farm), which won global fame in 2017 as TripAdvisor's #1 Restaurant in the World! But while its "adventurous" nine-course tasting menu still hits "amazing" heights for most reporters, its overall ratings suggest it risks becoming a victim of its own success (including the constraints of Tommy Banks's TV commitments, and opening a second venue in York). "Sky high prices" are the main gripe, but slips in service are also a concern (one reporter "paid for a signed book and had to ask six times to receive it"). / www.blackswanoldstead.co.uk; @BlkSwanOldstead; Sat & Sun-Fri 8.30 pm; No Amex.

OMBERSLEY, WORCESTERSHIRE   2–1B

VENTURE IN   £62   4|3|3

MAIN ROAD   WR9 0EW   01905 620552

This "lovely traditional restaurant" in a Grade II-listed, timber-framed 16th-century house serves "high-quality" classic dishes. Chef-patron Toby Fletcher smokes his own fish and meat in-house, and his love of seafood is reflected in daily specials and fortnightly fish evenings. / www.theventurein.co.uk; Tue-Sat 9.30 pm, Sun 2 pm; Take bookings all week via phone and/or online.

ONGAR, ESSEX   3–2B

SMITH'S BRASSERIE   £60   4|4|3

FYFIELD RD   CM5 0AL   01277 365578

This "excellent seafood and fish restaurant" features "traditional/classic cooking", and "its high turnover means the fish is never less than perfectly fresh". It attracts a clientele of "Essex luminaries including Rod Stewart and Alan Sugar, who once described it as his 'posh chippy'": "a lot of the diners are a surprising shade of orange that is rarely observed in nature… but it's still a confident recommendation for fish lovers!" / www.smithsrestaurants.com; @SmithsOfOngar; Tue-Thu 10 pm, Fri & Sat 10.30 pm, Mon 9.30 pm, Sun 9 pm; No trainers; Take bookings all week via phone and/or online; children: 12+.

ORFORD, SUFFOLK   3–1D

BUTLEY ORFORD OYSTERAGE   £45   5|3|2

MARKET HILL   IP12 2LH   01394 450277

It's "a simple environment and quite noisy" ("not at all flashy"), but "the fish and seafood could not be better" at this famous venue, owned by the Pinney family, who provide much of the catch from their own boats. "The unbeatable, overall quality ensures that you hardly notice the school canteen feel": "beautiful, very simple, incredibly fresh, plain dishes" all delivered in an "unfussy and unpretentious manner" right by the sea ("maybe could do with a green vegetable more, but the side salad is perfect"). / www.butleyorfordoysterage.co.uk; @Pinneysoforford; No Amex; Take bookings all week via phone and/or online.

THE CROWN & CASTLE   £59   4|4|4

IP12 2LJ   01394 450205

"Consistently good, flavoursome local food" (with "fish a strong point, landed on the nearby village quay") is abetted by "efficient but laidback service" at this crowd-pleasing hotel; while TV's 'Hotel Inspector' Ruth Watson sold it to a local hotel group recently, longtime regulars report that standards have been preserved. / www.crownandcastle.co.uk; @CrownandCOrford; No Amex; Booking max 10 may apply; children: 8+ at D.

ORPINGTON, KENT   3–3B

XIAN   £41   5|3|2

324 HIGH ST   BR6 0NG   01689 871881

"Outstanding Chinese food on a suburban high street" – "Victor and his team deliver year after year" at this "faultless" (albeit somewhat "cramped and busy"), family-run Chinese. "It's hard to get a table, it's so popular" so book ahead. / Tue-Sun 11 pm; Take bookings all week via phone and/or online.

OSWESTRY, SHROPSHIRE   5–3A

SEBASTIAN'S   £68   3|4|3

45 WILLOW STREET   SY11 1AQ   01691 655 444

"A wonderful joy to visit and to eat at", say fans of Mark Sebastian & Michelle Fisher's "consistent" restaurant with rooms, whose beamed and panelled dining room has been a feature of the area for 30 years. / www.sebastians-hotel.com; No Amex; Take bookings all week via phone and/or online.

OTLEY, WEST YORKSHIRE   5–1C

BUON APPS   £52   3|4|4

WHARFEBANK BUSINESS CENTRE, ILKLEY RD LS21 3JP   01943 468 458

"A family-run Italian restaurant, with authentic food" – at a "beautiful location on a weir of the River Wharfe" – Alessandro and Elena Sofia's converted paper mill wins consistently good ratings after 16 years in business. "Sitting by the water on a sunny summer day could not be bettered" – and it helps that "the owners are always there". / www.buonappsotley.co.uk; @Buonapps.

OTTERSHAW, SURREY   3–3A

FOX DINING ROOMS   £84

STONEHILL RD   KT16 0EL   01932 872050

FKA 'The Manor at Foxhills': this "beautiful" dining room of a top golf course – set in an impressive Victorian manor house – "has been refurbished, with no carpets or window furnishings so it's noisier than it used to be". Too little feedback as yet from which to rate this new, more modern guise, but prices are not punishing and there is a menu for 'Young Adults'. A traditional afternoon tea in the adjoining plush lounge is still an option. / www.foxhills.co.uk; @FoxhillsSurrey; Mon-Sun 9.30 pm; No jeans; Take bookings all week via phone and/or online.

OUNDLE, RUTLAND   6–4A

TAP & KITCHEN   £49   3|2|3

STATION ROAD   PE8 4DE   01832 275069

"Consistently good" modern brasserie cooking "with beers from the adjacent brewery" (by sister company Nene Valley Brewers) makes for an attractive package at this modern wharfside warehouse operation. / www.tapandkitchen.com; @tapandkitchen; Mon-Sat 11 pm, Sun 9 pm.

OXFORD, OXFORDSHIRE   2–2D

AL-SHAMI   £29   3|3|2

25 WALTON CR   OX1 2JG   01865 310066

This Jericho veteran inspires remarkable loyalty from fans – "been coming since it opened 30 years ago and it's still the best Lebanese I've found in the UK" – "and great value too". Others find it "pleasant enough", with a "wide range of nicely flavoured dishes", but complain there's "no excitement". / www.al-shami.co.uk; No Amex.

ARBEQUINA £40 442

74 COWLEY RD OX4 1JB 01865 792777

"Top tapas in the somewhat unlikely environment of the Cowley Road" – this "small and noisy" former chemist's shop is "not a place to linger" with its "stools not chairs, where you sit at the bar, or at very small tables". All reports acclaim the quality of the small plates and interesting wine: "the meal didn't take much more than an hour, but we left feeling much happier". / arbequina.co.uk; @arbequinaoxford; Mon-Sat 10.30 pm.

ASHMOLEAN DINING ROOM £54 324

BEAUMONT ST OX1 2PH 01865 553 823

"A lovely spot to enjoy rooftop views of Oxford" – this better-than-average venue on the top floor of the museum has a "competent but limited menu that's good if rather pricey", and also serves afternoon teas. It opens out into a rooftop cocktail bar with deckchairs in the summer, but gets crowded in all seasons – so make sure you book to avoid being shunted into the basement refectory. / www.ashmoleandiningroom.com; Sun-Wed 4.30 pm, Thu-Sat 10 pm.

ATOMIC BURGER £37 333

92 COWLEY RD OX4 1JE 01865 790 855

An "imaginative selection of burgers and all the extras" is turned out in a dazzling mural- and memorabilia-bedecked setting at this "bustling", quirky local hangout; sadly their nearby spin-off and Bristol branch have now bitten the dust. / www.atomicburger.co.uk; @atomicburgers; No Amex; Take bookings all week via phone and/or online.

BRANCA £52 333

111 WALTON ST OX2 6AJ 01865 556111

A Jericho stalwart for more than 15 years – this "local Italian is always buzzing and reliable" for light lunches as well as more substantial meals. It now has a deli next door, and a garden terrace for al fresco summer dining. / www.branca.co.uk; @brancaoxford; Sun-Wed 10 pm, Thu-Sat 10.30 pm; No Amex.

BRASSERIE BLANC £53 222

71-72 WALTON ST OX2 6AG 01865 510999

The brasserie that Raymond Blanc originally used as the template for his national roll-out sits in the attractive Jericho site where Blanc made his name before scaling up to the magnificent Manoir aux Quat' Saisons. The food is generally rated as "reliable", but there are enough concerns ("bit of a 'chain' feel", "trying too hard", "slightly glum") to preclude an enthusiastic recommendation. /

www.brasserieblanc.com; @brasserieblanc; Mon-Sat 10 pm, Sun 9 pm.

CHERWELL BOATHOUSE £46 325

BARDWELL ROAD OX2 6ST 01865 552746

The "gorgeous setting by the river" is one perfect ingredient for a "romantic lunch" in the heart of north Oxford at this veteran fixture – a working boathouse, with punts gliding past on the Cherwell – and its "super wine list" is another. The "mainly good" food and "friendly service" also make a contribution, if sometimes in a supporting role. / www.cherwellboathouse.co.uk; @Cherwell_Boat.

CHIANG MAI £51 323

KEMP HALL PASSAGE, 130A HIGH STREET OX1 4DH 01865 202233

"Eating green curry in a Tudor house is still a novelty" and fans of this slightly incongruous stalwart, tucked away off the High Street, say it's "still very good in a city blessed with good Orientals". That said, its cooking "has declined" from when it was Oxford's top-rated venue in our survey ("how the mighty have fallen") and, given its "really crammed" and sometimes "noisy" interior, its overall performance only seems fair-to-middling nowadays. / www.chiangmaikitchen.co.uk; Mon-Sat 11.30 pm, Sun 10.30 pm; No Amex; Take bookings all week via phone and/or online.

CINNAMON KITCHEN OXFORD £42 332

309 THE WESTGATE, QUEEN STREET OX1 1NZ 01865 951670

"Up-market Indian food which is better than most in this city" – certainly "better than its chain neighbours at the top of the new Westgate shopping centre" – is found at this contemporary offshoot of London's ambitious Cinnamon Club. / www.cinnamon-kitchen.com/westgate-oxford; @CinnamonKitchen.

THE COCONUT TREE £89 322

76 SAINT CLEMENT'S STREET OX4 1AH 01865 421865

"A good-value array of Sri Lankan small plates" helps make for an "interesting" meal at this Sri Lankan street food operator: part of a south west England mini-chain, which has been in the City of dreaming spires for the last two years. / www.thecoconut-tree.com; @CoconutTreeUK; Sun-Thu 10 pm, Fri & Sat 11 pm.

GEE'S £52 234

61 BANBURY RD OX2 6PE 01865 553540

"Just on the edge of central Oxford", this "lovely" listed Victorian conservatory ("twinkly in the evenings") has been a local favourite for many years and is a natural choice for romance. Even fans, though, concede it's "not cheap" to an extent that's a turn-off for one

Arbequina, Oxford

or two reporters. / www.gees-restaurant.co.uk; @geesrestaurant; Mon-Sun 10.30 pm; Take bookings all week via phone and/or online.

THE MAGDALEN ARMS £52 333

243 IFFLEY ROAD OX4 1SJ 01865 243 159

"Sunday roasts are legendary, with care lavished on the ingredients", say fans of this well-known varsity gastropub – "a busy place" (some would say "too noisy to be enjoyable" when it's "packed out": i.e. often), which has just celebrated its 10th anniversary. But while it's rated consistently well, even so it can seem a case of "much hype about nothing", and its albeit good ratings are not in the same league as its famous stablemate, London's Anchor & Hope. / www.magdalenarms.com; @magdalen_arms; Mon-Sat 11 pm, Sun 10.30 pm; No Amex; No bookings.

MY SICHUAN £41 422

THE OLD SCHOOL, GLOUCESTER GRN OX1 2DA 01865 236 899

"Your tastebuds are in for a roller-coaster ride" at this "madhouse of a venue, packed with Chinese diners" – less on account of its spartan décor than its "very strong spice combinations" and "outstanding" dishes of offal, etc ("put your concerns behind you…chitterlings are lovely!"). "There's a lot more competition in the Chinese restaurant market nowadays, but this place still more than holds its own against the best". / www.mysichuan.co.uk; Sun-Thu 11 pm, Fri & Sat midnight.

NO.1 SHIP STREET £56 323

1 SHIP STREET OX1 3DA 01865 806637

"At last Oxford is getting some good restaurants" say fans of this very central Gallic-tinted British brasserie, est. 2017, who praise its "super" food and a well-appointed interior (green walls, copper tables) that "feels special" – partly due to fancy additions like the dedicated cocktail and Champagne/oyster bars. It did, though, also inspire the odd 'off' report. / www.no1shipstreet.com; @no1shipstreet; Mon-Sat 10 pm, Sun 4.30 pm.

OLI'S THAI   £35   5 4 3

38 MAGDALEN RD   OX4 1RB
01865 790223

"Still the best restaurant in Oxford" – especially if you're into Thai food – this cult café delivers grub that's "packed with flavour, in simple surroundings at immensely reasonable prices"; accordingly, it's "disappointingly impossible to get a table" (unless you book ages in advance). / www.olisthai.com; @olisthai; Tue-Fri 9 pm, Sat 2.30 pm; Take bookings all week via phone and/or online.

THE OXFORD KITCHEN   £70   3 2 2

215 BANBURY RD   OX2 7HQ
01865 511 149

"The food is imaginative and amazing" according to fans of chef Paul Welburn's noteworthy gem, buried on Summertown's main shopping street, and "recently M-starred". Feedback was more uneven this year though, with quite a few reporters disappointed, albeit acknowledging that the trip wasn't all that bad ("dishes were technically accomplished, but they felt like they each could have lost a few ingredients – too many competing flavours…"; "might have been one of those evenings, but service was up and down…"; "the food was good, but the wine pairings were odd…"). / www.theoxfordkitchen.co.uk; @Kitchenoxford; No trainers; Take bookings all week via phone and/or online.

THE PERCH   £52   3 4 3

BINSEY LN   OX2 0NG   01865 7228891

This famous thatched pub by Port Meadow, where the countryside encroaches into Oxford, is "lovely on a summer's day for a meal outdoors" – and "highly recommended after a walk along the Thames if you're staying in Oxford". There has been a pub here for 800 years and the current building has hosted real and imaginary drinkers including Inspector Morse, C.S.Lewis and William Morris. Landlord Jon Ellse is from Oxford pub royalty – his father ran the Turf Tavern. / www.the-perch.co.uk; @theperchoxford; Mon-Sat 9.30 pm, Sun 9 pm; Take bookings all week via phone and/or online.

PIERRE VICTOIRE   £45   3 3 3

LITTLE CLARENDON ST   OX1 2HP
01865 316616

This "utterly reliable bistro" – serving "simple, classic French food and quaffable wines" – "really hits the target for the price"; it has been "one of the best places to eat well and cheaply in Oxford" for more than 20 years. Once part of a franchised national chain that lost its way, this branch has remained true to "old-style charm and professionalism" – "it reminds me of the best bits of the Seventies!" "There must come a time when we'll tire of the overly fancy and return to the straightforward reassurance of Gallic culinary flair, done well for the time-poor". / www.pierrevictoire.co.uk; Mon-Sat 11 pm,

Sun 10 pm; No Amex; Take bookings all week via phone and/or online.

POMPETTE   £66   4 3 3

7 SOUTH PARADE   OX2 7JL
01865 311166

"A very welcome arrival on the Oxford map" – in Summertown – Pascal and Laura Wiedemann's charcuterie, wine bar and dining room offers "beautiful" dishes, in a similar Gallic mould to Pascal's former work at London's Racine and Terroirs. Many reporters note that the lunch prix fixe is "an especially great deal", while dinner is much less of a steal. / www.pompetterestaurant.co.uk; @Pompetterestau1; Tue-Sat 10 pm, Sun 3 pm.

THE PORTERHOUSE   £57   3 4 3

MILL STREET   OX2 0AL   01865 248546

"First class steaks" and "excellent wine pairings" help win enthusiastic reviews for this large, attractively converted pub near the train station, which opened a couple of years ago. / www.theporterhouse-oxford.com; @porterhouseox; Mon-Sun 9.30 pm.

QUOD, OLD BANK HOTEL   £50   2 3 4

92-94 HIGH ST   OX1 4BJ   01865 202505

"Right in the heart of Oxford", this "busy" and well-known bistro (part of the Old Bank Hotel) with a "lovely courtyard", has a solid reputation for "cooking that's not fancy but reliable and decent value". Attractions include "an excellent breakfast with first-rate coffee". / www.oldbank-hotel.co.uk; @quodrestaurant; Booking max 10 may apply.

SOJO   £39   4 3 2

6-9 HYTHE BRIDGE ST   OX1 2EW
01865 202888

"Every dish we have tried is a delight", say fans of this low-key haunt near the station, serving Cantonese, Shanghainese and Sichuan dishes. The "mezzanine floor is usually full of Chinese customers – a good sign for this well-priced, authentic, no-frills spot". / www.sojooxford.co.uk; Mon-Sat 11 pm, Sun 10 pm; No bookings.

TURL STREET KITCHEN   £46   3 3 3

16 TURL ST   OX1 3DH   01865 264 171

Bang, slap in the heart of the town, this almost "rustic" spot with "wooden floors and bare tables" is part of a social enterprise, with a dining room opening off a very busy coffee shop. "There's a limited choice, but always something of interest" – "simple dishes, simply served" by "sweet staff". Not a particularly foodie hotspot, but "there's nothing not to like here". / www.turlstreetkitchen.co.uk; @turlstkitchen; Mon & Tue, Sun 5 pm, Wed-Sat 11 pm; Take bookings all week via phone and/or online.

THE VAULTS AND GARDEN CAFE   £21   4 3 3

UNIVERSITY CHURCH OF ST MARY THE VIRGIN, RADCLIFFE SQ   OX1 4AH
01865 279112

"A great Oxford institution" set in the "fifteenth-century vaults of the university church" – this ethical and organic café makes an "excellent stop-off point during a busy day in Oxford" – whether you're shopping or studying texts next door in the Bodleian Library. "Superb coffee, decent food and a very civilised atmosphere, despite sometimes being crowded". / www.thevaultsandgarden.com; @VaultsandGarden.

ZHENG   £39   4 3 3

82 WALTON ST   OX2 6EA   01865 51 11 88

"Small space, big food!" – the winning formula behind this "great Far Eastern" venue, whose menu dexterously hops from Malaysia to Singapore and China (in a good way). It's "very noisy and appeals to the younger crowd because of the pricing and fairly large portions". / www.zhengoxford.co.uk; Mon, Wed-Sun, Tue 11 pm; Take bookings all week via phone and/or online.

OXTON, CHESHIRE   5–2A

FRAICHE   £116   5 4 3

11 ROSE MOUNT   CH43 5SG
0151 652 2914

"One of the best in the country" – Marc Williamson "never fails to please and delight with his superb food, excellent wine list, and friendly and knowledgeable staff" at this "very intimate" venture on the edge of Birkenhead. In December 2018 he closed the restaurant with plans to move across The Mersey into Liverpool and double in size from his existing 12 seats (it's so small, you need to book months in advance). After a March 2019 rethink, though, he decided against scaling up and decided to stay put and do a minor refurb. As he commented in the Liverpool Echo, after he'd decided against going down the expansion route: 'For good or bad, you get 100% of me – the décor is me, the visuals are me, the music is me. I care, I guess – it's a passion'. / restaurantfraiche.com; @marcatfraiche; Wed-Sun 9.30 pm; No Amex.

OXWICH, SWANSEA   1–1D

BEACH HOUSE   £60   5 4 4

OXWICH BEACH   SA3 1LS   01792 390965

For "a wonderful meal in a fantastic setting", it's worth a trip to this three-year-old venture: a stylish, airy dining room with vaulted ceiling, looking right onto the sand beach of Oxwich Bay. Chef Hywell Griffith and his team are on view in the open kitchen and offer a choice of à la carte and tasting menus (the latter five courses for £50 or eight for £80). In October 2019, it became one of six restaurants now blessed by Michelin in Wales. Top Tip – "it's that rarest of destinations with wonderful cuisine that also offers an excellent kids' menu and is a treat for that alone. Good for the foodie parent on holiday – no more pizza!" / www.beachhouseoxwich.co.uk; @beachouseoxwich; Take bookings all week via phone and/or online.

APPLETONS AT THE VINEYARD   £70   ３３４

DARK LANE PL27 7SE 01841 541355

"Windows overlooking the vineyard" afford views onto this peacefully located spot – run by Andy Appleton (a graduate of Jamie Oliver's Fifteen Cornwall) although the "huge barn" it occupies can feel a tad "quiet" at less busy times. Numerous "excellent" meals are reported this year from its Med-slanted modern British menu. / www.appletonsatthevineyard.com; @_Appletons; Wed & Thu 2.30 pm, Fri & Sat 9 pm, Sun 2 am.

PAUL AINSWORTH AT NO. 6   £88   ５４４

6 MIDDLE ST PL28 8AP 01841 532093

"Outstanding… that is all!". Paul Ainsworth's intimate and illustrious ten-year-old is nowadays the most-mentioned operation in town, far eclipsing Rick Stein's nearby Seafood Restaurant in terms of the excitement it generates. "The kitchen can be seen from the tables, and is a dream to watch", with "Paul himself almost invariably present". The cuisine is as you might hope for – "technically accomplished, with quality materials, some inventiveness, and carefully prepared to preserve flavours". "However, it's the attention to detail, and the overwhelming passion for the place from its staff" that seals the experience for some diners: "nothing was too much trouble". / www.number6inpadstow.co.uk; @no6padstow; Mon-Fri 6 pm, Sat 5 pm, Sun 3 pm; No Amex; children: 4+.

PRAWN ON THE LAWN   £55   ５４３

11 DUKE STREET PL28 8AB 01841 532223

"Just brilliant, incredibly fresh seafood" is the payoff for a visit to Rick & Katie Toogood's "very small" and "cramped" venture (24 covers), which – since they made the move from Islington in 2015 – has shown it can compete with the best of the best in this foodie enclave. (They still also own the restaurant of the same name in N1.) / prawnonthelawn.com; @PrawnOnTheLawn; Take bookings all week via phone and/or online.

RICK STEIN'S CAFÉ   £52   ３４２

10 MIDDLE STREET PL28 8AP 01841 532700

One of six Stein venues in the Cornish capital of his empire, this casual outfit is notable for its "very good value", and wins solid ratings for a "limited menu of well-cooked" fish and seafood. / www.rickstein.com; @TheSeafood; No Amex; Booking evening only.

ROJANOS IN THE SQUARE   £52   ４３２

9 MILL SQ PL28 8AE 01841 532 796

A Padstow institution since 1974, this Med-inspired outfit has been owned for the past 10 years by Paul Ainsworth of No 6. The menu runs from "delicious roast monkfish and really tasty pork chop and crackling" to "top pizza". "Friendly and informal service" too. / www.paul-ainsworth.co.uk/rojanos-in-the-square; @rojanos; Take bookings all week via phone and/or online.

SEAFOOD RESTAURANT   £86   ３３３

RIVERSIDE PL28 8BY 01841 532700

Harsher reports say the Stein family's "large and buzzing" HQ near the harbour wall (but without any views) is "overpriced and you're paying for the name". But, a more representative view on the cradle of Rick Stein's TV celebrity is that "despite the close proximity of the tables in the dining room, it's still worth a visit". Yes, probably there are restaurants "just as good but cheaper elsewhere in Cornwall" (and it's not in the same league as Nathan Outlaw's restaurants down the coast), but most reports still acclaim its "good choice" of "fantastic and well-prepared fish", agreeable atmosphere and "friendly, knowledgeable staff". / www.rickstein.com/eat-with-us/the-seafood-; @TheSeafood; Sun-Fri 9.45 pm, Sat 9.30 pm; No Amex; Booking max 14 may apply; children: 3+.

HURTWOOD INN   £63   ３３２

WALKING BOTTOM GU5 9RR 01306 731769

"Good Italian food in the Surrey Hills" is to be found in this substantial village pub, now operated by an Italian team that ran restaurants in Guildford for three decades. The bar menu of pizzas and pasta is complemented by a more formal menu in the restaurant. / hurtwoodinn.com; Sun-Thu 9 pm, Fri & Sat 9.30 pm.

SHILLINGFORDS AT THE FORAGERS RETREAT   £47   ４４４

THE COURTYARD CO10 2AN 01787 389123

Carl and Beth Shillingford have moved from nearby arts venue, The Quay in Sudbury, to these converted former stables, "in the middle of a small village". "With a carefully constructed ever-changing menu, Carl manages to forage for and produce the most wonderful food with ingredients garnered from the Suffolk countryside": "amazing!". / theforagersretreat.co.uk; Take bookings all week via phone and/or online.

CRINGLETIE HOUSE   £49   ３３３

EDINBURGH RD EH45 8PL 01721 725750

A "fabulous place to stay in the Scottish Borders", with "delicious food" (including afternoon tea) and a "great garden", this grand Victorian mansion in the Scots Baronial Revival style has been a hotel for almost 50 years. Less than an hour from Edinburgh, it has been lavishly restored by the current owners since 2003. / www.cringletie.com; @CringletieHouse; Take bookings all week via phone and/or online; children: 4.

RESTAURANT JAMES SOMMERIN   £88   ４２４

THE ESPLANADE CF64 3AU 07722 216 727

James Sommerin runs his Beach Cliff venue with the help of his wife, Louise, and it's a swish contemporary operation, with views internally through the long hatch into the kitchen and externally of the sea and pier. The chef is "an artist" and his "superb modern British cuisine" establishes "what a very seriously good restaurant this is". Even so, ratings slid a little this year amidst gripes about toppish prices and a few reports of service that was "not special". / www.jamessommerinrestaurant.co.uk; @RestaurantJS.

ASKHAM HALL   £73   ４４５

ASKHAM CA10 01931 712350

Talk about ticking the boxes! Set in beautiful Cumbrian countryside, check… "historical" mansion that looks a bit like a castle, check… wonderful grounds with kitchen garden, check – this Lakeland hotel makes a marvellous and "romantic" destination, and boasts a "fantastic restaurant in the old hall" serving Richard Swale's highly accomplished cooking, with the option of a tasting menu format. And as of October 2019, Michelin star, check. / www.askhamhall.co.uk; @AskhamHall; Take bookings all week via phone and/or online; children: 10.

THE PIG, HUNSTRETE HOUSE   £53   ３４５

HUNSTRETE BS39 4NS 01761 490 490

"Such a lovely setting" (a Grade II-listed shabby-chic hotel) and a "wonderful surrounding area" – the Chew Valley, just south of Brizzle – are hard to beat, but fans claim that there's "food and service to match" at this venture, boasting a "true provenance of all-local ingredients" (much sourced from the "beautiful kitchen garden"). "Hope the extension of the chain doesn't result in a loss of focus" (it's now seven-strong and counting). / www.thepighotel.com/near-bath; @The_Pig_Hotel.

Engine Social Dining,
Sowerby Bridge

THE SHORE £53 533

**13-14 ALVERTON STREET TR18 2QP
01736 362444**

"Bruce Rennie is a wizard with fish, which is fresh from day boats in nearby Newlyn" – the reason to discover this small, modern bistro. "He now only offers a set, taster-style menu, but the food is brilliant considering it is only him at the stoves. Well worth a visit, but booking is absolutely essential". / www.theshorerestaurant.uk/; @The_Shore_Pz; No Amex; Take bookings all week via phone and/ or online.

TOLCARNE INN £48 433

TOLCARNE PL TR18 5PR 01736 363074

The "freshest seafood right off the boat from Newlyn Harbour" is the formula behind Ben Tunnicliffe's "fantastic" boozer, occupying a 300-year-old inn on the harbour. / www.tolcarneinn.co.uk; @tolcarneinn; Take bookings all week via phone and/or online.

VICTORIA INN £50

TR20 9NP 01736 710309

Ancient, low-ceilinged coastal Cornish pub, not far from St Michael's Mount, with a sunny beer garden. The food has been well-rated in recent times, but reports this year – which saw the departure of chef Nik Boyle to start his own (short-lived) venture in Falmouth – have a little more up-and-down, so we've left a rating till next year. / www.victoriainn-penzance.co.uk/; @victoriainn_pz; Tue-Fri 9 pm, Mon 9.30 pm, Sun 3 pm.

ECKINGTON MANOR £68 322

**HAMMOCK ROAD WR10 3BJ
01386 751600**

"The quality of the chef is well known and the major attraction" at this timbered country house hotel, helmed by MasterChef: The Professionals winner Mark Stinchcombe; yet while his "excellent" farm-to-fork cuisine generally pleases, service strikes some reporters as "average": "a tremendous amount of attention has been paid to the design of the cooking school adjacent but seemingly less to what makes a good fine-dining restaurant". / @EckingtonManor; Thu-Sat, Wed 9 pm, Sun 3.30 pm; Take bookings all week via phone and/ or online.

CAFE TABOU £61 332

4 ST JOHN'S PL PH1 5SZ 01738 446698

"A tiny touch of France in the centre of Perth, Scotland!" – Marek Michalak's "little gem" of a city-centre bistro is a "longtime good place" where "the à la carte menu changes seasonally but the daily specials are as they should be – wiped off the blackboard as they sell out. Specialities are steaks and seafood, and the wine list isn't to be sniffed at either, and won't break the bank". / www.cafetabou.com; @CafeTabouPerth; Sun, Mon 8 pm, Tue-Sat 9 pm; No Amex.

THE NORTH PORT £50 443

8 NORTH PORT PH1 5LU 01738 580867

Extensive dark-wood panelling and low ceilings help create a cosy, enveloping ambience at this small, traditional venture, run by Andrew Moss (chef) and Karen Milne (front of house). Highly acclaimed by Scottish press critics for its unhackneyed Scottish cuisine, a "good value lunch" is singled out for praise in our feedback. / www.thenorthport.co.uk.

63 TAY STREET £63 333

63 TAY ST PH2 8NN 01738 441451

Set up in 2007 by Slow Food aficionado Graeme Pallister, who trained at Kinloch House Hotel and the restaurant at Gleneagles, this elevated Scottish dining room, on the western banks of the Tay, remains a Perth gem that's "exceptional value early evening". / www.63taystreet.com; @63TayStreet; No Amex.

PREVOST £57 342

20 PRIESTGATE PE1 1JA 01733313623

Lee Clarke's ambitious Priestgate two-year-old accounted for some reporters' best meal of the year, with both its three-course menu and more extensive options (running to nine courses) inspiring the highest praise. There is the odd duff report, but on most accounts the culinary experience is "innovative, very enjoyable and good value for the level of cooking and service". / @foodleeclarke; No trainers; Credit card deposit required to book.

INDIAN ESSENCE £51 533

**176-178 PETTS WOOD RD BR5 1LG
01689 838 700**

"Not just a neighbourhood gem, but just about the best place for miles and miles around" – Atul Kochhar is a perhaps-unlikely name to be associated with an ordinary-looking venture in a suburban parade of shops in Petts Wood, but which helps explain its "very subtle Indian food with terrific flavours" from a menu that's "always interesting, with some mainstays that are worth ordering every time". In other respects, "it's got that local curry house feel: it's simply the food (and some nifty wines) which make it a superb standout". / www.indianessence.co.uk; @IndianEssence1; Tue-Thu, Mon 10.45 pm, Fri & Sat 11 pm, Sun 10.30 pm; No trainers; Take bookings all week via phone and/or online.

EAST STREET BAR & GRILL £76 333

NEW STREET GU28 0AS 01798 345 111

With its stylish interiors and large garden, this modern brasserie in the heart of the town offers an "accessible" menu, majoring in "excellent steaks and grills (including venison)". / www.newstreetbarandgrill.co.uk; @NewStreetBar; Wed-Sat 11 pm, Sun 9 pm.

FRIENDS £66 434

11 HIGH ST HA5 5PJ 020 8866 0286

"A new chef is bringing style and ambition to this lovely period building" – an "intimate" five-hundred-year-old Tudor structure in central Pinner where Stelian Scripcariu has taken over from Terry Farr (owner for over 25 years) at the stoves. A trip "can work out expensive" (nothing new there) but all local reporters say it's "well worth a visit". / www.friendsrestaurant.co.uk; Take bookings all week via phone and/or online.

ROCK SALT £50 543

**31 STONEHOUSE ST PL1 3PE
01752 225522**

A "perennial favourite local relaxed foodie joint", this ex-pub turned "bistro-cum-cafe-cum-restaurant" goes from strength to strength as a showcase for the "inventive food" of chef-owner Dave Jenkins, whose dishes "always delight, with lovely little touches and innovations that make total sense once you've tasted them". They serve "great breakfasts, good-value lunches", and "the best Sunday roast in town". / www.rocksaltcafe.co.uk; @rocksaltcafeuk; Mon-Sun 11 pm; No Amex; Booking max 6 may apply.

THE GREEDY GOOSE £38 323

**PRYSTEN HOUSE, FINEWELL ST PL1 2AE
01494 863566**

A Grade I listed house from 1487 that was "one of the few buildings in Plymouth to survive WW2 bombing" – Ben and Francesca Palmer's "delightful" venture delivers "good food at great value". Top Tip: on Tuesdays the 11-course tasting menu is half price, at £45. / www.thegreedygoose.co.uk; @greedygooseplym; Take bookings all week via phone and/or online; children: 4.

SAMS ON THE BEACH £47 334

PL24 2TL 01726 812255

As per the name, this converted lifeboat station "couldn't be closer to the beach, and sandy children are made very welcome"; add in "excellent wood-fired pizzas", "friendly staff" and "well-cooked fresh seafood" and it's a major hit. / www.samscornwall.co.uk; @samscornwall; No Amex.

POOLE, DORSET   2–4C

BRANKSOME BEACH   £58 3|3|3

PINECLIFF RD BH13 6LP 01202 767235

This "seafront diner with great views" "in a great location" – an Art Deco 1930s solarium overlooking Poole Harbour – serves up an all-day mix of breakfast, snacks, fish and grills, with dinner in the summer months and plenty of al fresco tables. It also offers "rare good value" this close to Sandbanks. / www.branksomebeach.co.uk; @branksome_beach; Mon-Sun 5 pm.

GUILDHALL TAVERN   £55 4|4|4

15 MARKET STREET BH15 1NB 01202 671717

"Very good fresh fish and seafood" – "landed in the harbour 50 feet away" – is the USP at this French family-run operation, where staff "keep the entente as cordiale as possible". It's been "a favourite for more than 10 years", and "early booking is recommended". / www.guildhalltavern.co.uk; Tue-Thu 9.30 pm, Fri & Sat 10 pm; No Amex; Take bookings all week via phone and/or online.

POOLEY BRIDGE, CUMBRIA   7–3D

1863 BAR BISTRO ROOMS   £55

ELM HOUSE, HIGH STREET CA10 2NH 017684 86334

Small (about 30 covers) Lakeland bar-bistro with a high level of ambition; feedback was too limited for a rating this year – the cooking seems dependable, but if there's a complaint it's over portion sizes. / www.1863ullswater.co.uk; @1863Ullswater; children: 10.

PORT APPIN, ARGYLL AND BUTE   9–3B

AIRDS HOTEL   £84 3|4|3

PA38 4DF 01631 730236

A Relais & Châteaux property – "a wonderful hotel in a beautiful lochside location" (a former ferry inn) whose "very fine restaurant" has been "a top-notch destination for many, many years" thanks to its "first-class, French-inspired" food, including seafood and game – "long may it continue!" / www.airds-hotel.com; @AirdsHotel; No jeans; children: 8+ at D.

PIERHOUSE HOTEL £67 4|4|5

PA38 4DE 01631 730302

A former piermaster's house is the setting for this hotel dining room, which boasts epic views over Loch Linnhe to Lismore, and whose food focuses on simply cooked but superb fishy fare, be it oysters from nearby Loch Ceran or mussels and langoustines from Loch Linnhe (though game fans are also in for a treat). /

www.pierhousehotel.co.uk; @pierhousehotel; Take bookings all week via phone and/or online.

PORT ISAAC, CORNWALL   1–3B

FRESH FROM THE SEA   £23 3|3|3

18 NEW ROAD PL29 01208 880849

"Nathan Outlaw fully booked? Console yourself with the finest crab sandwich ever", from Calum & Tracey Greenhalgh's fishmonger and café. You won't find fresher seafood – Calum sets out in his boat the Mary D every day to catch crab and lobster using pots, and pollack, mackerel and bass by handline. / www.freshfromthesea.co.uk; No Amex; No bookings.

OUTLAW'S FISH KITCHEN   £56 5|4|4

1 MIDDLE ST PL29 3RH 01208 881138

"Fabulous, small plates of fishiness" – "each mouthful a truly memorable experience" – help inspire nothing but praise for Nathan Outlaw's "tiny and atmospheric" spin-off venture, which has a "fantastic location", "set on the quayside" of this Cornish fishing village and "doing full justice to the locally caught produce". Compared with his posh gaff, dishes are "simpler, but just as fine in their own way", and even fans of both establishments may feel that "although it's not as pricey or fancy as his main place in town, this is actually better value and more enjoyable". / www.nathan-outlaw.com/restaurants/outlaws-fish-kitchen; @outlawsgrubclub; Take bookings all week via phone and/or online.

PORT GAVERNE HOTEL   £55 3|2|3

PL29 3SQ 01208 880244

"Fish and seafood dishes are the ones to go for" at this privately run hotel and restaurant – a local "favourite" owing to the "consistent quality from the kitchen" (though service can be a tad "variable" at times). / www.portgavernehotel.co.uk; @PortGaverne; Mon-Thu 10.30 pm, Fri & Sat 10.45 pm; No Amex; Take bookings all week via phone and/or online; children: 7+.

RESTAURANT NATHAN OUTLAW   £173 5|5|4

6 NEW RD PL29 3SB 01208 880 896

"Certainly the best restaurant in the region, perhaps the country!" Nathan Outlaw's acclaimed flagship sits on a clifftop in a picturesque north Cornish village (home to TV's Doc Martin) and while "the exterior of the building is underwhelming", "the room itself is lovely, with perfectly positioned tables"… and "my god the view out of the windows is breathtaking". On the menu – "a procession of the most delicious fish and seafood imaginable": "supremely clean and pure in their premise and construction, with flavours that either hit you round the chops or melt down your throat in nuanced waves".

Service is "top class" – "warm, personal and professional, and with very appropriate wine suggestions". A quibble? Many reports note that a trip here is "so expensive", "even more so with the wine flight". But even so, the investment almost invariably "feels like money well spent": "was it worth the 625-mile round trip? – unquestionably YES". Top Tip – "use an app to book local parking if you are coming in season, as Port Isaac is tiny and parking is extremely limited". / www.nathan-outlaw.com; @ResNathanOutlaw; Take bookings all week via phone and/or online; children: 10.

STARGAZY INN   £55 4|4|4

1 THE TERRACE PL29 3SG 01208 811516

Some "outstanding" meals are reported at this newly refurbished hotel (formerly Bay Hotel (aka Wenn House in TV's Doc Martin) and under the same ownership as the nearby Port Gaverne Hotel and Pilchards Café. There's not yet enough feedback yet to back up those who claim it's "on a par with Nathan Outlaw opposite", but suffice to say that the comparison's not a preposterous one with unanimously high ratings awarded to Great British Menu chef, Andrew Sheridan's cuisine – either simpler items from the à la carte, or fancier five-course and seven-course tasting options. / stargazyinn.co.uk; @StargazyinnStay; Tue-Sat, Mon 10.30 pm, Sun 6 pm.

PORTHGAIN, PEMBROKESHIRE   4–4B

THE SHED   £39 4|3|3

SA62 5BN 01348 831518

"Set in a gorgeous spot looking out over the harbour in a surprisingly unspoilt village" – this "small bistro" is one of the better options for a meal in striking distance of St Davids: you get "sophisticated dishes of fresh-from-the-sea fish, plus friendly staff and a quaint ambience". Fish 'n' chips, here, are also some of the best: "melt in the mouth, crispy, light batter with the freshest of fish". / www.theshedporthgain.co.uk; @ShedPorthgain; No Amex; No bookings.

PORTHLEVEN, CORNWALL   1–4A

KOTA   £64 4|3|3

HARBOUR HEAD TR13 9JA 01326 562407

Jude Kereama's cooking takes inspiration from his half Maori and half Chinese Malay origin, and fans say it just "gets better and better" at this "wonderful restaurant full of atmosphere" in a "picturesque" fishing village on the "deep south-west Cornish coast", which he runs with his wife Jane. / www.kotarestaurant.co.uk; @KotaRestaurant; No Amex; Take bookings all week via phone and/or online.

KOTA KAI   £49 3|3|3

CELTIC HOUSE, HARBOUR HEAD TR13 9JY 01326 574411

The "more relaxed sister of Kota" is an "informal, light-filled room overlooking the harbour", and a "useful alternative for lunch when Kota is closed – (Great British Menu chef)

Jude Kereama's presence is much in evidence here": result? "assured" Pan-Asian cuisine that's "much more imaginative than the usual seaside fare" – www.kotakai.co.uk; @Kota_Kai; Mon & Tue, Thu-Sat 9 pm, Sun 2.30 pm; No Amex; Take bookings all week via phone and/or online.

RICK STEINS SEAFOOD RESTAURANT £64 3️⃣3️⃣4️⃣

MOUNT PLEASANT TR13 9JS 01841 532700

"A lovely harbourside location", plus a "glossy and glamorous" interior – created from a former warehouse – help win a very high level of feedback for this celebrity-branded fish and seafood restaurant; and "when all is on form, this branch of the Stein empire is one of the better ones", delivering on the promise of "excellent local fish, perfectly cooked" that the name leads you to expect. Some misfires are reported ("starter was gritty and main slathered in buttery sauce"), but mostly it earns a good rep. As one regular notes: "food and service is somewhat dependent on what you choose and which waiter or waitress you get: results can be very good, if not cheap, and service can be rather disinterested and impersonal, or friendly and efficient". / www.rickstein.com; @TheSeafood; Take bookings all week via phone and/or online; children: 3.

THE SQUARE AT PORTHLEVEN £35 3️⃣3️⃣3️⃣

7 FORE STREET TR13 9HQ 01326 573 911

Overlooking the harbour – and with an outside terrace for sunny days – this modern brasserie is well worth knowing about. "Its local reputation of this restaurant has not diminished at all over the last twelve months thanks to its excellent menu helpful staff and reasonable prices". / www.thesquareatporthleven.co.uk; @thesquarepl; No Amex; Take bookings all week via phone and/or online.

PORTMEIRION, GWYNEDD 4–2C

PORTMEIRION HOTEL £76 3️⃣4️⃣5️⃣

LL48 6ET 01766 772440

This intriguing Art Deco hotel dining room with "amazing views" has long been a major attraction of the famous Mediterranean-style village in the Welsh countryside, dreamt up in the early twentieth century by architect Clough Williams-Ellis. The food has been less reliable in recent times, but "over the past couple of years, the menu has improved dramatically", and the kitchen is starting to recover the "fabulous" form that for so long made the venue a "must-do experience in this part of the world". / portmeirion.wales/eat/hotel-portmeirion/the-dining-room; @portmeirion; Mon-Sat 1 am, Sun midnight.

PORTSMOUTH, HAMPSHIRE 2–4D

ABARBISTRO £47 3️⃣2️⃣3️⃣

58 WHITE HART RD PO1 2JA 02392 811585

A short stroll from the Historic Dockyard, Gunwharf Quays and sea front, this long-established bistro (with outside terrace in summer) is a "reliable" option for straightforward fare that's "good value for money". "Excellent wines too", as they run a bottle shop upstairs. / www.abarbistro.co.uk; @abarbistro; Mon-Sun 10 pm.

PORTSTEWART, COUNTY LONDONDERRY 10–1D

HARRY'S SHACK £47 3️⃣3️⃣4️⃣

118 STRAND ROAD BT55 7PG 028 7083 1783

The last of the local Harry's chain "does what it says on the tin – it's a shack on Portstewart Strand serving cracking seafood straight out of the sea" (as well as other dishes, using ingredients sourced from their organic farm). / www.facebook.com/HarrysShack; @Harrys_Shack; Sun & Mon 8.30 pm, Tue-Thu 9 pm, Fri & Sat 9.30 pm.

PRESTON BAGOT, WARWICKSHIRE 5–4C

THE CRABMILL £48 3️⃣3️⃣3️⃣

B95 5EE 01926 843342

"Much improved by a change of owners" (the all-conquering Brunning & Price), this seventeenth century pub in "beautiful surroundings" – a hamlet "out in Warwickshire's lush countryside" – wins applause for "upmarket pub food at a reasonable price point", and which comes "allied to lovely service" to boot. / www.crabmillpub.co.uk; Mon-Sat 11 pm, Sun 6 pm; No Amex; Take bookings all week via phone and/or online.

PRESTON, LANCASHIRE 5–1A

BUKHARA £28 3️⃣3️⃣2️⃣

154 PRESTON NEW RD PR5 0UP 01772 877710

This large, modern roadside outfit, just off the M6 near Preston, has established an enviable reputation for its "well cooked, authentic Indian food" over the last 15 years. "Pity it looks rather like a works canteen". Important to note: it is alcohol free. / www.bukharasamlesbury.co.uk; @bukhara; Mon-Sun 11 pm; Take bookings all week via phone and/or online.

QUEENSBURY, MIDDLESEX 3–3A

REGENCY CLUB £30 4️⃣3️⃣3️⃣

19-21 QUEENSBURY STATION PDE HA8 5NR 020 8952 6300

"High-quality grilled food and delicious, freshly cooked curries" as influenced by East Africa are the order of the day at this wood-panelled institution, established in 1991 and based on the Indian community's private clubs in Kenya.

It is "super-popular with northwest London's Indians" and with sports fans ("there's live TV sport most days"), while Lily Allen has also graced its tables. / www.regencyclub.co.uk; @RegencyClubUK; Mon-Sat 11 pm, Sun 10.30 pm; Take bookings all week via phone and/or online; children: 18+.

RADNAGE, BUCKINGHAMSHIRE 3–2A

MASH INN £86 5️⃣4️⃣4️⃣

HORSESHOE RD, BENNETT END HP14 4EB 01494 482 440

Nick Mash's three-year-old operation occupies a converted 18th century inn set in scenic countryside. Reporters "cannot fault it", from the "passionate" and "friendly staff" to the "perfect" cooking, using "mainly locally sourced ingredients" (many of them from the kitchen garden), which are "cooked with great flair" over a bespoke wood-fired grill. / www.themashinn.com.

RAMSBOTTOM, LANCASHIRE 5–1B

BARATXURI £47 4️⃣4️⃣3️⃣

1 SMITHY ST BL0 9AT 01706 559090

Levanter's "brilliant" sibling is nowadays "really two restaurants in one" since they expanded into the adjacent shop and added a 'comedor' (dining room) for larger dishes – suckling pig, etc – cooked in the wood-fired Pereruela oven. By most accounts "the original bar half is definitely better" thanks to its "interesting pintxos (some on colourful display along the bar, some to order) and small plates". The more substantial dishes "can seem to turn out less interesting than they sound", though, leaving an "overrated" impression with one or two diners. / www.levanterfinefoods.co.uk/baratxuri; @BaratxuriBar; Thu-Sat midnight, Wed 11 pm, Sun 6.30 pm.

EAGLE & CHILD £53 3️⃣3️⃣3️⃣

3 WHALLEY ROAD BL0 0DL 01706 557181

On the outskirts of Ramsbottom, this small inn on the village green was recently well-renovated and has a "good beer garden". "Any lack of polish service-wise is compensated for by the staff's enthusiasm and willingness". "Good quality, traditional British food, with regional variations, and some home-grown vegetables, works well". / eagle-and-child.com; @EagleChildRammy; Mon-Fri 9 pm, Sat & Sun 9.30 pm; No Amex.

THE HUNGRY DUCK £46 2️⃣3️⃣2️⃣

76 BRIDGE STREET BL0 9AG 01706 550899

Opened in 2015, Joe Kaczmar's small venture offers modern brasserie fare produced by chef Cassie Bond and her team. The rating was dragged down by the odd reporter who found it a little overpriced, given somewhat cramped conditions and a lack of smoothness service-wise, but all reports say the staff are pleasant and the food of good quality. / www.hungry-duck.co.uk; @HungryDuckUK; Mon-

Sat 9.30 pm, Sun 8 pm; Take bookings all week via phone and/or online.

LEVANTER £51 5 3 4

10 SQUARE ST BL0 9BE 01706 551530

"In the centre of this undistinguished Lancashire town, this two-tiered venue with its open kitchen comes close to taking your breath away" – "quite what Ramsbottom ever did to deserve such a bustling, authentic tapas bar remains a mystery". "Sparkling dishes ("often relying on specialist Spanish ingredients") are as fresh and delicious as they come", prices are "encouraging" and "the friendly staff make eating in this sometimes packed restaurant a pleasure". "It's also probably the only Andalusian bar in the UK to which you can travel by steam train!" / www.levanterfinefoods.co.uk; @levanterfoods; Wed 11 pm; Take bookings all week via phone and/or online.

RAMSGATE, KENT 3–3D

THE EMPIRE ROOM, ROYAL HARBOUR HOTEL £40 4 4 4

10-12 NELSON CRESCENT CT11 9JF 01843 582511

With its "deep red walls, low lighting and candles", this "romantic" basement dining room has a "lovely, old-fashioned and cosy ambience, and is decorated with framed covers of old editions of Empire magazine". Craig Mather's modern British menu focuses on "unfussy dishes, where the local seasonal ingredients are the star", in particular "fish that comes straight from the small boats which ply the harbour". / theempireroom.co.uk/; @EmpRoom; Wed-Sat 9.30 pm, Sun 3 pm.

FLAVOURS BY KUMAR £39 4 4 2

2 EFFINGHAM ST CT11 9AT 01843 852631

"Tasty and unusual Indian food with a modern twist" comes as a "big surprise" at Anil Kumar's "superb" pub conversion, "tucked away down an uninspiring narrow road" – it's "not your average curry house by a country mile". / www.flavoursbykumar.co.uk; @flavoursbykumar; Take bookings all week via phone and/or online.

LITTLE SHIPS £57 4 3 3

54-56 HARBOUR PARADE CT11 8LN 01843 585008

"Chef Craig Mather revels in the abundance of local, seasonal produce" and "the locally built Harrison charcoal-fuelled oven works its magic on meats, veg and fish" at this "great addition to the harbour front" (est. June 2018 together with hotelier James Thomas, also of Ramsgate's Empire Room). The name – and décor – nod to the flotilla of private boats that evacuated troops from Dunkirk. / littleshipsramsgate. wordpress.com.

The Clock House, Ripley

RAMSGILL-IN-NIDDERDALE, NORTH YORKSHIRE 8–4B

YORKE ARMS £108 3 2 4

HG3 5RL 01423 755243

Frances Atkins remains involved with the "beautifully situated" coaching inn that she helped make famous, and which she and husband Bill sold in 2018 to local entrepreneur Jonathan Turner. Its ratings slipped a notch this year, though – not due to grievous complaints, but on the back of a few mixed reports (e.g. "food good, but service rather haphazard and felt overhyped"; or "meal was good, but didn't hit the heights, and not good value at over £200"). But many reporters do continue to acclaim it as their best gastronomic experience of the year, or say "it's even better after the recent renovations". / www.theyorkearms.co.uk; @theyorkearms.

READING, BERKSHIRE 2–2D

LONDON STREET BRASSERIE £61 3 2 3

RIVERSIDE ORACLE, 2 - 4 LONDON STREET RG1 4PN 0118 950 5036

The "best thing in central Reading" (not to dismiss the city's charms naturally) – this "unexpected gem" enjoys a "wonderful location" in an eighteenth century tollhouse, and the food is "interesting" and "well-cooked" to boot. / www.londonstbrasserie.co.uk; @lsb_reading; Sun-Thu 10.30 pm, Fri & Sat 11 pm; Take bookings all week via phone and/or online.

THAMES LIDO £40 4 4 4

NAPIER ROAD RG1 8FR 0118 207 0640

"Reading? It feels more like you're in San Francisco" at this "fantastic" three-year-old venture, where "you can watch the swimmers" in the Edwardian lido, rescued after 40 years' dereliction by the people behind Bristol's Lido. "The décor, lighting, setting and service are modern, and the food Mediterranean/North African fusion, with fish and shellfish to the fore". "We love the lido!" – "anyone with a sense of adventure will not be disappointed". / www.thameslido.com; @ThamesLido.

REEPHAM, NORFOLK 6–4C

THE DIAL HOUSE

MARKET PLACE NR10 4JJ 01603 879900

"An excellent breakfast" is the top tip at Hannah Springham and Andrew Jones's good-looking, Georgian restaurant with rooms: sibling to Norwich's Farmyard. For other occasions, feedback on its straightforward, brasserie-style fare (fish pie, côte de boeuf, burger) is still too limited for a rating. / www.thedialhouse.org.uk/; @thedialhouse.

REIGATE, SURREY 3–3B

LA BARBE £59 4 4 3

71 BELL ST RH2 7AN 01737 241966

"Beautifully presented, authentically French food" – "some of the best I've tasted outside France" – earns consistently high ratings for Serge Tassi's veteran bistro as it approaches its 40th anniversary. The largely French staff ensure that service is "stylish but not over-complicated", and that the dishes are "cooked by somebody who really understands flavour and texture". / www.labarbe.co.uk; @LaBarbeReigate; Tue-Sat 9 pm, Sun 2 pm; Take bookings all week via phone and/or online.

RETFORD, LINCOLNSHIRE 6–2A

MARKHAM MOOR INN £40 3 3 3

OLD GREAT NORTH ROAD DN22 0QU 01777 838229

Just off the A1, this 300-year-old inn, run by Stephen & Laura Heath since 1999, "always delivers super food at a great price", and errs on the finer side of pub grub with "good mid-week deals to look out for". / www.markhammoorinn.co.uk; @markhammoorinn.

RICHMOND, SURREY 3–3A

CHEZ LINDSAY £49 3 3 3

11 HILL RISE TW10 6UQ 020 8948 7473

"One of the mainstays of Richmond over many years" – this "lovely little bistro" near the bridge provides "a touch of Brittany with its galettes (savoury and sweet) and cidre bouche (though they also do offer a wider menu as well"); added marks for the "river view (if you ask for it)". / www.chez-lindsay.co.uk; @Chez_Lindsay; Mon-Sat

Yorke Arms, Ramsgill-in-Nidderdale

11 pm, Sun 10 pm; No Amex; Take bookings all week via phone and/or online.

RIPLEY, SURREY 3–3A

ANCHOR £62 3 3 3

HIGH ST GU23 6AE 01483 211866

"Upmarket" Surrey village pub that's "maintained a very good standard": a meal is "always enjoyable, always good value and a friendly experience". Young chef Mike Wall-Palmer and colleague Dave Adams have recently bought out the previous owner, Steve Drake, who wants to concentrate on Sorrel, his well-known Dorking restaurant. / www.ripleyanchor.co.uk; @RipleyAnchor; Mon-Sat 9 pm, Sun 8 pm; Take bookings all week via phone and/or online.

THE CLOCK HOUSE £81 5 4 4

THE CLOCK HOUSE, HIGH STREET GU23 6AQ 01483 224777

"A sublime experience" – Serina Drake's "lovely" converted Georgian house is a "delightful building in a lovely village" which provides "fine dining, but without the associated pretentiousness". Fred Clapperton's deft but un-gimmicky cuisine is credited with many "exceptional" meals here, aided by the attitude of the "friendly and personable staff". "It's particularly gorgeous in the beautiful walled garden on a warm day". / www.theclockhouserestaurant.co.uk.

PINNOCKS £16 4 4 4

HIGH ST GU23 6AF 01483 222419

"The platonic ideal of the local caff: great brews, excellent cakes and top-quality sausage sandwiches, all in a ramshackle old building stuffed full of dog-walkers, cyclists and families, and run by lovely people". "The ample coffee, tea, hot chocolate and smoothie menu is extensive too, with good descriptions of all options". / www.pinnockscoffeehouse.com; @pinnockscoffee; Mon-Sat 5.30 pm, Sun 5 pm; Take bookings all week via phone and/or online.

ROCK, CORNWALL 1–3B

DINING ROOM £72 3 3 2

PAVILION BUILDINGS, ROCK RD PL27 6JS 01208 862622

"Still a favourite" – Fred & Donna Beedle's intimate, well-established restaurant (est. 2010) surpasses its humdrum setting, on a parade of shops, with its fine modern British cuisine. / www.thediningroomrock.co.uk; @TheDiningRmRock; No Amex; Take bookings all week via phone and/or online; children: 10.

ST ENODOC RESTAURANT, ST ENODOC HOTEL £59 2 3 4

ROCK ROAD PL27 6LA 01208 863394

Still a "lovely, relaxing" location, with views across the Camel estuary, but feedback at this hotel dining room has become very mixed since the departure of chef James Nathan and his illustrious predecessor, Nathan Outlaw (and the ownership of the hotel itself changed in January 2019, which "may not have helped"). Whatever the cause, while it does still have some fans, some regulars feel it's "just not in the same class" as it was formerly. / www.enodoc-hotel.co.uk/food.html; @Stenodochotel; Take bookings all week via phone and/or online.

THE MARINERS £50

PL27 6LD 01841 532796

Nathan Outlaw cut ties with this "lovely" Cornish pub, co-run with Sharp's Brewery, after five years, in early 2019, thus ending his reign in Rock; new tenants (and Outlaw buddies) Paul & Emma Ainsworth – also behind the Michelin-starred restaurant No.6 and boutique hotel Padstow Townhouse, plus casual pizzeria Rojano's in the Square – are still finessing their approach, with plans for a refurb' in 2020, though it continues to win praise for its "locally caught fish". / www.themarinersrock.com; @TheMarinersRock; Take bookings all week via phone and/or online.

ROCKBEARE, DEVON 1–3D

THE JACK IN THE GREEN INN £48 3 3 3

LONDON ROAD EX5 2EE 01404 822240

One of the better pubs in the Exeter area – this well-known gastropub near J29 of the M5 has been in the same hands for over 25 years, and wins praise for its "very reliable cooking" and "a great choice of local beers and ciders". / www.jackinthegreen.uk.com; @JackGreenInn; Mon-Sun 9 pm; No Amex; Take bookings all week via phone and/or online.

ROSEVINE, CORNWALL 1–4B

DRIFTWOOD HOTEL £97

TR2 5EW 01872 580644

This "beautiful restaurant" at a clifftop boutique hotel on the Roseland Peninsula has earned a fine reputation for "highly unusual presentations of local produce". But it lost Chris Eden in June 2019, who left after 12 years for rival Gidleigh Park (and subsequently it also lost its Michelin star). Chris's replacement, Oliver Pierrepoint, arrived from La Trompette in London, and has both Fera and Le Manoir on his CV. Ratings were very good all-round in the survey this year, but given all the change after its conclusion we've left the venue un-rated. / www.driftwoodhotel.co.uk; @DriftwoodHotel; Take bookings all week via phone and/or online; children: 7.

RUTHIN, DENBIGHSHIRE 4–1D

ON THE HILL £46 4 4 3

1 UPPER CLWYD STREET LL15 01824 707736

"Quirky, comfortable, friendly… with really good food" – "this is an absolutely fabulous restaurant tucked away in a small north Wales town". Husband-and-wife team Rowan and Imogen have built a strong following for their small bistro since 2008 – so it is well worth booking ahead. / onthehillrestaurant.co.uk/; Mon-Sat 9 pm; Take bookings all week via phone and/or online.

RYE, EAST SUSSEX 3–4C

LANDGATE BISTRO £45 4 3 2

5 - 6 LANDGATE TN31 7LH 01797 222829

Chef-proprietor Martin Peacock can be relied upon to provide "locally sourced food (including Rye Bay gurnard and Romney Marsh lamb) cooked with flair" at his small and stylish modern British bistro. A longstanding Rye favourite, fans sum it up as "fine-dining food at mid-dining prices". / www.landgatebistro.co.uk; Wed-Sun 9 pm; No Amex; Take bookings all week via phone and/or online.

TUSCAN RYE £40 3 4 4

8 LION ST TN31 7LB 01797 223269

Once more in the able hands of Franco (chef) and Jen (FOH), who had a brief stint away before stepping back into the fold in 2015, a "lovely intimate restaurant serving delicious Tuscan dishes" to an "enthusiastic clientele" ("advance booking necessary!"). / www.tuscankitchenrye.co.uk; Thu-Sat 11 pm, Sun 4 pm; Take bookings all week via phone and/or online.

WEBBE'S AT THE FISH CAFE £52 3 3 2

17 TOWER STREET TN31 7AT 01797 222 226

"Always reliable for fish cooked with flair", this popular venue in a listed Edwardian building serves sustainably caught local fish and seafood. Paul Webbe has three other restaurants and a cookery school in East Sussex. / www.webbesrestaurants.co.uk/the-fish-cafe/; @webbesrye; Take bookings all week via phone and/or online.

SALISBURY, WILTSHIRE 2–3C

ANOKAA £50 3 3 3

60 FISHERTON ST SP2 7RB
01722 414142

Colourful, smart Indian which has been going strong for nearly two decades, thanks to its gourmet cuisine – "some of the finest, most interesting you'll find anywhere" according to one fan (visiting from London). / www.anokaa.com; @eatatanokaa; No shorts; Take bookings all week via phone and/or online.

CAFE DIWALI £40 4 3 2

90 CRANE STREET SP1 2QD
01722 329700

A "tasty choice of Indian street food" is paired with craft beer in a straightforward café/conservatory setting at this "different twist on your standard subcontinental", which took over the premises of Cranes Wine Bar in 2016. / cafediwali.com; Mon-Sat 9 pm, Sun 5 pm.

SALTAIRE, WEST YORKSHIRE 5–1C

SALTS DINER, SALTS MILL £38 3 2 3

SALTS MILL, VICTORIA ROAD BD18 3LA
01274 530 533

"Hockneys in view" as you dine are the most famous attraction of this noisy but atmospheric venue: a large, post-industrial space in the UNESCO-listed Salts Mill complex, open from breakfast on for a coffee or fuller meal (Saltburger, Caesar salad, etc). / www.saltsmill.org.uk; No Amex; No bookings.

SALTBURN, COUNTY DURHAM 8–3C

THE SEAVIEW RESTAURANT £51 4 4 4

THE FORESHORE BUILDING, LOWER PROMENADE TS12 1HQ 01287 236015

Epic views of the sands and Saltburn pier reward a trip to this seafront café, set over two floors and with an outside terrace. It serves an all-day menu that goes beyond posh fish 'n' chips to more complex seafood dishes and steak. / theseaviewrestaurant.co.uk; Mon-Thu 8 pm, Fri & Sat 9 pm, Sun 7 pm.

SALTHOUSE, NORFOLK 6–3C

DUN COW £46 3 3 3

PURDY ST NR25 7XA 01263 740467

"One of those places you have to visit: the name does nothing for it, and the outside of the pub looks dull and uninviting, but persevere and you will find good honest seafood and fresh fish", a "friendly atmosphere with lots of locals chatting" and a "huge external sitting area with splendid views of the Norfolk expanse".

/ www.salthouseduncow.com; @salthouseduncow; Take bookings all week via phone and/or online.

SANDBANKS, DORSET 2–4C

RICK STEIN £64 3 3 5

10-14 BANKS RD BH13 7QB
01202 283 000

A "stunning location" by Poole Harbour ("if you can bag a table by the window upstairs, the view over the bay is superb") is an undisputed plus of this three-year-old outpost of the Stein empire. but the consensus over its other attractions became weaker this year. Most reporters feel that "the food is a match for the setting" and say "this is one of the better, non-Cornwall Ricks". The size of the bill, though, is a sore point for a fair few dissenters who feel it's becoming "overpriced, chainified and no longer of particularly good quality". / www.rickstein.com/eat-with-us/rick-stein-sandbanks; @SteinSandbanks; Mon-Sat 9.30 pm, Sun 8.30 pm; children: 3.

SANDIACRE, NOTTINGHAMSHIRE 5–3D

LA ROCK £67 4 4 3

4 BRIDGE STREET NG10 5QT
0115 9399 833

"Very good food" allied to "friendly and efficient service" wins considerable praise this year for chef-owner Nick Gillespie's accomplished venue. It's a rustic, brick-lined space with bare wooden tables in a rather offbeat location, close to the M1-A52 junction, but a "special occasion go-to" for its fans. / www.larockrestaurant.co.uk; @laRock_NG10; Wed-Sat 8.30 pm, Sun 1.30 pm.

SANDWICH, KENT 3–3D

THE SALUTATION HOTEL & RESTAURANT £79 4 2 3

KNIGHTRIDER ST CT13 9EW
01304 619919

This two-year-old venture in a Lutyens-designed boutique hotel surrounded by famous gardens builds on its positive start, with Shane Hughes (previously of the Connaught, Whatley Manor and Ynyshir Hall) turning out "outstanding" tasting menus (including, for the brave, a 'blind' option) in the Tasting Room overlooking the hi-tech kitchen. Top Tip – "a great choice for afternoon tea, with offerings on a par with Claridges or The Ritz!". / www.the-salutation.com; @Salut_Sandwich; May need + to book.

SAPPERTON, GLOUCESTERSHIRE 2–2C

THE BELL AT SAPPERTON £52 3 3 3

GL7 6LE 01285 760298

A "charming, lovely and well-run village pub" that "has had its ups and downs, but seems to be on an 'up' at the moment"; and serving an "interesting but not over-ambitious menu". / www.bellsapperton.co.uk; @bellsapperton; Mon-Thu 9 pm, Fri & Sat 9.30 pm, Sun 4 am; Take bookings all week via phone and/or online.

SAUNDERSFOOT, PEMBROKESHIRE 4–4B

COAST £67 4 4 3

COPPET HALL BEACH SA69 9AJ
01834 810800

You get "impressive views whilst enjoying great seafood" at this "light and airy", timber-clad venue, which has a "beautiful setting" right on the sands. Chef Tom Hine's cooking is excellent, be it from the à la carte or fancier five-course tasting menu for £59 (which must be taken by the whole table). "Great with kids too (there's a kids' menu) whilst serving exceptional food with an amazing view". / coastsaundersfoot.co.uk; @CoastRestaurant; Wed-Sat 9 pm, Sun 4 pm; Take bookings all week via phone and/or online.

SCARBOROUGH, NORTH YORKSHIRE 8–4D

LANTERNA £56 4 5 3

33 QUEEN STREET YO11 1HQ
01723 363616

Giorgio Alessio's "fantastic" outfit has long been a "beacon of light" in these parts ("excellent since our first visit… in 1975!") – the fish is "as fresh as you can get it, collected from the harbour at dawn" and it's well worth going in season for "some dishes with truffles they bring back from visits home to Italy". "We go every year while on holiday and I dream about the zabaglione!" / www.lanterna-ristorante.co.uk; No Amex; Take bookings all week via phone and/or online.

SCAWTON, NORTH YORKSHIRE 8–4C

THE HARE INN RESTAURANT £76 4 5 3

YO7 2HG 01845 597769

A "fabulous and ancient inn run by Paul Jackson and his wife Liz", overlooking the North York Moors. Paul is a "self-taught chef who produces some of the most spectacular food, in highly imaginative tasting menus" (the only option, and running at either six or eight courses, with "veggie options very good"). Once again, all who report can't rate the service highly enough. / www.thehare-inn.com; @harescawton.

SEASALTER, KENT 3–3C

THE SPORTSMAN £61 5 5 5

FAVERSHAM ROAD CT5 4BP
01227 273370

"It seems wrong just to call it a pub… it's so much more". Stephen Harris's epic inn – the UK's best – is "well worth the trip from London" (or beyond), and "is an adventure to reach, along a virtually deserted road and through the salt marshes beside the Thames Estuary near Whitstable". "The exterior is a bit of a shock: it looks like what it is – a weather-beaten, old building on the coast". And there's little hint of anything special from the "shabby chic" interior either; it's "lovely and casual" but "not plush"; with "an authentic,

Orwells, Shiplake

scrubbed-table pub atmosphere". But when it comes to the cuisine, "for once the hype is justified": "it deserves all its plaudits" for the "clever" and "distinctive" but "no-nonsense" food "with a very local touch". There's a "fantastic tasting menu which has to be pre-ordered, although they now do a daily tasting option that doesn't need to be pre-ordered". Or you can just choose from "the most dynamic chalkboard menu ever, regularly updated during service as they sell out of items, but always seemingly with 'reserve' to add in". The fish in particular is "wonderful and fresh" (Top Tips are "local native oysters in season" and "those slip soles. Oh my!"). "Also, there's no searching for sides (at extra cost) as the course is complete – a refreshing change, and to be applauded". Service is "sensitive, positive and inclusive" and "first class" in a "low key" kind of way. In fact, through and through, "for such excellence, prices are very reasonable, and the wine prices even more so, thus it's hardly surprising that even a mid-week, out-of-season lunch needs booking several weeks ahead!" / www.thesportsmanseasalter.co.uk; @sportsmankent; Mon-Sat 11 pm, Sun 10 pm; No Amex; Take bookings all week via phone and/or online; children: 18+ in main bar.

SEDBERGH, CUMBRIA 7–4D

THE BLACK BULL INN £54 333

44 MAIN STREET LA10 5BL 015396 20264

A stylish £2.5m refurbishment complete with Japanese influences adds pizzazz to this 17th century coaching inn with rooms at the heart of this lovely town, in beautiful countryside, bordering the Lakes and the Yorkshire Dales. Reports are not as numerous as we would like, but the well-sourced cooking (with an emphasis on local beef) is uniformly well rated. / www.theblackbullsedbergh.co.uk; @blkbullsedbergh; Mon-Sat 9 pm, Sun 8 pm.

SEER GREEN, BUCKINGHAMSHIRE 3–3A

THE JOLLY CRICKETERS £52 333

24 CHALFONT RD HP9 2YG 01494 676308

"A jolly place to eat..." – this "very traditional village pub" in the Chilterns has "some of the usual pub grub and so much more", including a selection of "really sophisticated and delicious dishes". Landlord Chris Lillitou, a local who played cricket for Seer Green in his youth, took the pub over with his wife Amanda 10 years ago. / www.thejollycricketers.co.uk; @jollycricketers; Mon-Fri 9 pm.

SHEFFIELD, SOUTH YORKSHIRE 5–2C

THE CRICKET INN £50 323

PENNY LN S17 3AZ 0114 236 5256

Classic pub dishes are supplemented by more unusual specials from chef/partner Richard Smith at this inn on the edge of the Peak District – with 'Bertha', a British-made indoor charcoal oven, put to good use. "Great beers" from local craft brewers Thornbridge – partners in the pub – complete the picture. / www.cricketinn.co.uk; @cricketinnshef; Mon-Fri 9 pm, Sat 9.30 pm, Sun 8 pm; No Amex.

JORO £70 533

294 SHALESMOOR S3 8US 0114 299 1539

"Such a great addition to the Sheffield scene" – Luke & Stacey Sherwood-French's "extraordinary conversion of a shipping container" provides some "outstanding" cuisine with its selection of 'hyper-seasonal' small plates, available also as part of ten-course (£65) or twelve-course (£75) tasting menus: "the food's so exciting… the opposite of style over substance". / www.jororestaurant.co.uk; @JoroRestaurant; Thu-Sat, Wed 10 pm.

NONNA'S £51 333

535 - 541 ECCLESHALL ROAD S11 8PR 0114 268 6166

Maurizio Mori's long-established Italian (est. 1996) has earned its local popularity with "good food that's consistently authentic" and "staff and an atmosphere that help improve your day". / www.nonnas.co.uk/sheffield; @NonnasCucina; Mon-Sat 11 pm, Sun 10.30 pm; No Amex; Take bookings all week via phone and/ or online.

RAFTERS £65 454

220 OAKBROOK RD, NETHER GRN S11 7ED 0114 230 4819

"Still one of the best", Tom Lawson & Alistair Myers's ambitious, small upstairs dining room, ten minutes from the city-centre (and named for its main architectural features) is a "Sheffield gem" combining "excellent service" with "brilliant" modern British cuisine. "The 'Experience' label (used to describe its more elaborate weekend menus) is a tad pretentious", but that's the only complaint. /

www.raftersrestaurant.co.uk; @rafterss11; Tue-Sat 11.30 pm; children: 8.

STREET FOOD CHEF £12 433

90 ARUNDEL ST S1 4RE 0114 275 2390

"Very cheap Mexican near the station" – you can "always taste something new" (besides burritos, tacos, nachos et al) at this well-established cantina, which also now has a Sharrow Vale Road sibling. / www.streetfoodchef.co.uk; @streetfoodchef; Mon-Sat 10 pm, Sun 9 pm; No Amex; No bookings.

TAMPER COFFEE £21 324

149 ARUNDEL STREET S1 2NU 0114 275 7970

"Quirky, high quality and a refreshing change" – this "Kiwi-influenced" joint in "trendy, old factory premises" (a former silversmiths) in the Cultural Industries Quarter is "good for coffee, lunch or just a good vibe any time". Approaching its 10th anniversary, it now has two offshoots: Westfield Terrace and Kommune in the old city centre. / tampercoffee.co.uk; @tampercoffee; Sun-Thu 3 pm, Fri 9 pm, Sat 5 pm.

VERO GUSTO £69 443

12 NORFOLK ROW S1 2PA 0114 276 0004

"Sheffield's best Italian" – "this small, family-run, city-centre fixture stands out for its delicious, authentic food and friendly atmosphere" – and is "packed from early on Fridays" for good reason: "genuine Italian bustle and lots of classic dishes served very much to standard". / www.verogusto.com; @vero_gusto; Tue-Sat 11 pm; Take bookings all week via phone and/or online.

SHELLEY, WEST YORKSHIRE 5–2C

THREE ACRES £63 224

ROYDHOUSE HD8 8LR 01484 602606

It's been "a staple in the locality for half a century" and fans of this "moorland destination" (near the Emley TV transmitter) say this posh pub is "well worth the effort of finding" for "solid" traditional cooking that's "top drawer". Even fans note that "it has become very pricey" over the years, however, and the impression is growing ever stronger that it's "resting somewhat on its laurels" nowadays and risks becoming "pretentious". / www.3acres.com; @3AcresInn; No Amex; Take bookings all week via phone and/or online.

SHERBORNE, DORSET 2–3B

THE GREEN £65 323

3 THE GREEN DT9 3HY 01935 813821

"Very popular with well-heeled types – businessmen, families, retired couples" – Russian chef/owner Sasha Matkevich's "upmarket" outfit, in a pretty stone building with a terrace, serves "well-presented and good quality" Med-style dishes, and is particularly of note for its bargain midweek menu du jour. / www.greenrestaurant.co.uk; @greensherborne;

Tue-Sat 9.30 pm, Sun 2.30 pm; Take bookings all week via phone and/or online.

KINGHAMS   £49 **343**

GOMSHALL LN GU5 9HE   01483 202168

"Fabulous cooking in a characterful building" – "an attractive 17th-century red-brick cottage once known as the Hangman's Cottage" – "in a pretty (but busy) Surrey village": chef-proprietor Paul Barker has built a legion of fans for his "real food" over more than 25 years. With a heated gazebo, it's "perfect for al fresco dining in the English countryside". / www.kinghams-restaurant.co.uk; @KinghamsShere; Take bookings all week via phone and/or online.

SHINFIELD, BERKSHIRE   2–2D

L'ORTOLAN   £94 **444**

CHURCH LN RG2 9BY   0118 988 8500

"This beautiful house on the outskirts of Reading is still a favourite for a special meal" – an impressive old vicarage that many reporters are lucky enough to visit regularly. "Chef Tom Clarke has made this restaurant his own" and there's a feeling of "relaxed attention to detail at all levels, with warm and friendly staff, plus beautifully judged cooking". The "wonderful tasting menu" features in many reports, as does the "fantastic chef's table": "when you see the kitchen, it's like a well-oiled machine". / www.lortolan.com; @lortolan.

SHIPLAKE, OXFORDSHIRE   2–2D

ORWELLS   £90 **543**

SHIPLAKE ROW RG9 4DP   0118 940 3673

"Love it, love it, love it!" is the universal theme in all feedback on Ryan & Liam Simpson-Trotman's gentrified pub, a short drive out of Henley, where, in summer, you can "eat the beautiful garden with views of the countryside". Service is "professional" and the well-judged cooking – "innovative" without being unduly 'cheffy' – is "exceptional". Michelin continue to miss a trick here. / www.orwellsatshiplake.co.uk; @Orwells_Rest; Wed-Sat 9.30 pm, Sun 2.30 pm.

SHIPLEY, WEST YORKSHIRE   5–1C

AAGRAH   £33 **332**

4 SALTAIRE RD BD18 3HN   01274 530880

"Still going strong after 20 years" [er, make that 43, Ed], this Kashmiri chain has long since conquered the north, with a catering division and a dozen-odd branches across Yorkshire; on the menu, "good value" and "reliably authentic cooking" in "large portions" (downstairs serves the full menu, upstairs is a carvery beloved for its buffet). / www.aagrah.com; @Aagrahgroup; Mon-Sat 11.30 pm, Sun 11 pm; Take bookings all week via phone and/or online.

WATERSIDE
BISTRO   £48 **433**

UNIT B, 7 WHARF STREET BD17 7DW
01274 594444

"What a (pleasant) shock! A good modern British restaurant in my home town of Bratfud!" – Ian Johnson and son-in-law (and chef) Paul Huddleston's bistro sits on the banks of the Leeds & Liverpool canal, and wins strong praise this year for its "precise, at times witty, dishes with well sourced ingredients, helpful, informative service… and we were even able to bring our dog! Marvellous". "Prices are pretty reasonable for this quality of cooking, and the wine list has a lot of reasonably priced bottles too: highly recommended!" / www.watersideshipley.com; @enjoywaterside.

SHIPSTON-ON-STOUR,
WARWICKSHIRE   2–1C

THE ROYAL OAK   £69 **443**

2 UPPER FARM BARN, WHATCOTE CV36
5EF   01295 688 100

"Well worth a slightly twisty drive" – this "beautifully modernised little place" on the edge of the Cotswolds was re-launched a couple of years ago by the team formerly at The Chef's Dozen in Chipping Campden, and has won a major reputation for its "really first class cooking" – "unusual dishes, all sourced with local ingredients" and "particularly game" (shot to order). In October 2019, Michelin awarded it a star. / www.theroyaloakwhatcote.co.uk; Wed-Sat 9 pm, Sun 2.30 pm.

SHIRLEY, DERBYSHIRE   5–3C

THE SARACEN'S
HEAD   £37 **333**

CHURCH LANE DE6 3AS   01335 360 330

"Really pleasing food", "very good service" and a "lovely location" have earned plaudits over many years from the locals for Robin Hunter's Derby Dales village gastropub, which has recently added the Church Lane Deli to its attractions. / www.saracens-head-shirley.co.uk; Mon-Sun 9 pm; No Amex.

SHREWSBURY, SHROPSHIRE   5–3A

CSONS   £44 **433**

8 MILK STREET SY1 1SZ   01743 272709

'Inventive and good-value café-style food' is the motto of this friendly venture, established by the four Crouch brothers (hence CSONS). Come early in the day for an "interesting alternative to traditional bacon and eggs" (it features chorizo and smoked chilli sauce), then enjoy cakes, bakes and focaccia by day; or drop in for their Friday and Saturday night dinners. / www.csons-shrewsbury.co.uk; @CSonsShrewsbury; Mon & Tue 3.30 pm, Wed-Sat 10 pm, Sun 3 pm.

NUMBER FOUR   £37 **333**

4 BUTCHER ROW SY1 1UW
01743 366691

"Top eggs Benedict and very good coffee" are staple attractions of this modern, light and airy venue in the town centre: an all-day and family-friendly operation with a variety of down-to-earth tapas, lunch, dinner and kids' menus. / www.number-four.com; @numberfourSY1; Tue-Thu 9 pm, Fri & Sat 9.30 pm, Mon 4 pm; Take bookings all week via phone and/or online.

SKELTON, CUMBRIA   7–3D

DOG AND GUN INN £43   **434**

CA11 9SE

"A fabulous little village gastropub" in "a gastronomic desert" near Penrith "with a chef who does everything on his own!" – Ben Queen-Fryer is "cooking his heart out" to deliver "really high quality pub food" from an "excellent-if-limited menu" that's "amazing value for money" at this "small, out of-the-way inn on the edge of the Lake District". "The venison suet pudding and triple cooked chips are to die for!" / Wed-Fri 4 pm, Sat & Sun 5 pm.

SKIPTON, NORTH YORKSHIRE   8–4B

THE BURLINGTON
AT THE DEVONSHIRE
ARMS   £104 **444**

BOLTON ABBEY BD23 6AJ   01756 718100

The Duke & Duchess of Devonshire's well-known luxury hotel is scenically located on the River Wharfe and one of the more renowned dining destinations in this part of the world. Paul Leonard (who joined in 2017) has yet to regain the Michelin star the property has held on-and-off over the years, but all reports this year are of "exceptional fine dining, with attentive yet unobtrusive service". You can eat from a three-course menu or the eight-course, £85 'Burlington Experience' tasting menu. Much of the appeal here is being able to raid the duke's fine, if not particularly budget-oriented, cellar. / www.thedevonshirearms.co.uk/home/dining/burlington/; @Dev_Hotels; No trainers.

THE DEVONSHIRE FELL
HOTEL, DEVONSHIRE HOTELS
& RESTAURANTS   £18 **344**

BURNSALL VILLAGE BD23 6BT
01756 729000

"Views are incredible" from this sixteen-bedroom hotel in the middle of the Yorkshire Dales. There's a wide variety of menus – for a "romantic" dinner the main choice would be the two-course or three-course menu which are £29.50 and £38 respectively. / www.devonshirefell.co.uk/index.shtml; @DevonshireFell; No shorts.

SLAD, GLOUCESTERSHIRE –

THE WOOLPACK INN £54 324

SLAD ROAD GL6 7QA 01452 813429

"An unspoilt country pub ,with fabulous views over the Slad valley" – "very friendly and worth a visit" if you're in that neck of the woods. / thewoolpackslad.com; @woolpackslad; Tue-Sat, Mon 9 pm, Sun 4 pm.

SLAUGHAM, WEST SUSSEX 3–4B

HERITAGE £64

THE CHEQUERS INN RH17 6AQ 01444 401102

Matt Gillan, who made his name at The Pass nearby, opened this first solo venture in September 2019 – a crowdfunded pub with rooms in rural Sussex (not far from South Lodge, where he first hit big) with bar and garden. Menus in the restaurant include an à la carte, and a seven-course tasting option. / heritage.restaurant; @Heritage_sussex; Wed-Sat 9 pm, Sun 2.30 pm.

SLEAT, HIGHLAND 9–2B

KINLOCH LODGE £118 444

SLEAT IV43 8QY 01471 833333

The Macdonald of Macdonalds clan's famed country house hotel, a former hunting lodge staring out over the Sound of Sleat to Knoydart, received superlative feedback this year for its "comprehensive" wine list, "excellent" staff and tasting menus tapping the Highlands' bounty. All reporters rate culinary results as "outstanding". / www.kinloch-lodge.co.uk; @kinloch_lodge; No Amex.

SNAPE, SUFFOLK 3–1D

THE CROWN INN £40 323

BRIDGE RD IP17 1SL 01728 688324

Owned by local brewer Adnams, this fifteenth-century tavern is well-served by landlord Garry Cook's kitchen skills, while a "real highlight" is the rare-breed pork raised by his wife Teresa on "the smallholding that provides much of the produce". It's a five-minute walk from Snape Maltings, which makes it ideal for a pre-concert meal – but you'll need to book. / www.snape-crown.co.uk; Mon-Sun 11 pm; No Amex; Take bookings all week via phone and/or online.

THE PLOUGH AND SAIL £36 333

SNAPE BRIDGE IP17 1SR 01728 688413

Set amid the artistic attractions, performance venues and shops of Snape Maltings, and therefore "very good for a light lunch mid-shopping or pre-concert", the Burnside twins' welcoming boozer is "noticeably better than many other pubs with a similar guaranteed clientele". / www.theploughandsailsnape.com/;

@PloughandSail; Take bookings all week via phone and/or online.

SOLIHULL, WEST MIDLANDS 5–4C

PEEL'S, HAMPTON MANOR £109 344

SHADOWBROOK LANE B92 0EN 01675 446080

The Hill family's classy restaurant-with-rooms, nestled in the Birmingham 'burbs, continues to win solid marks – if on limited feedback – for its refined and original food (spanning afternoon tea and tasting menus, best sampled in their intimate tasting room). Bonus points for their regular drinks tasting evenings ("first and last time I'll try orange wine but it was a great opportunity to experience something very different!") / www.hamptonmanor.com/; @HamptonManor.

SOMERTON, SOMERSET 2–3A

28 MARKET PLACE

28 MARKET PLACE TA11 7LZ

Due to open in late 2019, a new West Country restaurant from ex-Soho House director Ben Crofton, with Great British Menu finalist Dan Fletcher as head chef. Fletcher previously worked at London's Sky Garden, The Kitchen in Edinburgh and under Tommy Banks at the Black Swan, Oldstead. / 28marketplace.co.uk; Sun-Thu 9 pm, Fri & Sat 10 pm.

SONNING-ON-THAMES, BERKSHIRE 2–2D

THE FRENCH HORN £90 345

RG4 6TN 0118 969 2204

"A gorgeous aspect overlooking the river… perfect for a sunny Sunday or bank holiday lunch" creates a picture-book English scene at this Thames-valley fixture, just over the bridge from lovely Sonning. Known for its "outstanding duck, which roasts in an open fire" this "old-fashioned and traditional restaurant" is, say fans, "always a delight" and backed up by a heavyweight wine list too. Caveats? – "while the food is above average, it's not a show-stopper", and the occasional cynic feels that "the setting is so idyllic it is understandable that they squeeze you for every penny". / www.thefrenchhorn.co.uk; @The_French_Horn; Mon-Sat 9.30 pm, Sun 9 pm; Booking max 10 may apply.

SOUTH FERRIBY, LINCOLNSHIRE 6–2A

HOPE AND ANCHOR £50 343

SLUICE ROAD DN18 6JQ 01652 635334

Five minutes from the Humber Bridge, this bracingly-located estuary-side pub wins enthusiasm – if not quite universal – support for its high quality cooking from chef Slawomir Mikolajczyk. / www.thehopeandanchorpub.co.uk; @hopeandanchorsf; Tue-Sat 9.30 pm, Sun 3.30 pm.

SOUTH LEIGH, OXFORDSHIRE 2–2D

THE MASON ARMS £58 343

STATION ROAD OX29 6XN 01993 656238

It's the picture of a traditional thatched pub, but the "cosy" interior and "heartwarming" menu have been funked up at this rural inn, which was consistently highly rated this year. / www.themasonarms.co.uk; @mrhanburyspub; Mon-Sun 9.30 pm.

SOUTH MILTON SANDS, DEVON 1–4D

BEACHHOUSE £53 333

TQ7 3JY 01548 561144

A "tiny, rustic shed overlooking a stunning beach and with great, fresh seafood to match" (plus a "fabulous brunch"), so you'll need to "book well in advance"; to get there, take the footpath from the car parks at either Milton or Thurlestone Sands. / www.beachhousedevon.com; Sun-Thu 4 pm, Fri & Sat 10 pm.

SOUTH SHIELDS, TYNE AND WEAR 8–2B

COLMANS £31 542

182-186 OCEAN RD NE33 2JQ 0191 456 1202

"THE place to go in the north east if you want to experience a first-class chippy", this "classic fish 'n' chip shop" (run by four generations of the family since 1926) is "fantastic, as ever" – with "very fresh fish" and "scampi from locally caught langoustines". See also Colmans Seafood Temple, nearby. / www.colmansfishandchips.co.uk; @ColmansSeafood; No Amex; No bookings.

COLMANS SEAFOOD TEMPLE £44 443

SEA ROAD NE33 2LD 0191 511 1349

This "stunning cocktail bar with panoramic views" and "unbeatable fish and seafood" was opened by the local fish 'n' chip dynasty two years ago and is "already a winner – a must-visit venue" on the South Tyneside seafront. It's a "fabulous" re-purposing of a colonnaded 1931 "local folly" known as 'Gandhi's Temple' – and menu highlights include an "enormous fish mixed grill". / colmansseafoodtemple.co.uk/; @ColmansTemple; Mon-Sat 8.30 pm, Sun 7 pm.

SOUTHAMPTON, HAMPSHIRE 2–3D

LAKAZ MAMAN £41 433

22 BEDFORD PLACE SO15 2DB 023 8063 9217

"Such a great find" – Shelina Permalloo followed up her MasterChef win by opening this "bright and cheerful restaurant serving very tasty Mauritian street food. Add in "superb service and BYO as well and it's a really special place". / www.lakazmaman.com; @lakazmaman; Mon-Sun 10 pm; Take bookings all week via phone and/or online.

Pensons at Netherwood Estate, Stoke Bliss

RESTAURANT ROOTS   £72 4|2|3

**141 BELLE VUE ROAD BH6 3EN
01202 430005**

"The best food in the area by a country mile!" – Jan and Stacey Bretschneider's small, 26-cover Southbourne venture is very accomplished, and provides a variety of eating options, but mainly focused on a no-choice, nine-course tasting menu. But while fans say "I can't believe Jan hasn't got a Michelin star yet", it doesn't always hit the right note with folks: "given that they only essentially serve one menu (in either a short or extended form), with no choices, they need to get everything right. However, whilst the chef clearly has talent, the prices are high for the small portions and lack of choice, and we sat feeling we'd stumbled into a glorified dinner party at which we were unwanted guests". / restaurantroots.co.uk; @roots_kitchen; Wed-Sat 9 pm, Sun 2 pm.

THE PIPE OF PORT £54 4|3|3

84 HIGH ST SS1 1JN 01702 614606

This atmospheric bar and wine merchant – mahogany tables, sawdust floors – is "famous for its pies, but they also take their wines seriously and have a great selection to choose from" (40 wines by the glass and 150 by the bottle). Top Tip – "Watch out for their regular wine events and supper nights." / www.pipeofport.co.uk; @ThePipeofPort; Mon-Sat 11 pm, Sun 4.30 pm; No Amex; Take bookings all week via phone and/or online; children: 16+.

BISTROT VÉRITÉ £53 4|4|4

**7 LIVERPOOL ROAD PR8 4AR
01704 564 199**

"Cosy Birkdale bistro" – "low-ceilinged, but that's French bistros for you" – "whose menu offers plenty of tempting choices", whose food is "fabulous" and where the service is "professional and efficient". "It's always busy, so early booking is essential." / www.bistrotverite.co.uk; Tue-Sat 11 pm.

THE VINCENT HOTEL V-CAFE   £53 3|3|3

**98 LORD STREET PR8 1JR
01704 883 800**

A cool, contemporary boutique hotel whose "pleasingly modern" brasserie has a "buzzy atmosphere and an all-round good vibe". Not many establishments feature as much choice as the all-day menu here: an eclectic selection ranging from British classics through modern European and other dishes, alongside the products of their sushi bar, providing fresh, hand-made sushi and sashimi. All this plus breakfast and afternoon tea! / www.thevincenthotel.com; @vincenthotel.

OX BARN AT THYME   £70 3|3|5

**SOUTHROP MANOR ESTATE GL7 3NX
01367 850174**

"The coolest restaurant in the Cotswolds" right now – this gorgeous, new barn-conversion "designed for the London trendy set". It's part of Caryn & Jerry Hibbert's 'village within a village' adjoining the "stunning village of Southrop", recently described in The Times as "a Disney-perfect vision of the English countryside": a collection of restored barns and other buildings that now form a complex of hotel, spa, pub, restaurant and events centre. Even those who say it's "blindingly expensive" say Charlie Hibbert's eclectic modern British fare is perfectly "acceptable" and fans say it's "properly modern, excellent and unusual". / www.thyme.co.uk; @Thyme_England; Thu-Sat, Wed 9.30 pm, Sun 3 pm.

RESTAURANT 27   £69 4|4|4

**27A SOUTHSEA PARADE PO5 2JF
023 9287 6272**

"The best restaurant on Portsea Island – by far!" is probably a fair verdict on this "professional" and ambitious 'global French' establishment, just off the seafront, praised for its "delicious" cuisine allied with "knowledgeable, yet also friendly" staff. / www.restaurant27.com; @R27_southsea; Wed-Sat 9.30 pm, Sun 2.30 pm; Take bookings all week via phone and/or online.

THE CROWN, ADNAMS HOTEL   £51 1|2|4

90 HIGH ST IP18 6DP 01502 722275

This good-looking, "relaxed and enjoyable" Adnams-owned inn is unarguably a "really great place" with massive potential – but its food offering continues to leave too many guests disappointed – "it's nowhere near as good as it used to be". Perhaps its enviable position in this popular town means it can afford not to try too hard. / www.adnams.co.uk/stay-with-us/the-crown; @CrownSouthwold; No Amex; Take bookings all week via phone and/or online.

SOLE BAY FISH COMPANY   £33 4|3|3

**22E BLACKSHORE IP18 6ND
01502 724241**

"A shed on the harbour at Southwold" it may be, but this "quirky" fish shack (attached to a "terrific fish shop") has earned a big and enthusiastic following thanks to its "posh fish 'n' chips" and "wonderful shellfish platters"; and "their smokery (and hook-up with the local Adnams merchant) is now adding to the menu" too. / www.solebayfishco.co.uk; Take bookings all week via phone and/or online.

56 HIGH ST IP18 6DN 01502 724544

"A must when you're in the area" for the "variety of fish dishes on the menu" – Andy & Kinga Rudd's "comfortable restaurant-with-rooms" (the oldest house in Southwold) is "still the most reliable place to eat in town". / www.sutherlandhouse.co.uk; @SH_Southwold.

THE SWAN   £56 2|3|3

THE MARKET PL IP18 6EG 01502 722186

A major, much-needed overhaul in 2017 hasn't been quite the triumph intended at the Adnams brewery's seventeenth-century hotel, with the "overly designed Still Room restaurant rather soulless" ("looks fabulous but does not feel right for the town – is it styled to make Londoners feel at home?"); and a seemingly rapid turnover of staff suggests "the new concept just wasn't working". A glimmer of hope, though, according to one regular: there's been a "definite attempt to take a step back from the changes", with "far more approachable prices and cooking" of late. / www.adnams.co.uk/stay-with-us/the-swan; @swansouthwold; Mon-Sat 11.30 pm, Sun 7 pm; No Amex; No jeans; Take bookings all week via phone and/or online; children: 5+ at D.

ENGINE SOCIAL DINING   £52 4|4|4

**72 WHARF STREET HX6 2AF
01422 740123**

Wil Akroyd and Mark Kemp's minimally converted pub in this Calderdale mill town opened in late 2018 and has taken the local area by storm: "a young team working hard in an open kitchen, loving what they are doing and smashing it, and the front of house are the same". "Outstanding Spanish tapas" attract the most mention but the menu is much wider than this, with "a huge range of vegetarian and vegan options": "fire-roasted cauliflower with pomegranate, pine nuts and sesame/coriander dressing is something of a signature dish and other influences come from all round the world but don't jar at all – (Sobrasada/pulled pork gyoza anyone?)". / enginesocial.co.uk; @EngineSocialSB; Wed-Fri 4 pm, Sat & Sun 5 pm.

GIMBALS   £58 4|3|3

76 WHARF ST HX6 2AF 01422 839329

"Fantastic food" ("always plenty of interesting seasonal options, including great vegetarian choices"), that's "great value" too, ensures the continuing popularity of Janet & Simon Baker's eclectically decorated stalwart. / www.gimbals.co.uk; @gimbalsworld; No Amex; Take bookings all week via phone and/or online.

THE MOORCOCK INN £70 543

MOORBOTTOM LANE HX6 3RP
01422 832103

"It exploded onto the food scene last year garnering two broadsheet reviews in quick succession… serving cod collar with XO sauce, fire-roasted razor clams with wild garlic – what were they thinking? This is Calderdale for god's sake!" And Alisdair Brooke-Taylor and Aimee Turford are still absolutely smashing it at this converted moorland pub, ably delivering "mind-blowing meals" from a "surprising menu using exciting local ingredients". "You would expect to pay three times as much in London, and would still feel you had got a bargain!" / www.themoorcock.co.uk; @norlandmoorcock; Wed-Sat 11 pm, Sun 6 pm.

ST ALBANS, HERTFORDSHIRE 3–2A

DYLANS KINGS ARMS £51 333

7 GEORGE STREET AL3 4ER
01727530332

A "small" and "cosy" dining room tucked away behind a small pub – and with a new offshoot, The Plough, in the hamlet of Sleapshyde. "The food (the weightier 'Bill of Fayre' out back, and snacks up front) shows a great deal of thought and the staff obviously feel proud about what they do, as they deserve to". If you feel like a cocktail, make it a Martini – barman Roberto Fiorillo surprisingly snaffled the 'World's Best Martini' award in 2019! / www.dylanskingsarms.com; Mon-Thu 9 pm, Fri & Sat 10 pm, Sun 3 pm; Take bookings all week via phone and/or online.

LUSSMANNS £48 323

WAXHOUSE GATE, HIGH ST AL3 4EW
01727 851941

One of a small Hertfordshire chain, run by hospitality veteran Andrei Lussmann and whose backers include famous restaurant investor, Luke Johnson. The worst trip this year was from a disappointed London-based reviewer, but it attracts a good number of local reports, all praising "good quality food (with a focus on sustainability) served with precision and at a reasonable price". / www.lussmanns.com/ restaurants/st-albans-restaurants/; @lussmanns; Mon & Tue, Sun 9 pm, Wed & Thu 9.30 pm, Fri & Sat 10.30 pm; Take bookings all week via phone and/or online.

TABURE £54 332

6 SPENCER STREET AL3 5EG
01727 569068

This "very good modern Turk" uses high-quality ingredients, including organic meats from Wales, to produce some interesting meals in this under-served town, and it "gets busy and can be very noisy". There's a spinoff branch in Berkhamsted. / www.tabure.co.uk; @Tabure_Kitchen; Tue-Sat 11 pm, Sun 10 pm; Take bookings all week via phone and/or online.

THOMPSON £70 433

2 HATFIELD RD AL1 3RP 01727 730 777

"A perfect experience – superb canapés, mains and desserts": former Auberge du Lac chef Phil Thompson (from a family of chefs and butchers) wins consistently excellent ratings for his town-centre venue with a conservatory and terrace. "Never had a bad meal here". / www.thompsonstalbans.co.uk; @ThompsonDining; Wed & Thu, Tue 9 pm, Fri & Sat 9.30 pm, Sun 3 pm; book online only.

ST ANDREWS, FIFE 9–3D

HAAR £57

KINETTLES, 127 NORTH STREET KY16 9AG 01334 473387

Named for a 'cold sea fog on the east coast of Scotland', Haar, from MasterChef finalist Dean Banks, is part of five-star hotel Kinettles. It opened too late for much in the way of survey feedback, but early reviews in the Scottish press have been very complimentary about its sharing plates cuisine. / www.haarrestaurant.com; Tue-Sun 11 pm.

THE SEAFOOD RISTORANTE £92 335

THE SCORES, BRUCE EMBANKMENT KY16 9AB 01334 479475

"An idyllic location right on the shores of the beach", unfurling majestically through the floor-to-ceiling-windows, elevate a trip to this fish and seafood "glass box", "close to the R&A clubhouse". "The standard of cooking is good, the staff are helpful, and the approach has the right formula to make dining so enjoyable amidst such fine surroundings". / www.theseafoodrestaurant.com; @theSeafoodStA; Mon-Sun 9.30 pm; children: 12+ at D.

ST IVES, CORNWALL 1–4A

PORTHMEOR BEACH CAFE £47 435

PORTHMEOR BEACH TR26 1JZ
01736 793366

An "imaginative" tapas-style venue that's "bang on trend" and enjoys "an unrivalled location right on the beach and by the Tate". "The view alone would suffice", but there's far more on offer – the "food never fails to deliver" and is "reasonably priced" ("it shouldn't be this good!"). / www.porthmeor-beach.co.uk; @PorthmeorStIves; No Amex; Take bookings all week via phone and/or online.

PORTHMINSTER CAFÉ £60 335

PORTHMINSTER BEACH TR26 2EB
01736 795352

"A magical position overlooking Porthminster Beach just below the revamped Tate" with "brilliant views" creates an "amazing setting" for this beloved "hut/café makeover": one of Cornwall's better-known eateries. After middling reports in recent years, food is back on the up, winning nothing but praise this

year for its "excellent" standards, with fish and seafood tending to take centre stage. / www.porthminstercafe.co.uk; @PorthBCafe; No Amex; Take bookings all week via phone and/or online.

PORTHMINSTER KITCHEN £46

WHARF RD TR26 1LG 01736 799874

Overlooking the harbour and with a large terrace – impressive views are a highpoint at this contemporary (lots of wood, glass and steel) spin-off from the Porthminster Beach Café, situated closer to the centre of town. Too few reports this year for a rating, but such feedback as we have is positive all-round. / www. porthminster.kitchen.

ST KEW, CORNWALL 1–3B

ST KEW INN £40 434

PL30 3HB 01208 841259

"What a gem of a pub!" – this "lovely, old Cornish inn, with a wonderful history, picture-perfect setting and delicious, modern British, informal cooking" is "where the locals head for Sunday lunch, inland from the fleshpots of Padstow and Port Isaac". / www.stkewinn.co.uk; Mon-Sat 11 pm, Sun 9 pm; No Amex; children: no children in bar.

ST MARGARETS, SURREY 3–3A

THE CROWN £55 334

TW1 2NH 020 8892 5896

"Thoughtfully refurbished a few years ago, with a splendid dining room at the rear", plus "better than average pub food", and an "excellent and well-kept range of beers on the hand pump" – this Georgian boozer (handy for Twickenham) "ticks all the boxes". "The Canbury Arms in Kingston upon Thames, which reopened in Spring 2019 after a lengthy refurbishment, is now in the same group" (Pearmain Pubs). / www.crowntwickenham.co.uk; @crowntwickenham; Wed-Sat 11 pm, Sun 6 pm; Booking max 7 may apply.

ST MAWES, CORNWALL 1–4B

HOTEL TRESANTON £63 224

27 LOWER CASTLE ROAD TR2 5DR
01326 270055

Set foot in Olga Polizzi's "celebrated" hotel and restaurant – which has "wonderful views over the harbour and estuary" – and, say fans, "you just feel like a million dollars". But despite its huge potential, it has seldom, over many years, achieved fully consistent feedback: and whereas fans applaud "fresh fish and seafood prepared by a chef who really knows what he's doing" the odd reporter found the cooking disappointing and pricey, and service poor this year. In a similar vein, its "romantic" ambience has also, on some occasions, seemed somewhat elusive here of late. / www.tresanton.com; @hoteltresanton; Booking max 10 may apply; children: 6+ at dinner.

THE CORNISH ARMS £43 333

CHURCHTOWN PL28 8ND 01841 520288

TV chef Rick Stein's "highly recommended" village gastroboozer continues to put in a creditable performance, even if it's more of a decent place to booze and graze than a foodie magnet. The canine-averse should be prepared – it's a "dog-friendly" sort of spot (i.e. "too many dogs"). / www.rickstein.com/eat-with-us/the-cornish-arm; @rick_stein; No Amex; book online only.

DA NELLO £47 324

46 LE POLLET GY1 1WF 01481 721 552

Traditional, well-established Italian (est. 1978) which occupies an ancient building in the heart of St Peter Port, and which has many staff who have been around for years. Feedback was more limited this year, but remains positive. / www.danello.gg.

LE PETIT BISTRO £54 334

56 LOWER POLLET GY1 1WF 01481 725055

A "little piece of France" – this "beautiful little restaurant in St Peter Port, with lovely service and delicious, good-value food" has a "genuine Gallic bistro" menu packed with classics, from snails and frogs' legs to coq au vin. / www.petitbistro.co.uk; @PetitBistroGsy; Take bookings all week via phone and/or online.

ST TUDY INN £53 334

BODMIN PL30 3NN 01208 850 656

"Emily Scott's pub just gets better and better" – "the food is always first-class" (majoring in "'wow' seafood at its finest"), and ably abetted by a wine list with "some unusual choices". First-timers proclaim it a "wonderful find". / www.sttudyinn.com; @sttudyinn; Tue-Sat 9 pm, Sun 3 pm; No Amex; Take bookings all week via phone and/or online.

THE CRAZY BEAR £67 334

BEAR LN OX44 7UR 01865 890714

This lavish and wackily decorated converted country pub has been a feature of the area south of Oxford for over 25 years, and offers the option of either English or Thai dining (in separate dining rooms). Reports were quite limited in number this year, but praise "brilliant" results in either location, and also the bar and casual restaurant attached to their farm shop. / www.crazybeargroup.co.uk; @CrazyBearGroup; Take bookings all week via phone and/or online; children: 12+ at Fri & Sat D.

MOAT HOUSE £54 344

LOWER PENKRIDGE RD, ACTON TRUSSELL ST17 0RJ 01785 712217

A 600-year-old moated building with a dining room "overlooking a canal and the moat" creates a "superb setting" at this "lovely" small hotel (owned by Chris Smith and his family since 1955), whose staff "really look after you". The odd "decidedly average" meal led to rather middling ratings, but some reporters consider this "the best dining experience in Central

The Sportsman, Seasalter (Credit Philip Harris)

Staffs". / www.moathouse.co.uk; @themoathouse; Mon-Sat 9.30 pm, Sun 5.30 pm.

THE GEORGE HOTEL £82 235

71 ST MARTINS PE9 2LB 01780 750750

This "magnificent" and "wonderfully maintained" oak-panelled dining room, in a famous and splendidly "olde worlde" coaching inn, is one of the country's archetypal traditional venues. An onslaught on the famous carvery trolley or the wider menu, while admittedly far too "expensive" ("the Dover sole itself would blush if it could see its price"), is nevertheless a "rare treat" and the "sirloin of beef on the bone, cooked and carved to perfection from the silver domed trolley" is particularly hard to beat ("if you can walk from the table you've not done it justice"). / www.georgehotelofstamford.com; @GeorgeStamford; Jacket required; children: 8+ at D.

THE DUCK INN £53 343

BURNHAM RD PE31 8QD 01485 518 330

With its "delightful setting", "friendly service" and "well-cooked food in good portions" – including "lovely puds" – this cosy pub-with-two-rooms has it all. It's a family affair, too: chef Ben Handley met his wife and co-owner, Sarah, when they worked together at his parents' pub in nearby Thornham, while brother Sam is general manager. / www.duckinn.co.uk; @duck_inn; Mon-Sat 9 pm, Sun 7.30 pm; Take bookings all week via phone and/or online.

LEAPING HARE VINEYARD £59 434

WYKEN VINEYARDS IP31 2DW 01359 250287

"A stunning location, outstanding food and their own delicious wine" make this 400-year-old oak-framed barn conversion on the Wyken estate "a brilliant place to take friends from abroad" – while for locals it's "good enough to save seeking alternatives nearby". Open for more than 25 years, the restaurant "makes great use of local produce". / www.wykenvineyards.co.uk; Sun-Thu 6 pm, Fri & Sat midnight; Take bookings all week via phone and/or online.

LOCH BAY RESTAURANT £62 544

1 MACLEODS TERRACE IV55 8GA 01470 592235

"Fabulous seafood" is the standout at Michael Smith's "intimate restaurant" in a "wonderful picturesque location at the north end of Skye". "Well-cooked and presented" dishes of "excellent local produce" arrive on either a 'Skye fruits de mer' five-course set menu or three courses with meat and veggie options. / www.lochbay-seafood-restaurant.co.uk; @lochbayskye/; Tue-Sat 9 pm, Sun 1.30 pm; No Amex; children: 8+ at D.

STOCKBRIDGE, HAMPSHIRE 2–3D

CLOS DU MARQUIS £60 4|3|3

LONDON RD SO20 6DE 01264 810738

"A1 food on the A30!" has won a loyal following for this "excellent" South-African-run French restaurant: an auberge-style venue with a penchant for rustic Gascon cuisine, which has just celebrated its 15th anniversary. "The food is well worth a long journey, and the wine list is exceptional". / www.closdumarquis.co.uk; Sun-Wed 4 pm, Fri & Sat 11 pm, Thu 5 pm; Take bookings all week via phone and/or online.

GREYHOUND £63 3|3|4

31 HIGH STREET SO20 6EY 01264 810833

"Effortlessly smart" pub with rooms on the River Test, in prime fly fishing territory – a "vibrant" place with a "lovely", small sun-trap terrace in summer. It serves a very wide range of dishes, from an extensive array of tapas-y plates to substantial mains and steaks from the grill. / www.thegreyhoundonthetest.co.uk; @GHStockbridge; Mon-Sat 9.30 pm, Sun 7 pm; Booking max 12 may apply.

THYME & TIDES £35 3|3|2

THE HIGH ST SO20 6HE 01264 810101

"Rather nice brunches and lunches await at this deli-café, with half a dozen specials chalked on the board" plus a garden and fish 'n' chip Friday nights. Though it serves an "upmarket clientele in an upmarket village", it's still "good value, with charming young staff" to boot. / www.thymeandtidesdeli.co.uk; @thymeandtides; Mon-Thu 5 pm, Fri & Sat 6 pm, Sun 4 pm; No Amex; Booking weekends only.

STOCKCROSS, BERKSHIRE 2–2D

THE VINEYARD AT STOCKCROSS £103 3|4|3

RG20 8JU 01635 528770

"An extensive and esoteric wine list is the top reason to visit" Sir Peter Michael's swish, California-style property: "a real experience, which begins when the automatic doors open, and you enter a haven of calm, efficiency and luxury". The wine-pairings provide some "brilliant matchings (although some are seriously expensive)" to the cuisine itself, which is perhaps not as memorable as the cellar, but was slightly more highly rated this year – perhaps a good sign for Tom Scade who succeeded Robby Jenks at the stoves here just as our annual survey was getting underway. / www.the-vineyard.co.uk; @VineyardNewbury; Tue-Sat 9 pm, Sun 1.30 pm; No jeans.

STOCKPORT, GREATER MANCHESTER 5–2B

THE EASY FISH COMPANY £46 4|3|3

117 HEATON MOOR ROAD SK4 0161 442 0823

In the 'burbs of Stockport, this "quirky restaurant at the back of a fishmonger" is a "brilliant local" revolving, as you'd expect, around "excellent" freshly cooked catch produced in an open kitchen (including a "fabulous lobster bisque"); the "good-value" lunch menu is also worth a look. / www.theeasyfishco.com; Take bookings all week via phone and/or online.

WHERE THE LIGHT GETS IN £112 4|5|4

7 ROSTRON ROW SK1 1JY 016 1477 5744

"Just phenomenal – the tasting menu is sublime and the wine pairing so well matched" at Sam Buckley's "relaxing but luxurious" set-up in an old, Victorian brick-walled warehouse. There is the odd gripe that the hipster succession of numerous bite-sized dishes – often using produce from their own farm – is on the pricey side, but all reports acknowledge the "amazing tastes and ideas" the experience delivers, while "the service is just wonderful – you're made to feel important as soon as you walk in the door". / wtlgi.co; @wtlgi.

STOKE BLISS, WORCESTERSHIRE 2–1B

PENSONS AT NETHERWOOD ESTATE £67 5|4|4

NETHERWOOD ESTATE, PENSONS YARD WR15 8RT AWAITING TEL

"Utterly sublime on all counts" – Lee Westcott's follow-up to The Typing Room in Bethnal Green is quite a step, both physically and spiritually, from London's East End, occupying a "beautifully designed" newly converted barn (on a 1,200 acre Worcestershire estate), which opened in January 2019. All reports on it are a paean of praise to its "honest but elegant" approach and "staff who all work hard to ensure the food is the star of the show". "You start out with superbly home-cooked bread and then the interesting and accomplished dishes" – "mainly locally sourced" or foraged and "full of unusual, subtle flavours", "all brilliantly married together – just keep coming, using all types of ingredients (e.g. pig's head with smoked apple potato) but not pretentiously". "The scallop, yeast apple and monk's beard dish and asparagus with wild garlic veloute are the stuff of legend". "It deserves a lot of attention" (and received some from Michelin in October 2019 when it was quickly awarded its first star). / www.pensons.co.uk; @PensonsUK; Thu-Sat, Wed midnight, Sun 3 pm.

STOKE HOLY CROSS, NORFOLK 6–4C

STOKE MILL £59 3|2|3

MILL ROAD NR14 8PA 01508 493 337

"A very professional operation, run to a high standards" – this picturesque, converted old mill on the River Tas (dating from 700 years ago) was once home to the business that became Colman's Mustard. "A very good option for a fine Sunday lunch at a fair price". / www.stokemill.co.uk; @StokeMill; Sun-Thu 9.30 pm, Fri & Sat 10 pm; Take bookings all week via phone and/or online.

STOKE ROW, OXFORDSHIRE 2–2D

THE CROOKED BILLET £55 4|4|5

NEWLANDS LN RG9 5PU 01491 681048

"A divine rural location and consistently excellent, seasonal food" have drawn celebs and ordinary mortals alike to former punk bass guitarist (John Otway, Sweet) Paul Clerihugh's one-of-a-kind gastropub for 30 years. "We've eaten here maybe 350 times over two decades and I recall only one poor meal – what a standard to have maintained!". Prices can be "a bit too steep", but are easily justified "on a cloudless summer's evening, when the whole experience is magical". / www.thecrookedbillet.co.uk; @Crooked_Billet; Take bookings all week via phone and/or online.

STOKE-BY-NAYLAND, SUFFOLK 3–2C

THE CROWN £56 3|4|4

PARK STREET CO6 4SE 01206 262 001

"Spectacular views, smart accommodation and consistently good food" – this gastropub with rooms in beautiful Constable countryside is well worth the drive – and "the prices aren't crippling". / www.crowninn.net; @crowninnsuffolk; Mon-Sat 2.30 pm, Sun 9 pm; Take bookings all week via phone and/or online.

STOW ON THE WOLD, GLOUCESTERSHIRE 2–1C

THE OLD BUTCHERS £54 4|3|3

PARK ST GL54 1AQ 01451 831700

"A great little bistro" with "an emphasis on top-quality ingredients and thoughtful cookery", Peter & Louise Robinson's Cotswold venture serves "head and shoulders the best meals in town". Despite its name and landlocked geography, it's predominantly a seafood spot, where "kicking off with a half bottle of Chablis and a round of Porthilly oysters sets a high bar for both quality and freshness". / www.theoldbutchers.squarespace.com; @Theoldbutcher; Mon-Fri 9.30 pm, Sat 10 pm, Sun 9 pm; Booking max 12 may apply.

INVER RESTAURANT   £53   5 5 4

STRACTHLACHLAN PA27 8BU
01369 860 537

"Simply brilliant" – "head down the single track road until you are sure that you are on the wrong route, and then keep going another couple of miles" to find Pam Brunton and Rob Latimer's converted fisherman's croft: "one of the more unlikely locations for top-class dining". The white-walled room with small bare tables is very simple in style, but the food is "as delicious as it can be surprising" with a "a fierce focus on invention with local produce and foraged ingredients" (and especially, of course, fish and seafood). A "funky wine list" is also a feature with "a strong focus on organic and biodynamic wines". "It's a great location and with lovely bothies now" too. / www.inverrestaurant.co.uk; @inverrestaurant; Take bookings all week via phone and/or online.

LAMBS   £43   3 2 4

12 SHEEP STREET CV37 6EF
01789 292554

Occupying "a beautiful old building" – one of Stratford's oldest – this beamed venue remains most often nominated as "a fantastic place for pre-theatre dinner: consistent quality with a great-value set menu". / www.lambsrestaurant.co.uk; @lambsrestaurant; Mon-Sun 9 pm; No Amex; Take bookings all week via phone and/or online.

LOXLEYS   £52   2 2 3

3 SHEEP ST CV37 6EF   01789 292128

"One of the better pre-theatre places in Stratford" – this smart, two-floor, former clothes shop is barely a three-minute walk from the RSC. Even a reporter who felt the food was "nothing special" says "everything turned out well for a pleasant evening". / www.loxleysrestaurant.co.uk/; @Loxleys; Mon-Sat 11 pm, Sun 10.30 pm; Take bookings all week via phone and/or online.

NO. 9   £58   3 3 2

9 CHURCH STREET CV37 6HB
01789 415 522

"Imaginative and excellent-value pre/post-theatre menus" (as well as more relaxed dining options for those giving Shakespeare a miss), are to be had at chef/owner Wayne Thomson's highly rated town-centre venue, which celebrates its 10th anniversary this summer. / no9churchst.com; @dineno9; Take bookings all week via phone and/or online.

ROOFTOP RESTAURANT, ROYAL SHAKESPEARE THEATRE   £48   2 2 4

WATERSIDE CV37 6BB   01789 403449

"A rooftop restaurant with splendid views" makes "pre-theatre eating fun" at the RSC's HQ – as well as "taking away the fear of being late for the show" ("it's so convenient!"). Unsurprisingly, it's not the last word in top gastronomy, but most reporters are mellow about any trade-offs involved ("tasty if not special…", "nothing to frighten, but reaches a fairly good standard…", "a bit pre-prepared, but very good for an arts venue…") / www.rsc.org.uk/eat; @thersc; Mon-Sat 9.30 pm, Sun 3.30 pm; No Amex; book online only.

SABAI SABAI   £50   3 4 3

19-20 WOOD STREET CV37 6JF
01789 508 220

Brum's popular Thai mini-chain established this Stratford spin-off three years ago, and its consistent food rating is in line with its siblings. "Charming staff" also received a particular thumbs up this year. / sabaisabai-restaurant.co.uk; @sabaisabai1; Fri-Sun, Mon-Thu 10.30 pm; Take bookings all week via phone and/or online.

SALT   £81   3 2 3

8 CHURCH ST CV37 6HB   01789 263566

This ambitious two-year-old, in a classic Stratford timbered house, has hit big targets, including the crowd-funding which financed its debut and a star for chef-proprietor Paul Foster from the French tyre people within 12 months of opening. But feedback from reporters this year is split: some hail "top-notch dining" and an "excellent tasting menu", while others regret "the disastrous portion sizes (mere scraps)", "pretentions", and "diminishing returns with each trip". / www.salt-restaurant.co.uk; @salt_dining; Take bookings all week via phone and/or online.

THE WOODSMAN, HOTEL INDIGO   £53

CHAPEL STREET CV37 6HA
01789 331535

Game expert, Mike Robinson – co-owner of the acclaimed Harwood Arms in Fulham – has opened this traditionally housed newcomer in Stratford-upon-Avon's Indigo hotel, bringing with him his 'field to fork' philosophy, and a traditional British menu with a focus on sustainability, seasonality and locally-sourced produce. Adulatory press reports suggest it's 'vaux le voyage'. / www.thewoodsmanrestaurant.com; Wed-Sun 9.30 pm.

THE THREE LIONS   £62   3 3 2

STUCKTON RD SP6 2HF   01425 652489

The Womersley's "utterly reliable family-run restaurant on the edge of the New Forest"; the décor may be a tad '80s, and the food – from ex-Lucknam Park chef Mike – may not always plough new furrows ("you can be guaranteed to meet an old favourite amidst occasional new dishes"), but it's a winner overall. / www.thethreelionsrestaurant.co.uk; Tue-Sat 9 pm; Sun 2 pm; No Amex; No trainers; Take bookings all week via phone and/or online.

PIG ON THE BEACH   £54   2 3 5

MANOR HOUSE, MANOR ROAD BH19 3AU
01929 450 288

"An amazing place" with "views to die for" across Studland Bay – this clifftop establishment in the six-strong group of shabby-chic 'Pig' country-house hotels hits most of its targets, with "impeccable service" and "good use of local ingredients, including very fresh fish". It can sometimes be "a victim of its own success" – "so packed that the overall experience is less intimate and relaxed than expected". / www.thepighotel.com/on-the-beach/; @the_pig_hotel; Take bookings all week via phone and/or online.

SHELL BAY   £49   3 4 5

FERRY ROAD BH19 3BA   01929 450363

A "stunning location – especially as the sun sets over Poole Harbour" ("you could be in the South of France") – is the main asset of this "casual" operation (shack-like without, rustic within), but it's no one-trick pony: the seafood is also "superb". / www.shellbay.net; Take bookings all week via phone and/or online.

SECRET GARDEN   £40   4 4 3

17 - 21 FRIARS STREET CO10 2AA
01787 372030

The "super" setting – the beamed, medieval Buzzards Hall – pleases most who report on this three-year-old 'wine bar & restaurant' outpost of the adjoining café (although some fans think "its high quality of food and service really deserves crisp white linen and more elegant décor than something that looks like an old fashioned tea room"). No disputes, though, over cuisine stamped with "Gallic authenticity", and which "continues to improve". / www.tsg.uk.net; Wed-Sat 11 pm, Sun 2.30 pm; Take bookings all week via phone and/or online.

RABY HUNT   £214   4 3 2

DL2 3UD   01325 374 237

James Closes's "global-quality cuisine" – "enjoyed as part of a 15-course tasting menu" – and "stunning wines" ("make friends with the sommelier and you will drink a more interesting selection") have won foodie fame for this converted old pub with three rooms, out in the sticks of County Durham: the only restaurant in the north east with two Michelin stars. Even fans concede that it is "expensive", however, and critics feel that "there's too much hype and fuss" surrounding cooking that "at the eye watering prices, is good, but not that good". / www.rabyhuntrestaurant.co.uk; @therabyhunt; Fri & Sat, Wed & Thu 9.30 pm.

SUNBURY ON THAMES, SURREY   3–3A

INDIAN ZEST   £41   443

21 THAMES STREET TW16 5QF 01932 765 000

"Consistently good modern Indian cooking" and "engaging staff" win firm praise for Manoj Vasaikar's "lovely" colonial-styled outfit near the river – sibling to well-known Hammersmith star, Indian Zing; "from the first taste of the amuse bouche, on the table within seconds of sitting down, to the kulfi dessert, absolutely everything is excellent". / www.indianzest.co.uk; @Indian_Zest; Take bookings all week via phone and/or online.

SUNNINGHILL, BERKSHIRE   3–3A

CARPENTER'S ARMS   £56   333

78 UPPER VILLAGE RD SL5 7AQ 01344 622763

This smart village pub with a garden incorporates a very French dining room, 'La Cloche', which serves bistro classics with a nod to the hearty dishes of the southwest, along with a good selection of wine and beer. / www.laclochepub.com; Sun-Thu 10 pm, Fri & Sat 11 pm; Take bookings all week via phone and/or online.

SURBITON, SURREY   3–3A

THE FRENCH TABLE   £65   543

85 MAPLE RD KT6 4AW 020 8399 2365

"Eric and Sarah Guignard continue to command a loyal following with their innovative modern French cuisine, relaxed and friendly hospitality and carefully chosen wine list" at this long-standing bright spark in the 'burbs: "a surprising find" (if a "cramped" one) for first timers, providing "amazing value in the heart of suburbia". As one of Surrey's better restaurants, it commands a much-more-than-local clientele: "we travel for at least one and a half hours by car/taxi then train to eat here; if we lived closer we would dine at TFT at least twice a month". Top Top – "lunch is a steal that's well worth braving Surbiton for". / www.thefrenchtable.co.uk; @thefrenchtable; Tue-Thu 9.30 pm, Fri & Sat 10 pm; Take bookings all week via phone and/or online.

NO 97   £51   343

97 MAPLE ROAD KT6 4AW 020 3411 9797

"Top-quality food at an affordable price" is the recipe at Sam & Alex Berry's three-year-old, which makes a virtue of its suburban setting to be 'part city slicker, part country bumpkin'. So it's "well-executed and professional" but with a "relaxed and welcoming ambience". / no-97.co.uk; @no_ninetyseven; Tue-Sat midnight, Sun 2.30 pm; Take bookings all week via phone and/or online.

SUTTON GAULT, CAMBRIDGESHIRE3–1B

THE ANCHOR   £48   333

BURY LN CB6 2BD 01353 778537

This Fenland inn dating from the eighteenth century is "a lovely place". Even a reporter who felt "the menu looks a bit pedestrian" says "it's an excellent place to eat, with very good cooking". / anchor-inn-restaurant.co.uk/; @TheanchorinnSG; Mon-Fri 9 pm, Sat 9.30 pm, Sun 8.30 pm; No Amex.

SWANSEA, SWANSEA   1–1D

PATRICKS WITH ROOMS   £57   333

638 MUMBLES RD SA3 4EA 01792 360199

Well-established restaurant-with-rooms in the Mumbles of 27 years' standing, overlooking Swansea Bay. Feedback was quite limited this year, but all reports are positive. You can eat either in the restaurant or the 'Lounge Bar'. / www.patrickswithrooms.com; @PatricksMumbles; Mon-Sat 9.50 pm, Sun 2.30 pm; Take bookings all week via phone and/or online.

SWINTON, SCOTTISH BORDERS   8–1A

THE WHEATSHEAF AT SWINTON   £50   333

MAIN ST TD11 3JJ 01890860257

Feedback is limited but all upbeat on this attractive pub with rooms, whose contemporary dining room overlooks the village green. / www.eatdrinkstaywheatsheaf.com; @Wheat_sheaf; Take bookings all week via phone and/or online; children: 8+.

TAPLOW, BERKSHIRE   3–3A

THE DINING ROOM AT CLIVEDEN, CLIVEDEN HOUSE   £92   224

CLIVEDEN RD SL6 0JF 01628 668561

After the departure of André Garrett as executive head chef from this landmark destination in October 2018 (for London's Corinthia Hotel), former head chef Paul O'Neill was promoted to take his place. This "beautiful" property has received up-and-down feedback over the years, and variability was also evident in this year's reports: numerous "wonderful" meals are described, but there are also experiences of "slow service" and food that's "overly grand but underwhelmingly prepared… especially at these prices!" The most consistent hit is afternoon tea in the grand hall – "exceptional" (not least "the world's best scones"). / www.clivedenhouse.co.uk; @Cliveden_House; No trainers; Take bookings all week via phone and/or online.

TARLAND, ABERDEENSHIRE   9–2D

DOUNESIDE HOUSE   £65   444

AB34 4UL 01339 881230

"A great representation of modern Scottish cooking: when they say locally sourced ingredients they literally mean within yards of the building…". This "scenic country house" sits on the MacRobert Estate in the Scottish Highland; its Library dining room (open weekends only) serves chef David Butler's six-course tasting menu that's "creative and full of flavour". At other times (including afternoon tea) you can eat in their more brasserie-style conservatory, overlooking the gardens. ("The hotel overall is a charity and all the profits from it go back into the MacRobert Trusts"). / www.dounesidehouse.co.uk; Wed-Fri 4 pm, Sat & Sun 5 pm.

TAUNTON, SOMERSET   2–3A

AUGUSTUS   £56   343

3 THE COURTYARD, ST JAMES ST TA1 1JR 01823 324 354

"Outstanding food" – at "very reasonable prices" – wins increasingly high ratings for Richard Guest and Cedric Chirrosel's neighbourhood restaurant. The pair have built on their success with the opening of fish specialist the Albatross around the corner in 2018. / www.augustustaunton.co.uk; @augustustaunton; No Amex; Take bookings all week via phone and/or online.

THE CASTLE BOW RESTAURANT   £65   443

CASTLE BOW TA1 1NF 01823 328328

"A great local restaurant in every way" – this highly regarded dining room ("decorated in Art Deco style") is situated under an old archway in the centre of the town, and scores very creditable grades all round, including for Liam Finnegan's fine cooking from a "lovely menu with lots of local ingredients", and also for its "very professional service". / www.castlebow.com; @CastleBow; Take bookings all week via phone and/or online; children: 5.

TAVISTOCK, DEVON   1–3B

CORNISH ARMS   £51   333

15 WEST STREET PL19 8AN 01822 612145

The rough-around-the-edges pub that once stood here is long gone – these days it's "clearly popular and well-regarded" owing to chef-patron John Hooker's "consistently good" gastro fare that's "tremendous value for money" too. / www.thecornisharmstavistock.co.uk; @CornishArmsTavy; Mon-Thu 11 pm, Fri & Sat midnight, Sun 10.30 pm.

CRAB SHACK   £52   4 3 3

3 QUEEN ST TQ14 9HN 01626 777956

This casual outfit is "THE place for fruits de mer, as fresh as a daisy (it really is man-vs-beast when you take on their crabs)", and it's "extra special if the weather is good and there are seats outside"; and "it bucks the local trend of high prices". / www.crabshackonthebeach.co.uk/; @@CrabShack3; No Amex; Take bookings all week via phone and/or online.

THE SALT CELLAR £66   3 3 3

THE ESPLANADE SA70 7DU
01834 844005

Lovely views of the town's amazing beach and an outside terrace are obvious attractions of this three-year-old bar and dining room on the sea front; but its shortish menu of modernised but, at heart, fairly traditional fare is consistently highly rated. / www.thesaltcellartenby.co.uk; @SaltCellarTenby; Wed-Fri 4 pm, Sat & Sun 5 pm.

GUMSTOOL INN, CALCOT MANOR   £51   2 3 4

GL8 8YJ 01666 890391

With its "superior pub food in a delightful location" – a plush spa and hotel complex in the Cotswolds – this is far from your standard village boozer. But it has stood the test of time, and recently celebrated its 25th anniversary. / www.calcotmanor.co.uk; @Calcot_Manor; Mon-Sat 9.30 pm, Sun 9 pm; No jeans; No bookings; children: 12+ at dinner in Conservatory.

ERIC'S FISH & CHIPS   £33   4 3 2

DROVE ORCHARD, THORNHAM RD PE36 6LS 01485 472 025

"Exceptional fish and chips, fried in beef dripping" have won wide acclaim for this offshoot from Eric Snaith, chef-owner of nearby boutique hotel, Titchwell Manor. Its success has led to the launch of two futher chippies – in Holt and St Ives – as well as a range of homemade sauces in 2019. / www.ericsfishandchips.com; @ericsFandC; No bookings.

TWELVE RESTAURANT & LOUNGE BAR   £54   3 3 3

MARSH MILL VILLAGE, FLEETWOOD ROAD NORTH FY5 4JZ 01253 821212

"A top option on the Fylde coast" – Paul Moss and Caroline Upton's well-established and jazzily decorated bar/restaurant near Blackpool only attracted limited feedback this year, but still good all-round. / www.twelve-restaurant.co.uk;

Tue-Sat 1 am, Sun 8.30 pm; Take bookings all week via phone and/or online.

LAWNS RESTAURANT, THORNTON HALL HOTEL & SPA   £87   4 3 3

NESTON RD CH63 1JF 0151 336 3938

The restaurant of this lush Wirral country pile is "a little hidden gem", delivering some "unbelievable" food (including a "quite affordable" prix fixe at lunch); fans say that it's the "best on the Wirral (since Fraiche is always full up)". (This was the location, in October 2019, of the crunch Brexit talks between Boris Johnson and Irish Taoiseach, Leo Varadkar). / www.thorntonhallhotel.com; @thelawnsrest; Tue-Sun 9.30 pm; Booking max 8 may apply.

THE RED FOX   £46   3 3 3

LIVERPOOL ROAD CH64 7TL
0151 353 2920

A link in the ever-expanding Brunning & Price chain embodying their eye for gorgeous properties – like this former country club overlooking landscaped lawns – offering solid grub and quaffable booze (they've won CAMRA and GPG awards for their cider and whisky respectively). This year it attracted plaudits for its "good value afternoon tea", and approachable style with kids (and there's also an appealing beer garden). / www.brunningandprice.co.uk/redfox; @redfoxpub; Mon-Thu 9.30 pm, Fri & Sat 10 pm, Sun 9 pm; Take bookings all week via phone and/or online.

THE HORSE GUARDS INN   £48   4 4 4

UPPERTON RD GU28 9AF 01798 342 332

"Quirky", "laid back" old country pub ("nicer than most") just outside Petworth, which continues to win very consistent praise for its "excellent grub" – "every meal is original and exceptionally well-prepared". / www.thehorseguardsinn.co.uk; @horseguardsinn; Sun-Thu 9 pm, Fri & Sat 9.30 pm; No Amex; Take bookings all week via phone and/or online.

PYTHOUSE KITCHEN GARDEN   £53   3 3 4

WEST HATCH SP3 6PA 01747 870444

The "gorgeous" walled garden of a south Wiltshire estate provides a year-round setting for meals based around "vegetables and herbs from their plot" and "locally sourced meats" – "BBQ'd over a brazier in summer months". There's a "great atmosphere but slightly amateurish service and food – but it works". Glamping and pick-your-own fruit and veg are also on-site. / www.pythousekitchengarden.co.uk; @pythousegarden; Fri & Sat 11 pm, Sun-Thu 4 pm.

STAGG INN   £57   3 3 3

HR5 3RL 01544 230221

An "always reliable gastropub" (with rooms) smoothly steered by Steve & Nicola Reynolds for two decades, and whose "wide-ranging menu" – supplemented by a lengthy wine list, mostly from Tanners – is "cooked to perfection". / www.thestagg.co.uk; @thestagginn; Mon-Sat 11 pm, Sun 10 pm; Credit card deposit required to book.

THE POACHER   £52   3 3 3

HARTLAKE RD TN11 0PH 01732 358934

"Next to Tudeley church, with its stunning Marc Chagall windows" (unique in the world), this pub's "huge" scale is "quite staggering" for a tiny Kent village, and "they've obviously spent a fortune on the décor" (glass-walled and overlooking a garden with a play area). It's "well-attended" though, due to its "delicious" modern pub grub from a wide all-day menu incorporating a selection of steaks and pizza from a wood-fired oven. / elitepubs.com/the-poacher-and-partridge-home/; Mon-Sat 11 pm, Sun 10.30 pm.

THE MOLE INN   £48   3 3 4

OX44 9NG 01865 340001

"A lovely old characterful pub, tucked away in a tiny village near Oxford, with a pretty garden, plus a well-decorated interior preserving the original features". "Loyal regulars come back again and again" as the "service is cheerful and efficient" and the food is "excellent". / www.themoleinn.com; @The_MoleInn; Mon-Thu 8.30 pm, Fri & Sat 9 pm, Sun 8 pm.

THE SALUTATION INN   £39   4 4 3

68 FORE STREET EX3 0HL 01392 873060

With its "lovely, accomplished cooking" and "beautiful building in a riverside village", this smart, eighteenth-century inn near Exeter is "brilliant for a weekend break". All the food is highly rated – from the eight-course tasting menu to the "excellent beef sandwiches and moreish homemade soup" served in the less formal Glasshouse. / www.salutationtopsham.co.uk; Mon-Sat 8.30 pm, Sun 4.30 pm; Take bookings all week via phone and/or online.

ELEPHANT RESTAURANT & BRASSERIE   £70   3 2 2

3-4 BEACON TER, HARBOURSIDE TQ1 2BH 01803 200044

With his "technically accomplished" cooking of "ingredients he sources locally, including from his own farm in nearby Brixham" and

Raby Hunt, Summerhouse

"day-boat Brixham fish that remains a marvel", "much-admired chef" Simon Hulstone's well-known destination in a Georgian terrace provides "sophisticated dining in South Devon". Its ratings are dragged down however, by its toppish prices and those who query "where's the spark: perfectly OK but it didn't leave me jumping for joy". / www.elephantrest.co.uk; @elephantrest; Take bookings all week via phone and/or online; children: 14+ at bar.

NO 7 FISH BISTRO   £48   5 4 3

7 BEACON TERRACE   TQ1 2BH
01803 295055

"Outstanding, simply cooked fresh fish" features in all feedback on the Stacey family's bright, relaxed restaurant (est. 1993), where you can eat the catch landed at Brixham downstairs – specials are listed on various blackboards – or pair one of 95 wines with oysters upstairs. / www.no7-fish.com; @no7fishbistro; Mon-Thu 10 pm, Fri & Sat midnight.

THE GURNARD'S HEAD   £52   3 3 4

TR26 3DE   01736 796928

Named after the west Cornwall promontory it's located on, this "lovely, cosy pub" on the road between St Ives and Land's End is one of the county's best known, and fans say it's "worth travelling to the end of the UK for!". The kitchen features "locally sourced ingredients" including seafood, while "staff take pride in the restaurant and hotel". / www.gurnardshead.co.uk; @gurnardshead; No Amex; Take bookings all week via phone and/or online.

CROCKER'S TABLE   £55   4 4 4

74 HIGH STREET   HP23 4AF
01442 828971

"I felt like a judge on MasterChef!". The 2015 runner-up in MC:The Professionals, Scott Barnard has created "a great new addition to the town" with this year-old, "most-amazing, intimate chef's-table experience", which features 14 seats around the counter of an open kitchen. "The food is good, sometimes great" and "the concept of watching Scott and his team prepare the tasting menu in front of you, with the opportunity to ask questions and get involved in fabulous conversation makes this an amazing culinary experience". A Henley spin-off is planned to open next year. / www.crockerstring.co.uk; @crockers_tring; Credit card deposit required to book; children: 12.

HIDDEN HUT   £20   3 3 5

PORTSCATHO BEACH   TR2 5EW

"No longer hidden" owing to its rave reviews (not least for oversubscribed 'feast nights'), "but still great value after a coastal walk" – this "gem" of a shack on the Roseland Peninsula gets a "five for ambience because of that view". Add in "genuinely delicious, hearty food" (pasties, clotted-cream ice-cream etc) and "what's not to like?". (Open in British Summer Time months only, plus a week at Christmas.) / www.hiddenhut.co.uk; @TheHiddenHut; Cash only; No bookings.

HUBBOX   £36   3 3 2

116 KENWYN STREET   TR1 3DJ
01872 240700

"Good burgers", "good chips – both potato and sweet potato", "truly excellent onion rings and tortillas" and "an excellent selection of draught beers and cider" feature on the menu at this funky West Country fast-food chain with eight outlets. "Will def go back!" / www.hubbox.co.uk; @TheHubBox; Sun-Thu 9 pm, Fri & Sat 10 pm.

PENROSE KITCHEN   £68   4 3 5

PENROSE WATER GARDEN,
TREGAVETHAN   TR4 9ES   01872 225697

"Idyllically located" – in a timber building complete with log-burner and large outside terrace, and set "next to former water gardens, in a sheltered, quiet valley a little way out of Truro" – this three-year-old venue doesn't generate huge feedback, but such as there is lavishes it with praise. Prices are reasonable, and chef Ben Harmer offers a choice of four dishes for each course, with "an extensive local cheese board" a great way to finish a meal. / www.penrosekitchen.co.uk/; @PenroseKitchen; Wed-Sat 9.30 pm, Sun 6 pm; No Amex; Take bookings all week via phone and/or online.

TABB'S   £50   3 4 3

85 KENWYN ST   TR1 3BZ   01872 262110

"Hidden gem" – "a bit pushed for space" but "intimate" – "off the beaten track in Truro" that's "well worth seeking out" for chef Nigel Tabb's "skillful use of seasonal Cornish ingredients" and also the wine list: "well-chosen, with descriptions you can rely on; a good selection by the glass; and some really interesting bottles; all at very reasonable prices". / www.tabbs.co.uk/; @Nigeltabb; Tue-Sat 9 pm; No Amex; Take bookings all week via phone and/or online.

TUDDENHAM MILL, TUDDENHAM MILL HOTEL   £60   3 2 3

HIGH ST   IP28 6SQ   01638 713 552

Beautiful oak-beamed dining room in a "very well-preserved" eighteenth-century building – a watermill until its conversion into a boutique hotel almost 50 years ago. Chef Lee Bye's menu is "not huge" but results are often highly rated. Persistent gripes about "sloppy service", though, suggest that "staff need more training". Top Tip: "afternoon tea is always a treat, especially in the summer when you sit outside overlooking the large pond". / www.tuddenhammill.co.uk; @Tuddenham_Mill.

THE BEACON KITCHEN   £51   3 4 4

TEA GARDEN LANE   TN3 9JH
01892 524252

"So much love has gone into the design and décor of this Victorian pub you can't help feeling like country gentry when dining here!" – this Arts & Crafts house is part of Pete Cornwell's 'I'll Be Mother' group and fans say that "the food is perfectly good posh pub fayre... but the big deal is the pub itself" (with its wonderful views, it also operates as a wedding venue). / www.the-beacon.co.uk; @Thebeacon_tw; Wed-Sat 11 pm, Sun 6 pm; Take bookings all week via phone and/or online.

HOTEL DU VIN & BISTRO   £54

CRESCENT ROAD   TN1 2LY
01892 320 749

"For a thoroughly enjoyable traditional afternoon tea (HdV certainly make an occasion of this British tradition)", or "a very good full English", this fine-looking mansion still wins praise. However, more serious dining from its French bistro menu, as supported by its trademark wine list, attracted too little commentary for a rating this year. / www.hotelduvin.com/locations/tunbridge-wel; @HotelduVinBrand; Mon-Thu 10 pm, Fri & Sat 10.30 pm, Sun 9.30 pm; Booking max 10 may apply.

SANKEY'S THE OLD FISHMARKET   £50   3 3 3

19 THE UPPER PANTILES   TN2 5TN
01892511422

This small-scale outpost of the local Sankey's empire is a "good all-rounder in a handy location" – the old Fishmarket venue in The Pantiles – serving a fair range of oysters, fruits de mer and shellfish, plus Kent sparkling wines, Champagnes and beers. It's "no-nonsense" but "excellent". / www.sankeys.co.uk; @sankeysrtw; Sun-Wed 11 pm, Thu-Sat 1 am; Take bookings all week via phone and/or online.

THACKERAY'S £85 333

85 LONDON RD TN1 1EA 01892 511921

With its "lovely" yet formal ambience, this well-known Regency villa is the town's best known culinary destination, but has tended to split opinion in recent years; it "seems to have come back to form" of late, winning consistently high ratings this year. In particular, "set lunch is amazing value and always feels like a treat". / www.thackerays-restaurant.co.uk; @Thackeraysrest; Tue-Sat 10.30 pm, Sun 2.30 pm.

TWICKENHAM, SURREY 3–3A

UMI £28 442

30 YORK STREET TW1 3LJ
020 8892 2976

Despite the "very basic setting", this family-run Japanese is a superb performer, turning out "great sushi" (but not just) and elevated by the "super-friendly manager, Bobby, who always remembers and welcomes patrons". "It's great value for what you get and you leave feeling like you've had a banquet." / umiedinburgh.com; Tue-Sat 11 pm, Sun 10 pm.

TYNEMOUTH, TYNE AND WEAR 8–2B

LONGSANDS FISH KITCHEN £45 432

27 FRONT STREET NE30 4DZ
0191 272 8552

"Traditional fish 'n' chips or more sophisticated and unusual fish dishes" (with "quality sourcing proudly displayed") are on the menu at this "casual" yet "immaculate" haunt, "named after Tynemouth's famous blue-flag beach". / www.longsandsfishkitchen.com; @LongsandsFish.

RILEY'S FISH SHACK £33 434

KING EDWARD'S BAY NE30 4BY
0191 257 1371

"LOL… this is awesome!" – This "fantastic, on-the-beach" shipping container gets "five stars for its location" ("the views of the ocean are stunning") and offers "a unique experience" whereby you "sit outside in deckchairs, on the sand, with an open fire, even in the middle of winter in the north east of England" eating fish. "It's not churning out tourist fish 'n' chips' mind, but with fresh and imaginative use of sparkling seafood (and side orders of potatoes and salads are also real winners)". "Queues are long even at quieter times, but it is always worth the wait." / www.rileysfishshack.com; @rileysfishshack; Mon, Wed-Sat, Tue 10 pm, Sun 5.30 pm; No bookings.

TYTHERLEIGH, DEVON 2–4A

TYTHERLEIGH ARMS £48 333

EX13 7BE 01460 220214

Some "superb meals" and "service that's always friendly but discreet" win solid ratings for this inn, near the Devon-Dorset border, that dates from the sixteenth century. "The menu's not extensive but it's local and original food, and there's never a problem finding something good". / www.tytherleigharms.com; @TytherleighArms; Mon-Thu 9 pm, Fri & Sat 9.30 pm, Sun 8 pm; No Amex; Take bookings all week via phone and/or online; children: 5.

ULLAPOOL, HIGHLAND 9–1B

SEAFOOD SHACK £47 442

9 WEST ARGYLE STREET IV26 2TY

"What a find!" – for "brilliant, delightful fish as it should be (so fresh!)", Kirsty and Fenella's "popular seafood hut" (open April to October) can't be beat; be aware there's "outside seating only (no cover!)". / seafoodshack.co.uk; @Seafood_shack1; No bookings.

ULLSWATER, CUMBRIA 7–3D

SHARROW BAY £95 345

CA10 2LZ 01768 486301

"For a special celebration and the drive", head to England's original country-house hotel, now a septuagenarian setting, perhaps with a slightly "dated" approach, but still with a twinkle in its eye. For a romantic meal, enjoying the updated traditional fare, with "a table for two overlooking Ullswater – what could be more perfect?". / www.sharrowbay.co.uk; @sharrowbay; No jeans; children: 8+.

UMBERLEIGH, DEVON 1–2D

NORTHCOTE MANOR £76 344

BURRINGTON EX37 9LZ 01769 560501

"It keeps on surprising… there's nothing old or boring about it, so all good!" – this grand old hotel, set in 20 acres amidst gorgeous countryside and boasting a distinctive muralled dining room, is a "lovely place: so peaceful". All reports say the cooking is good value too: both the three-course dinner menu for £49.50 or the 'Gourmet Dinner Menu': six courses for £65. / www.northcotemanor.co.uk; @NorthcoteDevon; Mon-Thu 9.30 pm, Fri & Sat 10 pm, Sun 9 pm; No jeans; Take bookings all week via phone and/or online.

UPPER SAPEY, WORCESTERSHIRE 2–1B

THE BAITING HOUSE AT UPPER SAPEY £51 433

STOURPORT ROAD WR6 6XT
01886 853201

A "small but tempting" menu is "delivered with a good level of skill" at this "homely" village pub with rooms, "set in the middle of unspoilt countryside" on the Herefordshire/Worcestershire border – the original member of the The Baiting House Collection of local pubs. / www.baitinghouse.co.uk; @TheBaitingHouse; Tue-Sat 9 pm, Sun 4.30 pm; Take bookings all week via phone and/or online; children: 1.

UPPER SLAUGHTER, GLOUCESTERSHIRE 2–1C

ATRIUM AT LORDS OF THE MANOR £122

STOW-ON-THE-WOLD GL54 01451 820243

Following a recent refurbishment, a second restaurant has opened at this plush Cotswolds manor house, with Charles Smith at the stoves. No more than 14 diners at any one time can enjoy an eight-course tasting menu for £95. / www.lordsofthemanor.com; @CotswoldLords.

LORDS OF THE MANOR £72

STOW-ON-THE-WOLD GL54 2JD
01451 820243

"Never fails to impress with its superb cuisine and overall experience" say fans of this well-known, picture-book Cotswolds mansion (under the same owners as The Feathers in Woodstock), where reports this year were more consistently upbeat than in recent times. In April 2019 (rather late-in-the-day for survey feedback), the hotel changed its offer – simplifying the menu in the long-established main dining room – and launching a new dining space, 'Atrium', with a £95, eight-course tasting menu from chef Charles Smith. In the circumstances, it seems best to suspend a full rating till next year. / www.lordsofthemanor.com; @CotswoldLords; Sat & Sun, Mon-Fri 9 pm; No jeans; children: 7+ at D in restaurant.

VALLEY, ISLE OF ANGLESEY 4–1C

CATCH 22 BRASSERIE £45 323

LONDON ROAD LL65 3DP 01407 238220

There's a big thumbs-up in local feedback on this attractive, wood-clad modern brasserie: a sizeable 160-seat space, also with a big outside terrace, where praise goes to its "very well realised food in good portions and provision for people with food allergies". / www.catch22brasserie.co.uk; @C22Brasserie; Tue-Fri 8.30 pm, Sat 9 pm, Sun 8 pm; Take bookings all week via phone and/or online.

WADEBRIDGE, CORNWALL 1–3B

TINY THAI £34 343

1A MOLESWORTH STREET PL27 7DA
01208 455135

"At last a decent… well, actually quite a bit more than decent, Thai restaurant in North Cornwall!" – this "pretty tightly packed" café "lives up to its name, but this just adds to the fun" and its spicy scoff comes highly recommended. / www.thetinythai.co.uk; Wed-Fri 4 pm, Sat & Sun 5 pm.

WALL, NORTHUMBERLAND 8–2A

HJEM £64

THE HADRIAN HOTEL NE46 01434 681232

Run by Swedish chef Alex Nietosvuori ('Hjem' means 'home' in both the local Northumbrian

Magpie Café, Whitby

and some Scandinavian dialects) – this May 2019 newcomer opened just as the survey was concluding. With 24 seats, the aim is to deliver Scandi-inspired cuisine via either a six-course or 12-course tasting menu. Some initial adulatory press reviews suggest that visitors to Hadrian's Wall at last have a foodie stop-off as a competing attraction. / www.restauranthjem.co.uk.

CHEZ VOUS £65 322

432 LIMPSFIELD RD CR6 9LA 01883 620451

A French-accented wine bar and restaurant-with-rooms (est. 2011) whose very dependable cooking has won it a strong local fan club over the years. / www.chezvous.co.uk; @ChezVousLtd; Take bookings all week via phone and/or online.

THE STAPYLTON ARMS £46 343

YO61 4BE 01347 868280

"One of James Martin's favourite gastropubs (or his mum's anyway)" – this whitewashed seventeenth-century ale house in a North Yorkshire village serves "uncomplicated and delicious meals" from a "sensibly priced and fairly conventional country menu". Formerly the Wombwell Arms, it was taken over three years ago by Robert & Gill Thompson of the White Swan at Ampleforth. / www.stapyltonarms.co.uk.

FIFTEEN CORNWALL, WATERGATE BAY HOTEL £67 225

TR8 4AA 01637 861000

"With the sun setting over the Atlantic, what better place to woo someone", query fans of this sleek and "relaxed" venue, with gorgeous beach vistas from its large windows. Don't book it if you're trying to score with a foodie, though – it does an OK brunch, but strike unlucky and more complex meals here can turn out to "a bit of an expensive disappointment", and that seemed somewhat more of a risk this year. Famous for its connections with Jamie Oliver, it has, in fact, always been under separate ownership, and has always been operated semi-autonomously. Now – ironically given the collapse of the TV chef's dining empire – it's the only surviving bearer of the 'Fifteen' name and the charitable mission associated with it. / www.fifteencornwall.co.uk; @fifteencornwall; Mon-Sun 9.15 pm; children: 4+ at D.

SPORTSMAN'S ARMS £49 322

THE SPORTSMANS ARMS HG3 5PP 01423 711306

"Honest Yorkshire portions of high-quality local ingredients" set the tone at this remote seventeenth-century inn near Pateley Bridge, run by Ray & June Carter for more than 30 years. They serve copious amounts of game shot in the immediate area, and have fishing rights on the River Nidd. The décor either "needs a refresh" or is delightfully old-fashioned, according to your taste. / www.sportsmans-arms.co.uk; Mon-Sat 9 pm, Sun 2 pm; No Amex; Take bookings all week via phone and/or online.

GIACOMO £53 333

MORLEYS ROAD TN14 6QR 01732 746200

"Good-quality, family-style cooking with many old-favourite dishes" (e.g. 'Filetto alla Stroganoff') ensures this engagingly old-fashioned venture maintains its appeal – and the Michael Bublé and Abba tribute nights go down a treat too! Top Tip – the best seats are by the windows in the conservatory, overlooking the garden. / www.giacomos.uk.com; Tue-Sat 9 pm; Take bookings all week via phone and/or online.

INN AT WELLAND £53 323

HOOK BANK, DRAKE ST WR13 6LN 01684 592317

"A warm, welcoming, comfortable place with excellent food" – "line-caught Shetland cod and good steaks" are stand-outs – this family-run inn is "extremely popular" (hence "very busy" and "noisy at times"). / www.theinnatwelland.co.uk/; @innatwelland; Tue-Sat 9.30 pm, Sun 2.30 pm; Take bookings all week via phone and/or online.

WELLS CRAB HOUSE £48 343

38 FREEMAN ST NR23 1BA 013 2871 0456

"Fresh seafood platters and a range of imaginative dishes" have earned a good reputation for Kelly & Scott Dougal's three-year-old venue – enabling them to buy the premises. "Kelly's a superb front-of-house" – "the couple deserve their success because they work hard to serve delicious food and engage personally with their customers". / wellscrabhouse.co.uk; @wellscrabhouse; Mon-Sat 9 pm, Sun 3 pm.

GOODFELLOWS £58 423

5 - 5 B SADLER STREET BA5 2RR 01749 673866

"For a restaurant this far inland, the fish is truly amazing" ("cooked interestingly but simply enough to retain the delicate flavours") at Adam Fellows's classic French all-day venture – though you'll also find game on the menu. / www.goodfellowswells.co.uk; @goodfellowswest; Mon-Sat 11.30 pm, Sun 6 pm; Take bookings all week via phone and/or online.

UPPER RECTORY £47 434

BERRIEW SY21 8AN 01686 640930

"Set in the chef/owner's own home – which is a beautiful old black and white house, full of character and charm" in "a pretty village set in rural Welsh countryside" – Kerry Huber's "small, French-themed spot" offers "a fabulous seven-course tasting menu" (£32.95) that's "beautifully presented and cooked and served in a very intimate dining room reminiscent of that in a Jane Austen novel! Superb value for money too". / www.upperrectory.co.uk; @upperrectory1.

AUBERGE DU LAC, BROCKET HALL £88 324

AL8 7XG 01707 368888

The "beautiful setting" – right on the lake, within an old hunting lodge on Lord Palmerston's former estate – makes this rural hideaway a natural choice for a "lovely Sunday lunch" or "wonderful afternoon tea". Its glory days foodwise (under JC Novelli in the early noughties) are long gone, but those who go unburdened by great foodie expectations enjoy its modern French cuisine and say the overall experience is "superb". / www.brocket-hall.co.uk; @AubergeBrocket; Wed-Sat 9.30 pm, Sun 2 pm; No jeans; children: 12+.

THE WAGGONERS £48 333

BRICKWALL CLOSE, AYOT GRN AL6 9AA 01707 324241

"Friendly French owner" Laurent Brydniak oversees this "attractive" old boozer with separate dining room where the "menu changes regularly". The set-up is fancier than one might expect for the genre, and the "very reasonable fixed-price menu at lunch" is a major draw. / www.thewaggoners.co.uk; Tue-Sat 11 pm, Sun 6 pm.

THE CAT INN £51 433

NORTH LANE RH19 4PP 01342 810369

This village pub-with-rooms "continues to excel", turning out "some unusual fare", with "vegetarian and vegan offerings worth sampling too". The "ambience is best in the older parts", but agreeable throughout ("no muzak, no TV – what a joy!"). / www.catinn.co.uk; @TheCatInn;

The Seaview Restaurant, Saltburn

Mon-Thu 9 pm, Fri & Sat 9.30 pm, Sun 8.30 pm;
No Amex; Take bookings all week via phone and/
or online; children: 7.

WEST MALLING, KENT   3–3C

AMANO   £54   **3 4 4**

47 SWAN STREET ME19 6JU
01732 600128

"Sister to The Swan and gaining a great
reputation" – this year-old restaurant-with-
rooms (created from a former small pub)
generates limited feedback, but is winning
fans with its above-average Italian fare. /
amanorestaurant.co.uk; @Amano_Kent; Mon-Sun
10 pm.

THE SWAN   £54   **3 3 3**

35 SWAN ST ME19 6JU 01732 521910

With its menu of modern brasserie classics,
this traditional village inn with a contemporary
interior is "the go-to place for food in the area".
/ www.theswanwestmalling.co.uk; @swanwm;
Mon-Sat 11.30 pm, Sun 7 pm; Take bookings all
week via phone and/or online.

WEST MERSEA, ESSEX   3–2C

THE COMPANY
SHED   £36   **5 2 3**

129 COAST RD CO5 8PA 01206 382700

"The queuing and lack of finesse in customer
care (plus the uncomfortable shed setting) are
all part of the joy" at this rough-and-ready
veteran spot, turning out "amazing fresh
fish"… er, and that's about it, so you may want
to take advantage of the BYO bread and bottle
policy (though they do now have a licence too).
/ www.thecompanyshed.co; Tue-Sun 4 pm; No
bookings.

WEST MERSEA OYSTER
BAR   £37   **4 4 3**

COAST RD CO5 8LT 01206 381600

Arguably "a more rounded experience than
The Company Shed down the road" – this
stripped-back seafront diner is "friendly,
good value and busy"; and offers a "great
variety of hot and cold fish dishes" (not least
superlative oysters, their beds in sight). /
www.westmerseaoysterbar.co.uk; No Amex; No

shorts; Take bookings all week via phone and/or
online.

WEST WITTON, NORTH YORKSHIRE 8–4B

THE WENSLEYDALE
HEIFER   £65   **4 3 3**

MAIN ST DL8 4LS 01969 622322

"Fresh fish in the middle of The Dales!" – the
unlikely hero at this "wonderful" and "quirky"
village restaurant-with-rooms, be it "fish and
chips to die for" or the lunchtime prawn
sandwiches ("feels like you are eating an ocean's
worth"). Add in a "the warmest Yorkshire
welcome imaginable" and it "has it all". /
www.wensleydaleheifer.co.uk; @wensleyheifer;
Booking max 6 may apply.

WESTBURY-ON-SEVERN,
GLOUCESTERSHIRE   2–1B

SEVERN & WYE
SMOKERY   £47   **4 3 3**

CHAXHILL GL14 1QW 01452 760191

"A huge choice of delicious fish and shellfish
dishes" – "all beautifully fresh and in generous
helpings" – is available at Richard & Shirley
Cook's long-established smokery overlooking
the Severn estuary, which added 'The Barn',
with a "pleasant, modern café", a couple of
years ago. "A nice bonus is the wonderful
fishmonger and delicatessen on the premises". /
severnandwye.co.uk/restaurant; @severnwye; Thu-
Sat 9 pm, Sun-Wed 2.30 pm.

WESTFIELD, EAST SUSSEX   3–4C

THE WILD
MUSHROOM   £55   **4 3 3**

WOODGATE HOUSE, WESTFIELD LANE
TN35 4SB 01424 751137

"Paul Webbe's original venture – a pleasant
country restaurant – is starting to feel a little
old-school", but absolutely no one seems
to mind, given the "superb, fantastic value
for money" food ("less fish-based than his
other venues", and "including beautifully
cooked foraged produce"). The set lunch,
with an unusually wide array of dishes, is a
particular hit. / www.webbesrestaurants.co.uk;
@WebbesGroup; Wed-Sat 9.30 pm, Sun 2 pm.

WESTLETON, SUFFOLK   3–1D

THE WESTLETON
CROWN   £53   **3 3 3**

THE ST IP17 3AD 01728 648777

This comfortable old inn between Southwold
and Aldeburgh has generated all-round
enthusiasm since joining East Anglia's Chestnut
Group a couple of years ago: the food is well
rated and "friendly staff make a meal here a
real pleasure". / www.westletoncrown.co.uk; @
Westleton_Crown.

WEYMOUTH, DORSET   2–4B

CRAB HOUSE CAFE £52   **5 3 4**

FERRYMANS WAY, PORTLAND ROAD DT4
9YU 01305 788 867

"The freshest fish right beside Chesil Beach"
(of Ian McEwan fame) is all part of the
"exceptional experience" and "incredible
range of dishes" on offer at this "quirky" beach
shack, "just off Portland", owned by local
oyster farmers (and where the "yummy" crab
etc. comes "without costing a fortune", too). /
www.crabhousecafe.co.uk; @crabhousecafe; Wed
& Thu 9 pm, Fri & Sat 9.30 pm, Sun 8.30 pm; No
Amex; Take bookings all week via phone and/or
online.

AL MOLO   £51   **3 3 3**

PIER BANDSTAND, THE ESPLANADE DT4
7RN 01305 839 888

"Good-quality Italian food" in a "stunning
Art Deco building" at the end of a pier make
for a formidable combination. There's also
"excellent, friendly service", and of course
"great views of the sea". / www.almolo.co.uk;
@AlMoloWeymouth; Sat, Tue-Fri 9.30 pm.

WHALLEY, LANCASHIRE   5–1B

BREDA MURPHY
RESTAURANT   £46   **4 4 3**

41 STATION RD BB7 9RH 01254 823446

Right opposite the train station, an Anglo-Irish
deli/restaurant that's an "all-time favourite in
The Ribble Valley", and which, "from breakfast
to dinner to special events is consistently
excellent"; having doubled in size in 2017 (an
Irish gin bar was also thrown into the mix), it's
not "cosy" these days, but the atmosphere is
always buzzing". / www.bredamurphy.co.uk/;
@Breda_Murphy; Tue-Thu, Sun 3 pm, Fri & Sat
11 pm.

WHITBY, NORTH YORKSHIRE   8–3D

MAGPIE CAFÉ   £39   **5 4 3**

14 PIER RD YO21 3PU 01947 602058

"White flakes of fish, encased in crispy, golden
batter, plus chips reminiscent of childhood,
and still cooked in dripping, all provide a
taste to savour" at this famous (hence "noisy
and crowded") Harbourside veteran, often
justifiably nominated for being home to "the
best fish 'n' chips in the UK". "Most punters
go for the obvious, but the specials board is
always worth close scrutiny, as the kitchen

actually produces superb dishes using the wide variety of fish and seafood available in this amazing port". "Recommended, but it can get very busy so be prepared to queue in busy periods". "I was in Yorkshire for a week and went three times! Totally excellent!" Top Tip – marvellous views from the window tables, or you can just take away and sit by the water! / www.magpiecafe.co.uk; @themagpiecafe; No Amex; No bookings at lunch.

THE STAR INN THE HARBOUR   £54 2️⃣2️⃣3️⃣

**LANGBORNE ROAD YO21 1YN
01947 821 900**

North Yorks star-chef, Andew Pern's hometown venture is a conversion of the old tourist information centre, on the harbour. Most reporters do praise the "delightful" fresh fish, and "really enjoy the setting", but one or two sceptics feel that, despite foodie hype, "mediocrity reigns", and it inspires relatively limited feedback for a business from a 'big name'. / www.starinntheharbour.co.uk; @HarbourStarInn; Mon-Fri 9 pm, Sat 9.30 pm, Sun 7 pm; May need + to book.

TRENCHERS   £48 4️⃣4️⃣3️⃣

NEW QUAY RD YO21 1DH   01947 603212

"Posh", "fab" fish ("cooked in the lightest of batter") and chips have earned this Whitby stalwart of over three decades' standing a reputation as one of the top chippies "in a town packed full of 'em"; and staff are "always friendly and welcoming". It spawned a sibling at Whitley Bay's Spanish City in 2018. / www.trenchersrestaurant.co.uk; @Trencherswhitby; May need 7+ to book.

DOCKET NO.33   £64 4️⃣4️⃣3️⃣

**33 HIGH STREET SY13 1AZ
01948 665553**

"What a revelation!" – "a quality addition to the (fairly sparse) North Shropshire dining scene in fairly simple premises on the high street" – Stuart & Frances Collins's modern British venture wins nothing but high praise for

its "outstanding food", with the option of an "absolutely fantastic, six-course tasting menu for £45". "A must!" / docketrestaurant.com.

THE BEEHIVE   £65 4️⃣3️⃣3️⃣

WALTHAM RD SL6 3SH   01628822877

"Families having lunch overlooking the village green provides a quintessentially English atmosphere" at Dom Chapman's "very busy" converted pub. One or two reports are so-so this year, but the majority of feedback is outstanding, praising a "thoroughly enjoyable" experience including "very individual" food that's so good "I'm not sure it qualifies as pub food" – "amazing!" / www.thebeehivewaltham.com; @thebeehivetweet; Mon-Thu 9.30 pm, Fri & Sat 10 pm, Sun 4 pm; Take bookings all week via phone and/or online.

THE WHITEBROOK, RESTAURANT WITH ROOMS   £117 5️⃣4️⃣3️⃣

NP25 4TX   01600 860254

"The Wye Valley setting is remote and peaceful" at Chris & Kirsty Harrod's restaurant-with-rooms, which is again enthusiastically endorsed for its "fascinating (I had to ask about the ingredients, many of which seem to have been foraged or grown locally) cooking with a stunning level of skill, care and attention going into every plate", plus "interesting wine pairings" and "informed and professional service". In October 2019 the couple purchased the freehold, with plans to up the degree of luxury and number of rooms. / www.thewhitebrook.co.uk; @TheWhitebrook; children: 12+ for D.

HINNIES   £43 3️⃣4️⃣3️⃣

**10 EAST PARADE NE26 1AP
0191 447 0500**

'A rustic and earthy Geordie-influenced British menu' is promised by the website of this small café/restaurant, on the seafront, with views of the promenade, and which fans say is "cheap, cheerful but lovely". / www.hinnies.co.uk/; @hinniesrest; Tue-Sat 10 pm, Sun 5 pm.

CRAB & WINKLE   £44 3️⃣3️⃣3️⃣

**SOUTH QUAY, WHITSTABLE HARBOUR
CT5 1AB   01227 779377**

"Excellent fish and seafood, especially oysters" come at "reasonable prices" in this unassumingly decorated harbour-view café, also boasting its own agreeable terrace. / www.crabandwinklerestaurant.co.uk; @Crab_Winkle; Mon-Wed, Fri 8 pm, Thu, Sun 4.30 pm, Sat 8.30 pm; No Amex; Take bookings all week via phone and/or online; children: 6.

HARBOUR STREET TAPAS   £41 3️⃣3️⃣2️⃣

**48 HARBOUR STREET CT5 1AQ
01227 273373**

"Excellent moules flavored with tarragon – served with sourdough and a beer for a tenner": such is the appeal of this busy three-year-old serving Spanish tapas and charcuterie alongside small plates of more modern British inspiration. Front-of-house Lee Murray is well known locally from the Goods Shed in Canterbury, while co-founder and chef Tim Wilson worked for The Ivy and Groucho Club in London. / www.harbourstreettapas.com; @harboursttapas; Wed-Sat 9.30 pm, Sun 9 pm.

JOJO'S   £43 3️⃣3️⃣3️⃣

2 HERNE BAY RD CT5 2LQ   01227 274591

A "favourite" among locals for its "amazing Mediterranean tapas and super views", this appealing little venue at the Tankerton end of Whitstable has "great food and atmos, with a laid-back seaside vibe". / www.jojosrestaurant.co.uk; @jojostankerton; Thu-Sat 11 pm, Sun 3 pm; Cash only; Take bookings all week via phone and/or online.

THE LOBSTER SHACK RESTAURANT   £24 4️⃣2️⃣3️⃣

EAST QUAY CT5 01227 771923

"Just about the best lobster and fries I've ever had – for under £20!" – the appeal of this good-value spot "well hidden" by Whitstable harbour, with outdoor tables overlooking the sea. They excel by serving line-caught fish and local shellfish "just kept simple". Just one quibble this year: "why no puddings?". Sister venue the Oyster Shed is nearby. / www.eqvenue.com/restaurant; @brewerybarwhits.

The Whitebrook, Whitebrook

PEARSON'S ARMS £65 3 2 4

**THE HORSEBRIDGE, SEA WALL CT5 1BT
01227 773133**

"Quaint" old pub (downstairs) and
restaurant (upstairs) "with great views
over the beach" to the Thames Estuary.
Chef Richard Phillips's versatile menus
encompass a "good-value" set lunch, and
are marked by a "good use of fish and local
ingredients". "Slow service" can be a bugbear.
/ www.pearsonsarmsbyrichardphillips.co.uk;
@pearsonsarms; Mon-Sun 11 pm.

SAMPHIRE £57 3 3 3

4 HIGH STREET CT5 1BQ 01227 770075

"Always very busy", this "cosy little café/bistro"
on Whitstable's main drag has a "friendly
owner and staff" and an "interesting menu
using locally sourced products". It's "especially
good – and good value – for lunch or brunch".
/ www.samphirewhitstable.co.uk; @samphirewhit;
Sun-Thu 9.30 pm, Fri & Sat 10 pm; No Amex;
Take bookings all week via phone and/or online.

WHEELERS OYSTER
BAR £49 5 4 3

8 HIGH STREET CT5 1BQ 01227 273311

"With its unmissable, pink exterior, the
original Wheelers" (est. 1856, and for a time
the base of a now-defunct mini-chain) – this
"tiny", "snug" and "eccentric" oddity feels "a
little like eating in the back room of a small
house, decorated in a 'domestic style', with
ornaments on the mantelpiece and patterned
tablecloths, and with tables a little packed-
close". "But, it has a brilliant professional
kitchen out back" and serves "exceptional" fish
and "truly excellent seafood" ("so local oysters
are a must-have"), while the ability to "BYO
makes it very good value". "You need to book
well in advance", although it's "easier to get a
table now the extension has been built" with
the capacity recently doubled to about 30. /
www.wheelersoysterbar.com; @WheelersOB; Mon
& Tue, Thu, Sun 9 pm, Fri 9.30 pm, Sat 10 pm;
Cash only; Take bookings all week via phone and/
or online.

WHITSTABLE OYSTER
FISHERY CO. £61 3 2 4

**ROYAL NATIVE OYSTER STORES,
HORSEBRIDGE CT5 1BU 01227 276856**

"A fantastic, atmospheric location on the
beach at Whitstable, plus supreme seafood" is
an enduring recipe for success at this "lovely
venue, in a candle-filled, rustic, quirky
space" – both "large and lively but also with
intimate tables". "It's not clever cooking, but
they use good quality fish and the oysters are
excellent". "Service can be a little off-kilter at
times" but escaped any serious flak this year. /
www.whitstableoystercompany.com; Mon-Thu 9
pm, Fri 9.30 pm, Sat 10 pm, Sun 8.30 pm.

THE FOX £49 3 2 3

SG6 2AE 01462 480233

Prettily located home counties pub (with
rooms), just off the A1, that's "cheerful and
well-run". Some reporters feel results here are
"variable" but on most accounts its cooking
– in the bar, and also with a somewhat more
ambitious restaurant menu (majoring in
steaks) – is well rated. / www.foxatwillian.co.uk;
@FoxAtWillian; Take bookings all week via phone
and/or online.

5 NORTH STREET £78 4 3 2

5 NORTH ST GL54 5LH 01242 604566

"A true passion for inventive food is
demonstrated time after time" at Gus & Kate
Ashenford's "friendly and efficient" former
tearoom in a Cotswold village. "Meals are
as great as ever, whatever Michelin says",
say regulars bemused by the loss of a long-
held star in 2018 – "we've found exciting
and memorable flavours in every dish". /
www.5northstreetrestaurant.co.uk; Tue-Sun 9 pm;
No Amex.

THE BLACK RAT £61 4 3 4

88 CHESIL ST SO23 0HX 01962 844465

After over a decade in action, this
"atmospheric" gastropub just on the fringes of
the town centre "continues to produce some
of the most innovative food" in these parts:
"interesting ingredients are used to create
balanced and intriguing flavours in dishes
clearly made with love and care". Expansion
may be afoot, as owner David Nicholson
recently submitted plans for a new kitchen and
two new dining areas. / www.theblackrat.co.uk;
@the_black_rat; Mon-Sun 9.30 pm; Take bookings
all week via phone and/or online; children: 18+
except weekend L.

THE CHESIL
RECTORY £65 3 3 4

1 CHESIL ST SO23 0HU 01962 851555

"Flavoursome twenty first century food
pleasantly served in an attractive fifteenth
century room is a combination hard to beat"
at this "exceptional" medieval building, with its
"very amusing" sloped floor and surprisingly
successful "bold décor"…but "mind your
head!" / www.chesilrectory.co.uk; @ChesilRectory;
Mon-Thu 9.30 pm, Fri & Sat 10 pm, Sun 9 pm;
children: 12+ at D.

GANDHI
RESTAURANT £40 4 4 2

**163-164 HIGH ST SO23 9BA
01962863940**

"Amazingly consistent food" meets "slick
service" at this "cramped" and "noisy" (yet
relatively classy) family restaurant. Chef

Amnart Ubonrat's "great Indian dishes"
include "surprising and delicious options
(e.g. ox cheeks)", but even if you stick to
more usual suspects you "can't go wrong". /
www.gandhirestaurant.com; @thegoabalti; Mon-Fri
10 pm, Sat 10.30 pm, Sun 9.30 pm; Take bookings
all week via phone and/or online.

HOTEL DU VIN &
BISTRO £54 2 2 4

**SOUTHGATE STREET SO23 9EF
01962 896 329**

"The garden's a joy in summer" at the original
HdV, founded 25 years ago in a gorgeous
Georgian house – but there's a lingering
feeling that it fails to live up to its attractive
setting or extensive cellar, with diners too
often "disappointed" by their bistro fare. The
chain, which now numbers 19 boutique hotels,
has been sold twice in the last 10 years. /
www.hotelduvin.com; @HdV_Winchester; Mon-
Thu 10 pm, Fri & Sat 10.30 pm, Sun 9.30 pm;
Booking max 12 may apply.

THE IVY WINCHESTER
BRASSERIE £57 2 2 3

**103-104 HIGH STREET SO23 9AH
01962 790700**

Another newish link in the London celeb
haunt's growing empire, this "busy and most
attractive restaurant" (est. May 2018) attracts a
typical mixture of feelings for the brand. Fans
do see it as a "great addition to the Winchester
High Street" and say it's "hard not to have a
good time". Detractors feel "all the attention
has gone on the décor" and that value is sorely
lacking: "not as good as Côte and twice the
price!" / theivywinchester.com; Wed-Fri 4 pm, Sat
& Sun 5 pm.

KYOTO KITCHEN £43 4 4 3

**70 PARCHMENT STREET SO23 8AT
01962 890895**

Miff Kayum's "beautiful" Japanese won stellar
feedback this year for its "incredibly good"
cuisine, ranging from sushi to "stunning"
sashimi (of a "butter-like consistency") and
tempura ("as good as those I've had in Kyoto").
"The care and attention that goes into the
entire dining experience is second to none." /
www.kyotokitchen.co.uk; @Kyoto_Kitchen.

THE AVENUE, LAINSTON
HOUSE HOTEL £95 3 3 3

WOODMAN LN SO21 2LT 01962 776088

"A classical set-up with comfy armchairs and
a roaring fire, tea served with sandwiches,
scones, jam, cream and cakes – this picturesque
country house hotel takes us plebs all
back to a bygone age" and is very highly
recommended for afternoon tea. Feedback
on more ambitious fare in its plush dining
room was a little more up-and-down this year
and relatively limited, coinciding with the
departure of highly rated exec chef Andrew
Birch after only two years. His replacement,
Phil Yeomans, returns after leaving as head chef
in 2014. / www.exclusive.co.uk/lainston-house;

@lainstonhouse; Sun-Thu 9.30 pm, Fri & Sat 10 pm.

RICK STEIN £62 333

7 HIGH STREET SO23 9JX 01962 353535

"For Winchester, pretty darn good" seems a fair assessment of this city-centre six-year-old, which wins a good amount of praise for its "excellent" fish and seafood, "friendly and helpful service, and an atmosphere that's lively and fun, without being noisy" ("a bit like an upmarket canteen"). Reviews are not consistent enough, however, for a more gushing endorsement: some dishes are judged "a bit run of the mill" and it can be "hard to correlate the experience with the price level". / www.rickstein.com; @SteinWinchester; Fri & Sat, Mon-Thu 10.30 pm, Sun 10 pm; Take bookings all week via phone and/or online.

RIVER COTTAGE CANTEEN £55 233

ABBEY MILL, ABBEY MILL GARDENS SO23 9GH 01962457747

"Sitting on the verandah", enjoying "a good-value lunch on a summer's day overlooking the park" is particularly enjoyable at HFW's Winchester outpost, which benefits from its leafy setting, in Abbey Mill Gardens. Its "unmessed-about" cuisine is most praised for a family day out, and even if "some dishes can be less-than-spectacular", most reports this year judge results as good overall. / www.rivercottage.net/canteens/winchester; @WinCanteen; Take bookings all week via phone and/or online.

WYKEHAM ARMS £56 234

75 KINGSGATE ST SO23 9PE 01962 853834

Disused desks from the town's famous boarding school nowadays support drinkers' pints at this "very atmospheric" old inn near the cathedral – "an exceptional town pub" that's in recent times become part of the Fuller's chain. Food has been up and down in the past, but was nothing less than "competent" this year, if perhaps "rather expensive". / www.wykehamarmswinchester.co.uk; @WykehmarmsLL; Mon-Sat 11 pm, Sun 10.30 pm; Take bookings all week via phone and/or online; children: 14+.

WINDERMERE, CUMBRIA   7–3D

GILPIN SPICE, GILPIN LODGE £61 543

CROOK ROAD LA23 3NE 01539 488818

"A great addition to Gilpin Lodge" – this "funky, delightful restaurant" (the more casual of the hotel's two dining rooms overseen by Hrishikesh Desai) serves up "bold flavours and panache", with "a leaning towards India, particularly southern India, but also drawing inspiration from beyond": "undeniably gorgeous!" / www.thegilpin.co.uk; @gilpinhotel.

HENROCK £68

LINTHWAITE HALL, CROOK ROAD LA23 015394 88600

Simon Rogan is running this October 2019 newcomer at Windermere's extensively revamped Linthwaite House which, since 2016, has benefited from over £12m of refurbishment and expansion. Under head chef, Brian Limoges, the culinary style is much more straightforward and inexpensive than L'Enclume. / www.henrock.co.uk; Mon-Sat 11 pm.

HOLBECK GHYLL £99 335

HOLBECK LANE LA23 1LU 01539 432375

"Luxury, on all fronts" helps summarise the appeal of a meal at this well-known Lakeland hotel: originally built as a hunting lodge with a "gorgeous" wood-panelled, traditional dining room and "sensational views" over Lake Windermere. Fans applaud its "truly elegant" cuisine too, but ratings are capped by sceptics who consider the performance "overrated". / www.holbeckghyll.com; @HolbeckGhyll; No jeans; children: 7+ at D.

HOMEGROUND £26 343

LA23 1DX 015394 44863

"This place is never quiet" – "they serve the best coffee (from Carvetii) for miles around and their creative breakfasts and brunches are out of this world". / www.homegroundcafe.co.uk; @Homegroundcafe; No bookings.

HOOKED £57 331

ELLERTHWAITE SQUARE LA23 1DP 015394 48443

"Fresh fish perfectly cooked on the bone" is a highlight of a visit to this well-established if "basic" venue, which continues to garner positive reports in the main. The owners launched a sibling, Urban Food House, offering pizza and other casual fare, in Bowness, in August 2018. / www.hookedwindermere.co.uk; @hookedwindermer; No Amex; Booking max 6 may apply.

HRISHI, GILPIN LODGE £89 543

CROOK RD LA23 3NE 01539 488818

"The best local ingredients are married with spices and great originality" at Hrishikesh Desai's swish dining room – the posher of the two eating options at this plush hotel, set "in a gorgeous Lake District setting" (see also Gilpin Spice). It offers a variety of modern British menus which provide "a hint of Indian influence in some of the dishes, but the resulting food is in no way overpowering: rather it is delicate and full of wonderful flavours". "From the moment of arrival up to the moment of departure you are cosseted in a traditional but not suffocating way – a real pleasure". / www.thegilpin.co.uk; @chef_keller; No jeans; children: 7+.

THE SAMLING £100 444

AMBLESIDE ROAD LA23 1LR 01539 431922

"Magnificent views over Lake Windermere" are part of the appeal of this celebrated county hotel, which gained a fancy new glass-walled restaurant, wine cellar and chef's table a few years back. It attracted the odd middling rating this year, but most feedback has remained very upbeat as chef Robby Jenks (from Newbury's Vineyard at Stockcross) succeeded Peter Howarth in spring 2019, and we've maintained its ratings as an "amazing" all-rounder. / www.thesamlinghotel.co.uk; @theSamlingHotel.

WINDSOR, BERKSHIRE   3–3A

AL FASSIA £46 443

27 ST LEONARDS RD SL4 3BP 01753 855370

"This family-run Moroccan restaurant is one of Windsor's best-kept secrets", "tucked away down a backstreet away from the tourist drag" and now in its third decade. "The food is always great – authentic, well-cooked, and in generous portions. You can now sometimes get the specials without pre-ordering – they're so popular that some are now made on spec". / www.alfassiarestaurant.com; @AlfassiaWindsor; Mon-Thu 10 pm, Fri & Sat 10.30 pm, Sun 9 pm.

WINGHAM, KENT   3–3D

THE DOG AT WINGHAM £62 343

CANTERBURY ROAD CT3 1BB 01227 720339

The Bridgen family's "pleasant, well-decorated inn" opened three years ago, and sits just outside Canterbury, opposite the church of a cute village. All reports suggest it's a "wonderful place to wine and dine" with "pleasant" service and "well-executed" cooking. / www.thedog.co.uk; @dogwingham; Sun-Fri 11.30 pm, Sat midnight.

WINSTON, COUNTY DURHAM   8–3B

BRIDGEWATER ARMS £56 433

THE BRIDGEWATER ARMS DL2 3RN 01325 730 302

This classy former school is "particularly good at seafood dishes", part of its "extensive blackboard options", which also run to "excellent game in season"; credit too for the "fab portion sizes" and "well-priced lunch and early-bird menus". / www.thebridgewaterarms.com; Take bookings all week via phone and/or online.

WINTERINGHAM, LINCOLNSHIRE   5–1D

WINTERINGHAM FIELDS £100 544

1 SILVER ST DN15 9ND 01724 733096

"The long-overdue Michelin star has finally been awarded", say fans of Colin McGurran's rural restaurant with rooms, near the banks of the Humber, which he continues to reestablish as the leading destination it was under its Annie & Germain Schwab. "Imaginative" cuisine is "prepared with flair", you are "well looked after" and the overall package is "thoroughly enjoyable", especially if you stay. Top Tip – "the cheese board is to die for". / www.winteringhamfields.co.uk; @winteringhamf; Wed-Sat, Tue 9 pm; No trainers; Take bookings all week via phone and/or online.

WISWELL, LANCASHIRE   5–1B

FREEMASONS AT WISWELL   £79   5 3 4

8 VICARAGE FOLD CLITHEROE BB7 9DF 01254 822218

"Fine dining in a local pub" – "high quality ingredients and well-rehearsed techniques to ensure a top-class, punchily-flavoured product"; and with "a brilliant wine list" – again win massive acclaim for Steve Smith's "lovely" old inn, set in a tiny village in the Ribble Valley. In July 2019, it re-opened after a major investment, with the addition of a new kitchen, chef's table (min 6, max 12), kitchen bench (4 stools) and bedrooms. / www.freemasonswiswell.co.uk; @Wiswellman; Wed-Sat 10 pm, Sun 9 pm; No Amex; Booking max 6 may apply.

WIVETON, NORFOLK   6–3C

WIVETON BELL   £45   3 3 3

BLAKENEY RD NR25 7TL 01263 740 101

"Well-above-average pub grub" – "nothing too complicated, but all very well done (not to mention tasting delicious)" – is on the menu at this "fab boozer near the north Norfolk coast". Top Tip: "do choose a table in the pub rather than the conservatory restaurant". / www.wivetonbell.co.uk; @wivetonbell; Mon-Sat 9 pm, Sun 8 pm; No Amex; Booking evening only.

WOBURN, BUCKINGHAMSHIRE   3–2A

PARIS HOUSE   £93   5 4 5

WOBURN PARK MK17 9QP 01525 290692

"Beautiful deer park surroundings" provide an "exceptional setting" for this well-known destination, in the grounds of Woburn Abbey, which occupies a picture-book, Tudor building ("what could be more romantic than a glass of Champagne on the terrace before a lovely meal here!"). Phil Fanning's "genius" cuisine is presented either from an à la carte menu or the eight-course tasting menu (six courses at lunch). / www.parishouse.co.uk; @ParisHousechef; Thu-Sat 8.30 pm, Sun 2 pm; No Amex; No trainers; Take bookings all week via phone and/or online.

WOKING, SURREY   3–3A

THE INN WEST END   £50

42 GUILDFORD RD GU24 9PW 01276 858652

"Upmarket pub" with a dozen bedrooms, handy for Ascot Racecourse, which was taken over by new owners (Barons Pub Company) in late 2018. Not all reporters are happy with the new ownership, but upbeat feedback praises its "well-rounded menu, relaxed style and pleasant service". Reflecting the up-and-down reports, we've left a rating till next year. / www.the-inn.co.uk; @InnWestEnd; Mon-Sat 11 pm, Sun 10.30 pm; No trainers; Take bookings all week via phone and/or online; children: 5+.

WOLLATON, NOTTINGHAMSHIRE   5–3D

THE COD'S SCALLOPS   £27   4 4 2

170 BRAMCOTE LN NG8 2QP 0115 985 4107

For "British street food at its best" you can't miss this bright fish 'n' chippy, serving 20 types of catch deep-fried in beef dripping, and consumed in a smart, booth-lined setting. / www.codsscallops.com; @TheCodsScallops; No Amex; No bookings.

WOLVERHAMPTON, WEST MIDLANDS   5–4B

BILASH   £58   3 3 3

2 CHEAPSIDE WV1 1TU 01902 427762

Sitab Khan's local fixture is "not your usual Indian", but rather a "Premiership-class" performer, turning out "always fabulous" dishes in a "swish luxurious" setting (the latter courtesy of a megabucks refurb to celebrate its recent, 35th anniversary). / www.thebilash.co.uk; @thebilash.

WOODBRIDGE, SUFFOLK   3–1D

THE TABLE   £40   3 3 2

QUAY ST IP12 1BX   01394 382428

A pleasant, courtyard bistro (est. 2012) turning out non-pretentious grub, and now working with local suppliers to grow more exotic Far Eastern vegetables (they also run 'Street Food Sundays' in summer). The building perhaps shows a bit of the strain of having operated as a restaurant for 50 years, but it's still a "cheap 'n' cheerful" beacon in these parts. / www.thetablewoodbridge.co.uk; Mon-Thu 9 pm, Fri & Sat 9.30 pm, Sun 3 pm; Take bookings all week via phone and/or online.

WOODLANDS, HAMPSHIRE   2–4C

SPOT IN THE WOODS   £31   3 4 3

174 WOODLANDS RD, NETLEY MARSH, NEW FOREST SO40 7GL   023 8029 3784

"TerraVina's resurrection" – "in its new guise as a boutique B&B and café" – "has become a real favourite in the beautiful New Forest". Founder Gerard Basset, the famed wine expert behind the original Hotel du Vin, died in January 2019 after a two-year fight against cancer, and his widow Nina has kept the business going. There are "no evening meals now, but breakfasts and lunches are splendid" and "in summer it's lovely to sit in the garden". / www.spotinthewoods.co.uk; @Hotel_TerraVina; Mon-Thu 4 pm, Fri-Sun 5 pm.

Roots, York

WOOLSERY, DEVON   1–2C

THE FARMER'S ARMS   £55

EX39 5QS   01237 439328

Purchased in 2015 by internet millionaires Michael and Xochi Birch – co-founders of social networking site, Bebo – their project is to revive the fortunes of this small village including the fish 'n' chip shop (already open), post office and shop, four guest cottages and a hotel set within a Grade II listed Georgian manor house, all due to open by 2021. Initial reports on the pub (which serves light meals and snacks and has a separate restaurant) are too limited for a rating, but all positive: "the commitment of the owner, team and suppliers is clear!" / www.woolsery.com/pub; Wed-Sat 9 pm, Sun 3 pm.

WORTHING, WEST SUSSEX   3–4A

CRABSHACK   £44   3 3 3

2 MARINE PARADE BN11 3PN 01903 215070

"Fresh seafood right on Chesil Beach: what's not to like?" – the "shabby-chic room" at this four-year-old café is "perfect when the sun shines" and "has been expanded, so it's better than ever". "The freshness of the food can't be faulted", but some feel "they have a tendency to muck about with the exquisite ingredients" – "so stick to the crab and simply cooked fish". Top Tip: "the crab sandwiches". / www.crabshackworthing.co.uk; @CrabShack10; Tue-Thu 9 pm, Fri & Sat 9.30 pm, Sun 4 pm.

ETHICUREAN   £59 434

BARLEY WOOD WALLED GARDEN, LONG LN BS40 5SA 01934 863713

Brothers Matthew and Iain Pennington's hyper-ethical outfit near Bristol doesn't generate masses of feedback but its devotees say it's "nothing short of spectacular" – serving veg-dominated, 'gut-friendly' food that creates "an excellent and interesting meal that's distinctive and local". "From the moment you stroll through the Victorian walled garden to the restaurant, you're treated to a full sensory experience". / www.theethicurean.com; @TheEthicurean; Take bookings all week via phone and/or online.

THE WIFE OF BATH RESTAURANT, ROOMS AND TAPAS BAR   £57 434

4 UPPER BRIDGE ST TN25 5AF 01233 812232

"The attractive village of Wye is not where you'd expect Spanish food", but that's precisely what's on the cards at Rock Salt chef Mark Sargeant's "light and airy" hotel-restaurant – in action since 1962, but turning out something "different" (tapas but also a "wonderful breakfast") since he acquired it in 2016. / www.thewifeofbath.com; @TheWifeofBath2; Wed-Sat, Tue 9.30 pm, Sun 5 pm; No Amex.

THE SHIP INN   £105 333

MAIN ROAD NE41 8AQ 01661 854538

"Inventive pub food – a mix of small and bigger plates" wins enthusiastic, if still-limited feedback on this attractive, stone-fronted village pub, whose chef Paul Johnson (who owns the pub with his partner, Kelly) has a CV which includes working for Nathan Outlaw in Cornwall. / www.theshipinnwylam.co.uk; @shipinnwylam; Wed-Sat, Mon & Tue 9 pm, Sun 4 pm; Take bookings all week via phone and/or online.

AMBIENTE   £22 332

31 FOSSGATE YO1 9TA 01904 638 252

A "lovely, good-value Spanish restaurant" whose modern, industrial style interior has a "buzzy, relaxed and friendly atmosphere". This is the larger of two branches in York serving tapas and paella (there are offshoots in Leeds and Hull): "I love it and have never had a bad meal there". / www.ambiente-tapas.co.uk; Take bookings all week via phone and/or online.

ARRAS   £70 442

THE OLD COACH HOUSE, PEASHOLME GREEN YO1 7PW 01904 633 737

"The food is exceptional and the choice is not so large that you are left bewildered" at Adam & Lovaine Humphrey's "little" 18-seater, where

you choose either a conventional two-course or three-course meal, or go for a five-course taster selection. "The excellent short menu is happily low on cheffy tricks but very long on accomplished and flavoursome cooking, and with well-suited wine matches". The end of the meal is a highlight: an "outstanding cheese board" and "an amazingly generous selection of treats (ice cream cones, Turkish delight, jellies, donuts, chocolates…)". "The ambience can be a little underwhelming" but it's enlivened by the "lovely" service. / www.arrasrestaurant.co.uk; @ArrasRestaurant; Tue-Sat 9.30 pm.

BARBARKAN   £39 333

58 WALMGATE YO1 9TL 01904 672474

A "robust Polish food offering in central York", also serving other Eastern European specialities (notably textbook pierogi and borscht) and winning fans for its bargain prices; "if you can, leave room for the cakes which are truly delicious". / www.deli-barbakan.co.uk; @TheBarbakan; Tue-Sat 10 pm, Mon 3 pm, Sun 9 pm.

BETTYS   £41 344

6-8 ST HELEN'S SQUARE YO1 8QP 01904 659142

"A must-visit experience" – brave the queues which "move surprisingly fast" at this iconic tearoom, which turns out "great breakfast and brunch", but really "stands head and shoulders above others when it comes to afternoon tea". The latter features "traditionally clad waitresses and a range of old favourites (you "cannot beat a fat rascal") in surroundings that seem dated but somehow are just what you want". / www.bettys.co.uk/tea-rooms/locations/york; @Bettys1919; Sun-Fri & Sat 9 pm; No Amex; Booking lunch only.

CAFE NO. 8 BISTRO   £47 332

8 GILLYGATE YO31 7EQ 01904 653074

"Never had a bad meal", say fans of this "favourite" tiny bistro, off the Gillygate, serving "excellent ingredients prepared with some imagination". It can feel "rather cramped inside", though. Top Tip: "go for the garden room in summer, under the medieval city wall". / www.cafeno8.co.uk; @cafeno8; Mon-Sun 10 pm; No Amex; Take bookings all week via phone and/ or online.

LE COCHON AVEUGLE   £111 543

37 WALMGATE YO1 9TX 01904 640222

"Part of York's culinary renaissance, in the heart of the town, on Walmgate" – Josh & Victoria Overington's "intimate", "small" venture again put in one of the strongest performances in this culinarily up-and-coming town. "Josh has his eye on the ball and continues to excel" with his "properly impressive" tasting menu: "full of invention with truly gorgeous flavours" using "hyper-seasonal ingredients"; and "at a decent

price, too". "The knowledge of the front of house team compliments all that is done in the kitchen, they know exactly what they are serving you; and the choice of wines is extraordinary – if you decide to take the wine flight then rest assured you will have an elevated dining experience". Top Menu Tip – "The boudin noir macron is a thing of joy". / www.lecochonaveugle.uk; @lecochonaveugle; Wed-Sat 11.30 pm; Take bookings all week via phone and/or online; children: 10.

THE COUNTESS OF YORK, NATIONAL RAILWAY MUSEUM   £29

LEEMAN ROAD YO26 4XJ 01904 686295

A beautifully restored rail carriage at the National Railway Museum makes a unique location for a luxurious afternoon tea. It has received the odd recommendation so far: reports please! / www.railwaymuseum.org.uk/ visit/countess-york.

IL PARADISO DEL CIBO   £39 333

40 WALMGATE YO1 9TJ 0190 461 1444

"A slice of Italy in York complete with TV screen showing Inter Milan playing valiantly (but silently!)" and a menu of "super trattoria food at reasonable prices"; pizza pilgrims are also well catered for. / www.ilparadisodelciboyork.com; Take bookings all week via phone and/or online.

THE IVY, GRANGE HOTEL   £55 322

1 CLIFTON YO30 6AA 01904 644744

With their exposed brick walls and greige tongue-and-groove panelling, these attractive cellars below a venerable (but recently revamped), 41-bed hotel in residential Bootham confusingly have absolutely nothing to do with the expanding national chain, having traded as 'The Ivy Brasserie' in York for over a decade before Richard Caring's arrival. Less fancy than its namesake, but arguably better value for a dependable, hotel-brasserie experience. / www.grangehotel.co.uk; @grangehotelyork.

THE IVY ST HELEN'S SQUARE   £57 223

2 SAINT HELEN'S SQUARE YO1 8QP 01904 403888

Fans say it's a "great restaurant for socialising" and there are some "reliable" dishes on the menu, but there's a strong sense among reporters that, having only opened in December 2017, The Ivy's York outpost feels "very average" all round…perhaps "this chain is tired after all the expansion of late? / www.theivyork.com; @theivyyork; Mon-Sat 12.30 am.

MANNION & CO   £39 433

1 BLAKE ST YO1 8QJ 01904 631030

"Breakfast never disappoints" at this artisanal deli and café in a former greengrocer's where

Fraiche, Oxton

you'll find "consistently good" snacks and brunch fare spanning sarnies and quirkier options ("like in New Zealand"). "Be prepared to table share" and don't miss the walled garden out back. The "charming" three-year-old Hemlsley spin-off is also a hit. / www.mannionandco.uk; @MannionsofYork; Mon-Sat 5 pm, Sun 4.30 pm; No bookings.

MELTON'S £68 343

7 SCARCROFT RD YO23 1ND 01904 634 341

"Very reliable" through three decades, Michael & Lucy Hjort's modern British venue near the city walls has a "fantastic menu" – including a "lovely selection of experimental hors d'oeuvres". "More flashy and fashionable restaurants come and go in York, but Melton's consistency, excellent locally sourced food and fabulous wine list make it a favourite." Local lad Michael trained under the Roux brothers before heading home. He also owns the Walmgate Ale House and is the long-time artistic director of the York Food Festival. / www.meltonsrestaurant.co.uk; @meltons1; Wed-Sat, Tue 9.30 pm; No Amex; Take bookings all week via phone and/or online.

MIDDLETHORPE HALL £93 234

BISHOPTHORPE ROAD YO23 2GB 01904 641241

With its "lovely, old, grandiose atmosphere", the NT's William & Mary country pile is a "beautiful place to eat in high-ceilinged dining rooms" and its cooking is consistently well-rated, if seldom plugged as being terrifically exciting. Top Tip – "lovely surroundings for an excellent afternoon tea: really spoiling". / www.middlethorpe.com; No shorts; children: 6+.

LOS MOROS £44 432

15-17 GRAPE LANE YO1 7HU 01904 636834

"A good find" for its "authentic Moroccan street food" – Tarik Abdeladim started out with a stall in Shambles Market, which he still has, before opening this yearling where "the grub is still great value". / www.losmorosyork.co.uk; @Los_Moros_York.

MR P'S CURIOUS TAVERN £58

71 LOW PETERGATE YO1 7HY 01904 521177

The most curious thing about star chef, Andrew Pern's eclectically olde worlde gastropub in the city-centre and its funky selection of dishes is how little interest it generated amongst our reporters this year. Such feedback as we have remains good, but we've removed the rating for the time being. / mrpscurioustavern.co.uk; @MrPsTavern; Tue-Fri 9.30 pm, Sat 11 pm, Sun 4 pm.

MUMBAI LOUNGE £33 333

47 FOSSGATE YO1 9TF 01904 654 155

"Beautiful Indian food" from a "varied menu with a touch of the exotic" and some really "great flavours" has earned this 10-year-old Bengali a position as one of the town's top curry stops. / www.mumbailoungeyork.co.uk; Sun-Thu 11.30 pm, Fri & Sat midnight.

THE PARK - BY ADAM JACKSON £66 443

4 - 5 SAINT PETER'S GROVE, CLIFTON YO30 6AQ 01904 640101

Part of a rather traditional, 21-bedroom town house hotel in the centre of town, this dining room with Adam Jackson at the stoves provides the choice of a four-course menu (for £48) or a six-course tasting menu (for £65). All reporters rate it extremely highly – "a favourite whenever we are in town, with wonderful cuisine". / www.marmadukestownhousehotelyork.com/the-park/; @theparkrestaura; children: 14.

THE PIG & PASTRY £19 343

35 BISHOPTHORPE ROAD YO23 1NA 01904 675115

"Like walking into Central Perk (the coffee shop from Friends)" – this "quirky local café" in "glam Bishy Road" has "friendly staff who are happy to have a banter" along with "fabulous breakfasts" and "great plates of tasty food". "Loved it – if I lived in York I'd be there every week!". / thepigandpastry.com; @Thepigandpastry; Take bookings all week via phone and/or online.

RATTLE OWL £56 442

104 MICKLEGATE YO16 XÂ· 01904 658 658

Clarrie O'Callaghan's "under-the-radar" venue in a "lovely historic space" on Micklegate is a showcase for Tom Heywood's "inventive, brilliantly executed cooking" – some reporters even feel it "outshines the more vaunted Skoosh a couple of doors down" (although that's a minority view). "My most memorable meal of the year – perhaps because it was a surprise and understated". Top Tip: "the lunch deal is spectacular value at £15 for three small plates – go with a friend and taste all six!" / www.rattleowl.co.uk; @TheRattleOwl; Tue-Sat 9.30 pm, Sun 4 pm; Take bookings all week via phone and/or online.

ROOTS £53 554

68 MARYGATE YO30 7BH NO TEL

"A magnificent addition to York's burgeoning food scene" – "Tommy Banks does amazing things with the most simple of ingredients" ("how can anyone make a humble brassica such as kale so bloody tasty that we were all fighting over it?!"), at his family's "converted pub, close to York city-centre", which – in one short year – has become the survey's most-mentioned destination in this increasingly foodie town. "The intense flavours and imaginative combination of sometimes-unlikely ingredients are a delight" and "the wine to match is excellent, and very well thought out". "Young, friendly, helpful and enthusiastic service" contributes to a highly impressive debut. "Get in quick, before the prices match those at his Black Swan in Oldstead!". Top Menu Tip – "his best-known dish is the epic crapaudine beetroot, the beetroot cooked in beef fat". / www.rootsyork.com; @RootsYork.

SKOSH £46 543

98 MICKLEGATE YO1 6JX 01904 634 849

"Every time I know that I am going to Skosh I am excited days beforehand as I know that I'm in for a flavour sensation!" – Neil Bentinck's city-centre three-year-old invites some comparison with local rival Roots (the only York restaurant to generate more reports than here) and the tapas-style dishes his kitchen produces feature "stunning food combinations, brilliantly conceived and executed, with flavours that linger long after the meal ends". "It's a small place, and not fancy" but fans feel "it's lovely like this" thanks to its "modern and fun" approach and "chilled vibe". / skoshyork.co.uk/; @skoshyork; Wed-Sat 10 pm, Sun 4 pm; Credit card deposit required to book.

STAR INN THE CITY £66 124

LENDAL ENGINE HOUSE, MUSEUM STREET YO1 7DR 01904 619208

Andrew Pern's gastropub offshoot from the Star Inn at Harome continues to inspire unusually mediocre feedback, with a majority of reports finding it severely "overrated" and with "OTT prices for the quality of the food". Why, then, is it "very busy"? – it has a "lovely setting over the river" with "the best waterside terrace in the city" (worth a visit for a drink if nothing else!) / www.starinnthecity.co.uk; @Starinnthecity; Take bookings all week via phone and/or online.

31 CASTLEGATE RESTAURANT £47 323

31 CASTLEGATE YO1 9RN 01904 621404

A "consistently good" indie that has been open since 2005 and occupies the former house of Georgian architect G.T. Andrews, in the shadow of the Clifford's Tower; its continental cuisine continues to elicit solid ratings, and "their 2-for-1 special offers (once they have your email address) are superb value". / www.31castlegate.co.uk; @31castlegate; Tue-Sat 9.30 pm, Sun 9 pm; practically no walk-ins – you must book.

THE WHIPPET INN £50 332

15 NORTH ST YO1 6JD 01904 500660

"Better-than-average pub food" – especially the main event, making the most of Yorkshire meat – is the draw to this "very popular" and trendy brick-walled steak and ale house (14+ only, so don't bring the kids). / www.thewhippetinn.co.uk; @WhippetWhere; Sun-Thu 11 pm, Fri & Sat midnight; Take bookings all week via phone and/or online.

Opheem, Birmingham

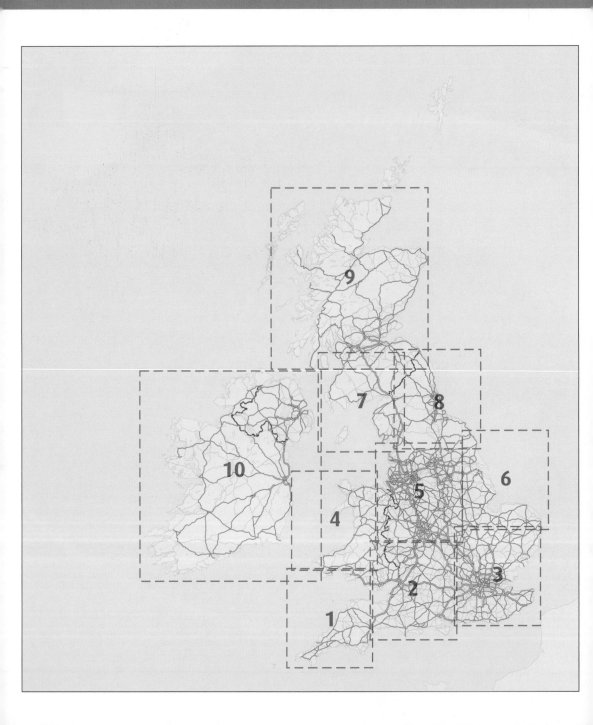

MAP 1

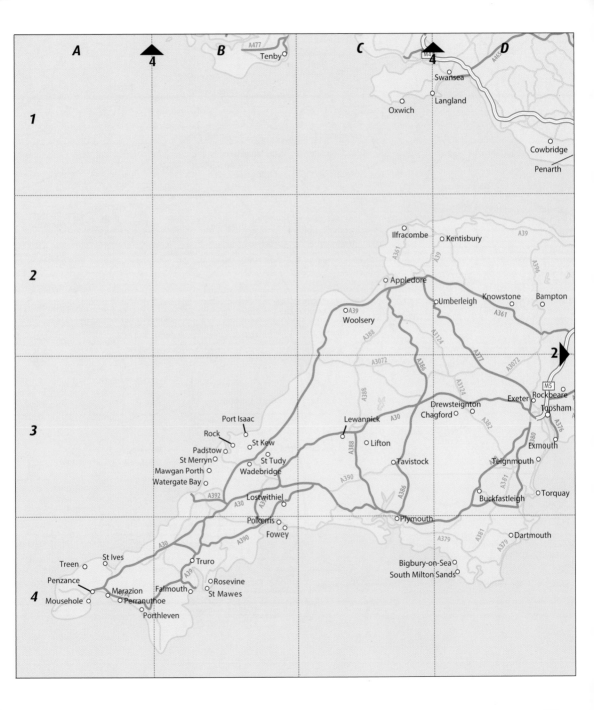

MAP 2

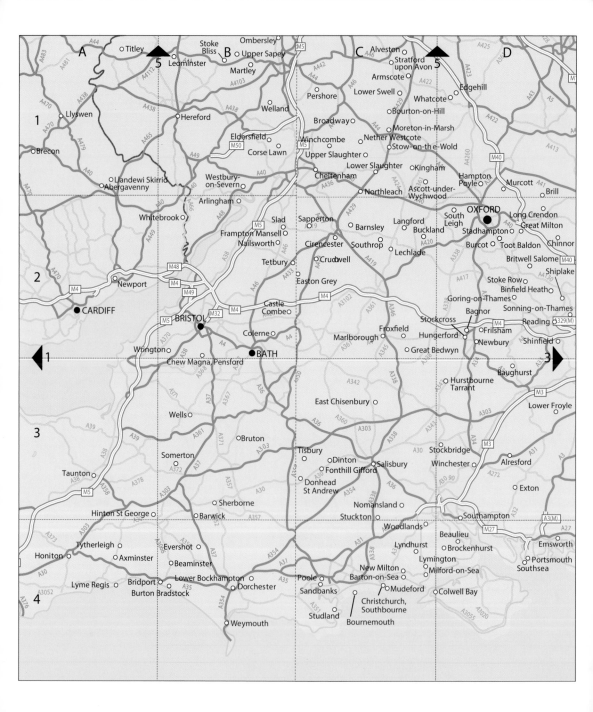

MAP 3

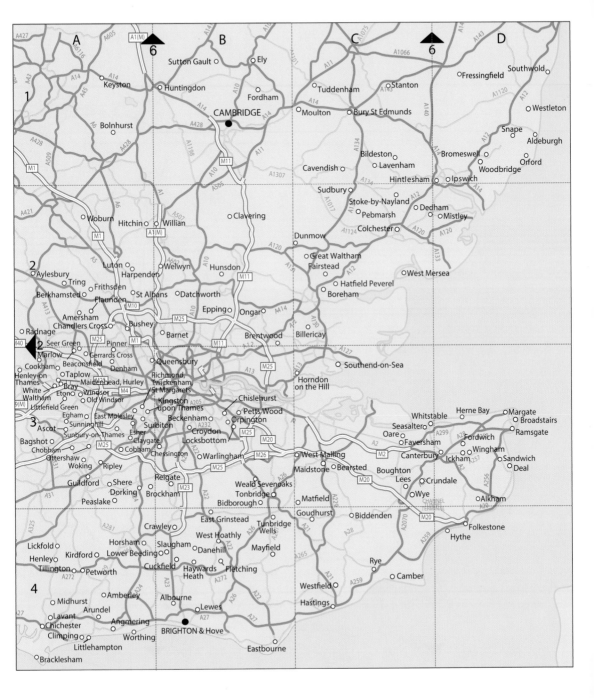

MAP 4

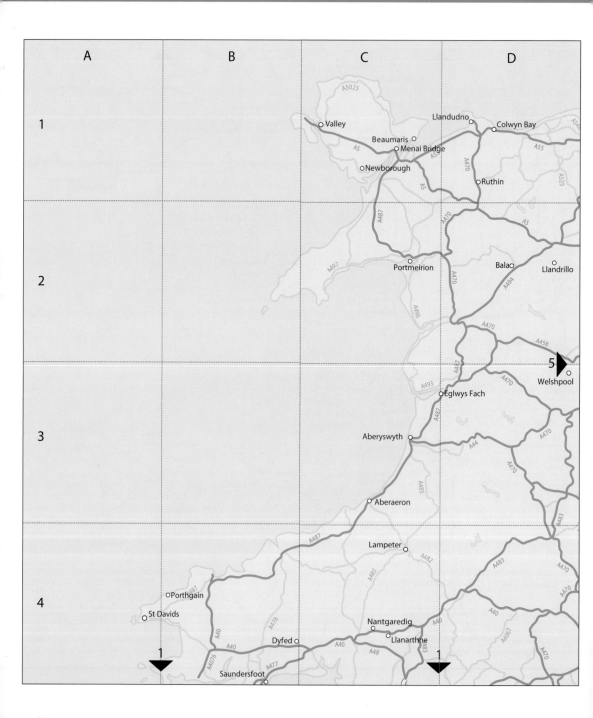

MAP 5

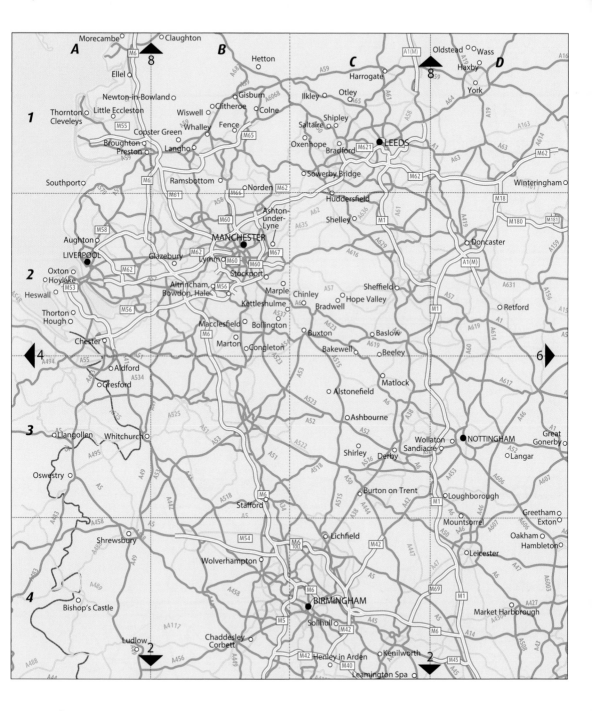

MAP 6

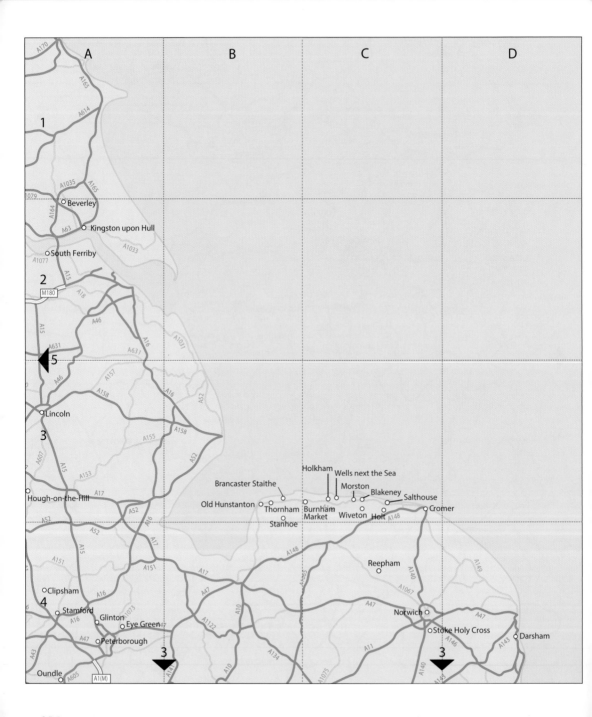

A   B   C   D

1

A170
A165
A614

A1035
A165
A1079
○ Beverley
A164
A63
○ Kingston upon Hull
A1033
○ South Ferriby
A1077
2
A15
M180
A18

A46
A15
A16
A1031
A631
A631
A52
5
A46
A157
A16
A158
A52
○ Lincoln
A158
3
A155
A607
A15
A52
A153
A17
Hough-on-the-Hill ○
A52
A17
A52

Holkham Wells next the Sea
Brancaster Staithe ○ Morston Blakeney
Old Hunstanton ○ Thornham Burnham ○ ○ Salthouse
Stanhoe Market Wiveton Holt ○ Cromer
A148
A148

A148
A15
A151
Reepham ○
A149
A151
A140
A17
A1067
A47
A151
A47
Clipsham ○
A16
A10
A1122 A47
Norwich ○
4
○ Stamford
A16
A1073
A146 A47
Glinton ○
○ Eye Green
○ Stoke Holy Cross
A43
A47
○ Peterborough
A134
A11
A143 ○ Darsham
3
A140
3
A10
A1075
A145
Oundle ○
A605
A1(M)

MAP 7

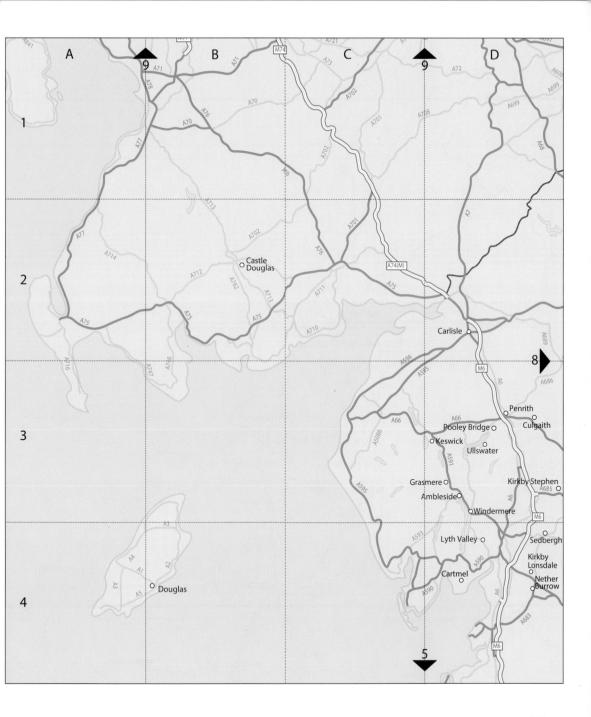

MAP 8

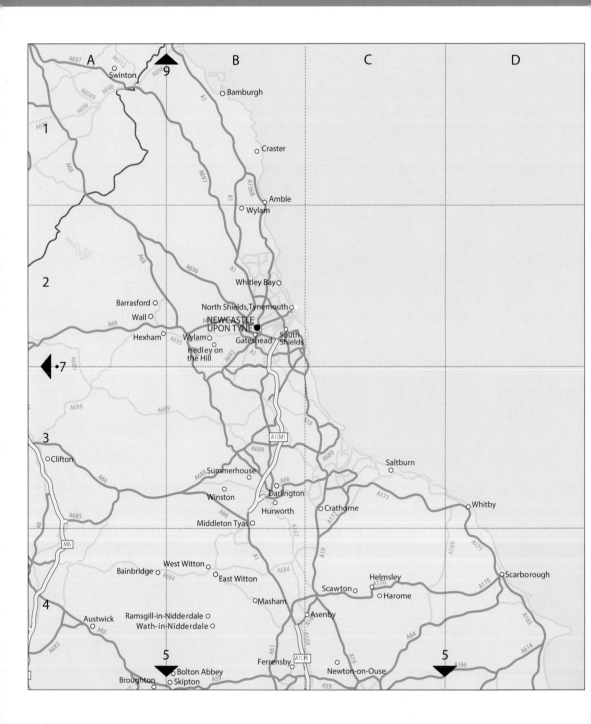

A697
Swinton
A6112
A6989
9
A1
Bamburgh
A6089
A698
A699
A68
A697
1
A697
Craster
A68
A1068
A1
Amble
Wylam
A68
A696
A1
2
Whitley Bay
Barrasford
North Shields,Tynemouth
Wall
A696
NEWCASTLE
UPON TYNE
A69
Hexham
A695
Wylam
Gateshead
South
Shields
Hedley on
the Hill
A692
A1
7
A68
A686
A689
A19
3
A1(M)
A689
Clifton
A66
Summerhouse
A688
A689
Saltburn
A66
Winston
Darlington
A171
Whitby
A685
Hurworth
Crathorne
A67
A172
M6
Middleton Tyas
A66
A169
A171
A1
West Witton
A684
Bainbridge
A684
East Witton
Helmsley
A170
Scarborough
Austwick
A65
Ramsgill-in-Nidderdale
Scawton
A170
Masham
Harome
Wath-in-Nidderdale
A19
A64
A165
A683
A1(M)
Asenby
A614
5
Ferrensby
A1(M)
Newton-on-Ouse
5
A166
Broughton
Bolton Abbey
Skipton
A59
A59

Saltburn
A688
M6
M6

MAP 9

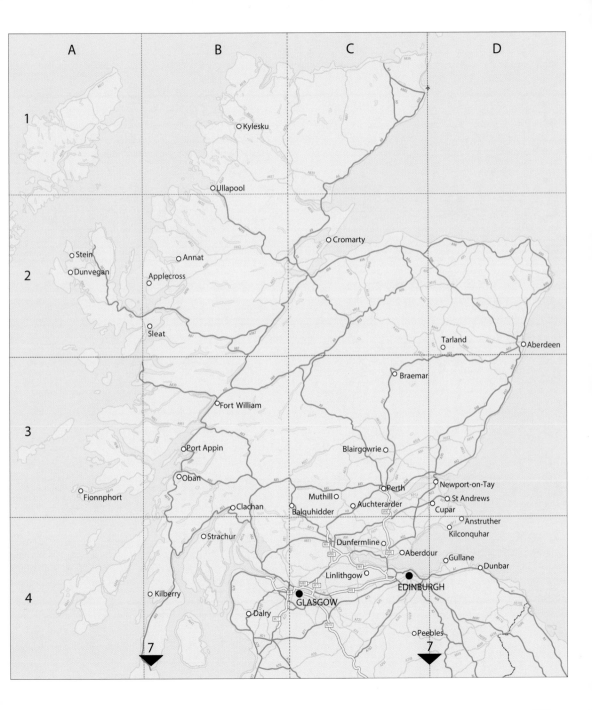

MAP 10

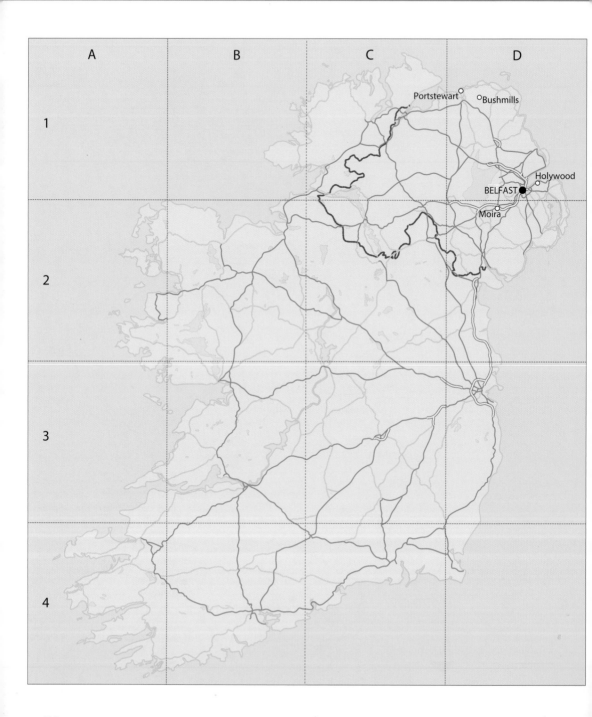

The Five Fields, London

ALPHABETICAL INDEX

314   ALPHABETICAL INDEX

Edera *London* 58

Edinburgh Food Studio *Edinburgh* 219

Edo *Belfast* 191

Educated Flea *Edinburgh* 219

Ee-Usk (Seafood Restaurant) *Oban* 264

Eggslut *London* 58

Eight *Bath* 188

1863 Bar Bistro Rooms *Pooley Bridge* 271

Ekte Nordic Kitchen *London* 58

El Cartel *Edinburgh* 219

Elderflower *Lymington* 248

Electric Diner *London* 58

Elephant Restaurant & Brasserie *Torquay* 286

Eliane of Hungerford *Hungerford* 237

Ella Canta *London* 58

Elliot's Café *London* 58

Elystan Street *London* 58

Ember Yard *London* 59

Emilia's Crafted Pasta *London* 59

Emilia *London* 59

The Empire Room, Royal Harbour Hotel *Ramsgate* 273

The Empress *London* 59

L'Enclume *Cartmel* 208

Endo at Rotunda *London* 59

Eneko Basque Kitchen & Bar *London* 59

Engine Social Dining *Sowerby Bridge* 280

English's *Brighton* 198

Enoteca Rosso *London* 59

Enoteca Turi *London* 59

The Enterprise *London* 59

Eric's *Huddersfield* 236

Eric's Fish & Chips *Thornham* 286

L'Escargot *London* 59

L'Escargot Bleu *Edinburgh* 219

Est India *London* 59

Estiatorio Milos *London* 59

Etch *Brighton* 198

Ethicurean *Wrington* 296

Ethos *London* 59

Etive *Oban* 264

Eusebi Deli *Glasgow* 228

Evelyn's Table at The Blue Posts *London* 60

Everest Inn *London* 60

Evuna *Manchester* 250

Falcondale Hotel *Lampeter* 240

Flavours By Kumar *Ramsgate* 273

La Famiglia *London* 60

Fancy Crab *London* 60

Farang *London* 60

Fare *London* 60

Farmacy *London* 60

The Farmer's Arms *Woolsery* 295

Farmer, Butcher, Chef *Chichester* 210

The Farmhouse at Redcoats *Hitchin* 236

Farmyard *Norwich* 262

Farzi Cafe *London* 60

The Fat Duck *Bray* 196

Fat Olives *Emsworth* 224

Fatt Pundit *London* 60

Fatto A Mano *Brighton* 198

Favorita *Edinburgh* 219

Fazenda *Birmingham* 192

The Feathered Nest Inn *Nether Westcote* 258

The Feathers Inn *Hedley On The Hill* 234

The Felin Fach Griffin *Brecon* 197

Fellini's *Ambleside* 183

Fellpack *Keswick* 238

Fenchurch Restaurant, Sky Garden *London* 60

The Fenwick Arms *Claughton* 211

La Ferme *London* 60

Fez Mangal *London* 60

Fhior *Edinburgh* 219

Fiddie's Italian Kitchen *London* 60

Field *Edinburgh* 219

Field & Fork *Chichester* 210

Fifteen Cornwall *Watergate Bay* 290

1539 *Chester* 210

50 Kalò di Ciro Salvo *London* 60

Finch's Arms *Hambleton* 232

Fink's Salt and Sweet *London* 62

Fischer's *London* 62

Fischers at Baslow Hall *Baslow* 187

Fish Central *London* 62

Fish in a Tie *London* 62

Fish Market *London* 62

Fish on the Green *Bearsted* 190

The Fish People Cafe *Glasgow* 228

fish! *London* 62

fish! Kitchen *Kingston upon Thames* 239

The Fisherman's Table *Marple* 256

Fishers in the City *Edinburgh* 219

Fishers Leith *Edinburgh* 220

Fishmarket *Edinburgh* 220

Fishworks *London* 62

Fitzroy *Fowey* 227

Fiume *London* 62

The Five Alls *Lechlade* 242

The Five Fields *London* 62

Five Guys (London) 62

500 *London* 62

500 Degrees *London* 63

5 North Street *Winchcombe* 293

Flank *London* 63

Flat Iron *London* 63

Flat Three *London* 63

Flat White *London* 63

Flesh and Buns *London* 63

Flint House *Brighton* 198

The Flitch of Bacon *Dunmow* 217

Flor *London* 63

Flora Indica *London* 63

Flotsam and Jetsam *London* 63

Flour & Ash *Bristol* 200

Flour & Grape *London* 63

FM Mangal *London* 63

Foley's *London* 63

Folie *London* 63

Folium *Birmingham* 192

The Folkestone Wine Company *Folkestone* 226

Food for Friends *Brighton* 198

The Fordwich Arms *Fordwich* 227

The Forest Side *Grasmere* 230

The Forester Inn *Donhead St Andrew* 216

Forman's *London* 64

Fortnum & Mason, The Diamond Jubilee Tea Salon *London* 64

The Fortnum's Bar & Restaurant *London* 64

45 Jermyn Street *London* 64

40 Maltby Street *London* 64

Forza Win *London* 64

400 Rabbits *London* 64

Four Legs at The Compton Arms *London* 64

Four Seasons *London* 64

The Fox *Crawley* 214

The Fox *Willian* 293

The Fox & Goose *Fressingfield* 227

Fox & Grapes *London* 64

The Fox and Hounds Hotel *Exton* 225

The Fox And Hounds Restaurant & Bar *Hunsdon* 237

Fox Dining Rooms *Ottershaw* 265

The Fox Inn *Moreton-in-Marsh* 257

Fraiche *Oxton* 267

Francesca's *Newcastle upon Tyne* 259

Franco Manca *London* 64

Franco's *London* 64

Frantoio *London* 64

Franzina Trattoria *London* 65

Freak Scene *London* 65

Frederic Bistro *Maidstone* 249

Frederick's *London* 65

Freemasons at Wiswell *Wiswell* 295

The French Horn *Sonning-on-Thames* 278

The French House *London* 65

French Living *Nottingham* 263

The French Rooms *Bushmills* 204

The French Table *Surbiton* 285

Frenchie *London* 65

Fresh From The Sea *Port Isaac* 271

Friends *Pinner* 270

Frog & Scot *Deal* 216

The Frog *London* 65

La Fromagerie *London* 65

The Frontline Club *London* 65

The Frustrated Chef *Nottingham* 263

Fucina *London* 65

Fugitive Motel *London* 65

Fuji Hiro *Leeds* 242

Fumo *London* 65

The Fuzzy Duck *Armscote* 185

Gallery Mess, Saatchi Gallery *London* 66

Gallipoli *London* 66

The Gallivant *Camber* 204

Galvin at the Athenaeum *London* 66

Galvin at Windows, Park Lane London Hilton Hotel *London* 66

Galvin Green Man *Great Waltham* 230

Galvin HOP *London* 66

Galvin La Chapelle *London* 66

Gamba *Glasgow* 228

Gambas *Bristol* 200

The Game Bird at The Stafford London *London* 66

Ganapati *London* 66

Gandhi Restaurant *Winchester* 293

The Gannet *Glasgow* 229

The Garden Cafe at the Garden Museum *London* 66

Garden Room *London* 66

Gardener's Cottage *Edinburgh* 220

Le Garrick *London* 66

La Garrigue *Edinburgh* 220

The Garrison *London* 66

The Gate *London* 66

El Gato Negro *Liverpool* 245

El Gato Negro *Manchester* 250

The Gatsby *Berkhamsted* 191

Gaucho *London* 67

Gauthier Soho *London* 67

Le Gavroche *London* 67

Gazette *London* 67

GB Pizza *Margate* 255

Geales *London* 67

Gee's *Oxford* 266

Gem *London* 67

General Tarleton *Ferrensby* 226

The George *Alstonefield* 183

The George *Cavendish* 208

George & Dragon *Hurstbourne Tarrant* 237

Number One, Balmoral Hotel, Edinburgh

If ocean plastic was the issue driving positive change in restaurants in 2018, the climate emergency has been very much front of mind in 2019. Countless reports have been published in the last 18 months highlighting the plight of the planet and the drastic action we need to take to ensure we keep temperature rises below 1.5C.

The good news for all of us is that our appetites are incredibly powerful. The choices we make about food have the greatest single impact on the planet – greater even than the car we drive or the planes we take. That provides chefs and menu developers with a big slice of power – the ability to influence what we eat and, through that behaviour change, a genuine shift towards less environmentally damaging diets. This chance to grab the sustainability bull by the horns also comes at precisely the time when the great British dining public is looking to satisfy its insatiable appetite to eat wisely.

And grab it they have. Hugh Fearnley-Whittingstall, he of River Cottage fame, described the Greggs vegan sausage roll as the most significant food story of the year. From high street to high end, the shift towards more veg-based dishes is accelerating at serious pace.

Vegetables, the eternal bridesmaids, are at long last taking centre stage. By dishing up more and more delicious and creative plant-based options, chefs are helping reduce the impact of their restaurant while also helping customers eat their way to a better food future. If, as UK citizens we all went plant-based for one more meal a week, it would reduce the nation's carbon footprint by a stunning 8%.

A desire to dine more consciously is growing faster than ever before and restaurants are striving to keep pace.

We've supported the SRA since soon after its launch in 2010 because we too believe in helping diners vote with their forks for a better food future.

Look out for those restaurants serving a One Planet Plate, the chef's sustainable special (www.oneplanetplate.org) and search in the guide for those with an SRA Sustainability Rating, either One, Two or Three Stars, achieved by proving they are doing these ten things:

• Support Global Farmers

• Value Natural Resources

• Treat People Fairly

• Feed Children Well

• Celebrate Local

• Source Fish Responsibly

• Serve More Veg & Better Meat

• Reduce Reuse Recycle

• Waste no Food

• Support the Community

w: www.foodmadegood.org / www.oneoplanetplate.org
Twitter: @the_SRA
Instagram: @foodmadegood